THE BIRDS OF THE THAI-MALAY PENINSULA

Dedicated in affectionate memory of Dato' Loke Wan Tho, lover and accomplished photographer of Asian birds, and patron of ornithological research.

... by his sister Lady Yuen Peng McNeice

THE BIRDS OF THE THAI-MALAY PENINSULA

Covering Burma and Thailand south of the eleventh parallel, Peninsular Malaysia and Singapore

Volume One
Non-Passerines

DAVID R WELLS

with contributions from
PHILIP D ROUND and UTHAI TREESUCON

Colour Plates by
PHILIP BURTON, GEOFFREY DAVISON, R DAVID DIGBY, DANA GARDNER, PETER HAYMAN, IAN LEWINGTON, DAVID QUINN and CHRIS ROSE

Woodcuts by
DANA GARDNER

ACADEMIC PRESS
San Diego · London · Boston · New York · Sydney · Tokyo · Toronto

This book is printed on acid-free paper.

Library of Congress Cataloging-in-Publication Data

Wells, David, Dr.

The Birds of the Thai-Malay Peninsula/by David R. Wells.

p. cm,

Includes index.

Contents: V.1. The non-passerine birds of southern Burma, southern Thailand, Peninsular Malaysia and Singapore

ISBN 0–12–742961–1 (alk. paper)

1. Birds—Thailand. 2. Birds—Malay Peninsula. I. Title.

QL691.T5W45 1998

598′ .09593—dc21 97-39326

CIP

ISBN 0–12–742961–1

ACADEMIC PRESS

24–28 Oval Road, London NW1 7DX, UK

http://www.hbuk.co.uk/ap/

AP Natural World is published by

ACADEMIC PRESS

a division of Harcourt Brace & Company

525 B Street, Suite 1900, San Diego, CA 92101, USA

http://www.apnet.com

Typesetting by Phoenix Photosetting, Chatham, Kent

Printed in Great Britain by The Bath Press, Bath

CONTENTS

LIST OF PLATES

LIST OF MAPS AND FIGURES

PREAMBLE

Alfred Russel Wallace collected birds in the neighbourhood of the Straits Settlements over a few months of 1854, and while passing through again in later years. Some of these specimens still exist, most now at the Tring branch of the British Natural History Museum where quite a few surfaced in the material researched for this book. Free of trade connections, they supply about the earliest dependable localizations that we have from the Peninsula although, typically, even Wallace found no use for more than a territory name and perhaps a year date on a label.

Recorders of scientific detail seem not to have arrived before the 1870s, including certain soldier-naturalists posted to the new Malayan garrisons and professional collectors sent from India by leading S Asian ornithologist of the day, Allan O. Hume. Hume's employees explored Tenasserim and, in the far south, Singapore and S Johor. Assisted by local recruits (including the Selangor police chief, H.C. Syers), they then worked intervening localities along the W coast, but were barred from the interior and eastern lowlands by security difficulties that were to set back knowledge of the uplands and beyond by one or more decades. Hume's plans for the writing of a companion to his *Birds of Tenasserim* (Hume and Davison 1878) must also have been dropped at about that time, but not before he had summarized interim results in issues of his house journal *Stray Feathers* (Hume 1879, 1880). The 20,000 specimens these are said to have covered mark the beginning of objective faunal studies in the Peninsula. One hundred and twenty years on, other, biological types of information contained in this immense collection have been tapped here probably for the first time.

No one survey project since has ever worked the ground of all four modern states of the Peninsula, but from the early 1900s ornithologists stationed locally produced occasional partial updates. H.C. Robinson and F.N. Chasen's handbook series *The Birds of the Malay Peninsula* (1927–1939) covered all non-Burmese territory, and a late concluded fifth volume (BMP5: Medway and Wells 1976) carried information forward to the end of 1973. This new book takes in extra ground, although still not a whole zoogeographical province, and Volume One on non-passerines covers 22 more years, to 31 December 1995. A few 1996 records have been added in proof where these materially alter conclusions but a separate addendum will be needed to bring fresh findings level with publication of Volume Two (passerines). Many collaborators have shared new data throughout, but ultimate choice of content and wording has been mine alone. In making this I have set out to be comprehensive over the review period and am reasonably confident of the outcome, but would never claim to have discovered every last source. The format of the species accounts, with its multiple subject-headings, is designed to cope with oversights by deliberately highlighting apparent information-gaps. These are for plugging, and over the coming 18 months of writing I would appreciate hearing from readers with items for an addendum that might help towards that end.

BMP5 emphasized a shift of interest to field ecology among bird students lately arrived at local universities and other research establishments in the region. The trend has continued, and with many more individuals participating since there has been no loss of continuity. Professionals have again made a large contribution, via theses and scientific papers, but more than evenly matched this time by the contribution of amateurs. Whereas organizations such as the British forces ornithology clubs serviced a minority of locally based expatriate birdwatchers in the past, thriving home-grown equivalents, including the Bird Conservation Society of Thailand (formerly Bangkok Bird Club) and Bird Study Groups of the Malaysian and Singapore Nature Societies, with their own record-handling procedures, now supply a whole new layer of co-ordination and information-exchange for all. The energetic Thais run a dependable monthly *Bulletin* and, at the opposite end of the Peninsula, Richard Ollington's personally produced *Birdline Singapore* approaches its eighth year. Elsewhere, the long-running *Bird Report* series of the Malayan Nature Society ceased publication in the early 1990s (as this book project started), overlapped and superseded by Bird Group publications *Enggang* (in Malaysia) and *Singapore Avifauna*, both now supplemented by yet more new titles, *Suara Enggang* and *Iora* respectively. Some local material also finds its way to the widely circulating *Bulletin* and journal *Forktail* of the international Oriental Bird Club. As text citations will show, all of these have been used to the full. Regrettably, nothing covers the relevant part of Burma, an area of special theoretical interest and deepening conservation concern (Blower 1985, 1985a).

Amateur and full time ornithologists have contributed, on balance, different kinds of information, though with no sharp boundary between their spheres of interest. Faunistics is shared, and with security problems on the wane (only Pakchan still totally off limits in the late 1990s), more of the Peninsula has been opened to field exploration recently than at any time since before World War Two. In certain environments this has developed into a race against habitat loss, but the many new range-records since BMP5 include some remarkable discoveries, and rediscoveries. In all over 50 species, including 34 non-passerines, have been added to the peninsular list against only two (Wood Snipe and Saunder's Tern) removed since 1973.

Research over the review period has included more long-term monitoring of forest bird communities, at one site into a third decade, relying as before on steady-effort mist-netting and ringing, but on a grander scale and with colour-ringing added to reveal more about sociality and individual ranging. Radio-tagging has aided work on the ecology and sociobiology of forest pheasants, daily ranging of arboreal frugivores, and the foraging of Barn Owls in oil-palm agriculture. Wing-tags and genetic markers (via DNA finger-printing) have helped unravel the social and breeding strategies of a colonial-nesting bee-eater. Direct bird/plant interactions remain under-worked, but have recently included observations on the response of a sunbird to rhythms of nectar production and, on a grander scale, resource partitioning by a forest fig-tree assemblage and its consumer community of birds. Interest in migration has continued, with intermittent work on nocturnal passage at Fraser's Hill (Malaysian Main Range) until the well-known trapping site there was lost to a housing development. Following the creation of INTERWADER, later re-named Asian Wetland Bureau and now the Asia-Pacific regional wing of Wetlands International, new attention given to migratory shorebirds (waders) is coordinated over their entire Asia-Pacific flyway, via regular monitoring of roosts, use of light aircraft to count whole standing populations and search out concentration points along remote coastlines, and mark-and-release for data on annual cycles, individual routes and mid-journey refuelling sites. Studies of physiological performance in other groups have included comparison of metabolic rates (among over-wintering migrants and others), chick-growth adaptations, and determinants of reproductive effort, mainly in aerial insectivores (swifts, bee-eaters and swallows). These birds have also been the subject of diet and foraging-space studies. In the meantime, interest in systematics has returned, with new kinds of taxonomic evidence (acoustic, behavioural, molecular) applied, among non-passerines, to cuckoos, owls and swifts. There has also been applied work, on urban nuisance species (mynas) and the role of birds as pest control agents, including use of managed populations of owls against rats in agriculture.

Conservation issues are taken up in the Introduction. They have begun to influence field exploration (e.g., the search for the last population remnants of Gurney's Pitta, an ornithological *cause célèbre*), and are set to dictate more of the research agenda to come. Some dedicated projects are already in place, including a programme of monitoring the impact of logging cycles on forest bird communities long-term, currently at only one site in Malaysia but ripe for replication elsewhere. Conservation is one of the species-account headings, and all species have been assigned an estimate of their security status. If treatments seem repetitive, this has been less a question of finding something meaningful to say than of dealing with issues that operate at community level. Over the past three decades, natural habitats particularly of the lowlands, and even certain agricultural systems of traditionally high biodiversity value, have suffered much deterioration and fragmentation. Finding rich or otherwise important sites is one thing, holding them in the face of other landuse pressures quite another. During this period some professional ornithologists in the Peninsula have diverted most of their resources to working directly for the rescue and management of sites (the Khao Nor Chuchi Lowland Forest project in Krabi province a prime example). 'Stake-outs' particularly of plains-level forest around which birders regularly trek give a comforting illusion of stability, disguising the meaning of the tracts of defaunated landscape that isolate such fragments. The message of real biogeographical significance is that except perhaps within Taman Negara national park (and even there now by no means certainly), complete representations of the community of these lowland forests, such as were widespread into the 1960s, seem no longer to be findable anywhere in the Peninsula. Pakchan has hardly been checked, but satellite imagery suggests forest destruction there has not slackened since ecologists last reported on conditions in the early 1980s. Global alarm bells about the state of this central part of the Sunda biogeographical sub-region may be ringing but, for various reasons, by no means as loudly as they should be.

June 1998

David Wells
Illington, Norfolk,
United Kingdom

ACKNOWLEDGEMENTS

Most countries of the Peninsula now have, or will soon acquire, their own national field guides, inevitably to be followed by attempts at a general handbook to the area. More easily proposed than delivered, of course, and much more time has been devoted to readying this one volume than most of those involved imagined would have been needed for the entire project. That it has actually come to pass is owed to a decision by Lady Yuen Peng McNeice to back production of a book that could be dedicated to her late brother, Dato' Loke Wan Tho. She has been repaid with a long wait, patiently borne, while her generous support bought writing time, the mobility needed for field and museum research, and a unique opportunity to commission a large amount of original artwork. One hundred and twenty new coloured plates encompass most of the avifauna. One immediate and public result of this art commission, and the associated publication subsidy, is that an altogether more ambitious book than would otherwise have been possible has appeared at a price, it is hoped, still within the pocket of its intended key audience, the bird students at work in the field.

For help and guidance on content, special thanks are due to collaborators Philip Round and Uthai Treesucon of the Center for Conservation Biology, Mahidol University, Bangkok. As advisors to the project on the Thai part of the Peninsula, and Thai ornithology in general, they steered me to material I would never otherwise have found, responded to numerous specialized queries, and made over the time to vet a full draft of the species accounts, adding much information of their own in the process. Sources for the Thailand part of the baseline habitat maps are theirs. I am completely in their debt also for locating and romanizing Thai bird names, and supplying non-speakers of this tonal language with a working guide to pronunciation.

While the research and writing have been fun, effectively absorbing a long set of field diaries and tidying away loose ends of my own making, this is really a review of the collective findings of many observers. Exactly how many has only become apparent as I have drawn up formal acknowledgement, it turns out, of eight times more people than were listed in the last large-scale review (BMP5). Most of the increase is due to amateurs, collecting data in spare time as they do everywhere, and numbers divide more or less equally between resident birdwatchers and visitors on tour (which was certainly not the balance 25 years ago). Many have corresponded directly, or will recognize that I have lifted information from limited-circulation reports. Others may be taken aback to discover a mention for unpublished material that has reached me indirectly. The back-up files of national recorders and report editors have been typical sources, raided routinely and which I have thought it right to process in the same way as other contributions.

For all of their new or confirmatory data, made available by whatever route, I am indebted to: Abdul Razak Jalalludin, Aini Zubedy, Aj Kasem, Amara (Tremongkol) Naksatit, C. Amdahl, L. Amdahl, F.G. Amigo, Amorn Liukiratiyutkul, K. Andersen, G. Anderson, P. Andrew, M. Ang, Apichart Nana, Arpha Triyan, J.S. Ash, P. Aston, M.L. Avery, T. Axelson, D.N. Bakewell, S. Baltz, R.J. Banham, H.S. Barlow, B. Barnacal, A. Barnes, S. Barnes, M. Barter, R. Battler, G. Baylis, C. Bealey, K.G. Beauchamp, the late H.L. Bell, N. Bell, B. Bengtsson, E.L. Bennett, P. Benstead, H.-U. Bernard, M. Betts, K.D. Bishop, A. Blakelock, B.D. Bond, C. Bosman, J. Boswall, R. Bowie, J. Bowlen, D. Bradford, C. Briffett, C. Brooks, J. Brown, E. Browning, D.M. Bryant, H.A. Buck, S. Buckton, P. Burgess, N. Burton, P. Burton, P.J.K. Burton, A. Camens, I. Camens, J. Carter, M.I. Carter, Chachada Hongvisitkul, L. Chan, Chan Yoke Keng, J. Chance, L. Chang, P. Chang, Chavalit Vidthayanon, J. Cheah, C. Cheong, H. Cheong, Chew Soo Hui, A. Chia, Chim Wai Main, Chin Kok Ann, Chin See Chung, Ching Koh An, M. Chong, M.H.N. Chong, Chong Swee Hor, Choy Wai Mun, S. Christensen, T.D. Christensen, E. Christopherson, J. Chuah, P. Chuah, D.L. Clugston, M. Cocker, P.D. Coe, S. Coe, S. Cohen, R.L. Cole, J.F.R. Colebrook-Robjent, G. Condell, M.A. Connor, R.T. Corlett, M. Cowlard, Earl of Cranbrook, N. Crockford, M. Crosby, R. Crossley, P. Cullen, P. Cunningham, S. Dabell, F. Danielsen, A. Darby, G.W.H. Davison, J. Dawn, N. de Sadeleer, L. Degnan, G. Dekkers, J. del Hoyo, E.C. Dickinson, D. Diskin, H. Dissing, R.J. Dobias, J. Drummond, Duangdao Suwanrungsi, J.E. Duckett, N.E. Duckett, J.A. Duggan, F.L. Dunn, J. Dunn, J.N. Dymond, A. Eaton, J.C. Eames, S. Eccles, C. Edelstam, P.J. Edwards, M. Eldridge, V. Esbensen, C. Escott, R. Eve, I. Ewing, T. Ewing, R.J. Fairbank, Faizah Jamal, Farid Hamid, D.S. Farrow, D. Fautin, Fauzee Yusof, C.J. Feare, L. Ferdinand, R.A. Filby, R. Flood, Fong Chee Wai, J. Forshaw, C.M. Francis, R. Frazier, D. Free, Gan Cheong Ann, L. Gan, S.K. Ganesan, D.G. Gardner, E. Gilston, H.G. Gilston, M. Giselet, L. Godfrey, M. Godfrey, Goh Si Guim, M. Golley, A. Goodwin, A. Gordon, P.T. Green, G. Greenblatt, J.L. Gregory, R. Gregory-Smith, R.F.

Grimmett, A.-M. Guigue, Gunasegeran Sellapan, T. Gunasegeran, E. Hagen, A.J. Hails, C.J. Hails, R.E. Hale, M. Hall, R. Harwood, A.F.A. Hawkins, P. Heath, P.A. Heathcote, P.E. Heathcote, T. Heatwole, A.J. Helbig, R. Hew, Hiew Kiam Phin, R.T. Hiscock, R.W. Hiscock, Ho Hua Chew, Ho Wah Loong, J. Hodge, D.A. Holmes, P. Holt, J. Hong, Hong Lee Tiam, D. Hosking, E. Hosking, M. Hosking, J.R. Howes, R.N. Hughes, L.H. Hurrell, P.J. Hurrell, S.A. Hussain, C. Inskipp, T. Inskipp, J. Izzard, H. Jacobs, F. Jarvis, R.P. Jaensch, O.F. Jakobsen, Jalalludin Mohamed Isa, Jarasri Sittiyot, Jarujin Nabhitabhata, D. Jeans, C.J.S. Jeffs, A. Jensen, H. Jensen, A. Jeyarajasingam, Jitraporn Satamaya, A.D. Johns, C. Johnson, S. Johnson, P. Joost, Jukrit Sareenonthachai, A.R. Kalai, Kalthom Abdul Latiff, Kampol Sukhumalind, Kang Nee, Kant Rattanajun, S. Karuppiah, Kashiyah M. Hashim, M. Kavanagh, K. Kee, P.R. Kennerley, R.R. Kersley, V.M. Kersley, Khoo Kim Choo, Khoo Soo Ghee, E.G.R. Kidd, B. King, R.D.W. King, P. Koh, K. Komolphalin, Koo Yuan Hsin, Kriengsak Jiajanpong, Krit Rerkwirun, K. Kumar, C. Kurian, R. Lai, K.C. Lam, M. Lambarth, S. Lambarth, F.R. Lambert, A. Lamont, N.P.E. Langham, R.V. Lansdown, A. Lau, J. Lee, Lee King Li, Lee Shek Hah, G.M. Lenton, Leong Kek Ping, Leong Siew Lin, R. Lévèque, A. Lewis, B. Li, Li Kok Wee, E. Liew, B. Lim, Lim Chan Koon, D. Lim, E. Lim, G. Lim, H. Lim, K. Lim, Lim Kim Chuah, Lim Kim Chye, Lim Kim Keang, Lim Kim Seng, Lim Lea Cheen, Lim Lee Hock, Lim Lin Heng, Lis Hartini Agdes, C. Loh, E. Loh, Loh Teng Huat, A. Long, L. Loo, T. Lund, P. Lutge, T. Lutge, S.G. Madge, G.C. Madoc, P. Magsalay, Mah Yoon Loong, D. Mahony, F. Maher, Mana Nakcharoen, C.F. Mann, M. Tharmalingam, R. Manoanmony, P. Marklevitz, J.T. Marshall, E. Marteijn, J. Martin, B. May, T. Mayer, K. McCarey, H.E. McClure, J. McCombie, P.J.K. McGowan, J. McKellar, J. McLoughlin, D.S. Melville, Mereek Singh, C. Mitchell, J.B. Mitchell, K. Mitchell, Mohamed Akhir Othman, Tungku Mohamed Nazim Yaacob, A. Moon, N. Moores, G.E. Morris, H.E. Morris, P. Morris, T. Mundkur, C. Murmann, K. Murphy, P.J.A. Murray, Musa, E.T. Myers, Nachatrasingam Raju, Nakin Khewboonsong, Napat Sirisambhand, J. Nathan, Ng Bee Choo, Ng Siew Lan, Ng Soon Chye, R. Ngim, R. Nicholls, S. Nicholls, L.R. Nielson, G. Nikolaus, J. Nilsson, Nivesh Nadee, Nomchit Nualnet, Noor Azli Yahya, Nora Ibrahim, G. Noramly, R.A. Noske, Nukul Ruttanadakul, C.E. Nuttall, R.F. Ollington, S. O'Neil, Ong Eng Eng, J. Ong, Ong Kiem Sian, M. Ong, R. Ong, Ong Soo Kiat, Ooi Beng Ean, R. Ottval, A. Owyong, Owyong Sue Lin, the late H.T. Pagden, Paipit Lekuthai, Pakorn Kanthong, N. Palaninathan, Panote Krairojananan, Panya Chaiyakum, F. Parish, J.W.K. Parr, M. Parr, Patcharee Komolphalin, J.C. Pearson, J. Penhallurick, B. Perry, M. Persson, P. Peterson, T. Peterson, J. Phang, A. Pierce, K. Phillipps, Pichitra Lawansiri, Pilai Poonswad, A. Poh, L. Poh, I. Polunin, A. Ponnambalam, C. M. Poole, S. Poole, Prakorn Kornlertvanich, Pranee Sachakamol, R.C. Prentice, Prinyakorn Voravan, P.J. Puncheon, H. Puppe, S.P. Quek, Rachit Lekvanich, J. Raemaekers, R. Rajathurai, B. Rapp, U. Remahl, Rajan Rajanathan, Rangsarit Kutkaew, H.T. Rask, A.J. Richards, F. Ridgley, E. Ritikos, D.G. Robertson, I.S. Robertson, D. Robinson, C. Robson, A. Rogers, S. Rooke, Roongroj Jugmongkol, C. Rose, P.D. Round, R. Rowland, F.G. Rozendaal, K. Rubeli, Rungsrit Kanjanavanit, S. Sabapathy, Saerah Yusof, Safizah Abdullah, P. Salaman, E. Salzman, L. Salzman, Santana Pluemshoosak, Sarala Aikanathan, M. Sato, J. Scharringa, F. Schepers, M. Schilthuizen, K.W. Scriven, D.A. Scott, See Swee Leng, A.C. Sebastian, J. See, the late Seub Nakhasathien, G. Seywald, R. Shamera, I. Sharp, R. Shaw-Brown, N. Shelton, P. Sheppard, S. Sheridan-Johnson, L.L. Short, H. Schritt, G. Shrubsall, J.B. Sigurdsson, A. Silcox, J. Silver, W. Silver, M.J. Silvius, J. Sim, D.M. Simpson, W. Simpson, Sin Chye Hock, Siripon Thongaree, Siriwan Nakkuntod, Siti Hawa Yatim, H. Skov, E.M. Smart, B.A.R. Smith, D. Smith, J. Smith, J.G. Smith, L. Smulders, Sng Hwee Lee, Somsak Saengsuriyothin, Sonapa (Wongrattana) Round, G.J. Speight, L.D. Stader, J. Starks, M. Strange, R. Struve, E.M. Stuart, Subaraj Rajathurai, D. Summers-Smith, J. Sunesen, P. Sung, Surapol Duangkae, Surapol Ardseungnern, Susanni Aziz, Sutari bin Supari, Suthee Supparatvikorn, M. Sutherland, T. Sutherland, W. Sutherland, Suvit Khruawan, P. Svensen, R.S.E. Swanquist, C. Swennen, Syed Ali Abdul Kader, Tan Boon Cheong, D. Tan, Tan Cheng Kim, Tan Choong Seng, Tan Hang Chong, J. Tan, Tan Kean Cheang, Tan King Pheow, Tan Lai Ping, Tan Mei Ling, Tan Soon Imm, T. Tan, Tanee Bhamaraniyama, I.B. Tarrant, P. Tatner, A. Tay, D. Tay, Teeranuch Invasa, I.D. Teesdale, R. Teo, Thanam Muthusamy, J.-M. Thiollay, Thiraphon Boonsuk, the late Tho Yow Pong, L. Thomas, R. Thomas, H.M. Thomsen, D. Thomson, C. Thompson, P. Thompson, B. Thong Kam Chuen, R.I. Thorpe, Thoswan Devakul, C. Ting, Tng Sok King, E. Tor, S.J. Toy, the late M.W.F. Tweedie, Uraiporn Wongthieres, Urium Nophakhun, Uthai Treesucon, J.D. Uttley, Valasini Trangkasetsin, S. van Balen, A.B. van den Berg, G. Vanderstichelen, N. Vann, D. Varripillay, N. Venning, A.C. Vilarasan, Vorapoon Ariratananond, Wachara Yusawat, G. Walbridge, Wallada Tesrumpun, P. Warham, Wasan Wattana, D.G. Watkins, D. Watson, D. Waugh, Wee Yeow Chin, A.M. Wells, Wen Foong On, N.J. Westwood, Wilai Chantarawang, D. Wilds, J. Wilds, Wimonrat Asavachaivisit, Wiphaphan Nakphaen, Wiroj Onganunkul, J.A. Wolstencroft, A. Wong, F. Wong, J. Wong, M. Wong, O.K. Wong, S. Wong, Wu Eu Heng, Yang Pah Liang, Yap Kok Thye, S. Yap, Yee Seng Hock, E. Yeo, K.L. Yeo, P.H. Yeo, Yeo Suay Hwee, S. Yeo, J.

Yeo-Ong, D. Yong, K. Yong, Yotin Meekaeo, A.C. Young, G. Young, and J. Ziarno.

This long list I believe covers all whose records have come my way, but in trying to name names comprehensively there is always the risk of someone having been let slip. This accident is particularly likely where an item has been due to a group of observers, and many regional residents do now organize their activities collectively through one or more of the national bird clubs. They will know who have been so missed, and I can only hope not to have offended too seriously.

The above list is of birdwatchers active in the Peninsula mainly over the period of this review. Some date from earlier years and a few are included whose field days are from well before the start of my own. Outstanding among these individuals is Guy Madoc who began a 30-year career in Malaya and Thailand in 1930, published voluminously throughout and witnessed much that, sadly, is now strictly a memory. One of few expatriate naturalists to have rescued some personal records at the outset of the Japanese military occupation (copies retrieved from the abandoned office of the director of the Raffles Museum) and to continue into post-war years, he has made available a large, densely typed file drawn up from diaries in response to publication of BMP5. As text credits show, this unique document has been used here to the full.

Other contributors deserving special mention are colleagues Chris and Sandra Hails, source of an earlier plan for a handbook that might well have been written jointly (and, no doubt, finished long since) had priorities elsewhere not intervened. Their ideas for that project have not been allowed to go to waste. Marina Wong and Charles M. Francis kindly made available large amounts of unpublished information from recent and ongoing ringing studies in Malaysian inland forests. The Malaysian Department of Wildlife and National Parks, Wetlands International Asia-Pacific, and the managers of Sungai Buloh nature reserve, Singapore, all gave me access to similar data on waterbirds.

Some sections of the species accounts were researched mostly at museums. By no means all of the holdings there are of material from the Peninsula were covered, but a good number of institutions around the world answered queries, were generous with study facilities, or made loans from the collections in their care. For this help, author and artists wish to thank directors and staff of: the Department of Ornithology, Academy of Natural Sciences, Philadelphia; the Department of Birds, American Museum of Natural History, New York (at which I held a Frank Chapman Fellowship during leave of absence from Malaysia in 1984); Dr Boonsong Lekagul's private museum, Bangkok; the Department of Zoology, Chulalongkorn University, Bangkok; Colchester Museums, Essex, UK; the Department of Wildlife and National Parks (PERHILITAN), Kuala Lumpur; the Institute for Medical Research Medical Ecology Laboratory, Kuala Lumpur; the Malaysian National Museum (Muzium Negara), Kuala Lumpur; the Department of Ornithology, National Museum of Natural History, Washington DC; the National Museum of Natural History, Leiden; the Zoological Reference Collections, National University of Singapore; the Sub-department of Ornithology, Natural History Museum, Tring, UK; the Department of Ornithology, Royal Ontario Museum, Toronto; the Division of Wildlife Conservation, Royal Thai Forest Department, Bangkok; the Division of Ecological Research, Thailand Institute for Scientific and Technological Research, Bangkok; the Zoology Department, University of Malaya, Kuala Lumpur (my work-base until 1995); the Western Foundation of Vertebrate Zoology (housing the F.G.H. Allen egg collection), Camarillo, California; and the University Museum of Zoology, Cambridge. Some of the above also offered access to libraries. Others well used were the Edward Grey Institute Alexander Library, Oxford University; the Linnean Society Library, London; the Natural History Museum Zoology Library, London; and the Worldwide Fund for Nature Malaysia Resource Library, Kuala Lumpur. For help over many years at these various institutions, special thanks are due to M.P. Adams, L. Birch, the late Boonsong Lekagul, P.R. Colston, G.L. Douglas, R.W.R.J. Dekker, J.C. Fisher, J. Heath, Jarujin Nabhitabhata, K.A. Joysey, M. Kavanagh, L.F. Kiff, Lim Boo Liat, G.F. Mees, Niphan Ratanaworabhan, Phairot Suvannakorn, R. Prŷs-Jones, K.W. Scriven, R. Simons, L.L. Short, P. Sweet, J.T. Marshall, Mohamed Khan bin Momin Khan, F.H. Sheldon, P. Sweet, M.P. Walters, F.E. Warr, Yang Chang Man and R.L. Zusi.

Two referees appointed by Academic Press Limited read trial text and influenced certain large decisions on layout. Nigel Collar scrutinized a late-stage draft of the systematic section, rescued me from errors and inconsistencies, and paved the way for a final revision. At the Press itself, executive editor Andrew Richford and production editor Roopa Baliga worked calm and indispensible magic at every stage of putting the book together. I am grateful to them all.

This publication is Project MYS 156/89 of Worldwide Fund for Nature Malaysia, and WWFM has provided financial management and accounting services throughout. In accordance with her interest in wildlife conservation, Lady McNeice has stipulated that all royalties from sales worldwide shall accrue to the WWFM Conservation Fund, for appropriate projects in the field.

INTRODUCTION TO VOLUME ONE

THE REVIEW AREA

Exploring lowland forests of Tenasserim in the 1870s, W.R Davison recorded a mainly Sundaic (zoogeographical 'Malaysian') bird fauna north to Tavoy (Dawei) district, several degrees beyond where one is generally accepted as having reached in Thailand. Malayan museums service (FMSM) researchers fixed the Thai part of the transition at about 10°30'N, level with the upper reaches of the Pakchan estuary, and this was the limit adopted by H.C. Robinson for his handbook series (Robinson 1927). Kloss (1929) preferred a 10° limit, coast to coast, and was followed by Chasen (1935) who hinted at a decision less to do with science than the avoidance of colonial territory administered from India (independent Thailand, it seems, presented less of a problem). Much later, and for a different reason, this was the limit adopted in BMP5.

Bioclimate, mapped from a selection of temperature and rainfall variables (Gaussen *et al.* 1967), reveals conditions capable of supporting a rain forest climax extend actually north even of the Robinson limit. In particular, most of the rest of Chumphon province appears to be wet and weakly seasonal enough for such forest to have occurred at plains level — a prediction P.D. Round and U. Treesucon were able to affirm on remote, valley-bottom sites at latitude 10°43'N, where they also found many typical Sunda forest birds (Round 1988).

This discovery prompted a decision to extend coverage of Thai territory by one degree of latitude to 11°N (approximately the Chumphon/Prachuap Khiri Khan provincial boundary) and having done that, rather than back-track in traditional fashion around the edge of Burma, move directly west to the Andaman sea. The area reviewed by this book thus includes: Burmese territory in the Pakchan division of Tenasserim (now Thanintharyi) state, 14 southern provinces of Thailand (including all of Chumphon), all territory of Peninsular Malaysia and all of the Singapore Republic, with associated islands and surrounding waters out to the sea boundary shown in Map 1. This follows roughly the break between continental shelf and deep oceanic waters of the Andaman sea, approximate international sea frontiers through the Melaka and Singapore straits, a line NNE over the S China sea to the Terengganu off-shore oil-field (longitude 105°13'E), then NW into the gulf of Thailand, incorporating the main zones of local shipping, hence of most observations at sea.

On land, the extra degree of latitude adds just a handful of species not treated in BMP5: Grey Peacock Pheasant, Yellow-legged Buttonquail and Asian Barred Owlet among resident non-passerines, and a single wintering passerine, Asian Stubtail (Sylviidae) (see page xxxv for the scientific names of all birds mentioned in the Introduction). Only the buttonquail is confirmed from Pakchan, and my real excuse for incorporating this slice of Burmese territory is the access it affords to large collections made by Davison and others at sites west of the Pakchan estuary (BMNH). Except to note the general level of deforestation revealed by remote sensing (Blasco and Bellan 1995) and probability that timber thieves have redoubled their efforts since Thailand halted domestic logging, only trivial items of modern information have been added from the field.

CHOICE OF A NAME

F.N. Chasen mapped an acceptable continential limit to the 'Malaysian' (Sunda) zoogeographical subregion, but failed to make use of it, and left no name applicable to a full zoogeographical province on the mainland (equivalent to Sumatran, Bornean, etc.). The search, it seems, is still on. As far as I have been able to ascertain, no zoologist has employed 'Malay Peninsula' in just the sense required, or even in any generally agreed sense. Hume's, Kloss's and Robinson's definitions all vary in detail, from which I conclude there should be no strong objection to the renaming of yet another arbitrary part. Borrowed from a geological source (Alexander 1962) and already in the zoogeographical literature (Boonsong and McNeely 1977), 'Thai-Malay Peninsula' serves to link past titles with the typical spread of recent field activity in the review area. Better than any more complicated alternative, it recognizes the contribution to local ornithology now being made from Thailand.

If and when a Burmese government re-opens the rest of the mainland to scientific exploration some more neutral term (such as 'Kra province', after the name of the isthmus) will be needed for the natural whole. Unless another meaning is clear from the context, hereafter, all unqualified references to 'Peninsula' or adjectival 'peninsular' are just to the review area. 'Malaysia' is likewise just Peninsular Malaysia, and 'west' and 'east' relate to appropriate coasts, not to any Bornean part of the country.

GEOGRAPHY

LANDFORM: The Thai-Malay Peninsula of the title is the outer 1200 km of the southernmost, SSW-trending finger of continental Asia: nowhere more than 320 km wide and barely 60 km opposite the point of mainland Burma (Kra isthmus), between co-ordinates 11° and 1°10'N (southern edge of Singapore's S archipelago) and 97°37' and 104°33'E (respectively, the Similan islands and outer edge of the Pahang-Johor archipelago).

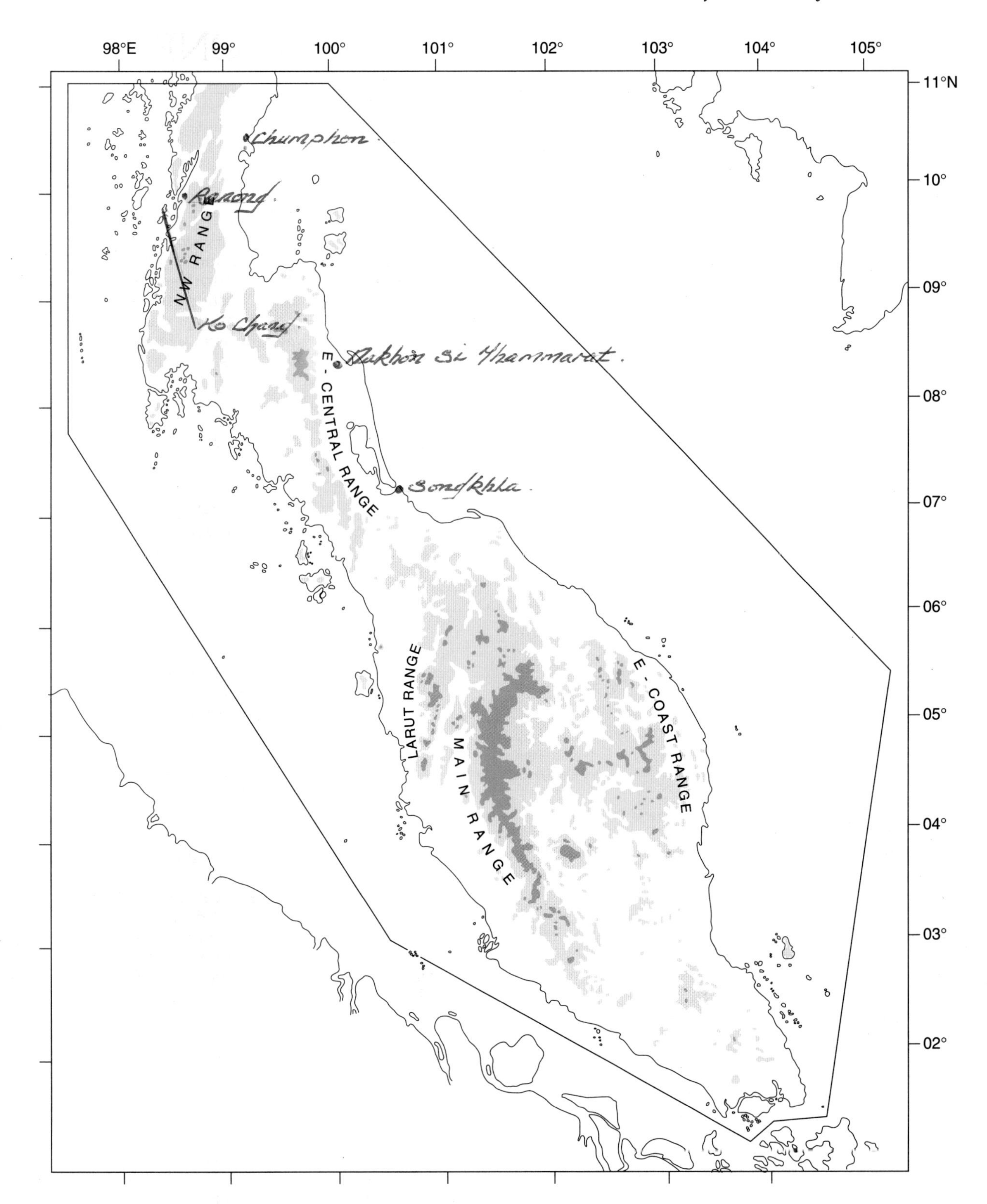

Map 1. The review area, showing sea boundary and main relief. Contours mark the average steepland boundary and lower edge of montane oak-laurel forest.

Long stable tectonically, this is an anciently exposed part of geological Sundaland. Its main topography is determined by a Mesozoic granite batholith upthrusted below older sedimentary strata and, locally in the eastern half of Malaysia, some volcanics. These surface with a roughly N–S strike, the granite as blocks and ranges of hills and mountains that rise abruptly from a distinct terrain-break (the hill-foot or steepland boundary, at an average 150 m above sea level) to maximum heights of around 2000 m. Upland plateaus (as at Cameron Highlands) are rare on granite, while sheer-sided, erosion-resistant quartz dykes with elfin vegetation resembling summit forest, regardless of altitude, are not uncommon.

Most individual peaks of ornithological importance bear well-established map names. This is not true of whole mountain ranges. The five most often referred to here (Map 1) have been fixed as: the *NW Range* (from the N Ranong/Chumphon border to low outliers on Phuket island, and high enough to support montane forest only at a few extreme summits, none explored); the *E-central Range* (from the Surat Thani/Nakhon Si Thammarat border south, with gaps, eventually to the Malaysian frontier, where continuous with a ridge of Palaeozoic limestone; highest in the north, to a maximum 1835 m); the *Main Range* (from the Yala/Narathiwat divide, where known as the Budo Range, south to the Negeri Sembilan/Melaka border; highest and longest, with by far the largest areas of land in all upland vegetation zones; maximum summit height 2182 m); the *Larut Range* (also known as the Bintang Range, west of the Perak river and connected via submontane ridges to high outliers along the E Kedah/Yala frontier; highest summit 1862 m); and the *E-coast Range* (on the border of Terengganu with Kelantan and Pahang, and incorporating the E edge of Taman Negara national park; maximum summit 1461 m). Only along the central spine of Malaysia do metamorphosed sedimentary rocks themselves form significant hill country, culminating in the high, mainly sandstone Tahan complex and outliers (maximum summit 2188 m). Mainly metamorphosed sedimentaries also cap one small area close to the position of Nong peak, E-central Range, Gagau and Tapis peaks, both flanking the E-coast Range, and, further south, form lesser hills adjacent, e.g., to the main uplands of the Endau-Rompin conservation area. Their terrain is often very steep, with cliff exposures not uncommon, and occasional plateaus that can be of significance to bird distribution.

Below the main mountains, the interior landscape ranges from steep ridge-and-valley to gently undulating, according to parent rock, with deep, level alluvial deposits on coastal plains and in the middle valleys of the larger rivers. Locally, north from about 3°N, limestone inselbergs of the tower karst type outcrop from a more general subterranean pavement, with many caves and fissures, overhangs behind external stalactites, and often spectacular cliffs ranging from a few tens to hundreds of metres high — key habitat for resident Peregrine Falcons, Dusky Crag Martins and Blue Rock Thrushes. Main concentrations of such outcropping are in the Kinta (Perak) and upper Kelantan valleys, on the NW coastal plain and islands from the Langkawi group and Perlis (where the border range is limestone) to Phangnga bay, and in the upper Sok valley, Surat Thani, with probably the tallest example in the Peninsula (Gua Peningat) isolated in western Taman Negara.

Apart from those draining swamp forests, all significant rivers rise on high ground and pass through a torrent stage before reaching the plains. Except for the Perak river, flowing nearly 400 km mainly southward to the mid-Melaka Straits, the largest (Bandon, Pattani, Kelantan, Terengganu and Pahang) all pass to the E coast. According to flow and flood regimes, successive stages are edged by characteristically different tree associations that, except in conservation areas, are well preserved now only on headwater slopes. Hardly any of the original lower-valley freshwater swamp forest fringe, believed to have been core habitat for birds such as Storm's Stork, is left anywhere. Last stands (with storks) along the lower Perak river were assigned to agricultural development during this review period.

The coastal plains themselves are Quaternary; flat, low-lying and most extensive opposite the Melaka Straits, up to 60 km wide in Perak, but on the E coast near this width also in Nakhon Si Thammarat. Seaward progression has at times been rapid: 24 km over 1500 years in S Pahang and a significant part of that within the last 200 years (Tjia 1988). The silt loads of many western rivers suggest that deposition rates near their estuaries may be close to a post-glacial maximum now. Comparing successive generations of 1:50,000 survey maps reveals some quite astonishing local shifts of the front edge of W-coast mangrove forests, by as much as one kilometre in a decade locally in W Johor.

Shore-fronts develop alternatively from land-derived muds, mud/sand mixes, or the marine sands of successive storm beaches, according to degree of exposure to monsoon wave action (mainly sand where fully exposed), creating different types of habitat. On storm-beach coasts, swales between the younger sand ridges are often water-filled, and behind prograding shores of all kinds long stretches of coast have been capped or infilled by peat, often metres deep, laid down since the highest standing of the sea 5–6000 years ago. The widest peat-bogs still bearing forest and not yet canalized are humped above the general level of the plain.

As would be expected, intertidal exposures, vital to the ecology of migratory shorebirds, ardeids, etc., are broadest (locally more than one kilometre) and muddiest on sheltered coasts, especially of the Johor and Melaka Straits; according to marine charts, also those parts of Pakchan in the lee of large islands. Elsewhere, as along the E side of the Peninsula, such habitat is confined to enclaves protected from strong wave action, including Bandon, Pak Phanang and Pattani bays, the Kelantan delta and Mersing bay.

CLIMATE: No part of the Peninsula is much beyond 100 km from the sea, most of it less. This proximity, and an inner tropical position determining only a small annual variation of daylength, fixes shade temperatures within a relatively narrow, equable span. Oscillation through the year is greatest in the areas of most seasonal rainfall, but nowhere in the lowlands do monthly means vary by much more than four degrees about an annual mean of close to 28°C, and in the SW lowlands by less than three degrees. As through most of the tropics, that is less than typical 24-hour amplitude. Apart from recent El Niño extremes and the still-local but increasingly obvious impact of air pollution on temperature cycling, the latter varies from less than ten to near 20°, but nowhere do dry-season maxima exceed the high 30s or (nocturnal) minima drop much below the 20s.

Ignoring likely effects of mountain size, height, isolation and proximity to the sea, mean ambient temperature falls by close to 1°C per 100 m of elevation. Hence at 1000 m, near the lower margin of the montane forest zone, it has cooled by about 10°C. Quicker change and more night cooling, owing to faster radiation of heat back into space, are other features of mountain climate, and rare night-time temperature extremes at high altitude have come within a few degrees of freezing. Through the year, however, means are no less stable than in the lowlands, hence in no way should the mountains of the Peninsula be thought of as 'temperate'. Regardless of height above sea level, temperature oscillations disappear a few centimetres into the soil, and root temperature may be one reason why vegetation boundaries on large slopes are so regularly linked to altitude.

Average annual rainfall varies from a little above 1500 mm to around 5000 mm, but not in any expected relationship to seasonality of precipitation, or even to latitude. E Negeri Sembilan to NW Johor, Jelebu district (Negeri Sembilan), a small area on the southern loop of the Pahang river, the W-coast plain from Kuala Selangor to Lumut, a narrow N–S strip of inland Perak, inland Perlis, and Pattani, Krabi and lowland Surat Thai provinces all register less than 2000 mm per annum. Areas of highest fall (over 3500 mm) are the E-coast Range and its immediate eastern fringe, the W-central face and foot of the Larut Range (Perak) and, above all, the NW from Ranong through Pakchan. Nowhere, it seems, is volume alone too low to support evergreen rain forests. Moderated by soils and ground-water, the main constraint on distribution of vegetation in the lowlands seems to be the length of a regular dry season.

Three factors (affected by El Niño events) influence rainfall in the Peninsula (Map 2): alternating on-shore (SW and NE) monsoons and associated N–S oscillation of the intertropical convergence zone of low pressure (ITCZ); orographic (mountain-range) effects; and convectional storms. Opportunities for convectional rain occur more or less everywhere. In the equatorial south, within the summer rain-shadow of the Sumatran highlands, this is an important source year-round, extremely localized but peaking overall during the light, variable wind conditions of the two equinoctial inter-monsoon periods. Details vary over relatively short distances but only along the E coast is this pattern overridden by a wet monsoon (blowing rain-laden off the S China sea during November–February). Crucially, nowhere south of latitude approximately 6°N is any month of the year dependably dry.

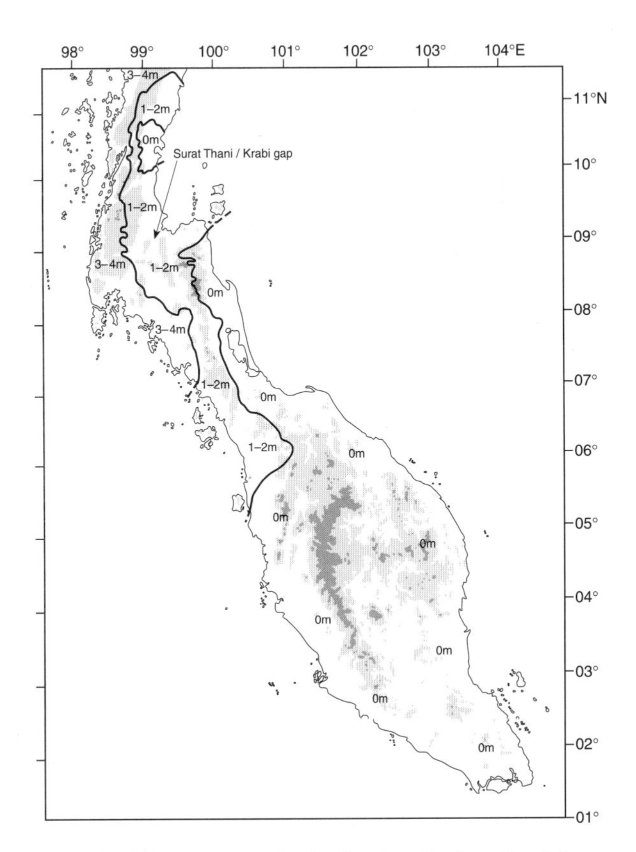

Map 2. Climate zones in the Peninsula: length of the dry season (number of consecutive, dependable drought months) shown against main relief. Adapted from Gaussen et al. *1967.*

Clear of Sumatra, weather is dominated by monsoons, and but for the strike of the E-central Range this whole northern part of the Peninsula would be ever-wet. Except where the system 'leaks', as apparently through the Krabi/Surat Thani gap, lowlands to the east of this range receive only a minor part of their total rain in summer, and in the inland shadow of the mountains experience a 1–2 month dry season. At this time, all western areas, plus Surat Thani, reach a rainfall peak. The opposite applies in winter. Eastern provinces, up to Nakhon Si Thammarat, are then at their wettest, whereas a 1–3-plus month dry season prevails in Surat Thani (then leeward of the highest stretch of the E-central Range) and throughout the west. Climatically rather isolated Chumphon province, clear of the northern tip of the mountains, appears to receive sufficient moisture off the Gulf of Thailand to suppress the winter drought of immediate E-coast neighbours. Northwards, the winter monsoon dries, whereas the SW monsoon off the Indian Ocean and Andaman Sea has by then gained the power to ensure the occurrence of a summer rain-peak everywhere.

The divide between ever-wet and seasonal climates is also the zone across which Malayan-type lowland rain forest gives way to the Thai-Burmese type (see below). This is defined as having run through Perlis to Pattani (Whitmore 1984), but E-coast bioclimates (Map 2) suggest the Malayan formation might once have ranged further north.

Montane habitats are exposed to the same seasonalities, but generally less convectional rain. On windward slopes and summit ridges, small-leaved, stress-adapted upland forests established on thin soils must gain significant amounts of their total water needs by 'combing' condensation directly out of ground-level cloud. This surely applies also to their many epiphytes, and combing and regular wetting of bark (stem-flow) account for the 'mossiness', especially of upper montane forest, down to the forest floor.

HABITAT CATEGORIES

The criteria by which wild populations recognize their own ecological space have rarely been studied. 'Habitats' are convenient substitute pigeon-holes; divisions of landscape or water recognizable in the field that encompass rather than actually define space used, coarsely enough, usually, to fit a whole set (assemblage) of species (see, e.g., Campbell and Lack 1985).

The following summary descriptions are of the categories of habitat used to compare the ecologies of species or populations. They vary in status from whole biomes or plant communities, supporting distinctive assemblages, to site variants characterized more by shifts of relative abundance, but most represent what I have termed 'core' space for at least one bird species in the Peninsula. Some constitute phases of recovery of vegetation after specified levels of disturbance. All are named as they appear in the species accounts, and sorted here as 'forest' (1–11) (see Ashton 1991; Ng 1988; Whitmore 1984, 1988; Wyatt-Smith 1997 for regional detail) or 'non-forest' (12–18), according to the importance of trees and other woody cover.

(1) *MANGROVE FOREST*: At global maximum richness (about 35 tree species) in equatorial SE Asia. A salt-tolerant forest colonizing estuaries and mud-accreting coasts that also receive good flows of nutrients off the land. Characterized by parallel zones of just a few dominants but generally increasing tree diversity back from the advancing shoreline, and varying in the frequency with which they are flooded by the tide (daily to equinoctial spring only). On prograding, accreting shores, typically, a pioneer *Avicennia/Sonneratia* zone gives way successively to *Rhizophora, Bruguiera* and multi-genus zones, with intrusions at the landward edge that often include the spiny-trunked palm *Onchosperma*. Stands of *Nypa fruticans*, a gregarious, stemless palm not recently extensive in the Peninsula, are a subsidiary back-mangrove habitat used by a few forest birds, hence may be just included in this category.

Old, untouched mangrove forest contains large-trunked, 20–30 m high emergents in all zones, hence is multi-layered. I have seen no recent information on the once-extensive mangrove forests of Pakchan, but elsewhere most mainland habitat has long been a commercial source of wood. Typical managed stands are immature pole forests of uniform age and low structural diversity, short in particular of old growth and dead wood, and with nothing like original stature. Some over-exploited Thai forests are now barely more than scrub. There has also been much outright habitat loss from the bunding-off of mid and back zones, with conversion of the land to other purposes. Where freshwater inflows have been blocked or diverted, bunding can further damage the remaining stand. Except on a few conserved islands, continuity of the mangrove succession with inland forests was lost long ago. Potentially, all remaining forest is under threat from the still-vibrant coastal aquaculture industry.

The main distribution of mangroves, in whatever condition, is along sheltered stretches of the W coast. Elsewhere, outliers are confined to deltas and bays of the E coast, and in the few small pockets of Singapore territory not yet subjected to the Republic's coastal land-claim programme.

(2) *STRAND WOODLAND*: Otherwise known as Beach Forest, a very narrow strip of low to medium-height woodland established above high-water mark on accreting sandy shores. It varies from a pure, pioneer stand of *Casuarina equisetifolia*, dense when young but showing little understorey growth later, apart from fringing shrubs (*Scaevola*, *Hibiscus*, etc.) and screw-pines (*Pandanus*), to rather low, even-crowned, mixed woodland of which *Calophyllum*, *Barringtonia* and *Terminalia* are typical tree genera. This, too, tends not to show much sub-canopy layering.

(3) *LOWLAND (SUBCOASTAL) PEATSWAMP FOREST*: Just 'peatswamp forest' in the species accounts. Grows over deep, rain-fed, permanently water-logged, acid peat-muck; the climax a mixed, evergreen forest, layered, with a dense, palm-filled to relatively open understorey, and emergents up to 40 m high. Poor in tree species compared with dry-land rain forest, but many are peculiar to this habitat, as is the spectacular sealing-wax palm *Cyrtostachys*. Among non-trees, ground-level pitcher-plants, diagnostic of nutrient scarcity, are common.

Most of the original stand has been lost to agriculture. Logging has reduced much of what remains to well below natural stature, without emergents. Where interference has been severe, dense, almost pure stands of *Macaranga* may replace it as a secondary forest.

Under drought conditions, peatswamp forest can be fired, and the climax derivative after a history of burning is (4) *PAPERBARK FOREST*, an almost pure stand of *Melaleuca cajuputi*. Drainage and fire are serious and continuing threats. The only significant stretch of original mixed growth for which a reserve, Chalerm Prakiat wildlife sanctuary (Narathiwat province), has been created was torched during the latest El Niño, it is rumoured by squatters seeking to market extra farm land. There is a reasonable chance several bird species have been lost to the Thai fauna as a result of this action.

(5) *FRESHWATER SWAMP FOREST*: Hardly investigated by ornithologists and, as tall forest, nearly

extinct, but guessed to have been the core habitat of a few now-rare bird species. This is mixed to fairly species-poor, sometimes pure-stand, evergreen forest of very variable stature and structure, with or without emergents. In places, large screw-pines are a feature. It occurs on regularly to near-permanently flooded, sometimes shallowly peaty but typically non-acid, fertile sites along the lower reaches of large rivers and fringes of certain still-water wetlands. The latter include Tasik Bera, Pahang, now subject to conservation planning under the Ramsar Convention and one of few places left where some chance remains of preserving habitat samples reasonably intact.

(6) *LOWLAND MIXED DIPTEROCARP RAIN FORESTS:* Exceptionally tall, multi-layered, with large emergents, and by global standards outstandingly rich in tree species, but commonly dominated by members of one family of large trees, the Dipterocarpaceae. These constitute the near-total climax dry-land cover of the plains, lower hills and the submontane slope, hence were formerly the most extensive habitats in the Peninsula – by a wide margin. In the species accounts, the Malayan-type formation is abbreviated to 'evergreen forest' and the Thai-Burmese to 'semi-evergreen', perhaps unwisely as both are 'rain' forests and both predominantly evergreen (Ashton 1991, Round 1988). Deciduousness affects only the high canopy. It tends to be commoner in Thai-Burmese-type forest (typically no more than a stretching and synchronization of 'leaf-exchange' in just a small minority of Malayan forest trees: Ng 1988), but even there is conspicuous only over limiting soils (sands, hilly limestone) and among certain immature stands (Ashton 1991).

In places (Perlis), floristic and climatic boundaries convincingly coincide (Map 2), but at least a proportion of tree species may be able to adjust their leafing cycles to match local conditions. There is otherwise a large difference in the tree floras of the two rain forests, in their tree-species richness (much less in Thai-Burmese forest); also in incidence of giant emergents, proportions of woody climbers, bamboo, etc., although some local structural variation (e.g., of density of the understorey) tends to be in common. This said, there is still no clear understanding of the relative importance to bird distributions of phenological versus floristic factors, or indeed of the climate shifts that may accompany these. There certainly are effects to be unravelled, even though (as Map 3 shows) more bird species seem to come to a range-limit within respective forest zones than actually between them.

Lowland rain forests are the key to Sunda subregional biodiversity and of the highest conservation importance. Their status will be taken up separately (page xxxii).

(7) *LOWLAND HEATH FOREST*: A catch-all category for generally small areas of vegetation on nutrient-poor, sometimes shallowly peat-topped, sandy podsols of certain submontane sedimentary plateaus, tops of quartz ridges, etc. The typical heath forest habitat is a climax of dwarf, shrubby growth, intermingled sedges, etc., with well-spaced, small, often gnarled trees, and has features (even plant genera, such as *Leptospermum*) in common with montane summit forest. The shrub *Baeckia* is a good marker. As in summit forest, tree size and crown density increase sharply on the deeper soils of stream gulleys, forming woodland 'galleries'. Forest botanists use the term also for a, now rare, more or less closed-canopy, layered, medium-stature forest over old beach dunes. According to level of disturbance, this has a bird community somewhere between poor lowland rain forest and strand woodland. It degrades to an open, dune scrub looking not unlike heath forest as defined here, and supporting some of the same birds (see *Scrub*).

(8) *LOWER MONTANE FOREST*: Merged with upper montane forest as *Hill Evergreen* forest in the continental SE Asian literature. Forest botanists include an Upper Dipterocarp zone, continuous with Lowland rain forest and still with many individual trees of that family, but lacking large emergent crowns, and with more leaf litter on the forest floor. A far more important range-boundary for birds is latter's ecotone with forest in which oaks and chestnuts (Fagaceae) and laurels (Lauraceae) are generally the commonest trees, conifers (*Agathis, Dacrydium*, etc.) are fairly common, large tree ferns appear in edge situations, and dipterocarps are relatively rare, occurring at around 900 m elevation more or less everywhere. This forest has medium but variable stature, according to site, is multi-layered but lacks strikingly large emergents, and its canopy often carries a heavy load of epiphytes. Understorey vegetation is nearly always dense, variably mossy, and the floor has much litter, plus usually some shallow peat.

(9) *UPPER MONTANE FOREST*: Cloud forest, taking over from oak-laurel forest at about 1450 m (soonest where exposure is greatest), dominated by Ericaceae, with conifers often common. Many older trunks are gnarled, and the characteristically smooth-topped canopy is rarely above 10 m up. This meets a dense understorey directly, with no obviously distinguishable middle stratum. The floor is of peat developed often almost directly on weathered rock and, like most lower trunks, is heavily fern- and bryophyte-laden. *Sphagnum* moss beds occur here.

Over exposed ridge-crests and summits the forest shrinks to a dense, unlayered elfin form, mostly less than man height, and where exposed to moisture extremes, as on the plateau tops of high sedimentary mountains, can be so stunted as to leave patches of mineral surface bare. Such habitats, like some extreme Lowland heath vegetation, verge on non-forest status.

(10) *FOREST EDGE*: A narrow, linear habitat characterized by dense vegetation growing where full sunlight invades along natural or man-made margins, bringing the leafy 'skin' of the forest, followed by some of its birds, from general canopy height down to ground level. Unrestricted by altitude or forest type, but 'edge' develops most luxuriantly below the mon tane forest ecotone.

(11) *WOODY PLANTATIONS*: Single-species stands of oil-palm, rubber, coconuts and exotic wood or pulp sources (acacias, *Albizzia*, teak, pine), on plots of a few to thousands of hectares, mainly at plains level. Most develop a closed canopy but, by definition, have simple, uniform structure. Well-managed, they tend to lack shade-layer vegetation, but soon develop some

if neglected. Traditionally and commercially, subcoastal coconuts are underplanted with woody secondary crops, including coffee, fruit trees and cocoa. Coffee and cocoa are also grown independently but, along with pulp and timber crops, and tea (closed-canopy woodland on a dwarf scale; a single-species simulation of montane summit forest), have not yet been well studied in the Peninsula.

All forest habitats are qualified according to stage of development. *Mature* means a stand containing a wide range of structure, from gaps due to natural tree-fall through to full, closed-canopy stature, but in equilibrium, no longer gaining net mass overall (commonly called *Primary*, but this implies never having been touched, which is an unnecessary assumption). *Regenerating* means a stand re-gaining form and mass after damage (including from logging) rather than after total destruction, hence retaining a layered structure throughout. *Secondary* means a stand at more or less closed-canopy stage after growing in afresh following total clearance; commonly made up of different, faster-developing, shorter-lived tree species, and more bamboo, etc., than grew there before. Tracts of bamboo tend to be a slope phenomenon in the south but extend to plains level in the north, mostly under the influence of temporary agriculture rotating too fast to allow many trees back into the system.

(12) *MARINE*: With a distinction made between in-shore waters and the open sea. By in-shore waters is meant the larger estuaries and bays, and first 1–2 km of shallow sea beyond low-water mark on mainland and large-island coasts. Open sea encompasses the rest, although only off the Thai W coast does any part of the review area reach oceanic water. Turbidity varies much: permanently high by any standards in in-shore waters of the Melaka and Johor Straits, lowest in open waters of the Andaman and S China seas, where it is influenced seasonally by monsoon wave action.

(13) *INTERTIDAL*: Covering the useful divisions of low-tide exposure, generalized as mudflats, sand-flats, back-reef coral rubble and rocky (as around headlands), with any special vegetation, e.g., scarce and threatened sea-grass (*Zostera*) beds and salt-marsh. Details of actual substrate composition favoured, for example, by foraging wader species, relate to the solidity (clayiness or ripeness) of mud deposits, and the proportions of mud against sand in the substrate.

(14) *BRACKISH WETLANDS*: Including tidal rivers and creeks; subcoastal lagoons forming after storm bars or beaches have impeded a river-mouth, as often along the S China sea coast exposed to NE monsoon wave action (the inland sea, opening at Songkhla town, being by far the largest example); and, locally in Perak and Selangor states, natural mangrove lagoons. Deep in forest, cut off from re-colonizing species of the frontal zone of the forest, these could be the outcome of clear-felling but are more likely to have been areas of die-back of trees that were fouled at former large-waterbird nesting stations. One at Ketam island, Kelang estuary, described as a colony site in the early 1930s, is still open.

Man-made categories include a still-increasing hectarage of aquaculture ponds cut out of mangrove forest, and the fly-ash collecting ponds of a coal-fired power-station on the coast of Selangor (important as a wader roost).

(15) *FRESHWATER WETLANDS*: An even more diverse category, covering rivers inland to the point at which headwater tributaries in forest no longer break the overhead canopy; agricultural irrigation canals; rare natural lakes including blackwater lagoon systems (e.g., Tasik Bera), flooded sinkholes in limestone; sealed-off subcoastal lagoons (Thalae Noi is continuous with the relatively enormous fresh to near-fresh section of the Phatthalung/Songkhla inland sea only during high-water periods); and large impoundments behind flood-control, water-supply or power-generating dams. Most such reservoirs are deep and dendritic, with steeply shelving shores that lack an aquatic vegetation fringe (except a temporary one of emergent tree skeletons). A few large lowland examples, such as Timah-Tasoh (Perlis) or, as in Singapore, claimed from sea-creeks, show signs of becoming good new waterbird sites. Flooded opencast mine-workings (including dredge-mine lagoons), disappearing much faster than they are now replaced and, very locally, inland fish-pond complexes are two other man-made categories.

The only really extensive natural marsh recorded is the zoned sweep of waterlily, *Eleocharis*, sedge and reed growth around much of Thalae Noi, variably exposed according to water level. Other types of marsh of localized significance are: floating sedge and water-hyacinth mats, the latter widespread, but particularly extensive on Thalae Noi and some of Singapore's coastal reservoirs; *Acrostichum* fern, natural in back-mangroves but forming extensive beds at the edge of some coastal reservoirs; fringing sedge, bulrush (*Typha*) and reed (*Phragmites*), a formerly widespread succession on tin-mine sludge-drying beds, now a fast-declining resource; grass-marsh on flooded land-fill, recorded mostly in Singapore; and, most extensive of all, paddyland. Rice agriculture supports most biodiversity where the field-cycle includes a long, weedy fallow stage. This traditional pattern of cropping is now confined mainly north of Malaysia, with a few isolated areas of ornithological interest also on the coast of Pahang. Malaysia's large, irrigated, multi-crop schemes are now dry-seeded, with a shortened flood phase and critical fallow weed stage brief, or totally suppressed by herbicides.

(16) *OPEN GROUND*: Another catch-all category, covering: recent dunes, mainly along the E coast; coastal fill, notably in Singapore; bunded-off and cleared back-mangrove land; shores and shoals of large rivers; dry-tilled and stubble-stage ricelands; open-cast mine-tailings; *Imperata* grassland maintained by burning; and grassland grazed by stock, or mowed short on airfields, golf courses, municipal grounds, (called *PARKLAND* where these also support a scatter of trees). Locally in S Malaysia, grazing habitat has received a boost from the development of ranches. Rough grazing may also incorporate wetlands, as at Thung Thong wildlife sanctuary (Surat Thani) and around the inland sea.

(17) *SCRUB*: Covering any type of low, open woody vegetation or mosaic of bushes, rank grass, etc., from pioneer growth on disturbed land to the early regrowth of clear-felled forest (in which bananas, gingers and other large herbs may also be prominent). Essentially a developing vegetation, versus the climax state of similar-stature heath and elfin summit forests. Plentiful throughout the lowlands.

(18) *OUTCROPS AND URBAN*: Lumped because many of the bird species they support are the same. Covers cliffs, mainly of limestone inselbergs, commonly with overhung niches, recesses and caves, and their man-made analogues: the walls, ledges, solid awnings and interiors of buildings, bridges, culverts and other infrastructure, of all sizes and types.

SPECIES ASSEMBLAGES AND BIOGEOGRAPHICAL BACKGROUND

680 bird species have been recorded wild in the review area, representing approximately 303 genera. Only 18 (six per cent) of the latter are Sunda subregional endemics, all of them land-birds of various forest habitats. There are no such endemic families. Affinities are otherwise mainly with the rest of tropical and E Asia, aided by a large contingent of northern visitors or species possessing at least one such migratory population (37 per cent of the avifauna overall, dominating most non-forest assemblages). Only a small part of the avifauna is due to invasions from beyond Wallace's Line, including, apparently, the pigeon genera *Ptilinopus* and *Ducula*, hanging parrots *Loriculus*, perhaps *Collocalia* swiftlets and, among passerines, presumably whistlers *Pachycephala* and (by Sibley and Ahlquists' classification) the pardalote *Gerygone*. The Golden-bellied Gerygone has been followed by a brood-parasite, Little Bronze Cuckoo, itself in a section of the genus *Chrysococcyx* that is otherwise nearly all Wallacean/Australasian. A congener, Horsfield's Bronze Cuckoo, is the only Australian-breeding land bird known to migrate as far north as the Peninsula, confirmed so far just in Singapore.

With overlap, and including a very small cluster of apparently self-sustaining introduced species, the fauna splits into five main assemblages (the term 'community' is reserved to particular sites), of inland forests up to the montane oak-laurel forest ecotone; forests above this ecotone; mangrove and strand forests; the sea and open intertidal zone (i.e., not directly implicating coastal vegetation); and of inland non-forest habitats. Apart from recent dunes, cliffs and some naturally open freshwater wetlands, the last are due to clearance and development of a landscape formerly totally forested.

Fairly obviously, the two non-forest assemblages are convenient amalgams of several more or less distinct sub-categories (not much contact, for example, between open-sea and intertidal foragers). The three forest assemblages, on the other hand, are natural units. All show variation of species richness between the types of forest included, and attenuation of richness towards their overall margins, but somewhere within each most of the species that could possibly co-occur do so. Apart from composition, they differ in size and, strikingly, in sub-regional endemism at species level.

THE LOWLAND INLAND FOREST ASSEMBLAGE: Three hundred and twenty species, or slightly over half of the total non-marine bird fauna of the Peninsula, make or are known to have made regular use of one or more of habitats 3–7. Species of all status, resident and part to full non-breeding visitor, are included, and only a few have spread in from core populations in other habitat categories. Forty-two per cent of this greater assemblage is endemic to the Sunda sub-region. Among the subset of 240 resident species found mainly to exclusively in lowland inland forests, and dependent on them for survival (of course, there are long-distance migrants for which this could also be true), endemism rises to 56 percent. Compared across regions, this equates to more than half the total endemic birds of all land habitats in neighbouring 'oceanic' Wallacea (White and Bruce 1986). No other habitat assemblage comes close to such a figure, which is another way of pointing out that the limit of usable forest and the continental edge of the Sunda sub-region are one and the same thing.

Among the forest types included in this category, most bird species have been found in dry-land mixed dipterocarp forest. From this peak, richness declines along three main axes. The first of these is latitudinal, north towards the edge of the sub-region. Map 3 tracks the mainly Sundaic non-passerines (pending a full revision of passerines, and without the benefit of a modern survey of S Tenasserim) by half degrees of latitude out to their historical range-limits. Losses pick up north of rather than at the Malayan/Thai-Burmese floristic transition and peak close to the accepted edge of the sub-region, at 14°N in Tenasserim, 10.5–11° in Thailand. In other words, most have gone as far as the habitat itself (in Tenasserim at 14°N the dry season expands to 5–6 months even though forest remains evergreen) except that, in Thailand, two sharp, additional peaks occur. They represent distributional pockets in patches (habitat islands) of atypically humid forest along the eastern foot of the border range. Some of the birds involved might have reached these by slow infiltration across the mountains from Tenasserim; others are perhaps the stranded survivors of a formerly more widespread Sunda environment that has since withdrawn south. Certain nineteenth century records from S Vietnam (of Blue-rumped Parrot and Black and White-crowned Hornbills among non-passerines), mostly rejected by Delacour (1970), might be worth reconsidering in the same light.

Even though many endemics appear to have followed usuable forest to its terminus, the general assumption has been that Thai-Burmese forest would be less rich in birds per unit area of habitat than its southern counterpart. A thorough search of the lowlands of Khao Nor Chuchi wildlife sanctuary (former Khao Pra-Bang Khram non-hunting area), on the Trang/Krabi border, offers one last chance to check (Round and Treesucon 1998), and suggests otherwise.

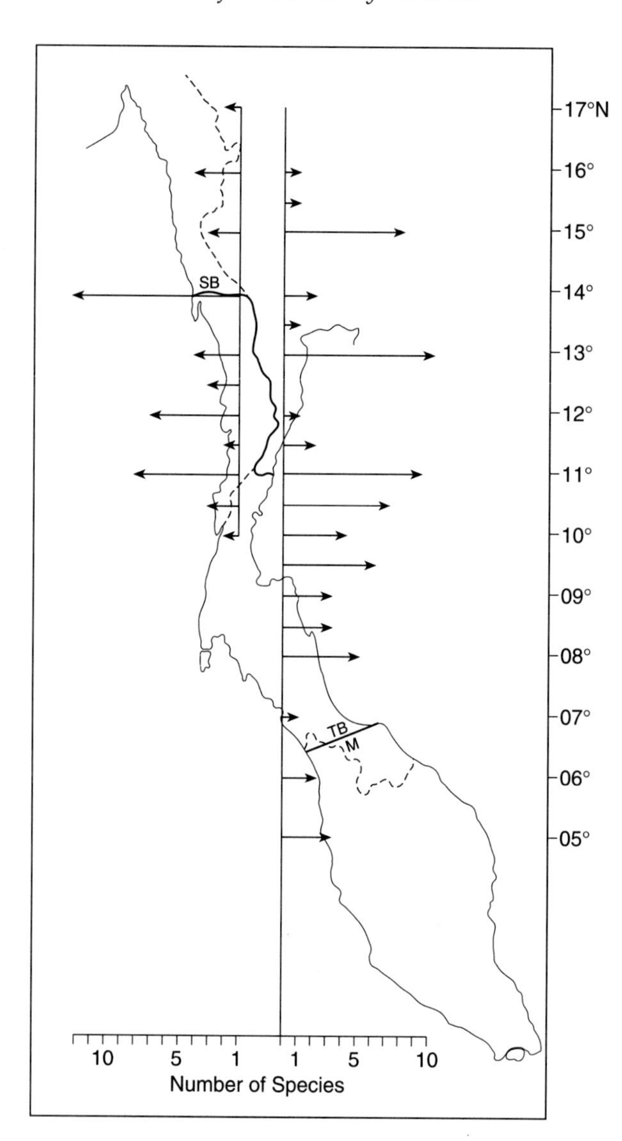

Map 3. Historical limits of occurrence of lowland inland forest non-passerines northward through the Peninsula, to the nearest half degree of latitude: right-hand column in Malaysia and Thailand; left-hand column in Burma. SB, northern limit of Sunda zoogeographical sub-region; TBM, zone of convergence of Thai-Burmese and Malayan-type forests.

Most now agree that alpha- (within-habitat) diversity peaks at the mature stage of the plains-level part of inland forest, below the terrain-break at the foot of main slopes. Over several years of censusing, roughly 2 km² unit areas of Malayan forest at Pasoh, eastern Negeri Sembilan, and the Kerau game reserve at Kuala Lompat ranger post, Pahang, produced 188 and 195 species overall. The equivalent figure for a more diffuse but probably not very much larger total area of Khao Nor Chuchi's Thai-Burmese forest, including species formerly present but recently hunted out, is around 190, and 3–4 more recorded there in regenerating forest should eventually be found in mature growth as well.

A few Malaysian birds are indeed missing from the northern site, but off-set by others actually appearing with latitude. From all sources, at least 11 such extra residents reach Khao Nor Chuchi. Two, Fulvous-chested Flycatcher and the famous Gurney's Pitta, are Sunda endemics that occur almost no further south in the Peninsula. Others (Ferruginous Partridge, Orange-breasted Trogon, Ochraceous Bulbul, Streaked Wren Babbler, Grey-throated Babbler) parallel the behaviour of certain forest trees (Wyatt-Smith 1997) by descending from high submontane or entirely montane, southern ranges into plains-level forest at the Perlis-Pattani transition.

Khao Nor Chuchi's Thai-Burmese type forest also hosts more overwintering migrants than the Malaysian sites, as a function of latitude (Swinhoe's Minivet) or, perhaps, actual forest type (Ashy Drongo, Golden-spectacled and Yellow-browed Warblers, Pale-legged Leaf Warbler and Hill Blue Flycatcher, all of which reach closer to the floristic transition). More large, migratory thrushes at Khao Nor Chuchi suggest a different availability of fruit. In the south, Eyebrowed and Siberian winter either in montane forest or non-forest habitats; except occasionally to reach canopy figs, they hardly enter mature lowland forest.

A second axis of diversity runs from dry-land rain forest to other, including wet, lowland forests. Old-growth freshwater swamp forest is now so scarce in the Peninsula that opportunities for study have probably already passed. Excluding 'edge' records, surveys of logged to well-regenerated peatswamp forest in N Selangor (Prentice and Aikanathan 1989, UMBRP), produced 139 species, just one of them additional to the Malayan dry-land forest lists (Crimson Sunbird, in place of related Temminck's). Several expected species were missed but there are grounds for believing in certain real differences. Shade-layer aerial insectivores seem genuinely to be under-represented in comparison with dry-land sites: just two muscicapid flycathers and four monarchs (only one of each common), compared with a collective 15 species at both Pasoh and Kuala Lompat. These also support two large forest robins, White-rumped and Orange-tailed Shama, together at floor and understorey levels. White-rumped was recorded at the edge of peatswamp forest but only Orange-tailed Shama occupied the interior, as though just one shama niche were supportable there. Parallel findings at Bornean and Sumatran peatswamp sites (A.J. and C.J. Hails; Silvius *et al* 1984) imply such differences could be fairly general.

Lowland heath forest as defined above has not been studied at plains level. The largest example searched occupies a submontane plateau of Keriong mountain in the Pahang state sector of the Endau-Rompin conservation area (Wells 1990), and represents the extreme bottom end of recorded lowland inland forest bird diversity. Elfin forest of its central core supported just three rain-forest or forest-edge species, all small-sized: a generalist frugivore, Cream-vented Bulbul; a generalist nectarivore, Purple-throated Sunbird; and an insectivore, Dark-necked Tailorbird. As recorded at a similar site in Sabah state, NW Borneo, the guess is that more invade during communal fruiting events, but only as temporary opportunists.

Diversity axis number three lies entirely within dry-land rain forest, up an altitudinal gradient to its limit against montane oak-laurel forest. In Malaysia, 14 lowland forest residents are exclusive to this submontane slope (or lap over into montane forest). Another ten are commoner there, and a few (not as many as sometimes claimed) appear to replace a down-slope relative. Crested Argus, 'trapped' in a narrow belt astride the montane ecotone of the Taman Negara national park mountains, meets lowland Great Argus; the calling zone of Black-browed Barbet meets that of similar-sized, lowland Yellow-crowned Barbet edge to edge, typically, at around 800 m; and Ochraceous and Ashy Bulbuls, respectively, meet or closely approach Grey-cheeked and Streaked Bulbuls. They may exclude one another but, to my mind, more convincing evidence of competition at work is supplied by pairs such as Grey-cheeked and Yellow-bellied Bulbuls that overlap widely but whose peaks of population density are partitioned by altitude. As indicated, not all of these restrictions hold up across the Perlis-Pattani transition, and only a few extra slope-specializing residents (Scaly Thrush, Spot-necked Babbler) appear on the northern mountains.

Such ecological replacements are of special interest, but do not disguise the trend of progressive loss of species across the submontane slope as a whole. In Malaysia, 38 species (about 17 per cent of a representative plains-level community), most of them resident but also including a few overwintering migrants (see below), halt at or soon after crossing the steepland boundary. Thereafter, the rate at which others drop out seems to vary with local conditions: generally slower over better vegetated, better watered granite slopes, on which a fair proportion of lowland species reach the montane boundary; faster up steeper, more rugged, sedimentary slopes where, in extreme cases, hardly any lowland species (at least of the shade layers) reach the ecotone. It is perhaps faster also north of the floristic transition, where typically steep mountains seem not to support certain species widespread on slopes in Malaysia. This life-zone effect continues through the sub-region as, in turn, certain of the Peninsula's plains-level specialists appear on the slopes of Bornean and Sumatran mountains.

The forest may show no obvious change of appearance as it crosses the steepland boundary, but Table 1 includes as many canopy as shade-layer species, implying a quite general effect. Observed in Borneo, the breeding success of widespread species can be lower on mountain slopes than in nearby plains-level habitat, and low also compared with the performance of slope specialists at the same site. This hints at a population recruitment problem overcome, perhaps, by upward colonization from more productive parts of the population. It becomes possible to speculate that a given submontane slope community is only as good as the steepness of the decline of its key resources up-slope, balanced against the capacity of adjacent habitats to supply colonists. A shift of either one should take its toll on species richness.

From the level of endemism shown by the assemblage as a whole, much speciation must have occurred within the Sunda sub-region itself. Three sets of circumstances could have produced the disruptions of range needed for the process to have begun:

(1) Inter-glacial flooding of the Sunda basin, although the highest sea levels of the Quaternary are believed to have been reached only during the Holocene era. Earlier floodings may not have caused as much fragmentation as now.

(2) Mega-rivers draining a vast, exposed Sunda basin during phases of continentality. Their routes across the Sunda shelf have been traced seismically, but all evidence of effectiveness at hindering the spread of forest birds has, of course, been lost.

(3) Disruption of forest cover owing to climate change.

Many lines of evidence, including an overwhelming number of lowland forest species in common, indicate the now-separate lands of the sub-region were once parts of a continent. Models of the climate

Table 1. Forest birds specializing in plains-level habitat; (m = exclusively migratory).

Black Partridge *Melanoperdix nigra*
Chestnut-necklaced Partridge *Arborophila charltonii*
Crested Fireback *Lophura ignita*
Crestless Fireback *Lophura erythrophthalma*
Malayan Peacock Pheasant *Polyplectron malacense*
Storm's Stork *Ciconia stormi*
Jerdon's Baza *Aviceda jerdoni*
Wallace's Hawk Eagle *Spizaetus nanus*
Masked Finfoot *Heliopais personata*
Chinese Banded Crake *Porzana paykulli*[m]
Cinnamon-headed Green Pigeon *Treron fulvicollis*
Little Green Pigeon *Treron olax*
Green Imperial Pigeon *Ducula aenea*
Blue-rumped Parrot *Psittinus cyanurus*
Long-tailed Parakeet *Psittacula longicauda*
Short-toed Coucal *Centropus rectunguis*
Brown Boobook *Ninox scutulata*
Large Frogmouth *Batrachostomus auritus*
Gould's Frogmouth *Batrachostomus stellatus*
Cinnamon-rumped Trogon *Harpactes orrhophaeus*
Wrinkled Hornbill *Aceros corrugatus*
Black Hornbill *Anthracoceros malayanus*
Oriental Pied Hornbill *Anthracoceros albirostris*
White-bellied Woodpecker *Dryocopus javensis*
Great Slaty Woodpecker *Mulleripicus pulverulentus*
Red-crowned Barbet *Megalaima rafflesii*
Hooded Pitta *Pitta sordida*
Garnet Pitta *Pitta granatina*
Black Magpie *Platysmurus leucopterus*
Slender-billed Crow *Corvus enca*
Bar-bellied Cuckooshrike *Coracina striata*
Narcissus Flycatcher *Ficedula narcissina*[m]
Malaysian Blue Flycatcher *Cyornis turcosa*
White-chested Babbler *Trichastoma rostratum*
Ferruginous Babbler *Trichastoma bicolor*
Grey-breasted Babbler *Malacopteron albogulare*
Hill Myna *Gracula religiosa*
White-bellied Munia *Lonchura leucogastra*

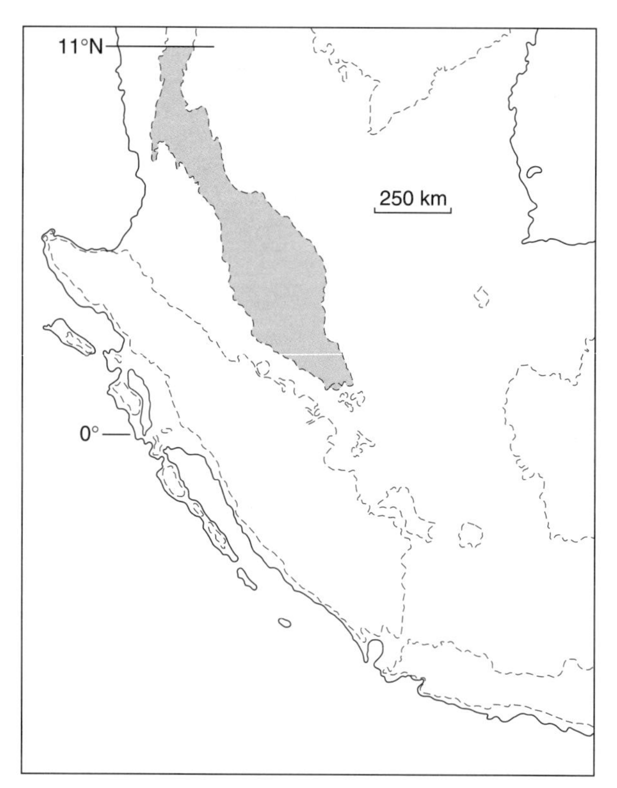

Map 4. Position of the recent Peninsula in the western part of an ice-age Sunda continent at postulated maximum draw-down of the sea (about 18 000 years ago).

of a fully exposed, ice-age Sundaland reveal more seasonality under the influence of a stronger and, with less sea to cross, drier Asian monsoon pushing further south than now. Effects would have been greatest away from the ameliorating influence of the sea, which, of course, is exactly where the southern part of the modern Peninsula would have found itself (Map 4).

There is no real possibility that tree-rich rain forest actually disappeared from this area during the ice-ages, but evidence that forest cover ruptured is reasonably firm. The small assemblage of northern savanna birds now isolated in Java and Bali, and Quaternary savanna mammals whose remains have been found even beyond Java, could only have spread from Asia through corridors of suitable habitat. Pollen recovered from ancient peat horizons (Batchelor 1983) reveals what these might have been like: on the Selangor plain, rich remains of a pine/grassland vegetation such as is now found in higher and drier parts of continental SE Asia but which survives in the Sunda sub-region only as a localized fire-climax relic on the volcanic uplands of Sumatra.

As the latest El Niño has demonstrated, dried-out Sunda rain forest burns, and seasonal fire (perhaps even including man-made fire), may have assisted in keeping ice-age forest at bay, confining it to pockets of the dampest climate and best ground-water conditions. If reasonably large habitat islands persisted for long enough, population isolates trapped by savanna could have experienced as much evolutionary divergence as is assumed may once have occurred among others trapped by the sea.

Where in the Peninsula these areas could have been bears on where conservation action might now prove (or have proved) most valuable. The local bird data alone give few clues other than, perhaps, to point to the NW, where distance to the Andaman sea would never have been great and the exposed coastal plain should have benefited climatically. This happens to be where Gurney's Pitta, one of the Peninsula's two lowland forest hyper-endemics, has been found, and spans the local range also of Fulvous-chested Flycatcher, a sub-regional endemic occurring in the Greater Sunda islands but unrecorded from the mainland south of Trang province. A good number of other, non-endemic species in various families is represented by a special subspecies in that area, and two that terminate there (Scaly Thrush and Spot-necked Babbler), like the flycatcher, reappear on one or more of the Sunda islands. Their habitat-island has either always been this restricted or they were pushed back from the Sunda heartland, including the southern Peninsula, as less seasonal conditions re-advanced after the end of the last ice age. Like Taman Negara's mini-populations of Crested Argus, also believed to be relics of a post-glacial retreat (Davison 1980), they found a durable refuge.

The second lowland forest hyper-endemic, Malayan Peacock Pheasant, has occurred widely enough not to be pinnable to a particular formation or possible refuge area in the Peninsula. Differences from Bornean and Palawan Peacock Pheasants are considered to be sufficient for recognition of separate species, and all that may be guessed about origins is that polygynous/promiscuous mating systems have driven the divergence of plumage ornamentation in this group unusually fast.

THE MONTANE FOREST ASSEMBLAGE: Occasional lowland forest birds reach the highest summits, and if records are pooled there is actually no point on the 'average' mountain slope in the Peninsula at which the lowland forest community could be said to terminate. Even so, the lower edge of oak-laurel forest is a major faunal boundary for birds. Except where the odd competitive replacement appears to have occurred (e.g., Rufous Piculet spreads into lower montane forest where Speckled Piculet is missing), most of the lowland species regularly penetrating far into montane forest belong in just one foraging sub-set, ranging long distances after fruit and nectar. Except also where montane frugivores commute to the lowlands to feed, or a few species jump habitats as described above, this boundary is an even more effective block to the downward spread of montane birds. A few may be curbed by competitive interactions with lowland relatives, but montane birds foraging close to the boundary typically turn aside as they reach it, reacting to evident alien space. Wanderings further down the slope occur, but rarely.

Peninsula-wide, 195 species are on record from montane forest, including a core of just 76 residents exclusive to this habitat. Fifty per cent of the latter's genera are unshared with lowland forest. There are two (possibly three) montane hyper-endemics, including another peacock pheasant, but only 16 species (just 20 per cent of the core assemblage) are endemic to the Sunda sub-region. All the rest are in common with a larger continental mountain fauna that extends to S China. No reconstruction of past environments manages to connect a continuous corridor of montane habitat through the Peninsula, but this has been less important to bird dispersal histories than the absence of anything in SE Asian mountain (as opposed to lowland) climate and ecology that determines a Sunda boundary. Evergreen montane forest is recognizably one habitat, throughout SE Asia, tempting purists to claim that the real continental edge of the Sunda sub-region is as much a matter of altitude as latitude.

Models of glacial maximum climate-change in the SE Asian tropics claim a range of temperature effects, from an annual mean 1–2°C actually warmer than present in the area of what is now the southern part of the Peninsula to as much as 14° cooler (Gates 1976). A lowering by about 5°C is the most widely agreed average. Assuming the rate of change with altitude to have been more or less as now, and other climatic factors to have been equal (which surely they were not), this amount of cooling could have expanded montane forest down to the current 500, or even 400 m contour. This would have much enlarged, and supplied some extra, montane habitat islands, but would not have been enough to have bridged the larger lowland gaps evident today. Invasion of the Peninsula, and the rest of the sub-region, it seems, would always have been by island-hopping, but at rates of onward colonization that could have been greater than now. Chance depends on the number of potential colonists available per step, and standard island biogeographical theory predicts this would have increased with island size (BMP5, and confirmed by comparative surveys).

The first of two axes of modern species diversity, between habitat islands, shows by far the largest community of core residents, 72 (close to scores for the spinal ranges of Sumatra and Borneo), on the largest 'island', the Main Range; 55 on the Larut Range, near but not recently linked to the Main Range; 50 each on outliers Benom and Tahan, both above 2000 m with over 200 km^2 of montane forest each; and 30 on the E-central Range. Among smaller outliers, Rabong, northwest of the Tahan massif and evidently once a part of it, has 20 species; Lawit, perhaps always isolated north of the E-coast range, 23; Tapis, south of the E-coast range, nine; and remote Jerai peak (coastal Kedah) and Tioman island just one each (Streaked Wren Babbler). Spotty distributions among habitat islands, and a few disjunctions directly between the continent and Greater Sunda islands, imply individual communities suffered the random extinctions ('relaxation') expected as habitat contracted and fractured. About the only obvious effects of latitude are the restriction of Sunda sub-regional endemics to mainly Malaysian mountains and of continental Blue-throated Barbet and Green-tailed Sunbird to northern ones. More Tenasserim species may once have reached the now rather too low NW Range but, as mentioned, its summits have never been explored.

The second diversity axis runs altitudinally, from a high point in taller, better layered, floristically more diverse lower montane forest. Thus, 65 of the 72 possible obligate montane species occur between 1000 and 1300 m on the Main Range at Fraser's Hill. As expected, individual abundances tend to vary over the slope, coming to a peak that, in more and more instances, shows altitudinal displacement relative to one of some similar species. Black-browed and Golden-throated Barbets replace one another sharply whereas the three laughingthrushes (*Garrulax*) overlap almost completely, but still peak separately: Black below Chestnut-capped below Chestnut-crowned.

At the low end of this diversity axis, about 12 species are exclusive to or commonest in upper montane forest, and a few specialize in summit forest. Green-tailed Sunbird at the N end of the E-central Range is of special interest as it completes a typical continental 'stacking' of ecological niches in the genus *Aethopyga*: Green-tailed at the top, Black-breasted in lower montane forest, and one of the red species below the ecotone. Southward, Black-breasted spreads up to absorb the untenanted space of Green-tailed, and on isolated peaks (Jerai, Ledang, etc.) that lack both of these, Temminck's Sunbird takes over all space. Hill Prinia, an endemic subspecies of which occurs in the review area only on the sedimentary summit plateau of Tahan, is another example of special interest. With 'edge' to almost non-forest adaptations, relatives elsewhere are known to be able to descend into cleared lowland gaps. Ice-age prinias may thus have reached, or retreated to, Tahan across a seasonal lowland savanna. Were they able to break out of their trap now, these birds would find plenty of usable space around settlements of the Main Range, etc., but why (if they were ever there) none survived naturally in the Main Range's own summit zone is a mystery. Their Tahan home is certainly an old bio-refugium, and could be more special than has generally been assumed. Even though much collected-over in the past, it has never been searched with modern equipment.

THE MANGROVE FOREST ASSEMBLAGE: Smallest of the three forest assemblages, and peculiar in a number of ways. Excluding coastal waders making facultative use of mangroves when denied access to more favoured open-ground roost sites, I find records of 135 species in this habitat (BMP5, Nisbet 1968, Noske 1995). Within their peninsular ranges, seven (nine south of latitude 7°N) still depend exclusively on mangrove forest, or this forest out to an immediate fringe of nipa palm swamp or strand or plantation (typically coconut) woodland. These are: Brown-winged and Ruddy Kingfishers, Greater Flameback, Mangrove Pitta, Black-hooded Oriole, Great Tit, Dusky Warbler (a non breeding visitor), Mangrove Blue Flycatcher and Copper-throated Sunbird. Six others: Great-billed, Grey, Little and Black-crowned Night Herons, Great Egret and Milky Stork, depend on it exclusively for nesting but feed elsewhere. A now-extinct W-coast population of Black-headed Ibis may also have fitted into that category. Only Brown-winged Kingfisher, Mangrove Pitta and Copper-throated Sunbird are global mangrove specialists in all respects. The one Sunda sub-regional endemic, Mangrove Blue Flycatcher, is not among them; indeed, the whole assemblage is only 12 per cent Sundaic, symptomatic of yet another habitat without a Sunda 'frontier'. Brown-winged Kingfisher and Mangrove Pitta, for example, follow mangrove forest round the head of the Bay of Bengal.

Where then does the rest of the mangrove assemblage belong? Forty-six residents and a minimum six non-breeding visitors (39 per cent of total species) are in common with one or more of the original inland forest formations (foraging Mountain Imperial Pigeons reach mangroves from at least the lower montane zone), or inland forest edge. Had more of the interface between mangroves and inland forest survived, and had more plant-rich back-mangrove been explored before clearance, undoubtedly, others would have been found (in 1989, Richard Noske added four during just three surveys of a small area of mid- and back-zone habitat near Kelang, Selangor). This sub-set also includes all the other Sunda endemics of the assemblage, hence inland forests may have been the main colonizing, or re-colonizing source. Ashy Tailorbird is an exception, being fairly thinly distributed through inland edge and peatswamp forest, but one of the commonest of mangrove birds (25 per cent of all survey contacts in Selangor habitat: Noske 1995). Mangrove forest may always have been its main habitat.

Considering that mangrove and inland forests abutted over long stretches of the coast until well into the present century, a one-third faunal overlap is not great — and by no means all overlapping species have yet been shown to breed in mangrove forest. Less expected, and often remarked upon is the fact that almost as many other mangrove species are in common with open coasts and the agricultural and even urban habitats that truncated mangrove successions now meet inland. Along with large waterbirds, some non-forest land-birds (Spotted Dove, Jungle Myna, Asian Glossy Starling, etc.) roost or nest in mangroves but for lack of appropriate foods could never exist there exclusively. A minimum 12 others are still-common permanent residents of mangrove forest (former mangrove specialists, perhaps) that must have expanded out of this habitat recently. The local inland invasion histories of Collared Kingfisher and Laced Woodpecker are actually documented.

This role of the mangrove assemblage as an exporter of colonists to non-forest habitats has long been assumed to be due to foraging niches evolved in a plant-poor environment (unstable on various time-scales) being broad enough to predispose mangrove birds to simplicity and instability elsewhere (Noske 1995, Ward 1968). Between-habitat comparisons have still to be made, but Richard Noske measured a sample of mangrove species (woodpeckers and passerines) also now well-established in non-forest habitats against others still locked into mangroves and found all of the latter to have narrower niches. Interestingly, a species shared with inland forest but rare in non-forest habitats (Ruby-cheeked Sunbird) showed a niche-breadth closer to that of the specialist group (Noske 1995).

What may now be found in the average logged and bunded-off mangrove forest of the Peninsula can be only a part of the community that once occurred there. All floral zones are occupied. A few species show an attachment to just one (Black-crowned Night Herons prefer to nest in the frontal *Avicennia* zone), and certain woodpeckers are reported to focus most foraging on single tree species (Noske 1995). If an axis of diversity is definable, it is of increase towards the land. The more complex back-mangrove zones may well have been the main habitat of most colonists from inland forests. Their near-total clearance might help explain why most of the overlapping forest birds that remain are now rather rare in mangroves (Nisbet 1968), and why some formerly widespread members of this category (including giant woodpeckers) have all but disappeared from mangrove haunts.

THE OPEN INLAND ASSEMBLAGE: A convenient lumping of the faunas of non- and de-forested landscapes: sea dunes, natural cliffs, river shoals, urban and suburban, open agricultural and industrial (mainly derelict open-cast dredge-mine) landscapes, and freshwater wetlands of all kinds, but also including scrub before its development into closed secondary forest.

Naturally non-forested habitats are ancient but of tiny extent, narrowly linear along large rivers and windward coasts (surely an early post-glacial corridor from the continent) or, as rock outcrops, patchy and scattered. A small, resident community of about a dozen rock specialists inhabits cliffs, according to height and availability of overhangs, fissures and caves: Peregrine Falcon, House Swift, up to three swiftlets (depending on proximity to the coast), three swallows, two thrushes and, near habitation, Rock Pigeon, Eurasian Tree Sparrow and Jungle Myna (White-vented Myna will certainly follow and, in the north, at least one more swift is expected). Towns and other built-up infrastructure (road culverts, bridges, etc.) simulate the physical environment, and most of these outcrop birds have made the connection (to date, excluding only Dusky Crag Martin and Blue Whistling Thrush). Where cross-colonization has occurred some, such as House Swift in the southern half of the Peninsula, must have increased vastly over their original numbers.

De- (as opposed to non-) forested landscapes are historically recent but have now replaced all except small remnants of the plains-level lowland rain forests, taking over their status as the Peninsula's largest, most continuous environment. Collectively, just under 300 bird species are on record from this modern landscape, i.e., not many fewer than in the assemblage displaced, although far less evenly distributed, and continuously affected by the patterns and pace of changing land-use. Less than half the total (136 species at latest count) actually breeds there.

The new assemblage draws from open coastal and riverine corridors (as conduits and, perhaps, refugia in their own right) and directly from non-forest environments outside the equatorial zone; also from adjacent forests. Not all forest-derived species are safely traceable to one source, and some of the emphasis placed on the mangrove assemblage as a populator is in need of adjustment, perhaps because most component species likely to break out have by now already done so.

On evidence ranging from comparative abundance in source habitats to the matching of song types (Golden-bellied Gerygone), I place mangrove versus inland-forest derivatives at 32 and 126, a four-fold difference in favour of inland forest, whereas between actual breeders in non-forest the difference is only 23 against 41. Including species derived from edge habitat and a few non-breeding migrants (Arctic Warbler, Asian Brown Flycatcher, etc.) able to maintain themselves in more or less any tree cover, over nine times as many inland forest as mangrove birds merely wander through man-made habitats, settling individually for days, weeks or even a few months (Red-bearded Bee-eater, Banded Broadbill, Crested Jay, etc., in overgrown rubber plantation behind my own suburban Selangor garden) then disappearing. Moreover, even among full colonists, most inland forest-derived birds remain uncommon to sparse, whereas some from mangroves (Oriental Magpie Robin, etc.) have broken decisively into new ecological space to become among the most familiar of open-country species. Another point applying especially to the inland forest immigrant list is its heavy dominance by canopy species. Except where edge habitat could have been the source (White-rumped Shama, Abbott's Babbler, Little Spiderhunter), shade-layer, especially understorey, birds are either unable to cope ecologically or blocked by some particular piece of behaviour, such as avoidance of strong sunlight. One exception is the migratory Siberian Blue Robin, but actual overwintering outside forest by this altogether unusual bird has still to be confirmed.

Very locally in Malaysia, stretches of mountain forest, too, have been replaced by resorts and agriculture, including golf courses, tea plantations and market-gardens, connected with lowland open country only by roads. Despite the surroundings, their main bird assemblage is an impoverished version of that which occurs at plains level, filtering up across the forest barrier. The contribution of montane forest is not yet on proper record, but smaller.

Several colonists from one or other forest source registered extensions of range during the review period (see Collared Kingfisher, Laced Woodpecker, Barred Eagle Owl, etc.), but none to compete with the part of the assemblage derived elsewhere. This now numbers 139 species (about half of them waterbirds), including 72 assumed breeders that illustrate all facets of the invasion process: from expansion complete (e.g., Spotted Wood Owl now at its Singapore terminus); spread ongoing, even and steady to rapid (e.g., Black-naped Oriole, White-vented Myna) or via large-scale leap-frogging, typical of waterbirds (Yellow Bittern), followed up by infill (Little Grebe); to incomplete but, for unknown reasons, static over many decades (Indian Roller), or sharp retreat (e.g., vultures). Discounting definite release or escape events, a minimum four non-migrants invaded afresh during the review period: from the continent, Black-collared and Vinous-breasted Starlings; and from the south (over water-gaps, raising the S hemisphere tally to a minimum 14) Savanna Nightjar and White-breasted Woodswallow.

Non-breeding visitors to open country constitute the fastest-growing sector of the peninsular avifauna (receiving much attention from birdwatchers); up 20 to 67 species during the review period. In season, these supply some of the largest populations of the assemblage (e.g., Barn Swallow). They will be examined in Volume Two.

LAND-BIRDS ON SEA ISLANDS: The broad outlines of this analysis were laid down long ago (BMP5) but stand up well enough to the extra information gathered since. By the end of 1995, 260 species of resident land and freshwater birds (up 25% during the review period) were on record from one or more of 105 islands. This score, too, is up by almost 60 per cent but still represents only a fraction of the real number of islands on which such birds must occur (including, no doubt, many extra species in the Burmese Mergui archipelago). Once again, only a handful of those actually visited has been searched thoroughly.

No meaning is extractable from census results without first considering the history of islands, and the divergent histories of their forest versus non-forest bird assemblages.

Every island in the review area sits on the continental shelf, and up to 10,000 years ago would have been no more than a hill or set of hills standing out of a broad lowland plain. All would then have been cut off over a relatively short span of time, certainly well before the high standing of the sea (a few metres above present) some 5000 years ago. What habitats they then supported cannot be known but in a post-glacial climate, by the sea, probably most were already well forested. While not necessarily holding all of the forest bird species that co-occur in the lowlands of the mainland now, at point of isolation most may have held a good part of this assemblage. Modern coastal erosion effects imply rising post-glacial seas would not have been good for mangroves, but if islands passed through such a forest as they formed, whatever amount of this habitat remained attached should likewise have been fed a fair complement of mainland birds.

Big sea islands in the review area hold larger forest communities than small ones, but among those well explored, the very biggest and best searched now holds nothing approaching mainland forest diversity; at most, a little over 80 species (Penang). On mainlands, localized chance die-offs are assumed to be made good from surrounding habitat rapidly enough to pass unnoticed, whereas even a small impediment to immigration should begin to make these count. On 'land-bridge' islands, therefore, previously supportable diversity must necessarily fall away to a new lower equilibrium, sustainable through the worst conditions experienced in isolation.

This begs the question of what kinds of forest bird have survived, what seem to have disappeared, and what governs the evenness or otherwise of distributions through peninsular waters. Why, for example, are there so few records of hornbills on S China sea islands whereas up to three species co-occur off the W coast? (Penang should have some of these, but much of its forest may have re-grown after early colonial clearances that probably extirpated such birds). A wider comparison shows that communities are not as randomly constructed as the hornbills might suggest.

On small islands in particular, certain species occur far more often than chance alone would predict. These, we assume, have special properties. One ought to be adaptability, measured here just as the number of habitat categories (one versus more than one) occupied by parent stocks on the mainland.

Figure 1 compares this statistic across the lowland rain forest communities of seven large islands, off both E and W coasts, and unit areas of mainland habitat (updating totals given in BMP5 and adding an extra mainland site representative of the Thai-Burmese flora). Regardless of forest type, it is immediately obvious (i) that unit areas of habitat on the mainland hold several times more specialists than occur in any island forest, (ii) that the proportion of specialists in the community is much greater at mainland sites. There, they convincingly outnumber generalists but are themselves outnumbered on even the largest of islands.

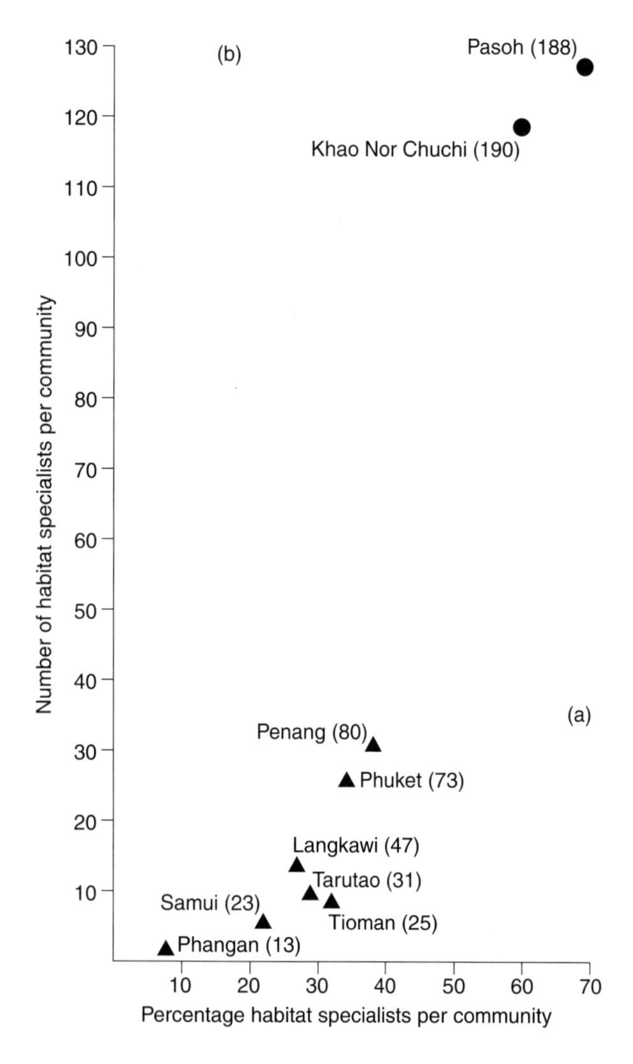

Figure 1. Number and proportion of resident single-habitat specialists versus multi-habitat generalists in the lowland inland forest communities (a) of islands versus (b) of unit areas of mainland. Site community sizes are given in parentheses.

The common-sense prediction that as island forest communities 'relax' they lose specialists ahead of generalists is vindicated. It follows as well that the smaller the ultimate total community, the smaller will be its proportion of specialists. Figure 1 shows Tarutao and Tioman islands stepping out of line in this respect, but if specialist but nomadic, gap-crossing frugivorous pigeons are deducted from scores across the board the trend is established absolutely. Without its pigeons, at the bottom of the scale, Phangan island holds zero specialists. A preponderance of specialists among deep shade species may further help to explain why island forests are so obviously deficient at understorey and ground levels.

The immediate message for conservation of diversity in forests is that birds (and presumably other groups) are ill-served by the transfer of nature reserve options from mainlands to islands, however large, and that the smaller the island chosen, the worse the impact. An often-pointed-out corollary is the role datable land-bridge ('continental') islands could play as natural laboratory test-beds, predicting the effects of forest fragmentation on the mainland, i.e., what mainland habitat islands of various characteristics may be expected to retain in the medium to long term.

Those familiar with an inland forest patch that has become isolated by encircling clearance will know how quickly certain birds begin to respond. Quite probably, the relaxation apparent on sea islands happened relatively fast; long enough ago at least to have allowed some surviving generalists to claim vacated ecological space. Typical responses range from enhancement of population density to occupation of new habitats. For example, in the Langkawi group Laced Woodpecker has spread from mangroves into rain forest in the absence of other shade-layer picids; Chestnut-breasted Malkoha and Tickell's Blue Flycatcher have spread from rain forest and edge into mangroves in the absence, respectively, of mainland Chestnut-bellied Malkoha and Mangrove Blue Flycatcher; and Abbott's Babbler has spread into all closed forests in the absence of regular floor and understorey relatives. A few supposed shifts are parallelled by morphological change: the very long bill of Dark-necked Tailorbird on Tioman and some other S China sea islands, the generally large size of Collared Scops Owl on Langkawi (both presumed to give a foraging advantage) and, also on Langkawi, the outsize tail of White-rumped Shama (evidently not for foraging).

These changes reflect isolation, but island forests do receive outside visitors, e.g., in the form of dispersing pigeons, occasional fruit-seeking hornbills, and even small nectarivores, such as Purple-throated Sunbird (Subharaj 1988). This tiny bird appears not only to have colonized Redang island (Terengganu state) with the last half century but actually to have replaced a relative there (Yellow-bellied Sunbird, in the mid-1970s found only on a small outlier apparently unused by Purple-throated).

Barring cliffs, permanent non-forest habitat on islands can only be a matter of centuries old, populated from scratch exclusively by over-water colonization. Ringing results, and the speed at which some non-forest specialists on the mainland discover newly cleared habitat, imply active dispersal is a well-developed behaviour of such birds. It should be no surprise, therefore, to learn that most have reached at least one of the explored islands (BMP5). Among residents, other than those marginal to the review area or only recently arrived, I know of only seven found just on the mainland.

Finally, a few land-birds in the peninsular fauna, the so-called island 'tramps', actually depend on islands. Parties of Pied Imperial Pigeons visit mainland coastal woodland but find most of their food, and breed and roost on small islands, between which they commute more or less continuously (and whose ecology they affect by spreading seeds). Two others (and a shorebird) are in the 'super-tramp' league, exclusive to small islands and characteristically able to make sometimes long inter-island journeys. They are Nicobar Pigeon and a still not certainly identified form of scops owl. Both should be generalists, able to live in a variety of habitats, usually wooded (but a pair of the owls bred successfully on Perak island, 140 km from nearest alternative land and, at the time, totally treeless).

THE COASTAL AND MARINE ASSEMBLAGES: Small, graspable in general ecological outline (waders have been a focus of attention) but harder to place in historical context than terrestrial assemblages. Certain of the latter are now at high risk yet even today many bird students have personal experience of what most would have been like in something close to their untouched state. Not so at sea or on the coasts of the Peninsula, where a tradition of bird harvesting is as widespread and well-entrenched as fishing in these environments (witness the many 'bird' rivers, creeks and islands of the review area). Clues from old specimens, comments in the early literature, and comparison with surveys of the still-remote coasts of modern SE Sumatra (Danielson and Skov 1986, Silvius *et al.* 1986) convince me these now hold just the remnants of altogether grander, past communities whose decline began before the end of the nineteenth century and which have slipped away almost unnoticed.

This applies particularly to sheltered coasts fronted by broad intertidal zones still prodigiously rich in benthic invertebrates and supporting what, until very recently, had seemed to be inexhaustible fisheries. The tide-flat fauna is grazed seasonally by over 30 species of non-breeding Palaearctic waders, whose modern numbers and distribution have only just been assessed (Mundkur 1993, Mundkur *et al.* 1992). Some have come under pressure locally (Pattani bay; now the site of a conservation programme) or at migration halts in the N temperate zone, but most population regulation must operate on the breeding grounds and this part of the shoreline community may be much as ever. Only two coastal waders (Beach Thick-knee and Malaysian Plover) are resident, the thick-knee now confined to islands of the extreme south and northwest, where sparse and threatened, but evidently once commoner and more widespread.

What really do seem to be missing, especially from sheltered coasts, are the large waterbirds. Instead of just a handful of Grey Heron colonies and last struggling groups of Great Egrets, Milky Storks and Lesser Adjutants, I picture globally important numbers of ardeids and storks occupying hundreds of kilometres of coastline at relatively high density. Among them would have been a healthy population of Great-billed Heron (when did it disappear?), most probably also Black-headed Ibis (locally frequent into the 1930s), and Spot-billed Pelican ('prodigious numbers' along the Selangor coast a century ago need not all have been migrants). Darter (still in Sumatra) and Great Cormorant (colonies in Sumatra until the 1920s) are other quite feasible past components. All of the resources they would have needed were widely available until relatively recently, indeed enough intertidal food probably still is available. Apart from boobies and, perhaps, frigatebirds, these are the only birds of the peninsular fauna that a local appetite for eggs and nestlings, collectable at fixed, traditional sites and by simple means, may actually have managed to eliminate before serious recording began; certainly well before coastal land-claims damaged crucial parts of the habitat.

Out of sight of land, birds can be as sparse in Peninsular waters as they are over open, tropical oceans, notoriously poor in surface nutrients (BMP5); yet these are not oceanic waters. On the broadest continental shelf in the world, shallow, enclosed Sunda seas receive a huge and continuous, nutrient-rich inflow of fresh water, and long stretches of shore are backed by mangrove forests, reckoned among the most productive of all ecosystems. Non-breeding terns are numerous enough in shore, yet only nine species of seabird (including the strictly coastal and partly riverine Little Tern) are accepted as having bred in the review area (BMP5, Wells 1991). All, except possibly Little Tern (which has benefited from transient conditions on coastal landfill and other earthworks), are in historical decline, in less than expected numbers considering the great array of potential breeding islands available, or, as breeders, have actually disappeared. Egging at traditional sites is behind most of this.

Boobies have been particular victims. I have speculated elsewhere that Red-footed and Masked may never have prospered in the relatively turbid waters of the Melaka straits, but why that should be so when Brown Boobies fished and bred there in multiple thousands is not obvious. Masked did once occur, nesting amongst Browns on Perak island. It might also have done so off the E coast (site of most recent records of birds at sea), but why no Red-footed Booby has ever been found breeding on any of the myriad, totally suitable-looking, wooded islands of peninsular waters has never been explained — other than that these have all long been reachable by fishing boat. We do have a fair idea of the local history of Brown Boobies. Common at sea throughout the Melaka straits a century ago, they are assumed to have bred there at a minimum two stations (S Arua and Perak islands), and at one (presumably in the Kra group) off the E coast. At Perak ('silver' island; surely a reference to white-washed rock, numbers declined from around 5000 pairs in the mid-1950s (perhaps by then already in decline) to fewer than 200 in 1980, plundered regularly for eggs and young by trawlermen (whose boats have also introduced rats). A few old adults persist in the area, but if these have fledged any young at all over the last 15–20 years it would be surprising. I know of no attempt whatsoever to protect them. S Arua was abandoned, or the colony died out, in the early twentieth century, and the Kra site, off Nakhon Si Thammarat, is hardly more than a rumour. Both are substantially closer in shore than Perak island.

The S Aruas are also the site of possible former breeding by Lesser Frigatebirds, known to have visited 'frigatebird stack' there up to the late 1940s. From near this have been collected males in breeding colours and a female carrying an oviduct egg. Perhaps they declined after the ouster of neighbouring boobies.

Overall, resident terns are far out-numbered by non-breeding visitors. Greater Crested numbers may depend on breeding sites peripheral to the review area; possibly no permanent site has ever existed within it. Black-naped, the species least obviously limited by availability of breeding stations (but whose usual sites are the very easiest to reach), has by common observation declined steeply more or less everywhere. Common Noddies (now) nest only on Perak island. Since some also once occurred on islands in the inner Gulf of Thailand, there is no clear ecological reason why use should not also be made of stacks in, e.g., the Arua group or Pahang-Johor archipelago. Both have been colonized by almost equally pelagic Roseate and Bridled Terns. E-coast Bridled colonies have formed the basis of an egging industry that even involved 'farming', to the extent of modifying habitat to attract birds. At one time it was regulated by social consent but such local-level control of collecting has long lapsed. How far this has caused a drift away from the 3000-plus pairs censused in Malaysian waters in the late 1940s (Gibson-Hill 1950) needs to be assessed. So, rather urgently, does the current whereabouts and status of much rarer, more easily reached, breeding Roseate Terns. Do any survive at all?

Needless to say, no sea or coastal bird species is a Sunda endemic.

IMPLICATIONS FOR CONSERVATION

There can be few wildlife conservation issues in the tropical world that do not apply somewhere in the Peninsula, offering scope for an essay. That has been resisted in favour of a single priority, relevant to interpreting the species-account distribution maps and illustrated in Map 5. This, of course, is the state of the lowland rain forests, from which must already have been lost globally important amounts of biological diversity, and upon whose fate hangs the survival of close on one half of the Peninsula's bird species.

As explained under the Assemblage headings, there are reasons for considering the survivorship of all but a handful of their species to be linked to the availability of plains-level forest, i.e., apparently, forest on gentle terrain. Why this might be so is still a matter of guesswork (and in urgent need of study). Longer-lasting surface water and damper soils on flat land could affect floor or understorey invertebrates such that weather-related dips in animal food supply might be less extreme below the steepland boundary. Again, thermoregulatory needs are perhaps greater on slopes, cutting into the foraging time of lowland breeders by extending brooding requirements. Many mutually inclusive possibilities wait to be tested.

There is also reason to suppose that species whose specialized ecologies evolved in the most continuous and extensive of all Sunda sub-regional biomes are peculiarly susceptible to localized, chance extinction, hence to the effects of habitat fragmentation (possibly more so than montane forest specialists). If ever enough inventories of sea islands of different sizes are completed, it should be possible to derive a doubling ratio specifically for rain forest birds, and from this, in theory, a working estimate of the continuous area needed to support a mainland-sized community in the long term. If this could not be contained within the borders of the largest nature reserve that already exists (Taman Negara national park, only relatively small, dislocated patches of whose terrain count as gentle), inspection of Map 5 suggests it might not now be found anywhere in the Peninsula — certainly not in the Thai provinces.

Map 5 includes the contour that scale and readability made it difficult to add to the standard background of the species distribution maps: at 150 m (the average position of the steepland boundary), superimposed on forest cover. In conjunction with Map 1, it defines the living space left to lowland rain forest birds compared (inset) with that available shortly before the start of the review period. The part of the habitat lost in the interval is obvious at a glance. Full accuracy cannot be an issue. Two quite separately derived, hand-drawn simplifications were superimposed to make the figure and, in a sense, are authenticated by the very roughness of their fit. The inescapable suspicion is that forest and contour on this map are *meant* to fit and that by the 1990s (earlier in Thailand) land clearance had reached or exceeded the steepland boundary, almost everywhere. If the notion of a plains-level core habitat versus dependant steepland fringe (in Malaysia, itself now a main target of the logging industry) is accepted, it must also be accepted that sustainability of the largest, most characteristic bird species assemblage of the Peninsula could be near (has perhaps already passed) a point of no return. Students of some other lowland forest animal groups, such as fish, will find this unsurprising. For them, the great Holocene extinction event is already with us.

In Malaysia at least, there are scraps of plains-level forest still that could be put to extra protective use, following the lead of Thailand's Khao Nor Chuchi project. Regional hard times will hurt wildlife conservation at every level, but on the basis that no effort should be spared under any circumstances, those able to carry out the fieldwork have a clear and urgent duty to find, search and put these sites on record.

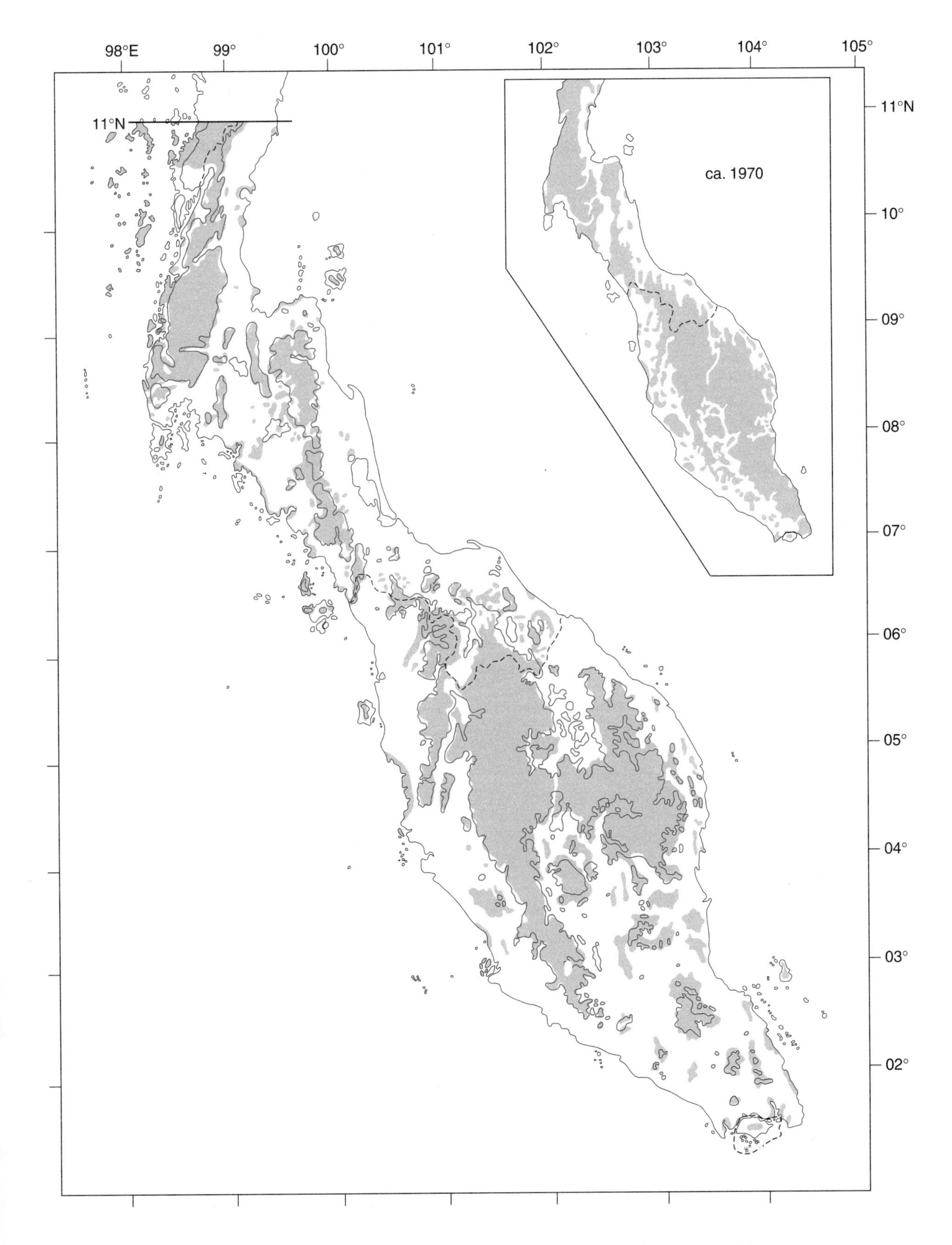

Map 5. Recent forest cover (including logged forest) relative to the position of the steepland boundary, and (inset) loss of cover over the review period. Sources: Directorate of National Mapping, Malaysia, 1974; P.D. Round and U. Treesucon; Smitinand et al. *1967; Thang Hooi Chiew 1995.*

VOLUME TWO

This will include subsidiary biogeographical information; ecological sections (including coverage of migrants and migration) that cannot be written up effectively without access to revised information on the whole fauna; systematic treatment of the passerines; a short history of ornithology in the Peninsula, up to the start of the review period; and a summary addendum to non-passerines.

REFERENCES

Alexander, J.B., 1962. A brief summary of the geology of Malaya. *Malayan Nature Journal* 16: 30–35.

Ashton, P.S., 1991. Toward a Regional Classification of the Humid Tropics of Asia. *Tropics* 1: 1–12.

Batchelor, B.C., 1983. *Sundaland tin placer genesis and late Cainozoic coastal stratigraphy in western Malaysia and Indonesia*. Ph.D. thesis, University of Malaya, Kuala Lumpur.

Blasco, F. and Bellan, M.F., 1995. *A Vegetation Map of Tropical Continental Asia*. Institut de la Carte Internationale de la Végétation, Toulouse.

Blower, J., 1985. Conservation priorities in Burma. *Oryx* 19: 79–85.

———, 1985a. Species conservation priorities in Burma. Pages 53–58 of Mittermeier, R.A. and Konstant, W.R. (editors), *Species conservation priorities in the tropical forests of Southeast Asia*. IUCN/SSC Occasional Paper 1, Gland, Switzerland.

BMP5. Medway, Lord and Wells, D.R., 1976. *The Birds of the Malay Peninsula*, Volume 5. H.F. & G. Witherby, London.

Boonsong Lekagul and McNeely, J.A., 1977. *Mammals of Thailand*. Association for the Conservation of Wildlife and Sahakarnbhat Co., Bangkok.

Campbell, B. and Lack, E. (editors), 1985. *A Dictionary of Birds*. British Ornithologists' Union and T. and A.D. Poyser, Calton.

Chasen, F.N., 1935. A Handlist of Malaysian Birds. *Bulletin of the Raffles Museum* 11: i–xx, 1–389.

———, 1939. *The Birds of the Malay Peninsula*, Volume 4. H.F. and G. Witherby, London.

Danielsen, F. and Skov, H., 1986. *Observations of waterbirds along the coast of South-east Sumatra, July–August 1985*. Unpublished report, Copenhagen.

Davison, G.W.H., 1980. The evolution of the Crested Argus. *World Pheasant Association Journal* 5: 91–97.

Delacour, J., 1970. The contribution of Gilbert Tirant to Indochinese ornithology. *Natural History Bulletin of the Siam Society* 23: 325–329.

Directorate of National Mapping, Malaysia, 1974. *Peninsular Malaysia; the forest area 1972*.

Gates, W.L., 1976. Modelling the ice-age climate. *Science* 191: 1138–1144.

Gaussen, H., Legris, P. and Blasco, F., 1967. Bioclimats du Sud-est Asiatique. *Institut Francais de Pondichéry. Traveaux de la section scientifique et technique* 3(4): 1–115.

Gibson-Hill, C.A., 1950. Notes on the Sea Birds breeding in Malayan Waters. *Bulletin of the Raffles Museum* 23: 5–64.

Hume, A.O., 1879. A first Tentative List of the Birds of the western half of the Malay Peninsula. *Stray Feathers* 8: 37–72, 151–163.

———, 1880. The Birds of the Western Half of the Malay Peninsula, third notice. *Stray Feathers* 9: 107–132.

Hume, A.O. and Davison, W.R., 1878. A Revised List of the Birds of Tenasserim. *Stray Feathers* 6: i–viii, 1–524.

Kloss, C.B., 1929. The Zoo-geographical Boundaries between Asia and Australia and some Oriental Sub-regions. *Bulletin of the Raffles Museum* 2: 1–10.

Mundkur, T., 1993. *A status overview of shorebirds in the East Asian – Australasian flyway*. Report to the Australian National Parks and Wildlife Service.

Mundkur, T., Yus Rusila Noor, Rudyanto and Lane, B., 1992. *A status overview of shorebirds in Malaysia and Indonesia*. Asian Wetland Bureau, Kuala Lumpur.

Ng, F.S.P., 1988. Forest Tree Biology. Pages 102–125 of Cranbrook, Earl of (editor), *Key Environments: Malaysia*. IUCN and Pergamon Press, Oxford.

Nisbet, I.C.T., 1968. The utilization of mangroves by Malayan birds. *Ibis* 110: 348–352.

Noske, R.A., 1995. The ecology of mangrove forest birds in Peninsular Malaysia. *Ibis* 137: 250–263.

Prentice, C. and Aikanathan, S., 1989. *A preliminary faunal survey of the North Selangor peat swamp forest*. WWF Malaysia and Asian Wetland Bureau, Kuala Lumpur.

Robinson, H.C., 1927. *The Birds of the Malay Peninsula*, Volume 1. H.F. and G. Witherby, London.

———, 1928. *The Birds of the Malay Peninsula*, Volume 2. H.F. and G. Witherby, London.

Robinson, H.C. and Chasen, F.N., 1936. *The Birds of the Malay Peninsula*, Volume 3. H.F. and G. Witherby, London.

Round, P.D., 1988. *Resident forest birds in Thailand*. ICBP Monograph 2. International Council for Bird Preservation, Cambridge.

Round, P.D. and Treesucon, U., 1998. *Birds of Khao Nor Chuchi; Check-list and Guide to Bird Finding*. Bird Conservation Society of Thailand, Bangkok.

Sibley, C.G. and Ahlquist, J.E., 1990. *Phylogeny and Classification of Birds. A study in molecular evolution*. Yale University Press, New Haven.

Silvius, M.J., Simons, H.W. and Verheught, W.J.M., 1984. *Soils, Vegetation, Fauna and Nature Conservation of the Berbak Game Reserve, Indonesia*. Research Institute for Nature Management, Arnhem.

Silvius, M.J., Verheugt, W.J.M. and Johan Iskandar, 1986. *Coastal wetlands inventory of Southeast Sumatra*. ICBP, Cambridge, and University of Utrecht.

Smitinand, T., Ana Na Lamphun and Vanek, D.V., 1967. *Map of Thailand, showing types of forest*. Royal Thai Military Research and Development Center, Bangkok.

Subharaj, R., 1988. Migrating sunbirds! *Singapore Avifauna* 2(2): 27–29.

Thang Hooi Chiew, 1995. *Sustainable forest management*

and conservation practices. Report to the Malaysian Timber Council, Kuala Lumpur.
Tjia, H.D., 1988. The Physical Setting. Pages 1–19 of Cranbrook, Earl of (editor), *Key Environments: Malaysia*. IUCN and Pergamon Press, Oxford.
Ward, P. 1968. Origin of the avifauna of urban and suburban Singapore. *Ibis* 110: 239–255.
Wells, D.R., 1990. Bird Diversity in the Sungai Kinchin area. *Malayan Nature Journal* 43: 326–332.
——————, 1991. Status and conservation of seabirds breeding in Malaysian waters. Pages 213–223 of Croxall, J.P. (editor), *Seabird status and conservation: A supplement*. ICBP Technical Publication 11. International Council for Bird Preservation, Cambridge.
White, C.M.N. and Bruce, M.D., 1986. *The Birds of Wallacea. An annotated check-list.* British Ornithologists' Union, London.
Whitmore, T.C., 1984. *Tropical Rain Forests of the Far East* (second edition). Oxford University Press, Oxford.
——————, 1988. Forest Types and Forest Zonation. Pages 20–30 of Cranbrook, Earl of (editor), *Key Environments: Malaysia*. IUCN and Pergamon Press, Oxford.
Wyatt-Smith, J., 1997. Manual of Malayan Silviculture for Inland Forests (second edition). *Malayan Forest Records* 23. Forest Research Institute of Malaysia, Kuala Lumpur.

Table 2. Alphabetical list of the species mentioned in the Introduction, with scientific names.

Abbott's Babbler *Trichastoma abbotti*
Arctic Warbler *Phylloscopus borealis*
Ashy Bulbul *Ixos flavalus*
Ashy Drongo *Dicrurus leucophaeus*
Ashy Tailorbird *Orthotomus ruficeps*
Asian Barred Owlet *Glaucidium castanopterum*
Asian Brown Flycatcher *Muscicapa dauurica*
Asian Glossy Starling *Aplonis panayensis*
Asian Pigmy-goose *Nettapus coromandelianus*
Asian Stubtail *Urosphena squamiceps*
Banded Broadbill *Eurylaimus javanicus*
Barn Owl *Tyto alba*
Barn Swallow *Hirundo rustica*
Barred Eagle Owl *Bubo sumatranus*
Beach Thick-knee *Esacus neglectus*
Black-breasted Sunbird *Aethopyga saturata*
Black-browed Barbet *Megalaima oorti*
Black-collared Starling *Sturnus nigricollis*
Black-crowned Night Heron *Nycticorax nycticorax*
Black-headed Ibis *Threskiornis melanocephalus*
Black-hooded Oriole *Oriolus xanthornus*
Black Hornbill *Anthracoceros malayanus*
Black Laughingthrush *Garrulax lugubris*
Black-naped Oriole *Oriolus chinensis*
Black-naped Tern *Sterna sumatrana*
Black-winged Kite *Elanus caeruleus*
Blue-rumped Parrot *Psittinus cyanurus*
Blue-throated Barbet *Megalaima asiatica*
Blue Whistling Thrush *Myophonus caeruleus*
Bornean Peacock Pheasant *Polyplectron schleiermacheri*
Bridled Tern *Sterna anaethetus*
Brown Boobook *Ninox scutulata*
Brown Booby *Sula leucogaster*
Brown-capped Woodpecker *Picoides moluccensis*
Brown-winged Kingfisher *Halcyon amauroptera*
Buffy Fish Owl *Ketupa ketupu*
Changeable Hawk Eagle *Spizaetus cirrhatus*
Chestnut-bellied Malkoha *Phaenicophaeus sumatranus*
Chestnut-breasted Malkoha *P. curvirostris*
Chestnut-capped Laughingthrush *Garrulax mitratus*
Chestnut-crowned Laughingthrush *G. erythrocephalus*
Chestnut-crowned Warbler *Seicercus castaniceps*
Collared Kingfisher *Halcyon chloris*
Common Noddy *Anous stolidus*
Collared Scops Owl *Otus bakkamoena*
Common Sandpiper *Actitis hypoleucos*
Copper-throated Sunbird *Nectarinia chalcostetha*
Crab-plover *Dromas ardeola*
Cream-vented Bulbul *Pycnonotus simplex*
Crested Argus *Rheinardia ocellata*
Crested Jay *Platylophus galericulatus*
Crimson Sunbird *Aethopyga siparaja*
Dark-necked Tailorbird *Orthotomus atrogularis*
Darter *Anhinga melanogaster*
Drongo Cuckoo *Surniculus lugubris*
Dusky Crag Martin *Hirundo concolor*
Dusky Warbler *Phylloscopus fuscatus*
Eurasian Tree Sparrow *Passer montanus*
Eyebrowed Thrush *Turdus obscurus*
Ferruginous Partridge *Caloperdix oculea*
Fulvous-chested Flycatcher *Rhinomyias olivacea*
Golden-bellied Gerygone *Gerygone sulphurea*
Golden-spectacled Warbler *Seicercus burkii*
Golden-throated Barbet *Megalaima franklinii*
Greater Coucal *Centropus sinensis*
Greater Flameback *Chrysocolaptes lucidus*
Great Argus *Argusianus argus*
Great-billed Heron *Ardea sumatrana*
Great Cormorant *Phalacrocorax carbo*
Great Crested Tern *Sterna bergii*
Great Egret *Casmerodius albus*
Great Slaty Woodpecker *Mulleripicus pulverulentus*
Great Tit *Parus major*
Green Imperial Pigeon *Ducula aenea*
Green-tailed Sunbird *Aethopyga nipalensis*
Grey-capped Woodpecker *Picoides canicapillus*
Grey-cheeked Bulbul *Criniger bres*
Grey Heron *Ardea cinerea*
Grey Peacock Pheasant *Polyplectron bicalcaratum*
Grey-throated Babbler *Stachyris nigriceps*
Gurney's Pitta *Pitta gurneyi*
Hill Blue Flycatcher *Cyornis banyumas*
Hill Prinia *Prinia atrogularis*
Horsfield's Bronze Cuckoo *Chrysococcyx basalis*
House Swift *Apus affinis*
Indian Roller *Coracias benghalensis*
Jungle Myna *Acridotheres fuscus*
Laced Woodpecker *Picus vittatus*
Lesser Adjutant *Leptoptilos javanicus*
Lesser Frigatebird *Fregata ariel*
Little Bronze Cuckoo *Chrysococcyx minutillus*

Little Grebe *Tachybaptus ruficollis*
Little Heron *Butorides striatus*
Little Spiderhunter *Arachnothera longirostra*
Little Tern *Sterna albifrons*
Malayan Peacock Pheasant *Polyplectron malacense*
Malaysian Plover *Charadrius peronii*
Mangrove Blue Flycatcher *Cyornis rufigastra*
Mangrove Pitta *Pitta megarhyncha*
Masked Booby *Sula dactylatra*
Milky Stork *Mycteria cinerea*
Mountain Hawk Eagle *Spizaetus nipalensis*
Mountain Imperial Pigeon *Ducula badia*
Nicobar Pigeon *Caloenas nicobarica*
Ochraceous Bulbul *Criniger ochraceus*
Orange-breasted Trogon *Harpactes oreskios*
Orange-tailed Shama *Trichixos pyrropyga*
Oriental Honey-buzzard *Pernis ptilorhyncus*
Oriental Magpie Robin *Copsychus saularis*
Osprey *Pandion haliaetus*
Palawan Peacock Pheasant *Polyplectron emphanum*
Pale-legged Leaf Warbler *Phylloscopus tenellipes*
Peregrine Falcon *Falco peregrinus*
Pied Imperial Pigeon *Ducula bicolor*
Purple-throated Sunbird *Nectarinia sperata*
Red-bearded Bee-eater *Nyctyornis amictus*
Red-footed Booby *Sula sula*
Rock Pigeon *Columba livia*
Roseate Tern *Sterna dougallii*
Ruby-cheeked Sunbird *Anthreptes singalensis*
Ruddy Kingfisher *Halcyon coromanda*
Rufous Piculet *Sasia abnormis*
Saunder's Tern *Sterna saundersi*
Savanna Nightjar *Caprimulgus affinis*
Scaly Thrush *Zoothera dauma*
Siberian Blue Robin *Luscinia sibirica*
Siberian Thrush *Zoothera sibirica*
Speckled Piculet *Picumnus innominatus*
Spot-billed Pelican *Pelecanus philippensis*
Spot-necked Babbler *Stachyris striolata*
Spotted Dove *Streptopelia chinensis*
Spotted Wood Owl *Strix seloputo*
Storm's Stork *Ciconia stormi*
Streaked Bulbul *Ixos malaccensis*
Streaked Wren Babbler *Napothera brevicaudata*
Swinhoe's Minivet *Pericrocotus cantonensis*
Temminck's Sunbird *Aethopyga temminckii*
Tenasserim Hornbill *Aceros subruficollis*
Tickell's Blue Flycatcher *Cyornis tickelliae*
Vinous-breasted Starling *Sturnus burmannicus*
White-bellied Woodpecker *Dryocopus javensis*
White-breasted Woodswallow *Artamus leucorynchus*
White-crowned Hornbill *Berenicornis comatus*
White-rumped Shama *Copsychus malabaricus*
White-vented Myna *Acridotheres cinereus*
Wood Snipe *Gallinago nemoricola*
Yellow-bellied Bulbul *Criniger phaeocephalus*
Yellow-bellied Sunbird *Nectarinia jugularis*
Yellow Bittern *Ixobrychus sinensis*
Yellow-breasted Warbler *Seicercus montis*
Yellow-browed Warbler *Phylloscopus inornatus*
Yellow-crowned Barbet *Megalaima henricii*
Yellow-legged Buttonquail *Turnix tanki*

THE SPECIES ACCOUNTS

GUIDE TO FORMAT

COVERAGE: The systematic section includes separate accounts of all species judged to have occurred naturally in the review area, or for which wild status cannot safely be excluded, plus definitely introduced species whose populations are self-sustaining or survive with only occasional, suspected topping up from releases. At 31 December 1995 this totalled 686 species, 385 of them non-passerine. Introduced species not regarded as fulfilling the above criteria, and those formerly on but for taxonomic or other technical reasons now removed from the peninsular list, receive only text mentions, in a family introduction or appropriate related species account. All of these categories have been indexed.

CONSTRUCTION: The book is not a part of a set series, and individual species accounts are as complete historically as I have been able to make them. Long descriptive passages called for under *IDENTIFICATION/DESCRIPTION* lapse into telegraphic style as appropriate, consistent with clarity and quick reference. Use of jargon has been kept to a low level and assumes only some general knowledge of life-cycle, ecology and classification terms. The avian morphology mentioned should already be familiar to those interested in bird identification. It is easily enough sourced in existing books, including some widely-owned regional field guides, to require no separate airing here, and I have not supplied a glossary. All the other short-hand special to particular subject-headings is explained below, as it arises.

I have also maintained a policy of using English rather than regional language terms for topography, habitats, etc., even though many of these are widely understood in the area, and often succinct. The only allowed circumstance is where a term is integral to the accepted proper name of a place. All those made use of in this way are translated in the Gazetteer (page xliv).

Sources are cited after the manner of a scientific paper, and because so much of the content of the species accounts has depended on original contributions, limited-circulation reports, etc., even after pruning, there are more of these than usual in a handbook format. To improve readability, where feasible, they have been clumped at the ends of paragraphs. Under *BREEDING*, with its formalized sub-sections, I have taken the further step of rolling often several usages into just one final citation; thus items attached to sub-section *Seasonality* may actually apply across the whole subject. Greatest problems of overloading occurred in the drafting of *GLOBAL RANGE* (served mostly by secondary sources, many widely shared) and *DISTRIBUTION* (with its many island details). The extreme solution here has been to strip these two back almost to no citations in the text at all. On balance, compensatory savings in other sections would have been proportionately more damaging. Unsourced statements elsewhere in the text are generally from personal records.

LAY-OUT: The splitting of material between 16 standard subject-headings per species is an experiment, focusing separate attention on a far wider span of topics than previously attempted for the avifauna of the Peninsula, or anywhere else in SE Asia. As will be evident, some headings have been hard to service, and rather few species escape without at least one 'No information' entry. Unless otherwise stated, this means no information available strictly from the review area, and draws purposeful attention to a gap in need of local filling. Collectively, of course, empty slots tend to emphasize topics of relative neglect across the board. Metric units are standard throughout and where reference material has been in other units, these have been converted.

SEQUENCE OF ORDERS AND FAMILIES: Subject of a modern revolution that many feel demands an outright choice between the mainly morphology-based Wetmore (or Peters Check-List) sequence and one built mainly on molecular data (Sibley and Ahlquist 1990). A third possible option, such as devised by Christidis and Boles (1994) for the Australian avifauna, capitalizes on change itself. Their approach is to substitute phylogenetic information in a baseline Wetmore sequence, progressively, as and when particular new results gain acceptable support. This I have attempted to extend to Asia. Change would be inherent in all updates, but should be driven at a pace slow enough most of the time to be digestible by non-specialists. No superior objectivity is implied, and the sole merit of the baseline sequence is its background familiarity.

The suborder and superfamily categories of the Wetmore sequence have been excluded. There has also been a small amount of switching about of families within orders to more closely approach the sequence of the Oriental Bird Club (OBC)'s Indomalayan *Checklist* (Inskipp *et al.* 1996). Substitutions made at order level result in: Galliformes and Anseriformes being placed next to each other at the head of the sequence, before grebes, petrels and pelecaniforms; and buttonquails, hornbills and hoopoes being elevated to orders (Turniciformes, Bucerotiformes, Upupiformes). At family level: darters (Anhingidae) are split from Phalacrocoracidae; Osprey is sunk into Accipitridae; phalaropes are sunk into Scolopacidae; Crab-plover is sunk into Glareolidae; skuas are sunk into Laridae; coucals (Centropodidae) are split from Cuculidae; and tree kingfishers (Halcyonidae) are split from Alcedinidae.

SEQUENCE BELOW FAMILY LEVEL: This is close but not identical to that of the OBC *Checklist*. Purposefully introduced differences here cover opinion on lumping versus splitting of species and, in a few instances, the relatedness of genera. One among parasitic cuckoos involves the moving of monotypic *Surniculus* (Drongo Cuckoo) away from its traditional slot by *Eudynamys* (koels) to a position next to *Cacomantis* (banded cuckoos). All such changes are explained and referenced in the text.

NAMES IN ENGLISH: The first large tranche introduced into the Peninsula came from Indian ornithology. Robinson (1927) acknowledged particularly the two editions of *The Fauna of British India* as sources, but admitted having substituted in his handbook where names offered seemed inappropriate. For the non-Indian species he coined new ones but considered 'the day ... far distant when any general agreement will be arrived at in respect of them'. Prophetically true, but with the OBC *Checklist* selection now available, and the involvement of a programme of the International Ornithological Congress, global agreement could at last be in sight.

Barring some taxonomy to be accommodated, most of the names used here agree with the *Checklist*. Only a handful of experimental substitutes has been too tempting to resist. In Volume One these are: 'Asian' Pigmy-goose; Brown 'Boobook' (for Hawk Owl, see Andrew 1992; part of a proposal to extend this Australian epithet from the current two to all small *Ninox* species, reserving 'Hawk Owl' to the Holarctic genus *Surnia*); 'Tenasserim' Hornbill (for Plain-pouched, since the gular pouch is unmarked in most *Aceros* species); and 'Yellownape' for all *Picus* woodpeckers showing a yellow-fringed crest (given that the traditional two among five found in the review area are not each others' closest relative).

NAMES IN THAI: I have seen no figures but understand that only a proportion of the species on the national list is dependably identified by a classical name. Other names in Thai are collectives for groups with features in common, but not always of birds related taxonomically, and some are dialect terms that have been familiar only locally. K.G. Gairdner, E.G. Herbert, Sir Walter Williamson and others began publishing both Thai script and romanized versions of reliable names early in the twentieth century, and started the long process of inventing new ones where classical sources failed. Dr Boonsong Lekagul much expanded this work (Boonsong 1968, Boonsong and Cronin 1974), and the latest country guide (Boonsong and Round 1991) includes a full set in Thai script — transcribed by Uthai Treesucon and Philip Round for use here.

Inevitably, most coined names are heavily influenced by already overly wordy names in English, and romanized versions can be astonishingly long; up to seven parts, five or more not uncommon, versus none above four in English. Those traditional names retained are typically tidier. Commonly, they allude to a habitat or some well-known behaviour (e.g., *Nok Dao Din* for the bobbing of Common Sandpiper) or, as often in Malay, are a rendition of some familiar call. *Nok*, the collective word meaning 'bird', applies in the names of most species, except for culturally important groups such as ducks (*Ped*) and diurnal raptors (*Yieow*). These have acquired their own separate terms. As names become more widely known such group collectives are likely to become commoner.

Here, spelling conventions indicate pronunciation without recourse to diacritical marks, but no more than hint at the tonality of spoken Thai (relative pitch, hold, and inflections up and down). This may hinder but should not block understanding, except in the case of certain words with romanized spellings fixed for other purposes but whose tone determines quite different, alternative meanings in a bird name. These must be learned separately. Otherwise, the following apply:

(1) Consonants as in standard English, except that *d* is always hard, unaspirated, as in English 'dog'; *g* never carries a *j* sound; *k*, where still retained at the beginning of a word is *g*, as in English 'gun'; *kh* is soft, aspirated, as in English 'carp'; *l* as a terminal letter is *n*, e.g., 'Satul' province is pronounced 'Satun'; *p* is an unaspirated *pb*, between English *p* and *b*; *ph* is a soft, aspirated *p*, as in English 'plume'; *t* is a *dt* sound, made with the tongue-tip touching the upper lip; *th* is a soft, aspirated *t*, as in English 'time'.

(2) As in English, double consonants in the middle of a word divide syllables.

(3) Vowels are short when single, as in English 'rat', 'net', 'tit', 'rot', 'rut'. Combinations take the following values: *aa* is as in English 'father'; *ae* has two just-separable sounds hence is not a full diphthong; *ai* is closest to English long *i*, as in the pronoun; *ao* is as in 'brown'; *aw* is as in 'paw' (*or* for this sound has been dropped); *ee* is as in 'meet'); *eh* has almost the same value as *ae*, but only a few names retain it; *ie* has two just-separable sounds, as in 'yew'; *oh* is as in 'hope'; *oi* is as in 'joy'; *uu* is as in 'moon' (*oo* itself has been dropped).

The most troublesome tonal meanings relevant to bird names involve the word spelled *khao*. With a long first vowel on a rising tone it means 'white', as in *Yieo Khao* (Black-winged Kite). With a short first vowel on a rising tone it means 'mountain', as in *Yieo Phuu Khao* (Mountain Hawk Eagle). With a short first vowel, uninflected, it is a collective for most owls, *Nok Khao ...*; anomalously, also for certain doves and pigeons, as in *Nok Khao Yai* (Spotted Dove).

NAMES IN MALAY: H.C. Robinson guessed around 250 traditional names dependably identified a scientific species. Quite a number are local dialect terms. They have been collected in dictionaries, including those published by the government body responsible for language development. Unfortunately, the latter's programme has yet to extend to a national vocabulary of wildlife terms. For birds, the task of selecting and inventing fell to the Federal Department of Wildlife and National Parks (PERHILITAN) (Abdul Rahman Ismail 1981).

Again, most of PERHILITAN'S new names were translated more or less direct from descriptive English. As many as possible I have used here, but have not shrunk from substituting where meanings could lead to confusion (thus 'Burung Tropika', meaning a tropical bird, does no justice to Tropicbirds of the genus *Phaethon*). Many of the alternatives offered in Volume One may be short-lived, but will have served if they generate a profitable argument amongst knowledgeable users of Malay. Without access to sets of good, communicable names for wildlife species the non English-reading public can hardly be blamed if it is not in the forefront of concern for biological conservation.

The general collective 'Burung' will continue in use as long as bird names remain relatively unfamiliar. Once a popular vocabulary is in place, the expectation is that group collectives will take over.

As a phonetic language, officially romanized, Malay presents none of the pronunciation problems faced in transcribing Thai. The following rules apply:

(1) Vowels are as in English 'part', 'pet', 'pit' (or 'police'), 'pot' and 'poop'. There are no diphthongs; in combination (including doublings), each vowel retains a separate value.

(2) Single consonants are as in standard English except that *c* is always *ch*, regardless of position, as in English 'chat' or 'batch' (written *ch* survives only in some place names), and *c* never doubles for *k*; single *g* is hard only as an initial letter, otherwise soft as in 'sing', and it never carries a *j* sound. A hard *g* sound in the middle of a word, as in 'mangle', is conveyed by doubling, to *gg*.

(3) *Kua* and *eks* are 'qu' and 'x', respectively.

(4) In general, two-syllable words are stressed lightly on the first syllable, three-syllable words on the second. For convenience, names at the head of the species-accounts have stress indicated by a subscript bar. Lack of a bar under certain short words means no stress appropriate.

SCIENTIFIC NAMES: Champions of the lineage-based 'phylogenetic' versus reproductive boundary-based 'biological' species concepts have for some time been debating the relative usefulness of these concepts to taxonomy. Ultimately, the only winners of this extraordinary argument will surely be those who come to accept complementary, even reinforcing, roles for separate systems run in parallel for different purposes (and agree to different terms for their units). In the process, some names could be upset but, as Inskipp *et al.* (1996) point out, at the moment none of this matters; so little of the right research has been conducted on Asian birds that only a few of the species-limits accepted amount to more than a subjective preference. Generally, the names used here are as found in the OBC *Checklist*, but err towards keeping species as broad as the biological evidence seems to allow. This has caused just a few suppressions, e.g., of *cuculoides* for continental Asian Barred Owlet, sunk into older *castanopterum* to cater for the Indonesian population.

Each species-account header includes the accepted species name and authority, followed by a full citation (except for the *Systema naturae* of Linnaeus and Gmelin), in line with a policy of not abbreviating the bibliography. This may seem excessive, but helps restore life to the work of over 80 taxonomists in four continents, spread across one and a half centuries. The library searches needed gave an opportunity for checking original dates, pagination, issue number and other such error-prone details at source.

Names of genera used are those generally accepted at present, loosely reflecting a tendency towards shrinking the size of this category for birds, worldwide. Exceptions in Volume One include: the sinking of *Dupetor* into an enlarged *Ixobrychus* (bitterns), *Haliastur* into *Milvus* (kites), *Gelochelidon* into *Sterna* (terns), *Rhinoplax* into *Buceros* and *Rhyticeros* into *Aceros* (hornbills), and *Pelargopsis* into *Halcyon* (tree kingfishers), plus the retention of *Hierococcyx* (hawk cuckoos) within *Cuculus*.

No synonymies are given, but no recent name-change in either category is adopted here that has not already been published elsewhere, and most such cases receive extra mention in the text.

GROUP RELATIONS: This first formal subject-heading gives notice of any taxonomic changes at level of genus or above that are controversial or could be unfamiliar, but is routinely about membership of superspecies (comprising two or more biological species at their closest level of relatedness). Such generally similar taxa would be isolated geographically or, where they have re-met, do not invade each other's space apparently because they have not evolved ecological compatibility. The concept helps in reconstruction of recent phylogenies, dispersal histories, etc., and a terminology has grown up around how members of a superspecies are posited. Here, they are treated only as each other's 'allospecies', emphasizing occupation just of different space.

No superspecies grade exists in nomenclature, and groupings represent little more than educated guesses, put forward to suggest research. As more kinds of evidence on relationships become available many are likely to be revised. It is also likely that phylogeneticists less concerned with biological boundaries in nature will use cladistic methods to define a category, and re-align clusters numerically.

By the end of 1995, a little over one third of non-passerines (142 species) in the review area had been identified as possessing one or more allospecies world-wide. Most of these superspecies have at least one member outside the Indomalayan zoogeographical region. Less than one quarter is entirely Indomalayan and only one, the cluster that includes Malayan Peacock Pheasant, is exclusive to the Sunda sub-region. As would be expected, none is restricted to the Peninsula alone.

All of the other non-passerines of the area (243) are what elsewhere have been called 'isospecies' but here are described simply as 'free-standing', believed not or no longer to be a part of a superspecies.

GLOBAL RANGE: Drawn mostly from secondary sources but researched to at least the end of 1995. Global range is described rather than mapped, and in more detail than some might consider necessary for a review of so small a part of Asia. Land-bird treatments are in more or less standard geographical sequence, as needed: the Americas, Africa and islands, Eurasia and islands, then Australasia and Oceania, with a gradation of detail up from global via Indomalayan to SE Asian. Within the Indomalayan region, regular order of treatment is: the Indian subcontinent and islands, margins of Tibet, political divisions of China and islands (after Cheng Tso-hsin 1987), SE Asia and islands, and Wallacea. 'Tenasserim' here always means peninsular Burma north of latitude 11°N. All detail within the review area is deferred to *DISTRIBUTION* and *STATUS AND POPULATION*. For seabirds, the cover is global seas, as needed, focusing in greater detail on Asian, then SE Asian waters.

Where substantially different, breeding and non-breeding ranges are described separately, if known, also with an indication of main passage routes, plus significant records of vagrancy that apply to SE Asia.

IDENTIFICATION/DESCRIPTION: Virtually all species accounts are indexed to an illustration, and plates and the text of this section are mutually supportive, to be consulted together. Opening sentences summarize identification pointers (other than vocalizations) regarded as useful or worth testing in the field. Where relevant, they also indicate the commoner field errors. Not set up in competition with specialist field guides, this short section should function as a supplementary, desk-top check on personal field-notes.

The rest of the text is in-the-hand description, pitched at a level of detail appropriate to the problems of identifying and separating age/sex classes expected in any one case; also, of course, to the quality of information actually available. Treatments range from a summary of key features, relying on illustrations where no special difficulties are anticipated, or where no useful characters have yet been found, to tract-by-tract detail, particularly where research has thrown up new features or clarified uncertainties (as, for example, in some parasitic cuckoos). If a particular class has not been described or is inadequately known, this is stated. Ordinary language is used throughout, with no reference made to colour standards at any stage.

Three sub-headings cover non-plumage characters and measurements:

Bare-part colours. As many as possible of these have been described from live birds observed at close range or, better still, actually in the hand. Unfortunately, not many non-passerines are regularly taken in ground-set mist-nets, the main tool available to field-workers during the review period. Waders at open-ground night roosts are an example of an exception. In forest, non-passerines typically constitute less than 30 per cent of capturable species and only a small fraction of the individuals handled. For this reason, some descriptions in Volume One have been pieced together from secondary sources. All such information has been cross-referenced as widely as possible to weed out copied-on errors and the sometimes extraordinary gaffs in museum collections where labels seem to have been muddled at the preparation stage, or the scribe was someone other than the collector or preparator.

The body-parts covered are: iris, eyelid (ranging from just the bare rim to full periorbital ring); other bare skin of the head and neck, exceptionally elsewhere; bill, cere and casque (of hornbills); and feet (toes plus exposed tarsus). Wherever the data are good enough they have been recorded separately for the different age/sex classes, also for different stages of cyclical change (as found, e.g., in most herons and egrets). Bare-part (particularly iris) colours are often a reliable way of detecting sexual maturity.

Size. Except where an unusual parameter has special identification or other biological importance, I have stayed with the traditional set: wing-length, measured flat and straightened as a chord from the flexed carpal ('wrist') joint to the tip of the longest primary; tail, closed and flattened, from the base (point of entry) of the central pair of rectrices to the tip of the longest pair; bill, as a chord from tip to point of connection of the upper mandible with the skull or, where access is difficult, to the anterior edge of the cere or level of the front or rear edge of the nasal opening; and tarsus, from the rear indentation in the tibio-tarsal joint to the basal joint of the middle (third) toe. Sample-sizes vary greatly but have generally been as large as I could make them. Unless stated otherwise, measurements apply exclusively to adults, sexed wherever the data were considered reliable. Measurements of free-flying juveniles are given only where these range significantly outside limits set for adults, but in many species juveniles need further study.

Overall, there have been two sources of data: fresh kills or live birds handled for ringing, and museum study skins that have ranged from recent to more than a century old. Storage should make no practical difference to skeletal and hard feather-part dimensions, but some inter-skeletal tissues shrink perceptibly while drying *post mortem*. With time, this reduces standard wing measurement by a small fraction below condition in life and, as skin draws back from feather-bases, may actually increase tail-length. For sample-size reasons it has not been practical to sort museum data, but an indication that study skins have been included as a source warns of one more variable to be considered when testing fresh material against the information given.

Weight. Accurate weighing, for the biological information it can yield, became a routine part of handling procedure in this area with the advent of mist-nets and ringing in the late 1950s. Some of the data given here have been published elsewhere; most are lifted direct from the files of the University of Malaya Bird-Ringing Project, or taken from affiliates working separately but with comparable equipment. In only a few instances have I resorted to museum labels for what many would now regard as pointlessly crude data on certain large birds not handled in modern times. If safely identified, age/sex classes have been quoted separately, and where the spread of handlings of long-distance migrants has been good enough (in this volume, mainly among coastal waders) I have summarized seasonal changes.

As will be seen, a fair proportion of non-passerines (including some relatively common ones) is still wanting good local weight data from any source.

DISTRIBUTION: Strictly within the review area, from the start of detailed field recording in the last quarter of the nineteenth century. Land distributions are summarized at the level of the 27 main geopolitical divisions (provinces, states, territories) of the review area, by direct or, for widespread species, negative listing in standard, roughly north to south sequence (Map 6). The space-saving abbreviations of division names used are from BMP5 and the Bird Report series of the Malayan Nature Society (BR, MBR), except that mainland Penang is now *Pra*, standing for Seberang Prai, the official name in place of former Province Wellesley (*Wel* of BMP5, etc.).

This is followed by occurrence on islands or island groups, also listed in standard north to south sequence: off the west (Andaman sea/Melaka straits) then the east (S China sea) coasts of the Peninsula, and east to west through Singapore waters. It has been convenient to classify metropolitan Singapore and also Phuket as political divisions rather than islands, treating them as 'mini mainlands' each with its own set of satellites. Neither of these large, extensively urbanized, mostly deforested islands has been used in biogeographical analyses.

Some have queried the need of so much space devoted to inventories of individual islands. As explained, all of the islands in peninsular waters are continental, hence are ageable, and many show at least some original forest cover. They are of special interest because of the forest bird communities retained, theoretically and due to the bearing these could have on conservation expectations in habitat 'islands' of the mainland. Only a few island forests of the review area are known thoroughly and the detail attempted should help stimulate yet more searching, while opportunities last.

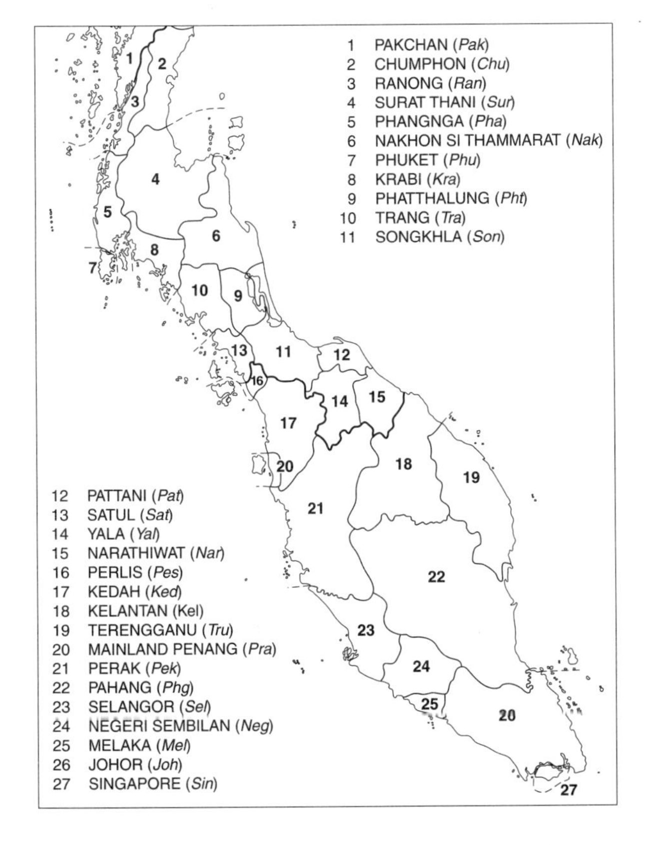

Map 6. Geopolitical divisions of the review area used to describe range. Heavy lines are the international land frontiers.

Marine bird distributions are described directly by sea area, with or without reference to political divisions or other land features, according to whether they are in-shore or mainly open-sea species.

The range map accompanying each species account rationalizes information given in the text except that, to minimize clutter at the scale demanded, land borders are reduced just to the international frontiers. Other than where occurrences are only sporadic (occasional to vagrant visitors or unusually rare residents), the convention is that range-margins run parallel with division boundaries, external to coastlines (enclosing the coast for land and shore species) but external also to the boundaries of divisions registering no occurrence, excluding these completely.

The second convention is that, except where occurrence is sporadic, adjacent divisions positive for a species are linked. This generates a gross range from historical data but without regard to distribution of habitats, whereas real distributions are, of course, habitat-dependant. The pink background area represents approximately what early 1990s remote-sensing recorded was then left of forest cover in the Peninsula. As explained, to gain an idea of the real range available to the main inland assemblages, this needs to be compared (a) with forest cover before the review period, (b) with the position of the steepland and montane boundaries (Maps 1 and 5).

Map and text are to be consulted together, and in combination should help distinguish between information-gaps and range-limits that are real on the ground. Comparison across sets of species will soon show up the under-worked parts of the Peninsula, and those divisions (Pattani, mainland Penang, Melaka, etc.) that were extensively deforested before ornithological exploration began.

At sea, some marine bird ranges are mapped as approaching but not actually reaching mainland coasts. Where unrecorded opposite a given political division on land, the range boundary is shown as interrupted, with question-marks at its broken ends. Marine ranges are considered to be seaward of any limit given, but distances off shore are shown only approximately. The text must be consulted for better detail. Important colonial breeding concentrations in the review area are arrowed on the map.

Because of the constraints of text-column shape, map height has been maintained at the expense of width by trimming sea off the right-hand margin. This affects the far-eastern (outer S China sea) fringe of the review area. To recover the position of the Terengganu off-shore oil field, compare with Map 1 and extrapolate NE and SE sea boundaries out to their point of intersection.

GEOGRAPHICAL VARIATION: Summarizes the essential features of morphological variation within the review area, and lists subspecies, giving author, date, type locality and an indication of global range. No fresh names have been introduced but space is taken both to highlight problems at this level and present options for the revisions that seem to be needed. Examples include Buffy Fish Owl and Greater Flameback. Where no variation has been described, the treatment is merely to name and outline the global range of the one taxon occurring.

Variation among non-breeding visitors is often, but not always, non-geographical. Where found among resident land birds it is mostly latitudinal, involving plumage tones and patterns and, commonly among non-passerines, a southward decline of size. Green Imperial Pigeon and Greater Coucal are about the only examples of a trend towards larger size in the south. Boundaries are by nature fuzzy and one useful let-out has been the discovery that zones of N–S intergradation between certain subspecies take in the entire Peninsula. On one or two of its bigger, more remote islands, a few species are larger (see Collared Scops Owl, Laced Woodpecker) or have some proportionately larger parts than on the mainland, a character-shift classically associated with oceanic islands (including some that fringe the Sunda sub-region). No altitudinal variation is known, and no geographical variation has been proven among marine birds. Claims of E–W differentiation between presumed local populations of Great Crested and Roseate Terns could not be confirmed from the material researched for this book.

STATUS AND POPULATION: Status has been given three components: *continuity*, covering presence through the year; *consistency*, covering presence in relevant habitats; and *abundance.*

The *continuity* categories used are: *Resident*, for populations that stay in the review area year-round, and breed there; *breeding visitor*, for populations that breed seasonally in the review area but mostly leave it at other times of year; *non-breeding visitor*, for populations present in the review area over at least the midwinter or mid-summer periods, but that do not breed there and whose adults migrate away seasonally; *passage migrant*, for populations that do not breed in the review area and occur there only on journeys between breeding and non-breeding ranges elsewhere. Where more than one distinctively behaving population of a species occurs, more than one category applies. Two or three per species is not uncommon.

All unqualified mentions of season in connection with *continuity* are to boreal seasons (of the N hemisphere), and terms such as 'overwintering' and 'oversummering' fit the N hemisphere. Where movements or other behaviour relate to austral (S hemisphere) seasons, this is specified.

Just two categories for *consistency* are used: *regular*, where the expectation is that, at appropriate seasons and in relevant parts of the review area, a species will be found wherever large enough amounts of suitable habitat occur; *local*, where suitable-looking habitat is demonstrably not occupied over large areas. The inferences could be that suitable-looking does not necessarily mean actually suitable, or that the population is constrained in other ways.

Objectively, *abundance* rates the size of the whole population or compares population densities. These pieces of information are rare, and even where density data are available they must take *consistency* into account. First impressions in the field are often just of relative conspicuousness, which by no means always ranks with population density. Particularly in forest, certain species maintaining relatively high densities may actually be quite hard to detect. To cope, my broad, purposely fuzzy categories here sink whatever hard data are yet available into a rating for what I consider to be findability by a competent and equipped field-worker operating at a relevant time, site and season. They are: *common*, for contacts on all or nearly all field days (*abundant* usually only applies locally and is used sparingly); *uncommon*, for contacts on less than half of field days; and *sparse*, for only occasional contacts even in prime sites. These may not be considered sufficient, but it is as important not to overstep reliability as to be able to record change over time.

Vagrant status is reserved for species recorded in the review area, individually or as parties, six or fewer times since 1950. This arbitrary cut-off date allows for long-term changes of status to be recognized; useful, e.g., for large waterbirds whose populations have declined since the mid-century. What appears to be a *continuity* category, therefore, is actually measured in terms of *abundance*. More often than not, occurrences of vagrants and near-vagrants fit the seasonality of known main movements of the species outside the review area. Where possible, treatments take that into account.

This subject-heading otherwise covers actual population sizes and density estimates: for groups such as coastal waders whose whole range in the review area has been reached and whose numbers have been counted through the year (turnover of migrants estimated from peak counts at traditional concentration points); and birds of the forest under-stratum studied by mark-and-release. This is also where I have pigeonholed information on range-boundary and other historical changes; interactions between populations of different status (typically, residents versus migrants); site-fidelity by returning migrants, etc. To a small extent, therefore, *STATUS AND POPULATION* treatment overlaps *DISTRIBUTION, HABITATS AND ECOLOGY* and *MOVEMENTS.*

HABITATS AND ECOLOGY: Lists the range of habitats used, plus any evidence of core versus only marginal occupation of a given habitat; selection of particular space within habitats; terrain and altitudinal range-limits; and any seasonal variation in usages. Where appropriate, it compares habitat selection by populations of different status, and enlarges on anything to do with the way similar relatives partition themselves ecologically.

The following terms cover divisions of the column height of forests, useful in describing activity spaces. The *floor* includes bare soil (and soil termite mounds, etc.), small streams and pools (wallows, etc.) not breaking the canopy, the litter layer, low stumps and fallen wood. The *understorey*, or *under-stratum*, covers roughly the first 3 m of vertical space, including the taller herbs, seedlings and saplings, stemless palms, and tree boles and buttresses. The *mid-stratum* is a diffuse but continuous zone above 3 m, including crowns of smaller trees and palms, and stems, trunks and lower boughs of larger trees, palms and climbers. Together, these sub-canopy strata are sometimes referred to as the *shade layer(s)*. The *canopy* layer is the uneven but more or less continuous leafy 'skin' of the forest, raised intermittently into the usually rather open crowns of giant emergents. Botanists often treat emergent crowns as an extra layer of forest structure (an upper versus general canopy) but this is not a required distinction here.

Usually in reference to forest cover, the term *submontane* means slope-land between the steepland boundary and lower limit of montane forest, i.e., within the altitude range of lowland forest. *Upland* or *uplands* means the higher hills in general, mostly without alluding to any particular class of vegetation.

FORAGING AND FOOD: Treats everything specifically to do with foraging-site and substrate preferences; food-finding, including ranging behaviour (such as revealed by radio-tagging); food-handling; food itself, and diet proportions. Aspects of ecological isolating mechanisms that relate directly to food or foraging space are also covered here.

SOCIAL ORGANIZATION: Describes the typical basic social group size and composition; also group spacing and territoriality, including seasonal changes or differences between populations of different status in the review area. There is some overlap between this section and *SOCIAL INTERACTIONS*.

MOVEMENTS: According to level of detail available, covers extreme annual dates of presence of migrants; seasonal limits of active migration; and intensity and progress of movements. Also describes the routes of visible passage (e.g., of raptors, swifts and bee-eaters); differences suggestive of more than one independent schedule operating through the review area; and features of migration and other movements revealed by controls and recoveries of ringed birds.

SURVIVAL: Except where enough individuals of a given species have been ringed at regular-effort mark-and-release sites to track survival in local populations, this section gives only the more extreme retrap intervals. Much work on typical survival rates still remains to be done.

SOCIAL INTERACTIONS: Covers miscellaneous behavioural interactions between members of the basic social group, usually just between pair-members; also behaviour (other than vocal) that appears to help maintain spacing between groups, including, e.g., drumming by woodpeckers.

VOICE: Most descriptions have been taken from personal field-notes and other unpublished sources, or from tape-recordings, unless expressly stated otherwise, all made within the review area. Rather than resort to the literature, in as many instances as possible I have made my own fresh attempt to verbalize vocalizations, on the basis that comparison across sources should aid interpretation. The vowel values and consonant combinations of standard British English apply throughout. It is hoped these convey at least the outline form of calls, with some hint of pitch and tone. The ultimate plan is actually to publish a parallel set of recordings.

It goes without saying that vocalizations have ordinarily been verified in the field before inclusion. Just a few identifications are only tentative, run down mainly by elimination (see, e.g., Ruddy Kingfisher). These are clearly marked, and have been added to draw attention to particular problems outstanding at time of writing.

BREEDING: According to the level of information available, summarized under four sub-headings:

Nest. Covers the range of sites selected, including substrate, height above ground, etc.; shape, size and materials; and any special building behaviour.

Eggs and brood. Describes egg colour, pattern and surface texture; egg shape, in categories adapted from Harrison (1975): *elliptical* = a symmetrical ellipse without obvious pointedness (sub-categories long, normal or short, the extreme of short being close to spherical); *subelliptical* = an unusually long version of elliptical; *ovate* = an asymmetrical ellipse, egg-shaped in the popular sense; *piriform* = unusually asymmetrical, bluntly rounded at one end, tapering to a distinct point at the other); *biconical* = long, more or less symmetrical, tapering at both ends; egg size, quoting a maximum and minimum diameter or sample ranges of these measurements, from the largest to smallest individual in each case; full (incubated) clutch size; brood size and typical number of young fledging; laying and hatching intervals, and incubation and nestling periods, or total development period; plus any information on breeding success levels (chicks fledging from eggs laid or eggs hatched).

Cycle. A catch-all for information on pair-member roles at successive stages of breeding, plus any special associated behaviour by pair-members or offspring; nest helpers; number of broods per breeding season (broodedness); and breeding-attempt intervals, etc.

Seasonality. Covers the combined occurrence (outer recorded limits by part month) of courtship behaviour, nest-building, eggs, chicks and fledging, pooling all data to give a theoretical total possible seasonal picture. This must exaggerate actual local population performance in any one year.

All references and other sources are grouped at the end of this last sub-section. Some of the most frequently used citations are unpublished, especially a detailed set of extracts made available from his Malayan diaries by G.C. Madoc and a field-book of the late V.W. Ryves covering the years 1915–1938. Found among papers with the Zoological Reference Collections, National University of Singapore, this was brought to my attention by Dr C.J. Hails.

MOULT: Summarizes special studies, but deals routinely only with primary-tract moult, covering sequence, intensity and estimates of individual duration of replacement, population-level synchrony, seasonal timing, and any convincing population or age/sex-class variations. Regardless of moult direction, primary-feather loci are numbered from P1, closest to the carpo-metacarpal joint, outward (descendantly) to the leading edge of the outer wing ('hand'). Moult activity (feather loss or regrowth) is indicated by a locus number, e.g., 'P1–3' means activity simultaneous at all three consecutive loci in a single wing; 'P1, 3' means no activity at the intervening locus; 'P1/3' means activity at a single locus, asymmetrical between wings. Where relevant, notation for the secondary tract and tail is the same, except that secondaries are numbered inward (ascendantly) from S1 near the carpo-metacarpal joint towards the body, and rectrices from the central pair (T1) outward (centrifugally). Body-moult intensity is given qualitatively as *light*, *medium* or *heavy*, and where successive or alternating plumages are distinguishable in the field, moult progress is *early*, *mid-stage* or *advanced*. Main sources of data have been the records of the University of Malaya Bird-ringing Project and collaborators, and museums. The latter have added many species never handled by mist-netters, hence not previously studied in this area.

CONSERVATION: Assesses local status relative to the condition of core habitat, or to any other special circumstances affecting population viability in the review area. Among lowland forest birds, the importance of plains-level versus slope habitat is a consistent theme. Where Birdlife International's *Birds to Watch—2* (Collar *et al.* 1994) gives a global rating for a species, this is also quoted.

THE ARTWORK

Eight artists painted the plates for Volume One, collectively over a period of seven years. Early ambitions of achieving uniformity were quickly abandoned in favour of the more attainable, ultimately desirable option of stylistic diversity within a general plan. From their individual technical standpoints, all members of the art team have worked towards ground between portraiture and the strictly functional aid to identification, shifting balance according to how difficult subjects were considered to be in the field. Large population and sexual differences, and typical phases of polymorphic species (e.g., Oriental Honey-buzzard, Changeable Hawk Eagle) are covered, but mostly only in adult plumage. Overall, rather few immature plumages have been illustrated, but key aging features are given in the text. In this and other respects, plates and text are interactive.

Volume One also includes a few monochrome woodcuts that stand in for plate illustrations. Non-passerines not given the full treatment, for whatever reason, it is hoped will be covered in extra plates of an addendum to Volume Two.

Standard abbreviations used in the plate captions are: 'ad.' = adult; 'subad.' = subadult; 'imm.' = immature; 'juv.' = juvenile; 'fw.' = first winter (applied to non-breeding visitors); 'br.' = breeding plumage; 'nbr.' = non-breeding plumage.

ADDITIONAL REFERENCES

Abdul Rahman Ismail, 1981. *Senarai nama-nama burung Semenanjung Malaysia dan Asia Tenggara*. Department of Wildlife and National Parks, Kuala Lumpur. [Bird names in Malay]

Andrew, P., 1992. *The Birds of Indonesia, a checklist (Peters' sequence)*. Indonesian Ornithological Society, Jakarta.

Boonsong Lekagul 1968. *Bird Guide of Thailand*. Association for the Conservation of Wildlife and Kurusapa Ladprao Press, Bangkok.

Boonsong Lekagul and Cronin, E.W., 1974. *Bird Guide of Thailand* (second edition). Association for the Conservation of Wildlife and Kurusapa Ladprao Press, Bangkok.

Boonsong Lekagul and Round, P.D., 1991. *A guide to the Birds of Thailand*. Saha Karn Bhaet Co., Bangkok.

Cheng Tso-hsin, 1987. *A Synopsis of the Avifauna of China*. Science Press, Beijing.

Christidis, L. and Bowles, W.E., 1994. *The Taxonomy and Species of Birds of Australia and its Territories*. Royal Australasian Ornithologists Union Monograph 2. RAOU, Melbourne.

Collar, N.J., Crosby, M.J. and Stattersfield, A.J., 1994. *Birds to Watch 2. The World List of Threatened Birds*. Birdlife Conservation series No. 4. Birdlife International, Cambridge.

Harrison, C.J., 1975. *A field guide to the Nests, Eggs and Nestlings of British and European Birds*. Collins, London.

Inskipp, T., Lindsey, N. and Duckworth, W., 1996. *An Annotated Checklist of the Birds of the Oriental Region*. Oriental Bird Club, Sandy.

UMBRP. Records of the University of Malaya Bird-ringing Project.

GAZETTEER

Sites and features mentioned in the species accounts are shown in Maps 7–12, accessed from the two directories that follow. One latitudinal sequence of reference numbers operates across all the maps, independent of scale, hence numbers boxed off in the local enlargements (Maps 8–12) should not be expected to make up complete independant series. Unless integral to a well recognized or purposefully coined proper name (capitalized), category words for locality-names in Thai and Malay (prefixes), and Burmese (suffixes), have been replaced by the equivalent suffix in English. Retained in occasional proper names here are: *Air (Ayer)* = water or waterway (M); *Anak* = satellite of a larger feature (M); *Ao* = bay (T); *Ban* = village, town (T); *Batu* = rock, outcrop (M); *Bukit* = hill (M); *Genting* = pass (M); *Kaki* = hill-foot (M); *Khao* = hill, mountain (T); *Khlong* = river (T); *Khuan* = hill (T); *Kota* = capital, fort (M); *Kuala* = river-mouth (M); *Negeri* = state, territory (M); *Padang* = field, open ground (M); *Pak (Pak nam)* = river-mouth, estuary (T); *Pantai* = coastline, open prospect (M); *Paya* = swamp, marsh (M); *Pekan* = town (M); *Pengkalan* = landing-point (M); *Phanom* = mountain (T); *Seberang* = beyond river, etc., implying an outer district (M); *Sungai* =

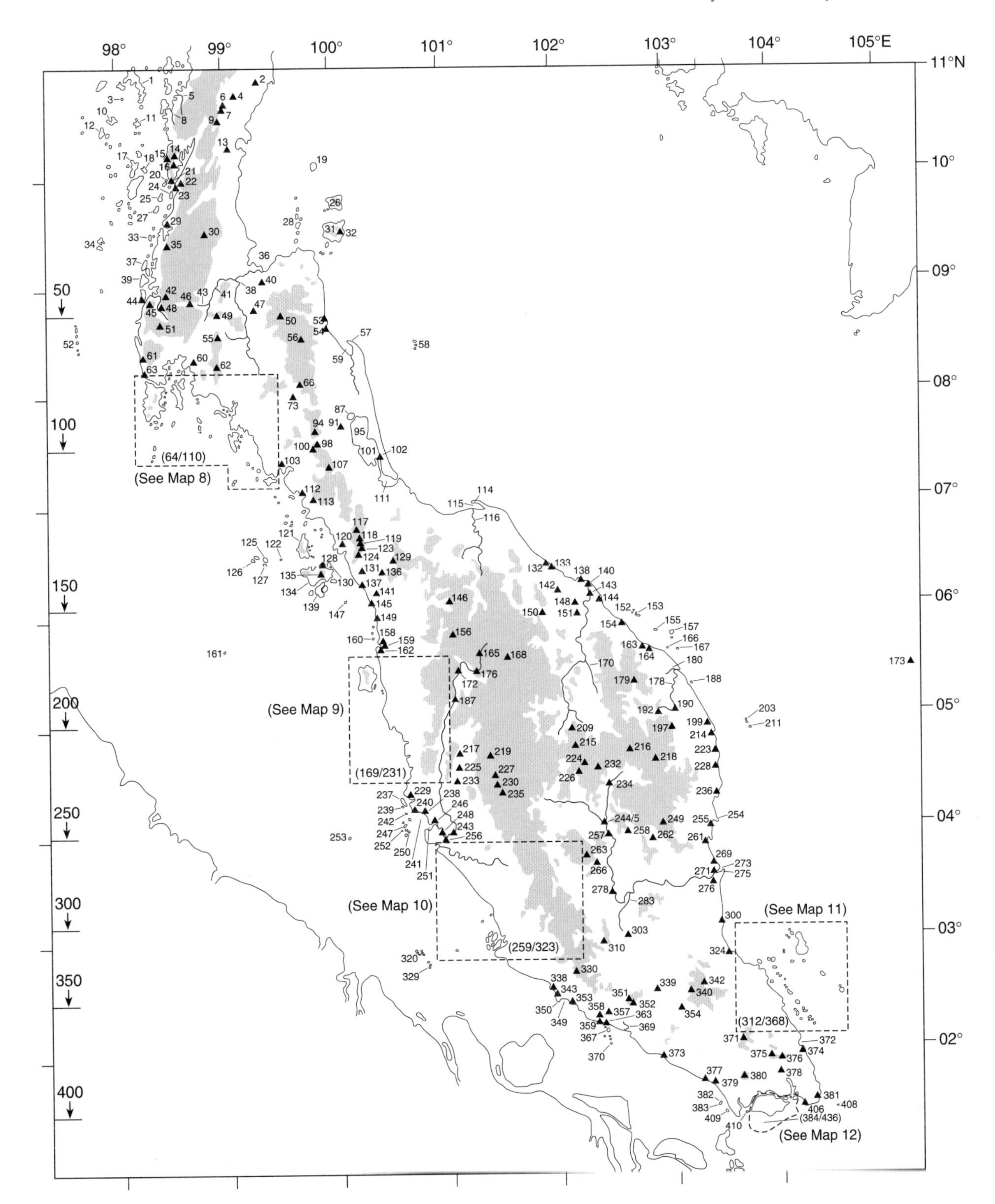

Map 7. Features and places mentioned in the text, accessed from gazetteer directories.

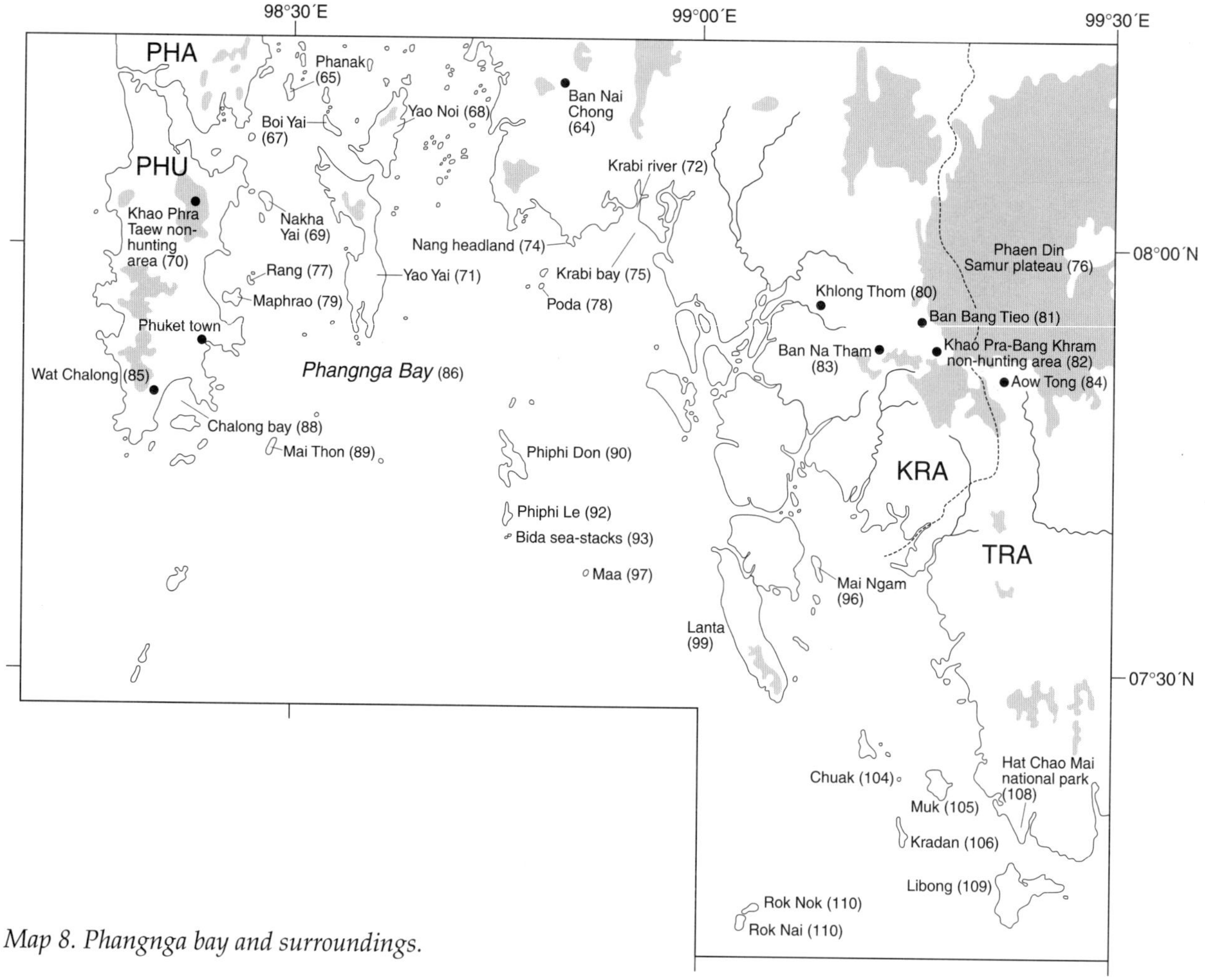

Map 8. Phangnga bay and surroundings.

river (M); *Tambol* = sub-district (T); *Tanjung* = headland (M); *Tasik* = lake (M); *Teluk* = bay (M); *Tha* = landing point (T); *Thalae* = lake (T); *Thung* = field, open ground (T); *Tokong* = rock-stack (M); *Ulu* = up-stream, headwaters (M).

MAPS CONSULTED: 1:500,000 series Tactical Pilotage Chart (Ministry of Defence/Ordnance Survey, UK, 1972); 1:63,360 series (GSGS, War Office, UK, 1954); 1:250,000 series Pakchan and Peninsular Thailand (US Army Map Service, 1963–64); 1:50,000 series Peninsular Thailand (Royal Thai Survey Department, 1973); 1:500,000 sheet Peninsular Malaysia (Directorate of National Mapping, Malaysia, 1977); 1:63,360 series Malaya and Singapore (Surveyor-General, Federation of Malaya, 1959).

LOCALITIES NUMBERED NORTH TO SOUTH: **1** – Lanbyi island; **2** – Ban Map Ammarit; **3** – Tika island; **4** – Ban Salui; **5** – Hankadaing river; **6** – Rap Ro wildlife sanctuary; **7** – Tha Sae district/Khlong Mala; **8** – Kanmawbya river; **9** – Tha Chana district; **10** – Pila island; **11** – Bada island; **12** – Loughborough island; **13** – Sawi district; **14** – Maliwun; **15** – Champang; **16** – Ban Kachon; **17** – St Luke's island; **18** – Hastings island; **19** – Tao island; **20** – Tonton island; **21** – Victoria point; **22** – Ranong town; **23** – Prapad beach; **24** – Lao island; **25** – Chang island; **26** – Phangan island; **27** – Phayam island; **28** – Ang Thong archipelago; **29** – Ban Bang Ben; **30** – Kaeng Krung national park; **31** – Samui island; **32** – Chawaeng marsh; **33** – Kam Yai island; **34** – Surin islands; **35** – Khlong Naka wildlife sanctuary; **36** – Bandon bay; **37** – Ra island; **38** – Ta Pi river; **39** – Phra Thong island; **40** – Khun Thalae wetland; **41** – Sok river; **42** – Khao Sok national park; **43** – Phrasaeng river; **44** – Pakarang point; **45** – Li river; **46** – Chiew Larn reservoir; **47** – Thung Thong wetland; **48** – Tambol Leh; **49** – Khao Si Suk wildlife sanctuary; **50** – Nong peak; **51** – Kapong district; **52** – Similan islands; **53** – Tha Sala coast; **54** – Pak Ying coast; **55** – Khlong Phraya wildlife sanctuary; **56** – Khao Luang national park; **57** – Thalumphuk spit; **58** – Kra islands; **59** – Pak Phanang bay; **60** – Ao Luk district; **61** – Thai Muang coast; **62** – Phanom Bencha national park; **63** – Kok Kloy; **64** – Ban Nai Chong; **65** – Phanak island; **66** – Thung Song; **67** – Boi Yai island; **68** – Yao Noi island; **69** – Nakha Yai island; **70** – Khao Phra Taew non-hunting area; **71** – Yao Yai island; **72** – Krabi river-mouth; **73** – Kapang; **74** – Nang headland; **75** – Krabi bay; **76** –

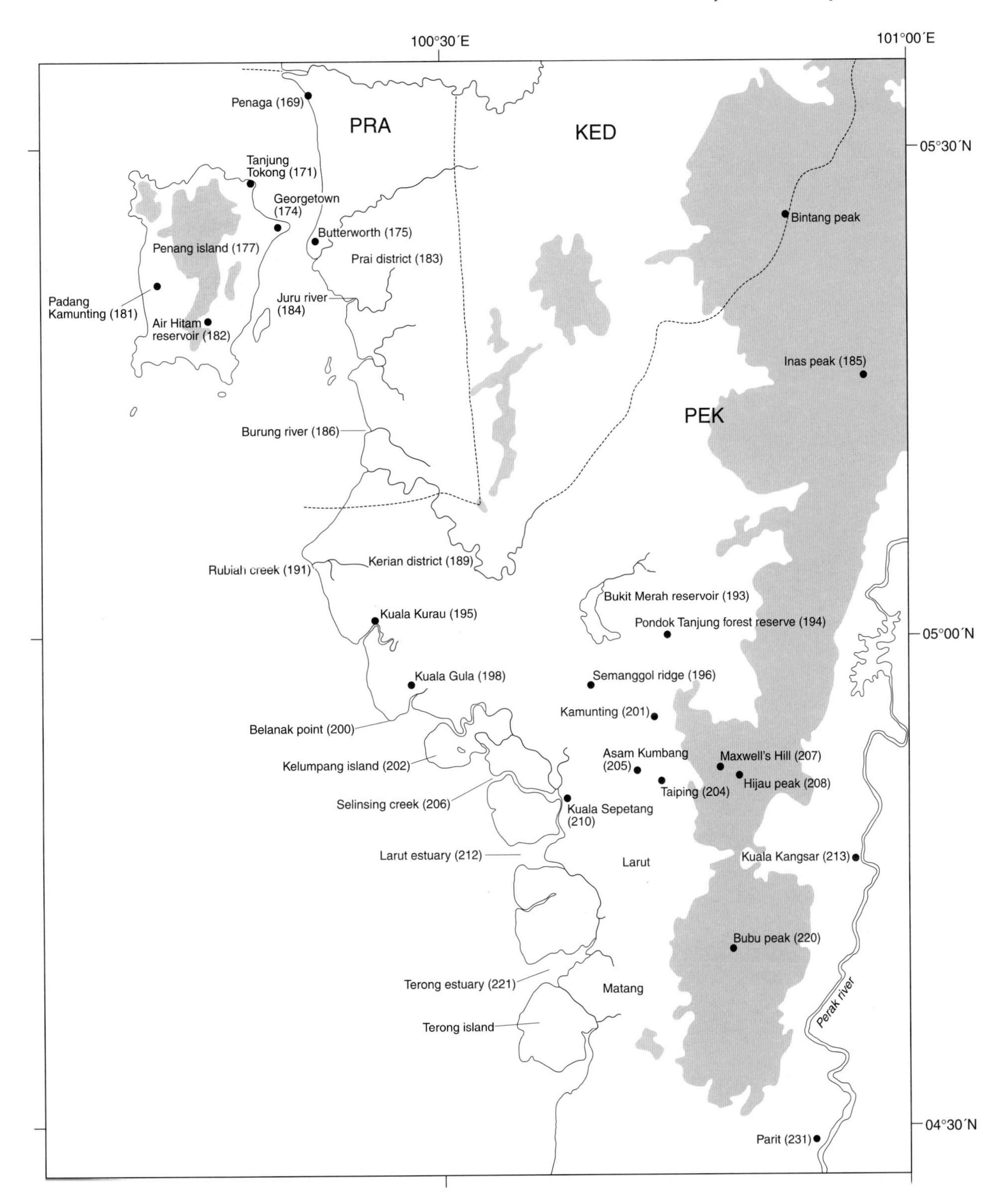

Map 9. Penang territory and mid Perak.

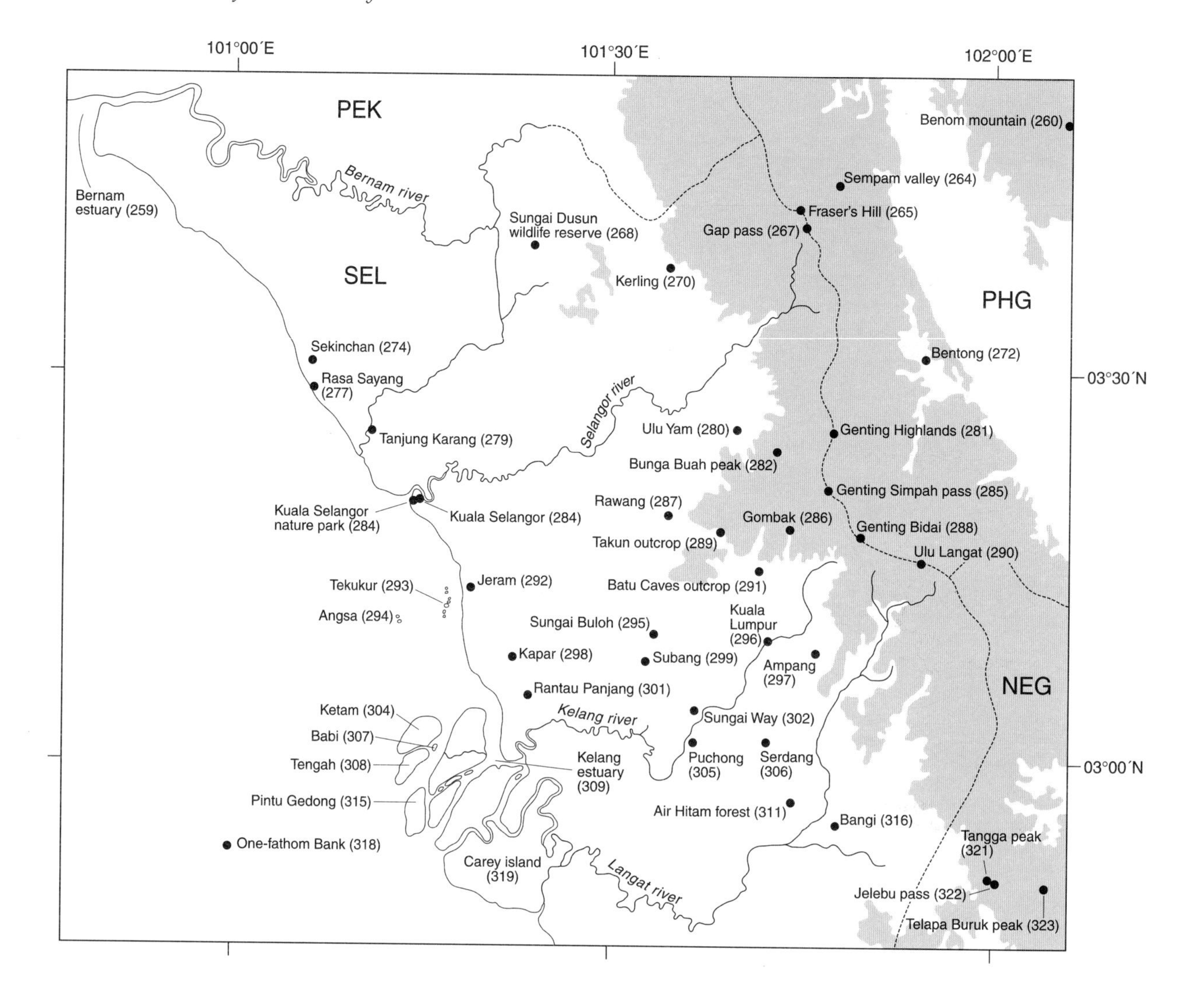

Map 10. Selangor and surroundings.

Phaen Din Samur plateau; **77** – Rang island; **78** – Poda island; **79** – Maphrao island; **80** – Khlong Thom district; **81** – Ban Bang Tieo; **82** – Khao Pra-Bang Khram non-hunting area/Khao Nor Chuchi wildlife sanctuary; **83** – Ban Na Tham; **84** – Aow Tong district; **85** – Wat Chalong; **86** – Phangnga bay; **87** – Thalae Noi wetland; **88** – Chalong bay; **89** – Mai Thon island; **90** – Phiphi Don island; **91** – Khuan Kanun district; **92** – Phiphi Le island; **93** – Bida sea-stacks; **94** – Khao Pu national park; **95** – Thalae Luang wetland; **96** – Mai Ngam island; **97** – Maa island; **98** – Nom Plu peak; **99** – Lanta island; **100** – Chong; **101** – Thalae Sap wetland; **102** – Kukut; **103** – Kantang; **104** – Chuak island; **105** – Muk island; **106** – Kradan island; **107** – Khao Banthad wildlife sanctuary; **108** – Hat Chao Mai national park; **109** – Libong island; **110** – Rok islands; **111** – Thalae Songkhla wetland; **112** – Palian coast; **113** – Thung Wa; **114** – Pattani spit; **115** – Pattani bay; **116** – Pattani river; **117** – Thaleban national park; **118** – Mata Ayer forest reserve; **119** – Kaki Bukit; **120** – Ban Banthung; **121** – Tarutao island; **122** – Ta Nga island; **123** – Timah-Tasoh reservoir; **124** – Air Jernih outcrop; **125** – Ladang island; **126** – Ba Hong island; **127** – Nipis island; **128** – Tanjung Ru coast; **129** – Sintok district; **130** – Langgun island; **131** – Arau; **132** – Narathiwat town; **133** – Tong Yong hill; **134** – Langkawi island; **135** – Raya peak; **136** – Kubang Pasu district; **137** – Kuala Sanglang; **138** – Tumpat lagoon; **139** – Dayang Bunting island; **140** – Kelantan delta; **141** – Keriang outcrop; **142** – Chalerm Prakiat wildlife sanctuary; **143** – Kota Baru; **144** – Kemasin estuary; **145** – Kuala Kedah; **146** – Pedu reservoir; **147** – Paya island; **148** – Pasir Mas district; **149** – Sala river-mouth; **150** – Hala-Bala wildlife sanctuary; **151** – To'Uban lake; **152** – Serenggeh island; **153** – Perhentian islands; **154** – Besut district; **155** – Lang Tengah island; **156** – Pengkalan Hulu plateau; **157** – Redang island; **158** – Jerai mountain; **159** – Bujang valley; **160** – Bidan island; **161** – Perak island; **162** – Merbok estuary; **163** – Setiu Baru lagoon; **164** – Penarik spit; **165** – Kenarong river; **166** – Barat sea-stack; **167** – Bidung Laut island; **168** – E-W highway; **169** – Penaga coast; **170** – Lebir river; **171** – Tanjung

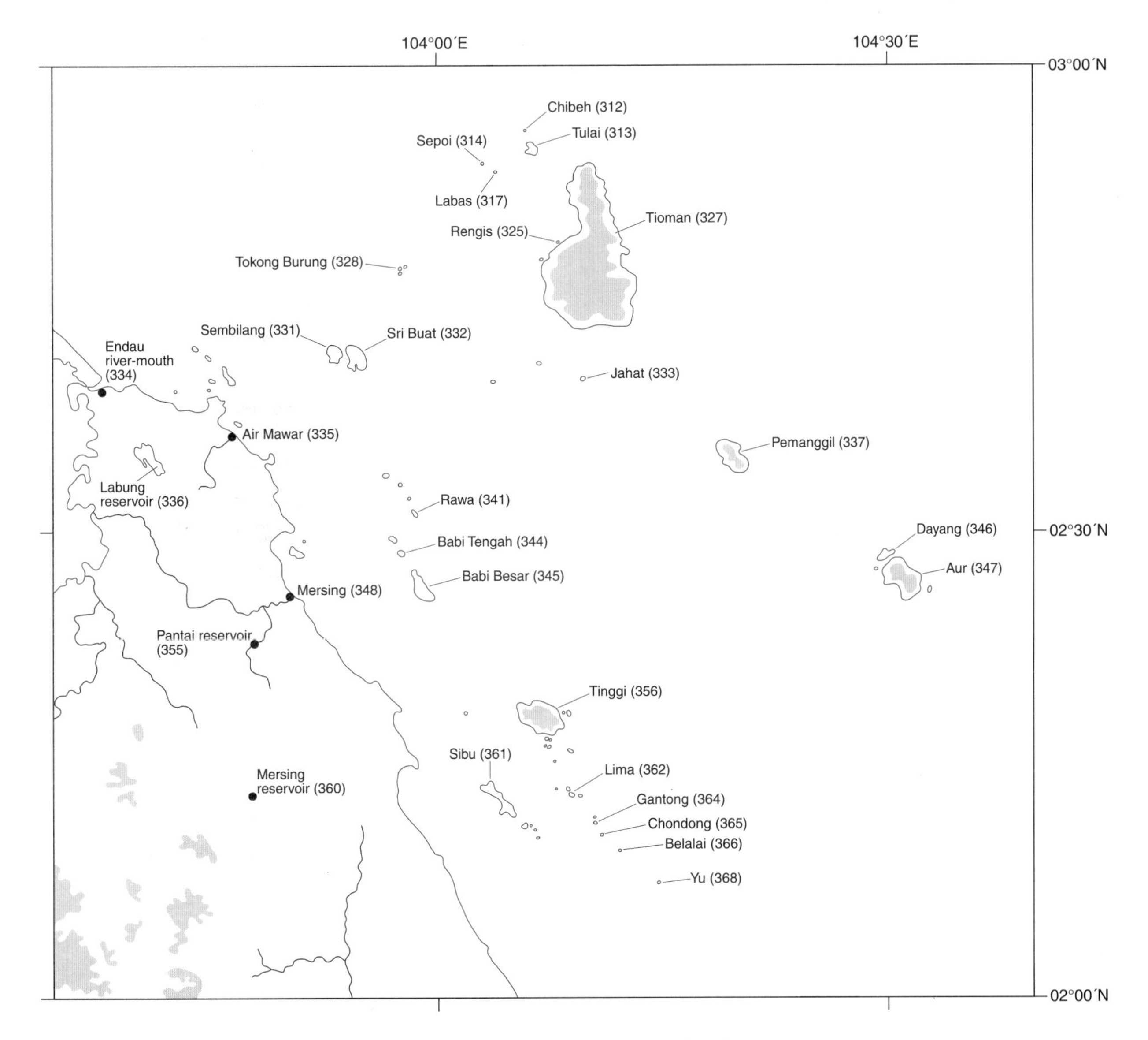

Map 11. The Pahang-Johor archipelago.

Tokong; **172** – Grik district; **173** – Terengganu offshore oil-field; **174** – Georgetown; **175** – Butterworth; **176** – Temengor reservoir; **177** – Penang island; **178** – Terengganu river; **179** – Petuang river; **180** – Nerus river; **181** – Padang Kamunting; **182** – Air Hitam reservoir; **183** – Prai district; **184** – Juru river-mouth; **185** – Inas peak; **186** – Burung river; **187** – Kenering reservoir; **188** – Kapas island; **189** – Kerian district; **190** – Kuala Berang district; **191** – Rublah creek; **192** – Kenyir reservoir; **193** – Bukit Merah reservoir; **194** – Pondok Tanjung forest reserve; **195** – Kuala Kurau; **196** – Semanggol ridge; **197** – Sekayu; **198** – Kuala Gula; **199** – Jambu Bongkok forest reserve; **200** – Belanak point; **201** – Kamunting; **202** – Kelumpang island; **203** – Tokong Burung (*Tru*) sea-stack; **204** – Taiping district; **205** – Asam Kumbang; **206** – Selinsing creek; **207** – Maxwell's Hill resort; **208** – Hijau peak; **209** – Rabong peak; **210** – Kuala Sepetang; **211** – Tenggol island; **212** – Larut estuary; **213** – Kuala Kangsar district; **214** – Dungun district; **215** – Tulang Rabong peak; **216** – Gagau peak; **217** – Chemor; **218** – Mandi Angin peak; **219** – Korbu peak; **220** – Bubu peak; **221** – Terong estuary; **222** – Matang forest reserve; **223** – Paka river; **224** – Tahan mountain; **225** – Ipoh; **226** – Taman Negara national park; **227** – Berinchang peak; **228** – Kerteh river-mouth; **229** – Dindings district; **230** – Cameron Highlands; **231** – Parit district; **232** – Teku confluence; **233** – Batu Gajah district; **234** – Kuala Tahan; **235** – Beremban peak; **236** – Kemaman river-mouth; **237** – Pangkor island; **238** – Sitiawan district; **239** – Pangkor Laut island; **240** – Katak point; **241** – Batu bay; **242** – Fairway rock; **243** – Kinta river; **244** – Jelai confluence; **245** – Kuala Tembeling; **246** – Seberang Perak district; **247** –

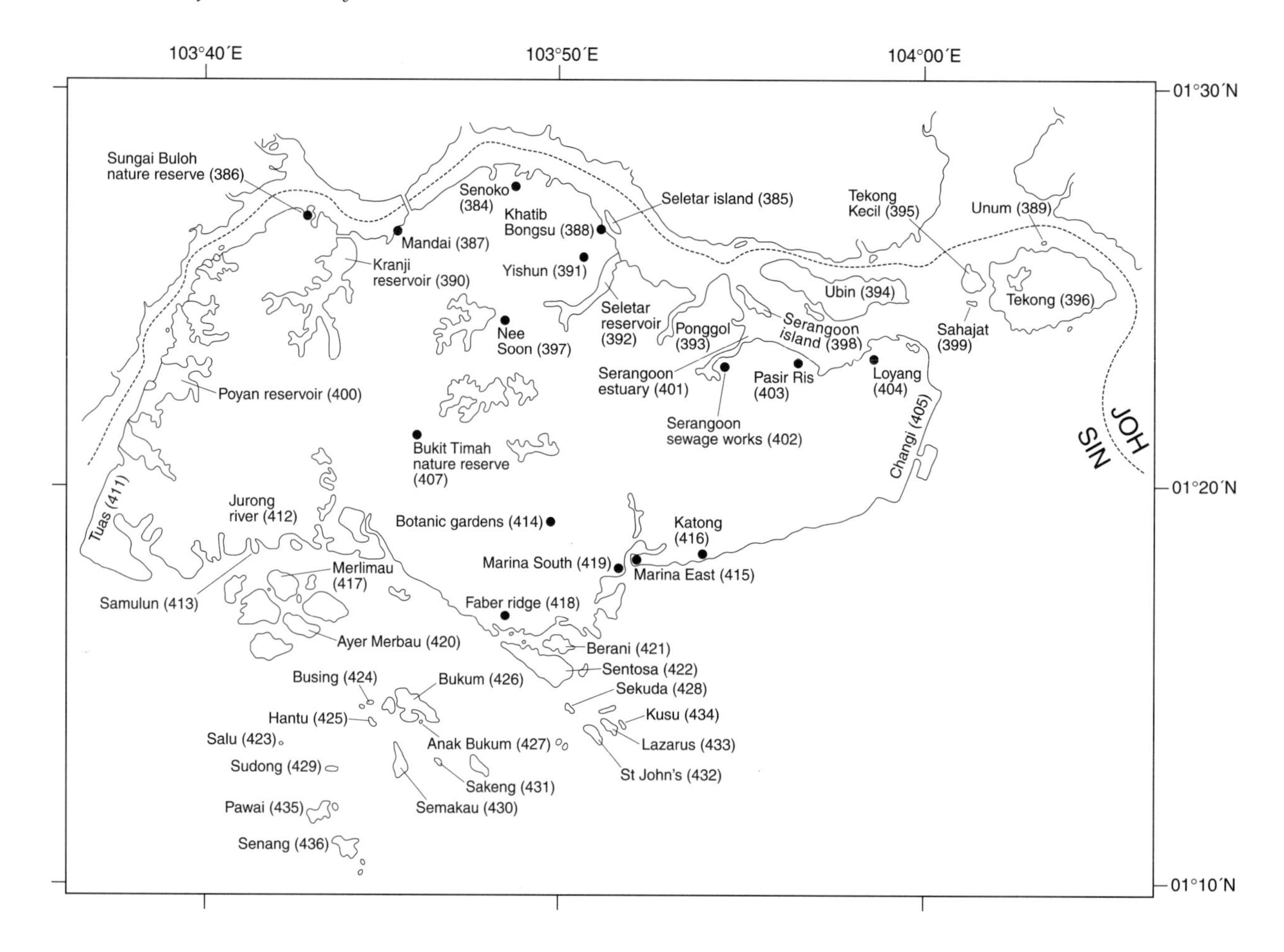

Map 12. The Republic of Singapore.

Rembia island; **248** – Teluk Intan; **249** – Tapis mountain; **250** – Lalang island; **251** – Perak estuary; **252** – White rock; **253** – Jarak island; **254** – Gelang headland; **255** – Kuantan port; **256** – Chenderong Bali; **257** – Jerantut district; **258** – Tekam forest reserve; **259** – Bernam river; **260** – Benom mountain; **261** – Kuantan estuary; **262** – Ulu Lepar valley; **263** – Kerau wildlife reserve; **264** – Sempam valley; **265** – Fraser's Hill resort; **266** – Kuala Lompat; **267** – Gap pass; **268** – Sungai Dusun wildlife reserve; **269** – Penor; **270** – Kerling district; **271** – Pahang Tua river-mouth; **272** – Bentong district; **273** – Pahang estuary; **274** – Sekinchan district; **275** – Agas point; **276** – Pekan; **277** – Rasa Sayang coast; **278** – Temerloh district; **279** – Tanjung Karang district; **280** – Ulu Yam district; **281** – Genting Highlands; **282** – Bunga Buah peak; **283** – Bera river; **284** – Kuala Selangor/nature park; **285** – Genting Simpah pass; **286** – Gombak district; **287** – Rawang district; **288** – Genting Bidai; **289** – Takun outcrop; **290** – Ulu Langat district; **291** – Batu Caves outcrop; **292** – Jeram; **293** – Tekukur island; **294** – Angsa island; **295** – Sungai Buloh district; **296** – Kuala Lumpur district; **297** – Ampang district; **298** – Kapar district; **299** – Subang airport/forest reserve; **300** – Bebar estuary; **301** – Rantau Panjang; **302** – Sungai Way wetland; **303** – Tasik Bera wetland; **304** – Ketam island; **305** – Puchong wetland; **306** – Serdang district; **307** – Babi island; **308** – Tengah island; **309** – Kelang estuary; **310** – Pasoh research forest; **311** – Air Hitam forest reserve; **312** – Chibeh sea-stack; **313** – Tulai island; **314** – Sepoi island; **315** – Pintu Gedong island; **316** – Bangi district; **317** – Labas sea-stack; **318** – One-fathom Bank lighthouse; **319** – Carey island; **320** – Arua islands; **321** – Tangga peak; **322** – Jelebu pass; **323** – Telapa Buruk peak; **324** – Rompin river-mouth; **325** – Rengis islet; **326** – Tekek bay; **327** – Tioman island; **328** – Tokong Burung (*Phg*) sea-stack; **329** – Tokong Simbang sea-stack; **330** – Angsi peak; **331** – Sembilang island; **332** – Sri Buat island; **333** – Jahat sea-stack; **334** – Endau river-mouth; **335** – Air Mawar; **336** – Labung reservoir; **337** – Pemanggil island; **338** – Port Dickson; **339** – Segamat district; **340** – Chabang Tiga peaks; **341** – Rawa island; **342** – Endau-Rompin conservation area; **343** – Si Rusa; **344** – Babi Tengah island; **345** – Babi Besar island; **346** – Dayang island; **347** – Aur island; **348** – Mersing; **349** – Kemang bay; **350** – Cape Rachado; **351** – Asahan; **352** – Ledang mountain; **353** – Linggi river; **354** – Labis; **355** – Pantai reservoir; **356** – Tinggi island; **357** – Ayer Keroh forest reserve; **358** – Batu Berendam district; **359** – Klebang district;

360 – Mersing reservoir; **361** – Sibu island; **362** – Lima islands; **363** – Melaka town; **364** – Gantong sea-stack; **365** – Chondong sea-stack; **366** – Belalai sea-stack; **367** – Besar island; **368** – Yu island; **369** – Kesang river; **370** – Undan island; **371** – Belumut mountain; **372** – Jason's bay; **373** – Batu Pahat; **374** – Sedili Kecil river-mouth; **375** – Muntahak peak; **376** – Panti peak; **377** – Suloh river-mouth; **378** – Kota Tinggi district; **379** – Benut forest reserve; **380** – Pulai mountain; **381** – Desaru resort; **382** – Sauh island; **383** – Pisang island; **384** – Senoko wetland; **385** – Seletar island; **386** – Sungai Buloh nature reserve; **387** – Mandai coast; **388** – Khatib Bongsu creek; **389** – Unum islet; **390** – Kranji reservoir; **391** – Yishun wetland; **392** – Seletar reservoir; **393** – Ponggol peninsula; **394** – Ubin island; **395** – Tekong Kecil island; **396** – Tekong island; **397** – Nee Soon catchment; **398** – Serangoon island; **399** – Sahajat island; **400** – Poyan reservoir; **401** – Serangoon estuary; **402** – Serangoon sewage works; **403** – Pasir Ris; **404** – Loyang; **405** – Changi district; **406** – Tanjung Sepang headland; **407** – Bukit Timah nature reserve; **408** – Horsburgh lighthouse; **409** – Kukup island; **410** – Merambong islet; **411** – Tuas district; **412** – Jurong river; **413** – Samulun island; **414** – Singapore botanic gardens; **415** – Marina East wetland; **416** – Katong; **417** – Merlimau island; **418** – Faber ridge; **419** – Marina South wetland; **420** – Ayer Merbau island; **421** – Berani island; **422** – Sentosa island; **423** – Salu island; **424** – Busing island; **425** – Hantu island; **426** – Bukum island; **427** – Anak Bukum island; **428** – Sekuda island; **429** – Sudong island; **430** – Semakau island; **431** – Sakeng island; **432** – St John's island; **433** – Lazarus island; **434** – Kusu island; **435** – Pawai island; **436** – Senang island.

LOCALITIES IN ALPHABETICAL SEQUENCE:

Aceh (northernmost province of Sumatra); **A**gas point (275); **A**ir Hitam forest reserve (311); **A**ir Hitam reservoir (182); **A**ir Jernih outcrop (124); **A**ir Merah (see Air Mawar); **A**ir Mawar village (335); **A**lang Yai (see Rang island); **A**mboyna Cay (atoll at 07°53′N:112°55′E); **A**mpang district (297); **A**nak Bukum island (427); **A**ngsa island (294); **A**ngsi peak (330); **A**ng Thong archipelago (28); **A**o Luk district (60); **A**ow Tong district (84); **A**rau (131); **A**rua islands (Sumatra) (320); **A**sahan (351); **A**sam Kumbang (205); **A**ur island (347); **A**yer Keroh forest (357); **A**yer Merbau island (420).

Babi island (307); **B**abi Besar island (345); **B**abi Tengah island (344); **B**ada island (11); **B**a Hong island (126); **B**an Bang Ben (29); **B**an Bang Tieo (81); **B**an Banthung (120); **B**andon bay (36); **B**angi district (316); **B**an Kachon (16); **B**an Map Ammarit (2); **B**an Nai Chong (64); **B**an Na Tham (83); **B**an Salui (4); **B**arat sea-stack (166); **B**atu bay (241); **B**atu Berendam district (358); **B**atu Caves outcrop (291); **B**atu Gajah district (233); **B**atu Pahat (373); **B**ebar estuary (300); **B**elalai sea-stack (366); **B**elanak point (200); **B**elawan district (NE coastal Sumatra at 03°47′N); **B**elumut mountain (371); **B**enom mountain (260); **B**entong district (272); **B**enut forest reserve (379); **B**era river (confluence) (283); **B**erani island (419); **B**eremban peak (235); **B**erinchang peak (227); **B**ernam river (estuary) (259); **B**ertam river (Cameron Highlands tributary of Jelai); **B**esar island (367); **B**esut district (154); **B**ida sea-stacks (93); **B**idan island (160); **B**idung Laut island (167); **B**oi Yai island (67); **B**ubu peak (220); **B**ujang valley (159); **B**ukit Merah reservoir (193); **B**ukit Serindit (paddyland at E edge of Melaka town); **B**ukit Timah nature reserve (407); **B**ukum island (reclaimed) (426); **B**unga Buah peak (282); **B**urung river (186); **B**using island (reclaimed) (424); **B**utterworth (175).

Cameron Highlands district (230); **C**ape Rachado (350); **C**arey island (319); **C**habang Tiga peaks (340); **C**halerm Prakiat wildlife sanctuary (142); **C**halong bay (88); **C**hampang (15); **C**hang island (25); **C**hangi district (405); **C**hawaeng marsh (32); **C**hemor (217); **C**henderong Bali (256); **C**hibeh sea-stack (312); **C**hiew Larn reservoir (46); **C**hondong sea-stack (365); **C**hong (100); **C**huak island (104); **C**oney island (see Serangoon island).

Damar rock (Anamba islands, Indonesia, at 02°45′N:105°23′E); **D**ayang island (346); **D**ayang Bunting island (139); **D**esaru resort (381); **D**indings district (229); **D**ungun district (214); **D**uri (Sumatra, at 01°16′N:101°13′E).

E-central Range (see Map 1); **E**-coast Range (see Map 1); **E**ndau river (mouth) (334); **E**ndau-Rompin conservation area (342); **E-W** highway (168).

Faber ridge (418); **F**airway (Tokong Perak) sea-stack (242); **F**ort Melawati (Kuala Selangor town); **F**raser's Hill resort (265).

Gagau peak (216); **G**alang island (Riau archipelago, Indonesia); **G**antong sea-stack (364); **G**ap (Semangkok) pass (267); **G**elang headland (254); **G**enting Bidai (288); **G**enting Highlands (281); **G**enting Simpah pass (285); **G**eorgetown (174); **G**ombak district (286); **G**rik district (172).

Hala-Bala wildlife sanctuary (150); **H**ankadaing river (5); **H**antu island (425); **H**ard Toop islet (SE satellite of Libong island); **H**astings island (18); **H**at Chao Mai national park (108); **H**ijau peak (208); **H**orsburgh lighthouse (408).

Inas peak (185); **I**poh (225).

Jahat sea-stack (333); **J**ambu Bongkok forest reserve (199); **J**arak island (253); **J**ason's bay (372); **J**elai river (confluence) (244); **J**elebu pass (322); **J**erai mountain (158); **J**eram (292); **J**erantut district (257); **J**ohor straits (between Johor and Singapore); **J**urong river (412); **J**uru river (mouth) (184).

Kaeng Krung national park (30); **K**aki Bukit (119); **K**am Yai island (33); **K**amunting (201); **K**anmawbya river (estuary) (8); **K**antang (103); **K**apang (73); **K**apar district (298); **K**apar power-station (on the Kapar coast); **K**apas island (188); **K**apong district (51); **K**atak point (240); **K**atong (416); **K**edah peak (see Jerai mountain); **K**elang estuary (309); **K**elantan delta (140); **K**elumpang island (202); **K**emaman river (mouth) (236); **K**emang bay (349); **K**emasin estuary (144); **K**enarong river (confluence) (165); **K**enering reservoir (187); **K**enyir reservoir (dam) (192); **K**erau wildlife reserve (263); **K**erian district (189); **K**eriang outcrop (141); **K**erling (270); **K**erteh river (mouth) (228); **K**esang river (mouth) (369); **K**etam island (304); **K**hao Banthad wildlife sanctuary (107); **K**hao Kachong (see Chong); **K**hao Luang national park (56); **K**hao Nor Chuchi wildlife sanctuary (see Khao Pra-Bang Khram non-hunting area); **K**hao Pra-Bang Khram non-hunting area (82); **K**hao Phra Taew non-hunting area (70); **K**hao Pu national park (94); **K**hao Si Suk wildlife sanctuary (49); **K**hao Sok national park (42); **K**hatib Bongsu creek (388); **K**hlong Bang Lai (see Ban Salui); **K**hlong Naka wildlife sanctuary (35); **K**hlong Phraya wildlife sanctuary (55); Khlong Thom district (80); Khuan Kanun district (91); Khun Thalae wetland (40); Kinta river (confluence) (243); Klebang district (359); Kok Kloy (63); Korbu peak (219); Kota Baru (143); Kota Tinggi district (378); Kra islands (58); Krabi bay (75); Krabi river-mouth (72); Kradan island (106); Kranji reservoir (390); Kuala Berang district (190); Kuala Gula (198); Kuala Kangsar district (213); Kuala Kedah (145); Kuala Kurau (195); Kuala Lompat (266); Kuala Lumpur district (296); Kuala Sanglang (137); Kuala Selangor (estuary and nature park) (284); Kuala Sepetang (210); Kuala Tahan (confluence and Taman Negara headquarters) (234); Kuala Tembeling (245); Kuantan port (255); Kuantan river (estuary) (261); Kubang Pasu district (136); Kukup island (409); Kukut (Thalae Sap non-hunting area headquarters) (102); Kundur island (Riau archipelago, Indonesia); Kusu island (434).

Labas sea-stack (317); Labis district (354); Labung reservoir (336); Ladang island (125); Lalang island (250); Lanbyi island (1); Langat river (see Kelang estuary); Langgun island (130); Langkawi island (134); Lang Tengah island (155); Lanta island (99); Lao island (24); Larut district (immediately S and E of Kerian); Larut estuary (212); Larut Range (see Map 1); Layang-layang island (S China sea, at 07°22′N:113°50′E); Lazarus island (433); Lebir river (confluence) (170); Ledang mountain (352); Li river (estuary) (45); Libong island (109); Lima island group (362); Linggi river (mouth) (353); Loughborough island (12); Loyang (404); Luang peak (see Khao Luang national park).

Maa island (97); Mai Ngam island (96); Mai Thon island (89); Main Range (see Map 1); Malaysian National University campus (see Bangi district); Maliwun (14); Mandai coast (387); Mandi Angin peak (218); Maphrao island (79); Marina East wetland (415); Marina South wetland (419); Mata Ayer forest re serve (118); Matang forest reserve (222); Maxwell's Hill resort (207); Melaka straits (between the Peninsula and Sumatra); Melaka town (363); Mengkuang Lebar peak (see Genting Highlands); Merambong islet (410); Merbok estuary (162); Merlimau island (being reclaimed) (417); Mersing (348); Mersing reservoir (360); Mohea (see Rok islands); Muk island (105); Muntahak peak (375).

Nakha Yai island (69); Nang headland (74); Narathiwat town (132); Nee Soon catchment (397); Nerus river (confluence) (180); Nipis island (127); Nom Plu peak (98); Nong peak (50); NW Range (see Map 1).

One-fathom Bank lighthouse (318); Ophir mountain (see Ledang).

Padang Kamunting (181); Pahang river (273); Pahang Tua river (mouth) (271); Paka river (mouth) (223); Pakchan estuary (straddles far-S Burmese/Thai border); Pakarang point (44); Pak Phanang bay (59); Pak Ying coast (54); Palian coast (112); Pangkor island (237); Pangkor Laut island (239); Pantai reservoir (355); Panti peak (376); Parit district (231); Pasir Mas district (148); Pasir Ris (403); Pasoh research forest (310); Pattani bay (115); Pattani river (mouth) (116); Pattani spit (114); Pawai island (435); Paya island (147); Paya Lebar wetland (long reclaimed; see Changi); Pedu reservoir (146); Pekan (276); Pekan Lama (on S side of Pahang estuary); Pemanggil island (337); Penaga coast (169); Penang island (177); Penarik spit (164); Pengkalan Hulu plateau (156); Penya shoal (*Sin*, at ca. 01°12′N:103°46′E); Penor (269); Perak island (161); Perak river (estuary) (251); Perhentian islands (153); Petuang river (179); Phaen Din Samur plateau (76); Phanak island (65); Phangan island (26); Phangnga bay (86); Phanom Bencha national park (62); Phayam island (27); Phiphi Don island (90); Phiphi Le island (92); Phrasaeng river (confluence) (43); Phra Thong island (39); Pila island (10); Pintu Gedong island (315); Pisang island (383); Poda island (78); Pondok Tanjung forest reserve (194); Ponggol peninsula (393); Port Dickson (338); Poyan reservoir (400); Prai district (183); Prapad beach (23); Puchong wetland (305); Pulai mountain (380).

Ra island (37); Rabong peak (209); Rang island (77); Ranong town (22); Rantau Panjang (301); Rap Ro wildlife sanctuary (6); Rasa Sayang coast (277); Rawa island (341); Rawang district (287); Raya peak (Langkawi summit) (135); Redang island (157); Rembia island (247); Rengis islet (325); Retan Laut island (reclaimed; at ca. 01°17′N:103°46′E); Riau (province of SE Sumatra); Riau archipelago (Indonesian islands immediately S of Singapore); Rok islands (110); Rompin river (mouth) (324); Rubiah creek (mouth) (191).

Sadet Kromaluang Chumphon wildlife sanctuary (see Rap Ro); Sahajat island (399); Sakeng island (431); Sala river (mouth) (149); Salu island (423); Samui island (31); Samulun island (re claimed) (413); Sanglang (see Kuala Sanglang); Sauh island (382); Sawi district (13); Seberang Perak district (246); Sedili Kecil river (mouth) (374); Segamat district (339); Sekayu (197); Sekinchan district (274); Sekuda island (428); Selangor river (see Kuala Selangor); Seletar reservoir (392); Seletar island (385); Selinsing creek (206); Semakau island (430); Semanggol ridge (196); Sembilan islands (see Rembia and satellites); Sembilang island (331); Sempam valley (264); Senang island (436); Senoko wetland (mostly reclaimed) (384); Sentosa island (422); Sepoi island (314); Serangoon estuary (reclaimed) (401); Serangoon island (398); Serangoon sewage works (402); Serdang district (306); Serenggeh island (152); Setiu Baru lagoon (163); Sibu island (361); Sime road (Singapore central catchment forest); Similan islands (52); Singapore botanic gardens (414); Singapore Straits (between Singapore and Riau archipelago, Indonesia); Sintok district (129); Si Rusa (343); Sitiawan district (238); Sok river (confluence) (41); Songkhla lake (see Thalae Songkhla); Spratly island (S China sea, at 08°18′N:111°59′E); Sri Buat island (332); St John's island (432); St Luke's island (17); Subang airfield and forest reserve (299); Sudong island (429); Suloh river (mouth) (377); Sungai Buloh district (295); Sungai Buloh nature reserve (386); Sungai Dusun wildlife reserve (268); Sungai Way wetland (reclaimed) (302); Surin islands (34); Swallow reef (see Layang-layang island).

Tahan mountain (224); Tahan river (see Kuala Tahan); Taiping district (204); Takun outcrop (289); Talumphuk spit (57); Taman Negara national park (226); Tambol Leh (48); Ta Nga island (122); Tangga peak (321); Tanjung Badak (not located, but near Victoria point, Pakchan); Tanjung Karang district (279); Tanjung Ru coast (128); Tanjung Tokong (171); Tanjung Tuan headland (see Cape Rachado); Tanjung Sepang headland (406); Tao island (19); Ta Pi river (confluence) (42); Tapis mountain (249); Tarutao island (121); Tasik Bera wetland (303); Tavoy (Tenasserim, at 14°03′N:98°12′E); Tekam forest reserve (258); Tekek bay (326); Tekong island (396); Tekong Kecil island (395); **T**eku river (confluence) (232); **T**ekukur island (293); **T**elapa Buruk peak (323); **T**eluk Intan district (248); **T**embeling river (confluence) (245); **T**emengor reservoir (176); **T**emerloh district (278); **T**engah island (308); **T**enggol island (211); **T**erengganu off-shore oil-field (173); **T**erengganu river (mouth) (178); **T**erong estuary (221); **T**erong island (mangrove forest S of Terong estu ary); **T**ha Chana district (9); **T**hai Muang coast (61); **T**halae Noi wetland (87); **T**halae Luang wetland (95); **T**halae Sap wetland (101); **T**halae Songkhla wetland (111); **T**haleban national park (117); **T**ha Sae district/Khlong Mala (7); **T**ha Sala coast (53); **T**hung Song (66); **T**hung Thong wetland (47); **T**hung Tieo (see Ban Bang Tieo); **T**hung Wa (113); **T**ika island (3); **T**ikus islet (off Tanjung Tokong, Penang island N harbour; reclaimed); **T**imah-Tasoh reservoir (123); **T**inggi island (356); **T**ioman island (327); **T**o' Uban lake (151); **T**okong Burung sea-stack (*Tru*) (203); **T**okong Burung sea-stack (*Phg*) (328); **T**okong Simbang sea-stack (Sumatra, S Arua islands) (329); **T**ong Yong hill (133); **T**onton island (20); **T**uas district (411); **T**ulai island (313); **T**ulang Rabong peak (215); **T**umpat lagoon (138).

Ubin island (394); **U**lu Langat district (290); **U**lu Lepar valley (262); **U**lu Yam district (280); **U**ndan island (370); **U**num islet (389).

Victoria point (21).

Wat Chalong (83); **W**aw islet (in Chalong bay); **W**hite Rock sea-stack (252); **W**ray's Camp (on Tahan mountain E trail, Taman Negara national park).

Yam Yai island (see Kam Yai); **Y**ao Noi island (68); **Y**ao Yai island (71); **Y**ishun wetland (391); **Y**u island sea-stack (368).

NOTE ADDED IN PROOF

(1) GREATER ADJUTANT *Leptoptilos dubius*. Reports from Narathiwat have been the subject of a misunderstanding. Occurrence of this stork in the review area remains unproven.

(2) SMALL-ISLAND SCOPS OWL *Otus* sp. P.C. Rasmussen (*Bulletin of the British Ornithologists' Club* 118: 141–153 (1998) believes the birds photographed by M.L. Avery on Perak island, Melaka straits, were *O. (sunia) nicobaricus* rather than members of the 'Small-island' *manadensis* superspecies. I follow J.T. Marshall, world authority on these subtly patterned owls, in suggesting no conclusion can be reached without knowledge of vocalizations.

Species Accounts

Order GALLIFORMES

Family PHASIANIDAE

Partridges, quail, junglefowl, pheasants and peafowl: 16 species

Long-billed Partridge; Nok Nual (Thai); Burung Siul Selanting (Malay)

Rhizothera longirostris (Temminck) 1815, *Histoire Générale des Pigeons et des Gallinacés* 3: 323 and 721. TL Sumatra.

Plate 3

GROUP RELATIONS. Free-standing; superficially francolin-like, but its nearest relative is not identified.

GLOBAL RANGE. Sumatra, Borneo (including Sabah) and the Peninsula north to about 11°20′ in Tenasserim and in hill-foot forest at close to 14°N in SW Thailand (AMNH, Inglis 1918).

IDENTIFICATION/DESCRIPTION. Hen jungle-fowl-sized but with tail-down, partridge shape. Upperparts intricately mottled brown; elsewhere mainly orange-chestnut, brightest on throat and breast, and adult males have a light grey collar, ventrally broad but narrowing to just close mid-dorsally. Both adults show an orange-chestnut supercilium above a black line through the eye, whereas juveniles have a strikingly striped face: throat up to moustache level, band from lores to below the eye and long supercilium buff-white, with blackish in between (BMNH).

The outsize bill has a distinct cere, and both sexes grow a stubby tarsal spur, larger in the male.

Bare-part colours. (Adult) iris light brown, eyelid reddish brown; bill black; feet pale yellow (BMNH, Riley 1938).

Size (mm). (Skins: 10 males, 5 females; adult): wing 197–212 and 188–200; tail 74–95 and 73–90; bill from cere 23.3–31.1 and 20.9–25.9; tarsus 54.0–60.7 and 54.3–60.1 (BMNH, ZRCNUS).

Weight. No data.

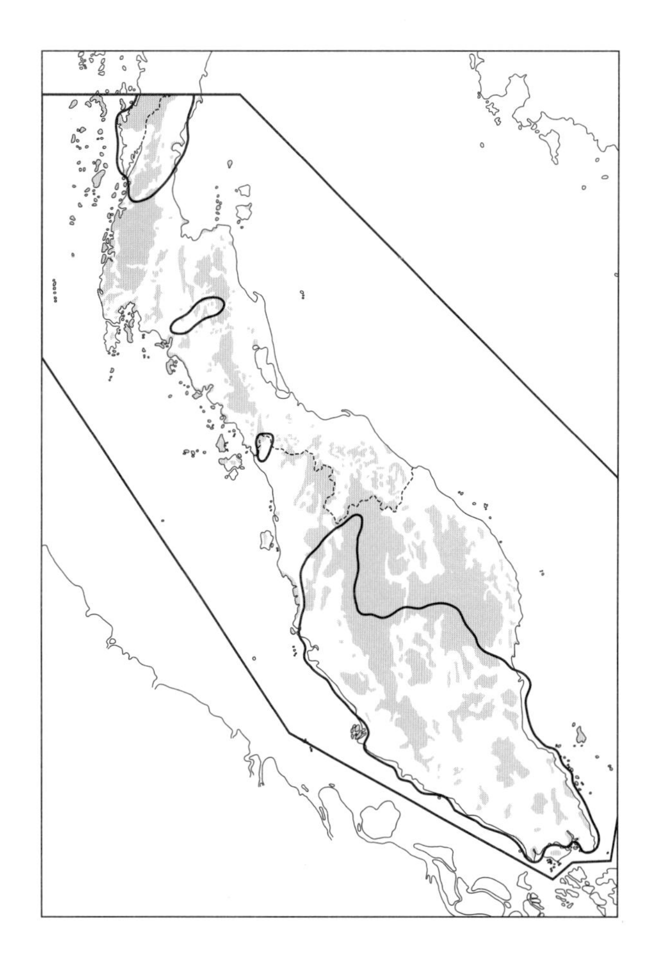

DISTRIBUTION. Historical summary: *Pak, Chu, Ran, Nak, Kra, ?Pes, Pek, Phg, Sel, Neg, Mel, Joh*. In the 1880s, C.B. Rickett bought many live birds, including Long-billed Partridges, off Malay vendors coming to Penang island from the neighbouring mainland. These traders are also likely to have been the main source of an earlier Penang collection, by T. Cantor. How long a stretch of coast this live trade drew upon is not known but two of Cantor's *Rhizothera* specimens are labelled 'Purlis' (Perlis) (BMNH). Penang island itself is not an accepted locality and there are no other island records.

GEOGRAPHICAL VARIATION. Nominate *longirostris*, of the global range except highland Borneo.

STATUS AND POPULATION. Resident, local and sparse to more or less common. Little known in the Thai provinces, from where there have been no formal records since 1955 (in Ranong: BLC), though may occur further up Thai mountain-slopes than has regularly been searched.

HABITATS AND ECOLOGY. The floor of mature and well-regenerated evergreen and semi-evergreen

Lowland forest, also bamboo jungle, at all altitudes, and Montane forest to (in Malaysia) 1500 m (Benom, Pahang: BR 1976–77). On evidence of calling, resident across the whole slope.

FORAGING AND FOOD. No information. The enlarged upper mandible, round-fronted and broadly overlapping the lower all round, seems likely to have a special function, not yet described.

SOCIAL ORGANIZATION. Apparently in permanent pairs. Duetting, and tarsal spurs in both sexes, suggest pair-members collaborate to defend a territory (Davison 1985). At night, they roost individually, 8–10 m up on mid-stratum branches (J. Chance).

MOVEMENTS. None known.

SURVIVAL. No information.

SOCIAL INTERACTIONS. No information other than on vocalizations.

VOICE. One sex (to be identified) gives a rather strident, slightly reedy double whistle, the second note a tone up, *tau hee* or *tyau wee*. Mates commonly duet, the above call running directly on from, or overlapping, a more compressed, non-inflected disyllable on a slightly lower frequency, *u ha*; the sequence verbalized *I'm a TUR KEY* (BMP5). Pairs ordinarily advertise in the early morning and late evening; after rain, sometimes at other times of day and occasionally also at night. The contact-call between mates is a single, soft whistle (G.C. Madoc, Robinson 1928).

BREEDING. Not recorded. Calling reported in February, April, May, August and November, but may not relate directly to breeding activity.

MOULT. Of 15 adults collected down the length of the Peninsula in July–August and October–March, only three showed bilateral wing-moult: P2 on 4 February, P3 on 24 July and P2-3 (P1 fresh) on 12 August (BMNH, ZRCNUS).

CONSERVATION. As with other obligate forest birds, has lost most of its plains-level habitat. In Thailand, where long-term survival in the lowlands is least likely, hill-slope forest may not be the habitat option it appears to be further south, but needs more exploration.

Black Partridge; (no Thai name); Burung Siul Bertam (Malay)

Melanoperdix nigra (Vigors) 1829, *Zoological Journal, London* 4: 349. TL Benkulen, SW Sumatra.
Plates 1 and 2

GROUP RELATIONS. Free-standing. Nearest relative uncertain, but the pattern of pale spotting on the dorsum of poults resembles same-stage Roulroul.

GLOBAL RANGE. Borneo (including Sabah), southern Sumatra and the southern Peninsula (AMNH). This partridge is one of a small (and shrinking) number of Sunda Lowland forest endemics not yet found north of Malaysia.

IDENTIFICATION/DESCRIPTION. Adult male from Roulroul in the poor light of the forest understratum by lack of a crown-band and crest, and slaty rather than red feet. Females are chestnut-brown, shading to whitish on throat and belly, with bold black bars across the inner secondaries and fine dark barring on lower tail-coverts. Spurless, and claw of hind toe reduced; bill deep and stout.

The downy chick is orange-buff, darker above than below, with forecrown to nape and a narrow band through the ear-coverts bay-brown. First mantle and scapular contour-feathers of the young poult have shaft and a small triangular tip-mark white (ZRCNUS). Immatures are buff-speckled brown with upper body and underparts from lower breast vermiculated blackish (feathers dark with a sub-apical whitish crescent, giving a scaly effect).

Bare-part colours. (Adult) iris dark brown; bill blackish (lead-grey in one live female); feet slaty.

Size (mm). (Live and skins: 8 males, 7 females; adult): wing 140–149 and 137–147; tail 54–62 and 56–68; bill 19.9–20.7 and 17.7–20.5; tarsus 43.6–46.7 and 43.0–45.7 (BMNH, UMBRP, ZRCNUS).

Weight (g). One adult female, 281 (UMBRP).

DISTRIBUTION. From S Johor north to the Pondok Tanjung forest reserve, lowland Larut district (Perak), and it may formerly have occurred in neighbouring mainland Penang. Historical summary: *Pra, Pek, Phg, Sel, Neg, ?Mel, Joh*. Virtually no habitat remains in S Johor, Melaka or mainland Penang. Nineteenth-century skins marked Singapore are likely to have been imports, perhaps from E Sumatra (whence this bird is still traded).

GEOGRAPHICAL VARIATION. None recognized.

STATUS AND POPULATION. Resident and local, sparse to uncommon. Its distribution may be patchy

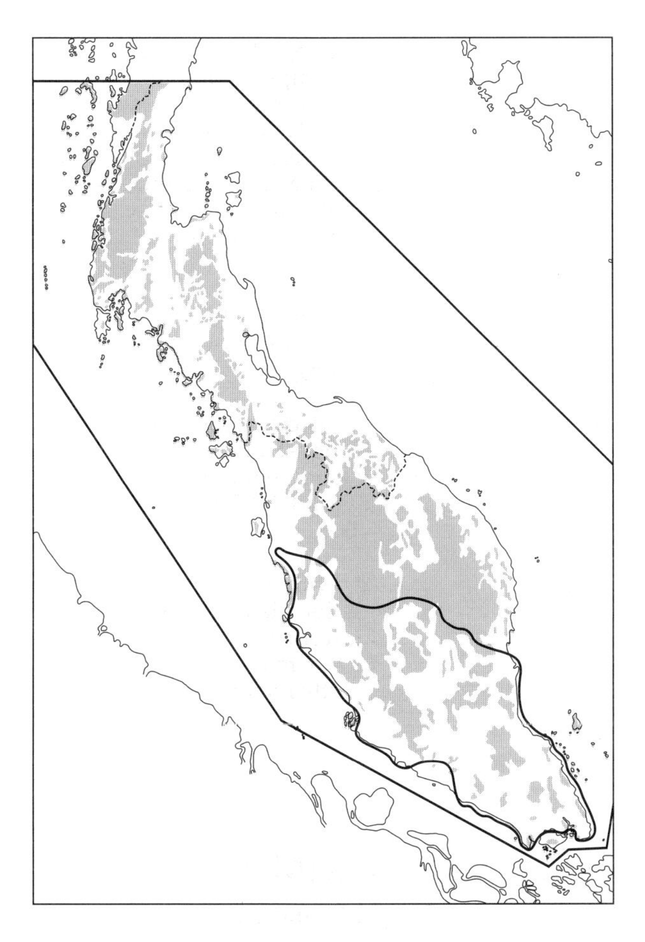

naturally but searching has been hampered by lack of information on calls, leaving open the possibility of confusion with other partridges such as Roulroul (see below). In the 1950s, Batchelor (1954a) saw birds regularly at Asahan, Johor/Melaka border, and museum collectors of 80 years ago found them not uncommon at Pondok Tanjung; also Rawang (Selangor) where in July 1912 eight were collected in five days (AMNH, BMNH, ZRCNUS).

HABITATS AND ECOLOGY. All definitely localized records have been from below the hill-foot boundary, with no confirmation of H.C. Robinson's claim of occurrence to 600 m, although found on hill-slopes in Borneo (Smythies 1981, Wilkinson *et al.* 1991). Black Partridge habitat is the floor of evergreen Lowland forest, mature and regenerated back to more or less closed-canopy condition after disturbance. Logging encourages invasion by the stemless, understratum bertam palm *Eugeissona tristis*, said to be favoured although the association needs confirming.

FORAGING AND FOOD. No specific information.

SOCIAL ORGANIZATION. Reported solitary and in pairs. An encounter in Subang forest reserve was with a pair (McClure 1963) and at Asahan Batchelor found them consistently in pairs.

MOVEMENTS. None known.

SURVIVAL. No information.

SOCIAL INTERACTIONS. No information.

VOICE. Batchelor (1954a) describes an evident short-range contact signal between foragers: 'a low creaking sound . . . like the opening of a heavy old door'. FMSM collectors reported a louder, two-note whistle resembling Roulroul (Robinson and Chasen 1936), but this has not been confirmed. A female released after ringing gave a brief, chicken-like cackle, *chor-ro-roh* (D. Yong).

BREEDING. Known from single, still mostly downy chicks collected at Pondok Tanjung (Perak) on 20 and 24 August, with poults there in August and September (BMNH, ZRCNUS).

MOULT. Replacement of primaries is mainly regular-descendant, but one undated female was moulting simultaneously at two loci, P4 and 8. Among 11 adults taken in March, July–September and December, July and December females were growing P3–4 and P10, respectively, and a male dated 15 July had recently completed P4 (BMNH, ZRCNUS).

CONSERVATION. One of a small assemblage of species stenotopic in plains-level forest, hence at risk from habitat-loss. Near-threatened globally (BTW2).

Blue-breasted Quail; Nok Khum See (Thai); Burung Pikau (Malay)

Coturnix chinensis (Linnaeus) 1766, *Systema Naturae* 12(1): 277. TL China.
Plate 1

GROUP RELATIONS. Has been lumped with Afrotropical *C. adansonii* (African Blue Quail). Differences in the pattern of male plumage-parts thought to have signal function are greater than variation within the Asian-Australian range, and these birds are more likely to form a superspecies.

GLOBAL RANGE. The Indian subcontinent (excluding the dry NW), Sri Lanka and the Nicobars;

China south of a line Fujian–S Yunnan, including Taiwan; SE Asia to the Greater Sunda islands, Bali and the Philippines; Wallacea, New Guinea and N, E and S Australia. Introduced on Guam. Some northern populations, including in parts of SE Asia, migrate or are strongly dispersive (McClure 1974).

IDENTIFICATION/DESCRIPTION. Smaller than either local buttonquail and flushes with more spring, rocketing away faster. Seen well, the male is distinctive. Females are black-barred on the lower body but not above and, in a rare good view, show broad, pink-chestnut supercilium and malar-stripe. Juveniles are black-barred dorsally but heavily streaked below. At all stages, yellow feet separate from Barred Buttonquail. In flight, male appears dark with deep chestnut lower rear body and, as the light catches them, silvery grey-cast flight-feathers.

Adult females show variation in the amount of pink-chestnut on the head; adult males in the extent of ventral chestnut: to centre-belly and base of legs at minimum, on to flanks and up the centre of the breast to meet the black throat (isolating blue on sides of breast) at maximum. These individual differences could have social significance.

Bare-part colours. (Adult) iris crimson (male), dark brown (female); upper mandible and bill-tip black, rest of lower mandible slaty; feet yellow to orange-yellow.

Size (mm). (Skins: 17 males, 14 females; adult): wing 68–75 and 66–75; tail not measured; bill 10.3–12.0, bill from front edge nostril 5.8–7.1 (sexes combined); tarsus 18.8–21.7 (sexes combined) (BMNH, ZRCNUS, UMZC).

Weight (g). Males, 36–49 (n=13); females, 28–54 (one laying and/or fat individual 73 on 16 March) (n=9) (UMBRP).

DISTRIBUTION. Probably under-recorded in the north. Historical summary: all divisions except *Ran*, *Sur*, *Pha*, *Nak*, *Phu*, *Tra*, *Pat*, *Sat*, with additional island records from Langkawi (unconfirmed) and Penang off the W coast; and Ayer Merbau, Singapore.

GEOGRAPHICAL VARIATION. Nominate *chinensis*, of mainland Asia.

STATUS AND POPULATION. Resident (ringed birds retrapped on site after intervals of up to 20 months). Night-time interceptions in unlikely situations also imply some long-distance movement. More or less regular and fairly common, but evidence of shooting-bags (BMNH) indicates populations in open agriculture were denser in the past.

HABITATS AND ECOLOGY. Typical habitats are a mosaic of open soil, dry and damp grassland and other herbage on and around stock-grazing areas, old dredge-mine sludge-beds, small-scale paddy agriculture with a long fallow stage, newly cleared land with leguminous, anti-erosion cover-crops, etc. Ventures

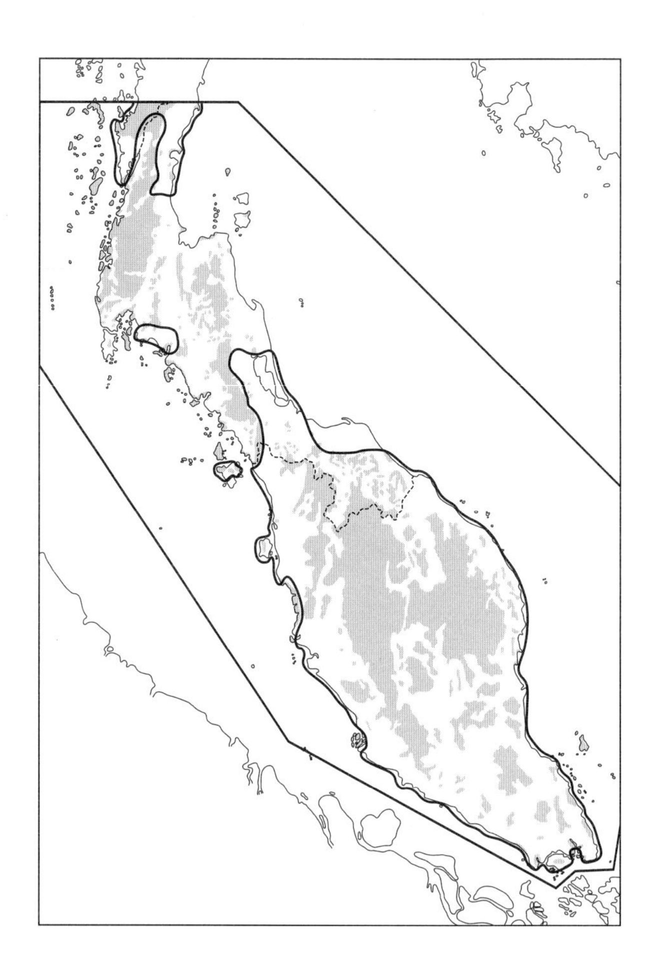

onto bare earth along the edge of tracks. Overlap of habitats with buttonquails appears fairly complete.

FORAGING AND FOOD. The crop of a Singapore poult held many grass-seeds and three termites, with more seeds, grit and insect chitin in its stomach (Spittle 1952).

SOCIAL ORGANIZATION. Solitary or in pairs (Wells 1958). Small coveys are likely to be family parties (Spittle 1949).

MOVEMENTS. Not monitored, but singles mist-netted at lights while crossing the ridge of the Main Range at Fraser's Hill on 25 October and 2 May, and birds striking the Kuala Selangor lighthouse on 20 August and 20 February (BR 1968, 1969) are assumed to have been on the move.

SURVIVAL. No information.

SOCIAL INTERACTIONS. No information.

VOICE. Gives a soft flight-call, *tirru, tirru, tirru*, when flushed in a covey. Not heard from loners, hence this may have contact function. Males advertise with a soft, fluty *puee pueh pau-oo*, on the same rhythm as the much louder call of Malaysian Eared Nightjar *Eurostopodus temminckii* (G.C. Madoc).

BREEDING

Nest. Mostly in tall herbage, occasionally in the open; a scrape lined sparsely with grass-stems in a slight hollow on the ground or on a tussock. On the latter, other material may be interwoven with encircling stems to convert the nest into a deep, loose-walled cup.

Eggs and brood. Eggs are olive-brown, commonly marked all over with fine, dark sepia-brown specks. Shape is from broad to long ovate to near-piriform. Size (mm): 28.0–26.0 × 21.0–19.0 (n=6), 25.1 × 20.0 (mean of 14). Incubated clutches of 3–8 eggs are on record but 5–6 is normal. Incubation period about 16 days.

Cycle. There are two reports of broods being escorted by an adult male, without definite mention of a hen.

Seasonality. Eggs found during October, December–April and June–August, with chicks up to 27 August (F.G.H. Allen, Berwick 1952, 1952b, Edgar 1933, G.C. Madoc, NRCS, Ryves 1938, ZRCNUS).

MOULT. Replacement of primaries apparently regular-descendant. Seventy-one adults, all from south of the Thai border but representing all months, showed two seasons of wing-moult, affecting both sexes and up to 78 percent of individuals per month. Limits of consistent activity are: mid May (P2–3)–early September (P6, P10) and early November (P7–8)–early February (P8–9, P9–10). One dated 15 September had halted at P5 and no October birds were active, implying the second season could be a resumption of suspended moult. However, single January and February birds were growing P1, with two dated 16 March at P4 and P5 (BMNH, UMBRP, UMZC, ZRCNUS). Winter moulters could be immatures or, possibly, the second season covers migrants, on a different annual schedule.

CONSERVATION. One likely cause of decline in agricultural habitats (see also buttonquails) is the spreading use of chemical herbicides on fallow and marginal land.

Grey-breasted Partridge; (no Thai name); Burung Sang-seruk Gunung (Malay)

Arborophila orientalis (Horsfield) 1821, *Transactions of the Linnean Society* 13(1): 184. TL Belambangan, E Java.

Plate 2

GROUP RELATIONS. From colour-pattern of breast and face, allied with *atrogularis, rufipectus, ardens* and *crudigularis* (White-cheeked, Sichuan, Hainan and Taiwan Partridges), replacing one another in hill forest from extreme NE India east across southern China (Davison 1982a). However, the advertising-call is virtually as in continental *brunneopectus* and Indonesian *javanica* (Bar-backed and Chestnut-bellied Partridges), of other plumage-groups but whose geographical ranges *orientalis* links (S. van Balen).

GLOBAL RANGE. By plumage definition, mountains of E Java, Sumatra and Peninsular Malaysia, but species-limits need more study.

IDENTIFICATION/DESCRIPTION. Hard to see and, like most forest partridges, identified mainly from calls. A reasonable view would show black-and-white head-pattern, mainly olive-brown upperparts and mainly grey underparts. There is individual variation in the amount of white on the head (frontal spot, supercilium, face-patch) apparent in both sexes (BMNH), and some have the head almost completely black – guessed by Robinson (1928) to be an age factor. The black of the head is slightly olive-washed in females, and juveniles have upperparts and breast washed rufous. Robinson reports an 'erythristic' morph (age/sex-class unclear) washed rufous dorsally and lacking black in the wings. Partridges in this genus are spurless.

Chick and poult plumages undescribed.

Bare-part colours. (Adult) iris brown; periorbital and sparsely feathered gular skin brick-orange; bill black; feet red (Robinson and Chasen 1936).

Size (mm). (Skins: 5 males, 8 females; adult): wing 141–156 and 130–144; tail 53–58 and 48–53; bill 19.5–20.7 and from front edge nostril 7.8–10.2 (sexes combined); tarsus 41.1–45.3 and 39.7–43.7 (BMNH, ZRCNUS).

Weight (g). Two unsexed adults, 320, 352.6 (McClure 1964, K.W. Scriven).

DISTRIBUTION. On the Main Range, from Ulu Langat, S Selangor/Pahang divide, north to Korbu (latitude 4°42'N), and on the Larut Range. Under-recorded but, apparently, not on any more distant outlier. Historical summary: *Pek, Phg, Sel.*

GEOGRAPHICAL VARIATION. Endemic *campbelli* Robinson 1904 (TL Cameron Highlands).

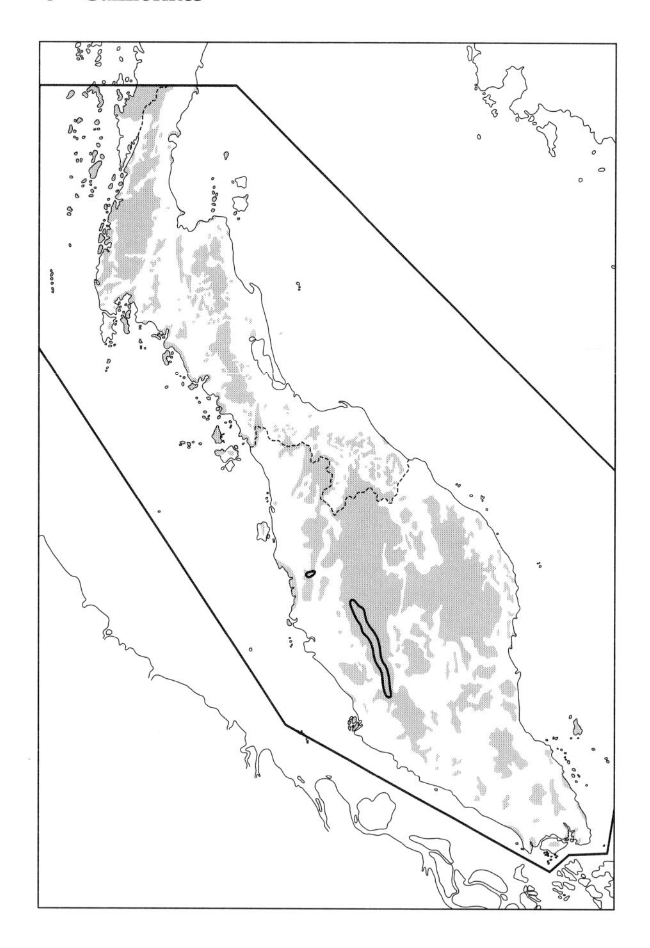

STATUS AND POPULATION. Resident, more or less regular and more or less common.

HABITATS AND ECOLOGY. The floor of Montane forest between about 1000 and 1600 m, selecting dense rattan and other undergrowth beneath well-grown forest, hence towards the upper limit of its range mainly in sheltered defiles. In Cameron Highlands, survives in quite small (down to 5 ha) forest isolates in tea plantations (G.W.H. Davison).

FORAGING AND FOOD. Stomachs of specimens collected in Genting Highlands held rattan fruits, the red fruits of the creeper *Pratia begoniaefolia*, termites and small gastropods (Robinson 1928).

SOCIAL ORGANIZATION. Occurs in pairs or small coveys that may be family parties (Robinson 1909).

MOVEMENTS. None known.

SURVIVAL. No information.

SOCIAL INTERACTIONS. Neighbours counter-call.

VOICE. The advertising-call is a set of up to 25 ringing whistles on a more or less level tone, giving way to commonly 12 shrill disyllables each dropping through about six tones of an octave . . . *oii oii oii oii oii, pi-hor pi-hor pi-hor* . . . The *pi-hor* section may also be given alone. Madoc (1956a) describes a soft, rapidly repeated, close-range contact-cheep, *wut-wit wut-wit*. Calling noted in October, November, January, March, April and June–August.

BREEDING

Nest. Only two recorded: one a loose, flat pad of twigs and leaves, 15 cm across, on the ground beneath a stemless palm, the second a short tunnel into a deep bed of leaves, perhaps heaped up by the birds themselves.

Eggs and brood. Eggs plain, rather glossy white. Shape near-piriform. Size (mm): 42.0 × 32.0, 42.0 × 31.5 (n=2). Full clutch uncertain but at least four.

Cycle. No information.

Seasonality. March is the only recorded egg-month (Madoc 1956a, Robinson 1909, 1909a).

MOULT. Primary moult recorded at one and two loci. Seven of ten adults collected on the Selangor/Pahang divide during 4 February–24 March showed active moult, between P1 and P4; eight others dated May, June, November and January none (BMNH, P.R. Sweet, ZRCNUS).

CONSERVATION. No issues identified beyond the general expectation of more disruption of mountain forest-cover on the Main Range and elsewhere in the near future.

Chestnut-necklaced Partridge; Nok Grataa Phaktai (Thai); Burung Siul Onak (Malay)

Arborophila charltonii (Eyton) 1845, *Annals and Magazine of Natural History* series 1(16): 230. TL Melaka (but perhaps imported).

Plate 2

GROUP RELATIONS. Forms a superspecies with continental SE Asian *A. chloropus* (Scaly-breasted Partridge).

GLOBAL RANGE. N Vietnam, Sabah, Sumatra and the Peninsula (a supposed juvenile, BMNH reg. 1936.4.12.92, from Hat Sanuk, SW Thailand, is a

Scaly-breasted Partridge). If the Vietnamese bird really is *charltonii*, the two parts of the latter's mainland range are interposed by its allospecies.

IDENTIFICATION/DESCRIPTION. Upperparts and wings mottled brown, long supercilium whitish, and ear-covert patch rufous-buff. Below, throat whitish, succeeded by black necklace and broader, rich chestnut horseshoe-collar. Remaining underparts rufous-buff, variably black-barred across lower breast and flanks. Tarsus spurless.

Downy chick and poult plumages undescribed, but several apparent adults showed some secondaries regularly mottled brown, others plain, rich chestnut with black barring on the inner web (one bird also with a similar back-feather). These chestnut feathers were smaller, more worn than adjacent brown feathers and are almost certainly juvenile. Scaly-breasted Partridge equivalents are not as richly chestnut and more extensively barred over both webs (BMNH).

Bare-part colours. (Adult) iris hazel to reddish brown, periorbital skin reddish orange; bill black in four specimens, black with reddish base and yellow-green tip to lower mandible in one, all olive-green in one, all brown in one and all yellow-brown in one – variation that is not yet understood; feet dull yellow to yellowish green (BMNH, ZRCNUS).

Size (mm). (Skins: 7 males, 9 females; adult): wing 163–166 and 151–160; tail 52–69 and 52–68; bill 17.5–19.7 (sexes combined); tarsus 39.9–43.0 and 37.1–41.5 (BMNH, ZRCNUS).

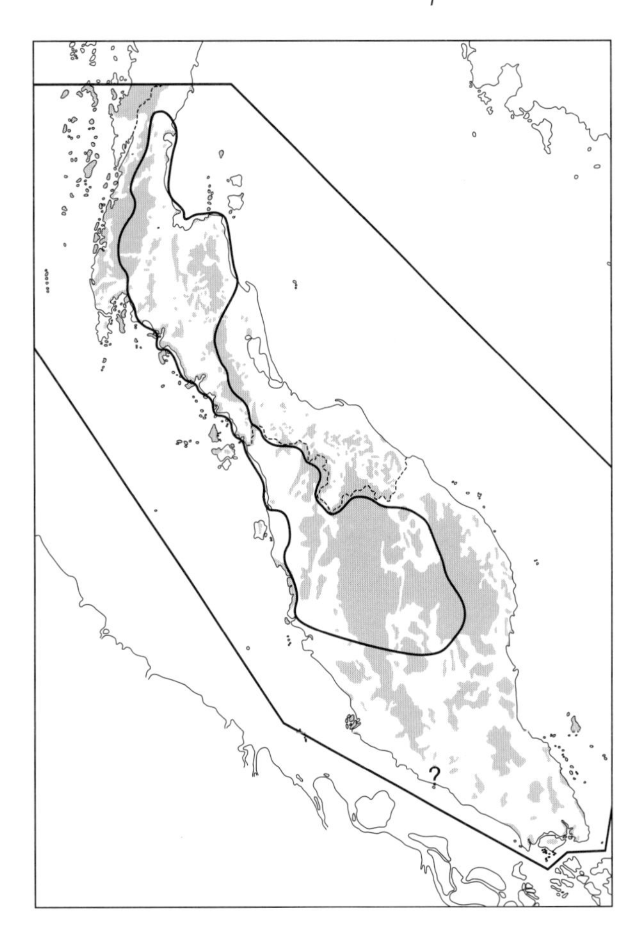

Weight. No data.

DISTRIBUTION. South definitely to N Pahang: at least one specimen has been collected from what is now the Pahang sector of Taman Negara (AMNH), recently with a party reported in Tekam forest reserve, Jerantut district, southeast of Taman Negara. Melaka type material is likely to have come from further north, or Sumatra. Historical summary: *Chu, Sur, Nak, Kra, Tra, Sat, Pes, Ked, Kel, Pek, Phg, ?Mel.* Hume's (1879) 'Penang' record is discounted. There are no other island records and in the 1880s C.B. Rickett bought captives on Penang island said to have been caught in Kedah (BMNH).

GEOGRAPHICAL VARIATION. Nominate *charltonii*, also of Sumatra (G.F. Mees).

STATUS AND POPULATION. Resident, local and (now) uncommon to sparse. Contacts in Khlong Phraya wildlife reserve, Krabi, in March 1990 are the only ones from the Thai provinces in 20 years (OBCB-12, RTFD). Boonsong and Round (1991) believe it may be close to extinction there. Probably much reduced from habitat-loss south of the border as well. Not found recently in the remains of former habitat in Perlis but no special searches have been made elsewhere.

HABITATS AND ECOLOGY. The floor of mature semi-evergreen and evergreen Lowland forest, also bamboo-dominated secondary-growth, and often under dense cover (G.C. Madoc); in the plains and on lower slopes of hills, but to not far above the hill-foot boundary.

FORAGING AND FOOD. No information.

SOCIAL ORGANIZATION. Found in small coveys. Nothing is known about the dispersion of breeders.

MOVEMENTS. None known.

SURVIVAL. No information.

SOCIAL INTERACTIONS. No information.

VOICE. 'A low, soft, double whistle' (Robinson and Chasen 1936). Partridges heard regularly at dawn in forest-edge gingers and scrub by the Tembeling river, Kuala Tahan (Taman Negara), in early April 1979 gave a trisyllabic *bee-a-bab*, the middle note fluctuating in clarity. This sequence is reminiscent of Ferruginous Partridge song, without its run-up component, but on habitat grounds Chestnut-necklaced Partridge would have been just as likely.

BREEDING. Not recorded.

MOULT. Replacement of primaries single-locus, apparently regular-descendant. Among 16 adults from Chumphon south to Perak and Kelantan dated November–January, March, June and July, six show wing-moult between 5 November (P6–7) and March (P10). A female dated 10 November had suspended at P3 (BMNH, ZRCNUS).

CONSERVATION. Probably dependent on plains-level forest, hence at risk from habitat-loss. Like other phasianids, open to trapping in small forest patches. Globally vulnerable (BTW2).

Ferruginous Partridge; Nok Grataa Song Deuay (Thai); Burung Sang-seruk Rimba (Malay)

Caloperdix oculea (Temminck) 1815, *Histoire Générale des Pigeons et des Gallinacés* 3: 408 and 732. TL central parts of the Malay Peninsula.

Plate 2

GROUP RELATIONS. Free-standing, with no known close relative.

GLOBAL RANGE. Sumatra, mountains of NW Borneo, the Peninsula, Tenasserim to about 14°10'N and SW Thailand to 14°57'N (Kanchanaburi) (BBCB-8).

IDENTIFICATION/DESCRIPTION. Generally orange-rufous and, apart from short black streak behind eye, face unpatterned; upper body black with white scallop-markings, large black drops on scapulars and wing-coverts, and sides barred black and white. From *Arborophila* partridges by longer, thinner bill, male tarsal spur and reduced hind claw (Davison 1982a). The short spur is occasionally doubled on one or both sides.

Bare-part colours. (Adult) iris dark brown; bill black, paling at extreme tip; feet light greenish.

Size (mm). (Skins: 11 males, 9 females; adults): wing 142–148 and 136–142; tail 59–67 and 57–64; bill 20.3–21.8 (males only) and from front edge nostril 9.3–11.0 and 8.4–9.5; tarsus 42.9–47.5 and 38.6–42.4 (BMNH, ZRCNUS).

Weight (g). A female from Pakchan, about 230 (BMNH).

DISTRIBUTION. Confirmed south to Ulu Langat, S Selangor/Pahang divide. Also occurs on Tahan (AMNH) and possibly on some of its lower outliers. Nineteenth-century 'Melaka' material is likely to have been imported. Historical summary: *Pak, Chu, Sur, Pha, Nak, Kra, Tra, Sat, Pes, Ked, Phg, Sel, ?Mel*, with no island records.

GEOGRAPHICAL VARIATION. Nominate *oculea*, of the mainland range.

STATUS AND POPULATION. Resident, local and sparse to more or less common, in the past more numerous towards the N end of its range (Robinson

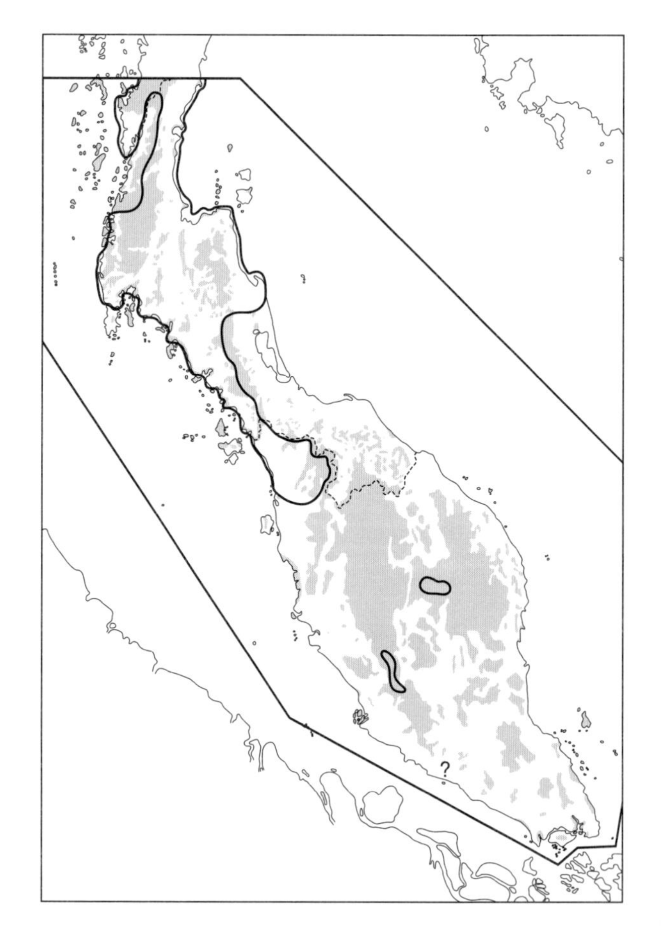

and Kloss 1910–11) and in 1986 still present in Tha Chana district, Surat Thani (P.D. Round). Formerly also fairly common in Perlis (Robinson 1913a) but several searches of the (since cleared) valley-bottom part of Mata Ayer forest reserve during both wet and dry seasons of 1987 failed to locate any. However, still present in hilly Thaleban national park (Satul) immediately to the north (Round 1988) and, southward, fairly common on the Main Range, including around Fraser's Hill.

HABITATS AND ECOLOGY. The floor of evergreen and semi-evergreen forest, dry and swampy; also bamboo-dominated secondary-growth. Said to favour streamsides (Robinson and Chasen 1936) but recent encounters give no particular evidence of this. Most plains-level habitat has been obliterated but birds also occur on hills, to about 1000 m in Thailand (P.D. Round) and 1200 m in Malaysia, and south from Kedah there are records only from slope-forest. On the Selangor/Pahang divide, found within a few hundred metres either side of the Lowland/Lower Montane forest ecotone, giving it the potential of ranging past the recorded Ulu Langat terminus to high ground further south.

FORAGING AND FOOD. No information.

SOCIAL ORGANIZATION. Said to have occurred in parties in lowland Perlis, but never confirmed. Recent encounters on the Main Range have been with loners and pairs only (B. King).

MOVEMENTS. None known.

SURVIVAL. No information.

SOCIAL INTERACTIONS. No information.

VOICE. The advertising-call is a sequence of clear whistles, rising (*contra* Grey-breasted Partridge) and breaking into three or four clanging trisyllables: *ee ee ee ee ee ee ii-ter-rang, ii-ter-rang, ii-ter-rang*. Neighbours counter-call. Around Fraser's Hill and the Gap, calling has so far been reported only in January, May, June and August.

BREEDING. A half-grown juvenile collected in Surat Thani on 16 September (Riley 1938). The record of a nest and egg attributed to H.C. Robinson by Baker (1922–30) is unsafe; Robinson never wrote it up and Baker misquoted him on another (obvious) item in the same publication.

MOULT. Only single-locus moult of primaries found in adults but an instance of double-locus post-juvenile moult (P2 and 10). Among 19 adults from Chumphon to Perlis dated October, November and January–April, four showed active wing-moult (P7, P8, P8, P8) between 18 October–13 November; others dated November, January and early March had recently completed. Post-juvenile wing-moult on 14 September (BMNH, ZRCNUS).

CONSERVATION. It is assumed the hill-slope population in the south is self-sustaining. This is less clear in the north and nowhere has response to logging and other forest disturbance been tested.

Roulroul; Gai Juk (Thai); Burung Siul Berjambul (Malay)

Rollulus rouloul (Scopoli) 1786, *Deliciae Florae et Faunae Insubricae* 2: 93. TL Melaka.
Plates 1 and 2

GROUP RELATIONS. Free-standing, with no certain close relatives (but see Black Partridge).

GLOBAL RANGE. Borneo, Bangka, Sumatra and the Peninsula, far-S Tenasserim and, in humid foothill forest, to latitude 14°57'N in SW Thailand (I.S. Robertson).

IDENTIFICATION/DESCRIPTION. Foragers are commonly detected by their litter-raking. The usual view is of dark birds scuttling ahead into undergrowth. Both sexes have a wispy forehead crest (inconspicuous in the field), but only males show the tall, maroon-rufous crown-fan with white band across its front edge. Spurless, and the hind toe lacks a claw.

Poults resemble the female. Downy chicks are mahogany-brown, paler below, with a darker streak down nape and back of neck, and another (bordered yellowish) from the mouth through the eye ending in a yellowish patch on the ear-coverts; iris black, bill brown and feet pinkish (BMP5, Ogilvie 1949).

Bare-part colours. (Adult) iris reddish brown, swollen and sculptured eyelids, produced to a point behind the eye, bright, waxy red; bill black, in male basal half of lower mandible and adjacent squared-off patch on upper, bright red; feet bright red.

Size (mm). (Skins: 17 males, 8 females; adult): wing 139–146 and 133–143; tail 58–67 and 51–62; bill 17.1–18.7 and 16.6–18.4, bill from front edge nostril 8.6–10.5 and 8.8–9.7; tarsus 41.8–47.0 and 40.3–46.5 (BMNH, ZRCNUS).

Weight (g). Means from Pahang, 280 (males) and 240 (females) (P. McGowan); two Negeri Sembilan males, 268.4 and 292.5 (UMBRP).

DISTRIBUTION. Historical summary: all divisions except *Phu, Son, Pat, Sat, Nar, Pes, Ked, Pra, Sin*. Specimens recorded from near Tonton island, close to Victoria Point, Pakchan, are assumed to have come from the opposite mainland. There are no confirmed island records; indeed, almost no strictly forest

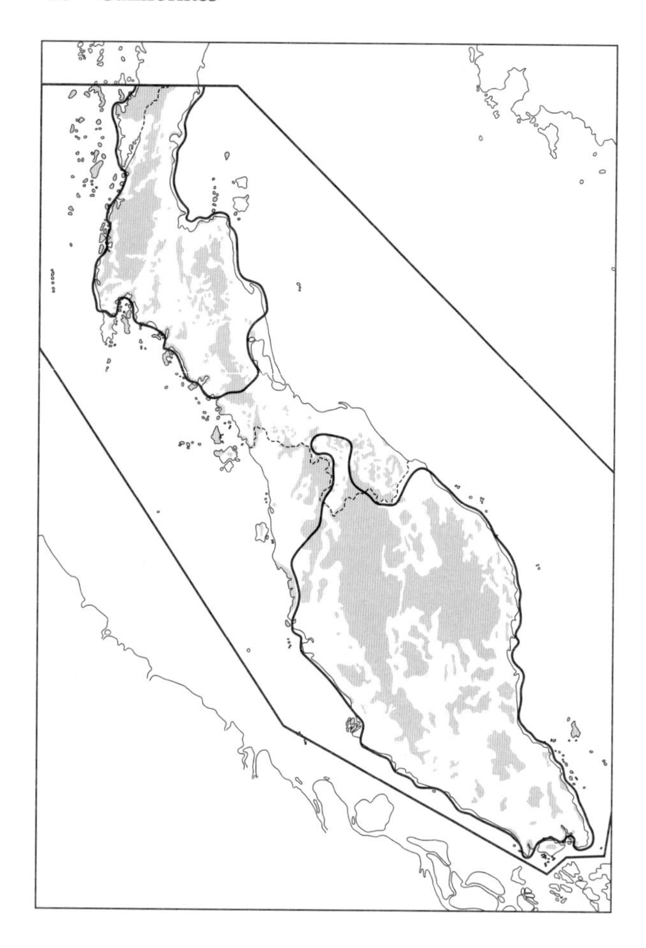

phasianids occur on islands off the Peninsula, suggesting the need for special long-term management also in habitat-islands.

GEOGRAPHICAL VARIATION. None recognized.

STATUS AND POPULATION. Resident, much reduced in Thailand but otherwise regular and more or less common. The most often-seen partridge in Lowland forest.

HABITATS AND ECOLOGY. The floor of evergreen and semi-evergreen Lowland forest, mature and recovering after selective logging, at all altitudes, plus Lower Montane forest to around 1200 m (on the Main Range, one Upper Montane record at 1550 m: Robinson 1909), but to a lower limit north of Malaysia.

FORAGING AND FOOD. Hunts mainly by raking litter for sub-surface invertebrates, but also takes prey (including the giant ant *Camponotus gigas*) on the surface, and pecks open soft, fallen figs (G.W.H. Davison).

SOCIAL ORGANIZATION. Occurs singly, in monogamous breeding-pairs, and family and larger parties (up to 13 birds on record: Davison 1986a). A large, all-male party reported but typically the sexes mix although, within parties, mates continue to associate as pairs (G.W.H. Davison). Pairs, together with their flying young, roost a few metres up in understratum saplings.

MOVEMENTS. None known.

SURVIVAL. No information.

SOCIAL INTERACTIONS. Pairing in a flock is initiated by the male blocking the approach of the female to other males and by a stretch display in which he raises his body, emphasizing red leg-colour. Later, both sexes perform a tail-quiver and the male courtship-feeds his mate. Occasionally he solicits brooding, like a chick (Davison 1986a). Broken-wing and other distraction display is recorded from the male of a pair shepherding small young (P.D. Round).

VOICE. The advertising-call is a melancholy, upturning whistle, *su-il*, steadily repeated; heard mostly at dawn and reported in February, June, August and September. Which sex, in what social unit, gives this call has not been checked.

BREEDING

Nest. A leaf-lined scrape on the forest floor, 15–20 cm across by 2–3 cm thick and hidden beneath loosely piled-up leaf and twig litter through which the parent burrows; difficult to recognize without observing a bird emerge but more than once found at the edge of a clearing, such as a path.

Eggs and brood. Eggs are matt white. Shape broad but near-piriform. Size (mm): 39.1–35.6 × 32.0–30.5 (mean 38.0 × 31.3, n=14). Full clutch 5–6, laid at intervals of up to three days but incubated as of the last egg. Incubation period 18 days.

Cycle. Both pair-members sit by turns in the nest-scrape, tuck leaves round the sides of their body and, as they walk away, toss back litter that eventually accumulates as the pile. Timed in captivity, males do about twice as much 'building' as their mates but all incubation is by the female. Both attend the young, with individual chicks progressively fixing on, and attempting to monopolize, either mother or father. In early life, they peck from the parent's bill and can get some food this way for several months. Chicks are also fed by older young. First short flights (enabling roosting off the ground?) have been observed at age two weeks.

Seasonality. In Malaysia south to Negeri Sembilan, eggs reported in October, December, February, April and July, and parents escorting chicks in October, December and February–June (BMP5, Chasen 1939, Davison 1986a, 1992a, G.C. Madoc, NRCS, Ogilvie 1949). Adult moult suggests October marks the start of a potentially long season (Wells 1988).

MOULT. Replacement of primaries is mostly regular-descendant but occasionally at two loci (BMNH, ZRCNUS). Among 74 adults from the length of the Peninsula and covering all months, only six of

32 dated December–mid April showed active bilateral wing-moult, the earliest (mid February) at P10. Others in March–April included starters and a few late-stagers that may have resumed after suspension. By contrast, 35 of 42 dated late April–November showed moult, including all those taken in May–June. Earliest birds finished by late July but with a few starters as late as September and even mid November. These may then suspend, and one in January had done so at stage P5 (BMNH, ZRCNUS).

CONSERVATION. The long-term security of Lowland forest phasianids confined to small habitat-islands has been questioned, but this partridge shows better than average resistance to the impacts of logging and can utilize early-stage regenerating forest.

Red Junglefowl; Gai Paa (Thai); Ayam Hutan (Malay)

Gallus gallus (Linnaeus) 1758, *Systema Naturae* 10(1): 158. TL Con Dao island, S Vietnam.
Plates 1 and 3

GROUP RELATIONS. Most like, and may form a superspecies with, *G. lafayetti* (Ceylon Junglefowl). Some hybridization with interposed *G. sonnerati* (Grey Junglefowl) occurs in a narrow zone of overlap across central India (HBI).

GLOBAL RANGE. Excluding driest parts of the NW, the Indian subcontinent from the Himalayan foothills south to about the latitude of Bombay; S Yunnan, S Guangxi and Hainan; and SE Asia to Sumatra, Java and Bali: also the Philippines, where it may not be native. Introduced in Wallacea east to Timor, and in Polynesia, etc.

IDENTIFICATION/DESCRIPTION. Bantam-sized. The bright-plumaged cock is an unmistakable chicken with black underparts. Dark slaty feet, a white puff at the upper base of the arched tail and, in the south, white ear-wattle help distinguish pure stock from domestic intergrades (but these characters are not individually diagnostic). Hens are dull brown, streaked pale yellow on the neck and light brown ventrally, and are the only local pheasant with tall, up-cocked tail. Young males are hen-like but blacker, especially on the underparts and tail, with broad black shaft-streaks to the neck-hackles. Adult males have a long, sharp tarsal spur; absent in hens.

The downy chick is buff with black-edged, mahogany-brown stripes: one median from crown to rump, one from the eye down the side of the neck, and a third dorsolateral along the back. Wings rufous-brown; throat, ear-coverts and underparts pale buff, with a darker breast-band (BMP5).

Bare-part colours. (Adult) iris hazel; comb and face- (except ear-) wattles blood red in cock, smaller and dull pink-red in hen (and immatures); bill dark horn; feet lead-grey. Ear-wattle colour varies geographically.

Size (mm). (Skins: 22 males, 13 females; adult): wing 211–234 and 191–208; tail 247–336 and 128–155; bill from front edge nostril 13.3–16.9 and 12.6–14.3; tarsus 69–82 and 58–66 (BMNH, UMZC, ZRCNUS).

Weight. No data.

DISTRIBUTION. Historical summary: all divisions except *Nak, Kra, Son, Pat*, with additional island records from Langkawi (perhaps introduced; not found there as of 1968), and Ubin (*Sin*) where introduced stock now breeds.

GEOGRAPHICAL VARIATION. Subspecies *spadiceus* Bonnaterre 1792 (TL Melaka), of SW China and

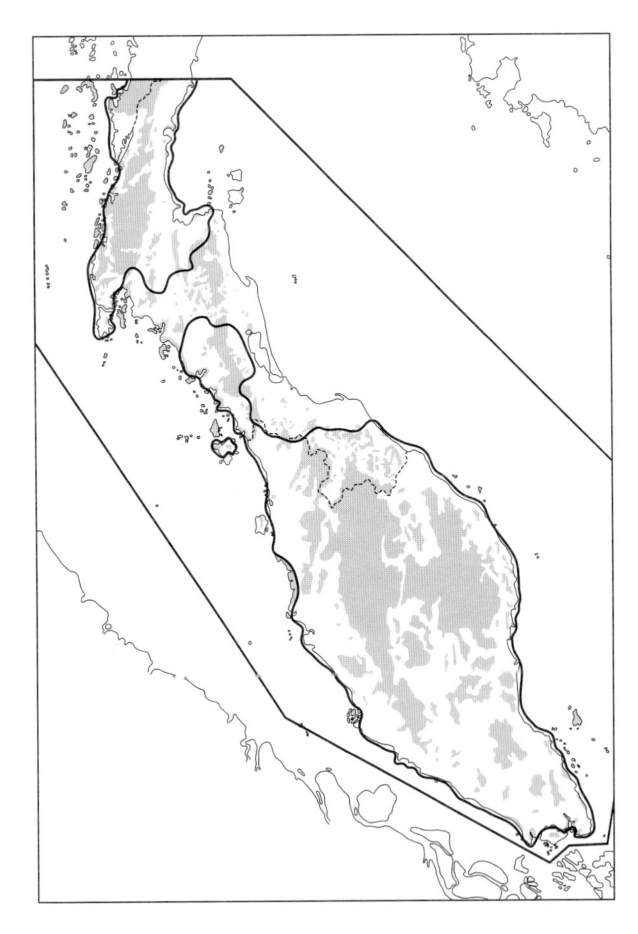

western SE Asia to N Sumatra (CLBS). The ear-wattle is non-contrasting red south to near the Thai/Malaysian border (but colour unrecorded in Yala–Narathiwat); white in Malaysia.

STATUS AND POPULATION. As far as known, resident throughout (but see Collias and Saichuae 1967). Much hunted but still regular and more or less common. Near rural habitation, mates with free-ranging domestic stock and obvious colour intergrades are quite common. It follows that some of the most stable wild populations in contact with man are those in wooded suburban parts of the larger towns, where few poultry are kept loose. No such intergrades seem to occur, e.g., in Kuala Lumpur.

HABITATS AND ECOLOGY. From the landward fringe of mangroves, following suitable edge habitat, to the summit of the mountain passes (in Cameron Highlands, two cocks seen on the road at 1800 m, close to the top of Mount Berinchang: BR 1965). Some may always have lived along the flood-damaged margins of large rivers or among the scrub of accreting coastal dunes, but agriculture has greatly aided dispersal. The typical modern habitat is a mosaic of openings (crops, grass, gardens, etc.) and dense cover, ranging from regenerating natural forest to tall *Saccharum* cane and including rubber, oil-palm and even tea plantations, especially where these are allowed to develop undergrowth. At plains level, fairly often found quite far into closed-canopy forest, perhaps chiefly in transit between gaps, but parties also litter-forage and may visit regular food-sources such as fruiting trees. Elsewhere in its range, congregates at seeding bamboos but this has not been documented locally.

In keeping with their preference for forest-edge habitat, Junglefowl routinely overfly quite wide barriers, including rivers and roads, at up to tree-top height.

FORAGING AND FOOD. In early mornings and evenings, Red Junglefowl range well out from cover, especially where termites or winged ants are emerging. These insects are prominent diet items; one male crop from Pahang contained nearly 1000 *Macrotermes carbonarius*. Invertebrates are otherwise uncovered mostly by raking but in Taman Negara Red Junglefowl have been seen taking items flushed by grazing Gaur, and in one instance a cock cleaned maggots out of a Gaur head-wound (Collias and Saichuae 1967). Beetles characteristic of cattle dung also figure. Plant food identified by Collias included tapioca tuber, rice and other seeds, and the fruit of luban *Vitex pubescens*, presumably after it had fallen or been knocked to the ground by other birds.

SOCIAL ORGANIZATION. Polygynous but parties of large young and often more than one adult cock as well as hens may have more importance as foraging than as mating units. Dominant cocks depress the vocalizing of sub-dominants (Collias and Saichuae 1967) and may disperse them but crowing birds are themselves often solitary, advertising from more or less fixed sites for a few days before moving on. Little is known about when and where most matings are actually obtained.

MOVEMENTS. None documented.

SURVIVAL. No information.

SOCIAL INTERACTIONS. No other local information.

VOICE. Delivered mostly during mornings and evenings, the male crow is a harsh, staccato *ka ka dee-dl*; less often *ka-deedl du*, i.e., typically of one note less than the common call of domestic breeds. The female cackle is as in domestic hens but rather high-pitched.

BREEDING

Nest. A shallow scrape in the ground, sometimes with a pad of dead leaves, in undergrowth among trees or scrub, dense weeds or cover-crops, or tunnelled into tall grass; sometimes off the ground, e.g., among litter collected in the axil of a low palm frond. Will also take to open baskets set out low in cover.

Eggs and brood. Eggs are glossy, creamy white. Size (mm): 49.0–45.0 × 36.0 (n=3). The regular full clutch is said to be six, but in Chumphon Robinson and Kloss (1921–24) recorded 5–7.

Cycle. Hens incubate and brood alone, and shepherd chicks close to cover until they are well grown.

Seasonality. In Malaysia, cocks commonly start calling in January but more observations are needed on seasonality. Eggs have been found in December–June and August, downy chicks on 22 November and 'month-old' poults on 28 November implying some laying as of October (Madoc 1956a, NRCS, Robinson and Chasen 1936, Ryves 1938, Sutari 1987, ZRCNUS),

MOULT. None of 26 adults taken from Pakchan south to Pahang and Perak during November–March showed any wing-moult, but ten of 11 dated May-October did, with apparent starts (P1) spread probably from April to October and earliest completion (P10) by September (BMNH, UMZC, ZRCNUS). Latest birds may suspend but direct evidence is lacking. In September in Selangor, cocks are replacing neck-hackles and tail-feathers; moult of plumage important for display may show stricter seasonality than that of wings.

CONSERVATION. Given most Junglefowl habitat is man-made, hunting and gene-flow from domestic stock are probably the main threats.

Crestless Fireback; (no Thai name); **Ayam Mata Merah** (Malay)

Lophura erythrophthalma (Raffles) 1822, *Transactions of the Linnean Society* 13(2): 321. TL Benkulen, SW Sumatra.

Plates 1 and 3

GROUP RELATIONS. Free-standing.

GLOBAL RANGE. Borneo north to Brunei, Sumatra north to about the equator, and the southern Peninsula.

IDENTIFICATION/DESCRIPTION. Apart from the male tail and back, both adults appear blackish in typical field views. The adult male has back coppery, darkening to maroon then purplish on rump and upper tail-coverts, and tail yellow-cinnamon with blue-black base; head and rest of body black, purple-shot except on belly, with wing-coverts and mantle to side of breast finely and densely vermiculated silver-grey; breast also with fine whitish shaft-lines. The female is all-black, and both adults have a tarsal spur, up to 26 mm long in males (Davison 1985).

Downy chick upperparts are reddish brown with a dark brown stripe from forehead to crown, one flanked by narrow buff-and-dark lines from nape to tail, another diagonally through the eye and two across the wing, continued on thighs as a dark spot; another dark spot on the ear-coverts and a broad, dark brown patch on the shoulder. Underparts from chin dull yellowish. Feet pinkish, bill reddish horn, culmen darker (BMP5). Poults are black with rusty brown feather-tips.

Bare-part colours. (Adult) iris hazel; facial wattle blood-red, larger and brighter in male; bill dirty greenish white in male, darker in female; feet and tarsal spur slaty blue.

Size (mm). (Live and skins: 7 males, 9 females; adult): wing 240–252 and 221–236; tail 150–170 and 139–150; bill from cere 19.2–21.6 and 18.0–20.2; tarsus 78.4–81.6 and 68.7–72.8 (UMBRP, ZDUM, ZRCNUS).

Weight (g). An adult male, 1194 (UMBRP).

DISTRIBUTION. S Johor to S Kelantan (the Lebir drainage) and Kedah. Nineteenth-century reports from Singapore and Penang islands are likely to have been of trade captives. Historical summary: *Ked, Kel, Pek, Phg, Sel, Neg, Joh.*

GEOGRAPHICAL VARIATION. Nominate *erythrophthalma*, also on Sumatra.

STATUS AND POPULATION. Resident and regular, uncommon to more or less common.

HABITATS AND ECOLOGY. The floor of mature and well-regenerated, closed-canopy Lowland forest from swampy valley-bottom to hilly terrain but rare more than a short distance up major slopes. Two adults labelled 'Wray's Camp', in the Lower Montane forest zone of Tahan (ZRCNUS) seem likely to have been collected further down that mountain. Where Crested Fireback is present, observed to avoid the favoured valley-bottom habitat of this larger bird (Davison 1981a), but ecological interactions deserve more study. They could throw light on why Crestless Fireback has such a limited distribution northward.

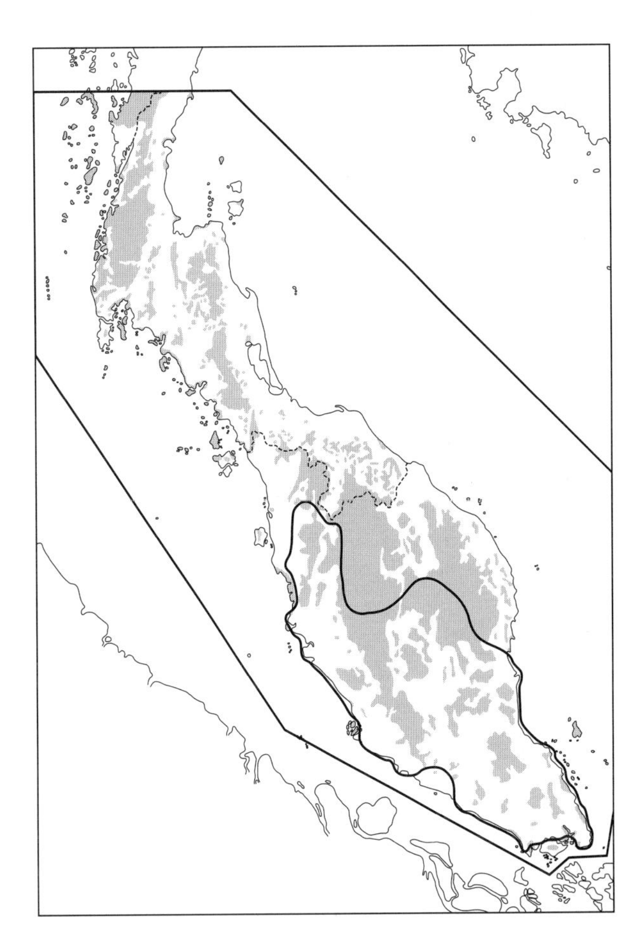

FORAGING AND FOOD. Little known but, like Crested Fireback, takes fallen fruit; also rakes for concentrations of invertebrates hidden beneath litter, for which group-searching should be efficient and from which groups would benefit. It has been suggested both loners and groups (at different times of year) work restricted patches for short periods before moving on within an overall larger activity-space (Davison 1981a).

SOCIAL ORGANIZATION. Solitary adults of both sexes, a lone female shepherding young and groups of large young together with more than one adult, including males, fit with a probably seasonal, polygynous mating system, as in other local 'gallo-pheasants'. In late February in the Kerau wildlife reserve, Pahang, I have seen a prolonged fight between two males, implying defence of some exclusive space at what, from the date, could have been the start of the breeding-season. Female tarsal spur and black, male-type rather than cryptic plumage, unique among gallo-pheasants (Delacour 1977), indicate some special need to advertise aggressiveness by this sex as well. Defending access to a mate from other females has been suggested (Davison 1985) although, in an aviary, females killed a newly introduced adult male.

MOVEMENTS. None known.

SURVIVAL. No information.

SOCIAL INTERACTIONS. Apart from male fighting, no specific information.

VOICE. Short-range vocalizations that may include low-intensity alarm are a throaty, vibrating purr and a low-pitched *tak-takrau*. The scare-call is a loud *kak*, and males advertise at a distance with a brief, throbbing wing-whirr (BMP5).

BREEDING

Nest. Only four recorded; three were depressions in dry leaf or twig litter between the buttresses of forest trees or stumps, one a shallow, leaf-lined depression by a stemless palm on top of a soil termitarium.

Eggs and brood. Eggs are pale pink-brown variably freckled chalky white. Size (mm): 49.0–46.5 × 36.5–35.0 mm (n=8). A captive female laid six eggs and, in the wild, incubated clutches of four and five reported.

Cycle. A captive started to lay in February of its third year. All incubation and chick-tending is by the lone female, and they can be close sitters. A 2-m length of rotten wood that fell right beside a nest under observation in Pasoh research forest, Negeri Sembilan, showered the hen with dust and debris but did not flush her.

Seasonality. Two clutches in March, one in April and one in June (from which young hatched on 3–4 July); a hen shepherding a poult of uncertain age in Taman Negara on 10 September (BMP5, BR 1965, 1976–77, 1978–79, Chasen 1939, MBR 1986–87).

MOULT. Eighteen birds taken in January, March, May, July–October and December (BMP5, ZRCNUS) showed wing-moult in every month except December (n=3), without obvious seasonal progression (including starts in July and September and completions in March and August).

CONSERVATION. Another plains-forest specialist at risk from habitat-loss. Its future may depend on maintaining what little forest of this type lies within Malaysian nature reserves. Globally vulnerable (BTW2).

Crested Fireback; Gai Fah Naa Khieo (Thai); Ayam Pegar (Malay)

Lophura ignita (Shaw & Nodder) 1797, *Vivarium Naturae or The Naturalist's Miscellany* 9: plate 321. TL Borneo.

Plates 1 and 3

GROUP RELATIONS. Free-standing.

GLOBAL RANGE. Borneo, Banka, Sumatra and the Peninsula.

IDENTIFICATION/DESCRIPTION. Almost as big as Great Argus and both have blue facial skin and red legs, but the Fireback eye-wattle is distinctive, and rich chestnut head and upperparts of the hen contrast with subtle body-tones of both sexes of Argus. Juvenile males lack the adult's white flank-streaking and coppery back but have maroon rump and a short crest. The adult male tarsal spur, contrastingly coloured and up to 40 mm long, is among the largest of all pheasants.

Bare-part colours. (Adult) iris clear light red; face-wattle large, angular and bright cobalt-blue in males, smaller and purplish blue in females; bill jade-white in males, browner in females; feet bright red, paler behind; spur and claws whitish.

Size (mm). (Skins: 14 males, 16 females; adult): wing 280–304 and 250–267; tail 240–291 and 171–200; bill from cere 21.6–23.1 and 20.2 (one only); tarsus 103–112 and 84–93 (BMNH, ZRCNUS).

Weight (g). Approximate only: males 2050–2500 (n=7 from Pakchan) and 1810, 2040 (Trang); females 1350–1600 (n=4 from Pakchan) (BMNH, Riley 1938).

DISTRIBUTION. From Melaka and NE Johor to latitude about 10°30'N. Historical summary: all divisions except *Pha, Pht, Son, Pat, Sat, Yal, Ked, Tru, Pra, Sin*. Certainly now extinct *Phu* and there are no other island records.

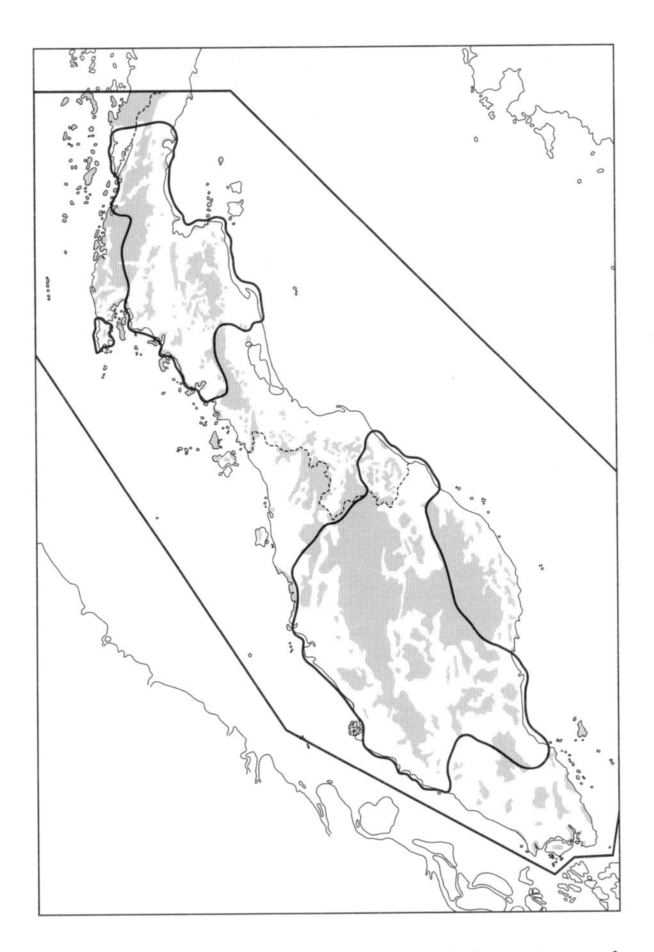

GEOGRAPHICAL VARIATION. Subspecies *rufa* Raffles 1822 (TL Benkulen, SW Sumatra), of the mainland and most of Sumatra, in which males have all-blue rather than part-coppery underparts, and pale-streaked flanks. High body-weights in the far north are not supported by any obvious increase in standard measurements (BMNH). Far-northern males have flank-streaks orange-buff rather than white, although Delacour (1977) believed this to be a character only of younger birds.

STATUS AND POPULATION. Resident, local and sparse to more or less common.

HABITATS AND ECOLOGY. The floor of tall, closed-canopy Lowland forest, apparently at all altitudes, and to 1200 m in Lower Montane forest, but with a strong bias towards damp valley-bottom habitat, especially close to rivers. At Kuala Lompat, Kerau wildlife reserve (Pahang), 40 percent of contacts were within 100 m of a river, most at the outer and back edges of the river terrace, thus in areas occasionally flooded but not permanently swampy (Davison 1981a). No contacts were made above the terrace and the only definite record from a major slope anywhere is of a female found dead in Lower Montane forest of the Main Range in Selangor (MBR 1984–85).

FORAGING AND FOOD. The diet is mainly fruit and invertebrates (Davison 1981a). Fruit-fall varies seasonally and it is believed social insects with a clumped distribution beneath the litter increase in importance towards the end of the year. They are most efficiently uncovered by the search-efforts of a group (Davison 1981), and flocks have more often been recorded at this season than earlier in the year.

SOCIAL ORGANIZATION. Adults of both sexes occur mainly alone during early and middle months of the year, like other local gallo-pheasants, working small patches of habitat for a few days before moving on within a presumed larger total activity space (Davison 1981a). Mobility could increase opportunities for polygamous matings as well as for feeding.

At times, a male may be accompanied by more than one adult female (never seen in Crestless Fireback), but larger parties usually include poults and are thought to function mainly to improve food-finding. In central Malaysia, flocks with young form as of about September and regularly include more than one brood, with several adults of both sexes (a record total 16 birds). Occasional parties, presumably of young birds, persist into the new year, as late as April (G.W.H. Davison, ENGGANG-1).

MOVEMENTS. None known.

SURVIVAL. No information.

SOCIAL INTERACTIONS. Wing-whirring signals presence at a distance, and advertising males can be pugnacious. W.R. Davison (Hume and Davison 1878) describes one wing-whirring at a display-court off which it repeatedly drove the Great Argus owner.

VOICE. Vocalizations are similar to Crestless Fireback, including a low, vibrant *chukun-chukun* and a loud *kak* scare-call. The wing-whirr is a brief throb, given persistently by males and heard once from a lone female (Davison 1981a). It is likely to have both spacing and mate-attracting functions.

BREEDING

Nest. Only one described: 'composed of dead leaves, grass and bamboo spathes under some thick, low bushes in dense evergreen jungle' (Baker 1922–30).

Eggs and brood. Eggs are plain, stone-white. Size (mm): 56.8–50.6 × 43.6–39.3 (n=14). The full wild clutch is unknown but local captives have laid up to five eggs. Incubation period 24 days among zoo birds.

Cycle. Only females incubate and tend young. Chicks erupt flight-feathers on day three and tail on day seven.

Seasonality. Eggs obtained by H.N. Coltart and J. Waterstradt from Melaka in April of 1896 and 1899 fit *ignita* on size and description. In Pahang, a group including five poults not more than six weeks old seen on 15 October (Baker 1922–30, Davison 1981a, M. Nazim Yaacob, M.P. Walters).

MOULT. A December-moulting female showed replacement of primaries at three loci (P2, 4 and 9). Among 30 adults from Pakchan south to Pahang covering all months except June and September, seven showed wing-moult in March, April, July and October–December, with apparent starts (P1) in April, July, November and December, i.e., without obvious seasonal progression (BMNH, ZRCNUS).

CONSERVATION. Seems to need valley-bottom, river-terrace forest, hence this is another species under direct threat from habitat-loss. A disproportionately large amount of key habitat has already been lost to agriculture and dams, and little is retained in nature reserves. Unlike Crestless Fireback, has not been seen in logged forest. Globally vulnerable (BTW2).

Mountain Peacock Pheasant; (no Thai name); Burung Kuang Cermin (Malay)

Polyplectron inopinatum (Rothschild) 1903, *Bulletin of the British Ornithologists' Club* 13: 41. TL Tahan massif, Peninsular Malaysia.

Plate 4

GROUP RELATIONS. Free-standing.

GLOBAL RANGE. Endemic to the mountains of Peninsular Malaysia.

IDENTIFICATION/DESCRIPTION. The only pheasant (as distinct from partridge) in its habitat; deep, rich brown with longish, pointed, strongly graduated tail; dark in a fleeting glimpse. Fine white dorsal spotting may show but the iridescent, blue-green ocelli need not be obvious.

Back, scapular and lesser- and median wing-covert feathers of the adult male carry a single subterminal ocellus, countershaded black and peaked buff-white fore and aft. The outer eight of his ten tail-feathers have a large ocellus on the outer web and a smaller one on the inner, in broad contact on the outermost feather, progressively less so inwards. Female ocelli are smaller and, except on the tail, non-iridescent. Males have one or two spurs per tarsus (in one instance a left lower and a right upper); females are spurless.

Bare-part colours. (Adult) iris dark brown, on a fully feathered face; bill bluish horn; feet slaty grey (Robinson 1928).

Size (mm). (Skins: 9 males, 9 females; adult): wing 195–210 and 180–192; tail 321–354 and 211–243; bill 22.0–22.7 and 20.2–21.0; tarsus 68.0–74.5 and 61.3–69.8 (BMNH, ZDUM, ZRCNUS).

Weight. No data.

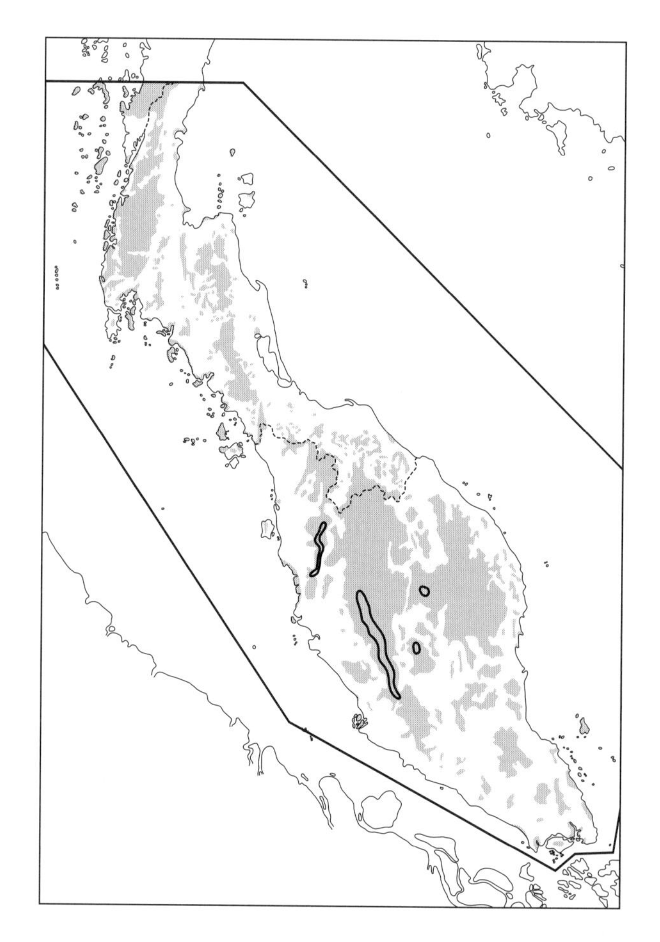

DISTRIBUTION. The Larut Range, the Main Range, recorded between Ulu Langat, S Selangor/ Pahang divide, and Korbu peak, Perak/Pahang divide, and on eastern outliers Tahan and Benom. Historical summary: *Kel, Pek, Phg, Sel.*

GEOGRAPHICAL VARIATION. None recognized.

STATUS AND POPULATION. Resident, regular and uncommon to more or less common.

HABITATS AND ECOLOGY. The floor of Lower and Upper Montane forest, recorded from about 820 m (one anomalous report of a shed tail-feather picked up at about 600 m, well below the Montane ecotone) to at least 1600 m, including in elfin forest of summit ridges where it is the only pheasant present (G.W.H. Davison, MBR 1986-87, Robinson 1909).

FORAGING AND FOOD. No information.

SOCIAL ORGANIZATION. Little known.

MOVEMENTS. None known.

SURVIVAL. No information.

SOCIAL INTERACTIONS. Male displays in the presence of a female, described from captives (Davison 1992), include ten main actions: body-shakes; rapid walking with flouncing of alternate wings; walking erect, with a flap of the spread wings; a stationary lateral pose with flight-feathers nearest the female drooped and tail tilted towards her; (once) a near-frontal display with breast dipped, far wing raised over back and tail cocked past the vertical; high-stepping with head and neck ruffled; head-bobbing; and ritual food-passing.

VOICE. The male's advertising-call, given mostly from a perch off the ground, is a series of bursts, 5–6 seconds apart, each of 1–4 (commonly two) fairly loud, harsh clucks or squawks about half a second apart (Davison 1992). When disturbed, one or both sexes give a chicken-like clucking.

BREEDING

Nest. One of two found in Cameron Highlands: a virtually unlined scrape roughly 26 cm across × 10 cm deep in peat under a rhododendron less than 1 m from a path through dense elfin forest on a high summit.

Eggs and brood. Eggs are plain, faintly glossy, pale cream-terracotta. Size (mm): 51.3 × 43.8 and 53.0 × 44.0 (n=2). Full clutch two.

Cycle. No information.

Seasonality. Both nests are dated January, including one clutch of slightly incubated eggs on 12 January. Poults moulting out of downy plumage have been collected on Genting Highlands in late February and a half-grown young escorted by a hen seen on nearby Bunga Buah peak, Selangor, on 11 June (G.W.H. Davison, Gibson-Hill 1949b, G.C. Madoc, Robinson 1909).

MOULT. Primaries are replaced at one or two loci, up to nine feathers apart. Eleven of 16 adults collected in January–April, June and October showed wing-moult in all of these months, with starts (P1) in January and March, and apparent mid-stage moult in other months, revealing no obvious seasonal progression (BMNH, ZDUM, ZRCNUS).

CONSERVATION. Unique among pheasants, hardly encroached upon. This situation is not expected to last but populations on isolated habitat islands, including Tahan and Benom peaks (both within protected areas), are assumed to be stable. Globally vulnerable by virtue of its limited range (BTW2).

Grey Peacock Pheasant; Nok Wen See Thao (Thai); Burung Kuang Kelabu (Malay)

Polyplectron bicalcaratum (Linnaeus) 1758, *Systema Naturae* 10(1): 156. TL Thaungya Sakan, N Tenasserim.

Not illustrated

GROUP RELATIONS. Forms a likely superspecies with allopatric Indochinese *P. germaini* (Germain's Peacock Pheasant), although *bicalcaratum* shows greater size-dimorphism (Delacour 1977).

GLOBAL RANGE. Hill-tracts of the NE Indian subcontinent; S Yunnan and Hainan; and SE Asia to the northern fringe of the Malay Peninsula and central Vietnam.

IDENTIFICATION/DESCRIPTION. Buff to white freckling gives adults a paler, more frosted appearance than Malayan Peacock Pheasant *P. malacense*. An adult male from Chumphon has head grey-white, without the iridescent, recurved crest of *malacense*; rest of plumage deep, dull brown finely spotted and freckled whitish, these spots forming obscure bars on the underparts. All ocelli are fully ringed with buff-white to buff-grey. They are purple on the body and wing-coverts, purple to green on the upper tail-coverts and tail, according to angle of view. Unlike *malacense*, all tail-coverts and tail-feathers have them double and fully separated. Males carry up to four spurs per tarsus, absent in females (BMNH, Davison 1985).

Poults lack white freckling on the body and are quite like same-stage *malacense* except for strong white fringes to blackish wing-covert and mantle feathers, and white bars on a dark tail (BMNH).

Bare-part colours. (Adult male) iris silvery; bill black; feet sepia-black.

Size (mm). (Skin: one adult male): wing 233; tail 390; bill 20.2; tarsus 75.4.

Weight. No data.

DISTRIBUTION. Known from only one specimen, adult male, in the E.G. Herbert collection from Khlong Bang Lai (modern Ban Salui) at 10°45'N, lowland Chumphon (BMNH). The date, 19 January 1916, fits with known activities at this locality and nothing about the bird suggests it was other than wild-caught. Historical summary: *Chu*.

GEOGRAPHICAL VARIATION. Nominate *bicalcaratum*, of the eastern mainland.

STATUS AND POPULATION. Formerly at least, a presumed resident. No suitable habitat is likely to survive in lowland Chumphon now but a relic population may still occur on steep ground of the dividing-range in the far north of the Peninsula.

HABITATS AND ECOLOGY. In adjacent SW Thailand, Grey Peacock Pheasants inhabit semi-evergreen and evergreen forest, now restricted more or less completely to the hills.

FORAGING AND FOOD. No information.

SOCIAL ORGANIZATION. No local information.

MOVEMENTS. None recorded.

SURVIVAL. No information.

SOCIAL INTERACTIONS. No local information.

VOICE. No local information.

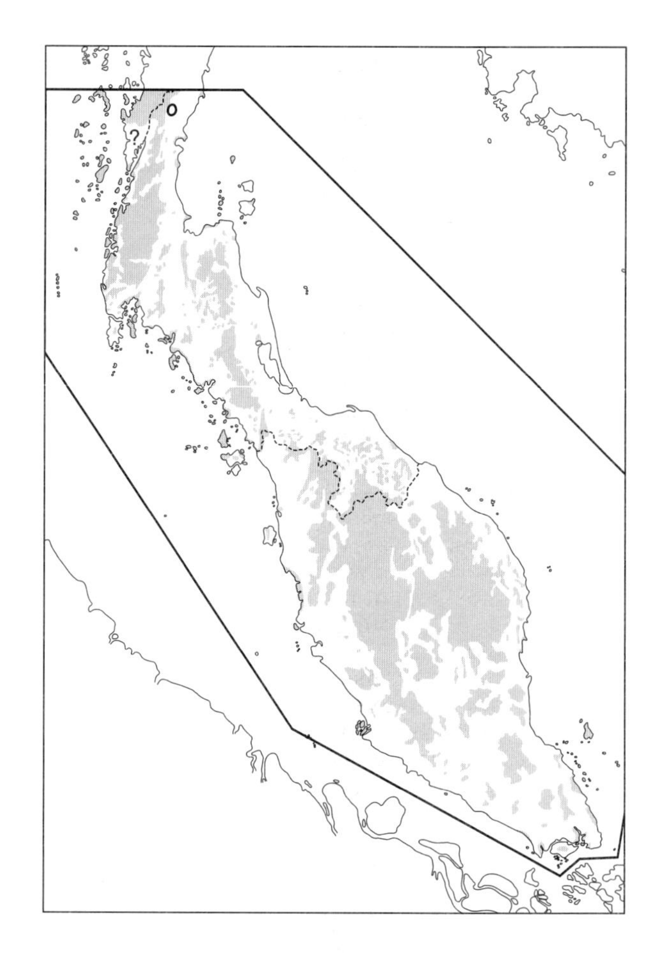

BREEDING. See Malayan Peacock Pheasant.

MOULT. The one mid-January specimen showed none (BMNH).

CONSERVATION. Pakchan is unchecked. On the Thai side of the border, pockets of plains-level forest survived until the 1980s but the only likely habitat now is probably on the Tenasserim border hills.

Malayan Peacock Pheasant; Nok Wen See Namtaan (Thai); Burung Kuang Pongsu (Malay)

Polyplectron malacense (Scopoli) 1786, *Deliciae Florae et Faunae Insubricae* 2: 93. TL Melaka.
Plates 1 and 4

GROUP RELATIONS. Allopatric *malacense*, *schleiermacheri* (Bornean Peacock Pheasant) and *emphanum* (Palawan Peacock Pheasant) show progressive plumage specialisation, but may still constitute a superspecies. There is no hard evidence of any member of the superspecies occurring in Sumatra (*contra* Chasen 1935).

GLOBAL RANGE. Endemic to the Peninsula.

IDENTIFICATION/DESCRIPTION. An elusive, clay-brown pheasant with full, square-cut tail carried flat, and crown-crest of male held sharply recurved over the bill. Ocelli on the upperparts appear dull black as the bird moves away (Davison 1983) and would not be conspicuous.

In adult males, the crest and grey-and-white-barred upper neck-feathers are tipped iridescent purple. Pale ochre-buff upper body and wing-coverts are densely mottled black. Underparts are finely peppered and vermiculated buff and black, unbarred other than on lower neck (versus barred in Grey Peacock Pheasant). Ocelli are largest on the tail. The central tail-feathers, upper tail-coverts, mantle, scapular and wing-covert feathers bear one on each web, other tail-feathers one on the outer web only. Where paired, ocelli make broad contact, pinched in along the shaft on tail- and tail-covert feathers, elsewhere forming a full round, encircled by black then clear buff. All ocelli are slightly domed and iridescent, reflecting according to aspect: in subdued light, purple-blue head-on to maximally green at right angles, as when the displaying bird tips its body towards the hen in a lateral pass or frontal bow. Those of the female upper body and wings are non-iridescent black.

Nearly all males, but no females, have up to three spurs per tarsus, erupting at age 8–9 months (BMP5, Davison 1983a).

The downy chick is mahogany-brown above with a deeper brown mid-dorsal band edged dark buff, a dark spot on the side of the nape, and pale supercilium and cheeks. The underparts shade from dark buff on the throat to dirty grey-white mid-ventrally. Bill dark, feet grey (BMP5).

Bare-part colours. Iris brown (immatures, adult female), clear blue-green (adult male); facial skin orange-pink margined by black feathering above, behind and below; bill blackish; feet and spurs blackish.

Size (mm). (Skins: 7 males, 5 females; adult): wing 208–219 and 184–189; tail 215–233 and 168–179; bill 21.6 (one only) and 19.8–21.0; tarsus 69.9–75.6 and 57.0–61.4 (ZDUM, ZRCNUS).

Weight (g). Two Negeri Sembilan males 581 and 586 (UMBRP, Wong 1985).

DISTRIBUTION. N Johor (Labis) (AMNH) apparently to Surat Thani (peacock pheasants in the now-drowned Phrasaeng river valley and one trapped in Tha Chana district are believed to have been this species: Nakhasathien 1984, P.D. Round).

Claims of presence across the Burma border rest on a hen and clutch of two eggs sent to E.C.S. Baker from forest in 'the extreme south of Tenasserim' (Baker 1916). The skin has disappeared, clutch-size is suspicious, and the one egg described: 'warm pink *café-au-lait* with innumerable freckles of white all over it . . . 47.7 × 36.8 mm' (later re-measured as 45.7 × 35.3 mm: Baker 1922–30), resembles Grey Peacock Pheasant. Malayan Peacock Pheasant eggs are now known to be broader and paler, without the white freckling.

Historical summary: *Sur, Phu, Kra, Kel, Tru, Pra, Pek, Phg, Sel, Neg, ?Mel, Joh*. A bird listed from *Nak* (Riley 1938) has been re-identified as *P. bicalcaratum*, apparently from a locality of the same name on the SW Thailand/Tenasserim divide.

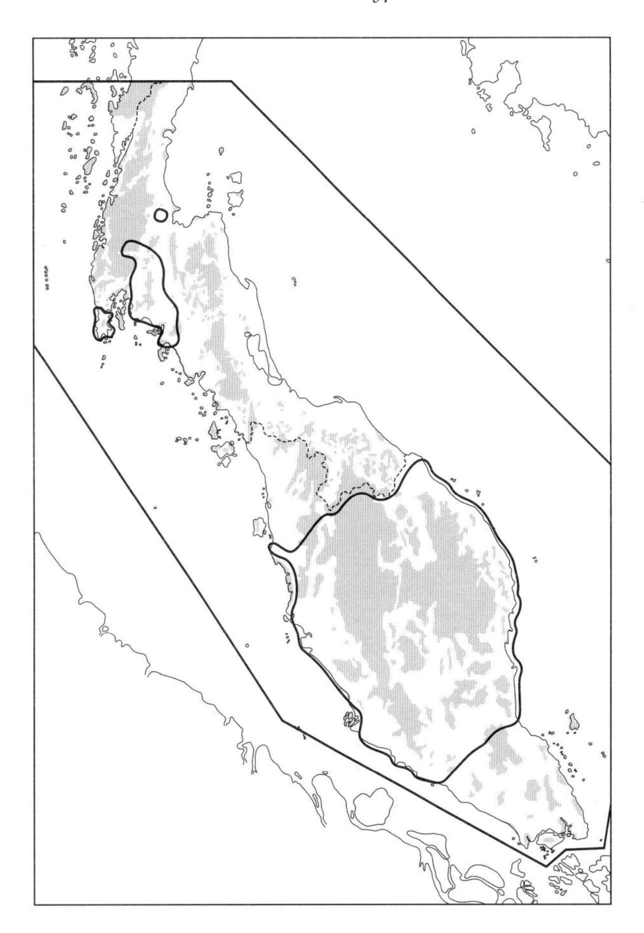

GEOGRAPHICAL VARIATION. None recognized.

STATUS AND POPULATION. Resident, local and sparse to more or less common. Forest clearance may already have ousted it from Thailand where none confirmed for more an a decade. Peacock pheasants recently reported from Tong Yong, a small coastal hill (and site of a royal palace) in Narathiwat, may not be wild there and have not been proven to be *malacense* (P.D. Round).

HABITATS AND ECOLOGY. Locally on small hills, e.g., beside the Petuang river, Terengganu (Cranbrook, G.W.H. Davison) but usually not past the terrain-break at the foot of big slopes. Everywhere, the strong preference is for well-grown to mature forest on level, low-lying, often temporarily wet sites (other than peatswamp) near streams, with dense understratum vegetation typically rich in small palms (*Iguanura, Pinanga*, etc.), Maranthaceae and other monocots (Davison 1983a). Even so, not all nominally good looking sites are occupied.

Adults roost alone, choosing slender, 1–2 cm thick horizontal branches or climbers 4–6 m up, and move site from night to night (G.W.H. Davison).

FORAGING AND FOOD. Little known but scrapes, common where peacock pheasants are present, imply the regular diet includes invertebrates from under forest-floor litter.

SOCIAL ORGANIZATION. Typically solitary, with a polygynous mating-system. The only prolonged association is believed to be between mother and chick, which she feeds bill to bill.

Adult males, but apparently not all in any one season (and perhaps no young adults), clear display-courts up to 2 m across, often including a soil termitarium or other hump, in relatively open spots such as on old forest paths. One bird may own two or more, typically close together, and use them over a few to 60 days in a season (longest during years of heavy fruit-drop). Courts are cleaned by raking with the feet and wing-flapping to waft off leaves.

In favoured habitat, the several hectares occupied per court-advertising male include some space defended by threat and fighting at boundaries. Calling also interrupts that of neighbours but the switching of roles between individuals implies no set order of dominance within a male cluster. However, the few observed visits by hens have been to males spending much time on their courts and calling persistently (Davison 1983a).

In the wild, displaying to a hen has only been seen at courts, but pairs met with elsewhere in the forest suggest a possible alternative strategy in which some matings could be obtained by males perhaps not advertising courts (Davison 1983a). Males are sexually mature before they attain full plumage, but if male ornamentation and female discrimination have evolved together, with or without a court, males are unlikely to succeed while still young. That nearly half the skins of males in the BMNH collection are in less than fully adult plumage suggests 'behavioural maturity' is deferred in this pheasant (G.W.H. Davison).

MOVEMENTS. None known.

SURVIVAL. No information.

SOCIAL INTERACTIONS. The male's sexual displays include the following actions and postures: head-feather ruffling; jumping; ritualized food-indicating; lateral passes with body, tail and secondaries tilted towards the hen; and a full frontal bow to the hen in which concentric ranks of progressively more eye-sized ocelli converge on the position of the male's real eye, tracking her movements so that she is continuously confronted over a wide angle (Davison 1983).

VOICE. Court-holding males intersperse three loud calls: (i) a short, two-note (but in some individuals more complex) whistle, the last note held and inflected upwards, given at intervals of about a minute, for up to 30 minutes per bout; (ii) a rasping *tchorr* repeated every few seconds for as long as three minutes; (iii) an explosive cackle running into a prolonged series of low clucks. It has not been proven that hens give any of these calls (Davison 1983a).

BREEDING

Nest. Only four reported, all from the mature forest of Kerau wildlife reserve, Pahang: in a slight, natural depression on a 1.4 m high *Macrotermes* termitarium (the incubating hen almost hidden by leafy cover); on the open ground among leaves (twice); and against a recent wind-throw.

Eggs and brood. Eggs are plain off-white. Shape broad ovate. Size (mm): 48.5 × 40.0 (n=1). Unique among pheasants, the full clutch is one, confirmed in captive breeders. Incubation period 25 days.

Cycle. A male chick erupted flight-feathers on day six and flew on day 23.

Seasonality. Eggs found on 15 March, 8 April, and 4 and (breeding attempt abandoned) 28 August (BMP5, BR 1980-81, Davison 1983a, C.M. Francis, ZDUM).

MOULT. Primaries are replaced at up to three loci, with active wing-moult of males seen in early July, September and late October, and of females in July and, once, late January (P5–6 and 10), i.e., in the latter half of the year, with the January record perhaps a late finish (BMNH, UMBRP, UMZC, ZDUM, ZRCNUS)

CONSERVATION. Calling males have been found in lightly logged forest but there is no certainty that suitable, natural forest will be maintained for any purpose in the plains. Ultimately, this pheasant will depend on scattered patches of what is already the most critically scarce habitat of Malaysian nature reserves. With a naturally patchy distribution in a very small total range, this local endemic is globally vulnerable, if not already endangered (BTW2, McGowan 1991).

Crested Argus; (no Thai name); Burung Kuang Raya Gunung (Malay)

Rheinardia ocellata (Elliot) 1871, *Annals and Magazine of Natural History* series 4(8): 119. TL central Vietnam.

Plates 1, 4 and 5

GROUP RELATIONS. Free-standing. Both sexes of the Malaysian form are more richly coloured than their Indochinese counterparts, brighter patterned on the head, the adult male also with blacker body regularly white-spotted rather than vermiculated. If, as suggested by Davison (1980), this character-shift has been driven by contact with Great Argus, these species could be closer than their separate generic names imply.

GLOBAL RANGE. Two widely isolated population-clusters, in the mountains of Taman Negara, Malaysia, and on outliers and both slopes of the Annamite range north from about latitude 12°N (OBCB-14).

IDENTIFICATION/DESCRIPTION. White crest and huge tail of the full-plumaged male are virtually unmistakable, and a combination of size and prominent pale eyebrow should identify other age/sex-classes. The female's light-and-dark-brown-barred upperparts resemble a young poult of Great Argus but size and wide-spaced black-and-brown barring of the tail are diagnostic. Neither sex has spurs.

Bare-part colours. (Adult) iris brown, periorbital skin bluish grey (male); bill horn-brown tinged pink on mouth (male); feet dark brownish grey (BMNH).

Size (mm). (Skins: 3 males, 2 females; adult): wing 367–382 and 312 (one only); tail 1213–1593 and 367 (one only); bill 35.8 (a male), from front edge nostril 17.6–18.8 and 15.8, 16.0; tarsus 92–102 and 86, 88 (BMNH, ZRCNUS).

Weight. No data.

DISTRIBUTION. Restricted to a narrow zone on the slopes of steep, sedimentary mountains at and within the borders of Taman Negara, including the Tahan massif, northwestern outlying peaks Tulang Rabong and Rabong and, to the east, Gagau and the western slope of the E-coast Range (Mandi Angin peak). The Terengganu slope offers further likely habitat but has not yet been explored. Past claimed voice identifications in the lowlands of W Pahang and on the adjacent Main Range have not been confirmed and are now generally rejected, as are claims from isolated (granitic) Benom peak, 80 km south of Taman Negara (see Davison 1980a, 1991). Recent searches of the whole Benom slope confirm only Great Argus occurs there. Historical summary: *Kel, Phg*.

GEOGRAPHICAL VARIATION. Endemic *nigrescens* Rothschild 1902 (TL Tahan massif, Pahang); possible variation between Malaysian sub-populations has not been investigated.

STATUS AND POPULATION. Resident, more or less common but highly localized. Some of the sub-populations in and around Taman Negara must be among the smallest avian breeding units in the region, potentially several thousand years old. In May 1976, Davison (1978) counted only 15 males calling (hence assumed to be getting most matings) on Rabong peak, Kelantan.

HABITATS AND ECOLOGY. Undisturbed tracts of the uppermost zone of Lowland forest and adjacent Lower Montane forest on precipitous slopes typical of

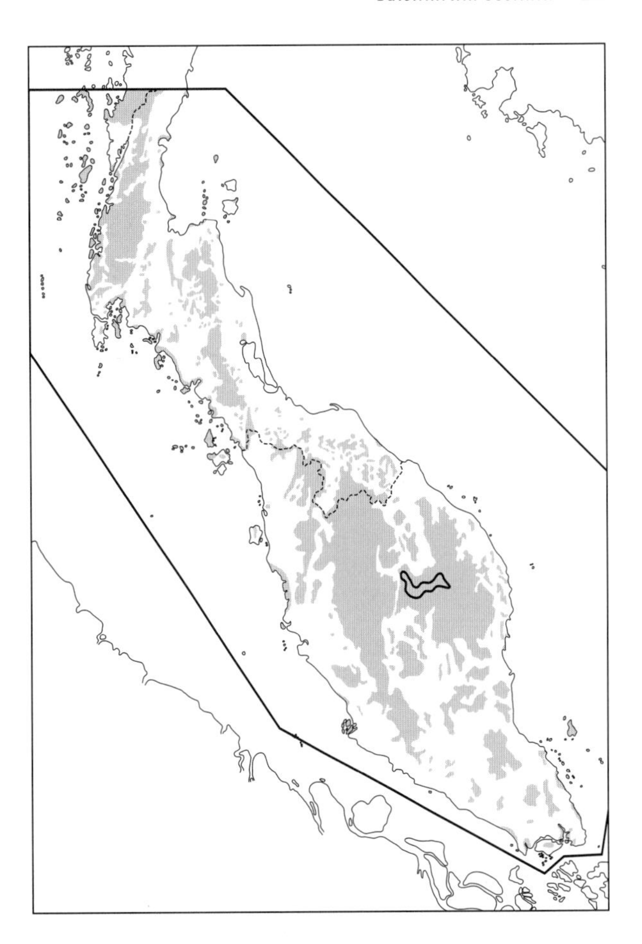

sandstone mountains, recorded between 790 and 1100 m and coming lowest along ridge-crests (BR 1978–79, Davison 1979, MBR 1984–85).

At the lower edge of its range, Crested Argus approaches or actually meets Great Argus. The latter may exclude it from lower ground and Malaysian populations are suspected to be relics of a northward retreat as Great Argus spread its range at the end of the Pleistocene (Davison 1980). Crested Argus is assumed to have been completely displaced from granite mountains (Benom, the Main Range, etc.).

FORAGING AND FOOD. Leaf, fern and liverwort fragments, and fruit remains including of *Calamus* rattans, together with insect (possibly ant) parts have been recovered from droppings on display courts (Davison 1978).

SOCIAL ORGANIZATION. Little known except that it seems to resemble that of Great Argus. Most encounters have been with loners and the only long-term social bond appears to be between hen and brood. The mating-system is believed to be promiscuous, or at least polygynous. Adult males individually maintain and call from a limited number of display-courts, up to 4 m across, often occupying all the space available on ridge-saddles and kept as bare and clean of vegetation as those of Great Argus. The only cleaning method observed so far has been forward-throwing of leaves and twigs with the bill (Davison 1978).

On Rabong peak, the mean distance between calling males was 1100 m, well within hearing range. With some individual and daily variation, males called on their courts from about 0700 to 1300 hours, and some called elsewhere in the evening and through the night, presumably from roost perches (BR 1972–73, Davison 1978). Vocalizing ceases during long spells of wet weather.

MOVEMENTS. None known.

SURVIVAL. No information.

SOCIAL INTERACTIONS. The sexual display sequence of Malaysian birds has not been seen. In captivity, that of nominate *ocellata* is dominated by lateral passes with arching of the extremely long and broad, ocellus-bearing tail around the female. Ocelli are lacking on body and wings of both subspecies, and nothing comparable to the frontal-fan posture of Great Argus has been reported.

VOICE. The commonest vocalization, given with head-feathers ruffled and white crest fully spread, is a rolling sequence of up to 12 powerful, hooting phrases, *oo kia-wau,* with second syllable shrill. Response to other males has not been studied but this call is given in reaction to extraneous noises, including hornbill wing-beats (Davison 1978) and distant human shouts. A second call, heard at other times, is 6-8 note sequence, *oo ki-iau, ki-iau, ki-iau . . .* with resonant introduction and shrill *ki* syllable (BMP5).

BREEDING. Not described. Calling by court-holding males recorded during mid March–mid June and, on Tulang Rabong, two half-grown poults escorted by a hen seen in mid June (BR 1972–73, 1976–77, 1978–79, Davison 1979, F.R. Lambert, BR 1980–81, 1984–85).

MOULT. Freshly shed male body- and wing- (but not tail-) feathers have been found at display-courts in March and May, implying mating and moult of plumage-parts not critical to display can occur at the same time. An adult male from Tahan was moulting primaries (P6–7) and had lost its central tail-feathers on 7 July; another dated 13 December showed no moult. A female dated 18 October showed no wing-moult but was growing its central tail-feathers (BMNH, ZRCNUS).

CONSERVATION. Globally vulnerable (BTW2) but, unless control of Taman Negara is lost, this pheasant's habitat must be considered among the most secure forest in the Peninsula. Its various tiny sub-populations also imply a resistance to chance extinction. Rumoured or potential threats include organized poaching and pressure from rising numbers of hunter-gatherers seeking refuge in the Park from land-clearance schemes. The spread of tour-trekking could also have an impact.

Great Argus; Nok Waa (Thai); Burung Kuang Raya (Malay)

Argusianus argus (Linnaeus) 1766, *Systema Naturae* 12(1): 272. TL Melaka.
Plates 1, 4 and 5

GROUP RELATIONS. Free-standing; see Crested Argus.

GLOBAL RANGE. Borneo, Sumatra and the Peninsula to about latitude 12°N in SW Thailand. The most northerly Tenasserim specimens seen are from the adjacent Kanmawbya and Hankadaing drainages at slightly above 10°30′N (AMNH, FAO 1983). J.C. Hopwood's claim of occurrence north to Tavoy district (14°N) has not been corroborated.

IDENTIFICATION/DESCRIPTION. Large size, with slender neck and head; elongated central tail-feathers only in the adult male. From red-footed female Crested Fireback by subtly mottled, subdued brown plumage throughout and lack of a face-wattle (although sparsely feathered face-skin is dull blue). Over the limited area of geographical contact with Crested Argus, foot colour, lack of a pale eyebrow and wings and tail without black barring are pointers in females and juveniles. Folded (hiding most ocelli), the large secondaries give the adult male body a log-like shape beyond which only the corkscrew tips of the central tail-feathers project.

As with Crested Argus, both sexes are spurless. They show no fighting behaviour.

Bare-part colours. Iris grey-brown (poult), greenish hazel to brown (adult); skin of sparsely feathered adult face and upper neck dull cobalt-blue (male), pale slaty blue (female); bill and cere black (poult), faintly blue-tinged white (adult male), pale horn-brown (adult female); feet orange (poult), light coral-red, duller in female (adult); claws whitish (BMNH, Baker 1930).

Size (mm). (Skins: 15 males, 8 females; adult): wing 453–504 (to longest secondary-tip 852–911) and 316–346; tail 1000–1367 and 265–327; bill 35.8 (one male only), from front edge nostril 18.6–20.4 and 15.4–18.8; tarsus 101–119 and 86–98 (109) (BMNH, UMZC, ZRCNUS).

Weight (g). Approximate weights from Trang and Pakchan are, males, 2040–2720 (n=8); females, 1360–1590 (n=3) (BMNH, Riley 1938).

DISTRIBUTION. Throughout, and in the early 1980s FAO found it still fairly common in Pakchan. Historical summary: all divisions except *Phu, Pht, Pat, Pra, Sin*, and present on Pangkor island (*Pek*).

GEOGRAPHICAL VARIATION. Nominate *argus*, of the global range except Borneo. Largest individuals are from Pakchan.

STATUS AND POPULATION. Resident, and more or less regular and common to, in Thailand, now uncommon. Abundance varies with substrate and terrain. Measured in terms just of the density of display-court-holding males, it is greatest on hilly land offering the steep ridges and crests from which advertising-calls carry furthest. Hilly terrain in W-central Malaysia gave sample densities of 1.5–2.25 per km^2, versus 0.15–0.54 in plains-level forest over the same years, with courts spaced a mean 375 and 435 m apart at representative hilly and flat sites in Selangor and Negeri Sembilan (Davison 1981, 1981b). Other age/sex-classes have not been censused.

HABITATS AND ECOLOGY. The floor of most tall, dry-land evergreen to near-evergreen forests in the plains and up slopes to about 950 m elevation, including selectively logged sites, but much sparser in significantly deciduous habitat and rare to absent in lowland peatswamp and white-sand heath forests. Replacement by Crested Argus in the uppermost fringe of Lowland forest on the steep-sloped sedimentary mountains of central Malaysia implies Great Argus is at a disadvantage in this marginal zone. Absence of both species from the upper slope of outlying sandstone peaks such as Tapis (Pahang) supports this.

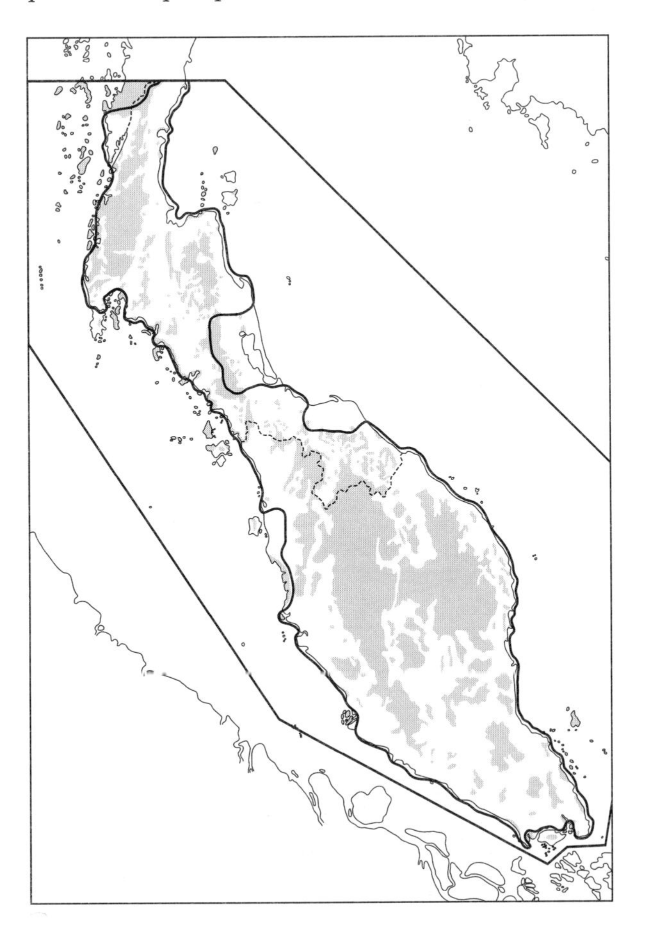

While the home-ranges of court-holding males are nearly always well-spaced, little is known about the dispersion of females, or of males not holding courts. The former call while nesting and raising chicks, during which increased food-needs may favour defending a territory (Davison 1981). Actual evidence that Great Arguses do approach their food-ceiling comes mainly from the observation that while the supply of males seems regularly to outstrip good court-sites, numbers calling (as an indication of being able to maintain a court while feeding themselves) vary year to year, being highest when forest trees fruit communally (Davison 1981). At the same time, there is no evidence display-courts are sited in special relationship to particular food-sources.

FORAGING AND FOOD. Great Arguses never rake litter to uncover the clumps of small invertebrates important to most more social pheasants. Instead, they walk slowly through the forest in search of rarer but larger items above the litter. Invertebrates identified from gut and dropping contents include various typically solitary arthropods, especially ants (commonly the giant *Camponotus gigas*). Mean size of bodies recovered whole exceeded the mean of arthropods sampled on the forest floor, suggesting selection. Birds also take much leaf material and fruit, some of which their long reach allows them to pick direct.

Climbers and under-stratum palms are favoured fruit-sources, as distinct from mass falls of more typical bird-fruits rich only in sugars (Davison 1981). This tendency to concentrate on richer but rarer rewards, it has been suggested, exposes Great Argus to more stress from periodic shortages than faced by dietary generalists. On the other hand, radio-tagging shows the core activity-space of a court-holding male can be very small (less than 1ha) and, typically, males forage only in the morning and evening, when surface invertebrates are most active. Declining returns make day-roosting the most efficient alternative behaviour, helped no doubt by energy conserved as an outcome of being large (Davison 1981).

SOCIAL ORGANIZATION. Apart from chick-care by the hen, both sexes lead solitary lives, a strategy associated with large size supported exclusively on well-dispersed, surface food.

Mating is polygynous, probably promiscuous, and at the start of the breeding-season older adult males begin to clear a court. This is often at a traditional site on an old game trail or where ground-layer vegetation is otherwise naturally sparse, typically on a spur or ridge-crest, or raised eminence in flatter country.

Court area is limited ultimately by space available but is rarely below about 12 m², and one irregular-shaped example at Pasoh, Negeri Sembilan, covered 72 m² (Davison 1981b). Clearing continues throughout, by scraping plants with the bill, pecking and tearing off overhanging vegetation, forward-flicking of fallen litter, and by bouts of 3–4 deep, fast wing-flaps with tail spread low, lifting the bird off the ground and fanning debris away from the court centre (Davison 1982).

Court positions are advertised by powerful calls, and neighbours respond to each other (and to other loud noises). However, there is a great difference in the audibility of calls over versus through forest vegetation, and whereas a female may hear several court-holders in succession on steep land this is less likely in plains forest. What she hears could be investigated experimentally but, to the human ear, male calling is stereotyped, varying individually only in loudness (according to distance) and persistence. For these and other reasons, the widely held concept of an 'exploded lek', in which females are guessed to select male quality by comparing voice features, may not explain the whole system. Given that young males take at least two long moults to develop a full array of feather-ocelli but reach sexually maturity before this, and that vacated display-courts are reoccupied within weeks or at most a month or so, it seems likely that 'subadults' waiting for a court-site would attempt matings as they meet females by chance in the nearby forest. While females are surely attracted by loud calling (and loudness and persistence might turn out to be what matters), Davison (1981b) implies their front-rank discrimination is between males of different plumage development – and also of different capacity to show it off since subadults do not make fresh courts of their own.

At the court, a mound or low branch serves as a regular day perch and calling station. At night both sexes roost alone on mid-stratum branches.

MOVEMENTS. None recorded.

SURVIVAL. No information.

SOCIAL INTERACTIONS. As display-court clearing begins, incumbent males start Short-calling (see below) and attend their court for around 40 percent of daylight hours, from dawn each day, alternating between bouts of cleaning and calling, with some displaying (Davison 1982). An habituated wild male visited by a female ceased calling and displayed for 34 minutes before being interrupted. Initially broken by brief rushes away from the court, its display included ten postures and actions (also seen in the complete display cycle of captives): front-end feather-ruffling; body shaking; ritual food-indicating; passes orientated laterally to the hen around the court perimeter or in arcs in front of her, with stamping, hissing, drooping the near- and raising the far-wing secondaries (to expose their ocelli?) or progressive forward-tipping of the sleeked body and tail. Ultimately, with body and tail tipped near vertical, wings are swept out and forward, and wrists reflexed past 180° so that their tips cross and scrape both each other and the ground. This concave fan is then skewed head-on to the hen, near-engulfing her in rows of ocelli that grow progressively smaller but more eye-like as they converge on the bird's real eye peering side-on through a gap left between the wrists (Davison 1982).

VOICE. Court-holding males have three very powerful, hooting calls audible for at least a kilometre over the forest. The Short-call advertisement is a shouting, *kau wow*, given from the display-court perch in bouts of up to 12 calls, and answered in kind by neighbouring court-holders; also given by these birds from roosts at night. The Irregular-hoot comprises 2–3 disyllables that sound like reversed Short-calls, given occasionally by males under various circumstances, but only during the Short-calling season; sometimes used to 'sign off' a final bout of Short-calling. The Long-call comprises 15–72 deliberate, spaced hoots, monosyllablic to the last few which then up-inflect to become disyllables, given throughout the year and at any time of day or night by adult and subadult males, occasionally also by breeding hens, and responded to by Long-calling from others. It is believed to space birds as they establish territories and court-sites but has also been recorded from a hen about to visit a court-holding male.

BREEDING

Nest. Only two sites described: on the ground between buttresses of a large forest tree on a river terrace, and in a litter-filled depression on the top of a 1.5 m tree-stump on steep land.

Eggs and brood. Eggs are smooth, creamy white to coffee-buff (though darker colours may be stain). Size (mm): 69.1–61.5 × 46.3–42.4 (n=5). Full clutch two, and two chicks are raised. In captivity in Malaysia, the incubation period is 24–25 days.

Cycle. Chicks are fed bill-to-bill by the hen for up to 11 weeks and can still be in her company when full-grown. At night, she broods them on a perch, one under each wing. There is a record from Zoo Negara, Kuala Lumpur, of a hen leaping up to a perch with a chick held under the base of each wing, implying they are on safe perches in forest before they can fly well (G.W.H. Davison).

Seasonality. The season over which males Short-call from display-courts varies year to year, starting between January and March and ending between July and September, unusually as late as November. Incubating hens have been flushed off full clutches on 4 May and 20 June. Other egg-dates, from the wild or from freshly captured birds, are 3 and 27 March, 20 May and 2 July. In years of mast fruiting, young poults have been seen as late as December (E.C.S. Baker, Baker 1930, BMNH, BR 1978–79, 1980–81, Davison 198l, MBR 1984–85, Robinson and Chasen 1936).

MOULT. Male flight-feathers have been picked up in Ampang forest, Selangor, during 19 May–16

October (G.W.H. Davison), and the few records of wing-moult obtained from museum skins concur: from Yala, P1 on 28 May and from Pahang, P6 and 8 (double-locus moult) on 27 July. Typically, flight-feather moult overlaps the individual's Short-calling by only 1–2 weeks, whereas body-moult starts 1–2 months ahead of flight-feathers. Adult females in wing-moult have been collected on Pangkor island and in Pahang and Kelantan in July (P3–5) and September (P2–3, P10) (BMNH, ZRCNUS).

CONSERVATION. Considering how easily court-holding males are shot or trapped, still surprisingly common. Within limits, resistance of the species to hunting lies in the solitary elusiveness both of females and the younger males waiting to replace incumbents. Adults are tolerant of some disturbance to forest but it is not known how this affects the survival of young.

Green Peafowl; Nok Yuung (Thai); Burung Merak Hijau (Malay)

Pavo muticus (Linnaeus) 1766, *Systema Naturae* 12(1): 268. TL Java.

Plates 1, 4 and 5

GROUP RELATIONS. Probably free-standing.

GLOBAL RANGE. Extreme SE Bangladesh and the India/Burma border (introduced in the Bengal terai); S and W Yunnan, and continental SE Asia to the Peninsula; also Java, but hunted out of much former range.

IDENTIFICATION/DESCRIPTION. Iridescent green plumage and full-webbed, up-standing crest of both sexes distinctive. On size, confusable only with escaped Blue Peafowl *P. cristatus*. Hens lack an upper tail-covert train and are less clearly squamated black on the back than males, and poults have mantle and chest mottled white and pale rufous (Robinson and Chasen 1936). Males have a large tarsal spur (occasionally unilateral: UMZC); females are spurless.

Bare-part colours. (Adult) iris dark hazel; anterior facial skin from bill around eye and slanting up in front of ear opening, clear blue (brightest behind the eye), below and behind, chrome yellow; bill black; feet black.

Size (mm). (Skins: 6 males, 3 females; adult): wing 470–508 and 386–425; tail 530–580 and 393–425; longest male upper tail-covert feathers 1310–1545; bill 44.3–47.0 and 40.0–41.6; tarsus 155–172 and 130–138 (UMZC, ZRCNUS).

Weight. No data.

DISTRIBUTION. In the late nineteenth century, along both coastal plains to the extreme south in the east and at least S Selangor in the west. Historical summary: all divisions except *Chu, Ran, Pha, Nak, Phu, Son, Pat, Pra, Neg, Mel, Sin*, with no island records.

GEOGRAPHICAL VARIATION. Nominate *muticus*, of the Peninsula and Java.

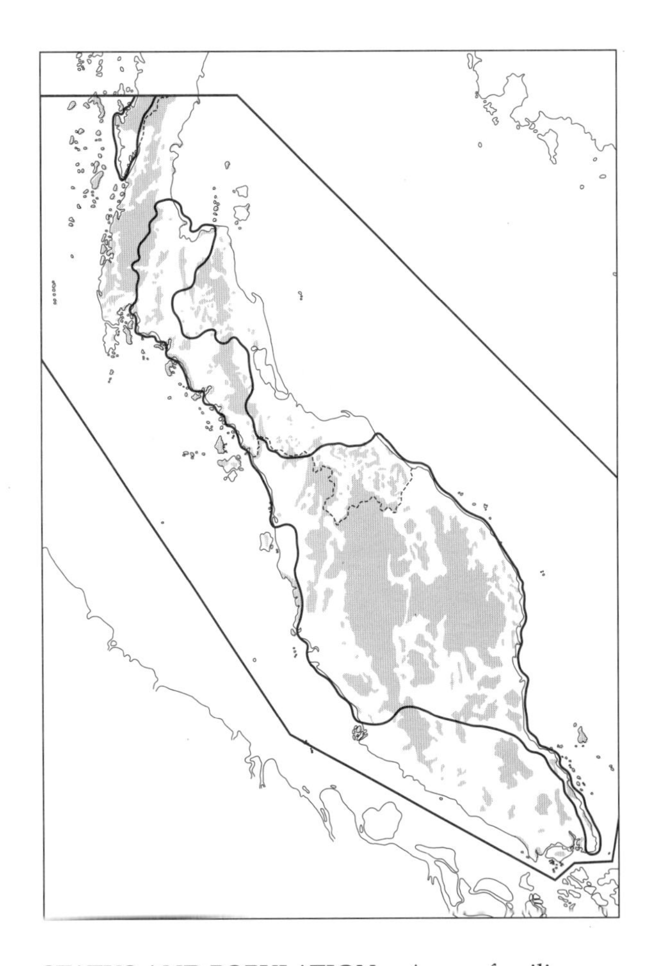

STATUS AND POPULATION. A once-familiar resident, now extinct; victim of locally changing attitudes to pot-hunting. Nothing is known about peafowl in Pakchan and nothing definite in the Thai provinces after Robinson (1914a) found them fairly common around cultivation in the interior of Surat Thani in 1913, and in early 1918 was able to collect several in a few days at a forest-edge site in Krabi (Robinson and Kloss 1918). Glenister (1951) found them pre World-War Two and villager accounts suggest pockets of population survived until the 1960s, or later.

History in the W Malaysian states is obscure, with no specific information later than the 1870s (Kelham 1881–83), except in Selangor. Some remained in Air Hitam forest reserve and adjacent rubber estates between the Kelang and Langat river valleys into the 1930s/early 1940s (Leyne 1941), but were not found post World-War Two (a rumour of presence in forest relics near Kerling, N Selangor, in the 1970s was never confirmed). Bangi, S Selangor, is the southernmost locality in this area.

East of the Main Range, neither the Skeat nor Waterstradt expedition reports mention peafowl on turn-of-the-century journeys along the Kelantan river (Gibson-Hill 1953, Waterstradt 1902) but they were numerous in the Pahang–Tembeling drainage (AMNH), and present on the Terengganu river until at least the 1950s (Wolfe 1951a). Along the Terengganu–Pahang coast (south to the Johor border and probably beyond), too, peafowl were common until the 1950s. It is rumoured that about then a local interdict on killing them was lifted, with rapid results. There have been no confirmed records from Pahang since, although a few are suspected to have survived there until much more recently. In Terengganu, last reported dependably in the early 1960s (Kemaman district), with a later rumour from Besut (Kelantan border) unconfirmed (BMP5).

HABITATS AND ECOLOGY. Glenister (1951) records meeting peafowl quite deep in closed forest but, like Red Junglefowl, they more typically selected the forest edge, including flood-damaged margins and sandbanks of large rivers through forest, margins of agriculture, and fire-maintained scrub over peaty and sandy 'beris' soils backed by forest along the E coast.

FORAGING AND FOOD. No local information other than a Selangor male recorded harvesting fallen fruit from the verge of a road through forest (Leyne 1941).

SOCIAL ORGANIZATION. For part of the year at least, associated in parties. A cock and four or five hens are described as the common grouping (Robinson and Chasen 1936) but ageing and sexing in the field could only have been provisional. Male-like plumage of the hen implies aspects of the social system may differ from the better-known polygamous Blue Peafowl.

MOVEMENTS. None known.

SURVIVAL. No information.

SOCIAL INTERACTIONS. No local information.

VOICE. The advertising-call of the male is an explosive, far-carrying *merak*, ear-splittingly loud at close range.

BREEDING

Nest. Only two described: slight depressions in the ground amid tall *Imperata* grass and in peaty soil under dense fern and scrub at the edge of forest clearings. Both were close to small, isolated tree stems, and this is believed to have been a regular feature.

Eggs and brood. The one egg described was cream-coloured with thick, glossy, pitted shell. Size (mm): 65.6 × 52.8 (n=1). Full clutch unknown; four eggs is the largest number reported.

Cycle. No informaton.

Seasonality. Along tributaries of the lower Kuantan river (Pahang), a nest with broken egg-shells on 6 March, one with four eggs ten days later, and a single, apparently abandoned, egg on 24 May (G.C. Madoc).

MOULT. Replacement of primaries apparently regular-descendant: an undated adult male in the Skeat collection (UMZC) showed P1–5 new, 6–7 growing, the rest worn, and central tail-feathers growing while most of the rest were new. In early July 1913, Surat Thani peafowl were in body-moult and males lacked upper tail-covert trains. A Malaysian bird dated 13 August showed P10 and train both half-grown. Trains are said to have re-grown by November/December and adult males dated January and March were in full plumage (Robinson 1914a, Robinson and Kloss 1918, ZRCNUS).

CONSERVATION. Globally vulnerable (BTW2). Reintroduction would need secure reserves. Isolated palm plantations on which hunting could be controlled are a proposed alternative, but exposure to the poison-baits still used against pest rodents is one of several foreseeable management problems.

Order ANSERIFORMES

Family ANATIDAE

Whistling ducks, pigmy-geese, dabbling and diving ducks: 11 species

Lesser Whistling Duck; Ped Daeng (Thai); Itik Belibis (Malay)

Dendrocygna javanica (Horsfield) 1821, *Transactions of the Linnean Society* 13(1): 199. TL Java.
Plate 6

GROUP RELATIONS. Free-standing. No separate family Dendrocygnidae has been accepted here, hence the need for a special group name, 'Whistling-duck', does not arise.

GLOBAL RANGE. The Indian subcontinent from the Indus valley, Sri Lanka and the Bay of Bengal islands; China south from the Changjiang valley, including Hainan and Taiwan, and (formerly) the S Nansei islands; SE Asia to Sumatra, southern Borneo, Java and Bali; and Sumbawa and Flores. Concentrations suggestive of wintering migrants occur south to Thailand.

IDENTIFICATION/DESCRIPTION. Flight (in loose packs or chevron skeins) appears slower, more laboured than in anatid ducks, on broader-tipped wings and with extended neck characteristically low-slung. The sexes are mostly alike: face and neck unpatterned, light bay-brown, with cap dark brown; lesser wing-coverts and rump rufous-chestnut, rest of upperparts dark purplish brown with rufous feather-edging. In the hand, adult males show a prominent flange on the emarginated inner web of the outer primary. Juveniles are duller brown than adults, especially below, with pale fringing dorsally.

Wandering Whistling Duck *D. arcuata*, free-flying in Singapore since the late 1980s (SINGAV-3), has fine black spotting on the breast of adults, black of cap extending down hind-neck to the mantle, and elongated marginal flank-feathers buff with black edging.

Bare-part colours. (Adult) iris dark brown, narrow eyelid-rim orange-yellow; bill slaty blue with black nail; feet slaty blue with webs paler.

Size (mm). (Skins: 14 males, 12 females; adult): wing 178–193 and 165–190; tail 40–53 and 42–52; bill 38.4–42.0 and 35.7–44.2; tarsus 41.7–47.5 and 43.0–48.4 (BMNH, ZDUM, ZRCNUS).

Weight. No data.

DISTRIBUTION. Historical summary: all divisions except *Nar, Pes, Kel, Tru, Neg*, with additional island records from Langkawi and Penang off the W coast; Samui off the E coast; and Tekong, Singapore.

GEOGRAPHICAL VARIATION. None recognized.

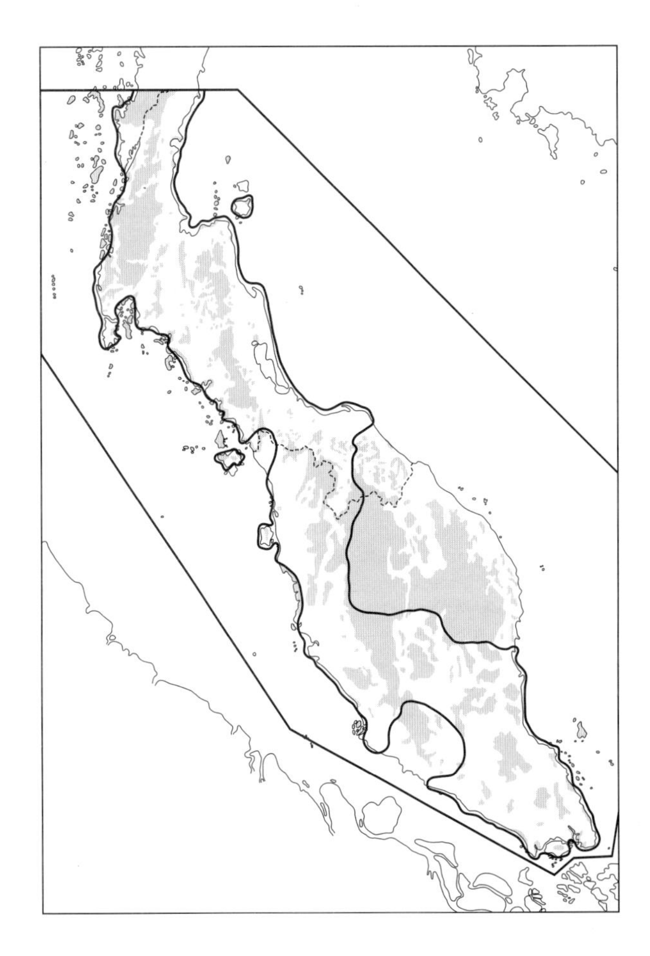

STATUS AND POPULATION. Resident but local; generally uncommon, moving with availability of suitable habitat. True non-breeding visitors may occur in the north and accounts dating from periods when this duck was more numerous in the south describe flocking in some areas as seasonal: February to June in the Perak river valley (Kelham 1881–83), with dispersal of most birds to breed elsewhere. However, recent monitoring in Selangor and Singapore shows flocks 20 or more strong can occur at any time of year.

Like many waterbirds, it must have gained from forest clearance but old accounts imply numbers have declined this century. Much shot, but the impact of hunting versus changing patterns of land-use has not been studied. Now more widely distributed in the Thai provinces and east of the Main Range than in the Malaysian W-coast plain, where reclamation of abandoned dredge-mine workings since the 1980s is believed to be having a particular effect. Recent polderization of coasts in Singapore, on the other hand, has seen an increase in numbers reported, with a flock of 107 at the Senoko wetland in June 1987 (MBR 1986–87, SINGAV-2). Complete control of gun-use and restricted public access to parts of the affected coast are other special factors there.

HABITATS AND ECOLOGY. Lowland, mostly freshwater wetlands combining open water and tall, weedy cover, ranging from the extensive natural lake/marsh systems of Thalae Noi–Songkhla to silted, part-vegetated dredge-mine lagoons (the main Malaysian W-coast habitat); also small-scale paddy agriculture, particularly when flooded, but mostly avoiding the larger, multi-crop paddy-plains. At Thalae Noi, birds shift habitats through the year, moving between small, weed-covered pools and the surrounding (evidently preferred) *Eleocharis dulcis* marsh, according to the level of the water (Storer 1976). Not usually attracted to blackwaters but small numbers occur in the peaty sedge/pandan swamp system of Tasik Bera, Pahang (BMP5, R.P. Jaensch). They visit lagoons along the Malaysian E coast, occasionally coastal prawn-ponds, and have been recorded from mangroves in Krabi (Madoc 1956a, Parr 1988, SINGAV-2) but are not regular in salt-water habitats.

Robinson and Chasen (1936) claim night-roosting on riverside trees but neither roosting nor nesting in trees has been confirmed in the Peninsula. On the Pahang river, flocks have been found at dawn loafing on sand-bars (Ryves 1938).

FORAGING AND FOOD. At Songkhla lake, mass flighting out to paddyland feeding-grounds occurs in the evening, and some foraging appears to be nocturnal. *Scirpus* and *Cyperus* fruit-bodies, and *Utricularia* bladders have been identified in stomachs of shot birds (Madoc 1956a, Meeswat and Prentice 1984, Robinson and Chasen 1936, Storer 1976).

SOCIAL ORGANIZATION. Mostly in pairs or groups of not more than potential family-party size. Larger flocks occur at any time of year but, except on the Thalae Noi–Songkhla wetland in winter, rarely number over 100.

MOVEMENTS. None monitored, but a winter concentration of up to 12 000, unlikely to be entirely local, has been reported in the Thalae Noi–Songkhla wetland (Scott 1989).

SURVIVAL. No information.

SOCIAL INTERACTIONS. A duck put off a full clutch of eggs at Songkhla lake gave injured-wing distraction display with loud calling, only 2 m from observers (Meeswat and Prentice 1984).

VOICE. In flight, flock members communicate with a light, whistling disyllable, *seasick* or *cheese-wick* (HBI, Madoc 1956a).

BREEDING

Nest. A shallow cup of grass, etc., apparently lacking added down, built in rank herbage on or close to the ground in wet marsh or the weedy neighbourhood of a pond or waterway. Vegetation sometimes pulled over as a roof, with access via a side-entrance.

Eggs and brood. Eggs are creamy white, slightly glossy. Size (mm): 49.6–45.6 × 39.7–38.1; weight (g): 36.0–39.5 (n=21). Full clutch 12, and 12 downy ducklings escorted by two adults on a small pond in Singapore are assumed to have been one brood.

Cycle. No information.

Seasonality. From Surat Thani south to Singapore, eggs and/or downy ducklings have been found on dates that imply laying in June (earliest actual eggs 24 June)–October and December–March. The latest records of dependant, downy young are 19 and 24 April, in Singapore (BMP5, BR 1976–77, ENGGANG-1, Madoc 1956a, MBR 1984–85, Meeswat and Prentice 1984, P.D. Round, SINGAV-2, -6).

MOULT. None of 14 males and 11 females from Nakhon Si Thammarat south to Pahang dated January, April–June, August, September, November and December (BMNH, ZDUM, ZRCNUS) showed wing-moult or significant feather-wear, but three dated December, April and June were growing central tail-feathers. Temporarily flightless birds have evidently been safe from collecting guns.

CONSERVATION. Takes readily to artificial wetlands in protected places but overall range can be expected to shrink as small-scale rice agriculture is squeezed out of the economy and dredge-mining for tin becomes a thing of the past.

Asian Pigmy-goose; Ped Khab Kheh (Thai); Itik Kapas (Malay)

Nettapus coromandelianus (Gmelin) 1789, *Systema Naturae* 13(2): 522. TL Coromandel, SE India.

Plate 6

GROUP RELATIONS. Probably free-standing.

GLOBAL RANGE. The Indian subcontinent, Sri Lanka and the Andamans; southern China, historically south from Hebei, and Taiwan; SE Asia to Borneo, Sumatra, Java (formerly?) and Luzon (vagrant); N Sulawesi, N New Guinea and NE Australia. Within SE Asia, there has been no definite record of breeding south of Indochina and the central plains of Thailand (Lekagul and Round 1991, Madoc 1950–51).

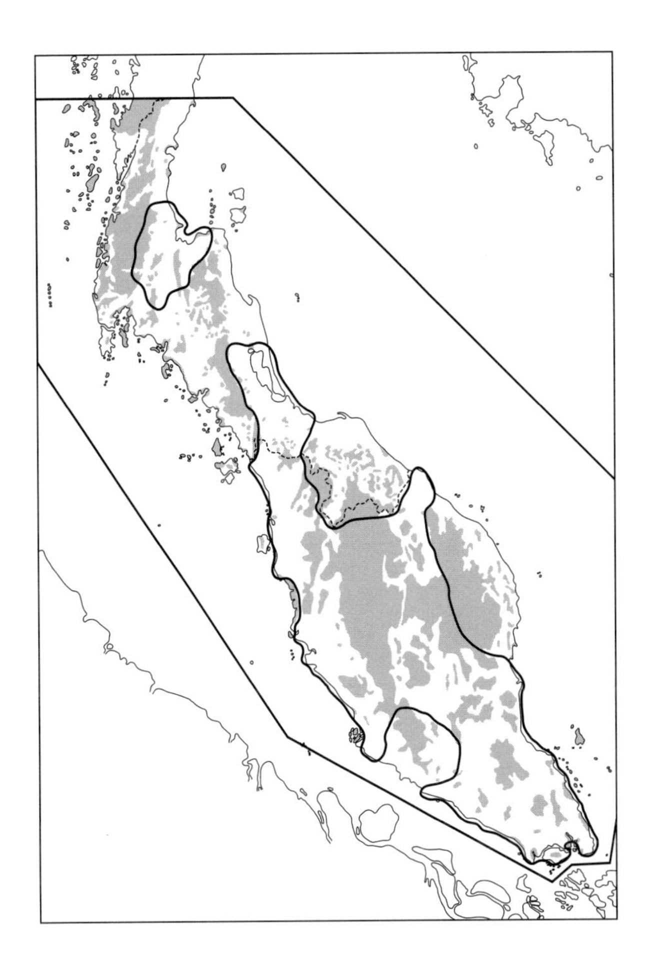

IDENTIFICATION/DESCRIPTION. A tiny, compact, short-necked duck; both sexes dark-capped and with dark, green-shot upperparts. Adult male face (to above eye), neck and underparts white, with a narrow, blackish ring round the base of the neck. The female has a dark eye-stripe, the male's white parts grey, and lacks his neck-ring. In flight (fairly fast and often low), shows a narrow white band across the upper tail-coverts and wings dark above and below except for a broad white band across all flight-feathers (male) or narrow white trailing-edge to the secondaries (female). The possibility of a male post-breeding eclipse plumage in this area has not been investigated.

Bare-part colours. (Adult) iris crimson (male), dark brown (female); upper mandible brownish, lower yellow (but breeding male has all-black bill); legs and feet greenish black with sides yellowish, toe-webs black (Kelham 1881–83, Robinson and Chasen 1936).

Size (mm). (Skins: 1 male, 1 female; adult): wing 168 and 152; tail 56 and 64; bill 23.3 and 22.6; tarsus 26.3 and 22.8 (UMZC).

Weight. No data.

DISTRIBUTION. Probably overlooked in the far north. The hub of distribution is the large, shallow Thalae Noi–Songkhla wetland, holding a major midwinter concentration. Historical summary: *Sur, Pht, Son, Pes, Ked, Kel, Pra, Pek, Phg, Sel, Mel, Joh, Sin*, with no additional island records.

GEOGRAPHICAL VARIATION. Nominate *coromandelianus*, of the global range except Australia.

STATUS AND POPULATION. Local and generally uncommon; status uncertain but some are likely to be resident. Near Sanglang, N Kedah coast, G.C. Madoc was shown a dead coconut palm in the hollow top of which it was claimed a duck had nested; possibly this species, but elsewhere in its range Lesser Whistling Duck also uses tree-holes (HBI). Other claims of breeding in N Malaysia (Cairns 1963) have not been accepted. However, groups occasionally met with on large rivers, including the Tembeling (Pahang), could be on the move in search of nest-sites in forest, and regular monitoring shows presence through most of the year south at least to Selangor.

Area details suggest a population mix. At Thalae Noi during October–November, groups of 5–15 concentrate in patches of floating waterplants. In mid December, flocks over 100-strong arrive on open water, swelling to over 300 by mid January (see also Little Cormorant at this site). During February, these flocks begin to break up and smaller groups retire to more secluded areas, with chases and multiple mountings noted from late March to August. Present during July–August also at Thung Thong wetland, Surat Thani (Annandale and Robinson 1903, BMP5, Meeswat and Prentice 1984, Storer 1976, 1978).

Southward, up to 500 were on the shallow, recently

filled Timah Tasoh impoundment, Perlis, in January, with multi-male chases common (G.W.H. Davison) but, as yet, no monitoring there later into the year. In the lower Perak valley, Kelham (1881–83) found them 'exceedingly plentiful', in groups of 4–10 on open waters until May, with pairing and retreat to secluded creeks in forest in June. He implies a continuous presence at that time, and recent monitoring of favoured open-country mine-lagoon sites elsewhere in Perak and Selangor has shown them absent only during August–October, with largest groups (up to 13) in January–early April (ENGGANG-1, -3, Phillips 1961). On Singapore island, where polderization of the coast recently increased freshwater habitat, largest groups (up to 35) occur during January–late May but here they are absent from late July to November/December (SINGAV-1, -2, -3, -4).

Coincidence of peak numbers on open waters and the widening of the seasonal gap in records southward implies some north-south ebb and flow. Birds pairing in Perak as late as mid June might still move to nesting sites farther north. On the other hand, a pair has been seen near Kuala Lumpur in early October (ENGGANG-2) and, on balance, some local breeding to at least this latitude seems likely.

HABITATS AND ECOLOGY. During the northern winter, Pigmy Geese favour open-country wetlands, including vegetated lakes, dredge-mine lagoons, occasionally also flooded paddy. The only indications of salt-water usage have been records from the Krabi mangroves and a female mist-netted by ponds on cleared back-mangrove land behind the sea-bund at Kuala Selangor (BR 1978–79, Parr 1988). At the end of winter, they move into still-water or slow-flowing sites hemmed in by reeds or woody cover and with plenty of floating and near-surface macrophytes (Kelham 1881–83, Storer 1976). Use of forest has still to be confirmed in this area.

To avoid detection among waterplants, birds float motionless and are able to submerge the body down to neck level.

FORAGING AND FOOD. Browses aquatic plants. Stomachs contained grit and vegetable matter, including seeds (*Scirpus*) (Anonymous 1981, Kelham 1881–83).

SOCIAL ORGANIZATION. Pairs and variable-sized flocks are the standard social units; loners exceptional.

MOVEMENTS. None monitored.

SURVIVAL. No information.

SOCIAL INTERACTIONS. No additional information.

VOICE. The squeaky, rattling call of males is widely described as *fixed bayonets*, and they are noisy during sexual chase-flights. Females give a subdued quack (HBI, Madoc 1950–51, Storer 1976).

BREEDING. No information.

MOULT. No data.

CONSERVATION. Residents may have declined in step with the removal of lowland waterside forest with trees mature enough to provide acceptable nest-cavities. A search is needed of the few low-lying, shallow-edged reservoirs still with big timber in their catchments.

White-winged Wood Duck; Ped Gaa (Thai); Itik Serati Hutan (Malay)

Cairina scutulata (S. Müller) 1842, *Verhandelingen over de Natuurlijke Geschiedenis der Nederlandsche overzeesche bezittingen . . . Land- en Volkenkunde* 1: 159. TL Java.

Plate 6

GROUP RELATIONS. Free-standing; closest to Neotropical *C. moschata* (Muscovy Duck) (Livezey 1991).

GLOBAL RANGE. Historically, far-NE India, Bangladesh and from Burma, central Laos and N Vietnam south to the Peninsula, Sumatra and Java. Sizeable parts of this range have not been open to modern fieldwork but while certainly gone, e.g., from Java, small pockets of population remain scattered through most of the original range, indeed, are still being discovered (Green 1992). Many are under continued pressure from habitat-loss and hunting.

IDENTIFICATION/DESCRIPTION. Large size; mottled white head and neck on blackish body, with white wing-coverts. None of the albinism noted in Indonesia has been reported on the mainland. Flight powerful but not especially fast (Robinson 1909a), showing white inner leading-edge of the wing separated from white-and-lavender speculum by a black bar across the greater wing-coverts.

Variation in the colour of the underparts, from chestnut-brown with a black collar to all black, is believed to be an age rather than a sex character, as also the amount of iridescence on neck-base and mantle. A bony concrescence on the wrist is larger in males, and males are larger overall.

Bare-part colours. Not described locally. Indian subcontinent adults have iris brown to red; bill lemon-yellow to rich orange, mottled and with base and tip black; legs and feet lemon-yellow to dull orange, mottled greenish.

Size (mm). (Skins: 12 males, 3 females; adult): wing 360–394 and 308–344; tail 134–149 and 145 (one only); bill 59.2–68.2 and 60.3–61.0; tarsus 56.5–64.8 and 51.1–56.8 (BMNH, ZRCNUS).

Weight. No data.

DISTRIBUTION. Formerly widespread south to about the Thai/Malaysian border, possibly to NW Malaysia. Historical summary: *Sur, Pha, Kra, Pht, Tra, Nar, Pek* (*contra* BMP5, apparently not *Nak*).

GEOGRAPHICAL VARIATION. None recognized.

STATUS AND POPULATION. Probably resident; now very local and close to extinction. Into the second decade of the century, widespread through the Thai provinces. In Trang during May 1902, 'common on the . . . coast, going inland every evening and passing in numbers over the town of Kantang', and December–January 1909/10, 'from various districts

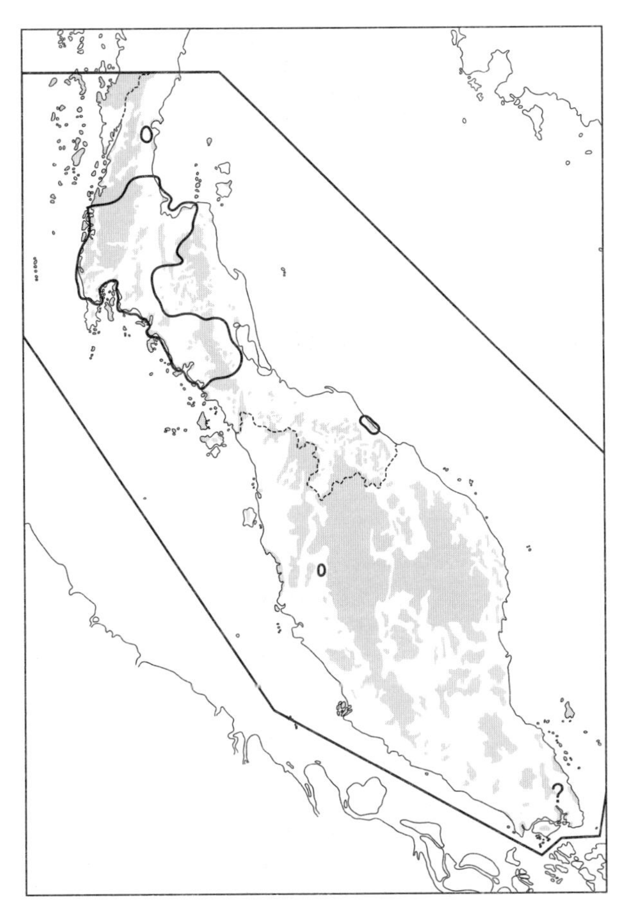

. . . over a dozen specimens'; in Surat Thani in June 1913, 'fairly common on the rice fields upcountry . . . and almost down to the coast'; and in Krabi, January 1918, four from a single location in less than ten days (Annandale and Robinson 1903, Robinson 1914a, Robinson and Kloss 1910–11, 1918). In the mid 1930s, two were collected near Kapang, Trang (Meyer de Schauensee 1946), and until about 1974 some occurred in Khlong Thom district, Krabi (P.D. Round). Presumed extinct until rediscovered at Chalerm Prakiat peatswamp forest, Narathiwat, in the late 1980s. Still there in June 1992, and in July 1996 two occurred in Sawi district, Chumphon (BBCB-9, BCSTB-13, P.D. Round).

South of the border, known certainly only from a nineteenth-century specimen said to have been collected near Ipoh (Perak), but A.T. Edgar (Gibson-Hill 1949b) believed rural people in Kedah were familiar with it before World-War Two. On 10 August 1981 a pair of ducks with some of the features of White-winged Wood Duck was seen escorting two young on a forest river upstream of Kota Tinggi waterfall, Johor (Green 1992). Grounds for accepting the identification are insufficient but swamp-forest of the type inhabited in Narathiwat once extended most of the way down the E coast, into Johor.

Overall, records fall in December, January and April–July (extreme dates 8 December and 24 July) (AMNH, BCSTB-13, BMNH, BMP5). This is just the period over which largest numbers of Pigmy Geese gather in open-water situations, and the same problem of status applies. Their use of forest appears similar and while people in Phatthalung believed Wood Ducks to be migratory (Bonhote 1901) they may simply have shifted habitat. No migration has been reported elsewhere in the range. At the same time, apart from the Johor sighting, there has never been a local record of a nest or juvenile.

HABITATS AND ECOLOGY. Contacts with this duck have mostly been at the interface of forest and paddy agriculture, favoured during flooding seasons (Robinson and Kloss 1910–11). The lack of records from Malaysia, it has been suggested, could be due to avoidance of blackwater peatswamp habitat as opposed to more seasonal freshwater swamp-forest. Narathiwat sightings and some from permanently wet peatswamp in NW Sumatra (on a latitude with Singapore) (Holmes 1990) now quash that argument. As suggested by Mackenzie and Kear (1976), perhaps some did once inhabit the Malaysian part of the Peninsula.

At Chong, foot of the E-central Range, Trang, birds day-roosted on forested knolls rising out of the paddyland, emerging to forage in fields at dusk (Robinson and Kloss 1910–11). Experience in more remote areas of Thailand suggests this may have been a reversal of the usual activity cycle, perhaps due to disturbance (P.D. Round).

FORAGING AND FOOD. Stomachs of two birds collected on Trang paddylands were crammed with large aquatic gastropods, together with a few freshwater bivalves (Robinson 1909a).

SOCIAL ORGANIZATION. Described as associating mostly in pairs, sometimes in (family?) parties.

MOVEMENTS. None confirmed.

SURVIVAL. No information.

SOCIAL INTERACTIONS. No information.

VOICE. Not recorded locally. In Sumatra and also in Burma flight-calls differ between the sexes: a mournful goose- or crane-like honk versus a high whistle, and pairs call antiphonally (Holmes 1976, Smythies 1953).

BREEDING. Not recorded.

MOULT. Among ten adults collected during 8 December–13 January, six (including both sexes) showed one to three pairs of inner tail-feathers in moult, and a male dated 17 January had the whole tail growing. Inevitably, these and all others seen showed no wing-moult (BMNH, ZRCNUS). Where and how temporarily flightless, wing-moulting birds maintain themselves is unknown.

CONSERVATION. It is unrealistic to suppose the last tiny population-remnant is completely protectable from hunting, but Chalerm Prakiat wildlife sanctuary may still provide scope for managed reintroductions from captive stock. Globally endangered (BTW2).

Eurasian Wigeon; Ped Pak San (Thai); Itik Puteri (Malay)

Anas penelope Linnaeus 1758, *Systema Naturae* 10(1): 126. TL Sweden.
Plate 6

GROUP RELATIONS. Forms a superspecies with New World *A. americana* (American Wigeon) (Delacour and Mayr 1945).

GLOBAL RANGE. Breeds at cool N temperate and arctic latitudes, in Iceland and across Eurasia to the Pacific, south in E Asia possibly to extreme NE China (Heilongjiang). Migratory; winters from the mid N-temperate zone to the northern tropics of Africa and Asia. In SE Asia, main movement terminates in the inner delta of the Mekong, but Wigeon are nowhere common in Thailand. Significant numbers reach Luzon, small numbers elsewhere in the Philippines, and NW Borneo; vagrant in the Peninsula, New Guinea and the western Pacific.

IDENTIFICATION/DESCRIPTION. A medium-small, compact duck with steep forehead. Bright-plumaged drake combines light rusty orange head and cream forecrown with pale grey upper body and black lower tail-coverts. The female is mottled brown, with black-tipped grey bill; eclipse-plumaged drake is similar but more rufescent. Legs and feet slate-grey to olive-grey. In flight, upper wing-coverts white in male, grey in female, sharp against dark (green) speculum. Both sexes show a whitish underwing and square-cut white belly-patch.

Bare-part colours. See above; no other local data.

Size. No data.

Weight. No data.

DISTRIBUTION. Historical summary: *Pat, Pek, Joh, Sin.*

GEOGRAPHICAL VARIATION. None recognized.

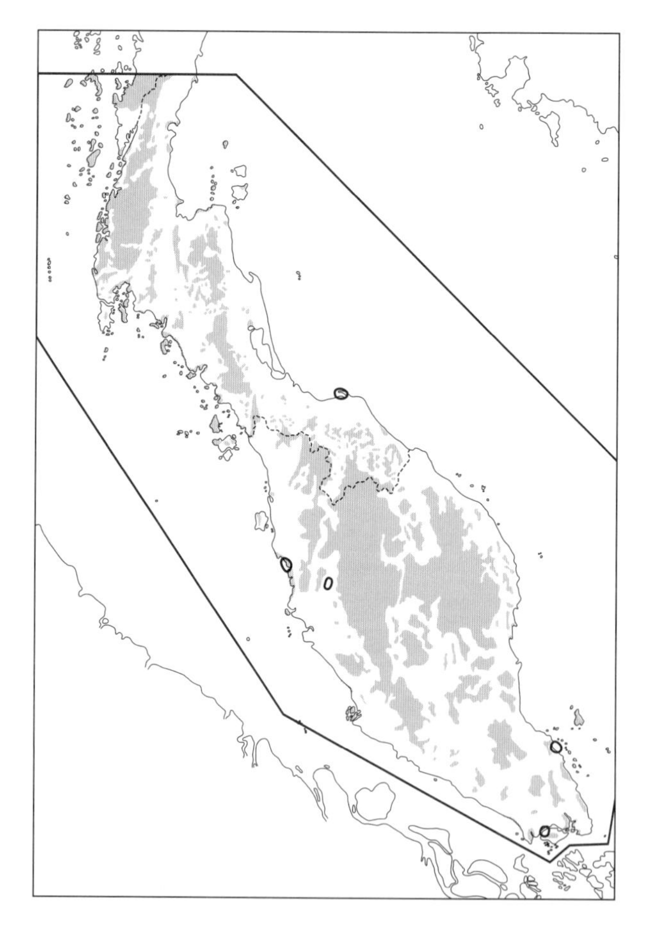

STATUS AND POPULATION. Vagrant; the five records (in different years) are from November through February. By latitude: one with a group of

Garganey *Anas querquedula* in Pattani bay; single adult males in a Garganey flock on the Matang coast and, with Pigmy-geese, inland near Batu Gajah, Perak; two birds in dull plumage but on vocal evidence including at least one male, at Mersing, Johor; an immature female at Sungai Buloh, NW Singapore island, staying for two months (BR 1980–81, MBR 1986–87, Phillips 1961, R. Subaraj, Swennen *et al.* 1986).

HABITATS AND ECOLOGY. Three of the five occurrences were on low-tide mudflats or (in Pattani bay) tidal salt-marsh pools, and a fourth on a brackish prawn-pond in cleared mangrove-land. Past concepts of the rarity of dabbling ducks have been too much influenced by the assumption that they select fresh water. The one inland record is from a dredge-mine lagoon.

FORAGING AND FOOD. No local information.

SOCIAL ORGANIZATION. Loners, and in association with other dabbling ducks.

MOVEMENTS. Extreme dates are 2 November and 22 February.

SURVIVAL. No information.

SOCIAL INTERACTIONS. No information.

VOICE. Males give a distinctive, ringing whistle, *hwee-eu*.

BREEDING. No population.

MOULT. No data.

CONSERVATION. No relevant issues.

Gadwall; Ped Thao Gon Dam (Thai); Itik Bemban (Malay)

Anas strepera Linnaeus 1758 *Systema Naturae* 10(1): 125. TL Sweden.
Plate 6

GROUP RELATIONS. Free-standing.

GLOBAL RANGE. Breeds around the N temperate zone east in Asia to NE China, Pacific Russia and Hokkaido, with a recently extinct outlying population on Teraina island, Kiribati (central Pacific). Northern birds migrate, reaching tropical E Africa and the Indian subcontinent. In SE Asia, regular only in the far west, to the S Burma plain; rare elsewhere, and vagrant in the Peninsula and Luzon.

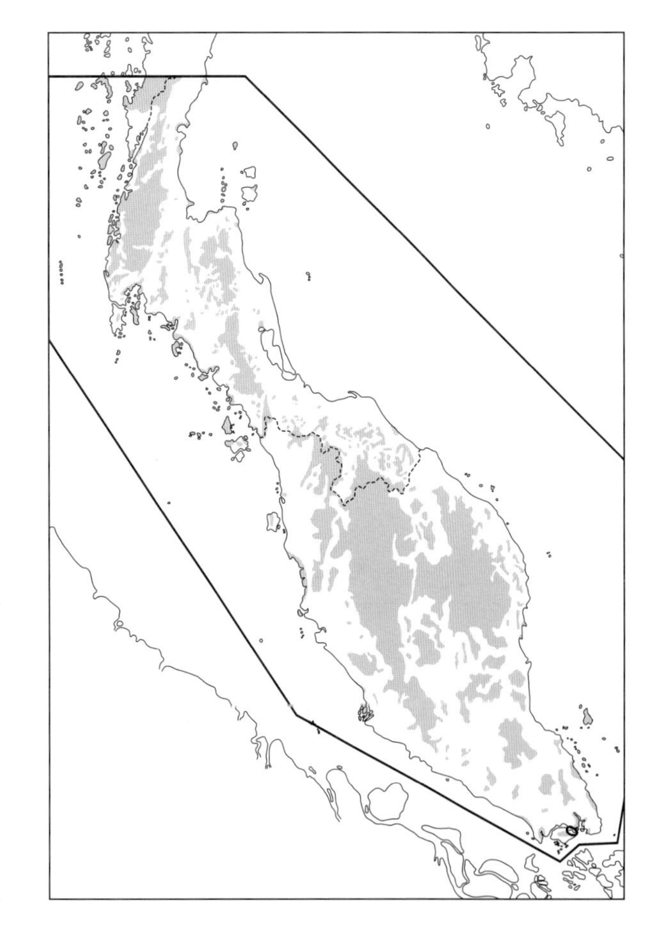

IDENTIFICATION/DESCRIPTION. Medium-small domestic duck size. At rest, female and eclipse drake are mottled brown, lighter on the head and neck, with crown and line from lores through eye to nape blackish; lower tail-coverts and outer tail-feathers whitish. Bright-plumaged drake has grey body with upper and lower tail-coverts solidly black. Legs and feet orange-yellow; bill blackish, except in bright drake, broadly edged orange-yellow. In flight, both sexes show white speculum bordered black in front, and drakes have median wing-coverts chestnut. Overhead, underwing is whitish and belly clean-cut white.

Bare-part colours. No other local data.

Size. No data.

Weight. No data.

DISTRIBUTION. Historical summary: *Sin* only.

GEOGRAPHICAL VARIATION. Asian populations are nominate *strepera*.

STATUS AND POPULATION. Vagrant. The one record is of a first-winterer present (and photographed) in the Ponggol area, NE Singapore island, during 1–19 January 1989 (SINGAV-3).

HABITATS AND ECOLOGY. Open freshwater ponds are the only habitat on record.

FORAGING AND FOOD. No information.

SOCIAL ORGANIZATION. No information.

MOVEMENTS. No information.

SURVIVAL. No information.

SOCIAL INTERACTIONS. No information.

VOICE. No local information.

BREEDING. No population.

MOULT. No data.

CONSERVATION. No relevant issues.

Common Teal; Ped Peek Khieo (Thai); Itik Eropah (Malay)

Anas crecca Linnaeus 1758, *Systema Naturae* 10(1): 126. TL Sweden.
Plate 6

GROUP RELATIONS. Forms a superspecies with S American *A. flavirostris* (Chilean Teal) (Johnsgard 1978).

GLOBAL RANGE. Breeds in arctic and cool N-temperate latitudes around the world, in E Asia south to NE China and N Japan. Migratory, wintering from the N-temperate zone to the outer tropics, in Asia south to the Indian subcontinent, Bay of Bengal islands and SE Asia, where the main movement terminates in N Burma and N Vietnam (the Red River delta). Uncommon as far as Gulf of Bangkok wetlands and Luzon; vagrant in Mindanao, Sabah and the Peninsula.

IDENTIFICATION/DESCRIPTION. Size and shape of much commoner Garganey. At rest, female and eclipse-plumaged drake are mottled brown, face and neck paler, with crown and nape dark brown and a single blackish line (bold in female) from the lores though the eye to the nape. Bill dark slate, legs and feet olive-grey. Chief features of the bright-plumaged drake are: dark head (deep chestnut with long green eye-patch outlined creamy-white), grey upper body and black-and-cream tail-coverts. In flight, both sexes show green speculum edged white fore and aft. Overhead, underwing pale and belly-patch white.

Bare-part colours. No other local data.

Size (mm). (Skin: 1 female; adult): wing 172; tail 64; bill 34.5; tarsus 26.6 (ZRCNUS).

Weight. No data.

DISTRIBUTION. Historical summary: *Sel*, *?Mel*, *Sin*.

GEOGRAPHICAL VARIATION. Presumably nominate *crecca*, the only subspecies so far identified in SE Asia.

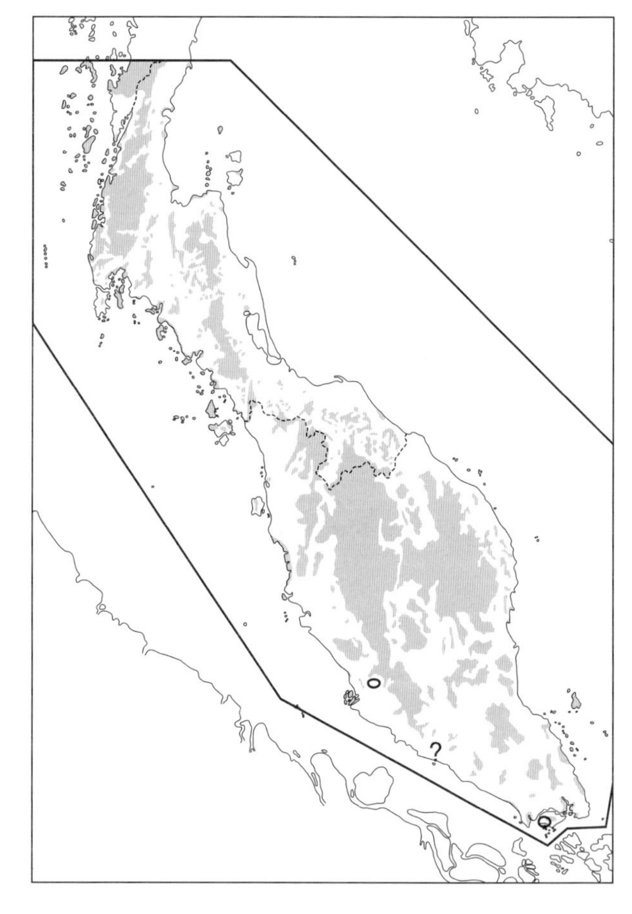

STATUS AND POPULATION. Vagrant. Only two definite records: a female shot near Kuala Lumpur in April 1912 and a bird with Garganeys on the Jurong river, Singapore island, on 29 October 1978. A female in the mid-nineteenth century Maingay collection is likely to have come from the neighbourhood of

Melaka (BMNH, BR 1978-79, Robinson 1913a, ZRCNUS).

HABITATS AND ECOLOGY. Open fresh water, but should also be looked for among salt-water Garganeys.

FORAGING AND FOOD. No information.

SOCIAL ORGANIZATION. With other dabbling ducks.

MOVEMENTS. No information.

SURVIVAL. No information.

SOCIAL INTERACTIONS. No information.

VOICE. No local information.

BREEDING. No population.

MOULT. No data.

CONSERVATION. No relevant issues.

Northern Pintail; Ped Haang Laem (Thai); I̱tik Mua̱ra (Malay)

Anas acuta Linnaeus 1758, *Systema Naturae* 10(1): 126. TL Sweden.
Plate 6

GROUP RELATIONS. Forms a superspecies with S American *A. georgica* (Brown Pintail) (Delacour and Mayr 1945).

GLOBAL RANGE. Breeds at arctic and cool N-temperate latitudes around the world, south in E Asia to Lake Baikal, with outlying populations on islands of the S-temperate Indian Ocean. N-hemisphere populations migrate, wintering from the temperate zone (in E Asia from Japan and the Changjiang valley) to the northern tropics. In SE Asia, large-scale migration terminates in N-central Thailand and the inner delta of the Mekong, S Vietnam (G.E. Morris, Scott 1989), with small numbers regular to Gulf of Bangkok wetlands and Luzon. Vagrant as far as Java, New Guinea and the S Pacific.

IDENTIFICATION/DESCRIPTION. Size that of a small domestic duck, with slender neck and round head. Female and eclipse-plumaged drake are mottled brown with indistinct line through the eye and blue-grey bill (blue-billed Wigeon has more compact shape). The most conspicuous features of the bright drake are: white front and spur up side of neck, contrasting with dark head and grey body; and black-and-white tail-coverts. Legs and feet dark grey. In flight, bright drake shows clean white under-body and other sex/age-classes a white belly. All have underwing dull with white trailing-edge to secondaries, and a pointed tail.

Bare-part colours. No other local information.

Size. No data.

Weight. No data.

DISTRIBUTION. Historical summary: *Pht, Mel, Sin.*

GEOGRAPHICAL VARIATION. All N-hemisphere populations are nominate *acuta*, distinguished from southern outliers by the bright plumage of the drake.

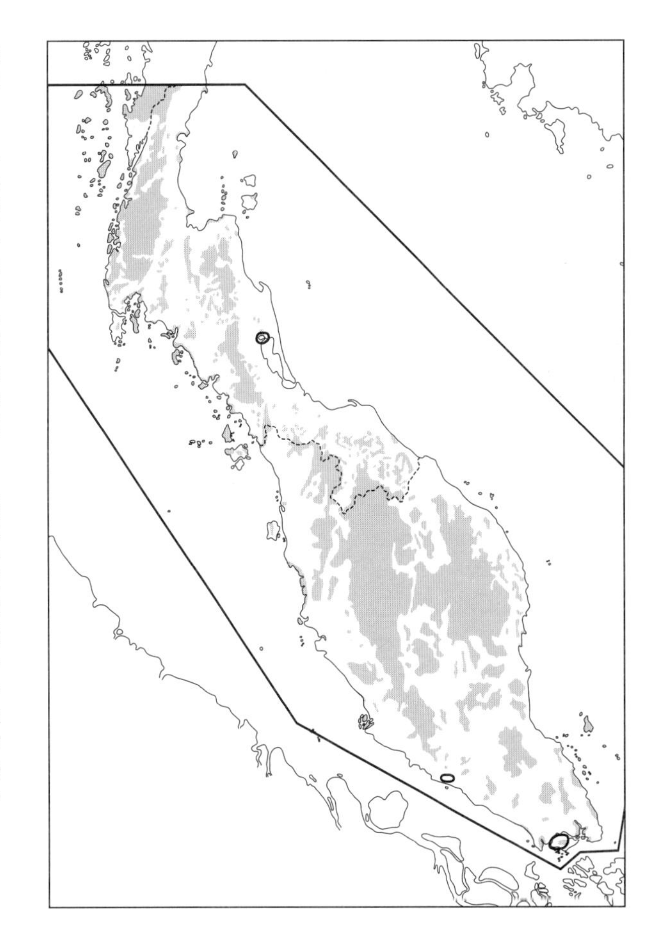

STATUS AND POPULATION. A non-breeding visitor; hardly more than vagrant. Recorded south from Thalae Noi during four winters: 1967–68,

1983–84, 1985–86 and 1992–93 (BIRDLINE 1992, 1993, BR 1967, 1968, A. Helbig, MBR 1982–83).

HABITATS AND ECOLOGY. Open freshwater marsh and reservoirs, and both freshwater and brackish ponds.

FORAGING AND FOOD. No information.

SOCIAL ORGANIZATION. Singles and small parties, not so far seen with other ducks.

MOVEMENTS. Extreme dates are 22 November and 31 January, recently with 2–3 at Senoko, Singapore, that stayed throughout this period.

SURVIVAL. No information.

SOCIAL INTERACTIONS. No information.

VOICE. No local information.

BREEDING. No population.

MOULT. No data.

CONSERVATION. No relevant issues.

Garganey; Ped Lai (Thai); Itik Berkik (Malay)

Anas querquedula Linnaeus 1758, *Systema Naturae* 10(1): 126. TL Sweden.
Plate 6

GROUP RELATIONS. Free-standing; closest to *A. discors* and *A. cyanoptera* (Blue-winged and Cinnamon Teal) of the Americas (Mayr and Short 1970).

GLOBAL RANGE. Breeds in mid N-temperate Eurasia from the Atlantic to Pacific Russia, NE China and Hokkaido. Migratory, wintering from warm N-temperate latitudes to the outer tropics of the S hemisphere, as far as southern Africa and N Australia, but in SE Asia large-scale migration terminates north of the equator, in the Gulf of Bangkok wetlands, S Vietnam, W Sabah and Luzon.

IDENTIFICATION/DESCRIPTION. Small size; only Asian Pigmy-goose is smaller. At rest, mottled brown female and eclipse-plumaged drake show dark cap and line from lores through eye to nape, as in Common Teal, with an additional thin dark line from base of bill arching across cheek to end in a dark blob on the ear-covert. Bright-plumaged drake is dorsally dark mahogany-brown with a broad white supercilium curving down side of nape and long, black-edged white scapulars overhanging closed wing. Bill and feet grey. Upper wing-coverts are grey in female, pale blue-grey in drake, conspicuous in flight, with green speculum edged white fore and aft as in Common Teal. From below, belly-patch is white, square-cut against breast in drake, and underwing whitish with characteristically dark leading-edge.

Bare-part colours. No other local data.

Size (mm). (Skin: 1 male; adult): wing 184; tail 64; bill 38.2; tarsus 28.9 (ZRCNUS).

Weight. No data.

DISTRIBUTION. Thalae Sap–Songkhla wetland is the distributional focus. Historical summary: *Son, Pat, Pes, Pek, Sel, Mel, Sin*, with no other island records.

GEOGRAPHICAL VARIATION. None recognized.

STATUS AND POPULATION. A non-breeding visitor and possible passage migrant, local and sparse

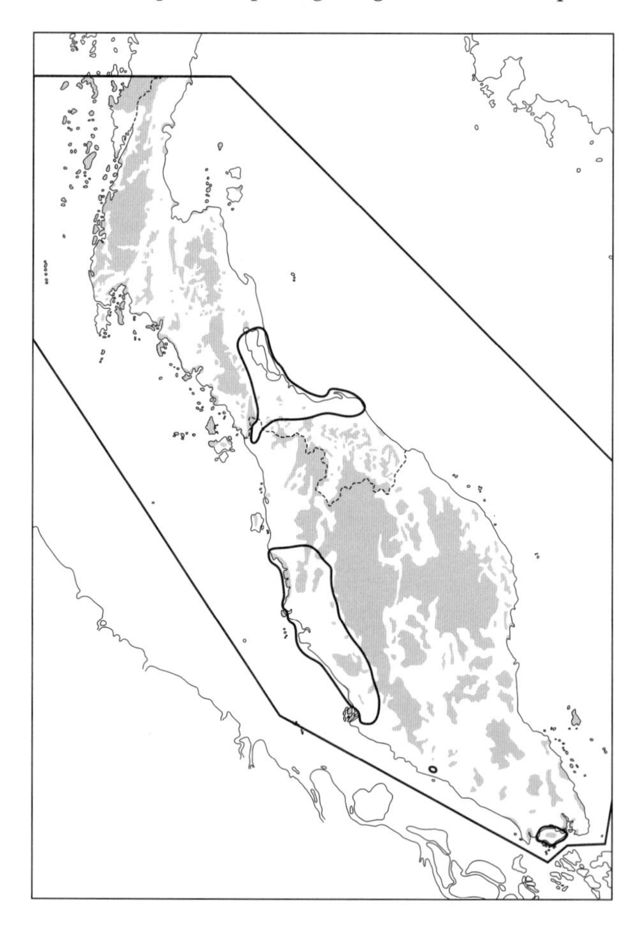

to common. The only Palaearctic duck species wintering annually, in fluctuating but larger numbers than formerly believed (see BMP5), with counts of up to 800 in the Thalae Sap wetland (Scott 1989, R. Gregory-Smith). Southward along the same coast, villagers on Pattani spit claim a large flock of duck, probably mostly this species, forms off shore in October–November, and groups of up to ten Garganeys have been seen in November resting and feeding at pools on the Pattani bay salt-marsh (now mostly reclaimed for aquaculture) (Swennen *et al.* 1986). In the Melaka Straits, in December and January flocks of up to 80 seen off Rasa Sayang beach (N Selangor), 50 on the Matang coast (Perak) in late January and, in mid to late March, 30 off Kuala Sanglang (Perlis) (R. Gregory-Smith, MBR 1984–85, R. Subaraj). Sparse inland and in much smaller groups; usually only ones and twos. At regularly monitored ponds and impoundments in Singapore the largest recent count has been 16 (SINGAV-4), but see below.

HABITATS AND ECOLOGY. Despite the numbers on Thalae Sap, significantly, none has been found on neighbouring, freshwater, Thalae Noi. Past searches focused on inland habitat, where birds have occurred on abandoned mine-lagoons, fish-ponds, rivers and flooded paddyland (BMP5). Much of the Thalae Sap–Songkhla system is brackish and it is now clear Garganeys prefer saline conditions including, as mentioned, salt-marsh and much more extensively available intertidal mud (MBR 1984–85, 1986–87). They may also roost at sea. In consistently well-watched Singapore, most sites of regular occurrence are brackish, or recently dammed-off parts of formerly tidal estuaries. Domestic supply reservoirs in the central catchment area of the island do not attract.

FORAGING AND FOOD. No information.

SOCIAL ORGANIZATION. Gregarious.

MOVEMENTS. Extreme dates overall are 6 October and late March (SINGAV-1, -2), but arrival in the far south varies year to year by as much as three months and may depend on wintering conditions to the north of the Peninsula. In good Garganey years, such as 1989–90, flock sizes in Singapore have been 2–3 times larger in November and March than in intervening months, implying small-scale through-passage.

SURVIVAL. No information.

SOCIAL INTERACTIONS. No information.

VOICE. No local information.

BREEDING. No population.

MOULT. The earliest date for drakes in bright plumage is 22 February (SINGAV-4).

CONSERVATION. No relevant issues.

Northern Shoveler; Ped Paak Plao (Thai); Itik Paruh Bajak (Malay)

Anas clypeata Linnaeus 1758, *Systema Naturae* 10(1): 124. TL Sweden.
Plate 6

GROUP RELATIONS. Unclear. Closest to S-hemisphere *A. platalea*, *smithi* and *rhynchotis* (Red, Cape and Southern Shovelers), although some of their resemblances may be convergent (Mayr and Short 1970).

GLOBAL RANGE. Breeds in the cool N-temperate zone around the world, extending to low arctic latitudes in Eurasia, and south in E Asia to Hokkaido and Heilongjiang. Migratory, wintering from the N-temperate zone south to the outer N tropics, in E Asia roughly from the Changjiang valley. Large wintering concentrations occur in the Indian subcontinent, mostly the northern half; not so in SE Asia where significant migration terminates at the latitude of the S Shan states (E Burma) and Red River delta (N Vietnam) (Scott 1989). Beyond that, small numbers occur south to Gulf of Bangkok wetlands and Luzon; vagrant as far as Mindoro and the Peninsula.

IDENTIFICATION/DESCRIPTION. Small domestic duck-sized, compact when at rest. Bright-plumaged drake has front and bold scapular patches clear white, head dark (green), underparts and flanks rufous-chestnut. Female and other male plumages are mottled brown (eclipse male dark-spotted on flanks), paler on face, with dark brown cap and nape, and thin dark line from lores though eye to nape. Speculum green, bordered white anteriorly, and both sexes show pale upper wing-coverts: grey in female, light blue in drake. Tail whitish. Outsize bill dark, edged orange in brown birds; and feet rich orange. In flight, underwing, but not under-body, white.

Bare-part colours. No other local data.

Size. No data.

Weight. No data.

DISTRIBUTION. Historical summary: *Pek, Sel, Sin.*

GEOGRAPHICAL VARIATION. None recognized.

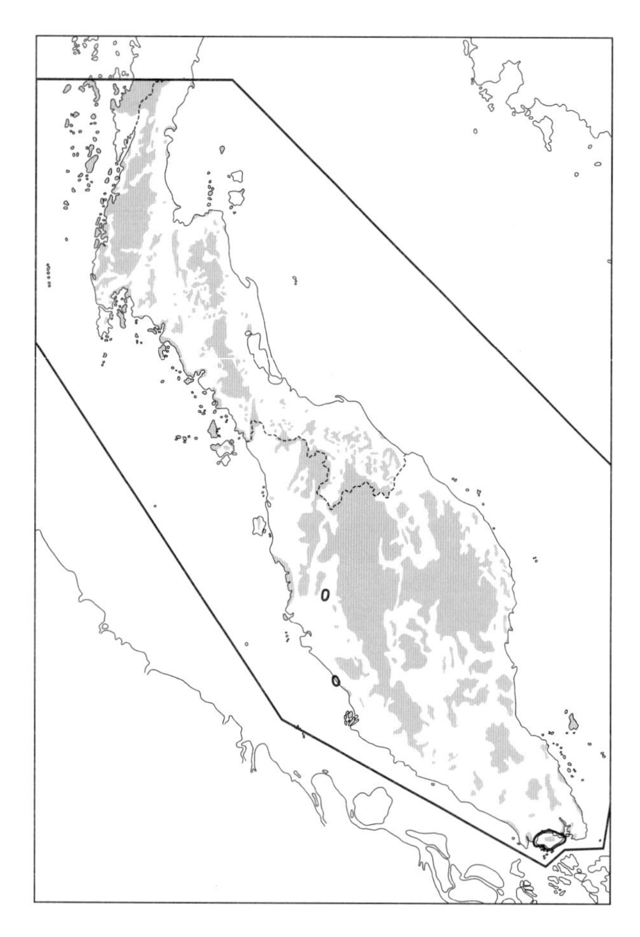

STATUS AND POPULATION. A non-breeding visitor, hardly more than vagrant, with six definite occurrences: in 1896, 1959, 1983, 1986, 1987 and 1988 (Allen 1961b, MBR 1982–83, 1986–87, R.F. Ollington, Robinson 1910, SINGAV-2), most in November. Increasing incidence through the 1980s, and a disproportionate number of recent reports from Singapore, reflect improved levels of coverage rather than any claimable change of status.

All records for which there are details have been of dull-plumaged birds, with three of four occurrences in Singapore during the likely eclipse season for drakes.

HABITATS AND ECOLOGY. Two, possibly three, records have been from genuinely freshwater situations; others from at least brackish sites, including tidal prawn-ponds in the mangrove zone, coastal impoundments and low-tide mudflats.

FORAGING AND FOOD. No information.

SOCIAL ORGANIZATION. Singles, in one instance two together, and on two occasions associated with Lesser Whistling Ducks (Allen 1961, SINGAV-2).

MOVEMENTS. Extreme dates are 6 November and 6 March.

SURVIVAL. No information.

SOCIAL INTERACTIONS. No information.

VOICE. No information.

BREEDING. No population.

MOULT. No data.

CONSERVATION. No relevant issues.

Tufted Duck; Ped Pia (Thai); Itik Berjambul (Malay)

Aythya fuligula (Linnaeus) 1758, *Systema Naturae* 10(1): 128. TL Sweden.
Plate 7

GROUP RELATIONS. Probably free-standing. Mayr and Short (1970) group it with N-hemisphere *A. marila* and *A. affinis* (Scaup and Lesser Scaup), and *A. novaeseelandiae* (New Zealand Scaup).

GLOBAL RANGE. Breeds in the arctic and cool N-temperate zone from Iceland across Eurasia to Pacific Russia, in E Asia south to Hokkaido and far-NE China. Mostly migratory, wintering in the N-temperate zone and outer tropics of Africa and Asia, in the east from roughly the Changjiang valley. Large-scale migration in Asia terminates in Pakistan, N India, N Burma and S China, with little penetration of SE Asia except in the east where some reach Luzon (also W Micronesia). Vagrant in the Peninsula, Sabah and Sulawesi.

IDENTIFICATION/DESCRIPTION. Compact, rotund, round-headed; obviously smaller than a domestic duck, swimming tail-low and diving to forage. At rest, bright-plumaged drake glossy black with sides of body clean-cut white. Female and eclipse-plumaged drake dark brown, sides of body paler brown and lower tail-coverts dusky to white; head bronzy with white often conspicuous around the bill-base, especially at the sides. In flight, shows a white wing-bar along the base of the flight-feathers, and underwing and belly white, sharp against black breast in drake.

Bare-part colours. (Adult) iris clear yellow in both sexes (see Baer's Pochard); bill grey-blue; legs and feet slate-blue.

Size. No data.

Weight. No data.

DISTRIBUTION. Historical summary: *Phg, Mel.*

GEOGRAPHICAL VARIATION. None recognized.

STATUS AND POPULATION. Vagrant, with two definite records: an adult female on the ponds of the fisheries research station, Batu Berendam, Melaka, during 3–7 February 1972 and a first-winter female mist-netted at floodlights as it crossed the crest of the Main Range at Fraser's Hill, Pahang, on 10 December 1975 (BR 1972–73, 1974–75). One bought as an already-prepared specimen at Temerloh, Pahang (Robinson 1910), may or may not have been collected locally but seems less doubtful now than before. A pale-eyed *Aythya* at Timah Tasoh dam, Perlis, on 3 January 1996 (G.W.H. Davison) was not confirmed to species but is likely to have been Tufted Duck.

HABITATS AND ECOLOGY. Open freshwater ponds and impoundments.

FORAGING AND FOOD. Dives for food but there are no local details.

SOCIAL ORGANIZATION. The Melaka bird associated with Garganeys.

MOVEMENTS. No information.

SURVIVAL. No information.

SOCIAL INTERACTIONS. No information.

VOICE. No local information.

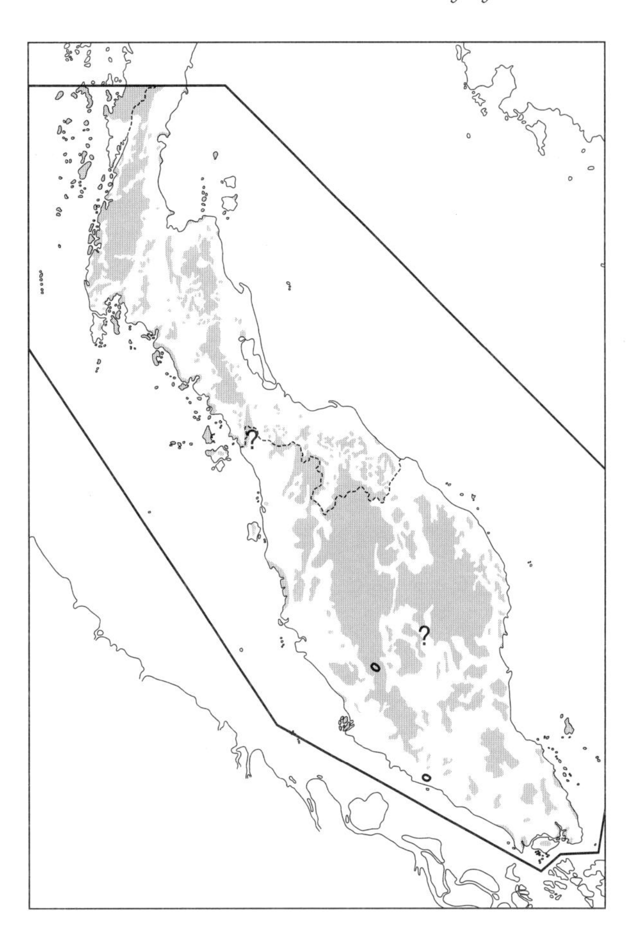

BREEDING. No population.

MOULT. No data.

CONSERVATION. No relevant issues.

Baer's Pochard; Ped Dam Hua Dam (Thai); Itik Baer (Malay)

Aythya baeri (Radde) 1863, *Reisen im Süden von Ost-Sibirien* 2: 376 and plate 15. TL middle Amur river, Pacific Russia.

Plate 7

GROUP RELATIONS. Forms a superspecies with W-central Eurasian *A. nyroca* (Ferruginous Pochard); perhaps also with S-hemisphere *A. australis* (Hardhead) and ?extinct *A. innotata* (Madagascar Pochard) (Delacour and Mayr 1945).

GLOBAL RANGE. Breeds in the Amur and Ussuri drainages, NE China and possibly N Korea. Winters from Japan, Korea and the Changjiang valley to NE India and SE Asia, in significant numbers as far as central Thailand. A few reach Gulf of Bangkok wetlands; vagrant in Luzon and the Peninsula.

IDENTIFICATION/DESCRIPTION. Larger, but comportment as Tufted Duck, and dives. At rest, bright-plumaged drake shows greenish black head and neck, chestnut front, blackish brown upper body, rufous-brown flanks and white lower tail-coverts. Female and eclipse-plumaged drake are duller with brownish black rather than greenish head, and are rufous (rather than white) lateral to the bill. Both sexes have a white chin-spot. In flight, pattern much as Tufted Duck, above and below, but lower tail-coverts show more clearly white (King *et al.* 1975).

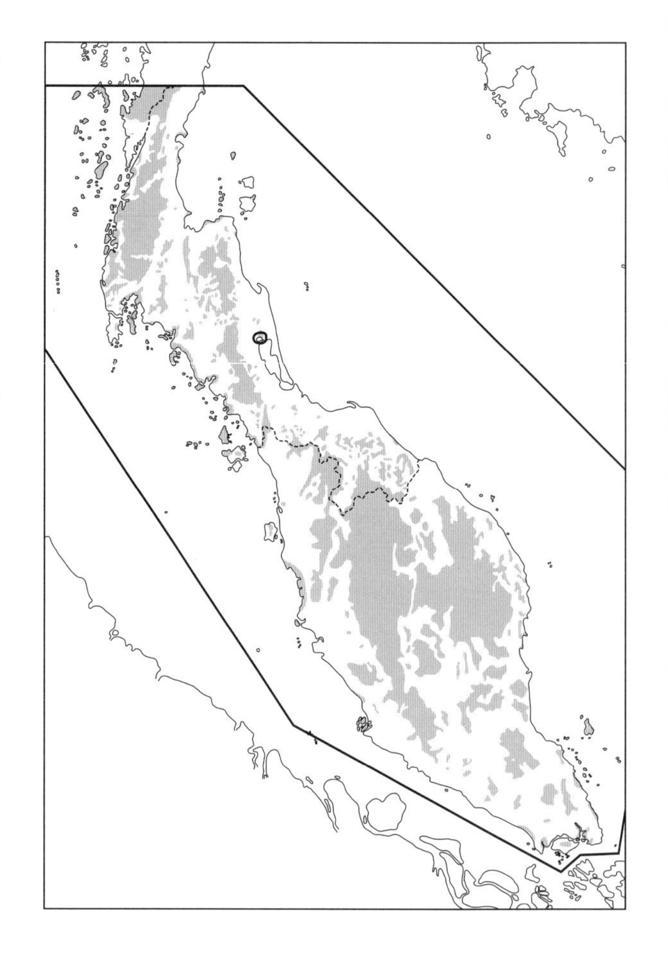

Bare-part colours. (Adult) iris pale yellow (male), brown (female, *contra* Tufted Duck); bill slaty; legs and feet slaty.

Size. No data.

Weight. No data.

DISTRIBUTION. Thalae Noi only. Historical summary: *Pht*.

GEOGRAPHICAL VARIATION. None recognized.

STATUS AND POPULATION. Vagrant; a party of five at Thalae Noi lake on 20 January 1991 (BBCB-8).

HABITATS AND ECOLOGY. Open fresh water.

FORAGING AND FOOD. Dives for food.

SOCIAL ORGANIZATION. Winterers gregarious.

MOVEMENTS. No information.

SURVIVAL. No information.

SOCIAL INTERACTIONS. No information.

VOICE. No information.

BREEDING. No population.

MOULT. No data.

CONSERVATION. No local issues, but globally vulnerable (BTW2).

Order PODICIPEDIFORMES

Family PODICIPEDIDAE

Grebes: one species

Little Grebe; Nok Ped Phee Lek (Thai); Burung Gerib Kecil (Malay)

Tachybaptus ruficollis (Pallas) 1764, Vroeg's *Beredeneerde Catalogus, Adumbratiunculae*: 6. TL Holland.

Plate 7

GROUP RELATIONS. Hybridizes with endemic Madagascan *T. rufolavatus* (Aloatra Grebe) and more or less parapatric with *T. novaehollandiae* (Australasian Grebe). They probably form a superspecies (cf. CLBS, Voous and Payne 1965, Weigant and van Helvoort 1987).

GLOBAL RANGE. Africa, Madagascar, temperate Eurasia from the Atlantic to Ussuriland; the Indian subcontinent and Sri Lanka; Japan, Korea, and China including Taiwan; SE Asia to the Greater Sunda islands (vagrant in Borneo), Bali and the Philippines; and Wallacea and New Guinea to Bougainville. Some northern populations are migratory.

IDENTIFICATION/DESCRIPTION. 'Tailless', swimming with body horizontal, not cocked at the rear, and without head-bobbing movements. Patters over the water surface to take off. Bright-plumaged adults show swollen edges of the gape (rictus) as a conspicuously pale streak, up-angled from the base of the bill. They vary individually in the amount of black on the chin, how far the dark of the crown extends down the face and in greyness of the underparts. In flight, some white shows on the secondaries of otherwise dark wings. All toes carry hard swimming-flanges.

The downy chick has not been described locally, but juveniles are dull brown with a whitish throat and foreneck.

Bare-part colours. (Adult) iris pale yellow; rictus creamy white; bill black; feet black.

Size (mm). (Skins: 7 adults, none sexed): wing 97–107; tail not measured; bill from mouth 24.0–29.0; bill-depth at gonys 5.0–7.4; tarsus not measured (Wells and Medway 1976, TISTR).

Weight. No data.

DISTRIBUTION. In Malaysia, no records east of the Main Range. Historical summary: *Sur, Pht, Tra, Son, Pat, Pes, Pek, Sel, Mel, Sin,* with additional island records from Pisang (Melaka Straits) and, on 5 May 1990, eight adults and two juveniles on Chawaeng marsh, Samui (R.S.E. Swanquist).

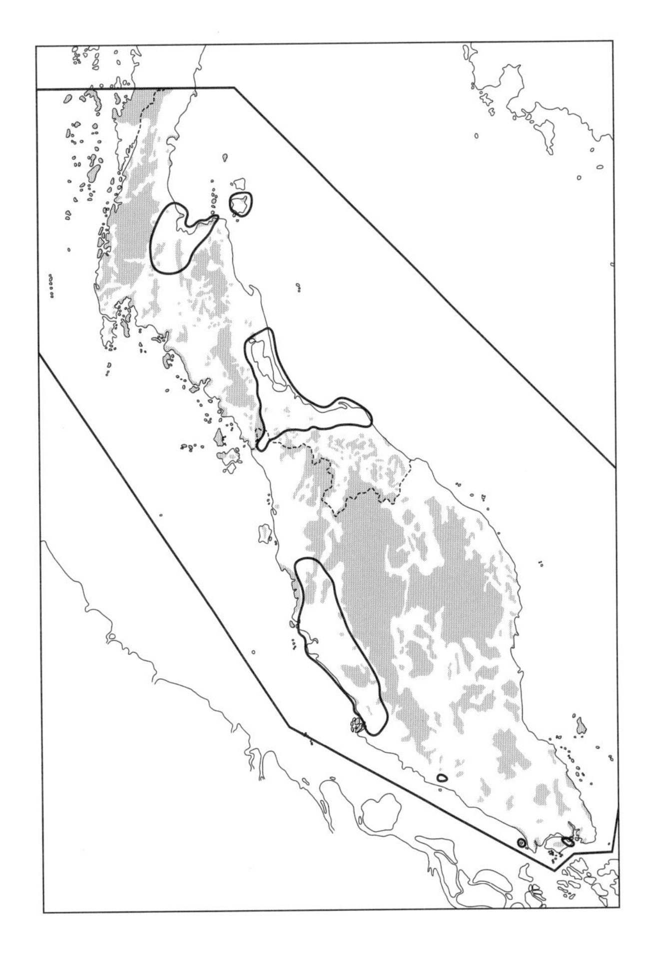

GEOGRAPHICAL VARIATION. Deignan (1963) identified Thai Little Grebes as subspecies *poggei* Reichenow 1902 (TL Hebei province, China). Based on two adults from Perak, Wells and Medway (1976) extended use of this name to Malaysian populations, which are likely to have spread from Thailand recently. Claims of a 'gradation' into *capensis* across southern Thailand–Indochina (Delacour and Jabouille 1931, Robinson and Kloss 1921–24) may be due to *poggei* being met by northern migrants in this area. A bird in eclipse plumage (wing-length 102 mm) collected on Pisang island on 15 January 1934, decades before breeders colonized the Malaysian mainland, had both inner and outer webs of the secondaries mainly white (dark confined to a sub-apical spot reaching the edge of the vane at only one point), as in central/S Asian *capensis*. Local *poggei* secondaries are white only at the extreme tip and along the outer margin of the inner web.

STATUS AND POPULATION. Resident and, in the north, a probable winter visitor; local but common where it occurs. First recorded on the Malaysian W-coast plain, in mid Perak, in 1958 and by 1967 had reached Melaka (BR 1967, Phillips 1960). There has been geographical in-fill since, including colonization of Selangor where many sizeable pools now have Little Grebes, and a large influx of breeders into Perlis with filling of the Timah-Tasoh dam in 1995–96 (G.W.H. Davison). A bright-plumaged bird at Ponggol, Singapore, in late December 1992 and two there in early 1994 were followed by a first Singapore breeding record, at Serangoon, in October 1994. In the meantime, the Republic's central catchment reservoirs are empty habitat (BIRDLINE 1992, 1994, BR 1978–79, SINGAV-8).

HABITATS AND ECOLOGY. Selects still waters, from large, marsh-lined natural lakes (Holmes and Wells 1975) to fish-ponds and relatively deep, flooded mine-workings, usually but not invariably with vegetated margins and some floating macrophytes.

FORAGING AND FOOD. Hunts during prolonged dives that may carry it 20 m or more from point of submergence; also by surface-picking. At Thalae Songkhla, small, actively feeding groups quickly attracted others, generating tight packs of up to 30, mass-feeding between bouts of resting and preening. Stomach contents from Thalae Noi included 40–70 percent insects, 20–60 percent prawns (Anonymous 1981, Meeswat and Prentice 1984).

SOCIAL ORGANIZATION. Nesting pairs space themselves but, where numerous, non-breeders tend to be gregarious. Thirty-five together at Kuala Lumpur on 19 December 1990 (ENGGANG-3) is a high count in the south but at Thalae Noi flocks of 50–300 form during September–May (Holmes and Wells 1975, P. Benstead). On evidence of plumage, these are likely to include both residents and migrants.

MOVEMENTS. No grebes have been intercepted at night but, evidently, some are migrants, and local breeders must make significant dispersal movements.

SURVIVAL. No information.

SOCIAL INTERACTIONS. Noisy chase-flights; the only flying undertaken in the daytime.

VOICE. Shrill, whinnying trills dropping away in pitch are commonly given during chases; also heard from large flocks (Holmes and Wells 1975, MBR 1984–85).

BREEDING

Nest. A floating weed-mat; one with eggs on a fish-pond in Melaka was 4 cm submerged, 1 cm above the water surface, and attached to growing waterplants.

Eggs and brood. Eggs are creamy but discolour rapidly in the damp nest. Size (mm): 39.3–33.0 × 29.8–24.1; weight (g): 11.0–14.5 (n=52). Full clutch four but broods of four are unusual (at Thalae Songkhla, 1–3, mean 1.7).

Cycle. Egg-covering behaviour before departure of the parent from the nest is reported from Melaka. Both parents tend and feed free-swimming chicks bill to bill.

Seasonality. Perhaps year-round, but with need of more summer records. Active nests and/or downy chicks reported in all months August–February and May, and immatures with traces of chick plumage on the head in May, September, November, December and January (BR 1970–71, 1974–75, M. Chong, G.W.H. Davison, ENGGANG-1, -2, -3, R.P. Jaensch, Meeswat and Prentice 1984, MBR 1982–83, 1984–85, NRCS).

MOULT. Bright-plumaged birds consistently outnumber others and have been recorded in all months except June. Dull, eclipse plumage may not occur at all among resident adults (BMP5). A bright-plumaged adult collected in Perak on 14 February was moulting several inner primaries (BMNH).

CONSERVATION. South of Songkhla, Little Grebes depend largely on man-made habitat. With a downturn in the tin industry, more mine lagoons have been lost than created in recent years, and tolerance of grebes by aquaculturists at now rapidly multiplying fish- and prawn-rearing ponds is generally low. Numbers may fall locally but dispersants are opportunistic and, for the moment, continue to spread.

Order PROCELLARIIFORMES

Family PROCELLARIIDAE

Petrels and shearwaters: four species

Bulwer's Petrel; (no Thai name); Burung Petral Bulwer (Malay)

Bulweria bulwerii (Jardine & Selby) 1828, *Illustrations of Ornithology* 2: plate 65. TL Madeira, N Atlantic.

Plate 8

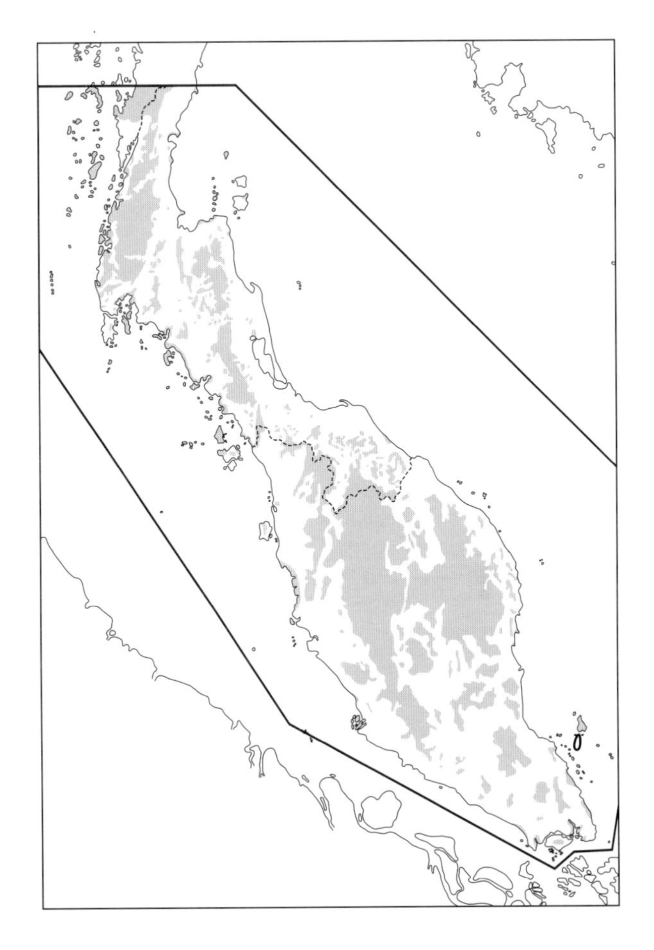

GROUP RELATIONS. Uncertain.

GLOBAL RANGE. Breeds colonially on coasts and islands of the N temperate to N tropical Atlantic and Pacific Oceans, west in the latter to the Taiwan Straits. Disperses within these oceans and also into the Indian Ocean where records in June, July and August imply over-summering by visitors and/or undiscovered breeding stations. Migrates across E Indonesia and some pass through the S China Sea, recorded off western Borneo in mid September and December, and the N coast of Java from mid September through November (P. Andrew). They may winter in this area or commute to the Indian Ocean via the Sunda Straits, where a few petrels thought to have been Bulwer's were noted on 13 September 1989 (S. van Balen).

IDENTIFICATION/DESCRIPTION. Medium-small and stocky, all sooty brown with a longish, wedge-shaped tail and pale bar along the upper coverts of proportionately long, narrow wings; bill short and thick. Flight steady and direct, on wings held angled at the wrist and beaten shallowly and fairly fast, with intermittent glides and side-slipping, mostly within 1 m of the sea surface. Occasionally swoops up to as much as 8 m before wheeling off in a new direction (MBR 1986-87). On shape, confusable with smaller, all-brown *Oceanodroma* storm petrels and potentially occurring Jouanin's Petrel *B. fallax*, but the latter is 25 percent larger and mostly lacks a pale wing-bar.

Bare-part colours. (Adult) iris dark brown; bill black; legs and feet greyish pink (HANZAB).

Size (mm). (Skins: 2 males, 4 females, from SE China; adult): wing 199, 213 and 200–212; tail 104, 110 and 108–112; bill 22.5 (one only) and 21.5–23.5; tarsus 27, 28 and 27–29 (BMNH).

Weight. No data.

DISTRIBUTION. SE coast.

GEOGRAPHICAL VARIATION. None recognized.

STATUS AND POPULATION. A passage migrant, local and sparse. The only record to date is of 15 birds scattered along a 10 km boat-run SW of Tioman island on 5 May 1986 (MBR 1986–87), presumably on northward spring passage.

HABITATS AND ECOLOGY. No specific information.

FORAGING AND FOOD. No information.

SOCIAL ORGANIZATION. No information.

MOVEMENTS. See above.

SURVIVAL. No information.

SOCIAL INTERACTIONS. No information.

VOICE. No information.

BREEDING. No population.

MOULT. No data.

CONSERVATION. No relevant issues.

Wedge-tailed Shearwater; (no Thai name); **Burung Olak Ekor Tirus** (Malay)

Puffinus pacificus (Gmelin) 1789, *Systema Naturae* 13(2): 560. TL Kermadec island, SW Pacific.
Plate 8

GROUP RELATIONS. Apparently free-standing.

GLOBAL RANGE. Breeds colonially on small islands in low temperate to mainly outer tropical waters of the Pacific and S-hemisphere Indian Ocean, including on N Keeling island, 1000 km southwest of Sumatra. Non-breeding migrants move towards/over the equator, including off the W and N coasts of Sumatra and in the Andaman Sea.

IDENTIFICATION/DESCRIPTION. Medium-sized, rather long-tailed shearwater with proportionately broad wings. Either all dark brown or with underparts from chin to belly (excluding lower tail-coverts) sharply demarcated white. Pale-phase lower wing-coverts are white outlined by a dark leading-edge and flight-feathers. Good views show relatively slender, greyish bill and pale feet (short of the tail-tip). Flight in calm conditions unhurried and buoyant, on flexed wings: 4–5 rather deep strokes and a long glide, briefly upward then skimming the water.

Bare-part colours. (Adult) iris dark brown, eyelid-rim black; bill grey to purplish grey, blackish at tip and above nostrils; feet off-white to pale pink with outer edge smoky grey or brown (HANZAB, ZRCNUS).

Size (mm). (Skins: 1 unsexed adult): tail 123; tarsus 43 (Junge 1941). Australian breeders measure wing 300–327; tail 128–149; bill 39.4–49.1; tarsus 47.1–53.5. Nine unsexed Cocos-Keeling breeders are smaller: wing 277–296; tail 123–134; tarsus 48.0–52.0 (HANZAB, ZRCNUS).

Weight. No data.

DISTRIBUTION. The Melaka and Singapore Straits.

GEOGRAPHICAL VARIATION. No subspecies currently recognized.

STATUS AND POPULATION. Passage migrant, local and sparse. The nearest area of regular occurrence

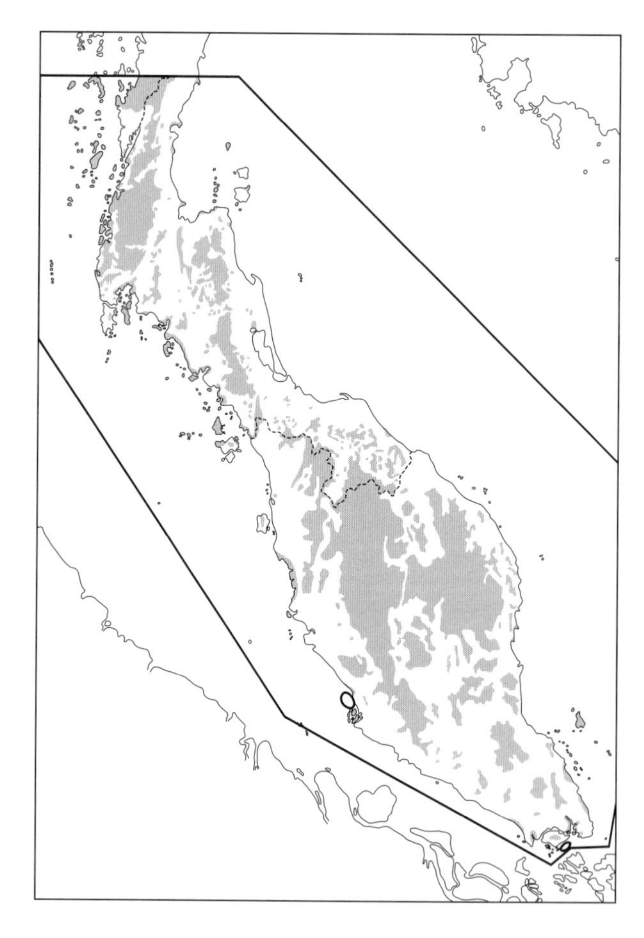

is the continental shelf-break off the N mouth of the Melaka Straits, including: several medium-sized, all-dark shearwaters with graduated tails, evidently this species, at about 7°N on 4 August 1951, and 15 including 2–3 pale-phase individuals in the same area on 10 July 1963. Within the Straits, a dark-phase bird close inshore at Kapar, Selangor, on 17 April 1992, but one collected by P. Buitendijk somewhere in the Straits on 30 July 1916 need not necessarily have been in shelf waters when it flew aboard his ship. SW of Singapore, some have been seen off Kundur island, Riau archipelago, on 19 July (E.F. Allen 1951, Bourne 1983, Colston 1980, P.J. Hurrell, R.N. Hughes, Junge 1941, G.F. Mees).

Not yet found off the E coast but four all-dark shearwaters, apparently this species, heading west through the Singapore Straits on 10 October 1989 could have come from the S China Sea, where a few dark-phase birds of Wedge-tailed size have been seen off NW Sabah in September, and one in the Gulf of Bangkok in March. To the south, a definite Wedge-tailed has been collected off NW Java, and a possible seen in the Sunda Straits on 13 September (BBCB-9, Lim 1989, NNML, D.M. Simpson, S. van Balen).

HABITATS AND ECOLOGY. No specific information.

FORAGING AND FOOD. No information.

SOCIAL ORGANIZATION. No information.

MOVEMENTS. Off E and W coasts of Australia, with minor variation, breeding runs from September through April and on N Keeling from late August to February (Abbott 1978, Gibson-Hill 1950b, Johnstone 1978, Milledge 1977). NE Indian Ocean (and the few local) migrant records fall exclusively during mid April–mid October, consistent with a S-hemisphere origin. This is also the period of occurrence from Java east through Wallacea (CLBW, Junge 1941, S. van Balen).

SURVIVAL. No information.

SOCIAL INTERACTIONS. No information.

VOICE. No information.

BREEDING. No population.

MOULT. The 30 July bird was growing its two outer primaries (Junge 1941).

CONSERVATION. No relevant issues.

Short-tailed Shearwater; Nok Jamuk Lawd Haang San (Thai); Burung Olak Ekor Pendek (Malay)

Puffinus tenuirostris (Temminck) 1835, *Nouveau Recueil de Planches Coloriées d'Oiseaux* 99: text. TL seas north of Japan.

Plate 8

GROUP RELATIONS. Apparently free-standing.

GLOBAL RANGE. Nests colonially on small islands off S and SE coasts of Australia, notably in the Bass Strait, migrating clockwise up the W side of the Pacific to high N-temperate latitudes and back down the centre during the non-breeding season. A few records from the Indian Ocean north to Pakistan, all in May, have been attributed to storm drift or navigational error through birds joining flocks of other species (Bourne 1967, Serventy *et al.* 1971).

IDENTIFICATION/DESCRIPTION. Medium-large, compact and with straight-set, proportionately narrow wings (cf. Wedge-tailed Shearwater). In a close view, toe-tips project past the tail-tip. All sooty blackish apart from grey (occasionally white) underwing, which shows a dark leading-edge and fringe to flight-feathers (Slater 1971). Feet and slender bill blackish. Rather rapid gliding is interspersed with bouts of hurried, stiff-winged flapping, quite different from the Wedge-tailed flight-mode, but no field identification based only on 'jizz' should discount the possibility of Sooty Shearwater *P. griseus*.

Bare-part colours. Iris dark brown; upper mandible and nasal tubes dull black, lower mandible dull black or blue-grey with a black tip; mouth-lining pale grey-blue or pale flesh-purple (an age difference?); outer surface of tarsus and outer toe black to purplish black, inner surface of tarsus and inner toes medium to pale purplish; toe-webs purplish grey to purple-flesh.

Size (mm). (Skins: two females): wing 258, 264; tail 83, 81; bill 32.1, 30.1; tarsus 52, 49 (bill/tarsus ratio 0.62 and 0.61).

Weight (g). 375 and 417 (Frith 1978).

DISTRIBUTION. Andaman Sea.

GEOGRAPHICAL VARIATION. None recognized.

STATUS AND POPULATION. Vagrant or a passage migrant, local and sparse. Known definitely from two females captured alive while roosting at night on the sea near Mai Thon island off the SE tip of Phuket, on 2 and 10 May 1977 (Frith 1978). Provisional sight identifications: between the Phangnga coast and Similan islands on 13 April 1991, near Phiphi island on 2 May 1991 and off the Surin islands, Ranong, on 2 October 1992 (BBCB-8, P. Heath, E.M. Smart). In the Pacific, all age-classes reach equatorial waters or cross into the N hemisphere by May (HANZAB), so that the

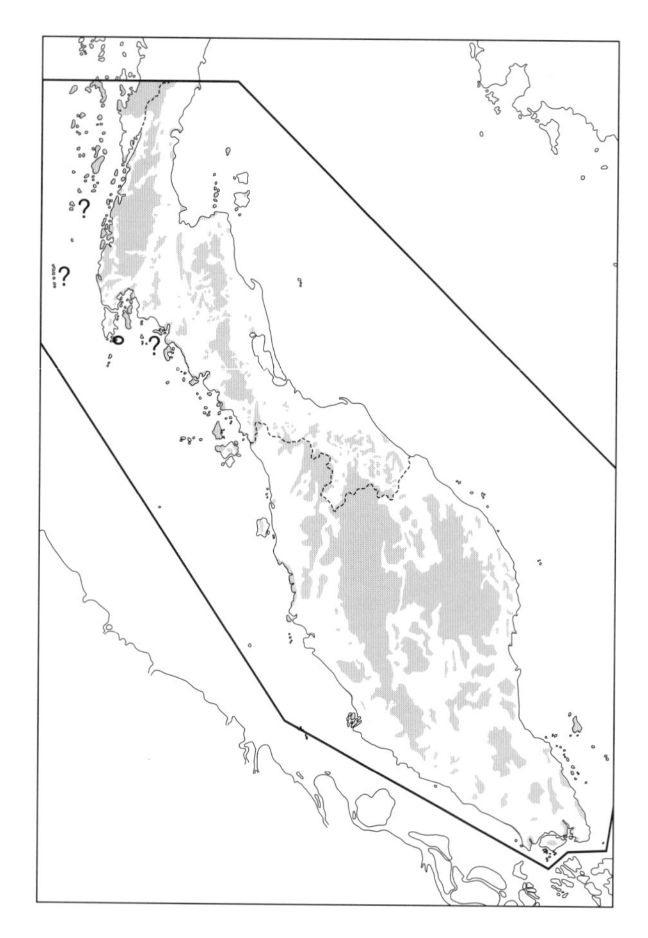

Phuket birds were on schedule by latitude. Frith says the Phuket fisherman who brought in the captives claimed to be familiar with dark shearwaters roosting in small groups around local islands during a brief season (presumably including May) each year. What species predominate in these groups is not known but the successive capture of two *tenuirostris* and no others is remarkable if this bird was not at least well represented that year.

HABITATS AND ECOLOGY. No specific information.

FORAGING AND FOOD. No information.

SOCIAL ORGANIZATION. No specific information.

MOVEMENTS. Dates imply the possibility of two brief passage seasons. It has been suggested some divert west from a route through the S China Sea (Colston 1980), but with no records anywhere in Indonesia and only one from the S China coast (OBCB-16) a more parsimonious explanation would be that occasional groups of immatures follow other shearwaters (Flesh-footed?) on a direct ocean route off the 'wrong' end of Australia.

SURVIVAL. No information.

SOCIAL INTERACTIONS. No information.

VOICE. No information.

BREEDING. No population.

MOULT. One of the two specimens shows slight wear of the primaries, but no moult.

CONSERVATION. No relevant issues.

Streaked Shearwater; Nok Jamuk Lawd Lai (Thai); Burung Olak Berjalur (Malay)

Calonectris leucomelas (Temminck) 1835, *Nouveau Recueil de Planches Coloriées d'Oiseaux* 99: plate 587. TL seas of Japan.

Plate 8

GROUP RELATIONS. Forms a superspecies with Atlantic–Mediterranean *C. diomedea* (Cory's Shearwater).

GLOBAL RANGE. Breeds colonially on small islands from Hokkaido south to the Bonins. Winters primarily off N New Guinea but also to tropical Australia and west through Indonesian and Philippine waters to the S China Sea. Regular wintering concentrations occur off NW Borneo, where present from December through March. A few tentative identifications have also been made in autumn in the Sunda Straits (P. Andrew, S. van Balen) via which some may enter the Indian Ocean, where recorded west to Sri Lanka (van den Berg *et al.* 1991).

IDENTIFICATION/DESCRIPTION. Large. Clean-cut white below, including white lower wing-coverts that contrast with dark flight-feathers; mid-brown above often appearing to include face, on which the white streaking is not always conspicuous at sea. Flight-modes include stiff-winged, wave-front soaring in windy weather, but more often leisurely flapping flight up to several metres above the sea surface. Not attracted by ships.

Bare-part colours. (Adult) iris dark brown; bill pale grey; feet pinkish, outer toe and outer face of tarsus darker (HANZAB).

Size. No information.

Weight. No data.

DISTRIBUTION. The Melaka Straits and Andaman Sea.

GEOGRAPHICAL VARIATION. None recognized.

STATUS AND POPULATION. A probable winter visitor, local and sparse. Definite records from the mid Melaka Straits are: flocks at 3°53′N on 8 December 1973 and about 100 birds at 4°22′N, just south of the zone of rough monsoon seas, on 25 January 1980 (Bourne 1983, BR 1980–81). Bourne (1960) states Streaked Shearwater fairly often strays through the Melaka Straits but these are unlikely passage dates and a small concentration may winter in this area. Also occurs in the Andaman Sea, with three probables between Phuket and Phiphi island on 12 November 1987 (P. Edwards) and three near the continental shelf-break off Phuket on 20 November 1990 (Kiørboe 1991).

HABITATS AND ECOLOGY. No information.

FORAGING AND FOOD. No information.

SOCIAL ORGANIZATION. Melaka Straits 'winterers' occur in small, loose flocks.

MOVEMENTS. See above.

SURVIVAL. No information.

SOCIAL INTERACTIONS. No information.

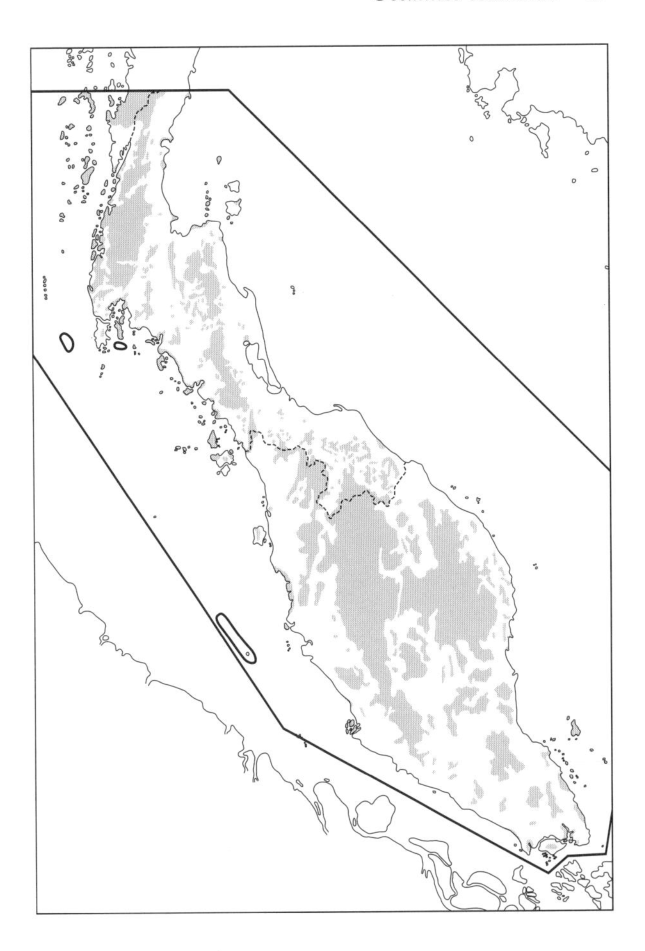

VOICE. No information.

BREEDING. No population.

MOULT. No data.

CONSERVATION. No relevant issues.

Family HYDROBATIDAE

Storm-petrels: two species

Wilson's Storm-petrel; (no Thai name); Burung Petral Wilson (Malay)

Oceanites oceanicus (Kuhl) 1820, *Beiträge zur Zoölogie und Vergleischenden Anatomie* 1: 136 and plate 10. TL South Georgia.

Plate 8

GROUP RELATIONS. Apparently free-standing.

GLOBAL RANGE. Breeds gregariously on coasts and islands around Antarctica, and winters north over the equator in all other oceans. Recorded to approximately 14°N in the Andaman Sea and is seasonally common in oceanic waters off the W and N coasts of Sumatra (CLBS, Lewin 1960).

IDENTIFICATION/DESCRIPTION. Small, sooty black, with squarish tail, white, square-cut rump-patch, and a greyish bar along the upper wing-coverts. In flight, toes project slightly beyond the tail-tip but this can only be seen close up (yellow toe-webs on otherwise black feet are perhaps checkable only in the hand). In calm conditions, flight light, steady and unhurried, within a few metres of the water surface; not noticeably 'fluttery, erratic, bat-like' (cf. King 1967), though it may be during foraging. Lewin (1960) described the flight of foragers in the wake of his ship off Sumatra as resembling a small bat, but birds seen off Penang in July 1973 took no notice of the passing boat and continued steady, northward flight uninterrupted.

Bare-part colours. No local information.

Size. No data.

Weight. No data.

DISTRIBUTION. The Melaka Straits.

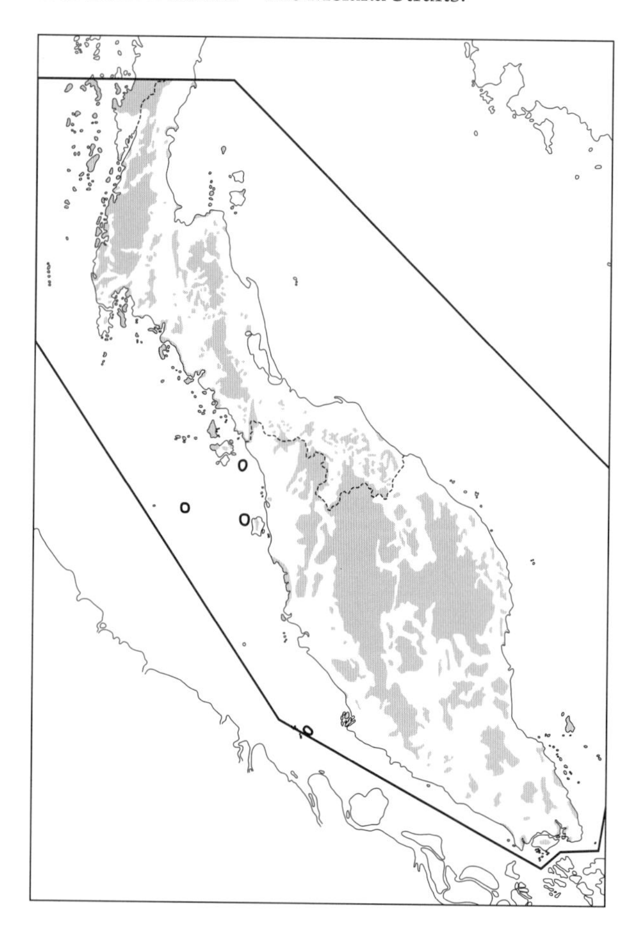

GEOGRAPHICAL VARIATION. No specimens collected but Ripley (1982) puts this area within the migration track of nominate *oceanicus*.

STATUS AND POPULATION. A passage migrant and possible 'over-summerer', local and sparse. Dark, square-tailed, white-rumped storm-petrels, presumed to be Wilson's (the only white-rumped species yet found in the E Indian Ocean) have been seen as follows, in date order: one in the northern mouth of the Melaka Straits, on the Sumatran side, on 28 June; two and one respectively 100 and 4 km WNW of Penang island on 20 and 22 July; a few near the Arua islands on 19 and 30 September; and 3–4 between the Kedah mainland and Langkawi island on 12 December (Bourne 1983, BR 1972–73, Bromley 1949, Gibson-Hill 1948).

HABITATS AND ECOLOGY. No specific information.

FORAGING AND FOOD. No information.

SOCIAL ORGANIZATION. No specific information.

MOVEMENTS. December is two months outside the period of consistent presence north of the equator, suggesting a few birds may stay in this area through the southern summer. Dates in and around the Melaka Straits are otherwise more or less in line with the schedule of migration recognized elsewhere in the Indian Ocean (Gibson-Hill 1948, Harrison 1985). There are no records off the E coast, indeed, anywhere in Sunda-Shelf waters east of the Peninsula apart from a mid-August sighting of two probables in the eastern Java Sea (Jespersen 1933). Numbers in the Melaka Straits are too low to be sure this is a true migration conduit rather than being just marginally invaded from regular deep-water range off its northern mouth. To the south, the situation in the Sunda Straits (CLBS, Hoogerwerf 1953, S. van Balen) could be similar.

SURVIVAL. No information.

SOCIAL INTERACTIONS. No information.

VOICE. No information.

BREEDING. No population.

MOULT. No data.

CONSERVATION. No relevant issues.

Swinhoe's Storm-petrel; Nok Toh Khluen See Khlam (Thai); Burung Petral Swinhoe (Malay)

Oceanodroma monorhis (Swinhoe) 1867, *Ibis* series 2(3): 386. TL Xiamen, Fujian province, China.

Plate 8

GROUP RELATIONS. From analyses of morphology and voice characters, Bretagnolle *et al.* (1991) have suggested *monorhis* is not more than a well-differentiated subspecies of Holarctic *O. leucorhoa* (Leach's Storm-petrel). Here, they are ranked at superspecies level (cf. BWP).

GLOBAL RANGE. Breeds on islands from the Taiwan Strait to Korea and Honshu, and has been found under conditions that suggest breeding also in the NE Atlantic. Its main recorded wintering area is the W Indian Ocean. December and January records off Sabah and Sarawak suggest some wintering also east of the Peninsula. Specimens collected off NE Java (Junge 1941, van Oort 1911) are said to average shorter in wing and tail than migrants from SE Peninsular waters (Horsburgh lighthouse). If this is true, they could represent a separate population, with a different migration journey.

IDENTIFICATION/DESCRIPTION. Small, all-dark-brown, with a paler band along the upper wing-coverts and moderately forked tail. Flight is 'distinctive . . . bounding and swooping over water like a tern', 'very graceful and swooping, swifter and more powerful than Wilson's [Petrel]' (Lewin 1960, Tuck and Heinzel 1978). Barring dark-rumped Leach's, possibly not separable in the field but which migrates eastward into the Pacific (BWP), confusion is potentially most likely with Matsudaira's Storm-petrel *O. matsudairae*, reported on migration west to the Lombok Strait (Johnstone *et al.* 1993). Matsudaira's flies slower, is about 30 percent larger, with white on the primary shafts showing as a pale patch (Slater 1971).

Bare-part colours. (Adult) iris dark; bill black; legs and feet black.

Size (mm). (Skins: 10 adults, most not sexed): wing 150–167 including four males 150–159 and a female at 167; tail 75–80; bill 14.0–15.0; tarsus 22.5–25.0; mid-toe plus claw 24.0–26.0 (BMNH, ZRCNUS).

Weight. No data.

DISTRIBUTION. Mainly off the S and SE coasts.

GEOGRAPHICAL VARIATION. None recognized.

STATUS AND POPULATION. Local, and sparse to common, recorded during two discrete seasons that imply strictly passage-migrant status, between alternate ranges elsewhere. Most have been seen in

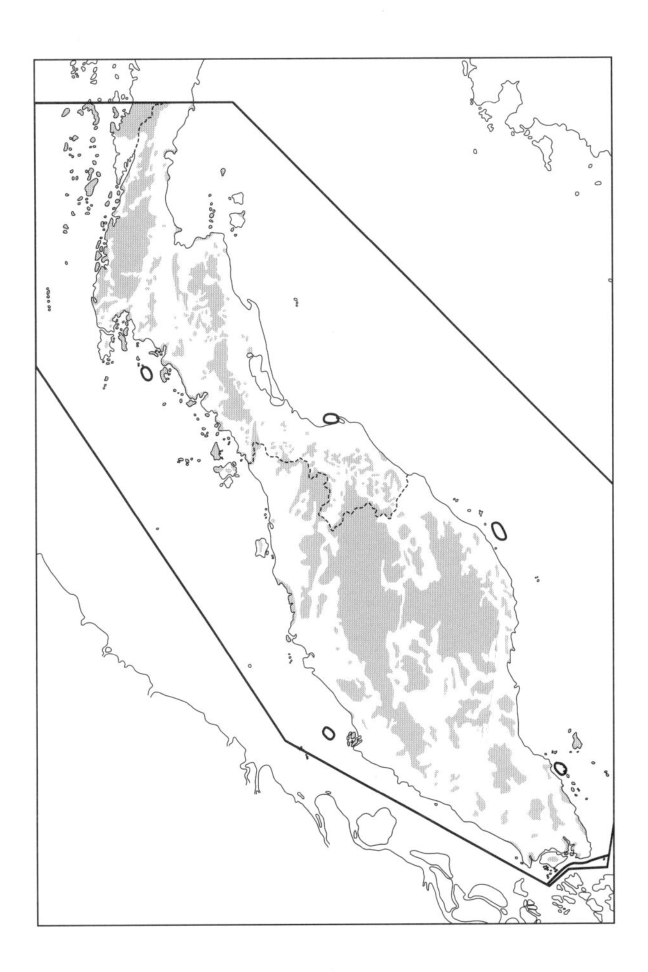

autumn, with singles and flocks of up to 30 moving down the E coast, south from Pattani (one netted in the bay on 18 September is the northernmost record) (MBR 1982–83, Parish and Ardseungnern 1989, Robinson and Chasen 1936) and much larger numbers passing west through the Singapore Straits: at an estimated 1000 per hour in early September (BIRDLINE 1993, Lim 1989).

Elsewhere, some reported over oceanic water off the N end of the Melaka Straits (S entrance to the Andaman Sea) in October, with a probable between Maa and Phiphi islands (Krabi) on 16 April (Lewin 1960, S. Rooke).

HABITATS AND ECOLOGY. No information.

FORAGING AND FOOD. D.M. Simpson reports foot-pattering over the sea-surface by birds feeding in a flock off Terengganu.

SOCIAL ORGANIZATION. No information other than that it is more gregarious on passage than Wilson's Storm-petrel.

MOVEMENTS. Extreme dates in autumn are 5 September–7 November, with numbers peaking in September. The migrant stream has not been followed out of Singapore waters but must turn south as only one autumn bird has been recorded in the Melaka Straits: collected at One-Fathom Bank lighthouse, latitude 2°51'N, on 7 November 1918. Sightings at the NW entrance of the Java Sea accord and birds have been seen and collected on appropriate dates in the Sunda Straits, which is perhaps this population's route to the Indian Ocean (BMNH, Bourne and Dixon 1973, Hoogerwerf 1969–71). Spring dates are 16 April–30 May (BIRDLINE 1994, Robinson and Chasen 1936, SINGAV-6), with records from the Singapore Straits east to Horsburgh lighthouse. Just one from the Melaka Straits, on 6 May (Bourne 1983), again implies they have mostly not come from the north. None in spring in E-coast waters suggests either insufficient sea-watching or a more complete shift seaward in what is then mainly calm weather.

SURVIVAL. No information.

SOCIAL INTERACTIONS. No information.

VOICE. No information.

BREEDING. No population.

MOULT. None of 13 specimens, covering April, May and early November (BMNH, ZRCNUS), shows wing-moult. Primaries are slightly worn in November, near-fresh in spring, implying moult is completed at sea during the wintering period.

CONSERVATION. No relevant local issues but near-threatened globally (BTW2).

Order PELECANIFORMES

Family PHAETHONTIDAE

Tropicbirds: two species

Tropicbirds show broadly overlapping ranges around the world and breed gregariously on cliffs and small islands close to deep water. Only vagrant in the area of the Peninsula though all three have breeding stations peripheral to the Sunda Shelf: Red-billed off Vietnam from the Xisha south to the Hon Trung islands (Cheng 1987, Scott 1989); White-tailed on Cocos-Keeling and Christmas islands, and eastward from SE Java (de Korte 1991); Red-tailed on Cocos-Keeling and Christmas islands and, it has been guessed from unique measurements of a bird collected off Aceh, somewhere in the Bay of Bengal.

There are five records from Peninsular waters: a mid-nineteenth century immature Red-billed *Phaethon aethereus* (subspecies *indicus*) 'shot in the Straits of Malacca' (BMNH); a White-tailed *P. lepturus* taken on board a ship somewhere in the Melaka Straits in November 1927 (G.F. Mees) plus one in Pattani bay in October 1984 (Swennen and Marteijn 1985a); a Red-tailed *P. rubricauda* in the mouth of Phangnga bay in August 1990 (O.F. Jakobsen); and two unidentified tropicbirds off Seletar, NE Singapore island, on 11 December 1963 (BR 1964). In addition, an immature *rubricauda* has been collected off the N coast of Sumatra (Gibson-Hill 1949) and a group recorded heading west over central Aceh in mid May (Meyer de Schauensee and Ripley 1940) on what could have been a coast-to-coast crossing of Sumatra.

All species seem possible, but old suspicions hang on the *aethereus* specimen (BMNH 1880.1.1.3423). Independent evidence suggests the collector, T. Cantor, acquired specimens off ships without reference to where they went aboard. *P. aethereus* sightings have been claimed in the Andaman Sea south to about 10°N (Hume and Davison 1878), but repeated checks since the 1970s (BR 1980—81, Langham 1976) confirm earlier findings that no tropicbirds occur at the seabird colony on Perak island, N Melaka Straits.

FAMILY IDENTIFICATION/DESCRIPTIONS. Stocky, pigeon-sized, with longish, pointed wings that row the body along in steady flapping flight, well above the sea-surface. Plunge-dive for food but submerge only briefly (Gibson-Hill 1947). Predominantly white, immatures are strongly dotted and barred black over the nape, upper body and wing-coverts. Their wedge-shaped tail lacks or has only short streamers. Adults retain the crescent-shaped, black eye-mask and are best separated by pattern of dorsum: black-barred including upper wing-coverts and with nape-band and distal primaries black in *aethereus*; all-pale in *rubricauda*; pale with distal primaries and bold bar from rear scapulars running obliquely across wing-coverts solid black in *lepturus*. Some *rubricauda* are flushed pink, some *lepturus* golden-apricot. Long, black-shafted centre tail-streamers (rather stiff in *rubricauda*: Gibson-Hill 1947) are concolorous with body in *aethereus* and *lepturus*, red in *rubricauda*, but are not always present. Dagger bill at first black in *rubricauda*, turning yellowy; yellow in other immatures; red or (*lepturus*) yellow in adults.

Red-tailed Tropicbird; Nok Rawn Thalae Haang Daeng (Thai); Burung Sinbad Ekor Merah (Malay)

Phaethon rubricauda Boddaert 1783, *Table des Planches Enluminéez d'Histoire Naturelle*: 57. TL Mauritius.

Plate 39

GROUP RELATIONS. Free-standing.

GLOBAL RANGE. Breeds on blue-water islands of the tropical Indian and Pacific Oceans, with nearest proven colonies on the Cocos-Keeling group and Christmas island, and islands in the Banda Sea, E Wallacea. Non-breeders are oceanic, in SE Asia reaching the W and N coasts of Sumatra and, to the east, the N and E Philippines.

IDENTIFICATION/DESCRIPTION. See Family introduction. A subadult male had shafts of the flight-feathers and primary-coverts mainly black, and short tail-streamers apricot-yellow, representing an intermediate plumage.

Bare-part colours. (Subadult male) iris dark brown; bill yellow-horn shading to blackish tip; tarsus, inner digit and base of other digits pale blue-grey, rest of the foot black.

Size (mm). (Skins: 1 male; subadult): wing 335; tail 206; bill 69.5, bill from mouth-corner 96; tarsus 28 (Gibson-Hill 1949).

Weight. No data.

DISTRIBUTION. The Andaman Sea.

GEOGRAPHICAL VARIATION. The Australasian–Indonesian subspecies *westralis* has been identified off W Sumatra (CLBS) but Gibson-Hill (1949) showed a bird from the SW entrance to the Andaman Sea to have atypical measurements, including an unusually long bill, for this subspecies.

STATUS AND POPULATION. Vagrant. An all-white, red-billed, adult tropicbird lacking streamers but otherwise answering the description of this species, seen off the Krabi coast on 3 August 1990 (O.F. Jakobsen).

HABITATS AND ECOLOGY. Typically oceanic.

FORAGING AND FOOD. Stomach contents of the outer Andaman Sea bird included 6 mm-long cephalopod beaks and vertebrae and fin-rays of probable flying-fish (Gibson-Hill 1949).

SOCIAL ORGANIZATION. Non-breeders are typically solitary and wander great distances.

MOVEMENTS. No information.

SURVIVAL. No information.

SOCIAL INTERACTIONS. No information.

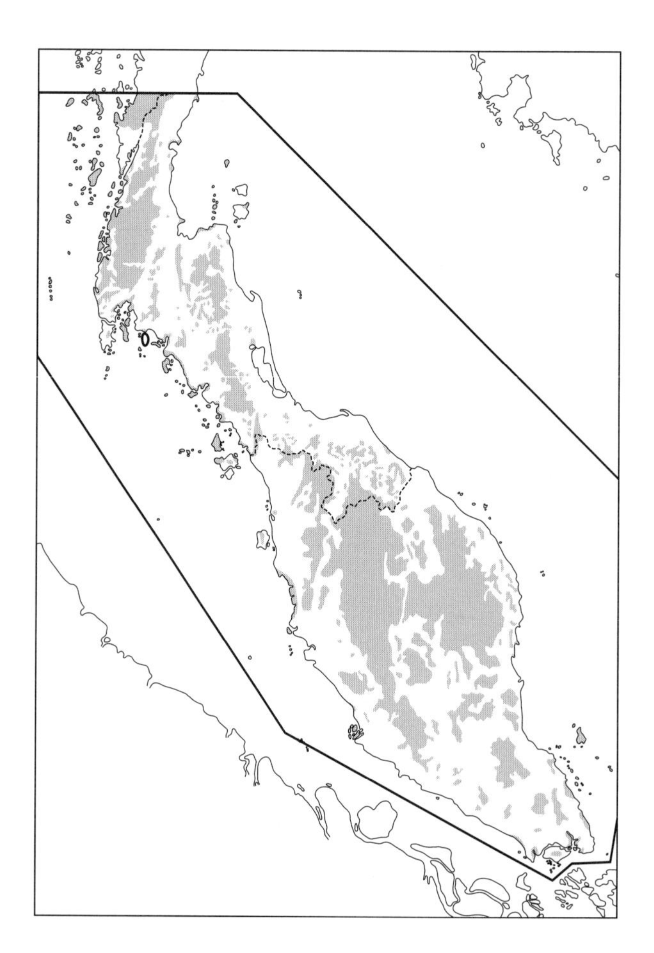

VOICE. No information.

BREEDING. No population.

MOULT. No information.

CONSERVATION. No relevant issues.

White-tailed Tropicbird; Nok Rawn Thalae Haang Khao (Thai); Burung Sinbad Ekor Putih (Malay)

Phaethon lepturus Daudin 1802, Didot's *Histoire Naturelle des Oiseaux, par Buffon* 14: 319. TL Mauritius.

Plate 39

GROUP RELATIONS. Free-standing.

GLOBAL RANGE. Pan-tropical, breeding gregariously on small islands and remote coastal cliffs close to deep waters of all oceans; golden-apricot-coloured *fulvus* on Christmas island south of Java, the white-plumaged, nominate subspecies everywhere else. Nearest known colonies of the latter are all S hemisphere: in the Cocos-Keeling group, on cliffs in SE Java and islands south of Bali and Lombok. Non-breeders are oceanic wanderers.

IDENTIFICATION/DESCRIPTION. See Family introduction. The smallest tropicbird, about the size of a Gull-billed Tern but more thick-set; flight direct and level, with regular wing-beats (Swennen and Marteijn 1985a).

Bare-part colours. (Adult) iris dark brown, eyelid-rim black; bill yellowish grey (yellow to greenish yellow in *fulvus*); feet black except for pale blue-grey inner toe and part of inner web (greenish white with black webs and toes in *fulvus*) (Gibson-Hill 1947, 1950b).

Size (mm). (Skins: 8 nominate *lepturus* from Cocos-Keeling; unsexed adults): wing 273–281, tail 355–501; bill from mouth-corner 67–76; tarsus 23–25 (ZRC-NUS).

Weight. No data.

DISTRIBUTION. The S China Sea and possibly the Melaka Straits.

GEOGRAPHICAL VARIATION. Both subspecies have been claimed although the status of *fulvus* Brandt 1838 (TL Christmas Island, Indian Ocean) is uncertain (see below).

STATUS AND POPULATION. Vagrant on the Sunda Shelf. It is not possible to say where an immature male *fulvus* collected by P. Buitendijk in November 1927 somewhere in the Melaka Straits actually went aboard his ship (G.F. Mees). The only certain natural occurrence is of an adult showing all essential characters of nominate *lepturus* flying along the low-tide mudflats of Pattani bay on 15 October 1984 (Swennen and Marteijn 1985a).

HABITATS AND ECOLOGY. Typically oceanic.

FOOD AND FORAGING. No information.

SOCIAL ORGANIZATION. Non-breeders are solitary.

MOVEMENTS. No information.

SURVIVAL. No information.

SOCIAL INTERACTIONS. No information.

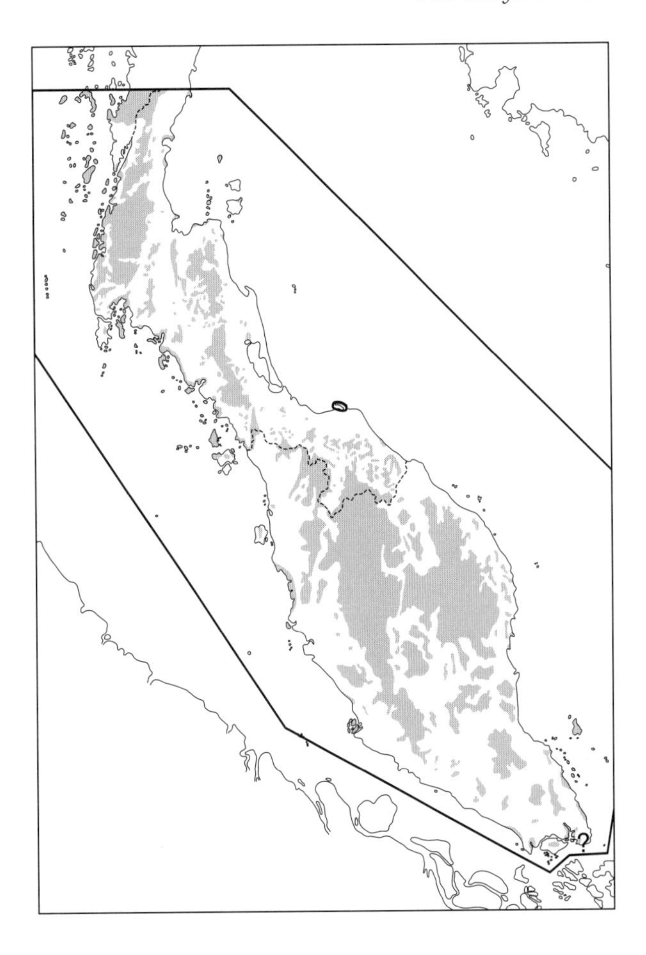

VOICE. No information.

BREEDING. No population.

MOULT. No data.

CONSERVATION. No relevant issues.

Family SULIDAE

Boobies: three species

Masked Booby; Nok Buu-bee Naa Dam (Thai); Burung Dendang Muka Hitam (Malay)

Sula dactylatra Lesson 1831, *Traité d'Ornithologie* 8: 601. TL Ascension Island, Atlantic Ocean.
Plate 9

GROUP RELATIONS. Free-standing.

GLOBAL RANGE. Breeds gregariously or in colonies of other booby species on small, remote islands scattered over the tropics and near-tropics of all oceans, with long-distance dispersal by some non-breeders, but missing from most of the NE Indian Ocean.

IDENTIFICATION/DESCRIPTION. Big dagger bill on extended neck and longish, wedge-shaped tail give all boobies a rakish, torpedo shape in flight.

Masked is said sometimes to plunge-dive for food vertically, like a gannet, instead of at the gentler angle of other boobies (Nelson 1978). Adults are white with tips of the longest scapulars, greater- and primary-coverts, and both surfaces of flight-feathers and tail black. Immatures are mostly brown above with a variable extent of white on rump and back, according to age, and white below; from adult Brown Booby *S. leucogaster* by brown of head extending back only to the throat rather than the breast, a white collar round the hind-neck, and in flight by less clean-cut white lower wing-coverts (Gibson-Hill 1950b, Harrison 1985). At all ages, from brown morphs of Red-footed Booby in this area by size and dark tail.

Bare-part colours. (Adult; a photographed captive) iris pale yellowish; facial and gular skin blackish; bill pale yellow; feet dark grey. N Keeling birds have bill yellow in males, yellow-grey in females; feet dull olive in males, lead-grey in females. Immatures resemble adult females.

Size (mm). (Live: 4 males, 1 female, from N Keeling island; adult): wing 424–434 and 446; tail 184–193 and 201; bill from mouth-corner 120–125 and 125; tarsus 51–53 and 53 (Gibson-Hill 1950b).

Weight. No data.

DISTRIBUTION. Off both coasts south to the vicinities of Melaka and Mersing.

GEOGRAPHICAL VARIATION. No collections, but the Peninsula is adjacent to the range of Pacific–Australasian *personata* Gould 1846 (TL N and NE coasts of Australia).

STATUS AND POPULATION. A former local breeder, now hardly more than vagrant. At Perak island Brown Booby colony, N Melaka Straits, two birds present on 9 April 1949, a pair with an egg on 4 February 1956 and three adults there on 24 June that year (Gibson-Hill 1950f, Madoc and Allen 1956). At sea further south, two tentatively identified as Masked Booby in Indonesian waters off the S Arua islands on 23 June 1951 (G.C. Madoc) and, evidently later, about ten 'flying in line ahead' (a fishing formation?) in the area of Melaka (Madoc and Allen 1956).

Subsequently on the W coast, a captive at Ladang island, Tarutao group, in 1980 and an adult beached and exhausted on Libong island (Trang) on 29 August 1992 (OBCB-15, RTFD). West of the Peninsula, Masked Boobies probably now breed no nearer than N Keeling island, 1000 km southwest of Sumatra (Grant 1990).

To the east, some (still?) breed in seabird colonies off Vietnam, south to the Hon Trung group, latitude 8°20′N, 500 km from the Peninsula (Scott 1989, D.M. Simpson). In early August 1963, at the same latitude but twice the distance out, Haile (1964) found a few pairs nesting among Brown Boobies on Spratly island, close to deep water at the SW edge of the Sin Cow reefs (later garrisoned by the Vietnamese military, with predictable results for big, meaty sulids). During

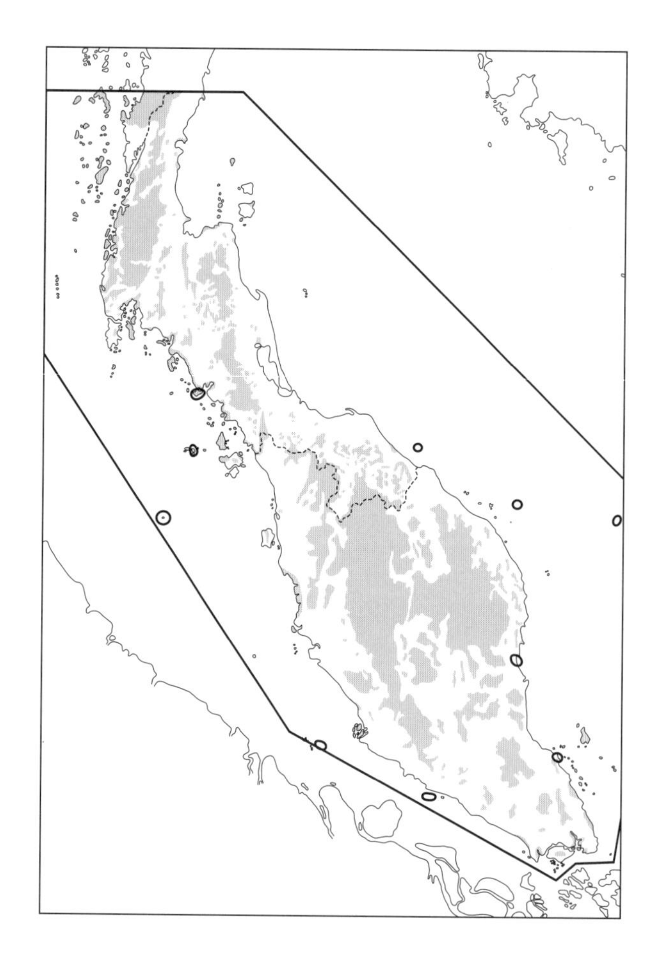

nine months of regular E-coast sea travel in 1982, D.M. Simpson saw only one, an adult at the Terengganu offshore oil-field on 30 October (MBR 1982–83). Three other E-coast records are of captives at fishing ports: a bird at Kuantan (Pahang) on 9 October 1964 (BR 1964); one at Kampung Air Mawar, Mersing (Johor) on 25 May 1975, said to have been caught the previous year (BR 1974–75); and one at Pattani on 23 October 1983 claimed by its captors to have been taken three days earlier from among a group of dark boobies (either immature Masked or Brown) resting on the sea about 20 km out, between Narathiwat and the Malaysian border (Chavalit 1985). The cluster of October dates could be of interest, at the opening of the NE monsoon. However, a white booby 19 km east of Redang island, Terengganu, on 17 May (Parry 1954) is also likely to have been this species (see Red-footed Booby), and two have been seen in the Inner Gulf of Thailand in December (OBCB-7).

HABITATS AND ECOLOGY. Typically selects bluer waters than found at least off the W coast of the Peninsula. Said to have a tendency to adopt breeding sites away from the natal colony (Nelson 1978).

FORAGING AND FOOD. No additional local information.

SOCIAL ORGANIZATION. At sea, from solitary to loosely gregarious.

MOVEMENTS. No information.

SURVIVAL. No information.

SOCIAL INTERACTIONS. No information.

VOICE. No local information. When threatened at the nest, N Keeling males gave a shrill, whistling hiss and females a loud, trumpeting quack (Gibson-Hill 1950b).

BREEDING

Nest. A low pile of stone chips, driftwood fragments and bones, on a bare, exposed rock ledge.

Eggs and brood. Egg whitish with a rough, chalky surface. Size (mm): 66 × 41 (n=1).

Cycle. No local information.

Seasonality. An egg on 4 February (Madoc & Allen 1956).

MOULT. No data.

CONSERVATION. Masked Boobies have reached a low ebb in SE Asia generally (de Korte 1991), but water conditions make it unlikely they were ever common around the Peninsula. At the same time, captives imply this bird is susceptible to some fishing technique employed locally, possibly the baited lines so devastating to Northern Gannet *Sula bassana* in the Atlantic. Captures at sea should not be ruled out as having aided in the removal of small breeding groups.

Red-footed Booby; (no Thai name); Burung Dendang Kaki Merah (Malay)

Sula sula (Linnaeus) 1766, *Systema Naturae* 12(1): 218. TL Barbados, West Indies.
Plate 9

GROUP RELATIONS. Free-standing.

GLOBAL RANGE. Breeds in colonies of a few to several thousand pairs on small, remote, wooded islands over tropical and near-tropical latitudes of all oceans, dispersing apparently farther than Masked Booby, but mostly absent from the NE Indian Ocean. No breeding has been recorded actually on the Sunda shelf but colonies exist on N Keeling and Christmas islands (Gibson-Hill 1947, 1950b), in Wallacea, in the Sulu Sea and, northward, (formerly?) in the Xisha islands off Vietnam (Cheng 1987). In early August 1963, Haile (1964) found two pairs nesting on Spratly island, an unlikely, treeless spot about 1000 km ENE of the Peninsula, and nearest site to date.

IDENTIFICATION/DESCRIPTION. The smallest booby. White-phase adults are all white (Christmas island birds washed apricot), with ventral carpal patch black and flight-feathers and primary coverts black on both surfaces. Juveniles are uniform brownish (compare well-demarcated pale belly of Brown Booby), with slightly darker flight-feathers and tail. Brown-phase adults vary from juvenile-like to grey-brown with white tail and rear body, to having brown restricted to mantle and wings. Feet show yellow-grey in perched juveniles, diagnostically bright red in adults.

Bare-part colours. (Adult) iris dark brown; lower eyelid and band of bare skin across forehead pink, gular skin blue-grey to, in breeding condition, black; bill pale blue-grey, pink at the base; feet bright rose-red. On N Keeling, the bill-base and bare facial skin are partly light green (Gibson-Hill 1947, 1950b). Juveniles have bill black-brown and feet grey-yellow (Harrison 1985).

Size (mm). (Live: males and females from N Keeling island; adult): wing 356–395 and 370–396; tail 177–233 (sexes combined); bill from mouth-corner 100–110 (Christmas island birds average slightly shorter-billed); tarsus 37–40 (Gibson-Hill 1947, 1950b).

Weight. No data.

DISTRIBUTION. See below.

GEOGRAPHICAL VARIATION. None collected but the surrounding subspecies is *rubripes* Gould 1838 (TL Queensland). Incidence of brown morphs varies. Gibson-Hill (1947, 1950b) implies they are rare in the Christmas island population but common (including the white-tailed variant) on N Keeling.

STATUS AND POPULATION. Vagrant. Included on the strength of two white-tailed, pale brown-phase adults seen together west of Galang island, Riau archipelago, on 10 August 1984 (A.M. Guigue and R. Eve), technically outside but not far from Singapore waters; and of an exhausted immature or brown-phase adult tentatively identified as this species off the mouth of the Kantang river, Trang, on 2 April 1990 (BBCB-7). CLBS lists a few sightings west of Sumatra and the supposition is that some non-breeders drift this far north of Christmas island or N Keeling. Gibson-Hill (1956a) is responsible for identifying as Red-footed a white booby seen at sea 19 km east of Redang island,

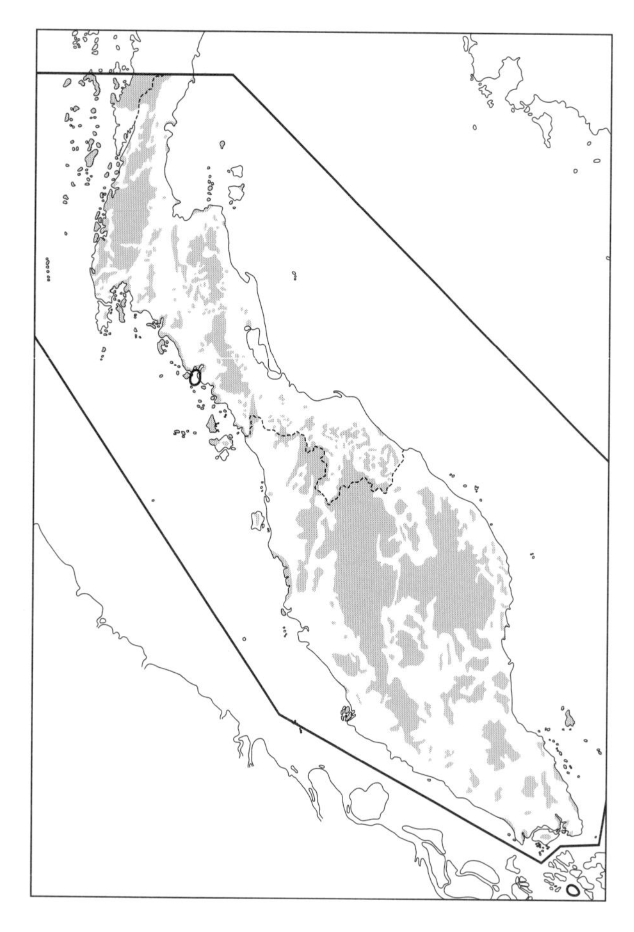

Terengganu, on 17 May 1954 (Parry 1954), on the basis that in a close view the observer made no mention of tail colour. Parry believed he had seen a Northern Gannet, 'long tail, black primaries . . . white plumage, they were all there', hence may as easily have half-described a Masked Booby.

HABITATS AND ECOLOGY. Another blue-water species. Red-footed Boobies have many apparently suitable, wooded breeding-sites open to them on the Sunda shelf yet seem more clearly to avoid shallow seas than either of the other two species. Though not directly relevant to the Peninsula, Haile's find on Spratly island is one of very few records anywhere of this booby nesting other than in trees. One pair had built a half-metre-high, conical pile of twigs and drift-wood, with a bird incubating on top, as far off the ground as it could get.

FORAGING AND FOOD. No local information.

SOCIAL ORGANIZATION. No information.

MOVEMENTS. No information.

SURVIVAL. No information.

SOCIAL INTERACTIONS. No information.

VOICE. No information.

BREEDING. No population.

MOULT. No data.

CONSERVATION. No relevant issues.

Brown Booby; Nok Buu-bee See Namtaan (Thai); Burung Dendang Laut (Malay)

Sula leucogaster (Boddaert) 1783, *Table des Planches Enluminéez d'Histoire Naturelle*: 57. TL Cayenne, Guyana.

Plate 9

GROUP RELATIONS. Free-standing.

GLOBAL RANGE. Breeds in colonies of up to several tens of thousands on small islands over the tropics and near-tropics of all oceans, with only limited dispersal away from home sites although in some areas a few non-breeders reach the N- and S-temperate zones.

IDENTIFICATION/DESCRIPTION. In flight, typical booby shape (see Masked). At all free-flying stages, from other boobies by entirely dark chocolate-brown upperparts, tail, wings, head and neck to lower breast, sharply demarcated from rest of underparts, which are white in adult, pale brownish in immatures. Contrast between belly and breast helps distinguish the latter from immature Red-footed Booby. At all ages, the lower wing-coverts show cleanly pale (white in adults) against dark flight-feathers.

Chicks hatch naked then acquire a dense, white down.

Bare-part colours. (Adult) iris pale blue; facial skin to bill-base cobalt-blue (male), grey (female); bill palest blue-grey to yellow-grey; feet lime-green (male), dull yellow (female). Young juvenile feet dull pink (Madoc 1954, UMBRP).

Size (mm). (Live: 7 males, 5 females; adult): wing 362–405 and 375–428; tail 200–230 and 213–247; bill 94–99 and 96–105, bill from mouth-corner 113–119 and 115–128; tarsus not measured (UMBRP).

Weight (g). Adult males, 960–1081 (n=7); adult females, 905–1260 (n=5).

DISTRIBUTION. Formerly common off the whole W coast, south to Singapore; little-known off the E coast.

GEOGRAPHICAL VARIATION. Indo-Pacific *plotus* Forster 1844 (TL New Caledonia), but Gibson-Hill (1950b) has pointed to the smallness of Melaka Straits birds compared with *plotus* from N Keeling island.

STATUS AND POPULATION. Resident; formerly common but in steep decline for several decades and now endangered. Not more than vagrant off Singapore and the Malaysian E coast but status less certain in the NE. During the late nineteenth century, common at sea off the whole W coast of the Peninsula, particularly between Penang and Singapore (Hume and Davison 1878), and probably many thousands bred locally at that time. In mid November 1906, Robinson (1906) collected specimens and saw 'some hundreds', all adult, visiting Tokong Simbang, a steep-sided rock-stack in the S Arua group, just outside Peninsular waters at latitude 2°50'N. He believed these birds were roosting, but others have concluded they were probably breeding in the area. Forty-five years on, visits in June 1951 and January 1952 (Madoc 1956) found Tokong deserted and no Brown Boobies anywhere around the Aruas.

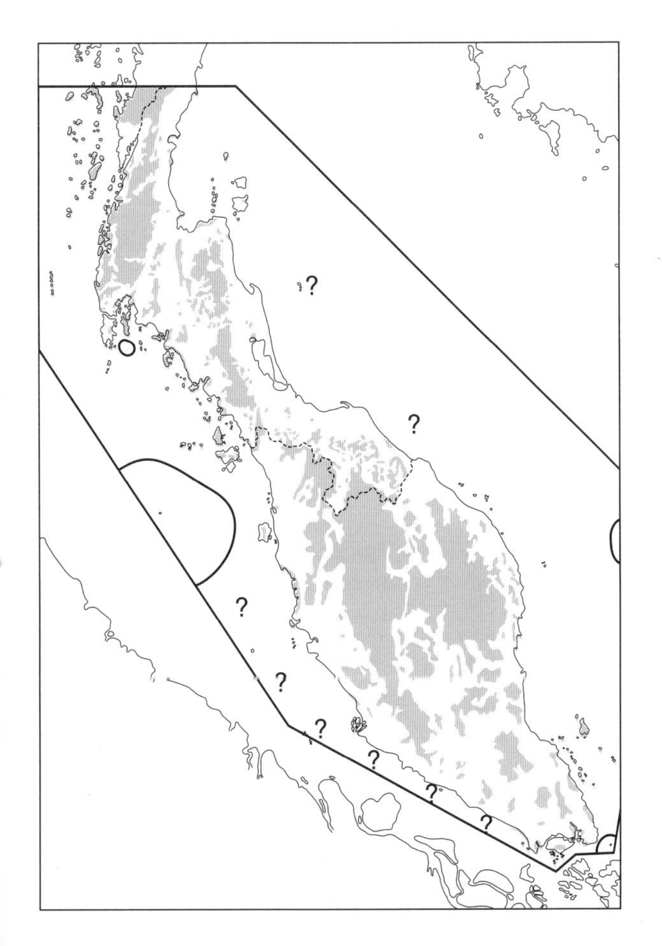

Three hundred and seventy km NW, boobies have been reported at Perak island, latitude 5°43'N, since the 1920s (Gibson-Hill 1956), but this implies nothing about colony start-up date and the Aruas and Perak could both be ancient breeding stations. A first census of Perak island birds (Gibson-Hill 1950c, 1950f), on 9 April 1949, estimated 4500–5000 pairs (possibly as many at this one site then as now breed through the whole of Indonesia) and numbers in January 1954 and February and June 1956 were judged to have been much the same (Madoc 1954, Madoc and Allen 1956). Nineteen years later, counts during 3–4 March 1973 suggested not more than 700–800 breeding pairs (450 occupied nest-sites actually found) (Langham *et al.* 1973). On the following 24–25 July, only 50 pairs among some 500 birds still attended nests (Langham *et al.* 1974), although boobies were more widespread at sea that month, implying fluctuating attendance at the colony. Six visits spread between 22 December 1975 and 19 November 1976 produced between 600 and 60 birds, and at the most recent count on 24–25 January 1980, about 250 (Langham 1976, BR 1980–81).

Extrapolating to a full population figure could only be guesswork, but even if counts were out by a factor of two or more a disastrous decline took place over the period in which Perak island graduated from remote, occasional practice bombing range to nightly anchorage and source of food and fun for fishing crews. Arua-group breeders, only 40 as against 136 km off shore, could have taken the same route much earlier.

In the S China Sea, Haile (1964) found many nesting on Spratly island, Sin Cow reefs, on 3–4 August 1963 (see also Masked Booby) and a few pairs each on neighbouring Amboyna Cay and Layang-layang (Swallow) atoll in the same week. Layang-layang, which has successively been turned into a Malaysian military post and a tourist resort, held a few pairs in March 1985 (Noramly and Noramly 1985) but rats have arrived and the situation there has become uncertain. Elsewhere, odd birds have been encountered on islands in the Inner Gulf of Thailand but without evidence of breeding. In actual E-coast Peninsular waters, a colony is rumoured to have existed on a small island off Nakhon Si Thammarat (Robinson and Kloss 1921–24) but no site has ever been identified. If breeding did once occur in that area it surely ceased long ago.

Recently, other than within about 100 km of Perak island, Brown Boobies have been recorded only sporadically: off the W coast, about 25 between Phuket and Phiphi island on 12 November 1987 (P. Edwards); and off the E coast, two adults and an immature in the Terengganu oil-field in late October 1982 (MBR 1982–83), plus a group possibly of this species 20 km off Narathiwat in late October 1983 (Chavalit 1985). The October dates are of interest relative to dates of Masked Boobies off this coast.

HABITATS AND ECOLOGY. The only SE Asian booby apparently well adapted to life in shallow, continental seas, including over the Sunda shelf.

FORAGING AND FOOD. No information except that it is attracted to shoals of fish pursued by tuna.

SOCIAL ORGANIZATION. Gregarious at breeding sites and, where common, often in groups at sea as well.

MOVEMENTS. No definite information.

SURVIVAL. No information.

SOCIAL INTERACTIONS. No local information.

VOICE. On the nesting ground, males give a goose-like, whistling hiss and a 'ko-el' call, apparently the disyllabic 'wheeze-whistle' greeting to the mate described elsewhere (BWP). Females give a variety of loud, honking quacks and crow-like growls (Madoc 1954).

BREEDING

Nest. On Perak island, nests are built of stone chips gathered into a shallow rim or bowl lined sparsely with feathers, bone fragments and miscellaneous flotsam, on bare summit ground and flattish ledges. Original nest-spacing at this colony was 3–6 m.

Eggs and brood. Eggs are whitish and rough-shelled. Shape subelliptical. Size (mm): 62.7–52.3 × 40.8–39.1 (n=16). Regular full clutch two, with single records of three and four, perhaps from egg-dumping by other females.

Cycle. Of 12 sitting birds captured at night for ringing, five were females and seven males, implying no regular incubation roster, with free mates away perhaps longer than a day at this stage. Incubated from egg one, young hatch asynchronously and only one chick survives long past hatching (the second egg an insurance against early loss of chick one?).

Seasonality. Because Perak island boobies have so constantly been plundered, it has never been possible to work out the colony's natural cycle of breeding, other than to note that stage of activity has at times been fairly well synchronized. Only young were seen in April 1949, perhaps before the era of serious interference. Chicks have otherwise been found in January–April, June, July and November, and eggs in all visit-months, i.e., other than May, September and October. One year's data suggest continuous activity with peaks of egg-laying 6–7 months apart, but there is no knowing how often individual birds would have participated (Gibson-Hill 1950c, Langham 1976, Langham *et al.* 1973, 1974, Madoc 1954).

MOULT. A mid-November adult male from the Arua islands had been flying on three generations of primaries: P8 old and very worn, P1–2 new, the rest, including the wing-tip, intermediate (ZRCNUS), showing that not all moulting bouts run to completion. At Perak island, active wing-moult overlaps breeding. Of 12 incubating birds, of both sexes, captured for ringing on 4 March 1973, 11 were growing 1–3 primaries per wing, mostly at two loci 3–7 feathers apart, with only loose synchrony between wings. Four individuals were renewing the outermost large feather and three the innermost, one of them both. All were also growing tail-feathers, again mostly at two loci per side. At sea in the Straits, adults collected in August and November were moulting P6, P7 and P7 but another on 1 December showed the whole wing fairly new (BMNH, ZRCNUS).

CONSERVATION. By March 1973, Perak island supported a dense population of Malaysian House Rat *Rattus diardii*, introduced and reinforced from fishing boats (Langham *et al.* 1973). While they are unlikely to get past the bill of an ordinarily tight-sitting booby, during night-time ringing operations that month, rats found and broke all eggs within 15 minutes of the sitting bird being removed for processing. Any disturbance that kept birds off their nests after dusk could, therefore, be calamitous – and might help to explain some of the synchrony of breeding events (due to mass replacement) noted in the 1970s. The second-egg insurance adaptation breaks down where rats are involved.

Another, less anticipated, import onto Perak has been plant-life. By 1980, much of the formerly bald island, including parts of the favoured summit ridge, had been colonized by a dense, in places waist-deep mat of grass and ferns (*Nephrolepis*), completely excluding ground-nesting birds and no doubt benefiting from a reduction of trampling by large, webbed feet. However, such effects have been secondary to unfettered predation by people. Other possible colonies this century have been abandoned or hunted out. Without drastic and expensive action (Wells 1991) Brown Boobies will shortly be extinct as breeding residents, indeed perhaps already are since the Perak island colony has not been checked for more than a decade. In the unlikely event that effective protection did become available while a nucleus of population survived, conditions for extensive recolonization would have to be restored by habitat management.

Family ANHINGIDAE

Darters: one species

Darter; Nok Ai-ngua (Thai); Burung Kosa (Malay)

Anhinga melanogaster Pennant 1769, *Indian Zoology*: 13 and plate 12. TL Sri Lanka.
Plate 7

GROUP RELATIONS. Unique sexual dichromatism of Australasian *novaehollandiae* has raised doubt about its status (McAllan and Bruce 1988). Pending other evidence, it stays merged with Old-World Darters in one species, *melanogaster*, of which American *A. anhinga* is probably not more than an allospecies (cf. Johnsgard 1993).

GLOBAL RANGE. Sub-Saharan Africa, Madagascar, W Asia formerly to S Turkey; the Indian subcontinent and Sri Lanka; SE Asia to the Greater Sunda islands and (formerly?) the Philippines; Wallacea, New Guinea and Australia. Vagrant in New Zealand.

IDENTIFICATION/DESCRIPTION. Significantly larger than Little Cormorant and looks big due to proportionately large wings and long, bulky tail. From cormorants by small head, scarcely wider than thin, very long, conspicuously kinked neck, and dagger (rather than hook-tipped) bill. Flies with neck part-stretched, on rather shallow wing-beats, and glides and occasionally soars (with tail part-fanned). Adult females are said to be slightly duller than males. Immatures have body brown and head and neck whitish. Fine 'barring' on the tail is an optical effect of the horizontal corrugation of the outer webs.

Bare-part colours. (Adult) iris yellow; upper mandible brown or blackish, lower yellowish; feet black (Oates 1883).

Size (mm). (Skins: 3 adults, none sexed): wing 343–358; tail 232–238; bill 72–105; bill from mouth-corner 98–114; tarsus 40–41 (BMNH).

Weight. No data.

DISTRIBUTION. Known only from the W-coast plain. Historical summary: *Pak, Phu, Pra, Pek, Sel, Mel, Joh*, including Dayang Bunting island (Langkawi group, *Ked*). One claimed from Nakhon Si Thammarat (Riley 1938) is wrongly located. A check against itineraries shows that on the date in question the collector was in Nakhon Ratchasima, E Thailand.

GEOGRAPHICAL VARIATION. Subspecies *melanogaster*, of S and E Asia.

STATUS AND POPULATION. A possible former resident, local and apparently sparse; now vagrant. Darters vanished from the Peninsula in advance of declines over most of the rest of continental SE Asia, where some still breed in S Vietnam and probably Cambodia. Most local records date back more than a century, including one from Phuket (Deignan 1963) and mid-nineteenth century specimens from mainland Penang, Melaka and Johor (BMNH). Kelham (1881–83) reported small numbers in the Perak river valley in 1877, and in April 1879 collected one out of a party of some 15 on a swampland pool along the Kesang river, Melaka/Johor border. W.L. Abbott took one at Maliwun, Pakchan, in March 1900 (Riley 1938) and Robinson and Chasen (1936) give the impression of a regular presence on Dayang Bunting lake. One was definitely there in late November/early December 1907. Sight-records of about that period claimed from the headwaters of the Perak and Pahang rivers were rejected (Robinson and Kloss 1910–11) and the only certain record since is of an adult at Puchong, Selangor, on 14 December 1991, evidently in transit.

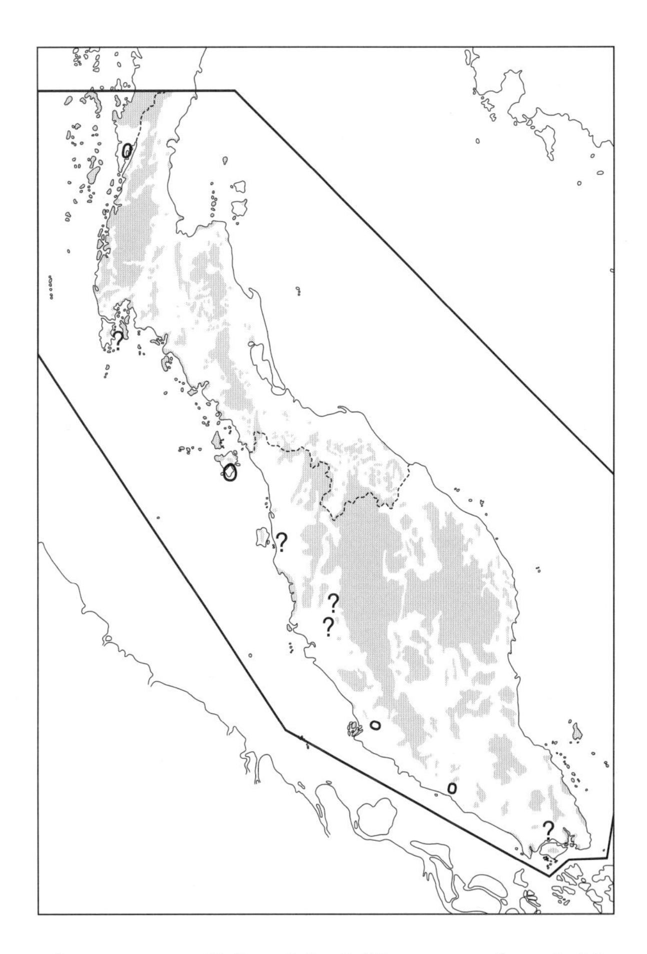

The Puchong record demonstrates capacity for long-distance wandering. Perhaps such visits were once commoner. If some did once nest in the Peninsula, such easily approached birds, probably flightless after breeding, would long ago have been egged and hunted out from boats, as is now happening in Sarawak (E.L. Bennett). On the other hand, Darters have never been recorded from that part of Sumatra directly opposite the Peninsula (CLBS), whereas they are still quite widespread south of latitude about 1°S (Verheugt *et al.* 1993).

HABITATS AND ECOLOGY. Kelham reported them from lowland river-courses through swamp-forest. The Puchong bird was on flooded tin-workings. Like cormorants, Darters spend much time sunning outstretched wings from some exposed snag.

FORAGING AND FOOD. Said to dive from low perches but the main hunting mode is to swim quietly with body submerged, smoothly withdrawing the head under water at intervals to forage for a few metres. Impales prey on one or both mandibles, and back-inclined serrations at the tip of the mandible cutting-edges are an efficient holdfast. Held up, the disembodied head and neck bob forward and twist about, evoking the alternative popular name of Snakebird.

SOCIAL ORGANIZATION. Where they are still numerous elsewhere in the Sunda region, Darters breed in loose groups in low trees over lakes, rivers and mangrove creeks, and roost gregariously, often on a high, dead crown.

MOVEMENTS. Evidently some long-distance dispersal, but no specific information.

SURVIVAL. No information.

SOCIAL INTERACTIONS. No information.

VOICE. No information.

BREEDING. No population.

MOULT. No wing-moult seen. A Johor adult (undated) showed all-new, fine-pointed flight-feathers and the whole tail growing in unison.

CONSERVATION. No relevant local issues although Asian populations are near-threatened (BTW2). Perhaps large mangrove reserves such as envisaged on the Perak and Selangor coasts could be re-stocked.

Family PHALACROCORACIDAE

Cormorants: two species

Great Cormorant; Nok Gaa-nam Yai (Thai); Burung Pependang Air (Malay)

Phalacrocorax carbo (Linnaeus) 1758, *Systema Naturae* 10(1): 133. TL northern Scandinavia.
Plate 7

GROUP RELATIONS. Less marine than NE Asian *P. capillatus* (Japanese Cormorant), but these similar-looking birds breed more or less parapatrically and are treatable as a superspecies.

GLOBAL RANGE. Breeds between the arctic and S-temperate zones: from extreme E Canada and the N Atlantic islands across Eurasia to Sakhalin and Japan; patchily through Africa; through the Indian subcontinent and Sri Lanka; historically, China including Hainan; SE Asia to Sumatra and the N Philippines; and New Zealand and Australia, mainly south of 20°S. Gone from most of SE Asia. Sumatran lake-dwelling groups vanished in the 1920s and possibly the only recent breeders of the region have been at mixed waterbird colonies in extreme S Vietnam (Scott 1989).

Many continental populations migrate, in E Asia reaching N Luzon, NW Borneo and, formerly, the Peninsula; perhaps also Sumatra.

IDENTIFICATION/DESCRIPTION. Muscovy Duck size. Swims tail-low, body often deep in the water and with long, heavy, hook-tipped bill canted up at a slight angle. Flies with rather shallow wing-beats and, as in all cormorants, neck extended. Adult from Little Cormorant by size and by white of lower face. Immatures of both lack iridescence and are extensively white below, from the chin. At rest, both species spend long periods upright on an exposed perch sunning spread wings (see also Darter).

Bare-part colours. Iris blue- to pale green (immature), emerald-green (adult); bill tip and culmen black, the rest dirty white (immature), yellowish (adult); gular skin chrome-yellow; feet black (BMNH, Kelham 1881-83, ZRCNUS).

Size (mm). (Skins: 1 adult male, 2 unsexed immatures): wing 354 and 331, 334; tail 162, 163 (immatures only); bill 64.2–64.8 (all); tarsus 60.2–62.5 (all) (ZRCNUS).

Weight. No data.

DISTRIBUTION. Historical summary: *Sur, Nak, Tra, Son, Pat, Ked, Pek, Phg, Sel, Mel, Joh,* with additional island records from Lalang (Perak estuary) and Phangan.

GEOGRAPHICAL VARIATION. Given nearest records of possible southern *novaehollandiae* are from the further edge of Wallacea (CLBW), all Peninsular occurrences are presumed to have been Eurasian *sinensis* Blumenbach 1798 (TL China).

STATUS AND POPULATION. A former non-breeding visitor, now extinct. All documented records are of immatures or, except one, adults in non-breeding plumage. Once common on the NE coast but in decline by at least 75 years ago. Thus, 'fairly numerous' in Pattani bay in 1901; four off the entrance to Songkhla lagoon in early May 1913 and 'common' round Phangan island (Surat Thani) at the end of that month (Ogilvie-Grant 1906, Robinson 1914b). Subsequently, singles taken in Songkhla in 1915, Nakhon Si Thammarat in 1924 and NW Trang apparently in 1926 are the only reports from the Thai provinces (AMNH, Baker 1919–20, BMNH, ZRCNUS).

South of the border, about ten recorded up to 1910, from Kedah (uniquely, one in breeding plumage, undated but with bare-part details that could only have been taken fresh) south to Johor (AMNH, BMNH, Hartert 1902, Kelham 1881–83, Robinson and Chasen 1936, ZRCNUS). An immature identified at the Lake gardens lake, Kuala Lumpur, on 10 August 1951 (G.C. Madoc) is by far the most recent record anywhere. After this interval, and in contrast to Borneo where occasional birds still occur (Perennou *et al.* 1990), it would be safe to conclude that whatever breeding population once fed the Peninsula with migrants is now extinct.

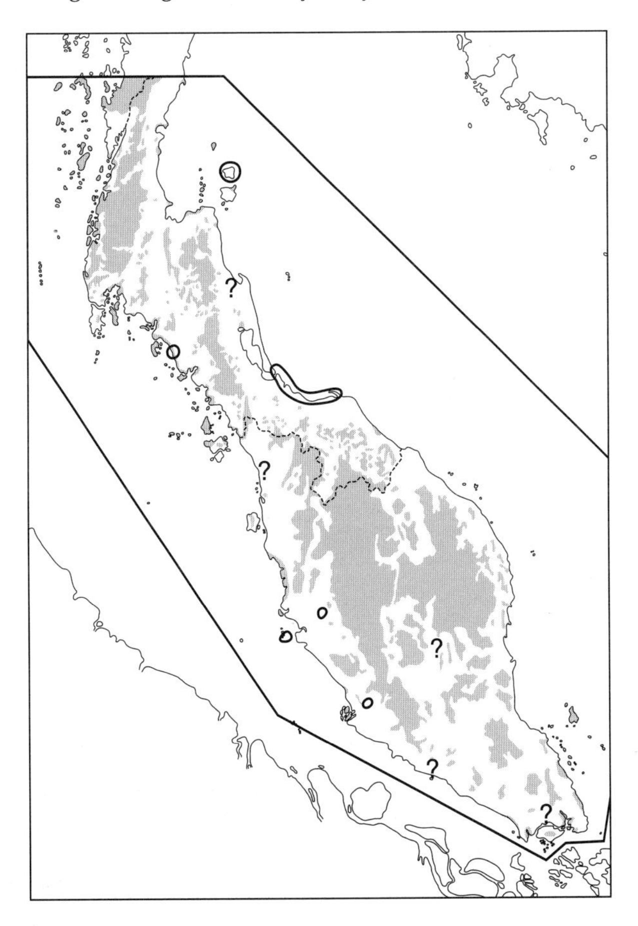

HABITATS AND ECOLOGY. Records divide fairly equally between fresh water and the sea, suggesting no particular habitat bias. Inland collection sites include river sand-bars and ponds.

FORAGING AND FOOD. No specific information.

SOCIAL ORGANIZATION. Generally solitary, with a few records of loose groups.

MOVEMENTS. Dated records fall during late April–early November, with most in August, implying a tropical rather than temperate-zone source of migrants (former large colonies on the lower Sittang river, Burma, are said to have been active in the northern winter: Oates 1883).

SURVIVAL. No information.

SOCIAL INTERACTIONS. No information.

VOICE. No information.

BREEDING. No population.

MOULT. Replacement of the inner primaries is regular-descendant, but an undated adult growing P6 had only P7 old, implying precocious moult of the wing-tip. Adults in active wing-moult in late May (P2) and mid August (P6); immatures suspended in April and August, but one growing P7 in mid October.

CONSERVATION. No relevant issues.

Little Cormorant; Nok Gaa-nam Lek (Thai); Burung Pependang Kecil (Malay)

Microcarbo niger (Vieillot) 1817, *Nouveau Dictionnaire d'Histoire Naturelle* 8: 88. TL Bangladesh.
Plate 7

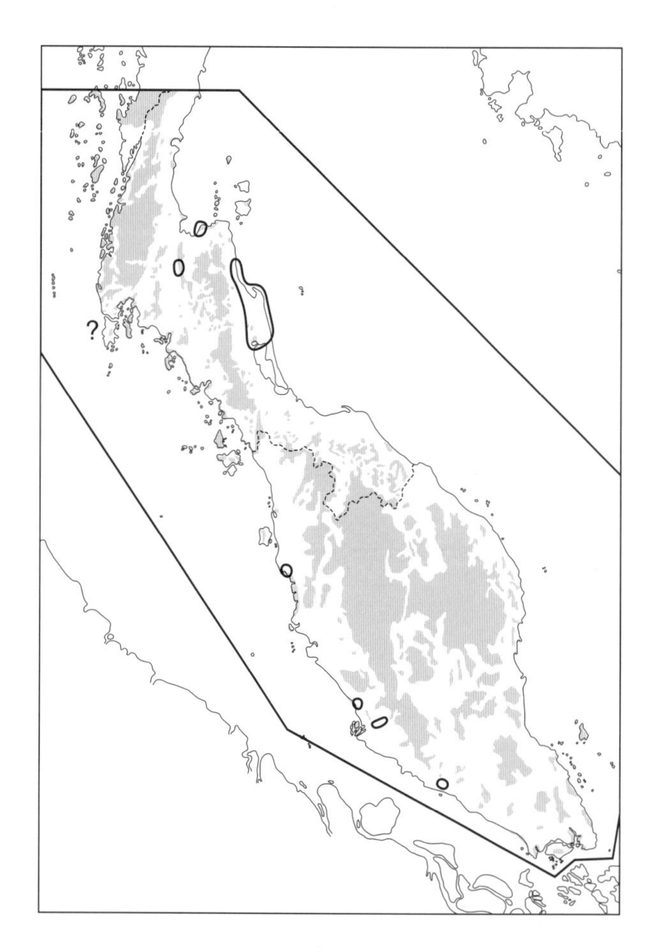

GROUP RELATIONS. Commonly not split from genus *Phalacrocorax* but skeletal anatomy and behaviour (Siegel-Causey 1988, van Tets 1976) suggest the Old-World–Pacific 'reed' cormorants are a separable group. *M. niger* forms a superspecies with allopatric Wallacean–Australasian *M. melanoleucos* (Little Pied Cormorant).

GLOBAL RANGE. From S Pakistan through the Indian subcontinent and Sri Lanka; S Yunnan (AMNH); continental SE Asia to the Peninsula and, south of the equator, the Barito basin and probably other Kalimantan wetlands, Java and far-S Sumatra (possible dispersants from W Java: D.A. Holmes).

IDENTIFICATION/DESCRIPTION. Black, crow-sized, with tapering (and for a cormorant comparatively stubby) hook-tipped bill. Swims 'tail-low', basks with outstretched wings, and flies with neck straight and on relatively rapid wing-beats, like Great Cormorant. From it by much smaller size, proportionately shorter bill and longer tail, and from possibly occurring Indian Cormorant *Phalacrocorax fuscicollis* by lack of yellow on gular skin. A light scatter of white filoplumes over the head of adults is lost post-breeding, and non-breeding adults have chin and throat white. Immatures are mostly white below, dull sooty brown above.

Bare-part colours. (Adult) iris green; facial skin blackish, gular pinkish to (summer) purple-black; upper mandible and bill-tip black-brown, lower mandible base pinkish to purplish; legs and feet black (Johnsgard 1993, Robinson and Chasen 1936).

Size (mm). (Skin: 1 female; adult): wing 205; bill from mouth-corner 57.1 (TISTR).

Weight. No data.

DISTRIBUTION. Local in the north; hardly more than vagrant south of Thalae Noi. Historical summary: *Sur, Nak, Phu, Pht, Son, Pek, Sel, Mel,* with no additional island records.

GEOGRAPHICAL VARIATION. None recognized.

STATUS AND POPULATION. Local, and sparse to common; an apparent non-breeding migrant but seen on inland rivers of Surat Thani in late June/early July; in June 1995 over 400 roosted in mangroves at Pak Ying, Nakhon Si Thammarat (BCSTB-11, -12); and entirely absent from Thalae Noi only in July, hence presence overlaps the breeding-season in continental Thailand. Most are at Thalae Noi, where numbers build up in October, with evening flights rising to 300–400 birds as of January and remaining high until April (Anonymous 1981, Holmes and Wells 1975, Storer 1976). West of the dividing range, an undated record from Phuket (Deignan 1963) and a handful of sightings of non-breeders or immatures on the Malaysian W-coast plain south to Melaka (AWB, BMP5, MBR 1984–85, 1986–87).

HABITATS AND ECOLOGY. In parts of SE Asia, breeds in mangrove forest but, like other 'reed' cormorants, forages only in fresh water. The Thalae Noi system is fresh; other habitats have been subcoastal paddyland, aquaculture ponds, flooded tin-mine workings and, perhaps on passage, forested rivers. Exceptional brackish sites include a marshy pond on bunded former mangrove-land of the Kuala Selangor Nature Park.

Roosts gregariously. Sites at Thalae Noi have not been located but the mass evening flight is typically northward (Storer 1976), towards paperbark forest. At Sungai Way, Selangor, during 1–29 January 1969, one roosted nightly with Cattle and other egrets in a *Phragmites* reedbed (BR 1969).

FORAGING AND FOOD. Hunts by diving from the surface, socially where numerous (packs of up to 100 birds noted at Thalae Noi).

SOCIAL ORGANIZATION. In their regular range, non-breeders are gregarious at all times.

MOVEMENTS. Extreme dates of non-breeders on the Malaysian W-coast plain are 3 November and 7 February; the season is much longer in the north.

SURVIVAL. No information.

SOCIAL INTERACTIONS. Apart from collective hunting, no information.

VOICE. No information.

BREEDING. No confirmed population.

MOULT. An adult from Thalae Noi dated 12 December showed central tail-feathers in growth (TISTR).

CONSERVATION. Sensitive to management of waterfowl habitat at Thalae Noi reserve. A defect of the reserve is that it incorporates none of the hinterland of marsh on which most life-forms ultimately depend, undoubtedly including some of the cormorant diet. The planning concept needs re-thinking.

Family PELECANIDAE

Pelicans: two species

Spot-billed Pelican; Nok Gra-thung (Thai); Burung Undan Paruh Titik (Malay)

Pelecanus philippensis Gmelin 1789, *Systema Naturae* 13(2): 571. TL Philippines.

GROUP RELATIONS. Most similar to and probably forms a superspecies with African *P. rufescens* (Roseate Pelican), to which some have added much larger, N-temperate-zone *P. crispus* (Dalmatian Pelican).

GLOBAL RANGE. Formerly, bred through the Indian subcontinent and Sri Lanka; perhaps SE China; continental SE Asia to Cambodia and S Vietnam, and Sumatra and parts of the Philippines. Currently, only in SE India and Sri Lanka, around Tonle Sap lake, Cambodia (AWB, ICF), with perhaps a few pairs left in mixed waterbird colonies of extreme S Vietnam (G.E. Morris, Scott 1989), and a small group of possible breeders on the Banyuasin delta, SE Sumatra. Forest clearance up to the 1930s eliminated the largest recorded colony (of any pelican species) from the lower Sittang river, S Burma (Smythies 1953).

Dispersants have occurred from southern China to Mindanao and Java, and a small remnant of former large congregations in the central plains and Inner Gulf of Thailand (Gyldenstolpe 1916) is still annual, mostly during December–March. Vagrant in the Peninsula.

IDENTIFICATION/DESCRIPTION. Line drawing, page 64. All pelicans fly with deep, deliberate wing-strokes and long, interposed glides; head tucked well back into body. Groups adopt line-ahead formation but also soar on thermals. Non-breeding adults are pale grey with a short, upstanding crest (giving the hind-crown an angular shape) and mane fringing the back of the neck. Crestless juveniles are brown, often dark (discoloured?) on the underparts. Head, neck and upper body lighten as of the first moult. Apart from dark primaries, the underwing shows white at all ages (Harrison 1985). From Great White Pelican by wing-pattern, pouch-colour and, in close view, feathering of the forehead coming to a concave margin over the bill.

Bare-part colours. Iris dark brown (immature), pale yellow (adult); facial skin yellow, liver-pink anteriorly; gular pouch plain dull pink (immature), dull purple blotched and spotted blue-black (adult); bill pinkish yellow margined yellow to orange with, in adult, a row of blue-black spots along the side of the upper mandible; legs and feet clay-pink to grey (immature), black-brown (adult) (Oates 1878).

Size (mm). (Skins: 1 adult male, 1 unsexed immature): bill 340 and 283; bill from mouth-corner of adult 355 (BMNH). No other data.

Weight. No data.

DISTRIBUTION. No records east of the Main Range. Historical summary: *Sur, Nak, Pht, Tra, Son, Pat, Ked, Pra, Pek, Sel, Mel, Joh, Sin,* and Penang island.

GEOGRAPHICAL VARIATION. None recognized.

STATUS AND POPULATION. Once numerous but with no record of breeding; now only vagrant. In the mid-nineteenth century, Maingay (1868) and Hume and Davison (1878) recorded the irregular appearance

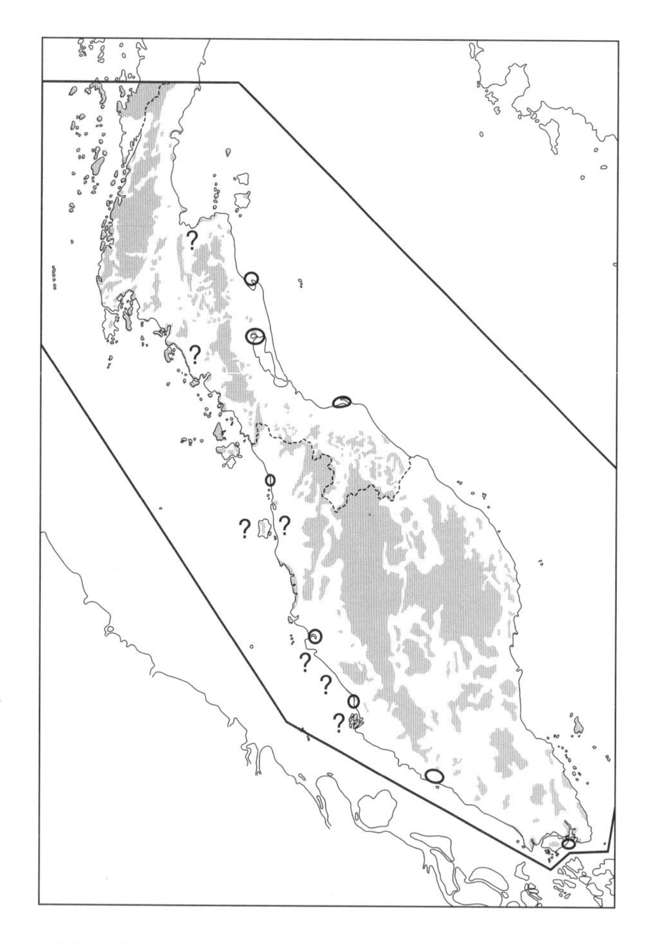

of 'prodigious' numbers of pelicans, guessed to have been mainly Spot-bills, on the Melaka Straits coast. Hornaday (1885) saw pelicans at Jeram, Selangor, in June 1878 and Robinson (1927) mentions great flocks that once gathered off Selangor between the Kelang and Bernam rivers. Elsewhere, he saw hundreds of pelicans in Pattani bay in 1901 (Annandale and Robinson 1903), some 'probably *P. philippinensis*' on mudflats off Kuala Kedah in late November 1907 (Robinson and Kloss 1910–11) and in later years this species in Surat Thani and the marshes of Songkhla, Phatthalung and Trang (Robinson and Kloss 1921–24).

These gatherings have vanished, and loners at Thalae Noi in July and September 1979 plus 26 pelicans, presumed to have been Spot-bills, off Talumphuk spit, Pak Phanang bay, Nakhon Si Thammarat, on 30 August 1988 (Anonymous 1981, OBCB-8) are the only ones reported from peninsular Thailand in over 50 years (Riley 1938). South of the border, modern pelican records are exclusively from the W and S coasts: a bird not identified to species over paddyland near Bukit Serindit, Melaka, on 14 July 1953, with local rumour of another there a year or two earlier (Bromley 1953); nine apparent Spot-bills (identified from museum specimens) on the lower Perak river in July 1957 and six in the same area 'about May' 1960 (Gee 1962); a flock of at least 15 pelicans, unidentified, flying off Ponggol point, Singapore, into the Johor Straits on 3 December 1960 (BR 1964).

No possible Spot-bill has been seen since and decline of southern records may be connected with the fate of estuarine pelicans in Sumatra.

HABITATS AND ECOLOGY. Coasts and tidal rivers, with use of freshwater wetlands in the north.

FORAGING AND FOOD. No local information.

SOCIAL ORGANIZATION. Gregarious, in the past evidently on a grand scale.

MOVEMENTS. The few clearly datable records cover May–September and November–December. Possibly more than one breeding population fed migrants into the Peninsula, on different annual schedules.

SURVIVAL. No information.

SOCIAL INTERACTIONS. No information.

VOICE. No information.

BREEDING. No population.

MOULT. No data.

CONSERVATION. No relevant local issues, but globally vulnerable (BTW2).

Top: Great White Pelican
Bottom: Spot-billed Pelican

Great White Pelican; (no Thai name); Burung Undan Putih (Malay)

Pelecanus onocrotalus Linnaeus 1758, *Systema Naturae* 10(1): 132. TL Caspian Sea.

GROUP RELATIONS. Free-standing.

GLOBAL RANGE. Breeds sporadically through Africa and temperate to subtropical Eurasia, historically from central Europe to the Kazakh/China border, south to Iran and the NW Indian subcontinent (Rann of Kutch). Old specimens exist from S Vietnam (BMNH) but breeding in the Mekong wetlands is unproven. Northern populations migrate, including into China, the N Indian subcontinent and Burma (where they arrive about August and leave in January/February), straggling as far as Java and Bali (Whitten 1989).

IDENTIFICATION/DESCRIPTION. Second largest living pelican. Immature head, neck and upperparts are pale grey, scapulars darker, upper wing-coverts pale brown and underparts white. The change to full white adult plumage occupies several moults. In overhead flight, at all ages, from Spot-bill by secondaries as well as primaries black to their bases, contrasting with pale coverts. Gular pouch dull to bright yellow rather than pink or purple; feathering of the forehead comes to a narrow point above the bill.

Bare-part colours. Iris orange (immature), red (adult); facial skin violet (immature), yellow (adult); gular pouch ochre-yellow (immature), rich yellow (adult); bill blue (immature), blue with red margins (adult); feet pale pinkish at all ages.

Size (mm). (Skins: 1 adult male, 1 unsexed immature): bill 382 and 282 (BMNH). No other data.

Weight. No data.

DISTRIBUTION. Perhaps passed over in the north. Historical summary: *Pra*, *Sel*, *Mel*, and Penang island.

GEOGRAPHICAL VARIATION. None recognized.

STATUS AND POPULATION. Vagrant from confirmable records, but migrant pelican flocks may once have included a proportion of Great Whites, as they are known to have done in Tenasserim. The few reports are all from the W-coast plain, south to Melaka (a bird claimed for Singapore appears to have been from a zoo: ZRCNUS), and mostly nineteenth century (Gibson-Hill 1949b). One on a dredge-mine lagoon at Puchong, Selangor, in November 1956 (Cant 1957–58) and an adult identified from wing-pattern and pouch-colour on coastal mudflats at Penaga, mainland Penang, on 19 August 1988 (ENGGANG-1) are the only modern occurrences. 17 July for an old specimen from Kelang, Selangor, is the only other firm date (BMNH).

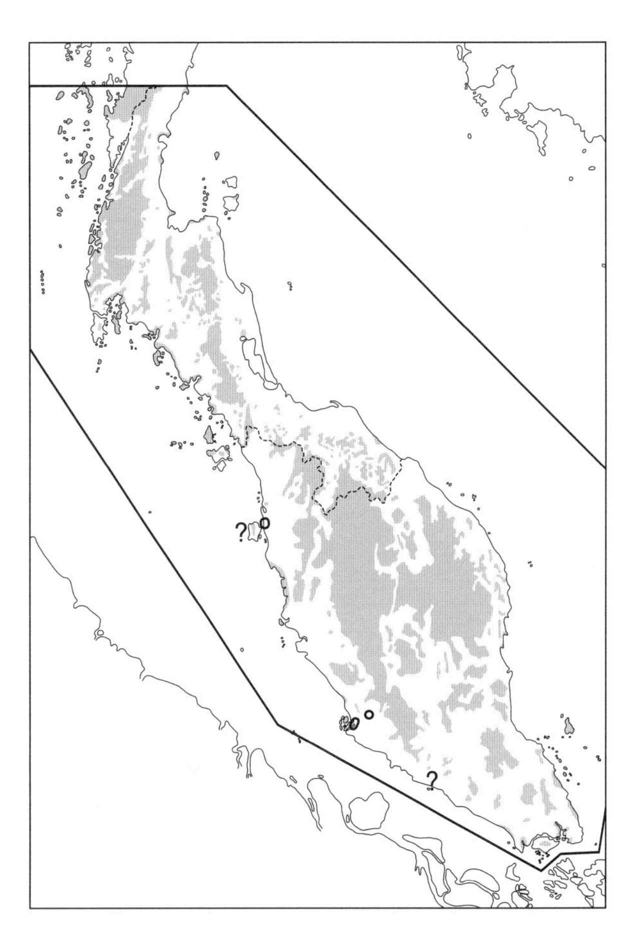

HABITATS AND ECOLOGY. Coasts and open fresh water.

FORAGING AND FOOD. No information.

SOCIAL ORGANIZATION. No information.

MOVEMENTS. Dates accord with the known migrant season in Burma.

SURVIVAL. No information.

SOCIAL INTERACTIONS. No information.

VOICE. No information.

BREEDING. No population.

MOULT. The July adult had primaries 1–5 fresh, others much older and more worn.

CONSERVATION. No relevant issues.

Family FREGATIDAE

Frigatebirds: three species

Frigatebirds spend most of their lives flying. With 40 percent more wing area relative to body weight than other seabirds of their size (Nelson 1975) they conserve energy by soaring, and may hang for hours on up-draught over small islands. Food they snatch in the air or from the water-surface while in flight, and neither swim nor plunge-dive. All species are large with very long, pointed wings angled forward and conspicuously flexed at the wrist in most flight-modes, a long, two-pronged tail and long, hooked-tipped bill – massive in Christmas Island Frigatebird. More or less instantly recognizable to family, they are hard to place at species level. Under most field circumstances, immatures are next to impossible (all with white to rusty head, white under-body and variable development of a dark breast-band, according to age). In good light, full adults can be separated by the distribution of white on otherwise black underparts.

Christmas Island Frigatebird; Nok John Salad Go Kristmaas (Thai); Burung Simbang Pulau Kristmas (Malay)

Fregata andrewsi Mathews 1914, *Austral Avian Record* 2(6): 120. TL Christmas Island, Indian Ocean.

Plate 9

GROUP RELATIONS. Free-standing.

GLOBAL RANGE. Endemic in SE Asia. Proven to breed only on Christmas island, south of Java, where three colonies totalling not more than 1600 pairs nest in the crowns of the taller strand-line trees, particularly *Terminalia catappa.* Non-breeders have wandered west to Kenya, east to Timor and northern Australia and, perhaps, north to the coast of S China, but main concentrations of population at sea are around the breeding island and in the southern S China Sea. Between these areas, apparently sparse though a few sightings have been made in the Sunda Straits (D.A. Holmes) and off SE Sumatra. Gibson-Hill (1947) believed in a second, S China Sea, breeding station somewhere in the Anamba or Natuna groups of islands but on no evidence beyond F.N. Chasen's report of a roost of 'thousands' on Rinji islet, Anambas, in September–October 1925. Some are now known to make regular use of non-breeder roosts as far north as Mantanani Kecil island, NW Sabah and, west of the Peninsula, islands in Phangnga bay.

IDENTIFICATION/DESCRIPTION. Largest frigatebird of the region. Adult males have the abdomen white back to near vent and more or less square-cut against the lower breast. In females, white extends forward to the upper breast and sides of the neck, with a narrow spur running out onto the base of the wing.

Bare-part colours. (Adult) iris dark brown; eyelids black with a light blue patch on the lower lid (male), all pinkish mauve (female); gular skin orange-red (male), pinkish mauve (female); bill blackish (male), rose-pink (female); feet black with pale pink soles (male), all pale pink (female) (Chasen 1933, Gibson-Hill 1947).

Size (mm). (Skin: 1 female from Tioman; adult): wing 650; tail 458; bill 134.5; within the ranges of 17 from Rinji and 4 from Christmas island. As in all frigatebirds, males are smaller. Five from these two sites measure: wing 605–632; tail 396 (1 Rinji bird only); bill 105–114 (BMNH, ZRCNUS). No other data.

Weight. No data.

DISTRIBUTION. Off all coasts but mainly the NW and E.

GEOGRAPHICAL VARIATION. None recognized.

STATUS AND POPULATION. A non-breeding visitor, more or less local, and sparse to common. Recorded over the whole E coast (Deignan 1963) including on 14 May 1988 one far inland over Chiew Larn reservoir, Surat Thani (OBCB-8). Apparently commoner in Malaysian waters, especially around the Pahang–Johor archipelago where they roost together with more numerous Lesser Frigatebirds *F. ariel* on Rengis, a wooded islet just off the beach of Tekek bay, Tioman island (BMP5, Medway 1966).

Southward, rare around Singapore, the only definite record a male over the main island on 30 May 1986 (C.J. Hails). Apparently scarce also in the Melaka Straits (groups of three and six reported from mid-Straits waters on 7 July and 6 August (E.F. Allen 1951a, Bourne 1966). Frigatebirds often seen over Perak

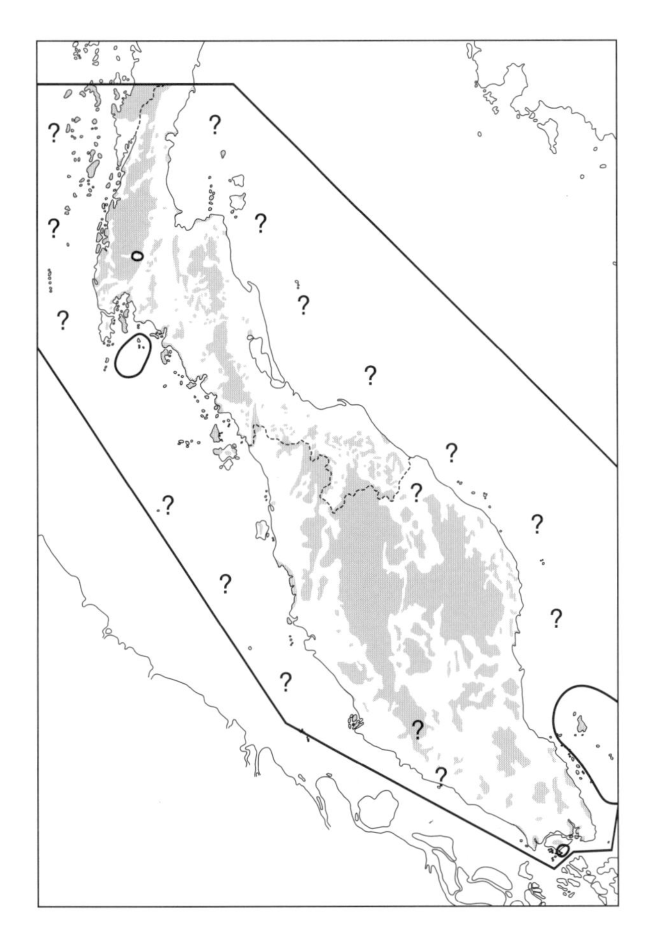

island have not been identified but north of the Straits numerous again at a mixed-species roost on the Ko Bida sea-stacks, Phiphi island group (a rumoured former frigatebird breeding-station at the mouth of Phangnga bay: P.D. Round). This gathering area may be reached directly from the ocean and, possibly occasionally, from across the Peninsula. Beside the Chiew Larn record, unidentified frigatebirds have been seen inland in Kelantan and Melaka, and over the summit ridge of the Main Range in Negeri Sembilan (BR 1965, 1967, Young 1940).

The breeding schedule is biennial but young stay at sea for up to seven years (Nelson 1975), which means that birds in all plumage states are likely to be found far from the breeding island, using non-breeder roosts in all months of the year. No local frigatebird roost has yet been monitored regularly but the impression is of usage by one or more species year-round. There are definite records of Christmas Island Frigatebirds around the Peninsula in December–February, April, May, July and August (but reflecting perhaps not more than the periods most comfortable for boat journeys).

HABITATS AND ECOLOGY. Off the E coast, found mainly beyond the 10-fathom contour, which may help to explain the paucity of records from the Melaka Straits. On Rengis islet, frigatebirds tend to roost on outer, exposed branches, giving themselves maximum launching space at dawn. Because of the take-off momentum they need to generate, Christmas Island Frigatebirds must also use relatively high perches (Gibson-Hill 1947, Medway 1966).

FORAGING AND FOOD. Nelson (1975) points out that all frigatebirds catch most food through their own fishing efforts and that much self-taken prey of this and other species is squid and flying-fish. There are few good observations of frigatebirds hunting in Peninsular waters but they actively follow fishing boats. One report of kleptoparasitism from near Mersing, Johor: five chasing a White-bellied Fish Eagle, which eventually relinquished its catch (MBR 1982–83).

SOCIAL ORGANIZATION. Gregarious at roost. Daytime soarers converge on the best atmospheric lift conditions.

MOVEMENTS. Not investigated.

SURVIVAL. No information.

SOCIAL INTERACTIONS. No information.

VOICE. No information.

BREEDING. No population.

MOULT. An adult female from Rengis growing P10 (the second longest) on 7 April. Among 18 collected on Rinji, about 200 km NE of Rengis, on 11 September (BMNH, ZRCNUS), 11 females and a male showed active moult between P5 and P9, mostly at two loci and with evidence of earlier renewal of the wing-tip. What, if anything, this implies about Rengis versus Rinji schedules is not yet clear. A well-known feature of tail-moult is that the long outer feathers are mostly not replaced together.

CONSERVATION. Not obviously at risk in Peninsular waters, but vulnerable globally (BTW2). Much depends on curbing poaching at the Christmas island breeding colonies (Stokes 1988) and solving its true status elsewhere.

Great Frigatebird; Nok John Salad Yai (Thai); Burung Simbang Besar (Malay)

Fregata minor (Gmelin) 1789, *Systema Naturae* 13(2): 572. TL Christmas Island, Indian Ocean. Plate 9

GROUP RELATIONS. Free-standing.

GLOBAL RANGE. Widespread in the Pacific and Indian oceans. Breeds on N Keeling and Christmas islands (where like *andrewsi* it chooses tall tree-crowns, but inland rather than along the shore) and at several sites in E Indonesia, formerly west to the Bawean island group, E Java Sea; also in the Sulu Sea.

IDENTIFICATION/DESCRIPTION. Intermediate size. Adult males are the only frigatebirds of the region lacking all white. Pale median wing-coverts, forming a grey bar along the dorsal surface of the wing (also in Christmas Island Frigatebird), make a further check against male Lesser Frigatebird (in which they match the rest of the upperparts). Like Lesser Frigatebirds, adult females have black up the centre of the belly. They are otherwise white to the chin (some individuals greyish on the throat), sharply demarcated against black cap, upper neck and axillaries, but lack a white spur out to the wing (Nelson 1975).

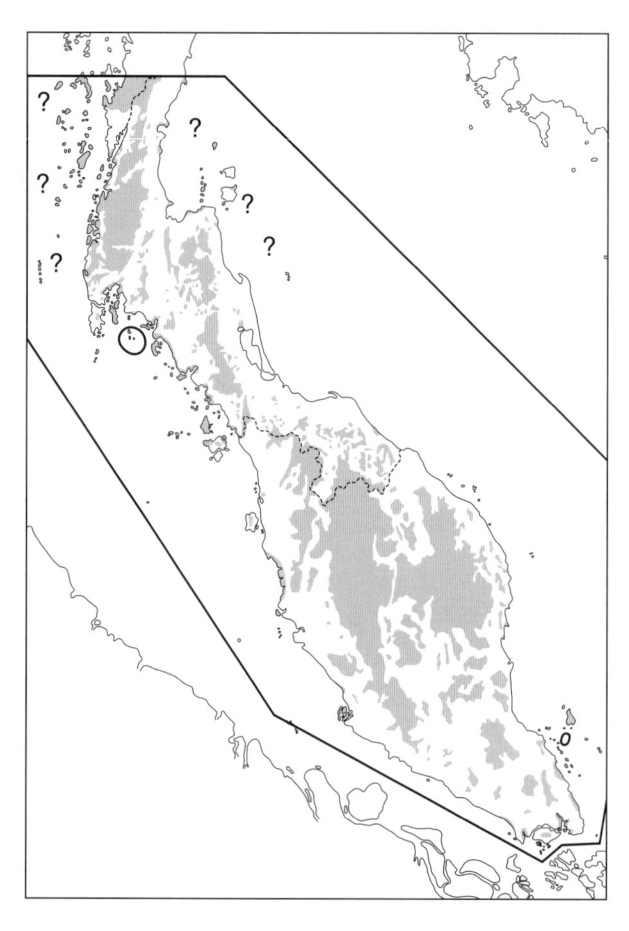

Bare-part colours. (Christmas and Cocos-Keeling adults) iris dark brown; eyelids black, with or without a white spot on the lower lid (male), all pink to red (female); throat-skin of non-breeders dull reddish; bill slaty blue (male); pink to slaty blue (female); feet dark reddish brown to dark slate with pale pink soles (male), all pale pink (female) (Gibson-Hill 1947, 1950b).

Size (mm). (Skins: males and females from Christmas and Cocos-Keeling islands; adult): wing 563–582 and 587–606; tail 379–391 and 404–415; bill 96–102 and 107–116; tarsus not measured (Gibson-Hill 1947, 1950b, Nelson 1975).

Weight. No data.

DISTRIBUTION. NW and E coasts.

GEOGRAPHICAL VARIATION. Great Frigatebirds of the surrounding region are nominate *minor* but central Pacific-ringed migrant *palmerstoni* have been recovered as far west as the Philippines (CLBP).

STATUS AND POPULATION. A non-breeding visitor, local and sparse (although more attention to frigatebird identification may revise this assessment). Deignan (1963) listed it off both Thai coasts south of the Kra isthmus and some have since been detected in the mouth of Phangnga bay: two males and a female in a flock of about 300 frigatebirds near the Phiphi group on 14 May 1990, three there again in May 1996 and two males near Maa island (BBCB-7, BCSTB-13, J. Eames, C. Robson). An adult male in a flock of 50 frigatebirds attending fishing boats northeast of Babi Besar island, Pahang–Johor archipelago, on 5 May 1986 (MBR 1986–87) is the only good southern record. CLBS lists sightings in the S Riau archipelago, but not recorded yet from Singapore waters. Coincidence of dates in May could merely reflect calm weather for sea-trips.

HABITATS AND ECOLOGY. More strictly a blue-water bird than other local species (Nelson 1975).

FORAGING AND FOOD. No specific information.

SOCIAL ORGANIZATION. As other species, with which non-breeders roost communally.

MOVEMENTS. No information.

SURVIVAL. No information.

SOCIAL INTERACTIONS. No information.

VOICE. No information.

BREEDING. No population.

MOULT. No data.

CONSERVATION. No issues identified.

Lesser Frigatebird; Nok John Salad Lek (Thai); Burung Simbang Kecil (Malay)

Fregata ariel (G.R. Gray) 1845, *The Genera of Birds* 3: 669 and plate 185. TL Raine Island, Queensland. Plate 9

GROUP RELATIONS. Free-standing.

GLOBAL RANGE. Pantropical, and to the subtropics of the Indian Ocean and Pacific. In SE Asia, breeds on N Keeling island and probably at one or more sites in E Indonesia (de Korte 1991); in the past, possibly also in W Indonesia (see below). Northward, colonies are on record from the Xisha group, off Vietnam.

IDENTIFICATION/DESCRIPTION. Smallest frigatebird. Adult males are separable from male Great by a white cross-bar on the side of the breast forming a short axillary spur, and uniform black upper wing-coverts. Like Great, adult females are black over the centre of the abdomen, sharply demarcated from pale rusty to white breast. White extends to a narrow collar but head and (importantly) throat are black.

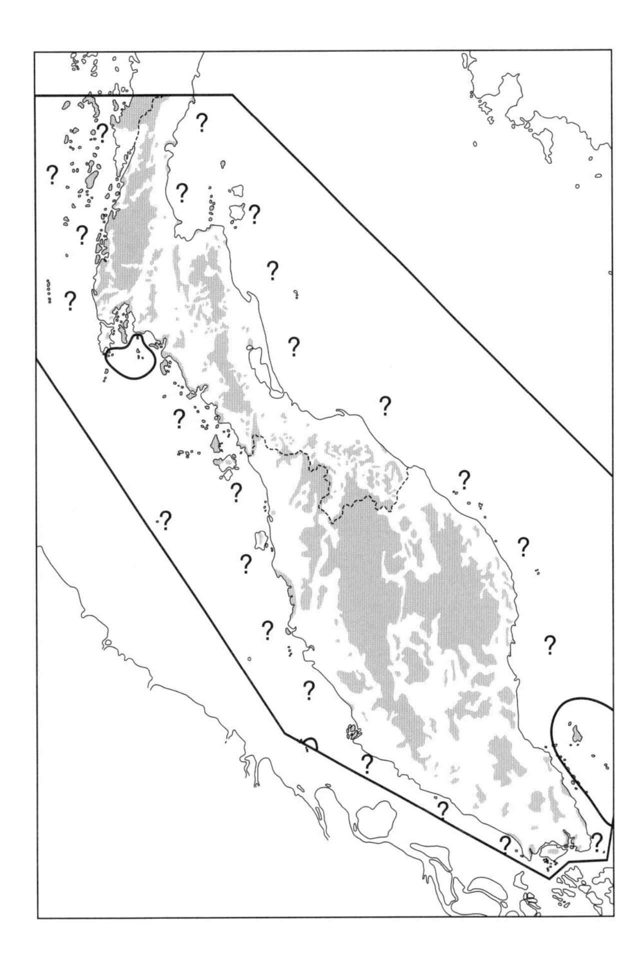

Bare-part colours. (Adults from N Keeling) iris dark brown; eyelids black (male), deep pink (female); gular skin orange-red (non-breeding male), greyish pink (female); bill dark slate to black (male), pink (breeding) to blue-grey (female); feet pale mauve to black (male), pinkish (female) (Gibson-Hill 1950b).

Size (mm). (Skins: 1 male and 1 female from Rengis; adult): wing 510 and 570; tail 325 and 345; bill 89 and 86; tarsus not measured (ZDUM). Respectively, these are smaller and larger measurements than given by Gibson-Hill for breeders on N Keeling island.

Weight. No data.

DISTRIBUTION. Throughout; probably the most widespread frigatebird in Peninsular waters.

GEOGRAPHICAL VARIATION. Assumed to be nominate *ariel*, of surrounding seas.

STATUS AND POPULATION. A non-breeding visitor, more or less regular and common. With the proviso that many go unidentified, Lesser is thought to be the most numerous frigatebird all round the Peninsula (BMP5). It dominates regular roost-gatherings in Phangnga bay (on the Bida stacks, Phiphi island group, with a suspected second site near Nang headland, Krabi coast) and at Rengis islet, Tioman (Medway 1966, P.D. Round, Slater and Slater 1988). Rengis has been in use for at least 30 years but could date from after 1948, when the local roost was in woods on Sepoi island 10 km northeast (Gibson-Hill 1950c).

As with other frigatebirds, generally less common than elsewhere around Singapore and in the Melaka Straits, but roosts have been reported on the Indonesian side of the Straits (Gibson-Hill 1950c), including on the southern stacks of the Arua group (G.C. Madoc). These are also the site of unique evidence that Lesser Frigatebirds may formerly have nested somewhere in the Straits. Six birds collected as they left this roost at dawn on 12 January 1952 were in breeding colours, including one with a full-sized but shell-less, oviduct egg (Madoc 1956). No nests were found but an overflight of the principal site, Tokong Simbang ('Frigatebird stack'), by Madoc in 1946 had shown numbers actually on it, which is most unusual daytime behaviour for non-breeders. This mystery has never been resolved.

HABITATS AND ECOLOGY. As with other frigatebirds, found mostly beyond the 10-fathom line but Lesser is evidently better adapted to relatively turbid conditions than the larger species. Several years are passed at sea before breeding is attempted, but seasonal changes in the size of roosting flocks have been noted in Sabah and Sarawak (Smythies 1981) and regular counting is needed at Peninsular sites. Since the frigatebirds' day can start before dawn, this is best done in the evening as they stream home from nearby gathering points at last light.

FORAGING AND FOOD. No specific information, but they follow fishing boats.

SOCIAL ORGANIZATION. As non-breeders of the other species.

MOVEMENTS. No information.

SURVIVAL. No information.

SOCIAL INTERACTIONS. No information.

VOICE. No information.

BREEDING. No population.

MOULT. A male dated 11 October from Horsburgh lighthouse, east of the Singapore Straits, showed asymmetrical wing-moult (P7/P9), and another from the S Arua group was growing P8 on 12 January. The female with the egg that day was not moulting, nor were a male and female at Rengis on 7 April (ZDUM, ZRCNUS).

CONSERVATION. Eggers in the Pahang–Johor archipelago (formerly?) burned woody vegetation off the tops of sea-stacks to expand the nesting habitat of Bridled Terns *Sterna anaethetus*. This must occasionally have affected frigatebird roosts.

Order CICONIIFORMES

Family ARDEIDAE

Herons, egrets and bitterns: 20 species

Great-billed Heron; Nok Gra-saa Yai (Thai); Burung Pucong Lembu (Malay)

Ardea sumatrana Raffles 1822, *Transactions of the Linnean Society* 13(2): 325. TL Benkulen, W Sumatra.

Plate 10

GROUP RELATIONS. Forms a superspecies with largely allopatric, continental *A. insignis* (White-bellied Heron) (cf. Payne and Risley 1976).

GLOBAL RANGE. From W Burma (Arakan) and extreme S Vietnam, south through SE Asia and Wallacea to Irian Jaya and N Australia; vagrant in E Australia (McAllan and Bruce 1988).

IDENTIFICATION/DESCRIPTION. Largest heron of the region, by far. In flight, from Lesser Adjutant by uniform, non-contrasting colour-pattern and lack of soaring; from Grey and Purple Herons by superior size and lack of contrast between flight-feathers and upper wing-coverts. On the ground, adults show long, white-streaked hackles on back and chest, and a wispy, grey-white nuchal crest. Immatures lack these features and have a rusty buff cast to the whole plumage. Huge bi-coloured, dagger bill.

Bare-part colours. (An adult female) iris bright yellow; facial skin (extending over and behind the eye) yellow-green; upper mandible blackish, lower yellow at tip shading to white then chrome-yellow at the base; legs and feet brown, tinged green at the joints, with soles pale yellowish (ZRCNUS).

Size (mm). (Skins: 5 males, 2 females; adult): wing 455–478 and 438, 451; tail 155–164 and 161, 172; bill 156–174 and 149, 155; tarsus 153–172 and 153, 164 (BMNH, ZRCNUS).

Weight. No data.

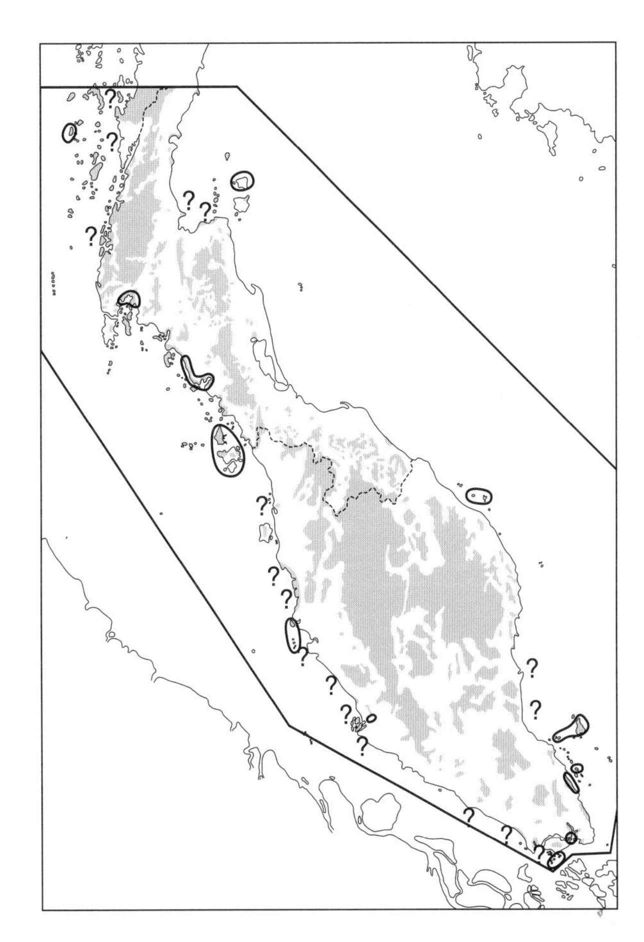

DISTRIBUTION. Historical summary: *Pak, Sur, Pha, Tra, Sat, Ked, Tru, Pek, Phg, Sel, Joh, Sin,* with additional island records from: Loughborough, Tarutao, the Langkawi group, Pangkor and the Sembilan group off the W coast; Phangan, Lang Tengah, Redang and the Pahang–Johor archipelago (Sri Buat, Tioman and Tinggi) off the E coast; and Ubin and the S archipelago (including Sentosa, St John's, Lazarus, Sakeng, Bukom, Anak Bukom, Semakau, Hantu and Sudong), Singapore.

GEOGRAPHICAL VARIATION. Asian nominate *sumatrana*, said to be slightly greyer, less bronzy brown in adult plumage than Australian *mathewsi*, but the difference has been questioned (HANZAB).

STATUS AND POPULATION. Resident, very local, and sparse to uncommon. Unlikely ever to have been 'abundant' (cf. Robinson and Chasen 1936), and a post World-War Two assessment: 'fairly plentiful along both coasts, and much more numerous than Grey Heron (Gibson-Hill 1949b), bears no relation to the modern record. This has been of a few pairs exclusive to the S archipelago of Singapore, patrolling favoured reef-flats over a wide area, but making only occasional visits to the coast of the main island and none, perhaps, to the mainland (BIRDLINE 1993, BR 1978–79, MBR 1986–87, SINGAV-3, -6). Reports in the late 1980s from Tarutao and the S anchorage of Redang island (ENGGANG-2, Scott 1989) remain unconfirmed, and contemporary surveys of most of the mainland coast of the Peninsula, on the ground and from light aircraft, drew a consistent blank (AWB).

HABITATS AND ECOLOGY. Almost exclusively coastal (an exceptional sighting about 10 km up the Kelang river, Selangor: Glenister 1951), whereas in island SE Asia and eastwards regular along rivers far into the interior (CLBS, Gilliard and LeCroy 1970, R.V. Lansdown). Typically, haunts secluded islands and mangrove forest fronted by consolidated mud- or back-reef flats, sitting out high water on some favoured rock, groyne or waterside tree (in Singapore with a liking for casuarinas).

FORAGING AND FOOD. Hunts over open, exposed flats or by waiting motionless in the incoming tide, poised for a strike. A record of swimming in the sea, with neck erect and body low, cormorant-like (Madoc 1947), suggests an occasional fishing method reported in some other giant herons (Hancock and Kushlan 1984). All food recorded taken to young in Singapore nests has been fish.

SOCIAL ORGANIZATION. Solitary or in pairs, and a non-colonial breeder. Four nests have been counted in mangroves on Anak Bukom islet, Singapore, but with only one pair of breeders confirmed in occupation at any given time.

MOVEMENTS. None recorded.

SURVIVAL. No information.

SOCIAL INTERACTIONS. Behavioural interactions between pair-members include upward stretching with throat puffed; arching, fluffing and twisting of the neck; and bill-grasping (Lansdown 1989).

VOICE. No good local information.

BREEDING

Nest. All records have been on small islands, 4.5–6 m up in mangrove trees. One large, stick-built nest in a horizontal fork 3 m out from the main trunk measured about 1 m across, with a shallow central depression.

Eggs and brood. Egg undescribed locally. Size (mm): 68.6 × 47.2 (n=1). Full clutch two, and both young are raised.

Cycle. No information.

Seasonality. Eggs (dead) on 23 June, nestlings on 14 April, 27 July and 1 and 9 August, and active nests, contents unchecked, up to 20 September (BIRDLINE 1993, BR 1978–79, Gibson-Hill 1952, Madoc 1936, MBR 1986–87, SINGAV-6).

MOULT. Replacement of primaries is regular-descendant but with P9–10 (the leading-edge of the wing) renewed precociously, coincident with P5–6. Five adults dated early March–late June (BMNH, ZRCNUS) all showed active wing-moult, between P3 and P6 (plus 10). One dated 1 August from Tioman island had recently finished.

CONSERVATION. The only difference between the Singapore S archipelago and much other coastal habitat in the Peninsula is effective gun control and progressive exclusion of the public by the military. The Republic's ultimate plan for the archipelago is reclamation but until that time birds should be relatively secure. Elsewhere, pot-hunting (could the Malay name, meaning cow heron, relate to taste?) appears to have pushed this bird to the brink of extinction. It is unlikely any remnant on Redang island has withstood the tourism developments of the 1990s, and a search for other pockets of population is needed urgently. Globally near-threatened (BTW2).

Grey Heron; Nok Gra-saa Nual (Thai); Burung Pucong Seriap (Malay)

Ardea cinerea Linnaeus 1758, *Systema Naturae* 10(1): 143. TL Sweden.
Plate 10

GROUP RELATIONS. Forms a superspecies with allopatric *A. herodias* and *A. cocoi* (Great Blue and Cocoi Herons) of the Americas (Hancock and Kushlan 1984).

GLOBAL RANGE. Breeds from the low arctic to the tropics, sporadically through Africa and the Malagasy region, across Eurasia from the Atlantic to Japan; in the Indian subcontinent, Sri Lanka and Bay of Bengal islands; China; and SE Asia to Sumatra and Java, though gone from some continental range, including Thailand (cf. Madoc 1950). Northern populations migrate into and beyond the tropical breeding-range, in SE Asia reaching the Peninsula, Borneo and the Philippines. Vagrant in Bali (Ash 1984) and W Micronesia.

IDENTIFICATION/DESCRIPTION. From Great-billed and Purple Herons by paleness, including almost white upper wing-coverts sharp against black wrist and flight-feathers. Juveniles are more uniform, duller grey and, apart from dark cap and flight-feathers, lack black parts, including crest. As other large herons, flies on steadily beaten, down-bowed wings, with head drawn back into the body. From Purple in flight silhouette by neck less obviously pouched below the ventral line of the body.

Bare-part colours. (W-coast adults) iris yellow (facial skin not well described); bill uniform bright orange-yellow (breeding), clay-yellow (non-breeding); legs and feet rosy flesh (breeding), dull clay-pink (non-breeding). Juveniles have dull horn upper mandible and dull, darkish legs and feet. There are no data on migrants.

Size (mm). (Skins: 4 W-coast females; adult): wing 400–420; tail 144–147; bill 108–114; tarsus 133–142 (Wells and Medway 1976, ZRCNUS).

Weight. No data.

DISTRIBUTION. Occurs in two populations that the record suggests meet only marginally, if at all: mainly along the NE coast south to Pattani, and the Malaysian W coast to Singapore. Historical summary: *Pak, Sur, Pht, Tra, Son, Pat, Pes, Pra, Pek, Sel, Neg, Mel, Joh, Sin,* with additional island records from the Kelang estuary (Ketam, Babi), Samui and Ubin.

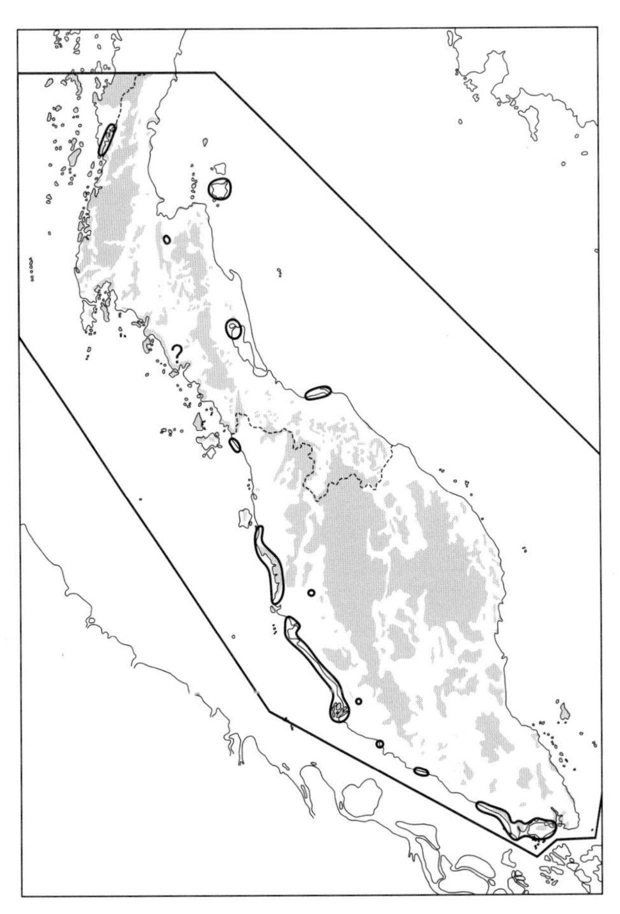

GEOGRAPHICAL VARIATION. Both populations are E-Asian *jouyi* Clark 1907 (TL Seoul, Korea), although Mees (1971) guessed breeders might conform with his big-billed Indonesian *altirostris*. Since bill-size varies individually over a wide area, they have not been so separated (Wells and Medway 1976).

STATUS AND POPULATION. Resident and a non-breeding visitor; local and uncommon to common. Barring odd birds seen or collected on the Pakchan estuary and in Trang, what are believed to be winter migrants inhabit mainly the NE coast, south to Pattani bay (Deignan 1963, Hume and Davison 1878, Ruttanadakul and Ardseungnern 1987; Scott 1989). Small colonies in Singapore and the W-coast mangrove zone north to Matang district (Perak), dispersing as far as mainland Penang (Kuala Juru) and possibly the Perlis mudflats (recent October–November records) (BMP5, BR 1980–81, R. Gregory-Smith), are certainly resident.

The number of groups recorded along the W coast has risen recently, probably through more intensive coverage of formerly remote habitat, although a March 1989 count of 107 birds represented a significant real increase in Singapore. Grey Herons were irregular there before the late 1970s and bred not earlier than 1983 (three pairs with Purple Herons *A. purpurea* at the impounded Kranji inlet in July: BR 1976–77, 1978–79, MBR 1982–83). Nearly 60 nests were counted there in February 1992, with at least 100 birds displaying and building later that year (SINGAV-6). On the mainland, 52 birds on mudflats fronting Benut mangrove forest, SW Johor, 50 km from Kranji, are presumed to have been from a separate colony, site not discovered (MBR 1986–87). In Selangor, a former stronghold in the Kelang estuary has been abandoned (last evidence of nesting there in 1971), but since the early 1980s at least three groups totalling a minimum 50 pairs have settled in mainland mangroves between the Kelang and Selangor rivers. As of 1991, they included up to 20 pairs in the Kuala Selangor Nature Park – gratifying start to a plan for artificially establishing a mixed large-waterbird breeding-colony there.

Current numbers and distribution of Grey Herons in the Perak mangroves need further study.

HABITATS AND ECOLOGY. While migrants in Thailand occupy both the shore and freshwater wetlands (Thung Thong, Thalae Noi, etc.: Storer 1976, 1978), Melaka Straits breeders rarely range behind coastal bunds, hunting mostly on low-tide mudflats. Records up to 30 km inland in open swamplands of Selangor and Perak, on dates outside the northern migrant season (Cant 1957–58, Glenister 1951), are exceptional.

FORAGING AND FOOD. Foragers hunt individually, by waiting or slow-wading in water or on freshly exposed tidal mud, peering with neck extended.

SOCIAL ORGANIZATION. Gregarious while nesting and roosting at customary sites, but foragers disperse.

MOVEMENTS. On the Thalae Noi wetland, migrants reported during October–April (Anonymous 1981, Storer 1976), but most arrive later and at other NE sites occur over a narrower range of dates.

SURVIVAL. No information.

SOCIAL INTERACTIONS. No local study.

VOICE. The regular flight-call is a loud, open *fraank*; when disturbed into flight, often gives a deep, grating *raark* (also heard from a bird threatened by a Brahminy Kite).

BREEDING

Nest. Apart from the circumstances of the Kranji colony, which shifted to a patch of drowned woodland, then to dry-land trees back from the present coastal bund, all recorded breeding has been in mangroves. Nests, one to several per crown, are invariably in emergent (including dead) tops that give above-canopy access. They are solidly built of twigs and lined with fresh, leafy branchlets (*Avicennia* sp. identified).

Eggs and brood. Eggs are blue, with rough shell texture. Shape elliptical to subelliptical. Size (mm): 58.4 × 40.4 (mean, n=11). Regular full clutch four but replacement clutches of three are on record.

Cycle. No information.

Seasonality. Attempts to define a local breeding-season have been frustrated by the effects of disturbance. Incubation is reported in months as far apart as July and January, but year-to-year and inter-colony differences have still to be worked out (BMP5, Madoc 1936).

MOULT. A resident female dated 26 May was growing P6 and 9 and had already renewed P1–5 and 7, suggesting complex, precocious moult of the wing-tip. Another dated 1 January showed no moult (ZRCNUS).

CONSERVATION. Although conspicuous where they occur, probably not more than ten breeding groups exist. Grey Herons relocate more readily than most other big colonial waterbirds but have been restricted in choice of site by the bunding-off and conversion of most of the width of the W-coast mangrove zone to other land-uses. Correspondingly greater access to what remains increases the ease with which colonies can be raided for eggs and chicks. Parts of Kuala Selangor nature park will be worth managing specifically for herons.

Purple Heron; Nok Gra-saa Daeng (Thai); Burung Pucong Serandau (Malay)

Ardea purpurea Linnaeus 1766, *Systema Naturae* 12(1): 236. TL River Danube, Europe.
Plate 10

GROUP RELATIONS. Free-standing.

GLOBAL RANGE. Breeds from the tropics to mid-temperate latitudes, patchily through Africa and Madagascar, and Atlantic Europe to W-central Asia (Iran, Kirghizstan); then through the Indian subcontinent, Sri Lanka and the Andamans; Ussuriland, E China, S Nansei islands and Taiwan; SE Asia; and Wallacea to Sulawesi and Flores. Northern populations migrate, wintering mostly in the tropics, in SE Asia as far as the Peninsula.

IDENTIFICATION/DESCRIPTION. Darker than Grey Heron, with upper wing-coverts only slightly paler than back. Head and neck thinner and more snake-like, obvious when alert and peering. Crestless immatures are predominantly dull rufous-buff, streaked on neck and underparts, without black markings. Flight-mode as in Grey Heron but folds base of neck conspicuously below ventral line of body. In hot weather, over short distances, often flies with neck slung semi-extended.

Bare-part colours. (Adult) iris chrome-yellow; facial skin greenish yellow; except for cutting-edge, upper mandible black-brown, rest of bill yellow to orange-yellow; legs and feet blackish, rear of tarsus yellowish (ZRCNUS).

Size (mm). (Skins: 6 adults, none sexed and status unknown): wing 357–384; tail 122–143; bill 118–128; tarsus 113–134 (BMNH, ZRCNUS).

Weight. No data.

DISTRIBUTION. Historical summary: all divisions except *Pak, Chu, Pha, Kra, Tra, Yal, Tru, Neg*, with additional island records from Penang, Samui and Ubin.

GEOGRAPHICAL VARIATION. All populations are S and E Asian *manilensis* Mayen 1834 (TL Manila), lacking dark marks down the foreneck (Hancock and Kushlan 1984).

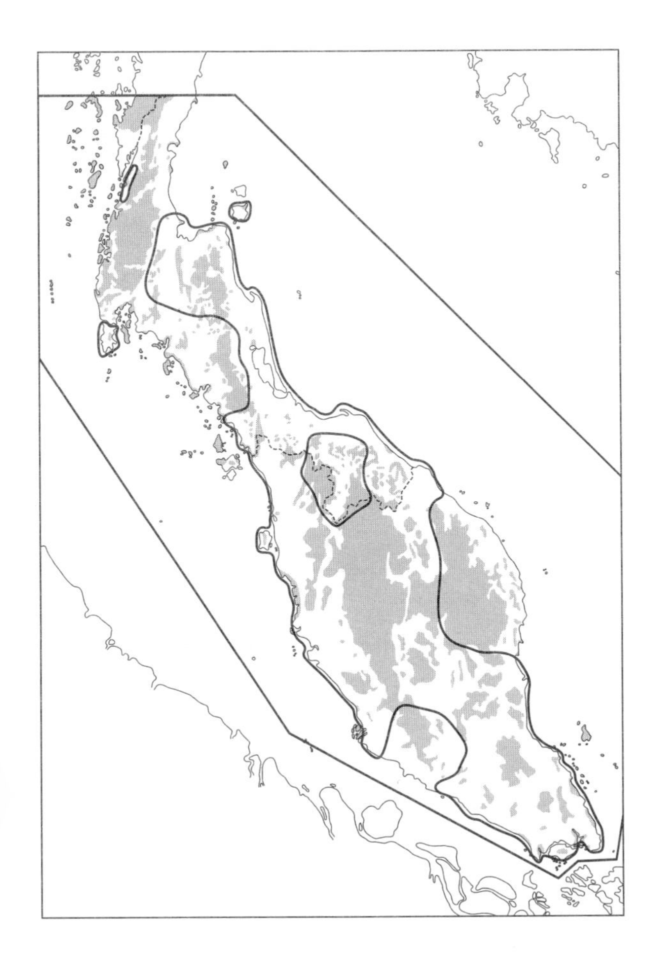

STATUS AND POPULATION. Resident and a non-breeding visitor, regular and more or less common. Purple Herons were formerly considered rare in the far south and 'only occasional' below Perak (Gibson-Hill 1949b, Robinson and Chasen 1936) though a juvenile from Singapore dated 1940 (ZRCNUS) implies at least some southern breeding. Winter migrants may still outnumber residents over much of the Peninsula but a state-wide count of 222 birds in Singapore on 26 March 1989 (SINGAV-3) is believed to have reflected new local nesting success.

Singapore breeders are now well-established. On 12 July 1983, Kranji reservoir held 20–30 pairs (at least 50 adults seen), nesting in *Acrostichum* fern-marsh. Some later joined nearby Grey Herons and a mixed, tree-nesting colony has continued there since. In the mid 1980s, a few additional pairs raised young in the top of an isolated clump of batai trees *Albizzia falcataria* by the Senoko wetland (since filled), and during 1988–90 some shared a patch of mangroves with Black-crowned Night Herons at Yishun (MBR 1982–83, 1986–87, SINGAV-2, -6).

On the mainland, more general in summer than the few reported colonies imply. The latter include about 20 pairs in mangroves near Kuala Sepetang (Perak coast), but not recently confirmed there, and during the mid 1980s large groups (80 and 267 nests) in swamp woodland near Thalae Noi (Gibson-Hill 1949, RTFD, U. Treesucon). Non-colonial nesting, reported on the lower Sala river, Kedah (Madoc 1950), is suspected to be widespread.

HABITATS AND ECOLOGY. Inhabits open marshland, reed-swamps on old dredge-mine land, the overgrown margins of irrigation and drainage canals in paddyland and other non-forest sitations, invariably freshwater or at most brackish. Apart from some nesting in mangroves, differs from Grey Heron in making no use of the intertidal zone (whereas it does in parts of island SE Asia). Purple Herons leave cover mostly at dusk and dawn, but their daily schedule is not well known.

FORAGING AND FOOD. Suspected to hunt mainly at night but some activity continues through the day, by motionless waiting more often than wading, and mainly within cover. An instance of fishing while swimming is on record (WWFM), and some non-aquatic items are taken: at Kranji, Singapore, an adult emerging from a water-hyacinth swamp with a half-swallowed rail or bittern chick (MBR 1982–83).

SOCIAL ORGANIZATION. Residents often nest and roost gregariously, but forage alone, and what are believed to be wintering migrants are typically solitary. Recorded nesting in mixed colonies alongside Grey Heron, Great Egret and Black-crowned Night Heron.

MOVEMENTS. Two ringed as nestlings on the Russian side of Lake Khanka, Ussuriland, in June 1961 and July 1962, were shot in Kelantan in December 1961 and March 1963 (McClure 1963a). An increase in regular dusk movements over dredge-mine swampland in Selangor during early November–late January may have been due to migrants passing through. In spring, an apparent actual departure witnessed on 13 May: at sunset, two birds circling up and disappearing north at an exceptional height. One in from the sea over the S coast of Singapore on 29 January may also have been on the move (BR 1964, 1968, SINGAV-3).

SURVIVAL. No information.

SOCIAL INTERACTIONS. No local information.

VOICE. A lone adult landing at an evening foraging site gave a loud, hoarse *raanka-raanka-raank*.

BREEDING

Nest. On the ground in reeds and *Acrostichum* fern-marsh, and in waterside trees, including mangroves. Groups readily switch between site-classes, according to availablility, but more consistently use trees. The stick nest has not been described in detail.

Eggs and brood. Not described locally.

Cycle. No local information.

Seasonality. Nest-building or repair noted in September, November–January and March–May, apparent incubation in late May and nestlings in

April, May, July–October and January (BR 1976–77, Madoc 1950, MBR 1982–83, 1986–87, SINGAV-2, -3). No clearly seasonal pattern emerges overall, but individual colonies have not been followed closely.

MOULT. Two (male and female) dated late February showed moult of P8 and P4–5. The female had already renewed P9–10, implying precocious moult of the wing-tip. An undated bird growing P5 and 9 simultaneously confirms this pattern (BMNH, ZRCNUS).

CONSERVATION. While habitat is scarce in Singapore, the skew of breeding records to the Republic reflects relative freedom of nest-sites there from hunters and eggers. Northward, most large, colonial species are under pressure from nest-raiding, even where guns are few.

Little Heron; Nok Yang Khieo (Thai); Burung Pucong Keladi (Malay)

Butorides striatus (Linnaeus) 1758, *Systema Naturae* 10(1): 144. TL Surinam.
Plate 13

GROUP RELATIONS. Forms a superspecies with exclusively New-World *B. virescens* (Green-backed Heron). Behaviour and molecular data (Sheldon 1987) imply these two are no longer conspecific.

GLOBAL RANGE. Tropics and subtropics around the world, including on many oceanic islands. Penetrates deep into the temperate zone in far-E Asia, north to Ussuriland and Sakhalin; vagrant in Europe. Some higher-latitude Asian populations migrate, reaching the Philippines and Greater Sunda islands.

IDENTIFICATION/DESCRIPTION. Small, compact and typically hunched when resting. Adults are dark grey with cap and long, drooping (but erectile) crest hanging down the back of the neck blackish, and contrasting bands along the side of the face white. Juveniles have short scapulars (versus long hackles in adult), buff tips to the upper wing-coverts, white triangular tips to the flight-feathers, narrow buff streaks on the crown, and pattern of grey-and-white stripes on ventral neck and underparts. Legs and feet vary from dull green to rich orange. In flight, from *Ixobrychus* bitterns by slaty grey colour and alarm-squawk when flushed.

Nestling down is light grey.

Bare-part colours. (Local residents) iris yellow; bill black (adult); facial skin olive-yellow; legs and feet dull green (juvenile) via clear green to bright orange-peach (adult), colour-change spreading forward from the rear of the tarsus.

Size (mm). (Live: 27 adult *javanicus* on Selangor and Singapore coasts; none sexed): wing 156–177; tail 50–59; bill from mouth-corner (61) 68–84; tarsus 43–52. Four presumed extra-regional migrants (live and skins) had wings 184–205, the largest individual with tail 76; bill from mouth 90; tarsus 58 (AMNH, UMBRP, ZRCNUS).

Weight (g). Many *javanicus*, 153–208. No data on migrants.

DISTRIBUTION. Historical summary: all divisions except *Chu*, *Yal*, *Nar*, including on most islands off both coasts. Migrants (?) on Perak and Jarak.

GEOGRAPHICAL VARIATION. Breeders and perhaps most migrants are subspecies *javanicus* Horsfield 1821 (TL Java), total wing-range 156–180 mm. Largest migrants have been identified as *amurensis* von

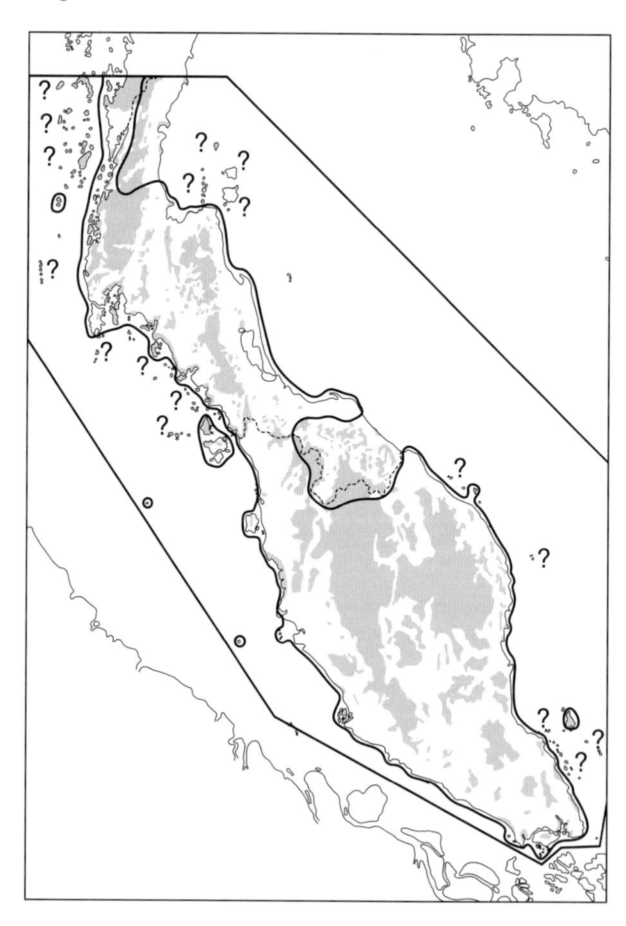

Schrenck 1860 (TL Heilong river, NE China), subspecies wing-range 200–214 mm (Hartert 1920). Intermediate migrants (wing 184, 189 mm) are perhaps *actophilus* Oberholser 1912 (TL N Pagai island, W Sumatra).

STATUS AND POPULATION. Resident and a non-breeding visitor, with some possible through-passage. *B.s. javanicus*, the breeding form almost to the head of the Bay of Bengal, is regular and common to abundant. It is also represented among migrants. Palaearctic birds, identified only by their larger size, have been intercepted on autumn migration over the Main Range and, on a likely spring-passage date (7 April), on Langkawi island (BR 1970–71). Others of wing-length appropriate to an intermediate, subtropical form have been collected in Nakhon Si Thammarat on 29 September and at Katong, Singapore, on 14 January (AMNH, ZRCNUS).

HABITATS AND ECOLOGY. Muddy coasts, tidal rivers lined with mangroves, open swampland and subcoastal paddyfields are the main habitats of residents, with no breeding recorded more than about 3 km from the sea (R.P. Jaensch, G.C. Madoc). At a lower density, Little Herons also occur on coral and other rocky shores (Gibson-Hill 1950e, Medway 1966), and at ponds and along rivers inland, far into forested headwaters. The Langkawi *amurensis* was caught by a forested hill-stream but because only some migrants are separable from residents, even in the hand, nothing can be said about possible segregation by habitat (cf. Hoogerwerf 1965).

FORAGING AND FOOD. Hunting methods include striking down into water from a low perch, and slow, stealthy walking or motionless waiting amongst flooded rice, mangrove roots, tideline flotsam and on open, inter-tidal mud. Less usual behaviour includes: foraging in the wake of wild pigs rootling along the edge of a brackish lagoon in mangroves (MBR 1986–87); repeated short flights from a low snag, dipping feet in the water, then splash-diving into the same spot to catch a tilapia *Oreochromis* almost too large to swallow, as though the fish had been attracted to the disturbance.

On open ground, the invariable stance is a forward crouch with head and neck low. While hunting, individuals space themselves out, with occasional short, low flights to sample fresh patches.

SOCIAL ORGANIZATION. Mainly solitary but breeding dispersion varies from lone pairs to colonies of up to ten nests, sometimes several per tree (Madoc 1956a, Ryves 1938). An unusual, close-packed flock of 40 birds flying along the shore at Kranji, Singapore, on 26 December (MBR 1982–83) may have been on passage.

MOVEMENTS. The only monitored movements of ringed birds, in Singapore and Selangor, have been coastal and within probable daily foraging distances. Genuine migration dates are from overnight interceptions at lights on Fraser's Hill: of *javanicus* on 2 and 21 November and a Palaearctic migrant on 10 November. Birds unidentified to subspecies have appeared on oil-rigs 200 km off Terengganu during 20 September–25 October and on 14 April (BMP5, BR 1969, 1976–77, MBR 1982–83, D.M. Simpson).

SURVIVAL. The longest retrap-interval to date is 32 months, a *javanicus* at Kuala Selangor (UMBRP).

SOCIAL INTERACTIONS. No information except that on open mudflats foragers react aggressively to conspecifics when they get close, and spacing seems to be maintained by brief chase-flights, with crest erected.

VOICE. Most obvious is a loud, explosive *chauk*, single or briefly repeated, when birds are flushed into flight. A clicking noise has been heard from parents whose nests were being threatened (Edgar 1933).

BREEDING

Nest. Mostly in mangroves, including within the regular tide-zone. Less usual sites are a tree in a sea-side park, an abandoned orchard, and mango trees on a paddyfield bund, up to about 3 km inland. The nest is a loose, flattish platform of small twigs, about 30 cm across × 5 cm deep, on a lateral branch within the canopy, 2–10 m up.

Eggs and brood. Eggs are pale bluish green with a chalky texture. Shape normal to short elliptical. Size (mm): 41.4–35.6 × 29.0–27.7 (n=8). Full clutch three, and as many chicks fledge.

Cycle. No information.

Seasonality. On the Perak coast, Edgar (1933) found a gap in egg-production during March–May but in Singapore and on the Malaysian W coast generally, eggs have been confirmed in all months 23 January–September (most records in May), with an occupied, defended nest seen in Selangor on 30 November (Edgar 1933, R.P. Jaensch, G.C. Madoc, Madoc 1956a, NRCS, SINGAV-2, Ryves 1938).

MOULT. A large sample of adult (presumed resident) *javanicus* covering all months showed active wing-moult during June–October but complicated by many instances of suspension. Up to three generations of feathers per wing, identified by fading and wear, suggest precocious replacement of leading edge primaries; also that no one moult episode necessarily runs to completion.

CONSERVATION. No critical issues.

Indian Pond Heron; Nok Yang Grawk Phan India (Thai); Burung Pucong India (Malay)

Ardeola grayii (Sykes) 1832. *Proceedings of the Committee of Science and Correspondence of the Zoological Society of London* 2: 158. TL Deccan, India.

GROUP RELATIONS. Forms a superspecies with *bacchus*, *speciosa* and *idae* (Chinese, Javan and Malagasy Pond Herons) (Snow 1978).

GLOBAL RANGE. The Persian Gulf, Indian subcontinent, Sri Lanka and Bay of Bengal islands; and lowland W, central and S Burma to mid Tenasserim (latitude about 16°N). Vagrant in SW Thailand and the Peninsula.

IDENTIFICATION/DESCRIPTION. Line drawing, below. Size between Little Heron and Cattle Egret, and from other pond herons only by breeding-colours: cap grey, face, neck, scapulars and upper breast buff-grey; lower breast vinous-grey with long, loose barbs tipped creamy white; mantle, including long, loose feathering overlapping back to the tail, mahogany-black; nuchal crest, chin and throat, wings and rest of body and tail contrastingly white. Up to five outer primaries have tips to whole outer web vinous-grey (variation perhaps age-linked).

Streaked winter and juvenile plumages not separated from other pond herons (see Chinese).

Bare-part colours. (Adult) iris clear, pale yellow, periorbital and facial skin pale greenish; bill yellow with black tip and (in breeding-colours) blue base; feet pale greenish yellow (BMNH).

Indian Pond Heron

Size (mm). (Skins: 2 S Burmese males; adult): wing 221, 230; tail 75, 75; bill 59.5, 64.5; tarsus 59.5, 64.9. Longest crest-feather up to 110 (BMNH).

Weight. No data.

DISTRIBUTION. *Pha.*

GEOGRAPHICAL VARIATION. None recognized.

STATUS AND POPULATION. Vagrant; confirmed from a bird in breeding-colours photographed at Tambol Leh, Phangnga, on 15 April 1995 (BCSTB-12).

HABITATS AND ECOLOGY. Not known to differ from other local pond herons; the Phangnga bird was in grassland.

FORAGING AND FOOD. No information.

SOCIAL ORGANIZATION. No information.

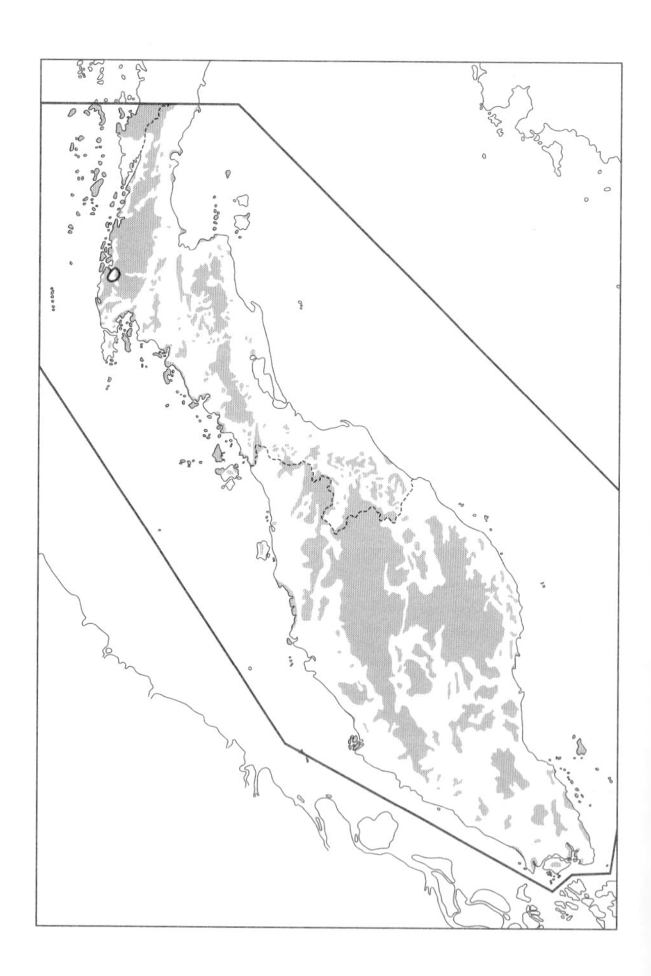

MOVEMENTS. No information.

SURVIVAL. No information.

SOCIAL INTERACTIONS. No information.

VOICE. No information.

BREEDING. No population.

MOULT. No data.

CONSERVATION. No relevant issues.

Chinese Pond Heron; Nok Yang Grawk Phan Jeen (Thai); Burung Pucong Cina (Malay)

Ardeola bacchus (Bonaparte) 1855, *Conspectus Generum Avium* 2: 127. TL Malay Peninsula.
Plate 12

GROUP RELATIONS. See Indian Pond Heron.

GLOBAL RANGE. Breeds in lowland Assam and Bangladesh; SE Tibet, China south from Jilin and the Huang Ho valley, including Taiwan and Hainan; and in E Indochina to far-S Vietnam. Migrants winter from parts of the breeding-range south to the Andamans, the Peninsula and Borneo.

IDENTIFICATION/DESCRIPTION. Maroon-mahogany head and neck of breeding plumage distinctive but winter and juvenile plumages not distinguishable from other pond heron species. All exposed upperparts are then shades of buff and vinous brown, boldly dark-streaked over the head and foreparts; hidden white of wings, rear body and tail 'explodes' on take-off. As in other Asian pond herons, the mainly yellow bill is tipped black at all seasons.

Males in breeding-plumage are identified by their slaty lower breast. Presumed first-winterers have lesser wing-coverts brown-streaked, versus plain white in adults. They are also more extensively brown on the outer primaries.

Bare-part colours. Iris chrome-yellow; facial skin greenish (immature), yellowish (winter adult); apical third of bill blackish, rest yellow (an early-winter immature has whole upper mandible, except for cutting-edge, black); legs and feet greenish yellow or yellow. By spring departure, some adults have facial skin to mid bill light bluish or greenish blue.

Size (mm). (Skins: 12 adults, most not sexed): wing 200–231 (largest confirmed female 206, smallest male 210; first-winterers down to 192); tail 68–88; bill 55.6–64.5; tarsus 54.9–64.4 (BMNH, ZRCNUS).

Weight. No data.

DISTRIBUTION. Historical summary: all divisions except *Yal*, *Nar*, and with additional island records from the Similan group, Yao Yai, Phiphi (spring passage), Langkawi and Penang off the W coast; and

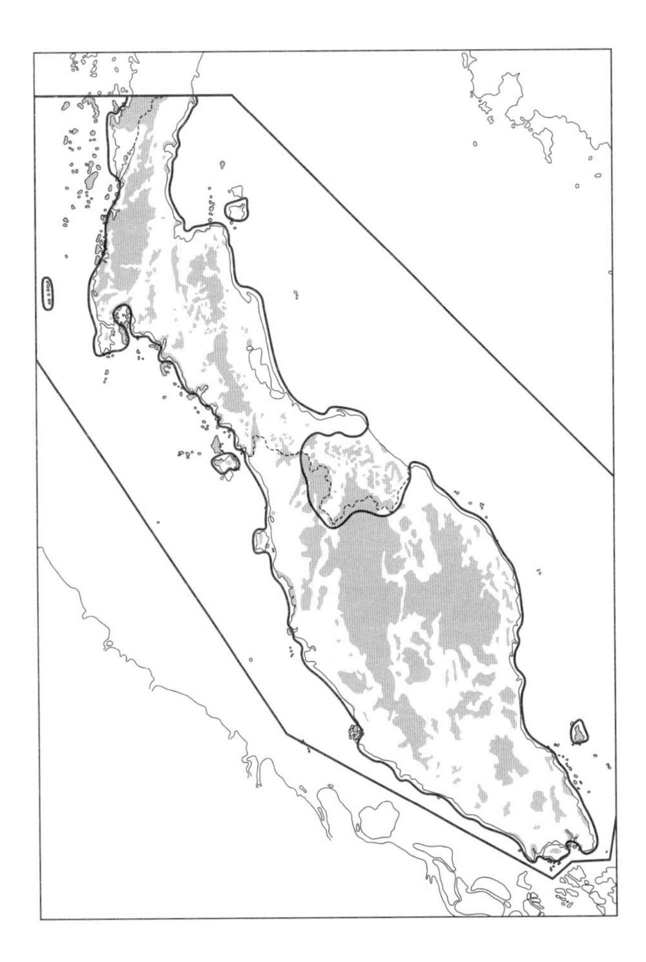

Samui and Tioman (a few records in January and April) off the E coast.

GEOGRAPHICAL VARIATION. None recognized.

STATUS AND POPULATION. A non-breeding visitor, more or less regular and common, increasingly so in the south but, as yet, no groups larger than 20 reported from Singapore. Roosts of 100 or more are known only north from coastal Perak and the Pahang estuary (Howes *et al.* 1986, SINGAV-3).

HABITATS AND ECOLOGY. A variety of open wetlands including grazing- and paddyland, and the margins of ponds, drains and wallows; occasionally dry beach strand, etc. Locally, loafs in groups and possibly also forages in degraded mangroves and on low-tide mudflats. Roosts always in trees, at customary sites usually over water, including the outer zone of mangrove forest. At dusk in early January, over 300 counted entering the Perak Black-crowned Night Heron colony (MBR 1986–87). There and wherever numerous, dusk and dawn flights are conspicuous. Over the Thalae Noi marshes, these last at least one hour and involve much larger numbers than found together anywhere in Malaysia (Storer 1976).

FORAGING AND FOOD. Hunts diurnally by slow-walking and motionless waiting, when the cryptic winter plumage melts into a background of waterside vegetation. Does not wade, and much prey must be terrestrial, but diet hardly known.

SOCIAL ORGANIZATION. Forages alone, but loafs socially and is strongly gregarious when on the move and at roosts.

MOVEMENTS. Earliest arrival dates: 19 September at Songkhla lake, 20 September in Penang, 28 September near Melaka and 29 September on Singapore island (BR 1968, Holmes and Wells 1975, K. Kumar, SINGAV-3), indicate a rather rapid spread south in autumn. Records from rigs in the Terengganu oil-field during 11–25 October 1982 (MBR 1982–83) imply some direct crossing of the Gulf of Thailand at that season. By late April, most birds have returned north, with last spring sightings on 1 May in Singapore, 3 May on Tioman island, 5 May (quarter moulted into breeding-plumage) at Kuala Selangor and 10 May at Khun Thalae swamp, Surat Thani (R.P. Jaensch, MBR 1986–87, R.S.E. Swanquist).

SURVIVAL. No information.

SOCIAL INTERACTIONS. No information.

VOICE. No information.

BREEDING. No population.

MOULT. Some arrive in part-breeding plumage, seen up to 18 October (Holmes and Wells 1975, SINGAV-2), and renewed as of February. A male dated 2 February from Perak showed early-stage body-moult, and advanced moult is recorded in late March (Phuket, Singapore) (BMNH, SINGAV-2). By early April, full colours are common.

Latest adult wing-moult (a Trang female growing P9–10) is dated 25 January. Birds taken later, up to 30 March, showed none, and fairly unworn primaries imply a general finish at or before mid winter. A late September adult from central Thailand, suspended after renewing P1–7 and 10, must have started before arrival. Immatures dated late October–late February showed no wing-moult and relatively more tip-wear, indicating a different schedule (BMNH, ZRCNUS).

CONSERVATION. No critical issues although, as with other herons, pesticides now exclude it from most Malaysian paddyland.

Javan Pond Heron; Nok Yang Grawk Phan Chawaa (Thai); Burung Pucong Jawa (Malay)

Ardeola speciosa (Horsfield) 1821, *Transactions of the Linnean Society* 13(1): 189. TL Java.
Plate 12

GROUP RELATIONS. See Indian Pond Heron.

GLOBAL RANGE. S-central plains of Thailand through Cambodia to S Vietnam, and S Sumatra, S Borneo, Java, Bali, Mindanao, Sulawesi and Flores.

IDENTIFICATION/DESCRIPTION. In breeding-plumage, both sexes have chin, throat and nuchal crest white, rest of head and neck pale straw-beige shading to rusty across the lower breast, sharply demarcated from the white abdomen; mantle and back-plumes blackish, as in other Asian species. Not safely identifiable in juvenile and non-breeding plumages.

Bare-part colours. No local information.

Size. No data.

Weight. No data.

DISTRIBUTION. The W-coast plain. Historical summary: *Kra, Pek, ?Sel.*

GEOGRAPHICAL VARIATION. No information. Given that breeding-plumage occurs in March–April both north and south of the equator, plumage cycles are not helpful in field identification of subspecies.

STATUS AND POPULATION. A non-breeding visitor, hardly more than vagrant. Since 1979, recognized from a few individuals in breeding-plumage in

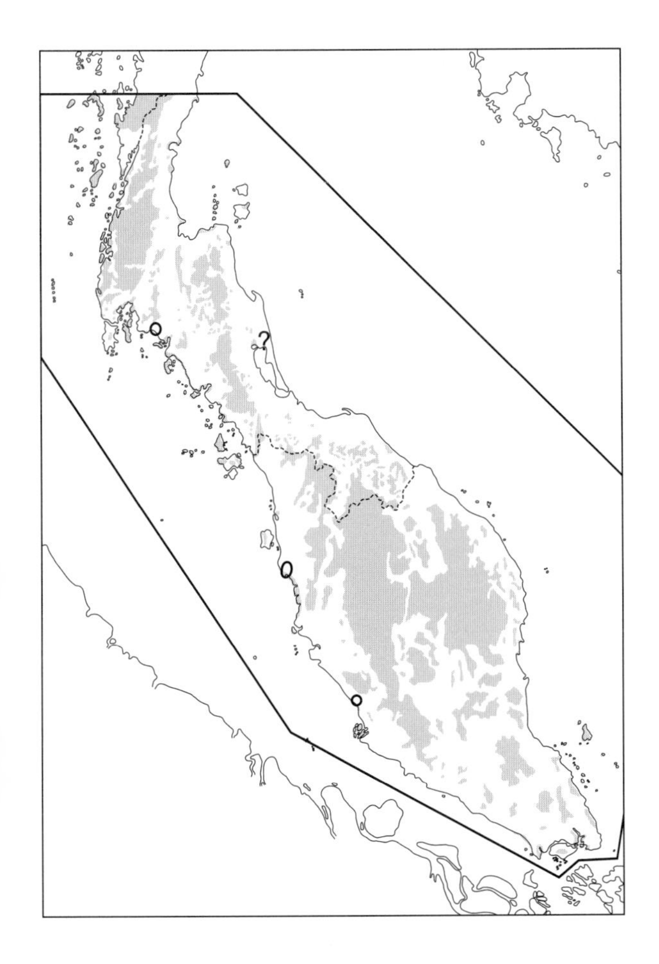

the W-coast mangrove zone within an eight-week period from 8 March, including around the Krabi river, at Kuala Gula (Perak) and, tentatively, Kuala Selangor; loners and in groups of up to three (BBCB-5, BCSTB-13, P. Benstead and R. Walker, BR 1978–79, Helbig 1987, MBR 1986–87).

A few records of pond herons up to early June at Thalae Noi might have involved this species. More summer visits to this site are needed.

HABITATS AND ECOLOGY. Cleared back-mangrove land and low-tide mudflats are the only habitats confirmed.

FORAGING AND FOOD. No information.

SOCIAL ORGANIZATION. No additional information.

MOVEMENTS. Extreme dates 8 March and 3 May, but these are only those between which summer plumage has been identified.

SURVIVAL. No information.

SOCIAL INTERACTIONS. No information.

VOICE. No information.

BREEDING. No population.

MOULT. No additional data.

CONSERVATION. No relevant issues, but discovery of many breeders in S Sumatra (Verheugt *et al.* 1993) suggests this heron's western range may be expanding.

Cattle Egret; Nok Yang Khwai (Thai); Bangau Kendi (Malay)

Bubulcus ibis (Linnaeus) 1758, *Systema Naturae* 10(1): 144. TL Egypt.
Plate 12

GROUP RELATIONS. Free-standing, assuming eastern and western Cattle Egrets are conspecific (cf. Payne and Risley 1976).

GLOBAL RANGE. Expansion over a century has carried Cattle Egrets around the world, to extreme outer limits of about 40°S and 47°N, but with a substantial land-gap still between African/W-Eurasian *ibis* and eastern *coromandus*. The latter now breeds through the Indian subcontinent, Sri Lanka and Bay of Bengal islands; Japan, China south from Shaanxi including Taiwan and Hainan; continental SE Asia, the Philippines, Java, Bali, possibly SW Kalimantan (Galdikas *et al.* 1985); and Sulawesi, Australia and New Zealand. Many northern populations migrate, in SE Asia reaching the equatorial zone. Directions of dispersal in the S hemisphere are less certain.

IDENTIFICATION/DESCRIPTION. Breeding-plumage is distinctive. At other seasons, a combination of dry-land foraging habits, size, all-yellow bill, all-blackish legs and feet, and relatively fast wing-beat should be enough to identify this species. At mixed-species roosts, from other all-white, yellow-billed egrets by small size, proportionately short, thick neck and pouchy throat ('jowl').

Bare-part colours. (Winter adult) iris yellow-white; facial skin yellowish; bill all-yellow; legs and feet blackish. Just before spring departure, lores and iris and then legs and feet turn rich orange-red. A photograph from Singapore (M. Strange) shows the beginnings of this change but full development has been reported only among spring migrants passing north across Langkawi island.

Size (mm). (Skins: 18 adults, most not sexed): wing 240–262 (birds sexed male span the full range, five sexed female 241–256, suggesting no significant size-dimorphism); tail 78–91; bill 55.4–65.0; tarsus 86.3–93.0 (BMNH, ZRCNUS)

Weight. No data.

DISTRIBUTION. Historical summary: all divisions except *Pes*, and with additional winter-dated W-coast island records from Yao Yai and Yao Noi (Phangnga bay), and Penang.

GEOGRAPHICAL VARIATION. Eastern *coromandus* Boddaert 1783 (TL Coromandel coast, SE India), distinguished by its slightly larger bill and more extensively golden-orange (versus pink-buff) breeding-plumage.

STATUS AND POPULATION. A possible local breeder and regular and more or less common non-breeding visitor. Many passage migrants reaching peak courtship colours pass through the Langkawi islands in the first two weeks of April (BR 1970–71) but rumour of an island nesting-colony off nearby Satul (Madoc 1950–51) was never verified, and confusion with Reef Egret seems likely. Recent June records of several hundred at Thalae Noi and over 700 roosting in mangroves at Pak Ying, coastal Nakhon Si Thammarat, imply some might breed in the north

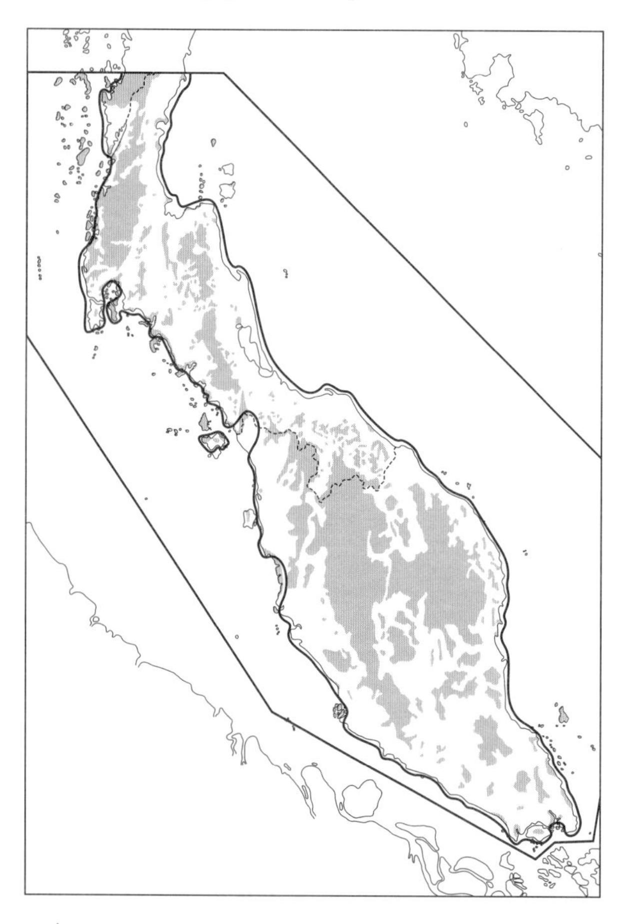

(BCSTB-11, -12), but age-classes were not identified and no nests have been found. The greater likelihood is that these areas are within the over-summering range of pre-adults not completing a full migration. Presumed northern migrants winter from Singapore at least to Surat Thani (Storer 1978) but avoid the driest conditions. Thus, not found in Langkawi and neighbouring Perlis at mid winter but they reappear on spring passage with the rain in March–April.

HABITATS AND ECOLOGY. On grazing-land and, in the past, commonly also stubble and fallow paddyfields, but most multi-crop paddyland is now so heavily dosed with pesticides as no longer to sustain egrets of any kind.

Communal roosts at customary sites may draw from more than one foraging area, flocks converging over the last hour of daylight from consistently different directions. Early arrivals form pre-roost gatherings before retiring and, where they have been hunted, make a final, jinking dash into the roost at cover-top height. Later birds go straight for the established nucleus. Mangroves and other waterside trees are used (BMP5, Kelham 1881–83) but, more often, tall, open reedbeds over water. The security of water seems crucial as a bund-burst at a monitored site in Selangor caused an immediate shift to an unaffected site 300 m away, even though nothing obvious happened to the quality of the original vegetation.

FORAGING AND FOOD. Hunts in loose groups in young, still-flooded rice, over stubble, and especially attracted to grazing stock around which birds slow-walk or stand about, making dashes for flushed animal prey. Food includes frogs and probably other small vertebrates, orthopterans, etc. Gaining a vantage by cattle-back riding is a habit they share with Black Drongos *Dicrurus macrocercus* and two or three species of mynas. Widely believed not to take ectoparasites but F.N. Chasen saw some removing ticks from the legs and bellies of cattle and tame banteng.

SOCIAL ORGANIZATION. Strongly gregarious at all times.

MOVEMENTS. Nowhere numerous before October. In the south, extreme early arrival dates are 1 September near Kuala Lumpur and 4 September in Singapore. Recently, in Kedah and NW Selangor, however, small flocks have been seen as of late July. All-white plumage at this early date indicates juveniles and/or, perhaps, one-year-olds (see above) moving ahead of post-breeders. A bird in the Terengganu off-shore oil-field on 28 October may have been on a direct crossing of the Gulf of Thailand (BR 1969, R. Gregory-Smith, MBR 1982–83, D.M. Simpson, R. Subaraj).

Best information on through-movements comes from a series of 24 counts at a roost at Sungai Way, Selangor, during early September–late April 1968/69 (BR 1969). From 42 birds at the end of September numbers rose steadily, with a large influx in the last three days of November, to peak at 550. Over 500 attended through December declining to around 300 in January but rose again by early February, with further peaks until late March, and numbers still appreciably above mid-winter levels into April. Oscillations imply waves of passage migrants making use of an established roost-site *en route*. Activity through most of April 1969 was missed but at the end of that month only 20 birds remained. Elsewhere in the south, most go by mid April (BR 1964) and at Sungai Way no birds have occurred after 10 May. The only later southern records have been of isolated stragglers (in breeding plumage) in Melaka territory on 22 May and 5 June (Batchelor 1958, BMP5).

SURVIVAL. No information.

SOCIAL INTERACTIONS. No information.

VOICE. Birds maintain a low, conversational rattle as they settle into roosts, but are otherwise silent in winter.

BREEDING. No confirmed population.

MOULT. Field data and a small sample of specimens suggest post-breeding body-moult is completed before arrival, although all adults retain some gold-buff on the centre of the crown. In Selangor, breeding-colours begin to reappear in early February (in one per about 30 individuals at the Sungai Way roost on 12 February) and by mid March many show colour additional to the crown. Full colours are common by April, but some birds (first-winterers?) depart white.

An adult from Krabi dated 5 January showed suspension of wing-moult with only P6 and 9 old, suggesting typical precocious renewal of the wing-tip. Two from Langkawi dated 26 and 27 November were growing P5 and P6, and all-fresh primaries have been seen on 28 December. The few examined in spring have shown virtually unworn wings, implying adults ordinarily complete around mid winter.

A still fully white bird moulting P2–3 on 2 April, was on a clearly different, possibly first-winter, schedule (wing and tail 234 and 78 mm, too short for an adult) (BMNH, ZRCNUS).

CONSERVATION. While Cattle Egrets may still be increasing worldwide, three decades of regular watching in the south of the Peninsula suggests numbers have actually decreased, with a contraction of foraging opportunities. Domestic water buffalo have gone from much of Malaysia, cattle-grazing has become more localized, and intensification of agriculture, with growing use of herbicides and other chemicals, has reduced the carrying-capacity of paddylands. The north has been less affected, and needs monitoring.

Great Egret; Nok Yang Thohn Yai (Thai); **Bangau Besar** (Malay)

Casmerodius albus (Linnaeus) 1758, *Systema Naturae* 10(1): 144. TL Sweden.

Plate 11

GROUP RELATIONS. DNA hybridization studies support the proposition that Great Egret is more closely related to *Ardea* than to *Egretta*, warranting a generic separation; also that American and Old-World forms have diverged to species rank (Mayr and Short 1970, Sheldon 1987). If accepted, they are treatable as a superspecies.

GLOBAL RANGE. Tropical to mid-temperate zones of the Americas, Africa, the Malagasy region, and Eurasia from the Atlantic to Amurland, Japan and N China; the Indian subcontinent and Sri Lanka; S China (Fujian, SW Yunnan); SE Asia; and Wallacea to New Guinea, Australia and New Zealand. Northern populations migrate, in SE Asia reaching at least to the equator.

IDENTIFICATION/DESCRIPTION. In steady flight, slow stroke rate and a marked down-fold of the flexed neck, as in Purple Heron, separate Great from other white egrets. On the ground, long bill, very long, distinctively kinked neck and comparative height are useful markers. The short, black streak back from the lower rear corner of the eye is diagnostic. In breeding plumage (acquired ahead of seasonal bare-part colours), erectile back-plumes extend beyond the tail. The common bare-part colours year-round now are yellow bill and black legs and feet.

Bare-part colours. (Winter adult) iris pale yellow; loral skin rather bright olive-yellow; bill chrome-yellow (some with extreme tip black; an age character?); legs, feet and toes grey to black. Breeders of both sexes show loral skin cobalt-blue; bill fully black; legs and feet to base of toes rose-pink, toes black. Last to be lost post-breeding is the blue face, seen as late as mid April (A. Jeyarajasingam).

Size (mm). (Skins: 6 Selangor breeders; not sexed): wing 324–357, tail 109–132; bill 95.8–113.7; tarsus 129–153; mid-toe plus claw 92.7–105.6. Birds of unknown status fall more or less within these ranges, but the sample is small (TISTR, ZRCNUS).

Weight. No data.

DISTRIBUTION. Historical summary: all divisions except *Pak, Chu, Pha, Pht, Sat, Yal, Nar, Pes, Kel, Phg,*

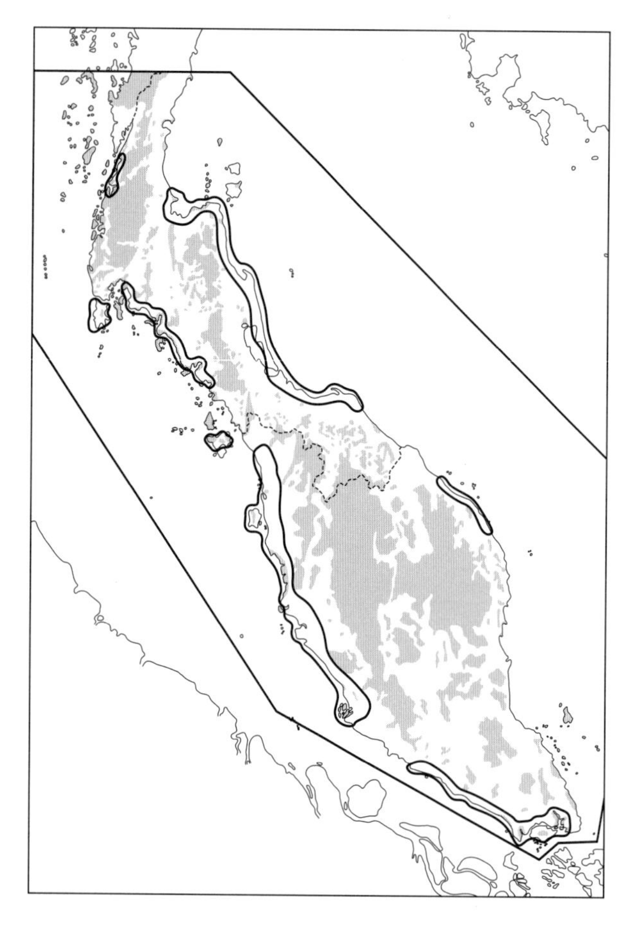

Neg, with additional W-coast island records from Langkawi, Penang and (breeding) the Kelang estuary group, Selangor.

GEOGRAPHICAL VARIATION. All populations are small-sized eastern *modestus* J.E. Gray 1831 (TL India).

STATUS AND POPULATION. A now sparse and very local resident but regular and more or less common non-breeding visitor. Until recently, parts of the NE coast, including Bandon bay, offered extensive potential breeding-habitat. Probable residents occurred there in the past (see Moult) but the only proven breeding has been in the Melaka Straits. Great Egrets dominated heronries of W-coast mangroves in the 1930s and 40s, including around 70 pairs at Ketam island (Selangor) and 50–100 near Kuala Sepetang (Perak) (possibly the same group, north side of the Larut estuary, still active in 1960) (BR 1964, Madoc 1936, Gibson-Hill 1949b). They have been decimated since. In the Kelang estuary, a few still visited Ketam to the mid 1960s but not above five in breeding colours could be found at what should have been the height of the 1968/69 season, with last nests (all emptied of young) recorded on nearby Babi island in 1971 (BMP5, BR 1966). Twenty km north, ten in full breeding-colours and plumes on newly opened salt-pans at Kuala Selangor on 1 December 1970 may have been from a separate population node (BR 1970–71), but no breeding was confirmed and, 20 years on (January 1991), a last, mateless, survivor joined the Grey Heron colony at nearby Kapar. Perak is less known and some residents may yet continue in the Matang–Larut mangrove belt, but with no breeding confirmed later than 1975 when a few pairs raised chicks among Black-crowned Night Herons at Tanjung Selinsing (Ratnam 1976). Elsewhere, one in part-breeding colours at Serangoon, Singapore, on 10 February 1985 must have been on the move.

For habitat reasons, non-breeding migrants are scarce along the Malaysian E coast (Berwick 1952), but widespread elsewhere. Main concentrations are on the NE and W coasts, from Bandon bay to Songkhla and in Perak and Selangor. Most are winter visitors but summerers (age unknown) occur in the NE including, in June 1995, 23 roosting in mangroves at Pak Ying, Nakhon Si Tammarat (BCSTB-12, Meeswat and Prentice 1984). A few summer birds have also been seen at Melaka, and in Singapore recently a yellow-billed loner spent several mid-year months visiting Kranji heronry (BR 1967, MBR 1986–87).

HABITATS AND ECOLOGY. Natural freshwater wetlands in the north do not seem to attract them (Storer 1976, 1978), and with pesticide contamination of intensively cultivated subcoastal paddylands in Malaysia, Great Egrets have mostly retreated to what must have been their ancestral local habitat: mangroves and intertidal mudflats. They roost there at customary sites in forest or reedbeds over water close to the coast. Intermittently through November, January, March and April 1968/69, a few joined the Cattle Egret roost at Sungai Way, inland Selangor (BR 1969), but are suspected of having been passing through.

FORAGING AND FOOD. Hunts alone or in small, loose groups, mostly on exposed mudflats close to the tideline.

SOCIAL ORGANIZATION. Residents nested gregariously and with other species, including Grey and Purple Herons, Black-crowned Night Heron and Milky Stork *Mycteria cinerea*. Migrants and other non-breeders also roost both gregariously and with other coastal ardeids, at mid winter some sites attracting up to 200 birds nightly.

MOVEMENTS. Not well studied. Numbers in non-breeding colours peak during late September–mid May (BMP5, BR 1967).

SURVIVAL. No direct information.

SOCIAL INTERACTIONS. No information.

VOICE. Winterers are mostly silent but when disturbed into flight occasionally give a deep, dry rattle.

BREEDING

Nest. All records are from mangrove forest. The twig nest, smaller than that of Grey Heron, and unlined, is built at crown height, usually on a lateral branch.

Eggs and brood. Eggs are pale greenish blue with a coarse, chalky shell-texture. Shape elliptical. Size (mm): 58.9–48.8 × 43.2–36.8 (mean 53.0 × 39.6, n=15). Full clutch three.

Cycle. No information

Seasonality. Bare-part breeding-colours reported in late July–September and November–April, eggs in August and September, and chicks in August (Madoc 1936). Year-to-year and between-colony variation not investigated.

MOULT. Most of 20-plus yellow-billed birds roosting at the Suloh Kecil river-mouth (W Johor) on 14 March had back-plumes (Hawkins and Howes 1986) but schedules of moult among migrants versus residents, and between age-groups, have not been worked out. Selangor-coast residents moulted flight-feathers during the nesting season: P5 on 2 July, P9 on 13 November, and one shot off a nest on 30 September had suspended at P7 (only P8–9 old). A dark-billed bird from the Bandon mangroves growing P2 on 4 June was on an evidently similar schedule. Two from Perak at P6–7 and P6 and 10 on 10 November were yellow-billed, hence of uncertain status. As among other herons, leading-edge primaries tend to be moulted precociously (ZRCNUS).

CONSERVATION. The main factor destabilizing residents has been nest-raiding at traditional sites. It remains to be seen whether stricter wardening and mangrove forest protection on the Perak coast can save an ageing nucleus (indeed, whether that nucleus is still fertile). In the meantime, recent rumours of egret-killing on the many fish-cage rafts now moored in Kelang estuary creeks should be taken seriously.

Intermediate Egret; Nok Yang Thohn Noi (Thai); Bangau Kerbau (Malay)

Mesophoyx intermedia (Wagler) 1829, Oken's *Isis* 22: 659. TL Java.
Plate 11

GROUP RELATIONS. Free-standing. Another egret that molecular studies suggest is nearer to *Ardea* than to *Egretta* (Sheldon 1987).

GLOBAL RANGE. Breeds through sub-Saharan Africa, the Indian subcontinent and Sri Lanka; S Japan, China south from Henan and Sichuan, including Taiwan and Hainan; SE Asia to Burma and the Mekong delta, and in S Sumatra, Java, Bali, possibly SW Kalimantan (Galdikas *et al.* 1985); and Sulawesi, New Guinea and Australia. Migratory probably in both hemispheres, in E Asia reaching the equator.

IDENTIFICATION/DESCRIPTION. Size between Little and Great Egrets; from the latter also by shorter, thicker-looking neck, lack of dark dagger-mark behind the eye, and posture often more hunched. On a tarsus 20–40 mm shorter, Intermediate has toes near the same length as Great Egret, and its bill is actually shorter than in many Little Egrets (proportionately shorter than in any other white egret). In breeding plumage, well-developed chest-plumes separate it from Great and at all times facial skin colour is more or less as bill. Yellow-billed Chinese Egret shows a heavy, drooping crest and yellow toes.

Bare-part colours. (Adult) iris pale yellow; bill yellow, generally paler than in Great Egret; facial skin as bill or with slight greenish tinge; legs and feet black (but see on).

Size (mm). (Skins: 3 adults, none sexed): wing 295 (one only); tail 118–119; bill 73.8–75.8; bill from mouth-corner 93.0, 94.5; tarsus 109.2–112.8; mid-toe plus claw 92.4–93.1 (BMNH, ZRCNUS).

Weight. No data.

DISTRIBUTION. Large gap on the Malaysian E coast. Historical summary: *Ran, Sur, Pha, Nak, Pht, Tra, Son, Pat, Sat, Nar, Ked, Pek, Sel, Mel, Sin,* with additional island records from Libong and (on spring passage) Langkawi and Penang off the W coast; and Tioman (*Phg*) off the E coast.

GEOGRAPHICAL VARIATION. Mees (1982) sank subspecies on the basis that claimed size-differences are not supportable, but left open the question of bare-part colours. Nominate Asian *intermedia* has been thought of as consistently black-legged, hence an April adult photographed in Singapore showing distinctly pink tibia and upper tarsi, as in African and Australasian breeders, is of special interest (M. Strange). The options are either a long-distance wanderer (unlikely in breeding colours) or more Asian variation than supposed, in further support of the new arrangement.

STATUS AND POPULATION. A non-breeding migrant, regular and more or less common, mainly along mangrove coasts hence predominantly in the

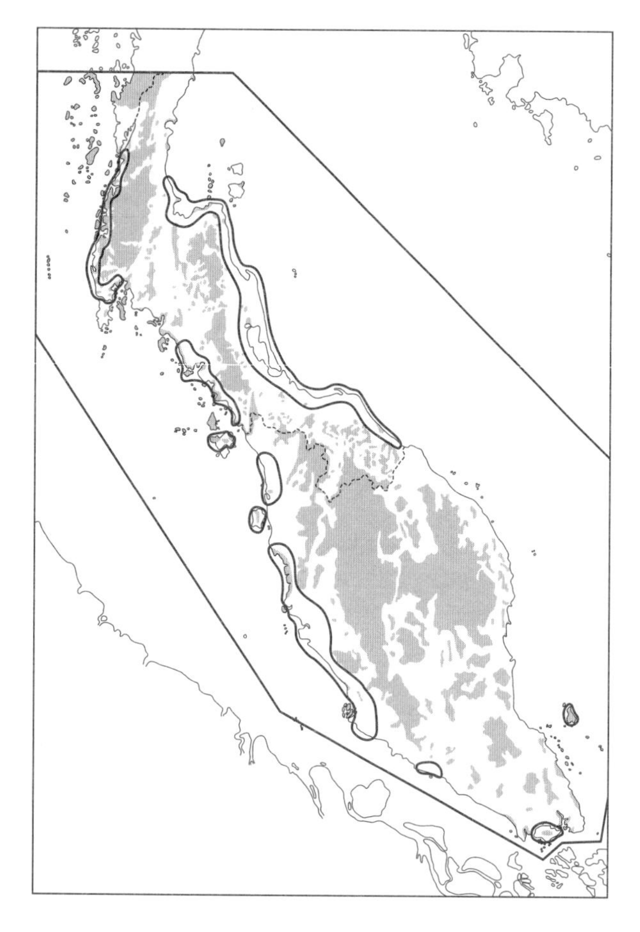

west and Singapore; indeed, there are no definite E-coast records anywhere between the Thai border and Tioman island (a bird in Tekek bay during 9–11 February 1990: A. Jeyarajasingam).

HABITATS AND ECOLOGY. Pesticide loads now keep most egrets off intensively worked paddylands, but Intermediates still make local use of freshwater sites, e.g., Thung Thong Reserve (Surat Thani), Thalae Noi and, in early February 1986, a party of 83 in fallows near Kuala Kurau, Perak (MBR 1986–87, Storer 1976, 1978). A few came to an inland Cattle Egret roost during late October–April 1968/69 but, in the south, most are now exclusively coastal, dependant on mangrove-backed intertidal mudflats. Like other migratory egrets, they roost in mangroves but where reedbeds over water are available nearby, these are favoured.

FORAGING AND FOOD. No specific information.

SOCIAL ORGANIZATION. At roosts, gregarious and mixes with other ardeids.

MOVEMENTS. Except in Singapore, absent during summer. Extreme dates are 22 August on the Songkhla lake wetland and 3 October in the Terong estuary, Perak; and in spring, 1 May at Kapar, Selangor, with northbound migrants crossing Langkawi island and neighbouring Satul province during April (Meeswat and Prentice 1984, P.D. Round, Silvius *et al.* 1987). May–August records from Singapore indicate either that superior coverage there has picked up individuals failing to migrate or that the extreme southern tip of the Peninsula is reached by a counter-flow of S-hemisphere birds (see also Little Egret).

SURVIVAL. No information.

SOCIAL INTERACTIONS. No information.

VOICE. No information.

BREEDING. No population.

MOULT. At least some acquire breeding-plumage before departure, e.g., five at Kuala Sepetang, Perak, on 21 March (BR 1965). The condition of Singapore summerers is not recorded.

CONSERVATION. Exclusion of waterbirds from paddyland through excessive use of chemical pesticides is a consistent issue for all egrets in the Peninsula. No other special factors identified.

Little Egret; Nok Yang Pia (Thai); Bangau Kecil (Malay)

Egretta garzetta (Linnaeus) 1766, *Systema Naturae* 12(1): 237. TL NE Italy.
Plate 11

GROUP RELATIONS. Inclusion of the western Indian Ocean and African reef egrets *dimorpha* and *gularis* in a species *garzetta* is contentious. Together with American *E. thula* (Snowy Egret), they may constitute a superspecies.

GLOBAL RANGE. The exclusive breeding-range spans warm-temperate Eurasia from the Atlantic to Korea and Japan; the Indian subcontinent and Sri Lanka; China south from Shaanxi and Sichuan including Taiwan and Hainan; SE Asia to the central plains of Thailand and Mekong delta, also Java, Bali and SW Kalimantan (Galdikas *et al.* 1985); and New Guinea and N and E Australia. Some populations of both hemispheres migrate, in SE Asia meeting across the equator.

IDENTIFICATION/DESCRIPTION. Similar to Chinese and Reef Egrets but from these by form of crest and, year-round, by combination of bare-part colours. The yellow lower foot of adult nominate *garzetta* is matched only by Chinese Egret in breeding colours.

Bare-part colours. Iris yellow; facial skin dull greyish (immature), clay-yellow (adult); bill entirely black or with extreme base of lower mandible pale yellow or bluish white; legs and feet black with soles yellow or (nominate *garzetta*) toes and base of tarsus yellow or greenish yellow.

Size (mm). (Skins: 3 adult *garzetta*; none sexed): wing 266–271 (juveniles smaller); tail 93, 94; bill 78.7–86.3; tarsus 97.1–101.8; mid-toe plus claw 71.7–73.0.

Weight. No data.

DISTRIBUTION. Historical summary: all divisions except *Pak, Chu, Pha, Sat, Yal, Nar, Kel, Neg*, with island records from Penang and, on autumn passage dates, Ubin, Singapore.

GEOGRAPHICAL VARIATION. Two forms occur: nominate *garzetta*, with toes and lowest part of the tarsus yellow, dominant everywhere; and much scarcer black-footed birds recorded north to Kuala Gula, coastal Perak (BR 1964). These may be subspecies *nigripes* Temminck 1840 (TL Java) of island SE Asia and beyond (but juvenile nominate *garzetta* could also lack yellow, and foot versus face colours need checking).

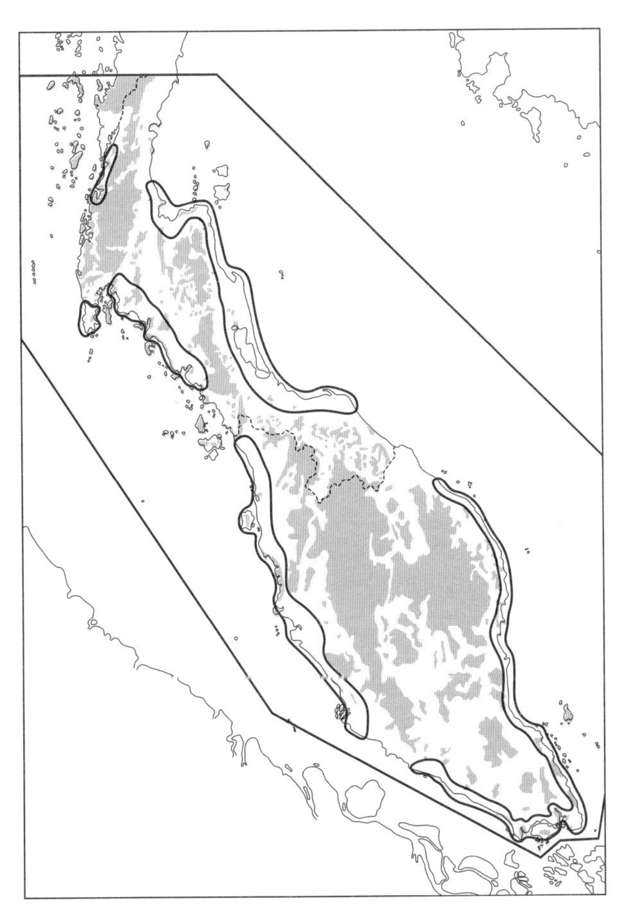

STATUS AND POPULATION. A non-breeding visitor and local over-summerer, regular and more or less common. During winter, fairly numerous along most of the W coast and in Singapore, with another concentration on the Bandon bay–Nakhon Si Thammarat coast. Formerly common on paddyland in N Terengganu but, recently, there have been few E-coast records anywhere south of Pattani (Berwick 1952b, Howes *et al.* 1986, P.D. Round, Swennen *et al.* 1986).

Outside accepted passage-dates, over 1600 roosted with other egrets in mangroves at Pak Ying, Nakhon Si Thammarat, on 24 June 1995, with records of small numbers in Pattani bay in June, a party of six coasting past Perlis on 21 July, and one in the Songkhla lake wetland on 11 August (Annandale and Robinson 1903, R. Gregory-Smith, Meeswat and Prentice 1984, P.D. Round, Williamson 1918). Southward, small numbers are regular year-round in Singapore, and some of a flock of ten at Serangoon on 11 June were black-footed, suggesting possible additional migration from the S-hemisphere. Black-footed birds have otherwise been recorded north to Perak, during 19 October–25 February (BR 1964, 1969, 1970–71, MBR 1986–87, SINGAV-2, -3). This prompts the suggestion that both northern and southern ends of the Peninsula might be within over-summering ranges of non-breeders that fail to complete a full migration back to respective breeding areas. More attention to age-class and moult schedule is needed.

HABITATS AND ECOLOGY. Makes local use of open, freshwater wetlands such as at Thalae Noi (Storer 1976) and, formerly, great use of paddylands. Pesticide contamination has all but excluded it from this habitat in Malaysia, where most now depend on mangrove-backed tidal mudflats. Yellow- and black-footed birds both occupy the full range of habitats used. Roosts, often with other ardeids, at customary sites in mangroves, nearby reedbeds or on snags over open water. As with Great and Intermediate Egrets, selects reedbeds if these are available close to the coast.

FORAGING AND FOOD. Hunts individually and has livelier searching action than most other egrets, constantly combing through wrack, etc., and fast-walking, with much foot-paddling to disturb prey in shallow water. Often dashes with semi-spread wings to capture prey spotted at a distance.

SOCIAL ORGANIZATION. Forages individually but roosts gregariously, and communally with other ardeids.

MOVEMENTS. 6 September (ENGGANG-2) is the earliest accepted autumn date in Malaysia, with main passage later. In Kedah, there is large-scale movement through subcoastal paddylands in

October–November. October was also the main arrival month in N Terengganu paddylands, is a month of increase on the Perak mudflats and marks the peak of arrival in Singapore (Berwick 1952b, BR 1964, Bromley 1949, SINGAV-3). At Sungai Way, inland Selangor, a few roosted with Cattle Egrets in open reedbeds through late October–November, but none later, implying use of an established site by passing migrants (BR 1968).

The latest spring date on the Malaysian E coast is 12 April, but large-scale passage through Kedah has been seen in May (Berwick 1952b, Bromley 1949) and in 1991 about ten were still visiting the Kapar power-station ash-pond roost (Selangor) on 1 May.

SURVIVAL. No information.

SOCIAL INTERACTIONS. No information.

VOICE. No information.

BREEDING. No population.

MOULT. Everywhere, adult nominate *garzetta* start developing breeding plumes by early February, and full plumage can be widespread by the end of the month, whereas a grey-faced immature photographed in Selangor on 10 April was in extremely worn plumage and may not have started moult by that date (BMNH, A. Jeyarajasingam, SINAV-3, Storer 1976, Williamson 1918). Among summerers, at least some Pattani bay *garzetta* were plumed, and an early June-dated male had nearly completed wing-moult (P1–7 new, 8 and 10 growing). Nothing is known of summer schedules in Singapore.

CONSERVATION. Pesticide contamination of former paddyland feeding-grounds is the probable main issue.

Chinese Egret; Nok Yang Jeen (Thai); Bangau Cina (Malay)

Egretta eulophotes (Swinhoe) 1860, *Ibis* 2: 64. TL Amoy island, Fujian, China.
Plate 11

GROUP RELATIONS. Uncertain. In general form and foraging behaviour it is closer to Little and Snowy Egrets than to Reef Egret.

GLOBAL RANGE. The only egret breeding predominantly in the N-temperate zone, formerly, from the the Sea of Okhotsk along the Asian coastal plain south to Guangdong. Colonies persist on small islands off the Korean Peninsula (Lansdown 1990) and, up to the 1980s, a few pairs bred in Hong Kong. There are no other recent reports. Migratory, wintering from the Philippines and N Sulawesi to Borneo, the Peninsula, SE Sumatra and SW Java, with largest numbers reported from Palawan (Gast and King 1985). Claims of occurrence on Christmas island (Indian Ocean) and in W Sumatra are based on specimens reidentified as white-phase Reef Egrets (Slater 1971, ZRCNUS).

IDENTIFICATION/DESCRIPTION. Tricky in winter, one useful difference from white Reef Egret being proportionate leg and foot length against folded-wing. A ratio wing-length/tarsus 2.8–3.3 (mean 3.1; close to Little Egret) compares with 3.4–4.3 (mean 3.8) in Reef Egret. In flight, feet project as far beyond the tail as in Little Egret; much more than in Reef Egret. The bill tends to taper more than in Reef Egret but this is a subtle, variable character dependant on lower-mandible shape. Bill length ranges overlap widely. In the hand, tarsus is longer than bill, versus always shorter in Reef Egret.

Before spring departure, some reveal themselves by bare-part colours, back-plumes and nuchal crest, which is drooping and shaggy, heavier and longer than in Reef Egret (up to 112 mm versus about 85). Where doubt remains about a plumed specimen, dorsal aigrette shape is decisive: barbs spaced and long throughout, forming a broad, lacy fan that reaches the tail-tip, whereas in Reef barbs are denser and shorten progressively to form a hackle-point that falls short of the tail-tip.

Bare-part colours. (Summer adult) iris pale yellow; facial skin light blue to grey-blue; bill orange-yellow; legs and feet black with toes and extreme base of tarsus yellow. (Winter) facial skin yellowish green; upper and apical half of lower mandible black or brownish black, base of lower mandible yellow to yellowish green; legs and feet sage-green, exactly as in many Reef Egrets wholly or patchily black down the front of the tarsus (remains of the seasonal colour-change).

Size (mm). (Skins: 7 males, 6 females, including from Fujian; adult): wing 255–275 and 230–249; tail 88 and 82 (singles); bill 75.7–83.5 and 66.0–75.8; tarsus 81.3–95.9 and 72.0–80.5; mid-toe plus claw 61.4–65.9 and 52.4–61.5 (BMNH).

Weight. No data.

DISTRIBUTION. Few known regular stopping points; none along the Malaysian E coast. Historical summary: *Pha, Phu, Kra, Tra, Pat, Pek, Sel, Mal, Sin*, with additional island records from Libong (Trang) and Ubin, Singapore.

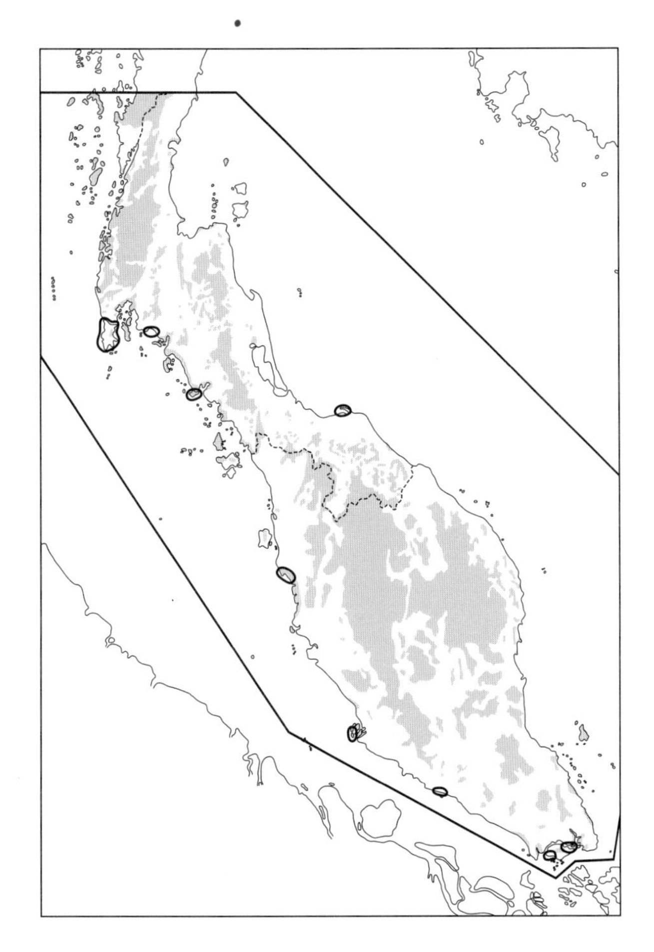

GEOGRAPHICAL VARIATION. None recognized.

STATUS AND POPULATION. A non-breeding visitor, local and sparse to uncommon. Problems of field identification (and the discovery that white Reef Egrets use tidal mudflats) weaken the record, but occurrence during both passage seasons is definite and some wintering has been assumed at a few favoured sites along the W coast and in Singapore. North to south: up to seven birds during recent winters (October–April) in Krabi bay, plus 2–3 in late March–early April at Libong island (BBCB-7, -9, BSCTB-10, G. Speight); 30-plus at Kuala Gula (Perak) in early November 1964 (fewer by mid December), up to five there through early January 1986, ten in mid March and 13 at nearby Rubiah river-mouth on 24 March (BR 1964, MBR 1986–87); about 30 on Tengah island, Kelang estuary, on 27 February 1967, and some or all of eight birds there on 9 March 1989 were believed to have been this species (BR 1967, ENGGANG-2). On the E coast, one from Pattani bay 'procured on the mud among mangroves' on 3 October 1901 (BMNH, Ogilvie-Grant 1906) may have been on passage (see also Reef Egret). In Singapore, recorded at Jurong and Serangoon, sites since lost to land-filling. As of 1990/91, a small group returned to the mudflats of the Seletar estuary, with at least one occurrence on nearby Ubin island (BMP5, BR 1963, MBR 1986–87, R.F. Ollington, M. Strange).

Largest recent groups (in breeding colours) anywhere have been the 13 at Rubiah on 24 March 1986 and a similar number at Serangoon six days later (MBR 1986–87).

HABITATS AND ECOLOGY. Not identified away from mangrove-backed, tidal mudflats and tide-flushed prawn-ponds in the mangrove zone. It is not known if they associate with other egrets at roost.

FORAGING AND FOOD. Foragers follow the receding tide and, like Little Egret, are typically active, often opening the wings as they run after prey (Lansdown 1990). Different behaviour quoted in BMP5 was described in November, i.e., after post-breeding moult and, with hind-sight, there is a risk that some of the birds studied were actually white Reef Egrets.

SOCIAL ORGANIZATION. No specific information.

MOVEMENTS. Extreme dates of occurrence are 5 August and 4 May, but with very few records before the last week of September. A bird colour-ringed as a chick on Shin-Do island, western Korea, on 6 July 1990 was sighted on Ubin island, Singapore, on 17 October 1992 (BCSTB-13, BIRDLINE 1994, BR 1965, T. Mundkur).

SURVIVAL. No information.

SOCIAL INTERACTIONS. No information.

VOICE. No information.

BREEDING. No population.

MOULT. Some in Singapore on 7 October still had orange bill-bases and blue facial skin but, apparently, no plumes. In spring, the latter have been seen as of 15 March, implying body-moult starts either on the wintering ground or at an early migration halt (BR 1980–81). Four of uncertain age collected during 3 October–24 January all showed slightly worn primaries, with no definite wing-moult (BMNH).

CONSERVATION. Globally endangered (BTW2). Recent rumours of egret-killing at fish-cage rafts moored in the Kelang estuary could involve this species. Of the regular stop-over/wintering sites, only Kalumpang (Perak coast) and Libong island are formally protected.

Reef Egret; Nok Yang Thalae (Thai); Bangau Batu (Malay)

Egretta sacra (Gmelin) 1789, *Systema Naturae* 13(2): 640. TL Tahiti.
Plates 10 and 11

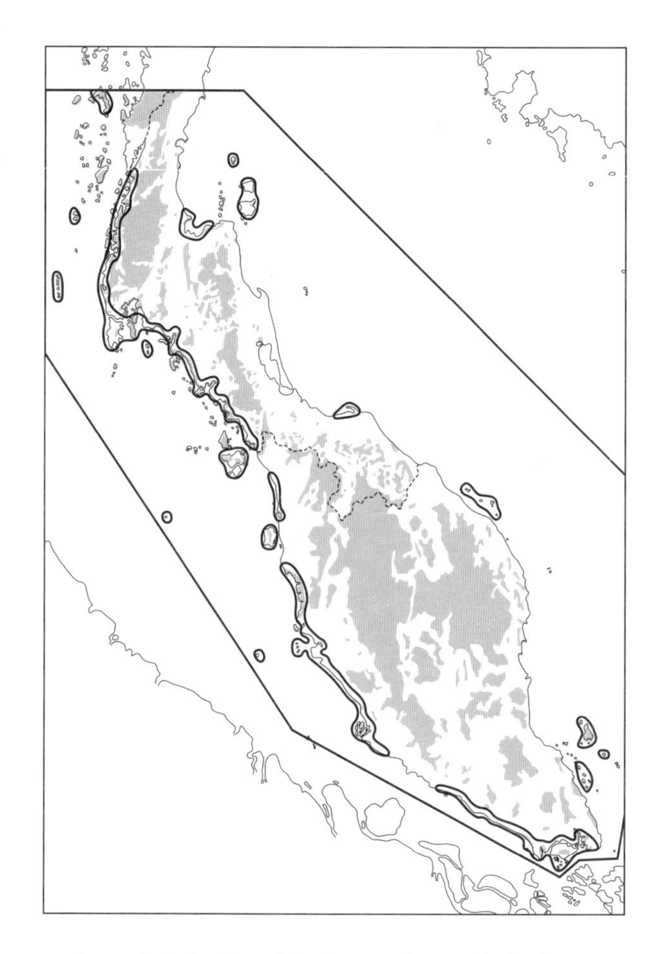

GROUP RELATIONS. Probably free-standing; affinities, especially with Chinese Egret, need more study.

GLOBAL RANGE. Coasts and islands, vagrant inland, from near the head of the Bay of Bengal and Bay of Bengal islands; S Japan and E China from the Changjiang mouth, including Taiwan and Hainan; SE Asia; Wallacea, Australasia and Oceania to the Tuamotu group and New Zealand.

IDENTIFICATION/DESCRIPTION. Dark morph from Little Heron by size, obvious egret shape and uniform slate-grey colour, without cap contrast or face pattern. From much larger Great-billed Heron also by darker plumage and lack of white neck and breast hackles. Pied plumage is reported among juveniles (Robinson and Chasen 1936) and the occasional white-phase adult shows a few dark marks, but real intermediates, if they occur, must be rare. For plume morphology and diagnostic proportions, see Chinese Egret.

Bare-part colours. (Adult) iris yellow; facial skin grey-blue in dark morph, greenish in white; upper mandible blackish to brown or greenish horn, lower horn- to greenish-yellow, apparently without the sharp base/tip colour difference of Chinese Egret; legs and feet olive to yellow- or sage-green, apparently often with dark markings on the front of the tarsus, as in Chinese Egret. Howes *et al.* (1986) report a dark bird with orange-yellow feet, a possible breeding colour. At no stage does tarsus sharply contrast with toe colour.

Size (mm). (Skins: 10 males, 8 females; adult): wing 275–292 and 268–279; tail 81–99 and 87–100; bill 78.0–85.7 and 72.4–82.4; tarsus 68.0–79.8 and 64.8–75.8. Sexual dimorphism less than in Chinese Egret, and not up to the seven percent size difference, without overlap, claimed by Mayr and Amadon (1941).

Weight. No data.

DISTRIBUTION. Historical summary: all divisions except *Pak, Chu, Nak, Pht, Son, Yal, Nar, Pes, Kel, Pra, Neg*, with records from many islands of all sizes and distances out, including: Lanbyi, the Surin and Similan groups, Boi Yai, Yao Yai, Phiphi and Libong, the Langkawi group, Perak, Penang, Jarak, Rembia and Pisang off the W coast; Tao, Phangan and Samui, the Perhentian and Redang groups and Bidung Laut, and the Pahang–Johor archipelago (Tulai, Tioman, Tokong Burung, Tinggi, Babi Besar, Sibu, Lima Besar and Pemanggil) off the E coast; and Ubin, Serangoon and most of the S archipelago, where relatively common, around Singapore.

GEOGRAPHICAL VARIATION. Peninsular populations are widespread nominate *sacra*.

STATUS AND POPULATION. As far as known, wholly resident; regular and uncommon to common. Generally more numerous on small islands than along mainland coasts. Roost-gatherings of up to 200 birds reported in Phuket (P.D. Round).

HABITATS AND ECOLOGY. A dark-phase bird in paddyland near Teluk Intan on 23 March 1986 is the only recent inland record, and even then close to the Perak river estuary (MBR 1986–87). Typical habitats are rocky shores and exposed back-reef flats, less often sandy beaches; also low-tide mud in and around mangroves, where white individuals heavily outnumber dark ones. On rocky shores, particularly those lacking a wide tide-flat, the reverse skew is just as obvious and on many small islands complete. Explanations of how the dimorphism might be maintained include anti-predation camouflage and camouflage affecting hunting success in different microhabitats (Holyoak 1973, Rohwer 1990). Itoh's (1991) claim that variation is geographical shows only that the white morph seems to be absent from mainland Japan. However, dark birds predominate along the entire Andaman Sea coast and roost-gatherings of 26 in Krabi and nearly 200 on Waw islet, Chalong bay, Phuket, included no white ones at all (BCSTB-13, Ewins *et al.* 1990).

According to habitat, roosts overnight or during high water on isolated rocks, mooring piles, snags overhanging water and, with other coastal egrets, in living mangrove trees. The large roost in Chalong bay was on a small, wooded islet.

FORAGING AND FOOD. Reef Egrets search by pacing over exposed ground from the high-tide splash-zone down, typically without the dash of Little and Chinese Egrets. Less usual hunting methods include: flying low and slowly out over the incoming tide, stabbing down into the water (by a white pair whose patch had been flooded); plunge-diving from a boulder; wading slowly in shallow water, wing-flicking (to flush prey?); and, by a dark bird, searching actually under the shade of an extended wing (Cairns 1955a, SINGAV-1).

SOCIAL ORGANIZATION. Hunts mostly alone but roosts gregariously and sometimes with other coastal egrets. Most pairs nest in isolation and rumours of colonies have not been confirmed.

MOVEMENTS. Believed sedentary but in mid-November 1985 apparent migrants moved through Pattani bay (Swennen *et al.* 1986), numbers rising to 83 birds on the 14th and falling to only seven five days later. That at least some white ones may have been Chinese Egrets cannot be ruled out for this locality.

SURVIVAL. No information.

SOCIAL INTERACTIONS. No information.

VOICE. No information.

BREEDING

Nest. All records are from small islands. Nests are about 45 cm across, a shallow cup built variously of sticks and grass in a low tree or under a rock overhang.

Eggs and brood. Eggs are pale bluish green. Size (mm): 43.4–40.0 × 34.3–32.5 (n=6). Full clutch three.

Cycle. No information.

Seasonality. In the Langkawi, Redang, Pahang–Johor and Singapore S archipelagos, eggs and chicks have been found on dates that imply laying during May–August; plus an active nest, contents not recorded, on Phiphi island, Krabi, in mid November (Dickinson 1966, Gibson-Hill 1952, Madoc 1936, 1947, SINGAV-6).

MOULT. Among 25 adults from Phangnga south to Johor, covering all months, 12 showed active wing-moult during April–early December. Synchrony is loose, with earliest completions by mid June and starts as late as July, and the picture further complicated by suspensions, recorded in March, June, September and late December. Barring these, the individual pattern is regular-descendant out to P7 or 8, then P10 precedes the rest of the wing-tip (BMNH, ZRCNUS).

CONSERVATION. No critical issues identified.

Black-crowned Night Heron; Nok Khwehk (Thai); Burung Pucong Kuak (Malay)

Nycticorax nycticorax (Linnaeus) 1758, *Systema Naturae* 10(1): 142. TL S Europe.
Plate 12

GROUP RELATIONS. A narrow breeding overlap exists with *N. caledonicus* (Rufous Night Heron) in parts of the Philippines, Sulawesi, NW Borneo and Java, with occasional hybridization (Hubbard 1976, Hoogerwerf 1966, Sheldon and Manuel 1985). They are treatable as a superspecies.

GLOBAL RANGE. Tropical to mid-temperate latitudes of both hemispheres around the world, except Wallacea and Australasia where replaced by the Rufous Night Heron. Higher-latitude populations migrate, some northern birds as far as the tropics, including the Philippines but not, apparently, continental SE Asia. Vagrant on Christmas island, Indian Ocean.

IDENTIFICATION/DESCRIPTION. In poor light, by chunky shape, calls and chevron flight-formation of flocks. Seen well, adults are distinctive. Juveniles are the only brown, bittern-shaped birds in this area with large, pale spots and streaks all over both head and body.

Bare-part colours. (Adult) iris carmine red (yellow in juvenile); facial skin blue-grey; bill black; legs and feet pink-orange. Courtship colours not described from this area.

Size. No local data.

Weight (g). Chicks hatch at around 25 and fledge at 650 (Ratnam 1976), but no adults have been weighed.

DISTRIBUTION. North to Songkhla but heavily concentrated (1) in the northern half of the Malaysian W-coast plain, (2) around Singapore. Historical summary: *Son, Pat, Pes, Ked, Kel, Pra, Pek, Phg, Sel, Mel, Joh, Sin,* with additional island records from Penang and Ubin, Singapore.

GEOGRAPHICAL VARIATION. Widespread nominate *nycticorax*.

STATUS AND POPULATION. Resident, local and sparse to common. Until the 1970s, vagrant away from NW Malaysia where a pioneer nesting-colony established itself on the Kerian coast of Perak, possibly before World-War Two (Allen 1948, Cairns 1956, Hamilton 1923, Young 1941). Developed as the first double-cropping 'rice-bowl' of the Peninsula, Kerian may have attracted colonists to new feeding opportunities supplied by extended irrigation (BMP5).

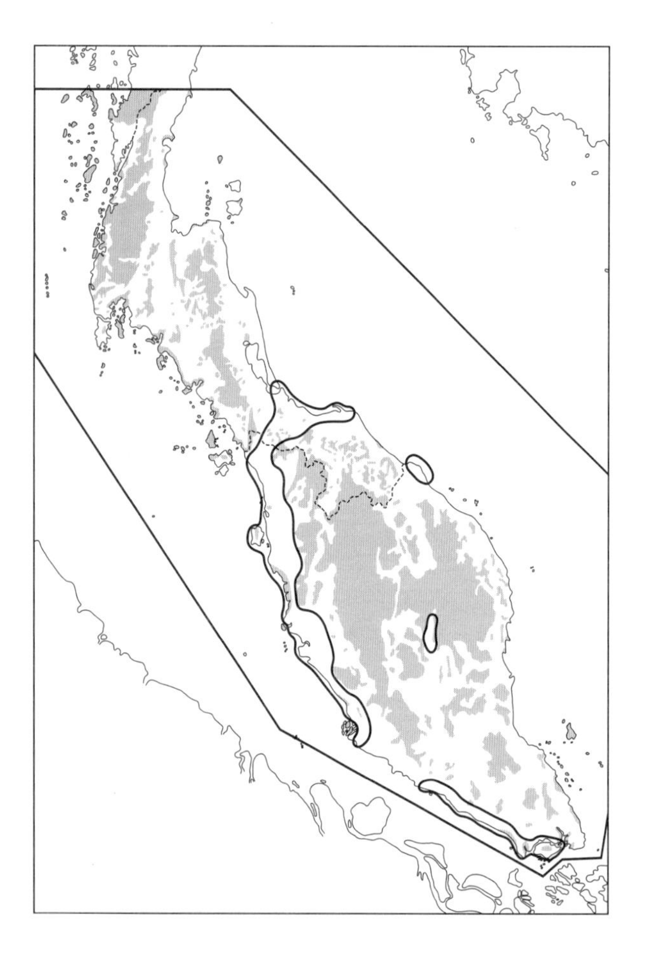

Important paddyland fishes have since been reduced by pesticides but over the last 30 years heron numbers have actually increased in the area, implying food has not been limiting. Wardening by wildlife guards, begun in the 1960s, is thought to have raised fledging success above the ceiling formerly imposed by hunting, although actual colony growth beyond the 2000 or so pairs estimated breeding in October–November 1964 is uncertain (BR 1964, Ratnam 1976, Silvius *et al.* 1987).

What does seem likely is that, barring possible release of captives, Black-crowned Night Herons now increasingly common elsewhere in the Peninsula all derive from the Kerian source. Outside the core zone of dispersal (see below), they became regular in coastal Selangor in the mid 1970s. In early April 1975, some were on the Tembeling river (Pahang) and in the same month birds appeared in Singapore (where previously known from just two old records), with singles and small groups at Kranji and elsewhere regular thereafter (BR 1974–75, Gibson-Hill 1950a, C.J. Hails). By April 1983, the evening flight over Serangoon, NE Singapore, topped 100 birds and on 22 May that year a dependant juvenile appeared there, tended by an adult (MBR 1982–83). Coastal reclamation in Singapore caused some shifts of population through the later 1980s but evening flights along the NE coast of the island had doubled in strength by 1986, with eventual discovery of a nesting colony of 200-plus pairs in a small, river-girt patch of mangroves near Yishun. Disturbance moved them on but some have since started re-visiting and are guessed to be nesting at one or more alternative sites (R.F.Ollington, Subaraj 1988).

HABITATS AND ECOLOGY. While mangroves are the regular nesting and roosting habitat, Kerian Night Herons hunt on open freshwater wetlands, to which they flight in long, chevron skeins each evening. Dawn returns to the colony-site occur year-round but some presumed non-breeders roost inland, typically in tree-thickets overhanging water. There are also reports of large groups spending the day in paddyland (BR 1964, 1974–75, MBR 1982–83, Silvius *et al.* 1987). These could be a source of onward emigration to other areas.

The two nest-colonies are in mangroves, with a preference in Kerian for dense stands of young, 2–6 m tall *Avicennia marina*. This implies a need to shift in step with seaward advance of the forest (Ratnam 1976), also with cycles of erosion of its frontal zone. Nesting activities create their own additional impact by killing foliage. In 1964, the first year of regular recording by wildlife officers, some nest-trees at the then Tanjung Selinsing site were reported defoliated or killed outright by heavy coatings of heron droppings. As a possible outcome of the spread of tree death, in 1978 the colony moved 20 km north to a new site at Sungai Burung. By mid 1986, many trees had been bared there, too, with evidence of a shift out into surrounding live crowns, expanding the total area occupied in the process (Silvius *et al.* 1987). Ratnam (1976) reported about 20 ha affected before abandonment of Tanjung Selinsing.

FORAGING AND FOOD. Fish regurgitated by nestlings handled for ringing at the Kerian colony (gouramis *Trichogaster*, etc.) are typical of flooded paddyland and irrigation ditches (BMP5, Medway and Lim 1970). On the other hand, a youngster being fed at the edge of the Serangoon mangroves and a dusk gathering on fish-trap piles off nearby Ubin island (SINGAV-2) imply Singapore birds may indulge in some shoreline hunting as well.

SOCIAL ORGANIZATION. Strongly gregarious except perhaps while actually hunting.

MOVEMENTS. No long-distance migrants have been shown to occur and, even though this is one of the commonest breeding herons in the central plains of Thailand (Round *et al.* 1988), there are no records in the Peninsula north of Songkhla. The proven outer limits of dispersal of birds ringed as nestlings at the Kerian colony (Medway and Lim 1970) are 6°45′N in Pattani (plus a record from the adjacent plain of Kelantan) and 1°50′N at Batu Pahat, Johor. However, only four of 72 rings recovered have been off the coastal plain between Perak and Perlis.

SURVIVAL. Of 9490 birds ringed as pulli at Tanjung Selinsing during 1964–71, 72 were subsequently recovered at a distance. Of these, 55 (76 percent) occurred during year-one, with no clear pattern from the second through the fifth year but only two thereafter, the most recent after 161 months (BR 1972–73, MBR 1982–83).

SOCIAL INTERACTIONS. No information.

VOICE. In flight, a loud *kuok* or *kuak* (the Thai and Malay names are onomatopoeic).

BREEDING

Nest. Often several nests per tree-crown (Subaraj 1988). Stick-built, but no good details of structure or size are available.

Eggs and brood. Eggs are pale blue when fresh laid. Shape normal to long elliptical. Size (mm): 50.7–43.3 × 36.5–32.7 (n=6). Regular full clutch three, but up to six eggs per nest have been reported, extras presumably dumped by other females.

Cycle. No information.

Seasonality. Activities at the Kerian colony are roughly synchronous but little is known about breeding intervals. At Tanjung Selinsing in October 1964, most nests contained eggs or small young and by December there were still a few of both. In the following August, only eggs were found, with widespread hatching at the end of that month. In 1968, young nestlings were present in early July. At Yishun, Singapore, some activity occurred year-round, but with no nests actually checked (BR 1964, 1965, 1968, Ratnam 1976, Subaraj 1988, ZDUM).

MOULT. No data.

CONSERVATION. A recent spraying of the Yishun colony with insecticide killed many adults and disrupted breeding but has not noticeably affected numbers in the Republic as a whole. In Malaysia, prime foraging habitat is contaminated with pesticides, and foraging herons are caught for food but, given some protection at the breeding site, the population has nevertheless expanded. At the moment, this is the most successful large colonial waterbird in the Peninsula.

Malayan Night Heron; Nok Yang Lai Seua (Thai); Burung Pucong Rimau (Malay)

Gorsachius melanolophus (Raffles) 1822, *Transactions of the Linnean Society* 13(2): 326. TL SW Sumatra.

Plate 12

GROUP RELATIONS. Probably forms a superspecies with *Gorsachius goisagi* (Japanese Night Heron)

GLOBAL RANGE. S Indian hill-tracts, Sri Lanka and Bay of Bengal islands, and far NE India; the S Nansei islands, Yunnan, Taiwan and Hainan; and SE Asia to the Greater Sunda islands and Philippines. In the east, breeds to central and SE Thailand, the Philippines, perhaps the Talaud islands (an August record), and possibly in W Java (an immature filmed in the Ujong Kulon Reserve in early August) (AMNH, BBCB-4, -5, -6, Compost and Milton 1986) – but see Moult. Strongly but perhaps not fully migratory. Even at the northern limit of range, in upper Assam, some remain as late as mid December (ROM), and on Hainan island are present again in March (AMNH). Vagrant W Micronesia and Christmas island.

IDENTIFICATION/DESCRIPTION. Much larger than von Schrenck's Bittern, in similar habitat. Stocky, thick-necked and, for a heron, short-legged, with relatively short beak decurved along its culmen profile. Rufous with a black cap (more or less white-spotted) that projects down the nape as a drooping but erectile crest. Immatures are grey-brown rather than rufous, vermiculated and spotted black and white (juvenile Black-crowned Night Heron lacks a black crest). At all ages, dark flight-feathers contrast with coverts and, in a good view, white tips of the primaries and primary-coverts could be a useful marker.

Bare-part colours. (Adult) iris yellow; facial skin yellow-green; all except cutting-edge of upper mandible black to blackish horn, rest of bill greenish; legs and feet olive-green to olive-brown (BMNH, ZRCNUS).

Size (mm). (Live and skins: 9 adults, most not sexed): wing 260–281; tail 90–102; bill 47.2–48.5; bill from mouth-corner 63–69; tarsus 66–76 (UMBRP, ZRCNUS, BMNH).

Weight (g). Autumn migrants, 377–451 (n=5, heaviest individual a male, lightest a female).

DISTRIBUTION. Historical summary: *Pak, Pha, Pht, Kra, Tra, Son, Sat, Ked, Pek, Phg, Sel, Joh, Sin,* with records from several additional W-coast islands: the Surins, Tarutao and Ladang (Tarutao national park), Langkawi, Penang, Rembia (Sembilan group) and Jarak.

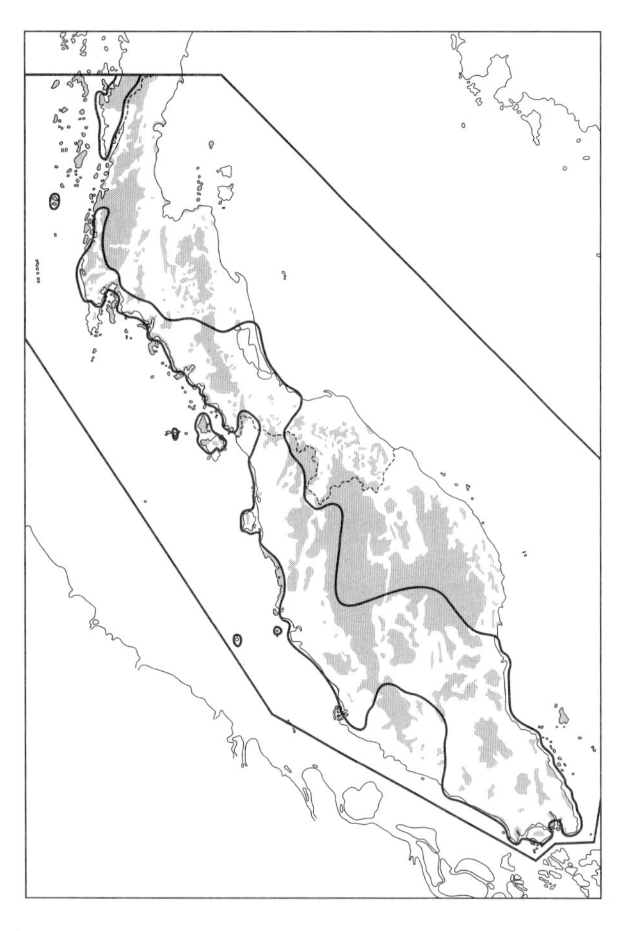

GEOGRAPHICAL VARIATION. Nominate *melanolophus,* if subspecies are accepted.

STATUS AND POPULATION. A passage migrant and probable non-breeding visitor, local and sparse to uncommon. Most records have been on likely migration dates but with some at mid winter south from Phatthalung. A presumed failed migrant, regular at the shrubby edge of Subang airfield, Selangor, during May–August 1991, is the only summer record (BLC, SINGAV-2, -3, A.C. Sebastian).

HABITATS AND ECOLOGY. Barring a few sightings in Selangor dredge-mine reedbeds, apparently during autumn, all daytime records have been from forest or secondary-growth, mostly along streams, from sea-level to about 500 m (BBCB-7, -8, BMP5, BR 1962, Cant 1957–58, Edgar 1947, Robinson and Chasen 1936). This includes upwards of ten recent sightings near reservoirs and streams in the Singapore central catchment area (C.J. Hails, SINGAV-1, -2, -3). Day-roosts alone in woodland trees.

FORAGING AND FOOD. Emerges onto clearings and open pool-margins at dusk (Cant 1957–58, SINGAV-3) but has been flushed from streamsides and puddles along forest tracks at mid morning so may not be wholly nocturnal in this area.

SOCIAL ORGANIZATION. Solitary.

MOVEMENTS. Night-flying migrants have been intercepted at lights at Fraser's Hill during 20 October–8 December and on 16 and 30 April, although from continental evidence (BBCB-4) spring passage starts at least a week sooner and continues later. Extreme dates area-wide are 16 October and 28 May (an immature) (BMP5, ENGGANG-1, C.J. Hails). One in the Terengganu off-shore oil-field on 6 November 1982 (D.M. Simpson) is likely to have been making a direct crossing of the Gulf of Thailand.

SURVIVAL. No information.

SOCIAL INTERACTIONS. No information.

VOICE. No information.

BREEDING. No population.

MOULT. About half the spring-season records, including on 28 May, have been of immatures, showing this plumage to be retained for at least the first one year of life. A bird collected at Pelarit, Perlis, on 5 November was in transitional plumage, at not less than 15–18 months old. Autumn migrants and winterers handled in all months up to 9 January show largely unworn wings, implying most adults will have completed a post-breeding moult before arrival. One with slightly worn flight-feathers at Penang on 14 March, and non-moulting spring migrants at Fraser's Hill, accord with this schedule.

CONSERVATION. No specific local issues.

Yellow Bittern; Nok Yang Fai Hua Dam (Thai); Burung Pucong Merah (Malay)

Ixobrychus sinensis (Gmelin) 1789, *Systema Naturae* 13(2): 642. TL China.

Plate 13

GROUP RELATIONS. Belongs in a superspecies of diminutive, thin-billed bitterns occupying tropical to mid-temperate latitudes around the world, also including *I. minutus* (Little Bittern) of Australia, Africa and west-central Eurasia and, apparently, American *I. exilis* (Least Bittern) although some molecular evidence is controversial (Sheldon 1987).

GLOBAL RANGE. Breeds through the Indian subcontinent, Sri Lanka and Bay of Bengal islands; Sakhalin, Japan and E China including Taiwan and Hainan; SE Asia to the Greater Sunda islands (including Borneo: Lansdown 1987), Bali and the Philippines; with outlying colonies in the Seychelles and W Micronesia. Migrants winter from parts of the breeding range on through Wallacea to New Guinea; vagrant in Australia.

IDENTIFICATION/DESCRIPTION. Smallest ardeid of the region. In flight, all age/sex-classes from Cinnamon Bittern by tail and all except innermost flight-feathers black, on both surfaces, contrasting with light body and yellow-fawn upper wing-coverts. Von Schrenck's Bittern is dorsally dark with a smaller pale area on the upper wing-coverts set against grey rather than black flight-feathers. Adult males have cap all black and back plain smoky; both streaked in females, which are also more obviously streaked orange-buff on otherwise white throat and lower neck. Juveniles resemble the female but are chestnut-streaked on the upper wing-coverts. In this species, the leg is feathered to the tarsal joint.

The downy chick is palest peach-pink, with iris yellow and other bare-parts pale yellow-green (Cairns 1954a).

Bare-part colours. (Adult) iris yellow with dark mark fore and aft of the pupil, facial skin not well described; upper mandible horn with culmen blackish, lower light yellow-horn; feet yellowish green, rear of tarsus and soles yellow (ZRCNUS).

Size (mm). (Live and skins: 41 adults, most not sexed): wing (125) 129–141; tail 34–52; bill 50.2–56.9; bill from mouth-corner 66–72; tarsus 44–51. The few sexed females did not exceed wing 131, tail 42, bill 50.9 (smallest definite male 52.1) and tarsus 47.1 (BMNH, UMBRP, ZRCNUS).

Weight (g). Range 70–114, but with a step between 95 and 101. Except for a nocturnal migrant intercepted on 3 December, all birds 101 or above were taken in April, implying fattening before or during spring passage.

DISTRIBUTION. Historical summary: all divisions except *Chu*, *Nak*, *Tra*, *Yal*, *Nar*, with additional island records (mostly at passage dates) from Surin Nua, Lanta, Penang and Pisang off the W coast; and Phangan and Tioman off the E coast.

GEOGRAPHICAL VARIATION. None recognized.

STATUS AND POPULATION. Both resident and a migrant or significant dispersant, regular and common. Up to the early 1980s, believed to have nested south only to Penang, including in the Thalae Noi–Songkhla wetland (Anonymous 1981, BMP5, Cairns 1954, 1954a, Loke 1954, Meeswat and Prentice 1984). The status of the odd southern bird as late as mid June had always been in doubt, but abruptly in 1983 undoubted over-summerers appeared in paddy and other open wetlands as far south as Singapore. On 12 July that year not less than 40 birds, including some displaying, were counted in open fern- and water-hyacinth swamp at Kranji impoundment; with

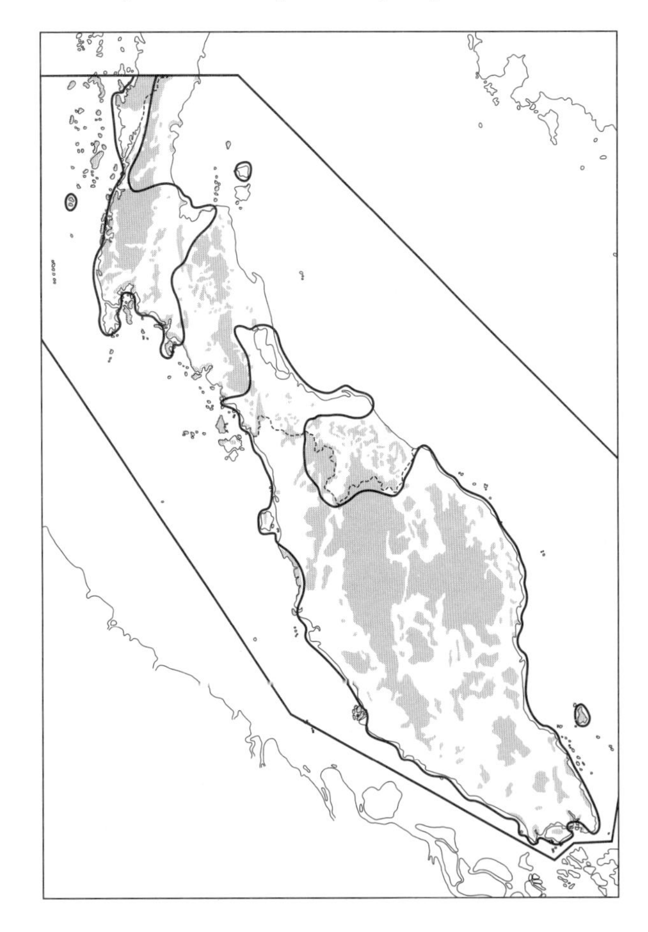

20 there again in late August and others over the same months in Perak and Selangor. By 1986, breeding had been proven in both Singapore and Selangor (BR 1968, MBR 1982–83, 1986–87).

HABITATS AND ECOLOGY. Densely vegetated freshwater wetlands, including the Thalae Noi marsh system, rice crops, *Typha* and *Phragmites* reedbeds on old dredge-mine lagoons, and ponds and channels fringed by tall herbage (amongst which bitterns climb with ease).

FORAGING AND FOOD. Forages mainly in or along the fringes of cover but also over more open, floating vegetation, especially water-hyacinth beds. Food includes small fish (*Trichogaster* identified), small frogs, prawns and terrestrial invertebrates (Cairns 1954, R.V. Lansdown).

SOCIAL ORGANIZATION. Where numerous, nests in clusters. Three to seven nests have been found in less than one hectare on Penang island (Cairns 1954) and up to 12 at Sekinchan, Selangor (Lansdown 1987), with five clusters in a radius of less than one km.

MOVEMENTS. Year-round mist-netting at Sungai Way reedbeds before the proven spread of breeders to Selangor caught presumed autumn migrants as of 13 September. Night-fliers have been intercepted at lights on the Main Range and at coastal and off-shore lighthouses in the Melaka Straits during 8 October–3 December, most in November (UMBRP), and birds collected on Pisang island in early January (Chasen 1932) are more likely to have been on the move than actually wintering there. None intercepted at lights, etc., in spring, but mist-netting at Sungai Way during the 1960s produced a surge of captures during April, interpreted as through-passage (BMP5). Of 65 ringed there overall, seven retrapped in later seasons demonstrated faithfulness to a wintering or staging site.

A bird grounded on a rig in the Terengganu off-shore oil-field on 18 October could have made a direct crossing of the Gulf of Thailand (MBR 1982–83).

SURVIVAL. The longest of few retrap-intervals is 24 months, a migrant back at site of ringing (UMBRP).

SOCIAL INTERACTIONS. Males advertise from bush-tops near nest-clusters, hunched with throat puffed out and base of the bill flushed bright red, uttering a soft, monotonous 'song'. From their post, they fly slow-flapping circuits and pursue females (R.V. Lansdown). A crest-raising display has been seen on the ground but sex and context were not recorded. When disturbed in vegetation, assumes a vertically stretched, cryptic 'bitterning' posture, but only females and juveniles have the plant-stem-simulating ventral neck-stripes.

VOICE. Male song is a soft *crrew crrew*. . ., and the flight-call when flushed a staccato *kak-kak-kak* (Boonsong and Round 1991).

BREEDING

Nest. Sites include tall rushes, flooded rice crops, scrub, reeds, *Saccharum* cane clumps and the lower boughs of dense-crowned (especially mango) trees fringing fields and irrigation canals. Of 42 nests checked in paddyland at Sekinchan, only three were in rice itself; the rest in other vegetation along field- and canal-margins. They are small, thick pads of grass or other leaf spears 10–300 cm above ground or water, and sometimes over-topped by a lattice of whatever materials are growing on site.

Eggs and brood. Eggs are pale blue-green. Size (mm): 30.0 × 23.0 (average). Full clutch typically four (3–5 on record), and repeat clutches are said to be smaller. Incubation period not reported but is said to begin with the first egg, such that chicks hatch at day intervals.

Cycle. Chicks climb before they can fly and stay away from the nest as of about day 15.

Seasonality. In Penang, eggs or chicks have been found in all months except January–March, the earliest clutch on 15 April. In 1986, first finds at Sekinchan, Selangor, imply laying began there not earlier than late March, but activity within clusters is not synchronized (Cairns 1954, 1954a, Lansdown 1987, R.P. Jaensch).

MOULT. Large enough autumn and spring samples have been examined to be fairly sure no moult occurs among migrants during the passage seasons (one suspension after P6, on 3 November). Among captures in Selangor reedbeds, the only instance of wing-moult was an adult growing P6–10 (i.e., half the wing) on 18 November (UMBRP). It is suspected birds in wing-moult fly little, hence are not susceptible to being netted or shot.

CONSERVATION. Like most other open-wetland birds, almost completely eliminated from herbicide-treated paddylands. See also Cinnamon Bittern.

Von Schrenck's Bittern; Nok Yang Fai Hua Thao (Thai); **Burung Pucong Gelam** (Malay)

Ixobrychus eurhythmus (Swinhoe) 1873, *Ibis* series 3(3): 74. TL Xiamen, Fujian, China.
Plate 13

GROUP RELATIONS. Free-standing, but has the same heavy bill as *I. cinnamomeus* (Cinnamon Bittern) and these two are likely to be close relatives.

GLOBAL RANGE. The only *Ixobrychus* bittern breeding mainly in the N-temperate zone, from Pacific Russia through Japan, Korea and E China, to an uncertain regular southern limit, but recorded in Guangdong. Nothing in the original reference to a juvenile live-caught in Sarawak in late November suggests it had fledged recently enough to be local (cf. Hancock and Kushlan 1984, Smythies 1957). Migratory, wintering possibly from Hainan through SE Asia to the Greater Sunda islands as far as Java (one record), and the Philippines; also Sulawesi. Vagrant in W Micronesia.

IDENTIFICATION/DESCRIPTION. Females and juveniles are the only local bitterns with deep brown upperparts liberally flecked white. Rich mahogany-chestnut face and upperparts, sharp against pale throat and underparts, and yellow-fawn wing-coverts pale against slate-grey (not black) flight-feathers identify the adult male. Underparts of females and juveniles are as boldly dark-streaked as Cinnamon Bittern, and a patch of long, black-streaked feathers on the lateral breast is conspicuous in both sexes of both. All sex/age-classes show the undersurface of the flight-feathers silvery grey against white coverts (versus black against buff in Yellow Bittern).

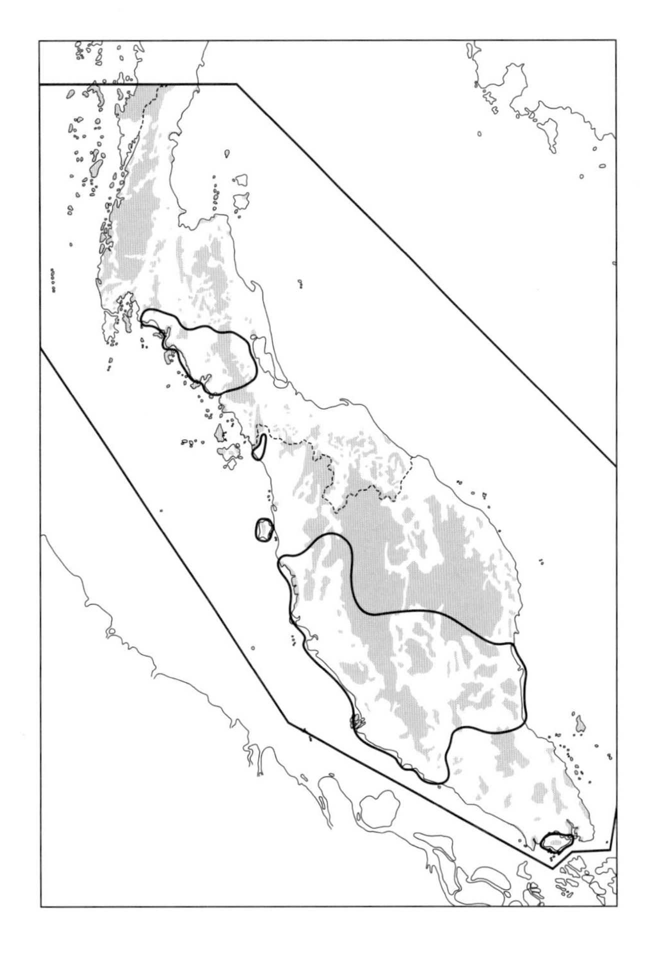

Bare-part colours. (Adult) iris chrome-yellow with dark mark fore and aft of the pupil as in other *Ixobrychus* species; facial skin yellow; culmen and separate cutting-edge of bill sharply demarcated blackish, the rest yellow; legs and feet greenish with yellow soles.

Size (mm). (Live and skins: 11 adults, sex mostly not recorded): wing 140–154; tail 40–55; bill 46.2–48.3; bill from mouth-corner 57–65; tarsus 45–55 (BMNH, ZRC-NUS, UMBRP).

Weight (g). All age/sex-classes, 90–123 (n=10) (UMBRP).

DISTRIBUTION. Probably overlooked in the north. Historical summary: *Kra, Pht, Tra, Pes, Pek, Phg, Sel, Neg, Mel, Sin*, with additional island records from Penang and Angsa (Selangor) off the W coast, and Ubin, Singapore.

GEOGRAPHICAL VARIATION. None recognized.

STATUS AND POPULATION. A passage migrant and non-breeding visitor, local and sparse. Only on passage in the Thai provinces and apparently also in Malaysia, but mid-winter (late December–February) contacts have been made in Singapore (Boonsong and Round 1991, SINGAV-1, -3, UMBRP).

HABITATS AND ECOLOGY. On passage, occasionally in open reedbeds, etc., alongside Yellow and Cinnamon Bitterns, but the mass of records at all dates has been from stream-, drain-, pond- or reservoir-sides near or actually under tree-cover (scrub to closed forest) (ENGGANG 2, MBR 1982–83, 1986–87, OBCB-8, SINGAV-2). Also recorded in or at the edge of mangroves (BR 1978–79, SINGAV-1, UMBRP), and this is the only local *Ixobrychus* bittern that may use brackish habitats.

FORAGING AND FOOD. Birds flushed off woodland streams after dark in Singapore and netted at night near the edge of the mangroves at Kuala

Selangor imply some foraging is nocturnal (BR 1978–79, SINGAV-3, UMBRP).

SOCIAL ORGANIZATION. Solitary.

MOVEMENTS. Interception of night-flying migrants at the Fraser's Hill floodlights during 5 October–8 November are matched by a wave of lowland sightings elsewhere between 2 October–19 November (BMP5, BR 1978–79, SINGAV-3, UMBRP). Limits of the sightings interpreted as spring passage are 4 March and 27 April, with occasional later records, recently up to 20 May at Kuala Lumpur and 21 June at Kranji reservoir, Singapore (in open situations suggestive of birds on the move: ENGGANG-2, C.J. Hails, SINGAV-3). These later dates fit an intra-tropical better than a N-temperate-zone migrant waterbird schedule (cf. Black Bittern), unless occasional non-breeders over-summer in the tropics.

SURVIVAL. No information.

SOCIAL INTERACTIONS. No information.

VOICE. No information.

BREEDING. No population.

MOULT. Autumn adults show more or less fresh wings and no moult, and may complete before arrival (one late October migrant had suspended after renewing P7–9). Autumn juveniles are less fresh than adults and may moult as first-winterers (ZRC-NUS).

CONSERVATION. No critical issues identified, but winter dependance on plains-level woodlands is a possible constraint. Globally near-threatened (BTW2).

Cinnamon Bittern; Nok Yang Fai Thammadaa (Thai); Burung Pucong Bendang (Malay)

Ixobrychus cinnamomeus (Gmelin) 1789, *Systema Naturae* 13(2): 643. TL China.
Plate 13

GROUP RELATIONS. Free-standing, but see von Schrenck's Bittern.

GLOBAL RANGE. Breeds through the Indian subcontinent, Sri Lanka and Bay of Bengal islands; the S Nansei islands and E and SE China from the Yellow Sea, including Taiwan and Hainan; SE Asia to the Greater Sunda islands, Bali and the Philippines; and Sulawesi. Migratory in the more strongly seasonal parts of its range, though movements are poorly understood. The few records further into Wallacea could be of migrants.

IDENTIFICATION/DESCRIPTION. All free-flying stages are distinguished by wings, upper wing-coverts and tail concolorous with the body. Adult males are more or less uniform orange-rufous above; females and juveniles browner and more speckled, with a dark brown cap and, below, darkish streaks prominent on the ventral neck (often only shadow-marks in males).

The downy chick is creamy white with iris yellow and other bare-parts pale yellow, to pale green over bill-base and lores (Cairns 1940).

Bare-part colours. (Adult) iris yellow with dark mark fore and aft of the pupil; facial skin bright green-yellow; culmen dark horn, cutting edge of upper mandible and all of lower yellow; legs and feet rather bright yellow-green. Juvenile duller, but not described in detail.

Size (mm). (Live and skins: 72 full-grown, most not sexed): wing 133–162 (largest female 148, smallest male 142); tail 34–48; bill 42.7–51.1; bill from mouth-corner 60–70; tarsus 46–55 (BMNH, UMBRP, ZRC-NUS).

Weight (g). Full-grown, sex mostly not recorded, 106–164 (n=28, but with only three, including two July males, over 150) (UMBRP).

DISTRIBUTION. Historical summary: all divisions except *Chu, Nak, Kra, Yal, Nar, Kel, Tru, Neg*, with a December record from the Similan group (*Pha*).

GEOGRAPHICAL VARIATION. None recognized.

STATUS AND POPULATION. Resident and a migrant or significant dispersant; regular and common. Throughout the year, easily the most numerous *Ixobrychus* bittern overall, matched only locally by Yellow Bittern.

HABITATS AND ECOLOGY. As might be expected from its similar morphology, more clearly partitioned by regular habitat from von Schrenck's than from Yellow Bittern, though also from the latter by its greater use of drier sites. Found in most of the kinds of situations that hold Yellow Bitterns, and frequently in rank herbage bordering waterways through more closed environments, such as plantations, although not entering actual tree-cover.

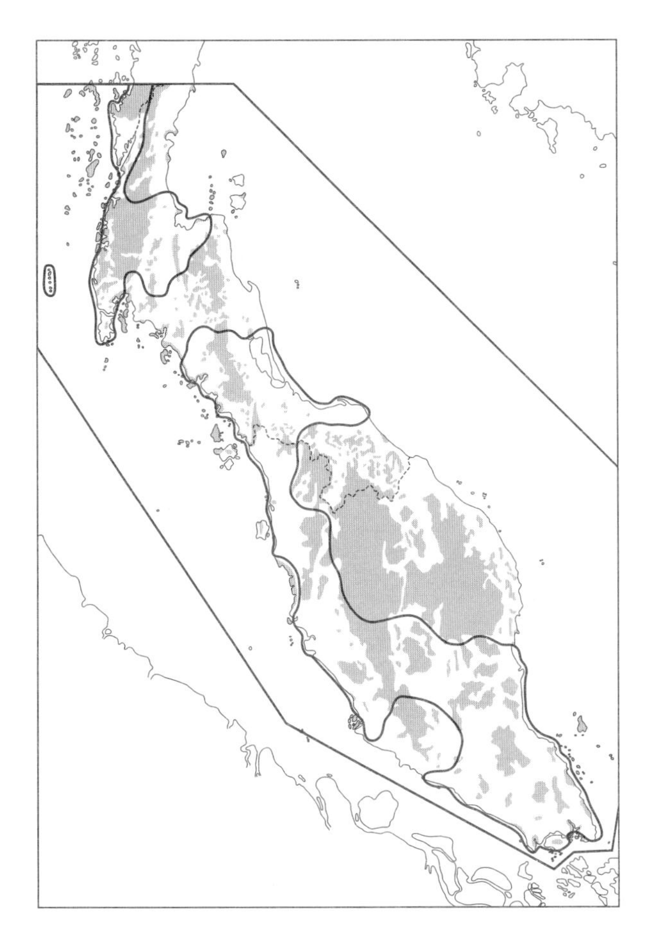

Weed-covered, fallow paddyland drained of water is another favoured situation but rice crops remain the key nesting habitat. Birds commonly roost individually, above ground on platforms of bent-over rice-stems.

FORAGING AND FOOD. Counts of flying birds in the Sekinchan paddy area, Selangor, showed strong peaks of activity in early morning and late evening, and the many bitterns caught in fish-nets hung up for this purpose attest to mobility during twilight hours. Feeding continues through the day but seems to be more intensive at these times. Unlike von Schrenck's, however, Cinnamon Bitterns have not been found active at night. Food includes fish (*Anabas, Trichogaster, Clarias* and *Ophiocephalus* spp. identified), amphibians and invertebrates, and items average larger than those taken in the same habitat by Yellow Bitterns - although food to chicks includes insects down to fly size (also vegetable material) (R.V. Lansdown, Meeswat and Prentice 1984).

SOCIAL ORGANIZATION. Nests are sometimes loosely clumped, males may advertise in loose groups, and on one occasion at Sekinchan (Selangor) R.V. Lansdown noted a cluster of what appeared to be day-roosters. Otherwise, solitary.

MOVEMENTS. Night-fliers have been intercepted at lights on Fraser's Hill during 26 September–5 December and on 26 February, 9 April and 2 May. An immature ringed and released at Fraser's on the night of 25 October was recovered 41 days later at Arau, Perlis, 350 km NNW, in reverse of the direction expected at that time of year. Straightforward latitudinal shifts controlled by monsoon weather may be too simple an explanation for the movements of this species (BR 1968, 1969, 1972–73, MBR 1986–87).

SURVIVAL. The longest of few retrap-intervals is 25 months, a bird at its site of ringing in Melaka (UMBRP).

SOCIAL INTERACTIONS. Solitary males advertise while perched on field-side bushes or among rice-stems such that their head shows above the crop. Stretched upright, with the base of the bill and facial skin flushing bright orange, they suddenly crouch and puff out the throat, with bill tilted upward. This exposes the white lateral throat-stripe and black tuft at the side of the breast. At the same time they give a long bout of soft *kok* calls. Alone or in groups, they also fly slow-flapping circuits, and slow-flapping displays are directed at passing females, as in Yellow Bittern. Aggressive encounters feature bill-snapping and calling (Lansdown 1988). Birds disturbed in vegetation may take up a 'bitterning' posture, and females and juveniles have appropriate neck- and breast-striping developed strongly.

VOICE. The male 'song' is a soft, repeated *kok*. Flight-calls include a sharp *kuok* and string of explosive *kuk* or *tuk* notes that may signal alarm (Lansdown 1988).

BREEDING

Nest. A pad of bent-over stems and leaves on or within a half metre of the ground, in tussocks and weeds but mostly over water in rice mixed with wild grasses (not in pure crop, reflecting either a mechanical need or side-effects of the herbicides that remove these grasses).

Eggs and brood. Eggs are white (cf. Yellow Bittern). Size (mm): 33.8 × 27.4 (average). Regular full clutch five, laid at daily intervals and incubated from number one. Chicks hatch in corresponding sequence as of day 23.

Seasonality. Peninsula-wide, eggs or young chicks found on dates that imply laying in all months. Cinnamon Bitterns are among a small number of waterbird species thought to be genuinely non-seasonal, although dependent on local agricultural crop-cycling (BR 1963, Cairns 1940, R.V. Lansdown, Meeswat and Prentice 1984, Wells 1988).

MOULT. As in some other ardeids, replacement of primaries is regular-descendant to P8, then P10 before 9. Among many handled (UMBRP, BMNH, ZRC-NUS), only eight adults showed active wing-moult, between 25 March (P4) and 26 December (P5–6), with evidence of most completing by the last quarter of the year. Scarcity of moulters among shot and mist-netted birds suggests they do not fly.

CONSERVATION. See Yellow Bittern. R.V. Lansdown suggests small bitterns take insects injurious to rice and contribute to a biological form of pest management. They should be protected in rice agriculture yet, with the decline of traditional paddyfield fish supplies through pesticide abuse, farming communities have turned more extensively to birds. Fine-grade fish-nets permanently erected in paddy are now a common sight and take bitterns in large numbers. Still more serious are the shortening of the fallow phase to a point where it barely supports a nesting attempt (direct losses due to ploughing), and post-harvest application of broad-spectrum herbicides that removes food and cover at a critical period. On certain large rice-schemes in S Perak and NW Selangor where they were numerous, recently, *Ixobrychus* bitterns have been all but eliminated.

Black Bittern; Nok Yang Dam (Thai); Burung Pucong Hitam (Malay)

Ixobrychus flavicollis (Latham) 1790, *Index Ornithologicus* 2: 701. TL India.
Plate 13

GROUP RELATIONS. Free-standing. Colour-pattern convergently similar to much smaller Afrotropical *I. sturmii* (Dwarf Bittern).

GLOBAL RANGE. The Indian subcontinent and Sri Lanka; China south from the Changjiang valley, including Taiwan and Hainan; SE Asia and Wallacea to New Guinea, the Solomons and Australia. Migratory in the more seasonal parts of its range, in SE Asia wintering in the equatorial zone. Vagrant to W Micronesia.

IDENTIFICATION/DESCRIPTION. The usual, dimly lit view is of a solitary bird flying low between roosting cover and feeding grounds, identified by its dark coloration, including feet, and larger size and slower, more deliberate wing-beat than other *Ixobrychus* bitterns or Little Heron. Females are deep bronzy brown rather than blue-black on the upperparts, with less admixture of black in the ventral streaking. First-winterers of both sexes retain pale fringing on the upperparts until at least February (ZRCNUS).

Bare-part colours. (Adult) iris hazel-yellow with dark mark fore and aft of the pupil; facial skin purple-brown; upper mandible and apical third of lower black (male) or very dark brown (female), rest horn-brown; legs and feet black (male), purplish brown (female) (UMBRP).

Size (mm). (Live and skins: 21 adults, most not sexed): wing 184–213 (confirmed males not below 207, females not above 210); tail 60–82; bill 74.0–80.6, bill from mouth-corner 91–105; tarsus 64–78 (BMNH, UMBRP, ZDUM, ZRCNUS).

Weight (g). Autumn-passage adults, 208–317; one mid-February winterer 321 (UMBRP).

DISTRIBUTION. Historical summary: *Pak, Sur, Phu, Kra, Pht, Tra, Son, Nar, Kel, Pek, Phg, Sel, Mel, Joh, Sin*, with additional (passage-dated) island records from Penang, Rembia, Jarak and Pisang in the Melaka Straits; and Samui off the E coast.

GEOGRAPHICAL VARIATION. Widespread nominate *flavicollis*.

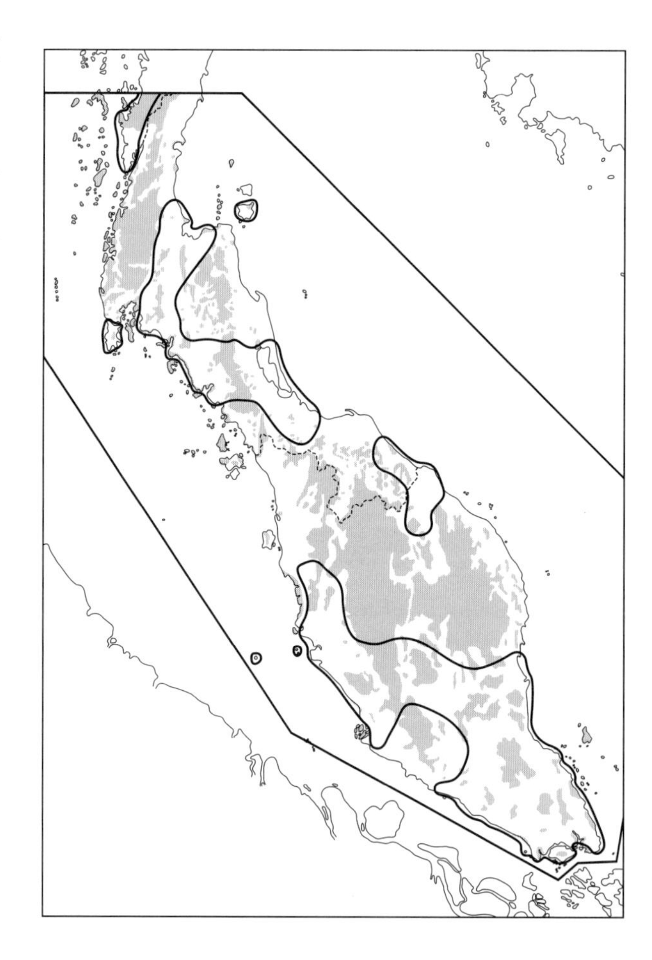

STATUS AND POPULATION. Local and sparse to uncommon. Apparently only a non-breeding visitor and passage migrant (strikes on One-Fathom Bank lighthouse, Melaka Straits), but dates imply movements are complex, and completely absent for a season of, perhaps, less than two months. June–July records have raised speculation that some may over-summer but the realization that Black Bitterns are mostly only (summer) wet-season breeding visitors south to the central plains of Thailand (Round *et al.* 1988) provides a good enough explanation of this schedule. What migrants are doing in the Peninsula through August and September, on the other hand, is less obvious. Perhaps a few northern birds really do over-summer (some at Chalerm Prakiat sanctuary, Narathiwat, in early June described as paired up), or perhaps the Peninsula also receives a small post-breeding contra-flow of migrants from the S hemisphere (BBCB-9, Holmes and Wells 1975, SINGAV-3, UMBRP). The nearest recorded S-hemisphere breeding locality is Belitung island, 2°50′S (CLBS).

HABITATS AND ECOLOGY. More clearly crepuscular than smaller congeners (even von Schrenck's) and rarely breaks cover by day. Main haunts are *Phragmites* reedbeds such as develop on old dredge-mine lagoons and mine-sludge settling-pools, and tall, rank grass-swamp/thicket mixes along rivers and channels, but not invariably linked to open water. A single record from mangroves: one at Loyang, Singapore, on 10 December 1992 (SINGAV-6).

FORAGING AND FOOD. May hunt mostly at night, but critical observations are lacking.

SOCIAL ORGANIZATION. Typically solitary.

MOVEMENTS. Extreme dates of intercepting presumed southbound migrants at floodlights on the Main Range, W-coast lighthouses, etc. (one recovery from a Singapore city building), are 5 October and early January (BMP5, BR 1970–71, Gibson-Hill 1952, MBR 1986–87, SINGAV-3, ZRCNUS). Of 23 handlings at the Fraser's Hill lights, 16 were in November. Accumulated daytime records elsewhere show no equivalent surge, beginning on 18 August (Singapore island) with a light, more or less even scatter through to late February (SINGAV-3, UMBRP). The most intensive autumn passage is, therefore, guessed to pass directly south of the Peninsula.

Numbers on the ground begin to rise again at the end of February, peak during March–mid May, and tail off through June to extremes of 24 June in Singapore, 25 June at Thalae Noi, 26 June on Phuket island and 15 July at Krabi town (BBCB-5, -8, MBR 1986–87). This long spring surge is interpreted as passage migration (and includes an evident migrant picked up injured in urban Georgetown, Penang, on 19 May: BR 1970–71). On the other hand, only one bird has been intercepted at Fraser's Hill in spring, on 16 April (BR 1969).

There has been one ring recovery, of a bird netted in reedbeds at Sungai Way, Selangor, on 11 December 1964 and shot at Tadubi, Manipur, on the following 1 November (BR 1965), i.e., on dates leaving open the possibility of both sites having been halts in a longer migration.

SURVIVAL. No information.

SOCIAL INTERACTIONS. No information.

VOICE. No information.

BREEDING. No confirmed population.

MOULT. Only one instance of active, double-locus wing-moult during migration seasons: a bird growing P1 and 4–5 on 5 October. Typically in autumn, flight-feathers are fairly fresh, implying most adults complete replacement before they reach the Peninsula. Two, a male and a female taken on Melaka Straits islands on 9 November and 7 January, showed suspension of moult after P8, leaving 9–10 old.

CONSERVATION. The decline of reedbed habitat as ex-mining land is drained and reclaimed for other purposes may already be pressuring migrants on the Malaysian W-coast plain.

Great Bittern; Nok Yang Daeng Yai (Thai); Burung Pucong Danau (Malay)

Botaurus stellaris (Linnaeus) 1758, *Systema Naturae* 10(1): 144. TL Sweden.

GROUP RELATIONS. Forms a likely superspecies with *B. poiciloptilus* (Australian Bittern).

GLOBAL RANGE. Breeds in southern and north Africa, and across temperate Eurasia from Atlantic Europe to Ussuriland and Sakhalin, south to N Japan and far-NE China, according to Cheng (1987) with an outlying population on Taiwan. Migrants winter to sub-Saharan Africa, the Indian subcontinent and Sri Lanka (OBCB-3); in Japan and southern China; and SE Asia regularly to central Thailand, with small numbers to Luzon. Vagrant in Palawan, Brunei (Mann 1987a) and the Peninsula.

IDENTIFICATION/DESCRIPTION. Line drawing, below. An outsize, thick-necked bittern, honey-brown in background colour, lighter below. In flight, broad wings are Night Heron-like. Larger than similar-shaped Malayan Night Heron and any confusion dispelled by coarse dark streaking over the head and body. Adults have cap and narrow moustachial streak black (sharp against white throat); this facial pattern less distinct in immatures.

Bare-part colours. No local information.

Size. No data.

Weight. No data.

DISTRIBUTION. Historical summary: *Mel*, *Sin*, but liable to have been overlooked.

GEOGRAPHICAL VARIATION. None handled; presumed to be widespread nominate *stellaris*.

STATUS AND POPULATION. Local and sparse; hardly more than vagrant. Singles collected in Singapore in autumn 1908 and near Melaka on the following 3 March (Robinson and Chasen 1936), with recent sightings in Singapore over three consecutive winters: singles on 16 March 1991, 4 January 1992 and 1 January 1993, and two on 27 March 1993, all at the Marina East or Tuas temporary wetlands (BIRDLINE 1993, R.F. Ollington, Ollington and Loh 1992).

HABITATS AND ECOLOGY. All recent records have been from areas of freshwater grass-marsh at least 1 m tall, in water at least 30 cm deep (BIRDLINE 1993).

FORAGING AND FOOD. No information.

SOCIAL ORGANIZATION. Typically solitary.

MOVEMENTS. The autumn date is lost; 27 March is the latest date in spring.

SURVIVAL. No information.

SOCIAL INTERACTIONS. No information.

VOICE. No information.

BREEDING. No population.

MOULT. No data.

CONSERVATION. In the south, recent records have all been from transient wetlands on land-claim sites.

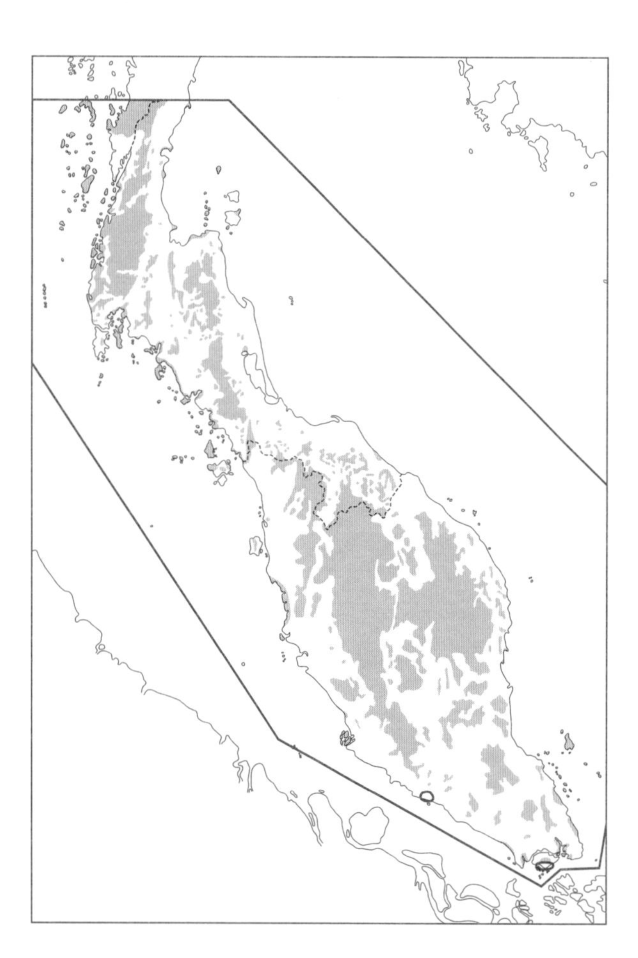

Great Bittern

Family THRESKIORNITHIDAE

Ibises and spoonbills: five species

Black-headed Ibis; Nok Gulaa (Chawn Hoi Khao) (Thai); Burung Sekendi Kepala Hitam (Malay)

Threskiornis melanocephalus (Latham) 1790, *Index Ornithologicus* 2: 709. TL India.
Plate 14

GROUP RELATIONS. Snow (1978) gives reasons for placing it in a superspecies with African *T. aethiopicus* (Sacred Ibis) and Australasian *T. molucca* (Australian Ibis).

GLOBAL RANGE. The Indian subcontinent (from the Indus valley) and Sri Lanka; far-NE and formerly also E and S China; and SE Asia to Sumatra and Java. Still present in Indonesia, including along the E coast of Sumatra, and recently numerous in S Vietnam (Scott 1989) but gone from much former E and SE Asian breeding-range, e.g., now only a visitor to central Thailand (Round *et al.* 1988). Migratory in the more seasonal parts of its range, wintering mainly on the continent but wandering occasionally as far as Japan, the Philippines, Borneo and Sulawesi. A few still reach the Peninsula.

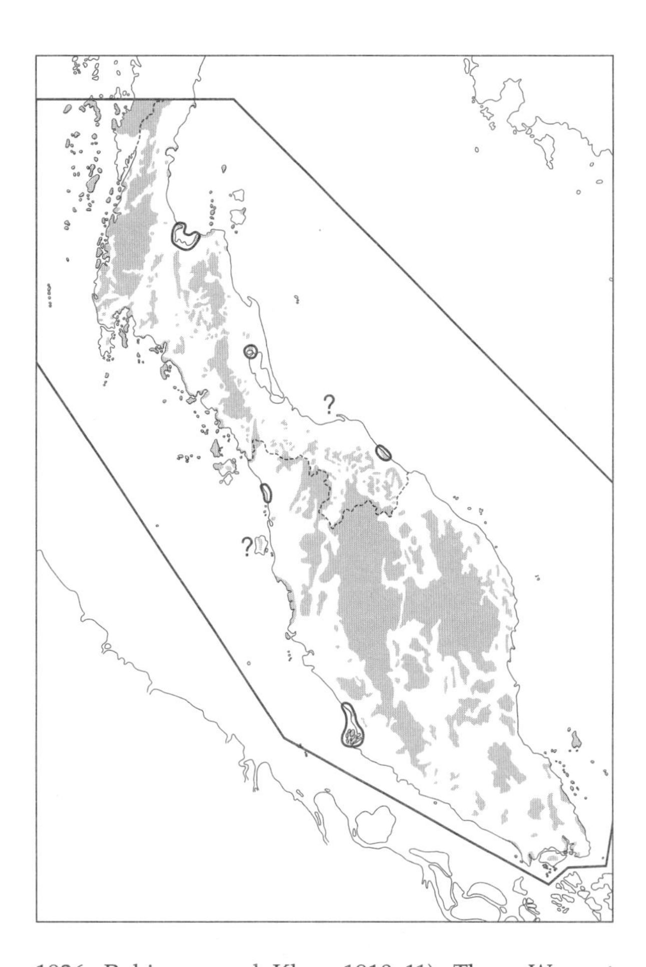

IDENTIFICATION/DESCRIPTION. All-white, with decurved bill and naked head and neck black. In breeding-plumage, has a drooping ruff of lanceolate feathers at the base of the neck, breast-plumes and plume-like scapulars and inner secondaries. Juveniles show some grey on head, neck and inner secondaries, with tips and shafts of outer primaries black.

Bare-part colours. (Adult) iris brown; skin of head and neck bluish black; legs and feet black (Oates 1883).

Size (mm). (Skin: 1 NE-coast male; adult): wing 345; tail 117; bill 145; tarsus 93 (ZRCNUS).

Weight. No data.

DISTRIBUTION. The NE and (formerly) Melaka Straits coasts. Historical summary: *Sur, Pht, Pat, Nar, Ked, Sel.*

GEOGRAPHICAL VARIATION. None recognized.

STATUS AND POPULATION. A non-breeding migrant, local and sparse. The museum-era collectors are mostly silent about this bird because it was always difficult to shoot. Its past distribution seems to have paralleled that of Grey Heron, i.e., the Melaka Straits and NE coasts, strictly littoral on the one but extending to freshwater wetlands on the other.

Early in the century, small numbers ranged along the Selangor coast north from Kelang, often in the company of Milky Storks, with records also from around the Kedah river-mouth (Robinson and Chasen 1936, Robinson and Kloss 1910–11). These W-coast birds have long since disappeared, with no definite record after 1934, although contemporary accounts imply they were then still common in the Kelang estuary, Selangor (Madoc 1936, 1956a). The few dated records fall in August, September and November, potential breeding months for large waterbirds on this coast, but apart from some reported visiting the then-active mixed-species colony at Ketam island, Selangor mangroves (Madoc 1936), status was never resolved.

In the NE, ibises have occurred south to Narathiwat (BCSTB-10) and still occupy at least one site annually. Pattani dates are lost but Robinson (1914a) records a flock of 20–30 on mudflats off the mouth of the Bandon river, Surat Thani, apparently in the first week of July 1913. This is within the span of non-breeder dates in central–SW Thailand but most modern records, all from the Thalae Noi and Chalerm Prakiat (Narathiwat) wetlands, are winter-dated (Anonymous 1981, BBCB-7, -8, BCSTB-10, RTFD, Storer 1976). Largest recent counts have been 52 in March 1979 and 27 on 20 January 1991, at Thalae Noi.

HABITATS AND ECOLOGY. Mudflats and freshwater marshland in the NE; elsewhere, apparently only the intertidal zone, and roosted in mangrove forest.

FORAGING AND FOOD. No information.

SOCIAL ORGANIZATION. NE migrants are gregarious but W-coast birds are described as having occurred mostly alone or in pairs, with Milky Storks, etc. (Robinson and Chasen 1936).

MOVEMENTS. Extreme dates of recent occurrences are November and 5 May (BCSTB-13).

SURVIVAL. No information.

SOCIAL INTERACTIONS. No information.

VOICE. No information.

BREEDING. No population.

MOULT. A Bandon bay adult male dated 4 July was moulting P2–3 (ZRCNUS).

CONSERVATION. A candidate for reintroduction as a breeder, if large-waterbird colonies can be planted in protected mangroves of the Malaysian W coast. Globally near-threatened (BTW2).

White-shouldered Ibis; Nok Chawn Hoi Dam (Thai); Burung Sekendi Bahu Putih (Malay)

Pseudibis davisoni (Hume) 1875, *Stray Feathers* 3: 300. TL Pakchan estuary, Tenasserim.
Plate 14

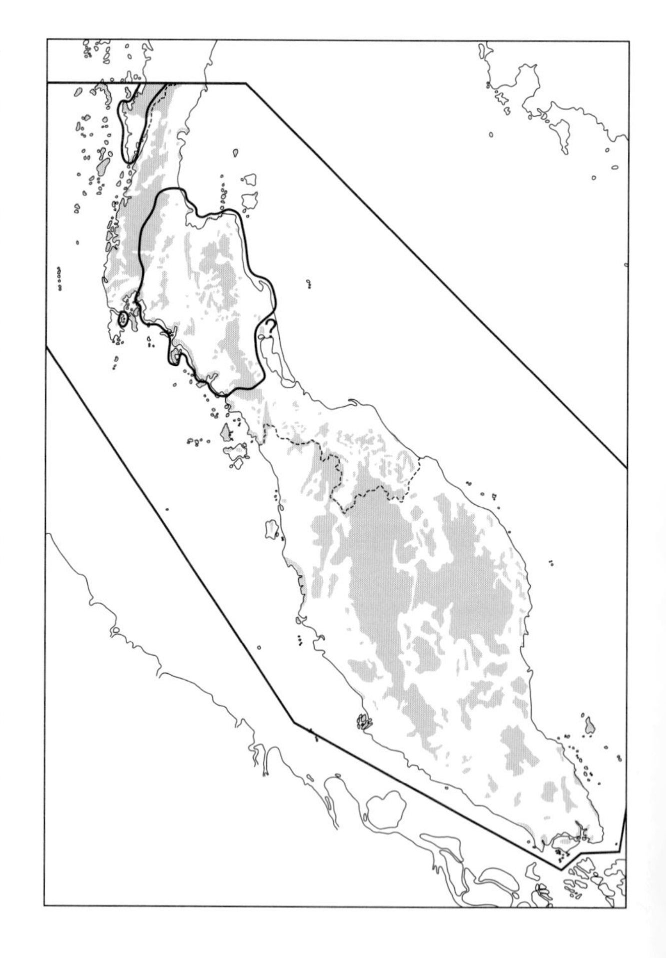

GROUP RELATIONS. Has been lumped with S-Asian *P. papillosa* (Red-naped Ibis) (Hancock *et al.* 1992) but is larger, lacks red on the crown, has bare collar a different colour and shape, and a longer, stouter bill. They are perhaps a superspecies.

GLOBAL RANGE. Historically, from W Burma to S Yunnan through continental SE Asia to S Vietnam and the Peninsula; also S-central and E Kalimantan, mostly in the Barito and Mahakam drainages (Holmes 1991); one record from S Sarawak. Survives in Borneo, S Laos and Vietnam (OBCB-14, -17, Petersen 1991) but has gone from most former range.

IDENTIFICATION/DESCRIPTION. Size of Black-headed Ibis but all-blackish except for pale nape-band and white inner lesser wing-coverts. Glossy Ibis is smaller, with a fully feathered head. The naked head of adults is covered in small brownish warts, absent in juveniles which have a tuft of brown feathers on the nape.

Bare-part colours. Iris pale grey-brown (juvenile), orange-red (adult); head black with broad collar at base of skull (narrowing to a peak on the nape) dirty white (juvenile), white tinged blue dorsally (adult); bill slaty blue; legs and feet dirty white (juvenile), coral-red (adult) (BMNH, Hume and Davison 1878; Riley 1938; Robinson and Kloss 1921–24).

Size (mm). (Skins: 3 males, 2 females; adult): wing 409–420 and 398, 406; tail 180–193 and 176, 178; bill 173, 180 and 155, 156; tarsus 83–88 and 76, 78 (BMNH,

ZRCNUS), suggesting some sexual dimorphism (also, that BMNH 'male' 1910.12.27.33, with wing, tail and tarsus 385, 173 and 85.4, may have been wrongly sexed).

Weight (g). A male, about 1588 (BMNH).

DISTRIBUTION. South to latitude about 8°N. Historical summary: *Pak, Sur, Nak, Kra, Pht, Tra*, with additional island records from Nakha Yai (*Phu*) and Lanta (*Kra*).

GEOGRAPHICAL VARIATION. None recognized.

STATUS AND POPULATION. Extinct, with last specimens from near Phanom Bencha (Krabi) and Kapang (Nakhon Si Thammarat) during 1934–36 (Meyer de Schauensee 1946), although in 1973 villagers at Thalae Noi, Phatthalung, claimed to recognize a field-guide illustration. Field-dates covering most months imply it was resident, although there are no actual nest records (a juvenile collected on the Pakchan river on 6 May: Hume and Davison 1878).

HABITATS AND ECOLOGY. Bush-studded grassland, dry and fallow paddyland, and open wetlands including marsh and riversides, with forest or other tree-cover nearby (Hume and Davison 1878, Oates 1883, Riley 1938, Robinson 1917, Robinson and Kloss 1910–11). Loafed, roosted and took refuge in the tops of tall trees (Hume and Davison 1878), and soared on thermals.

FORAGING AND FOOD. Active on the ground in the early morning and evening (Hume and Davison 1878).

SOCIAL ORGANIZATION. Where specific, most references are to loners or pairs, but at times sociable: W.L. Abbott (Riley 1938) saw 'dozens', with Giant Ibises, in a paddyfield apparently in Trang during the summer wet-season, and a June/July reference (Robinson and Kloss 1921–24) is to parties roosting with Painted and Woolly-necked Storks on big forest-edge trees along the banks of the Bandon river, Surat Thani.

MOVEMENTS. None recorded.

SURVIVAL. No information.

SOCIAL INTERACTIONS. No information.

VOICE. 'A weird and unearthly scream' uttered at intervals from tree-top perches, sometimes also in flight; audible 'two miles away' (Hume and Davison 1878, Oates 1883).

BREEDING. No information.

MOULT. Replacement of primaries apparently regular-descendant. Adults dated 27 January, 5 February and 7 July, respectively, were moulting P5, P10 and P8, and one dated 5 May from Pakchan had suspended after P6. Two others in late December–early January had recently completed (BMNH, ZRCNUS).

CONSERVATION. No remaining local issues. Globally endangered (BTW2).

Giant Ibis; Nok Chawn Hoi Yai (Thai); Burung Sekendi Besar (Malay)

Thaumatibis gigantea (Oustalet) 1877, *Bulletin de la Société Philomathique de Paris* series 7(1): 25. TL lower Mekong valley.

Plate 14

GROUP RELATIONS. Free-standing.

GLOBAL RANGE. Historically, S Vietnam, S Laos and Cambodia probably across the central plains to SW Thailand and the Peninsula. Long gone from its western range, apparently now also from Vietnam, and the only recent sightings have been in S Laos (OBCB-17). Cambodian wetlands are under-explored.

IDENTIFICATION/DESCRIPTION. Large size; silvery-grey, dark-barred upper wing-coverts without a white patch; entirely dark head and neck.

Bare-part colours. (Adult) iris crimson; head and neck grey, with a dorsal ladder of black bars across horizontal skin-folds back from level of the hind-crown; bill horn to greenish horn; legs and feet crimson to dark red (Riley 1938, Williamson 1916a).

Size (mm). (Skin: 1 male, adult): wing 530; tail 242; bill from rear edge nostril 212; tarsus 114 (BMNH).

Weight (g). A male, about 3515 (Riley 1938).

DISTRIBUTION. Apparently south to near what is now the Malaysian border. Historical summary: *Tra*, with a record from Tarutao island (*Sat*).

GEOGRAPHICAL VARIATION. None recognised.

STATUS AND POPULATION. Extinct, probably for many decades, and the scatter of field-dates gives no real clue to past status. In Trang paddyland during the

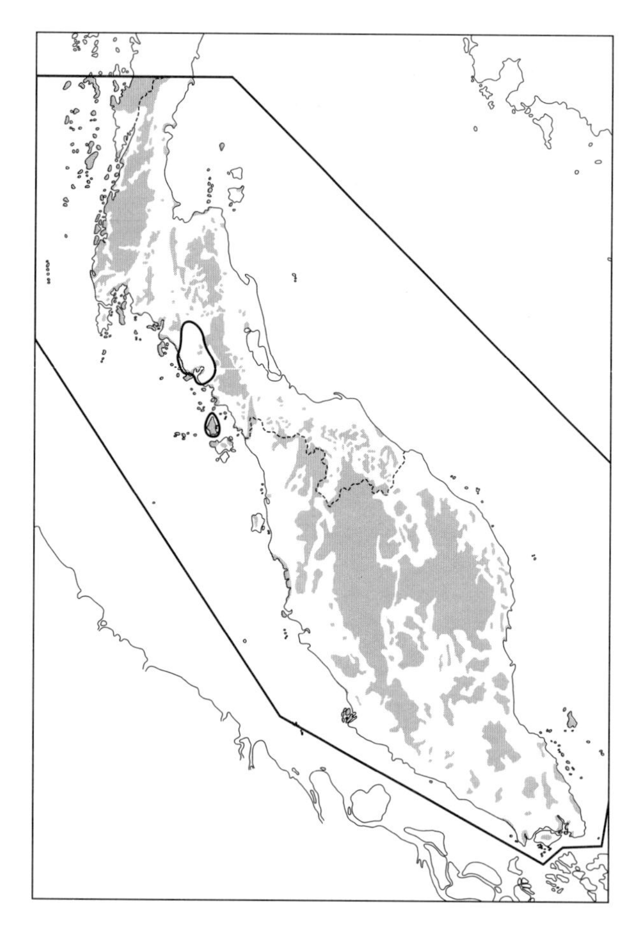

summer wet-season of 1896, W.L. Abbott saw dozens of dark ibises, both Giant and White-shouldered, and found local people were familiar with them (Riley 1938). He collected a lone bird in dry paddyland in NW Trang on 5 December that year and another on Tarutao island, Satul, on 6 April 1904, both adult. FMSM collectors got a third in NW Trang on 19 February 1910 but failed to find any elsewhere in the province. There are no other records, but Giant Ibises were still present in neighbouring SW Thailand a decade later, including a sighting in Prachuap Khiri Khan in early April 1919 (Robinson and Kloss 1921–24).

HABITATS AND ECOLOGY. The collection site on Tarutao island is not described but Trang records were all from paddyland. The Prachuap Khiri Khan bird was in a small marsh in savanna country, but elsewhere in SW Thailand habitat included streamsides and other wetlands in forest (Gairdner 1914, Williamson 1916a).

FORAGING AND FOOD. No information.

SOCIAL ORGANIZATION. Loners and pairs (Williamson 1916a), but apparently sometimes sociable (see White-shouldered Ibis).

MOVEMENTS. None known.

SURVIVAL. No data.

SOCIAL INTERACTIONS. No information.

VOICE. No information.

BREEDING. No information.

MOULT. A male dated 19 February had primaries worn but none moulting (BMNH).

CONSERVATION. No remaining local issues, but globally endangered (BTW2).

Glossy Ibis; Nok Chawn Hoi Dam Leuab (Thai); Burung Sekendi Licin (Malay)

Plegadis falcinellus (Linnaeus) 1766, *Systema Naturae* 12(1): 241. TL Austria and Italy.
Plate 14

GROUP RELATIONS. Forms a superspecies with *P. chihi* and *P. ridgwayi* (White-faced and Puna Ibises) of the Americas (Mayr and Short 1970).

GLOBAL RANGE. Breeds sporadically through the Caribbean and SE USA, sub-Saharan Africa, Madagascar, SE Europe to central Asia; the N Indian subcontinent; W Burma, S Vietnam, N Java and possibly Mindanao; Sulawesi and Australia (Silvius and Verheugt 1989). Higher-latitude populations migrate and some others disperse nomadically within and beyond the breeding-range, as far as Sri Lanka, SE China and, in the S hemisphere, New Zealand. Vagrant in Sumatra and the Peninsula.

IDENTIFICATION/DESCRIPTION. Smallest Asian ibis; near Curlew-sized. Looks black at a distance but adults are deep, rich chestnut with wings and tail shot purple-green; head and neck white-streaked in non-breeders. Immatures are paler, dun-brown rather than chestnut.

Bare-part colours. No information.

Size. No data.

Weight. No data.

DISTRIBUTION. Historical summary: *Pht, Sin.*

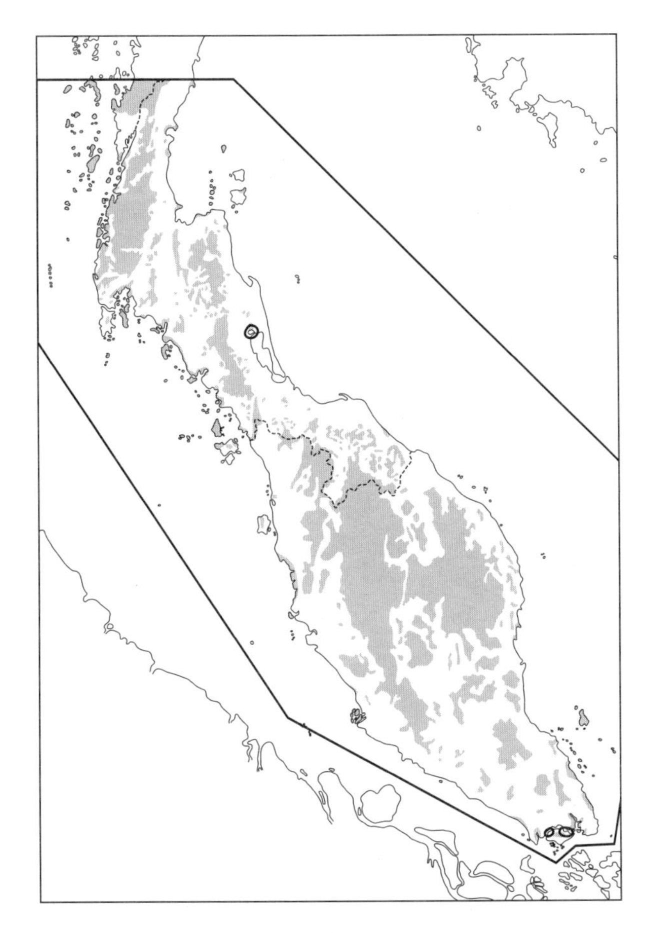

GEOGRAPHICAL VARIATION. The breeding populations of continental and island SE Asia have been separated subspecifically. There is no way of guessing which has occurred.

STATUS AND POPULATION. Vagrant; a loner at Thalae Noi on 14 December 1992 (OBCB-15) and two occurrences in Singapore, neither wholly above suspicion of a link with trade through the Republic: 11 at Serangoon during 12–16 June 1984, one individual staying a second week; two on the N coast at Sungai Buloh on 21 May 1989 (MBR 1984–85, SINGAV-3). The mixture of immatures and adults at Serangoon supports a wild occurrence given that big, colonial-nesting birds in trade have usually been taken as fledglings, and consignments of captives tend to be of uniform age.

HABITATS AND ECOLOGY. The Serangoon flock frequented sludge-drying beds of a sewage-farm, and birds at Sungai Buloh were on tidal mudflats.

FORAGING AND FOOD. No local information, except that the sludge-beds are known to have been rich in dipteran larvae.

SOCIAL ORGANIZATION. Non-breeders tend to be gregarious.

MOVEMENTS. No information.

SURVIVAL. No information.

SOCIAL INTERACTIONS. No information.

VOICE. No information.

BREEDING. No population.

MOULT. No data.

CONSERVATION. No valid local issues, but Serangoon works has since abandoned the open processing of sludge, and a valuable foraging-site for many migrant birds has been lost as a consequence.

Black-faced Spoonbill; Nok Paak Chawn Naa Dam (Thai); Burung Sekendi-sudu Muka Hitam (Malay)

Platalea minor Temminck & Schlegel 1849, Siebold's *Fauna Japonica, Aves*: 120 and plate 76. TL Japan.

Plate 14

GROUP RELATIONS. Most like Australasian *P. regia* (Royal Spoonbill), which breeds west to Wallacea (formerly to Java). They are a probable superspecies, to which Hancock *et al.* (1992) add *P. leucorodia* (Eurasian Spoonbill).

GLOBAL RANGE. A tiny world population, recently recorded breeding on only a few small islands off the W coast of Korea, though winter numbers imply other colonies must survive elsewhere, presumably in China. Two thirds of known numbers now winter on a single estuary in SW Taiwan. Elsewhere, others have wintered recently in Jiangzi, on the Guangdong coast and at Deep Bay (Hong Kong), and in the Red river delta, N Vietnam. Further into SE Asia, formerly reached Luzon, and odd spoonbill sightings in NW Borneo are also most likely to have been of this species (Mann 1987, Smythies 1981). Vagrant in Gulf of Bangkok wetlands and the NE Peninsula (BBCB-6).

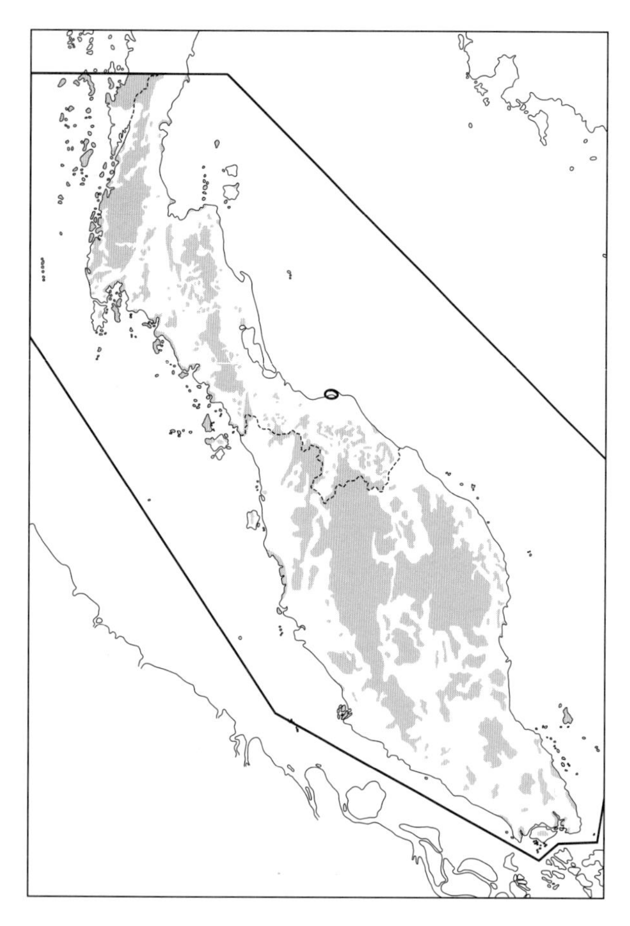

IDENTIFICATION/DESCRIPTION. From white egrets by stance, behaviour, face and bill-shape. All flying spoonbills hold neck extended and rather low-slung, with bouts of relatively shallow strokes interspersed by short glides on wings bowed slightly below the horizontal. They also soar. Apart from head, the winter adult is all-white, whereas immatures have tips and shafts of the primaries black. Size-ranges overlap and in the field probably difficult to distinguish from Royal Spoonbill. Both have head bare and black, back to level of eye, forehead warty in Royal, smooth in Black-faced (BMNH).

Bare-part colours. (Adult) upper surface of bill including spoon uniform grey-black (yellowish in Eurasian Spoonbill *P. leucorodia*); face black; legs and feet black.

Size. No local data.

Weight. No data.

DISTRIBUTION. *Pat.*

GEOGRAPHICAL VARIATION. None recognized.

STATUS AND POPULATION. Vagrant. Recorded twice: an immature (photographed) on the mudflats of Pattani bay on 29 February and 2 March 1988 (BBCB-5), and a sighting there again on 25 January 1992 (AWB).

HABITAT AND ECOLOGY. Winters on muddy coasts.

FORAGING AND FOOD. No information.

SOCIAL ORGANIZATION. In the main winter range, strongly gregarious.

MOVEMENTS. No information.

SURVIVAL. No information.

SOCIAL INTERACTIONS. No information.

VOICE. No information.

BREEDING. No population.

MOULT. No data.

CONSERVATION. No relevant local issues, but global status critical (BTW2).

Family CICONIIDAE

Storks: eight species

Milky Stork; Nok Gra-saa Paak Leuang (Thai); Burung Botak Upih (Malay)

Mycteria cinerea (Raffles) 1822, *Transactions of the Linnean Society* 13(2): 327. TL Benkulen, SW Sumatra.

Plate 16

GROUP RELATIONS. All *Mycteria* species are closely related (Hancock *et al.* 1992). Milky looks particularly like *M. ibis* (African Wood Stork) but *ibis* occupies habitats more like those of *M. leucocephala* (Painted Stork).

GLOBAL RANGE. Endemic in SE Asia, with a global population probably not above 5000: in central Cambodia (Tonle Sap) and (formerly?) extreme S Vietnam, coasts of the Melaka Straits and elsewhere in Sumatra (especially SE), Java and Bali; and parts of Sulawesi. Some outer-latitude breeders migrate or disperse (Ash 1984, Erftemeijer *et al.* 1988).

IDENTIFICATION/DESCRIPTION. Shares all-black tail and flight-feather pattern with Painted Stork and Asian Openbill. The latter has a different bill but gross distribution of plumage colours is the same and in distant flight they are confusable. Adult from adult Painted by all-white wing-coverts (both surfaces) and lack of a dark breast-band. Their grey-brown juveniles both have white rumps, feathered faces and the whole underwing blackish, confusable in the field.

Bare-part colours. (Adult) iris grey-brown to dark brown; bill orange-yellow (horn-brown in young juvenile); skin of head back to level of hind-crown and throat bright vinous-red; legs and feet magenta-pink, commonly whitewashed with uric acid.

Size (mm). (Skins: 3 males, 1 female; adult): wing 495–509 and 447; tail 155–180 and 143; bill from rear edge nostril 231 (1 only) and 191; tarsus 208–240 and 193 (BMNH, ZRCNUS).

Weight. No data.

DISTRIBUTION. The Melaka Straits coast and a short distance north. Historical summary: *Sat, Ked, Pek, Sel, Mel, Joh,* with additional island records only from Ketam, Kelang estuary (*Sel*).

GEOGRAPHICAL VARIATION. None recognized.

STATUS AND POPULATION. Resident, and sparse to more or less common, but very local; in long-term decline. Records cluster into five geographical nodes, suggestive of at least as many past colonies. (1) On the Thai/NW Malaysian border coast: sightings

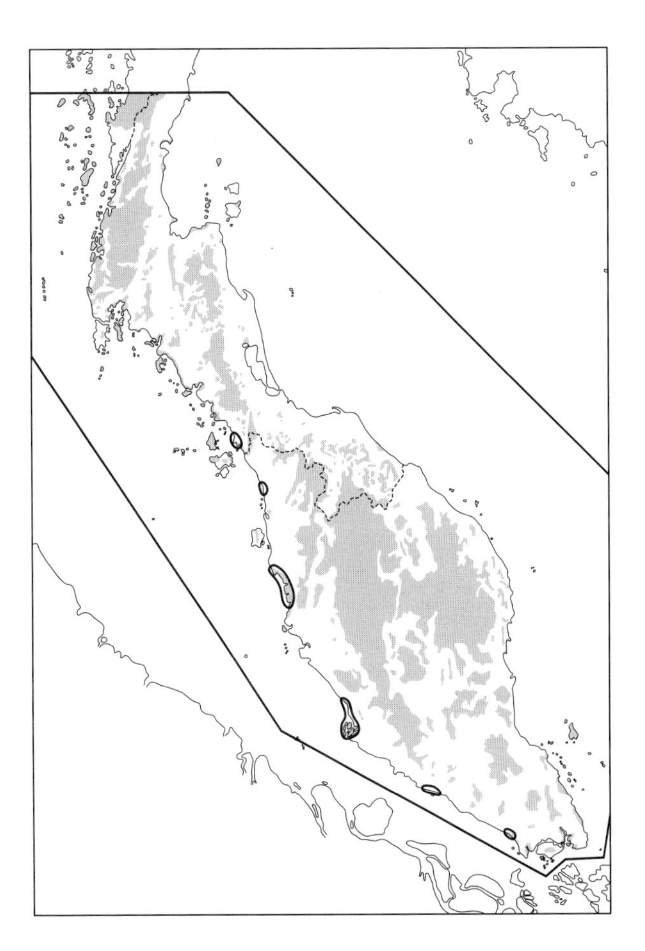

on low-tide mud at Kuala Kedah in late November 1907 (Robinson and Kloss 1910–11), an adult male from Satul dated 19 August 1935 (ZRCNUS) and, unconfirmed, in Kedah again in the late 1930s (Bromley 1949). (2) In Perak: a population censused at 115 birds in August 1983, 100 in October 1984 and 101 in July 1986 (MBR 1982–83, 1984–85, 1986–87, Silvius *et al.* 1987), occupying 45 km of coastline between the Burung river and Larut estuary (with low to nil breeding success in most years due to tree-felling and nest-raiding, though wardening by the Department of Wildlife has allowed a recent improvement). (3) In the Kelang estuary, Selangor: up to four pairs nested among Grey Herons and Great Egrets on much-raided Ketam island through the early 1930s (Madoc 1936) but with no record after 1935. (4) On the Melaka coast: mid-nineteenth century records (Gibson-Hill 1949). (5) In SW Johor: a few birds in the Benut mangrove forest in the 1950s; two there in February 1985 and a loner on 15 March 1986 (Hawkins and Howes 1986, I. Polunin).

One at Kuala Sala, mid Kedah, on 16 November 1992 (R. Gregory-Smith) had probably wandered from the Perak colony, but the likely longevity of adults means population relics could age, potentially, for decades after local breeding has ceased.

HABITATS AND ECOLOGY. While some dispersal between the coast and freshwater wetlands occurs in Indonesia, local Milky Storks are exclusively littoral, haunting mudflats and mangroves. They roost in mangrove tops and during high tides Perak flocks often loaf on shallow, open 'lakes' deep within the mangrove forests of Kalumpang and Terong 'islands'. Soaring on thermals is regular behaviour (Ratnam 1977).

FORAGING AND FOOD. Loners and loose groups forage well out from the mangrove front: (1) by slow-walking through soft mud or shallow water with half-opened bill three-quarters submerged and head scythed slowly from side to side; (2) by standing up to belly-deep in the incoming tide and passively allowing it to wash over the half-opened bill; (3) scanning the mudflat and flying to prey; (4) seeking mudskipper burrows on the exposed flat and probing in and around these, up to the full length of the bill and more. Prey seen taken by active methods have all been largish mudskippers. A Perak adult observed for 39 minutes probed an average two burrows per minute and caught a fish every four minutes (Silvius *et al.* 1987, Swennen and Marteijn 1987).

SOCIAL ORGANIZATION. Strongly sociable other than when foraging; even then, sometimes in loose groups.

MOVEMENTS. None confirmed.

SURVIVAL. No information.

SOCIAL INTERACTIONS. M.J. Silvius describes an 'up-down' greeting display between mates (cf. Kahl 1971): a bow then upward stretch, raising the bill to about 60°, repeated while partners stand facing each other, with some touching or crossing of bills and occasional interruptions for allopreening, mostly of the neck-feathers.

VOICE. Apart from mandible-clattering (Madoc 1936), no vocalizations recorded.

BREEDING

Nest. On Ketam island, stick-built and bulky, lined with fresh, leafy *Avicennia* sprigs and sited at the extreme, exposed top of a mangrove tree. At Kalumpang island, some support-trees were dead or defoliated yet held more than one active nest, almost touching in adjacent forks.

Eggs and brood. Eggs are plain, glossless white when fresh, one clutch with small red marks that may or may not have been original pigment. Shape subelliptical. Size (mm): 67.9 × 46.9 (mean, n=6). Full clutch three.

Cycle. No information.

Seasonality. In 1933, Kelang estuary breeders had large fledglings on 1 November and in 1935 eggs on 18 August. At least one out of 21 nests active in mangroves on Kalumpang island in November 1989 contained young by the end of December. It will be necessary to suppress poaching at Kalumpang completely to be sure of the true periodicity of breeding there (Madoc 1936, PERHILITAN).

MOULT. A Kelang-estuary female dated 17 September had primaries 1–10 fresh, the eleventh plus central tail-feathers growing (BMNH).

CONSERVATION. Hardly anywhere in the Melaka Straits have food and feeding opportunities for Milky Storks diminished. Population losses are due directly and exclusively to forestry and nest-raiding. Twenty-one nests at Kalumpang in 1989 were the first recorded in Perak since a few pairs occurred in a mixed heronry near Kuala Sepetang in the 1930s (Gibson-Hill 1949), although local people have surely been aware of sources of eggs and chicks in the area over many years. The site will require sustained wardening. Meanwhile, plans are afoot to establish a colony from zoo-bred stock at Kuala Selangor nature park, adjacent to rich feeding grounds. Success there will depend much on actively interesting the local community. Globally vulnerable (BTW2).

Painted Stork; Nok Gaab Bua (Thai); Burung Botak Padi (Malay)

Mycteria leucocephala (Pennant) 1769, *Indian Zoology*: 11. TL Sri Lanka.
Plate 16

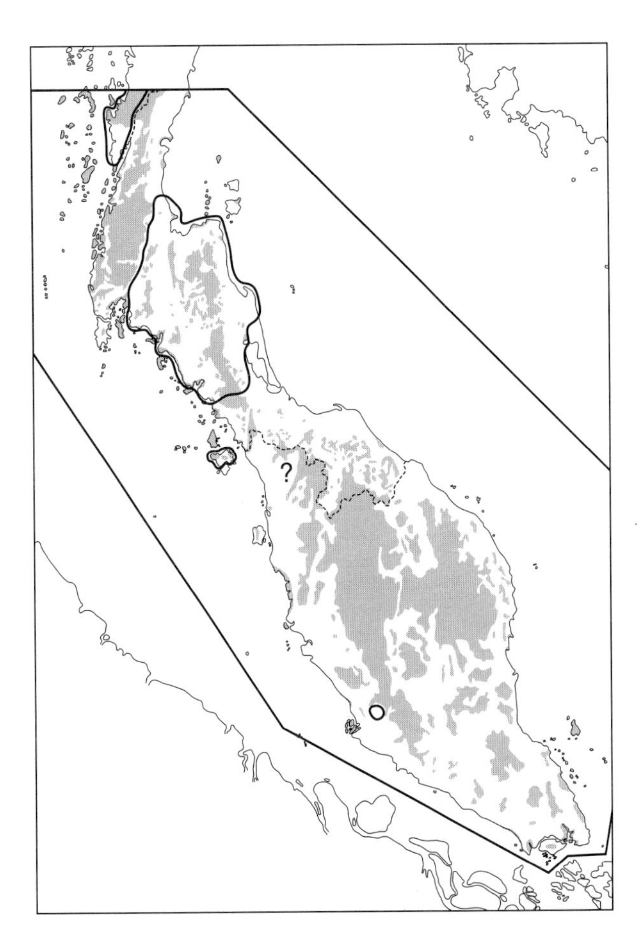

GROUP RELATIONS. See Milky Stork.

GLOBAL RANGE. The Indian subcontinent (from the Indus valley) and Sri Lanka; historically, S and E China as far as Hebei; and continental SE Asia to the Peninsula. Gone from much of its former range east of India, with proven recent breeding only in Cambodia, S Vietnam and at one site in the Peninsula.

IDENTIFICATION/DESCRIPTION. See Milky Stork. Adults have a blackish breast-band, black upper and lower wing-coverts edged white in a scaly pattern, and rose-pink scapulars. Juveniles are similar to same-stage Milky Stork.

Bare-part colours. (Adult) iris grey-brown to dark brown; bill orange-yellow (horn-brown in young juvenile); head back to level of skull-base orange-red, gular skin pinker; legs and feet magenta-pink or, in non-breeders, red-brown, commonly white-washed with uric acid.

Size (mm). (Skins: 3 males, 2 females; adult): wing 490–513 and 475, 485; tail 170 (one only) and 144, 163; bill 220–255 and 218, 224; tarsus 206–237 and 205, 207 (BMNH, ZRCNUS).

Weight. No data.

DISTRIBUTION. Formerly south to NW Malaysia. Historical summary: *Pak, Sur, Nak, Kra, Pht, Sel*, with island records from Langkawi (*Ked*).

GEOGRAPHICAL VARIATION. None recognized.

STATUS AND POPULATION. Resident or a breeding visitor; on the verge of extinction. Small flocks of non-breeders, possibly from Cambodia, are still annual in central and SW Thailand, mostly during August–January, but with no records south of Prachuap Khiri Khan. It is not known if extralimital migrants featured in the former population of the Peninsula.

Eighty-plus years ago, occurred along the western seaboard south to Langkawi island, where three were collected in mid December 1912 (BMNH, ZRCNUS). Locally common also in the NE including, in June–July 1913, along the lower Bandon river, Surat Thani; presumably also Phatthalung where a small and shrinking remnant has occurred at Thalae Noi within the last decade. From about 30 birds, including 4–5 breeding pairs, in 1980–81, only three individuals remained by 1987, but continued to attempt nest-building until at least 1990 (Anonymous 1981, BBCB-4, -7). Recorded in the area only during late January–June (once in September), they may have moved seasonally. A wandering immature has been collected at Kuala Lumpur, and three *Mycteria* storks flying east over N-central Kedah (well out of Milky Stork habitat) on 4 October 1993 could also have been this species (R. Gregory-Smith, Robinson and Chasen 1936).

HABITATS AND ECOLOGY. Flooded paddyfields are the only daytime habitat listed specifically. Towards evening on the Bandon river in 1913, gathered in large flocks that went to roost with Woolly-necked Storks and White-shouldered Ibises on tall, forest-edge trees (Robinson 1914a).

FORAGING AND FOOD. Food regurgitated for chicks included small fish.

SOCIAL ORGANIZATION. Like Milky Stork, a social breeder and rooster, but forages often independantly.

MOVEMENTS. No other information.

SURVIVAL. No information.

SOCIAL INTERACTIONS. No information.

VOICE. No information.

BREEDING

Nest. At Thalae Noi, nests built about 20 m up in crowns of a grove of old *Alstonia spathulata* trees.

Eggs and brood. Not described, but eggs said to be laid on alternate days; full clutch four.

Cycle. Both pair-members incubate.

Seasonality. Nest-building in late January–February (stick-carrying also reported on 1 April); young fledge in May (Anonymous 1981, BBCB-7).

MOULT. Replacement of primaries apparently regular-descendant. Four adults from Nakhon Si Thammarat and Langkawi collected during 26 September–16 December were in wing-moult, between P8 and P10; others dated 17 December and 4 July not (BMNH, ZRCNUS).

CONSERVATION. Problems at Thalae Noi include progressive loss of large trees, and poaching. Stringent wardening will be necessary to save any future nesting attempts, in addition to which too little is known about movements and diet. A group breeds at Zoo Negara, Kuala Lumpur and part of the free-flying flock, regular in wetlands over a radius of at least 15 km, may eventually settle outside. Globally near-threatened (BTW2).

Asian Openbill; Nok Paak Haang (Thai); Burung Botak Siput (Malay)

Anastomus oscitans (Boddaert) 1783, *Table des Planches Enluminéez d'Histoire Naturelle*: 55. TL Pondicherry, SE India.

Plate 16

GROUP RELATIONS. Apparently free-standing.

GLOBAL RANGE. The Indian subcontinent (from the Indus valley), and Sri Lanka; and the central plains of Thailand to far-S Vietnam. Ring-recoveries show juveniles from Thai colonies move over a wide compass arc, as far as Bangladesh westward and to central Cambodia in the east (McClure 1974), but southward no regular movements have been recorded below about latitude 13°N (BBCB-3, Williamson 1918).

IDENTIFICATION/DESCRIPTION. Smaller than Milky Stork and with fully feathered face and dark bill. In fresh non-breeding plumage, pale grey with shining black scapulars, flight-feathers and tail. Juvenile pattern the same but colours duller and browner.

Bare-part colours. (Adult) iris dark brown; facial skin blackish, gular deep blue; bill dull greenish-horn, tinged red ventrally; legs and feet flesh-pink (Herbert 1923–26).

Size. No local information.

Weight. No data.

DISTRIBUTION. *Kra.*

GEOGRAPHICAL VARIATION. None recognized.

STATUS AND POPULATION. Vagrant; two females collected in Krabi on 19 September 1936, i.e.,

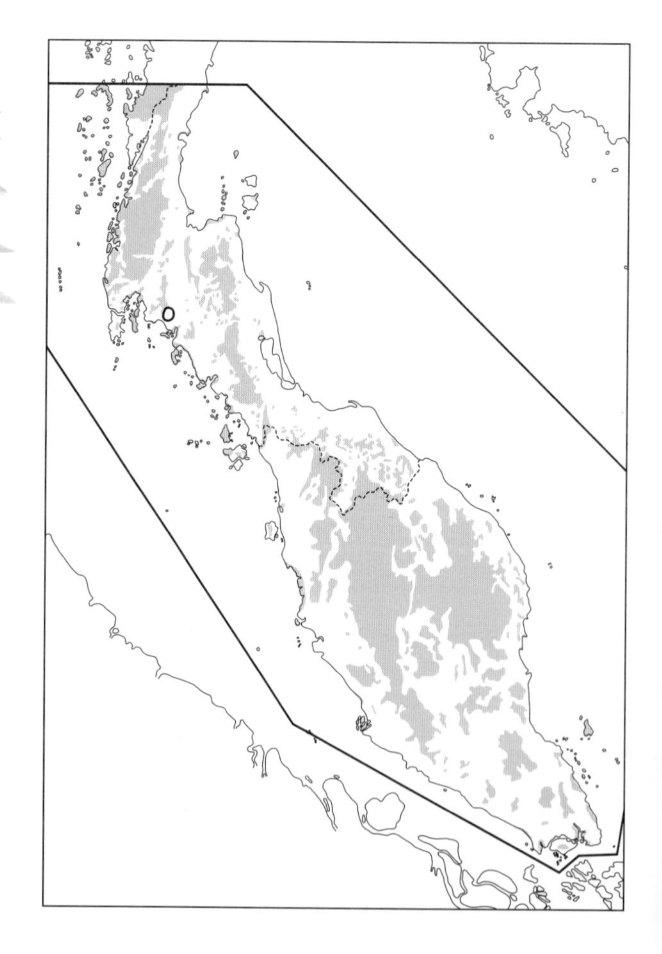

during the SW monsoon wet-season period of post-breeding dispersal (Meyer de Schauensee 1946).

HABITATS AND ECOLOGY. No local information but elsewhere, typically, open wetlands such as flooded paddyland. Soars on thermals.

FORAGING AND FOOD. Specializes on molluscs, mainly gastropods (including apple snails *Pila*), harvested from paddyfields and other open, strictly freshwater wetlands; also dug out of dried mud (Round *et al.* 1988). The pincer-shaped bill-tip cuts open the operculum and shakes out the body, leaving shell unbroken (Hancock *et al.* 1992, HBI).

SOCIAL ORGANIZATION. No information about dispersal-phase behaviour.

MOVEMENTS. No information but probable nearest breeding sources are in southern Indochina.

SURVIVAL. No information.

SOCIAL INTERACTIONS. No information.

VOICE. No information.

BREEDING. No population.

MOULT. Both September birds were in heavy moult (ANSP).

CONSERVATION. No local issues, but near-threatened globally (BTW2).

Woolly-necked Stork; Nok Gra-saa Khaw Khao (Thai); Burung Botak Padang (Malay)

Ciconia episcopus (Boddaert) 1783, *Table des Planches Enluminéez d'Histoire Naturelle*: 54. TL India.
Plate 15

GROUP RELATIONS. Forms a superspecies with Sunda endemic *C. stormi* (Storm's Stork), isolated by habitat.

GLOBAL RANGE. Sub-Saharan Africa and SW Asia (vagrant Iran); the Indian subcontinent and Sri Lanka; SE Asia to Sumatra, Java, Bali and the Philippines; Sulawesi and the Lesser Sunda islands as far as Flores. Increasingly sparse through most of SE Asia but resident where it occurs.

IDENTIFICATION/DESCRIPTION. Face, neck and lower abdomen to tail-coverts white; crown and rest of body and wings sharply demarcated glossy black; juvenile duller. Tail all-black and forked (depth 104–107 mm), overlaying stiff, tail-like, all-white lower tail-coverts that also form a fork.

Bare-part colours. (Adult) iris red with yellow outer ring; facial and gular skin slate-grey to black; bill black with tip and mid-dorsal and ventral lines dull red, or red with, at most, black base or black blotches; legs and feet dull red (BMNH, Riley 1938, Robinson and Chasen 1936).

Size (mm). (Skins: 12 males, 3 females; adult): wing 485–523 and 457–503; tail 175–195 and 160–168; bill 152–163 and 144–153; tarsus 155–174 and 154–187 (BMNH, ZRCNUS).

Weight. No data.

DISTRIBUTION. South to about what is now the Malaysian border. Historical summary: *Pak, Chu, Sur,*

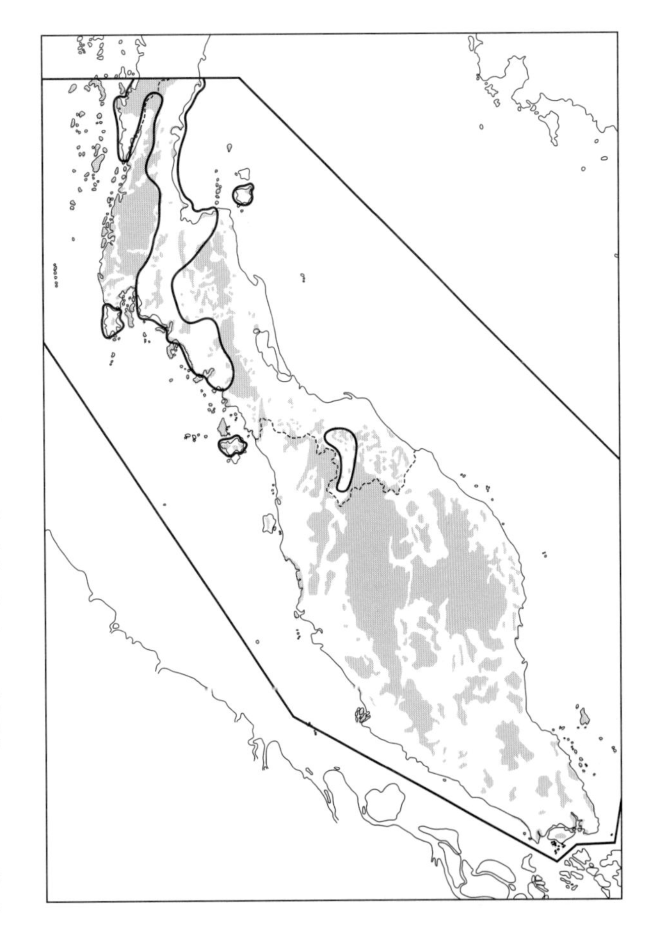

Phu, Kra, Tra, Yal, with island records from Langkawi (*Ked*) and Samui. A.T. Edgar (Gibson-Hill 1949) thought it might have occurred in Kelantan and N Terengganu, but supplied no evidence, and mid-nineteenth century specimens labelled 'Penang' in the Cantor collection (BMNH) show signs of having been captives.

GEOGRAPHICAL VARIATION. Deignan (1963) placed all Thai populations in nominate *episcopus*, with bill entirely black or only tipped red. Two females from Yala are described as having reddish bills and a male from Samui island red with a dark base (Ogilvie-Grant 1906, Robinson 1914b), which is either an age variant or identifies the form *'neglecta'*, not previously recognized in mainland SE Asia (cf. White 1974).

STATUS AND POPULATION. A presumed former resident, now virtually extinct. Early in the century, evidently numerous in the NE, including along the Bandon river and on Samui island; also west of the dividing range, but virtually gone, presumably hunted out, by the 1930s. A rumour of presence in Songkhla in the 1970s was never confirmed and the only recent record has been of a loner at Rap Ro wildlife sanctuary, Chumphon, on 4 May 1993 (BCSTB-10). Field-dates covering all months except September imply resident status but at its southern limit of range, on Langkawi island, recorded only during November–March, and the one actual breeding record (1904) is from the far north, at Tanjung Badak, Pakchan (BMNH, BMP5, Ogilvie-Grant 1906, Riley 1938; Robinson 1907, 1914a, 1914b, Robinson and Kloss 1910–11, 1918, ZRCNUS).

HABITATS AND ECOLOGY. Both wet and dry situations, including paddyfields, pool-margins, open grazing and other grasslands, and small wetlands in semi-deciduous forest. Along the Bandon river at mid summer 1913, roosted together with Painted Storks and White-shouldered Ibises in tall dead trees fringing the forest (Robinson 1914a). Regularly soars on thermals.

FORAGING AND FOOD. On dry land or at wetland margins rather than by wading. A male stomach contained fish, small crabs and grasshoppers (Riley 1938).

SOCIAL ORGANIZATION. Loners and, in the past, pairs and occasional small (family?) parties.

MOVEMENTS. None reported.

SURVIVAL. No information.

SOCIAL INTERACTIONS. No information.

VOICE. No information.

BREEDING. In Pakchan, nest-building by a female on 26 March (Riley 1938).

MOULT. Replacement of primaries apparently regular-descendant to P8, then P10 before 9. Adults dated 31 December, 11 February and 2 August showed moult of P5, P4 and P8/10 respectively; others dated December–March and May none (BMNH, ZRCNUS), revealing no obvious seasonality.

CONSERVATION. Critical in this area.

Storm's Stork; Nok Gra-saa Khaw Khao Paak Daeng (Thai); Burung Botak Hutan (Malay)

Ciconia stormi (Blasius) 1896, *Mitteilungen der Geographischen Gesellschaft und des Naturhistorischen Museum in Lübeck* series 2(10-11): 121. TL Pontianak, W Kalimantan.

Plate 15

GROUP RELATIONS. See Woolly-necked Stork. The breeding ranges of these two storks had been thought to meet only on Sumatra (Holmes 1977), but earlier this century geographical overlap also occurred in the Peninsula.

GLOBAL RANGE. Endemic to Borneo, the Peninsula and Sumatra, including N. Pagai and Siberut islands off W Sumatra (BBCB-3, BMP5, CLBS).

IDENTIFICATION/DESCRIPTION. From Woolly-necked Stork by black of underparts extending forward, leaving only the throat, feathered face and nape to hind-neck white, and bill entirely bright orange-red. Immatures are black-marked on the lower face and throat and have all bare-parts duller than adult; bill tipped dusky. Storm's has the same all-black, forked tail overlaying stiff, forked, white lower tail-coverts as Woolly-necked Stork but with shallower furcation (BMNH), only 60 mm in a Selangor female. The culmen of females is straight, that of males slightly concave, with basal knob (Tungku M. Nazim Yaacob).

Downy chicks are white with bill and bald crown black (Nakhasathien 1987).

Bare-part colours. (Adult) iris red; a broad

periorbital zone golden-yellow, rest of face dull orange; bill wholly bright orange-red (tipped brownish in juvenile); legs and feet pale orange.

Size (mm). (Skin: 1 female; immature): wing 420; tail 173; bill 149 (from an extra, unsexed skull, 168); tarsus 145 (ZDUM, ZRCNUS).

Weight. No information.

DISTRIBUTION. North to latitude about 9°N (Nakhasathien 1987). Historical summary: *Sur, Pek, Phg, Sel, Joh.*

GEOGRAPHICAL VARIATION. None recognized.

STATUS AND POPULATION. Resident, local and sparse; known from seven river systems. On the W-coast plain: lower reaches of the Perak (a bird collected near Sitiawan and several recent sightings in rapidly shrinking patches of flood-plain forest nearby: Chasen 1934, A.C. Sebastian); and the Gombak, upper Kelang drainage, Selangor (a shot immature picked up on 15 August 1963: BR 1963). In the east: on a tributary of the Phrasaeng (basin of the since-filled Chiew Larn reservoir), Surat Thani (Nakhasathien 1987); in the upper Pahang drainage, including Taman Negara, a since-cleared part of Tekam forest reserve (Jerantut district) and the Kerau wildlife reserve (BMP5, Gibson-Hill 1949b, MBR 1986–87); lower reaches of the Rompin and Endau rivers, Pahang/Johor border (up to three birds seen in March and May 1989, and three again in July 1990: ENGGANG-2, SINGAV-4); and in Panti forest reserve, source of the Johor and Sedili rivers (two on 22 January 1995: R. Subaraj).

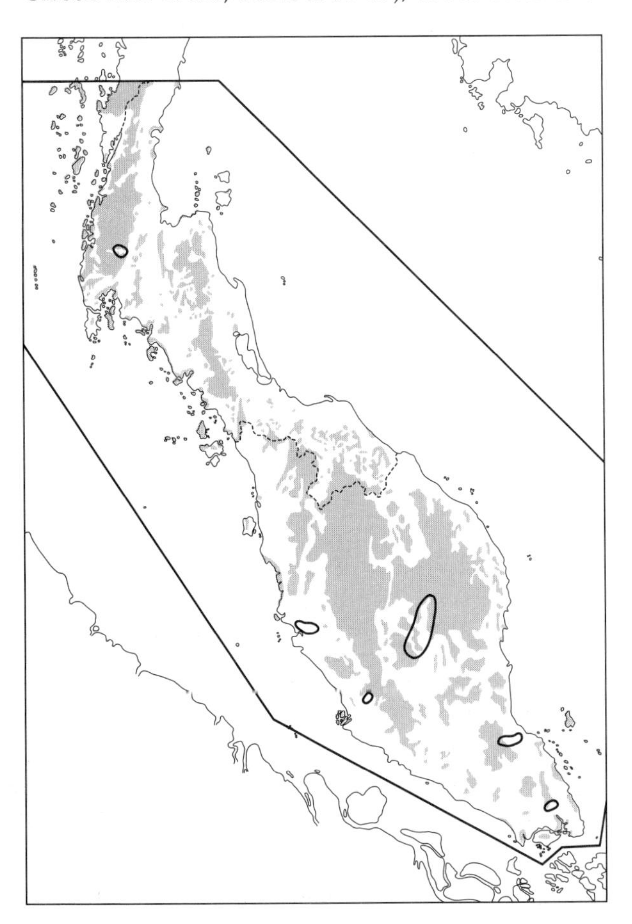

HABITATS AND ECOLOGY. Exclusively tall semi-evergreen and evergreen forest below the hill-foot boundary, core habitat almost certainly being the flood-plains of the larger rivers (incuding last fragments of riverine swamp-forest along the lower Perak, now being cleared for agriculture). Use of the peatswamp found in Panti forest reserve needs to be confirmed. Recorded in mangroves in E Sumatra but not in the Peninsula where contact between freshwater and coastal forests has mostly been lost. Several local records have been from selectively logged forest.

FORAGING AND FOOD. Hunts alone, commonly under the forest canopy, along margins of small streams (Nakhasathien 1987) and in boggy gaps such as maintained by the activity of large mammals at mineral-licks (BMP5, BR 1974–75). In the Kerau reserve, occasionally visited a former meadow clearing maintained for Gaur.

SOCIAL ORGANIZATION. Loners, pairs and occasionally small (family?) parties (larger soaring groups have been seen in Borneo). A dispersed nester; an unoccupied nest 200 m from an active one (Nakhasathien 1987) suggests pairs may maintain alternative sites within a regular territory.

MOVEMENTS. None recorded.

SURVIVAL. No information.

SOCIAL INTERACTIONS. A pair of chicks crouched and lay motionless in the bottom of the nest when a Crested Serpent Eagle called, and responded in the same way to human sounds (Nakhasathien 1987).

VOICE. Throughout their period of development in captivity, chicks gave loud, harsh and repeated *krack* calls (Nakhasathien 1987). No vocalizations have been recorded from adults.

BREEDING

Nest. Two in forest on the bank of a small river, 19 and 30 m up in the top and on a major lateral fork of tall dipterocarp trees (including *Dipterocarpus baudii*): flat platforms 50 cm across × 15 cm deep, built of sticks 15–60 cm long and lined with dry leaves and some down.

Eggs and brood. Egg undescribed. One record of a brood of two chicks, and successful clutches in captivity at Zoo Negara, Kuala Lumpur, have also been of two.

Cycle. Both parents incubate and tend nestlings. Chicks taken into captivity were able to fly at age about 90 days, but may not have developed at natural rates.

Seasonality. In Surat Thani in 1986, a pair incubated during late September–October and hatched two chicks between 21–24 October (Tungku M. Nazim Yaacob, Nakhasathien 1987).

MOULT. No information.

CONSERVATION. Globally vulnerable and, in the Peninsula, probably now endangered. Why Storm's Stork continues to be so rare in long-established Taman Negara and the Kerau wildlife reserve is not clear unless the headwater habitats offered are substantially below optimum for this species. No flood-plain forest is protected in the Peninsula and it is seriously possible that headwater population remnants will not maintain themselves once all immigration from below is cut off. A good case can be made for the captive breeding of genuine Peninsular stock while it lasts.

Greater Adjutant; Nok Ta-graam (Thai); Burung Botak Babi Besar (Malay)

Leptoptilos dubius (Gmelin) 1789, *Systema Naturae* 13(2): 624. TL India.
Plate 16

GROUP RELATIONS. Forms a superspecies with African *L. crumeniferus* (Marabou Stork) (Snow 1978).

GLOBAL RANGE. The northern Indian subcontinent east from Sind; Burma and the rest of continental SE Asia south of a line NW Thailand-central Vietnam. Large numbers once bred colonially, with other large waterbirds, in the lower Sittang valley and Tenasserim south to about latitude 16°N. Now dangerously reduced throughout its range and, in SE Asia, a few breeders remain only in Cambodia (AWB). Vagrant in the Peninsula.

IDENTIFICATION/DESCRIPTION. Huge size is of use only in direct comparison with Lesser Adjutant. Otherwise, by pendulous pouch and white ruff at base of neck, inner secondaries and secondary coverts pale grey against blackish of rest of upperparts and, in overhead flight, pale brown-and-white mottled lower wing-coverts contrasting with dark flight-feathers (all-dark in Lesser Adjutant). Both species fly with neck retracted.

Bare-part colours. (Adult) iris white or pale yellow, eyelid-rim pink, eyelids grey; forehead from bill-base black, rest of head red-brown, neck and pouch yellowish, the latter pink apically and spotted black; bill pale flesh-yellow; legs and feet grey-brown.

Size. No local information.

Weight. No data.

DISTRIBUTION. Historical summary: *Nar*.

GEOGRAPHICAL VARIATION. None recognized.

STATUS AND POPULATION. Vagrant. Two sightings, perhaps of the same individual, on 3 and 8 June 1992 at the Chalerm Prakiat wetland, Narathiwat, and a bird there again on 13 April 1993 (BBCB-9, BCSTB-10).

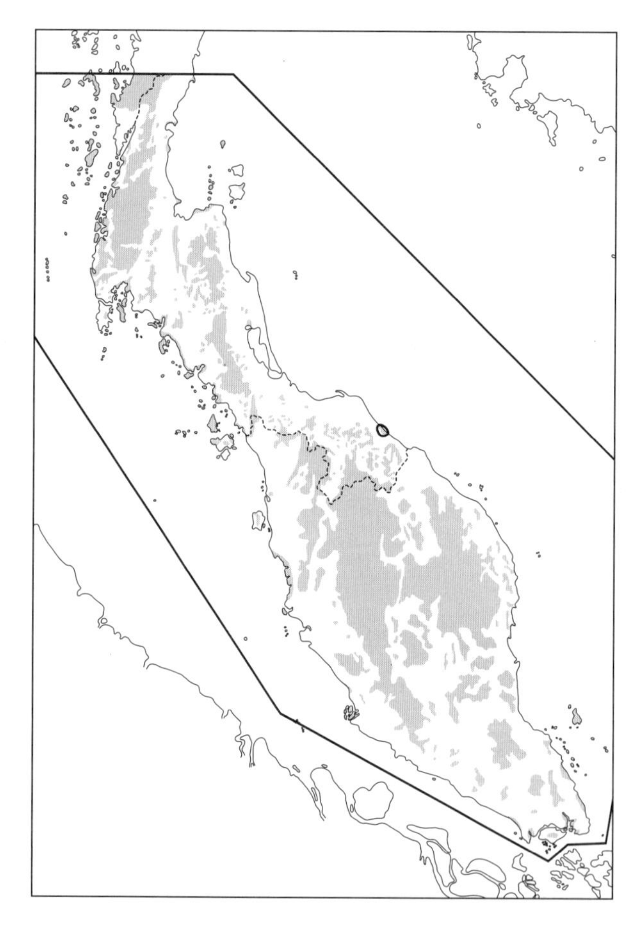

There is an outside possibility that one or two 'winter' in Narathiwat regularly. Reported intermittently at 12°N in coastal SW Thailand (OBCB-3).

HABITATS AND ECOLOGY. No direct information but likely habitats include open, freshwater marsh, fallow paddyland, etc.

FORAGING AND FOOD. No information.

SOCIAL ORGANIZATION. No local information.

MOVEMENTS. No information.

SURVIVAL. No information.

SOCIAL INTERACTIONS. No information.

VOICE. No information.

BREEDING. No population.

MOULT. No data.

CONSERVATION. Globally endangered (BTW2).

Lesser Adjutant; Nok Ta-grum (Thai); Burung Botak Babi (Malay)

Leptoptilos javanicus (Horsfield) 1821, *Transactions of the Linnean Society* 13(1): 188. TL Java.
Plate 16

GROUP RELATIONS. Free-standing.

GLOBAL RANGE. The eastern Indian subcontinent and Sri Lanka; historically, China south from S Sichuan and Jiangxi; and SE Asia to the Greater Sunda islands and Bali.

IDENTIFICATION/DESCRIPTION. On the ground, size and blackish upper body and wings against white underparts are a distinctive combination, though in fresh plumage the scapulars are white-margined. *Leptoptilos* species differ from other Old World storks by flying with neck retracted, heron-like; but no heron soars on widely splayed primaries and, in distant view when trailing feet might be missed, the resemblance is closer to a *Gyps* vulture. Seen overhead, a spur of white runs off the breast onto coverts of otherwise all-dark underwing.

Juveniles have a downy neck; in adults, apart from hair-like feathering on the nape, head and neck are bald.

Bare-part colours. (Adult) iris grey-white; crown stone- or pale green-grey, the rest of the head and neck yellow, blotched red on lower base of neck; bill yellow-horn; legs and feet black.

Size (mm). (Skins: 9 adults, most not sexed): wing 565–645 (smallest of 3 males 635, a female 578); tail 236–255 (smallest male 250, a female 237); bill 246–295; tarsus 215–256 (smallest male 243, a female 215) (BMNH, ZRCNUS).

Weight (g). Two adults, about 4000 and 5200 (Riley 1938).

DISTRIBUTION. Historical summary: all divisions except *Chu, Ran, Nak, Son, Pat, Yal, Pes, Neg, Mel*, with additional island records from Nakha Yai (*Phu*) and Penang, but no longer present on either.

GEOGRAPHICAL VARIATION. None recognized.

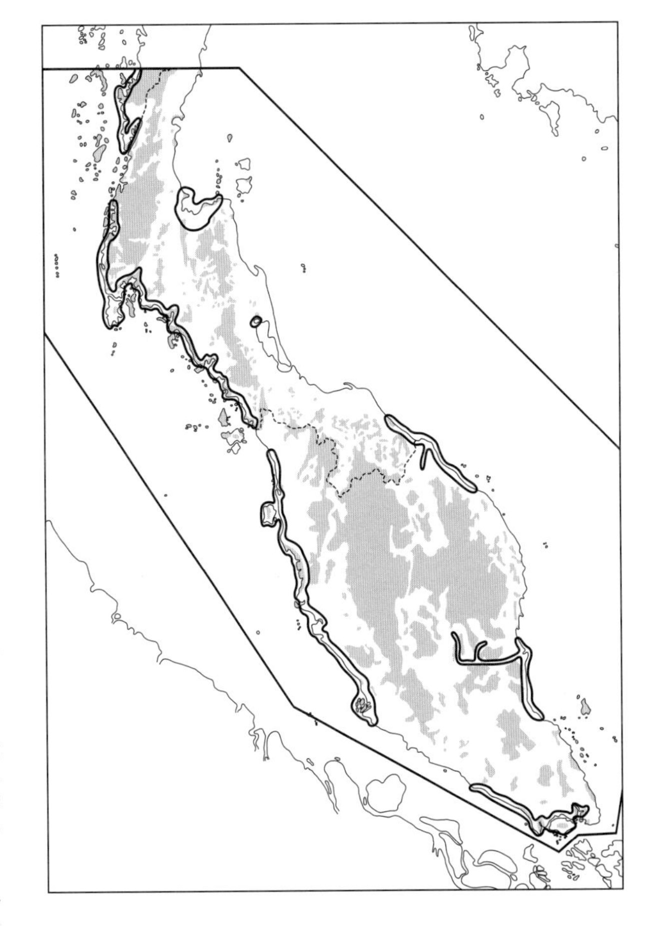

STATUS AND POPULATION. Resident and sparse to more or less common, but local. Declining everywhere due to nest-raiding and loss of acceptable sites as coastal timber is harvested or cleared. Early in the century, evidently general along the Thai W coast (Robinson and Kloss 1921–24). Over recent years: one tentative record from Ranong, a small, apparently still-active colony in Phangnga, a bird on Mai Ngam island (Lanta group), loners at Khlong Phraya wildlife sanctuary and Khlong Thom (Krabi), and one at Palian, Trang coast (BBCB-6, BCSTB-12, Y. Meekeow, J.W.K. Parr). Into the Melaka Straits, it has gone from Perlis and Kedah (Bromley 1949, Robinson and Kloss 1910–11) but an aerial census in August 1983 logged 128 between mainland Penang and Kelang, with a further 25 in W Johor (mostly Benut mangrove forest) in March 1986 and around 37 there on 18 July 1988 (ENGGANG-1, Hawkins and Howes 1986, Parish and Wells 1984). Not all habitat was thoroughly searched but the mid-1980s population of the W coast is unlikely to have topped 200, and few would have been breeding.

Still fewer survive on the E coast and most recent localities are freshwater wetlands, including scattered occurrences during the 1970s at the Thung Thong and Thalae Noi wetlands, but none reported there since May 1980 (Round *et al.* 1988, Storer 1976, 1978); and at Chalerm Prakiat wildlife sanctuary, Narathiwat, with a group of four breeding pairs active in March–April 1995 but whose nesting attempts have often been thwarted by chick-robbing (BBCB-4, -9, P.D. Round). Over the border, a capture at Pasir Mas, 30 km up the Kelantan river, in 1968 and two sightings that year on the Terengganu coast (BMP5, BR 1968) are the last records from these states. Southward, a few persist in mangroves and adjacent freshwater swamp-forest edge between Kuantan and the Rompin river-mouth (ENGGANG-2), and up the Pahang river for at least 150 km, including one over the Ulu Lepar lakes in April 1992 (A.C. Sebastian). Nine roosting near the Pahang estuary on 30 April 1986 (Howes *et al.* 1986) is the largest group seen in the area recently. Last Singapore nests date to the late 1930s (Gibson-Hill 1950a), with no birds recorded in the Republic now for several decades.

HABITATS AND ECOLOGY. On the W-coast plain, formerly made regular use of fallow paddy-lands (Gibson-Hill 1949b). At least in Malaysia, now, most foraging occurs in the intertidal zone, on mangrove-backed mudflats. On neither coast have any nests been more than 3–4 km from the sea or a major tidal river, implying no permanent use is made of remoter inland sites (BR 1969).

FORAGING AND FOOD. Hunts visually while striding slowly over tidal mud, etc., often along the tideline but sometimes back under the shade of the outer mangrove trees. Diet is not described but likely to be varied (an active nest contained a dead eel: Chasen and Kloss 1931).

SOCIAL ORGANIZATION. Mainly loners and pairs. At a few sites, has nested in small colonies, of up to eight pairs (Chasen and Kloss 1931, Madoc 1956a, MBR 1986–87).

MOVEMENTS. None recorded.

SURVIVAL. No information.

SOCIAL INTERACTIONS. No information.

VOICE. No information.

BREEDING

Nest. Exclusively a tree-nester in the Peninsula, up to 35 m above ground, favouring tall (including dead) emergents in secluded mangrove or freshwater swamp-forest; occasionally relic timber. Host-tree identifications include *Intsia, Alstonia* and *Bruguiera* species. The massive, stick nest is unlined, built alone or in small colonies.

Eggs and brood. Eggs are not described. Clutch said to be four, but no nest checked has contained more than a single chick.

Cycle. No information.

Seasonality. In the Perak mangroves, a pair building in late January–early February and an attended cluster of five-plus nests (contents unchecked) on 4 February; in W Johor, five nests in riverside mangroves each with a chick (four downy, one near-fledged) on 24 March; incubation or brooding by the Perak estuary on 5 April; and eight nests, most with a large young, in the top branches of a giant tree at Sekinchang, N Selangor, in June (E.F. Allen 1949, Chasen and Kloss 1931, Gibson-Hill 1949b, Madoc 1956a, MBR 1986–87, Robinson and Chasen 1936).

MOULT. Among very few examined, adults dated 17 January and 4 February were growing P10 and P6, respectively (ZRCNUS).

CONSERVATION. The undoubted longevity of adults may allow pockets of population to age for decades after breeding ceases, giving a false sense of the security of the species in most of its local range. Unless a concentration exists undetected in Pakchan, 220–250 would be an outside estimate of the recent population of the Peninsula as a whole. Globally vulnerable (BTW2).

Black-necked Stork; Nok Gra-saa Khaw Dam (Thai); Burung Botak Leher Hitam (Malay)

Ephippiorhynchus asiaticus (Latham) 1790, *Index Ornithologicus* 2: 670. TL India.
Plate 15

GROUP RELATIONS. Apparently free-standing; close to African *E. senegalensis* (Saddle-billed Stork) (Hancock *et al.* 1992).

GLOBAL RANGE. The Indian subcontinent (but no longer Pakistan) and Sri Lanka (Rahmani 1989); SE Asia, historically, from a line N Burma–central Vietnam to the Peninsula, and with one old record from Java (Bartels 1908); then in S New Guinea and N and E Australia. Sparse and declining throughout its Asian range; gone from most of SE Asia and may recently have bred only in Cambodia and far-S Vietnam (AWB, Scott 1989).

IDENTIFICATION/DESCRIPTION. Size, stilt legs, pied colour-combination and massive black bill are distinctive, but juveniles have head and upper body shades of brown. From below in flight, white except for head, neck, tail and band across wing-coverts, sharply demarcated black.

Bare-part colours. (Adult) iris dark brown (male), pale yellow (female); orbital skin black, loral and gular skin deep red mottled with black; legs and feet coral-red (Robinson 1917).

Size (mm). (Skin: 1 subadult, not sexed): wing not measurable; tail 211; bill from rear edge nostril 247; tarsus 342 (BMNH).

Weight. No data.

DISTRIBUTION. Recently only Trang. Claimed post-1980 occurrences on Tarutao island (Scott 1989) have not been confirmed but the species may once have ranged that far south. Mid-nineteenth century trade specimens from Penang include a subadult in the Cantor collection (BMNH) marked 'Purlis' (Perlis) that might have come from the border area. However, there are no records in support of 'Langkawi island' (Robinson and Chasen 1936). Historical summary: *Tra*.

GEOGRAPHICAL VARIATION. Nominate *asiaticus*, of the Asian range.

STATUS AND POPULATION. Resident but highly local and close to extinction. The one definite locality is Hat Chao Mai, on the mainland coast opposite Libong island, Trang, where the female of a breeding pair was collected on 1 January 1917 (Robinson 1917). Four were there in December 1980 but only one seen in January 1983, with a lone bird (and rumour of others) still present in 1992 (BBCB-9, OBCB-16, Round *et al.* 1988).

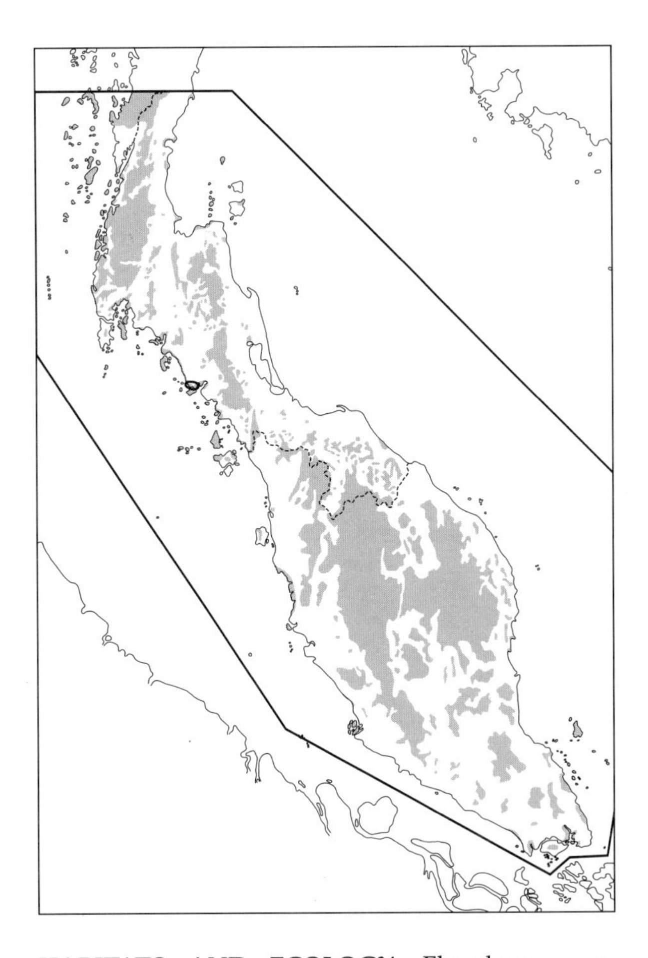

HABITATS AND ECOLOGY. Elsewhere, more often in freshwater wetlands but the only definite foraging habitat reported locally is intertidal mud- and sandflats supporting sea-grasses (*Zostera* spp). At least occasional breeding is likely to have occurred in the area but nothing is known about sites in recent time. Birds loaf and probably roost in the taller trees of paperbark woodland behind the Hat Chao Mai shore and, like other storks, soar on thermals.

FORAGING AND FOOD. Hunts while wading, but no local details.

SOCIAL ORGANIZATION. Loners and pairs; a dispersed breeder.

MOVEMENTS. None known.

SURVIVAL. No information.

SOCIAL INTERACTIONS. No information.

VOICE. No information.

BREEDING

Nest. The only one described, a very large, untidy stick structure built on a ledge some distance up a limestone crag (elsewhere in its range, including formerly in SW Thailand, mainly a tree-nester).

Eggs and brood. Eggs are rough-textured, matt to slightly glossy plain white. Size (mm): 71.9–70.3 × 54.0–52.4 (n=3). Full clutch four.

Cycle. No information.

Seasonality. Eggs, 'rather hard set', on 1 January (Gairdner 1914, Robinson 1917, ZRCNUS).

MOULT. No data.

CONSERVATION. It is not known if any viable pairs remain or if they could be adequately protected. Unusual local foraging habits imply it might be difficult to re-stock Hat Chao Mai from outside sources. In Asia generally, vulnerable to endangered.

Order FALCONIFORMES

Family ACCIPITRIDAE

Osprey, perns, bat hawk, kites, fish eagles, vultures, snake eagles, harriers, hawks, buzzards, booted eagles: 37 species.

Osprey; Yieo Osprey (Thai); Lang Tiram (Malay)

Pandion haliaetus (Linnaeus) 1758, *Systema Naturae* 10(1): 91. TL Sweden.
Plate 20

GROUP RELATIONS. Free-standing; no close relatives.

GLOBAL RANGE. Breeds in N and Central America; Eurasia mainly above about 40°N from the Atlantic to Kamchatka and Japan, with outlying populations south to the Cape Verde islands, SW and central Asia, the Himalayas, Assam and Taiwan; and in the S hemisphere: Java to islands of the Flores Sea, New Guinea and Australia. Northern birds migrate, wintering south to the tropics around the world, in E Asia to the Andamans, Greater Sunda islands, Bali, the Philippines and Sulawesi. S-hemisphere migrants occur north as far as the Philippines; possibly also to Borneo (Smythies 1981).

IDENTIFICATION/DESCRIPTION. Brahminy Kite-plus sized. Dark above, apart from buffy breast-band contrastingly white below, including wing-coverts. Long black mask through eye conspicuous against white of rest of head and nape, with cap of adult dark-streaked only mid-dorsally (more extensively in juveniles). Winter juveniles also retain narrow whitish fringing on the upperparts. In all flight-modes, tail appears relatively short, wings long, proportionately narrow and rather pointed, invariably flexed at the wrist and with a prominent, blackish carpal-patch (see also Common Buzzard, Oriental Honey-buzzard). Wing-beats are rather shallow, fairly rapid, and when soaring wings are held shallowly arched.

Bare-part colours. (Adult) iris yellow; bill blackish, cere pale blue-grey; feet pale blue-grey to greenish grey.

Size (mm). (Skins: 1 adult female; 1 immature, not sexed): wing 485 and 465; tail 210 and 200; bill from cere 34.0 and 32.9; tarsus 51.7 and 56.4 (ZRCNUS).

Weight. No data.

DISTRIBUTION. Historical summary: all divisions except *Chu*, *Nak*, *Yal*, *Nar*, with additional island records from Lanbyi, the Similan group (*Pha*), Phiphi, Libong, the Tarutao group (Ta Nga), the Langkawi group and Penang off the W coast; Hantu and Sakeng, Singapore.

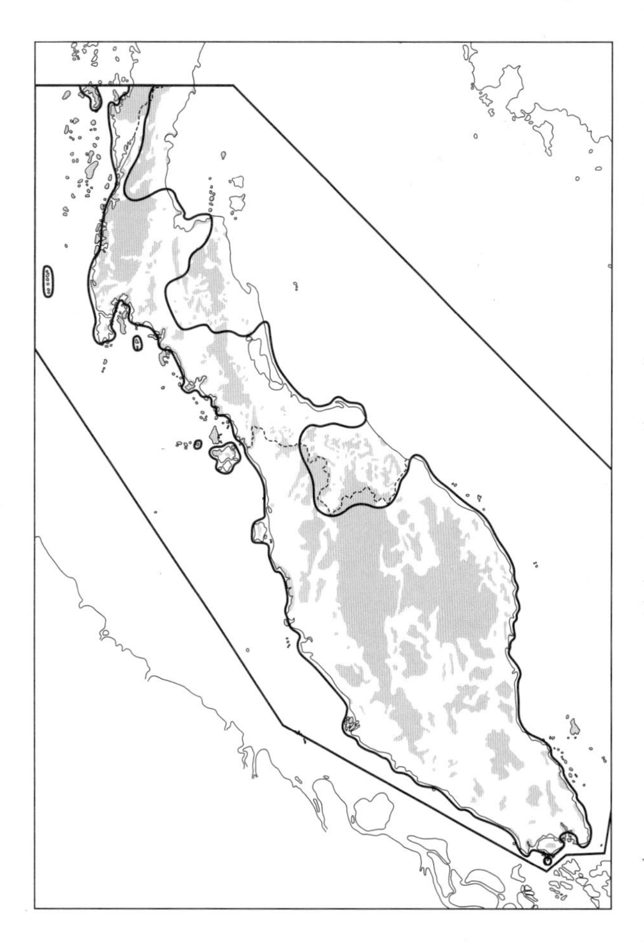

GEOGRAPHICAL VARIATION. Eurasian *haliaetus* is the only subspecies confirmed.

STATUS AND POPULATION. A non-breeding visitor year-round, local and uncommon but more present during October–March than in summer. It has been suggested over-summerers might be migrants from the south (Gibson-Hill 1949b) but at least one detailed description fits nominate *haliaetus*, and no maskless, southern-type birds have been reported. The greater probability is that northern subadults stay over, as they do elsewhere in the tropics (including S China: Chalmers 1986).

HABITATS AND ECOLOGY. There are few reports of open-sea hunting (Chasen 1924) but seen at off-shore fish-traps, and Ospreys regularly fish in estuaries, creeks and ponds within the mangrove zone (Eve and Guigue 1982, Madoc 1956a). Otherwise found in natural marshland (Thalae Noi); along the larger lowland rivers through both open country and forest; at reservoirs, especially where drowned trees provide loafing and look-out perches (several large dams have been closed ahead of basin-clearance, leaving many kilometres of attractive margin); and visits paddyland irrigation canals, dredge-mine lagoons and fish-pond complexes.

FORAGING AND FOOD. Mostly by quartering well above the water, with brief positioning hovers, then plunge-diving at a slant. Less often, by kite-like snatching from the water-surface. No reports of any food except fish, eaten on habitual perches that, in bare areas, can include the top of a pylon or service-pole.

SOCIAL ORGANIZATION. Typically solitary, even while migrating, but records exist of two, in a few cases three and, once in the Songkhla channel, seven fishing together apparently harmoniously (BR 1963, Hawkins and Howes 1986, Madoc 1950–51).

MOVEMENTS. Few definite records. South-heading loners over Trang on 19 October and the coastal plain of Selangor on 19 and 23 October and 17 December; in spring, with other returning raptors at Cape Rachado (Negeri Sembilan) on 23 March, over the Main Range (Perak) on 4 April and at sea off Phuket on 6 April (BCSTB-12). One in the Terengganu off-shore oil-field on 5 April (MBR 1982–83) could have been on a direct crossing of the Gulf of Thailand. Migrating Ospreys are less attracted to thermals than most other raptors in their size-class, hence may be less wedded to land routes.

SURVIVAL. No information.

SOCIAL INTERACTIONS. No details.

VOICE. Mostly silent. On a December evening, three birds interacting in the air over the Senoko wetland, Singapore, gave two kinds of calls: a long thin scream and sharp, piercing whistles reminiscent of the ringing *tiong* of Hill Myna *Gracula religiosa* (SINGAV-1).

BREEDING. No population.

MOULT. An adult female in wing-moult (growing P2) in February (ZRCNUS).

CONSERVATION. Loss of fish stocks through pesticide contamination of paddyland irrigation systems has reduced a locally important foraging option.

Jerdon's Baza; Yieo Gingkaa See Namtaan (Thai); Lang Baza (Malay)

Aviceda jerdoni (Blyth) 1842, *Journal of the Asiatic Society of Bengal* 11(1): 464. TL Bengal.
Plate 17

GROUP RELATIONS. Eck (1976) merged *jerdoni* with allopatric Wallacean–Australasian *subcristata* (Pacific Baza), *madagascariensis* (Madagascar Baza) and African *cuculoides* (Cuckoo-falcon) in a single polytypic species. A superspecies relationship is a less conservative but more acceptable guess.

GLOBAL RANGE. SW India and Sri Lanka, and the Himalayan foothills east from Darjeeling; SW Yunnan and Hainan; SE Asia to Sumatra, Borneo and the Philippines; and Sulawesi to the Banggai and Sula islands.

IDENTIFICATION/DESCRIPTION. Size of a small hawk eagle and crested apparently at all ages. Immatures are brown above, head and underparts more or less plain buff-white except for rather broad cinnamon-rufous barring on belly and flanks (in some, broken ventrally into large droplets). Adults are darker above, from cap, with side of face and broad hind-collar cinnamon-rufous, have a black gular stripe, and some are also black-streaked on the breast (an age factor?). Streak-breasted adults (possibly only males) become extensively black on crown, mantle and lesser wing-coverts, with ventral barring also invaded by black. The black, faintly barred crest is tipped white. In overhead flight, rather broad, butterfly wings show coverts cinnamon-and-white-barred against evenly black-and-white-barred flight-feathers.

When perched, from Wallace's Hawk Eagle by folded wing-tips reaching more than half way down the tail, lower tarsus unfeathered, and lower tail-coverts only sparsely marked (at all ages). In the hand, by prominent double denticle on upper mandible.

Bare-part colours. (Adult) iris yellow; bill and cere blackish; feet yellow.

Size (mm). (Skins: 5 males, 2 females; adult): wing 311–326 and 324–330; tail 193–225 and 228–238; bill from cere 24.4–25.4 and 25.7; longest crest-feather 51–57 and 45–48; tarsus 43.0 (one male) (BMNH, ZRC-NUS).

Weight. No data.

DISTRIBUTION. With certainty, only north of latitude about 4°N, but a nineteenth-century specimen in the Cuming collection from Melaka (BMNH) lacks the contemporary local trade-skin shape and might be genuine. Historical summary: *Pak, Sur, Pht, Tra, Nar, Pek*, ?*Mel*, with island records only from Langkawi (*Ked*).

GEOGRAPHICAL VARIATION. Subspecies *jerdoni* of the mainland and Sumatra, but variation related to possible colour-pattern mimicry needs more study.

STATUS AND POPULATION. Probably resident, recorded during October–March and recently also in June (BCSTB-10, BMNH, BLC, Holmes 1973, Riley 1938). Local and sparse, known from fewer than a dozen specimens and hardly as many sightings, but estimates of abundance are compromised by problems of identification in the field.

HABITAT AND ECOLOGY. All traceable records have been from the canopy or edge of tall Lowland forest, mature and logged, at plains level and on lower slopes, with one of birds using relic trees in a swidden clearing.

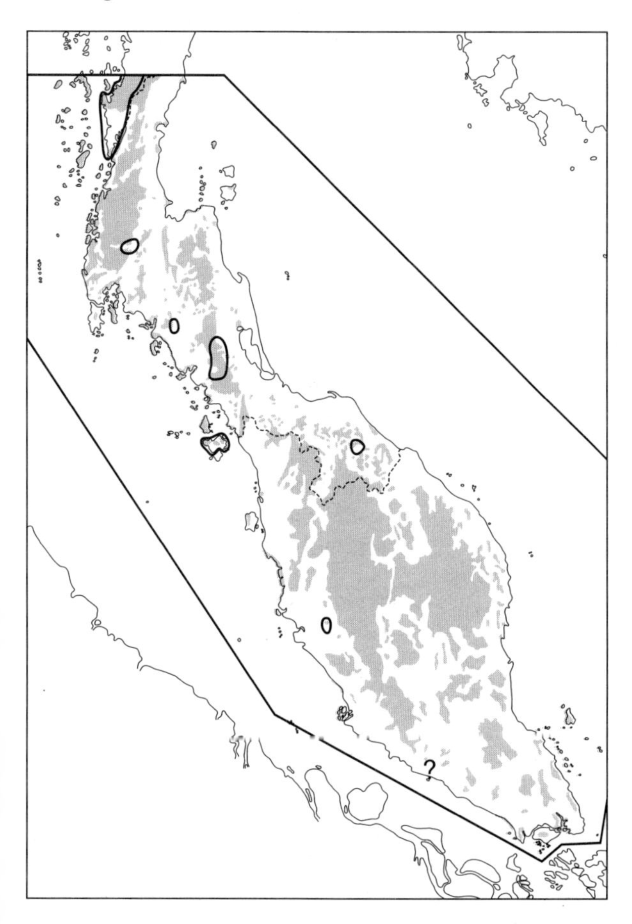

A possible reason why Jerdon's Baza is so little known in the Peninsula is that it resembles another raptor in the same habitat well enough to be mistaken. Parallels have been drawn with Crested Goshawk *Accipiter trivirgatus* and Oriental Honey-buzzard *Pernis ptilorhyncus* (Boonsong and Round 1991, King *et al.* 1975), but the really comprehensive resemblance is to Wallace's Hawk Eagle *Spizaetus nanus*. Immatures and some adults match brown-backed transitional-stage eagles before and after development of a gular stripe and breast-patterning. Adult males match the fully adult eagle in every important particular, including extent of black on the crown, mantle and wing-coverts, contrasting cinnamon collar and face, and pattern of black stripes and bars on the ventral body. Wing- and tail-barring, and length and common poise of the white-tipped crest are a fair match at all stages.

From its different appearance outside their common range, Jerdon's Baza appears to be mimicking *nanus*. *Spizaetus* species take mainly reptiles and small arboreal mammals, rarely large birds, hence the selective advantage it gains from this is unlikely to be direct protection from predation by the model. A diet overlap might favour interspecific spacing, or being taken for a more dangerous predator while foraging from high, exposed perches might reduce the risk of being mobbed. More than one factor could operate.

FORAGING AND FOOD. Two in disturbed forest in Narathiwat sallied for insects from high canopy perches, tending to return to a fresh perch each time (Holmes 1973). It was not clear whether they took prey flying or from foliage. Local diet information is lacking but, elsewhere, is said to include mainly invertebrates.

SOCIAL ORGANIZATION. At least three records have been of two adults together, whereas hawk eagles invariably forage alone.

MOVEMENTS. None recorded.

SURVIVAL. No information.

SOCIAL INTERACTIONS. No additional information.

VOICE. Quite different from Wallace's Hawk Eagle: a rather high-pitched, airy whistle, *fiweeoo*; also a shorter *ti-wuet* (reminiscent of a Violet Cuckoo *Chrysococcyx xanthorhynchus*) repeated 3–4 times and given frequently by foraging birds (Holmes 1973).

BREEDING. Not reported.

MOULT. No wing-moult in a December immature or three adults dated December and March (BMNH, ZRCNUS).

CONSERVATION. The extent of dependance on plains-level forest needs study. Globally near-threatened (BTW2).

Black Baza; Yieo Gingkaa See Dam (Thai); Lang Baza Hitam (Malay)

Aviceda leuphotes Dumont de Sainte-Croix 1820, *Dictionnaire des Sciences Naturelles* 16: 217. TL Pondicherry, SE India.

Plate 18

GROUP RELATIONS. Free-standing.

GLOBAL RANGE. Breeds in SW India and the Andamans (Abdulali and Grubh 1970); the Himalayan foothills and terai east from central Nepal; China west of a line Sichuan–Guangdong, including Hainan; and continental SE Asia south to latitude roughly 14°N. Northern populations (to an uncertain southern limit) are migratory, wintering in Sri Lanka and SE Asia to Sumatra and Java (van Balen 1984).

IDENTIFICATION/DESCRIPTION. Gregariousness, and pied pattern combined with tall, nodding crest cocked vertical are distinctive features. Soars often and in this flight-mode the lozenge- (almost leaf) shaped wings are equally distinctive. Their shape is due to a near-linear increase in the length of the secondaries out from the base of the wing, giving a slanting rather than bulging inner trailing-edge, not obviously nipped-in against the body.

Black Bazas show two pattern-morphs: (1) greater wing-coverts plus distal half of secondaries (apart from dark-freckled tips) white, and ventral barring confined to a narrowish zone across the lower breast and upper belly; (2) only greater coverts white, and ventral barring continued over the whole of the flanks. They occur in the same winter foraging-groups and museum data suggest a sex link, but collections show a large imbalance, and some individuals are intermediate (BMNH, ZRCNUS). Patterns may be age-related, but juveniles have not been distinguished.

Bare-part colours. (Adult) iris brown or purple-grey; bill pale slate with culmen and tip darker, cere slate; feet pale slate (BMNH).

Size (mm). (Skins: 18 presumed adults, none reliably sexed): wing 219–247; tail 128–142; bill from cere 15.7–18.9; longest crest-feather 47–64; tarsus 23.8–29.7 (BMNH, ZDUM, ZRCNUS). Pattern-morphs do not segregate by size.

Weight. No data.

DISTRIBUTION. Historical summary: all divisions except *Chu, Son, Yal, Nar, Kel, Tru,* with additional island records from Lanbyi, the Similan group, Pra Thong and Yao Yai (*Pha*), Libong, Tarutao, Langkawi and Penang off the W coast, mostly at wintering dates; and Ubin, Sentosa and St John's, Singapore.

GEOGRAPHICAL VARIATION. Deignan (1948) identified migrants reaching the Peninsula as long-handed *syama* Hodgson 1823 (TL Nepal), breeding between Nepal and S China. Wing-tips have not been measured here but standard wing-lengths fall in two ranges: 219–227 and 239–247 mm. Unrelated to pattern-morph, they are either sexual or of taxonomic significance. More research is needed.

STATUS AND POPULATION. A passage migrant and non-breeding visitor. Regular and common along migration routes.

HABITATS AND ECOLOGY. Mangroves and the fairly open canopy and edge of inland Lowland forest, mature and disturbed, including swamp-forest. Also in tall secondary-growth, mature oil-palm and rubber plantations and, locally, enters secluded, well-wooded gardens. Entirely at plains level.

FORAGING AND FOOD. Insects are grabbed by the feet in short, swooping sallies from high look-out perches; also by crashing onto and scrambling about

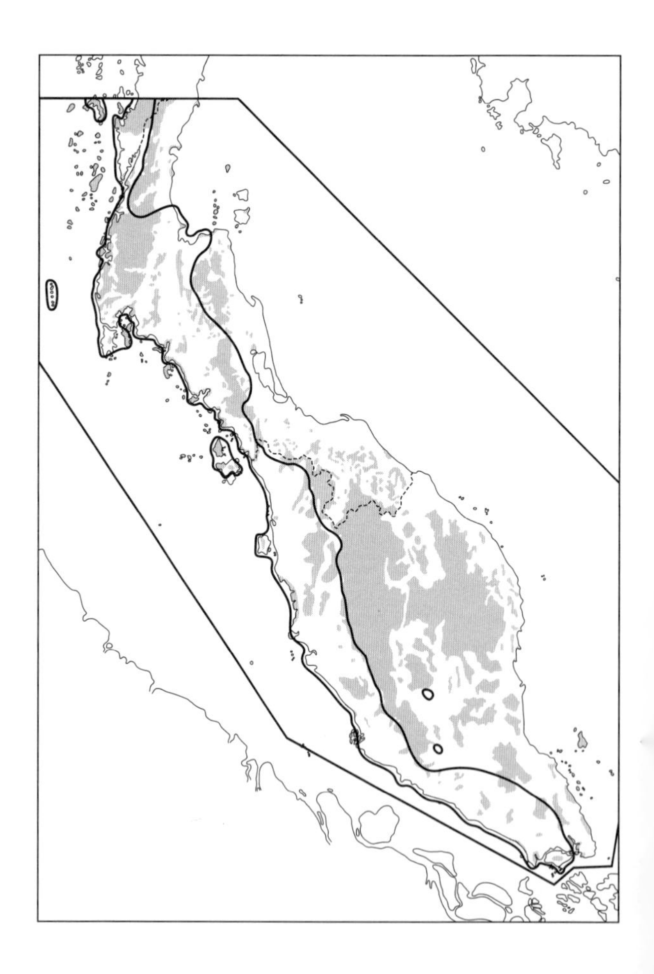

in foliage, mostly at canopy level but down to the ground at the edge of clearings (Edgar 1947). Beetles, orthopterans and alate termites are favoured prey, with occasional small vertebrates. Glenister (1951) describes a Baza leaping sideways on a branch to grab a perched Brown-throated Sunbird. Foragers have been noted following the movements of mixed-species flocks of woodland passerines (MBR 1984–85), perhaps on the watch for escaping insects. In *Sonneratia* mangroves, a group took hairy caterpillars (BBCB-4).

The suspicion that some food is vegetable is confirmed with a record of three birds on fruit-bunches of a Pahang roadside oil-palm, extracting nuts with the bill, transferring them to a foot then tearing off and eating strips of mesocarp (Duckett 1987).

SOCIAL ORGANIZATION. Loners are relatively unusual and winterers typically forage in parties of 3–10. These merge with others into larger loafing and roosting groups that gather at regular sites, including relic tree-clumps on the high tops of which 20 or more birds may sleep close together (Ludgater 1952). In undisturbed surroundings, roosts become traditional and one minimum 15-winter occupation is on record from suburban Kuala Lumpur (BMP5).

MOVEMENTS. Unlike most other migrating raptors, never seen over high ground. South at least of the Surat Thani/Krabi gap, heavily concentrated onto the W-coast plain. Not found at all among the raptors moving along the Malaysian E coast, and the only records of wintering between Surat Thani and E Johor appear to be of a few birds in Phatthalung, W-central Pahang, and at Pasoh, E Negeri Sembilan (ENGGANG-1, -2, -3, MBR 1986–87).

In three decades, first autumn arrival-dates over the SW coastal plain have varied by only seven days, between 23 and 30 October. East of the Main Range, a record of birds in a palm estate at Karak, Pahang, on 14 October is exceptional (MBR 1986–87). Passage past Selangor and Negeri Sembilan rises to full intensity in early November (largest autumn flocks during early/mid November) and falls away by mid December; extreme date 21st (19th in Singapore) (MBR 1982–83, SINGAV-6). Exodus over the Melaka Straits is believed to occur only as of the latitude of Cape Rachado (Tanjung Tuan), but more checks are needed. Southward, group-size decreases and parties reaching Singapore are rarely of more than ten (largest 63, on 1 November: R.F. Ollington). Most of these cross the western half of the main island, exiting for Indonesia via the S archipelago. Relatively few overwinter in Singapore (Ollington and Loh 1993).

Overall, northward return movement has been observed along the W-coast plain as far as Satul, during 18 February–8 April (SINGAV-2). Batchelor (1960) recorded a count of around 300 on 22 February but, typically, heaviest spring passage, and largest groups, occur through the last ten days of March: including day-scores of 460 and 450 over Thaleban national park (Satul) and 570 counted during a 15 km road journey near Kuala Lumpur (BR 1978–79). The only 3-figure flocks reported from Singapore also arrive in this period.

Returning parties clump before embarking on sea-crossings. In some years, flocks over 400-strong make landfall at Cape Rachado (BR 1976–77), but spring use of this headland (at the top end of the narrow part of the Melaka Straits) is inconsistent. A set of whole-day surveys there in February–early April 1983 (MBR 1982–83) registered almost no crossings by this or other small species, even on days when larger raptors were plentiful.

SURVIVAL. No information.

SOCIAL INTERACTIONS. Apart from obvious gregariousness, nothing recorded.

VOICE. Mostly silent but foragers give an occasional thin squeal or harsh squeak (Edgar 1947, Glenister 1951).

BREEDING. No population.

MOULT. Birds collected from November through February showed none, and fresh to only slightly worn flight-feathers imply a moult is completed before arrival (BMNH, ZRCNUS).

CONSERVATION. No critical issues identified.

Oriental Honey-buzzard; Yieo Pheung (Thai); Lang Lebah (Malay)

Pernis ptilorhyncus Temminck 1821, *Nouveau Recueil de Planches Coloriées d'Oiseaux* 8: plate 44. TL Java.

Plate 17

GROUP RELATIONS. Taken to form a superpecies with *P. apivorus* (Western Honey-buzzard), although apparent intergrades have been reported. A still more complicated situation is possible, deserving further research.

GLOBAL RANGE. Breeds in two probably discrete ranges: temperate-zone Siberia from the Yenisey drainage to Baikal, Amurland, Sakhalin, N Japan, and NE China to the Yellow Sea; and the Indian subcontinent and Sri Lanka, Sichuan and Yunnan, and SE

Asia to the Greater Sunda islands and Philippines. Northern populations migrate, wintering in S Japan, Taiwan and Hainan, and through the southern breeding-range to Bali and the Philippines; with a few Lesser Sunda island records east to Kisar.

IDENTIFICATION/DESCRIPTION. Roughly 30 percent larger than Brahminy Kite. Independant of size, from perched Jerdon's Baza by densely feathered anterior face and from *Spizaetus* eagles also by bare tarsus. Crest typically held flat against the nape. Where present, ventral barring is generally broad, well-spaced and broken. In flight, longish wing fairly parallel-sided, not strongly nipped-in at the rear base. Tail proportionately long and round-ended when closed, appearing narrow-based when fanned. Soars on flat, level to only slightly raised wings, and glides (e.g., off the top of thermals) typically with wings flexed. Flaps with deep, elastic beats that row the body along, and in all flight-modes slender head and neck project well forward, appearing low-slung in angled views. Below, lower wing-coverts are dark-barred or follow the colour of the under-body, with a black carpal patch in some darker birds (typically not in lighter ones, *contra* Osprey, Common Buzzard). Disposition of dark barring on the flight-feathers varies but all birds show a dark apical fringe backed by a pale zone without bars. At a distance, many tails show a broad, black tip and two narrower black bars across the basal half, leaving a wide, pale subterminal band. This is the adult male pattern. The other sex/age groups are separable by different tail-bar patterns (see Plate). Occasional apparent immatures show white on the upper tail-coverts.

While wing- and tail-patterns are more or less fixed, throat-pattern and head and body colours vary widely, individually and probably also with age (again, more research needed). Chin and throat range from fully outlined black, the bar across the lower throat produced forward into a mesial gular stripe, to unmarked apart from black malar-stripe. Main categories (independent of age) are otherwise: (1) upper body brown, whole head, neck and underparts white, lacking prominent dark marks; (2) all upperparts brown, underparts white from chin with breast finely to boldly black-streaked and trousers and belly barred rufous or dark; (3) more or less uniform dark chocolate, some with black streaks showing on breast; (4) upperparts all brown, underparts cinnamon, finely dark-streaked; (5) as (4) but with barred belly; (6) largely or entirely black and white, with prominent throat-pattern, black-streaked upper breast and strongly black-barred lower breast, trousers and belly.

Regardless of head-colour, the crest is black with slight to no pale tip, longest feather 51–62 mm in residents (including juveniles), not above 32 mm in migrants, and many of the latter are actually crestless (BMNH, Chasen and Kloss 1931, ZDUM, ZRCNUS).

Bare-part colours. Iris greenish (juvenile), clear yellow to orange (adult); bill horn with yellowish lower base (juvenile), black with grey-green base (adult), cere yellow (but full adults need more research); feet orange-yellow.

Size (mm). (Skins: 10 residents, 9 migrants; adult, most not sexed): wing 410–436 and 430–455; tail 252–273 and 240–280; bill from cere 21.3–26.3 and 21.3–24.4; tarsus 49.4–60.0 and 47.0–60.0 (BMNH, ZDUM, ZRCNUS). Wing-tip shape varies individually (also with age?) and may not be a safe guide to status.

Weight (g). One December-dated migrant female, 1350 (ZDUM).

DISTRIBUTION. Historical summary, from specimens and field evidence: (residents) *Chu, Sur, Nak, Kra, Tra, Tru, Pek, Phg, Sel, Neg, Joh, Sin*, with dispersants to Sentosa and St John's islands, Singapore; (migrants) all divisions except *Pak, Pha, Pat, Nar*, with additional island records from Langkawi and Penang off the W coast; and Ubin, Sentosa, St John's, Hantu and Sakeng, Singapore.

GEOGRAPHICAL VARIATION. Residents are subspecies *torquatus* Lesson 1830 (TL Sumatra), also of S Tenasserim (Oates 1883), SW Thailand and Borneo. Apart from one equivocal record from Trang (BMNH), all specimens and measurements identify migrants as Palaearctic-breeding *orientalis* Taczanowski 1891 (TL Ussuriland) (Wells and Medway 1976).

STATUS AND POPULATION. Passage migrant, non-breeding visitor and presumed breeding resident.

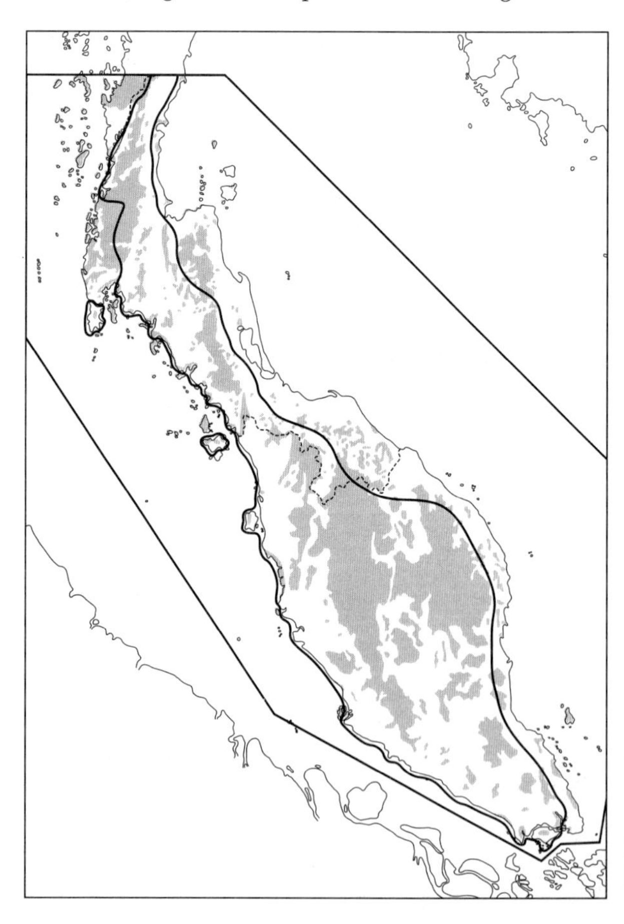

Sky-dance display that should reveal established residents has been reported only twice, suggesting breeding pairs are unusually secretive and/or widely scattered. Occasional summer appearances away from true forest habitat imply local wandering (MBR 1984–85, 1986–87).

Along migration routes during passage seasons northern migrants are regular and common; much less so at mid-winter. Hourly passage-rates of migrants, sampled in transects across the Selangor plain during October–November 1963 and 1964, extrapolated to roughly 121 000 birds moving south over the peak month of autumn migration; and during one early March day of 1965 an estimated 6000 returned north (BR 1964, 1965). Subsequently, checks have been made of spring landfall at Cape Rachado, Negeri Sembilan. In 1983, a set of day-counts spanning the passage season peaked at 1552, versus 1600 in 1963; on 1 March 1987 J.M. Thiollay counted 2761 making landfall over about 8 km of coast north from Rachado; and over two hours of 10 March 1994 1012 passed a single point on the coast 4 km north. Spot-counts are no substitute for consistent monitoring but the provisional impression is of no major status-change at this local level. There has been no confirmation of any migrants over-summering (as many young *P. apivorus* do in parts of Africa), but see below.

HABITATS AND ECOLOGY. Sky-dance records, and most specimen localities, imply breeders inhabit dry-land Lowland and Lower Montane forests, with a possible preference for edge habitat, from the plains to about 1220 m. Display has been noted (and a resident collected) over forested ridges around the Gap and Fraser's Hill (Selangor/Pahang boundary), and over disturbed forest by a large area of clear-felling in lowland N Terengganu (BR 1974–75). Where checked, summer-dated wanderers at the landward edge of W-coast mangroves, in coconut and overgrown rubber plantations, and even wooded urban parks (Singapore city) (BR 1963, MBR 1984–85, 1986–87, SINGAV-1) have all been juveniles, but are only assumed to have been local.

Few *orientalis* have been collected during mid winter but Honey-buzzards are seen more often then than in summer, implying some migrants overwinter (north at least to Trang: BMNH) rather than merely pass through. Separation from residents is an outstanding field identification problem, and sites at this season include forest-edge, secondary-growth at the edge of agriculture, etc., with several Selangor records in the subcoastal coconut belt (tall palms densely underplanted with coffee, cocoa and fruit-trees). Migrants may make less use of continuous forest than residents, but more research is needed.

Colour and pattern variations, it has been suggested, mimic an array of *Spizaetus* hawk eagles (C. Edelstam, B. King). Respectively, morphs (1), (2) and (3) suggest juvenile Changeable Hawk Eagle, light-phase adult Changeable or adult Mountain Hawk Eagle, and dark-phase adult Changeable; (4) matches juvenile Mountain; and (5) and (6) match subadult to adult Wallace's and Blyth's Hawk Eagles. A general relationship also exists between crest-lengths: short in migrants meeting SE Asian Changeable Hawk Eagle of forest-edge habitats in winter and, locally, short-crested northern Mountain Hawk Eagle in summer; long in residents meeting Wallace's, Blyth's and tropical Mountain Hawk Eagles in forest year-round. Some selective advantage to the mimic needs to be demonstrated but overall geographical matching is hard to ignore.

FORAGING AND FOOD. The only records are of raids on exposed arboreal bee nests (C. Kurian, MBR 1986–87), including one by a bird at a large nest of highly venomous tiger hornets *Vespa affinis*, near the top of a roadside tree at Fraser's Hill. Ripping with beak (rather than feet) into the side of the nest it was immediately attacked and its head, including eyes, smothered. No defence was attempted and after 30 seconds it dashed away, shaking insects into the air as it flew. Ten minutes later it returned for a second brief bout, at which stage observers withdrew. Two hours on, only a few hornets remained and the nest had been broken right through.

SOCIAL ORGANIZATION. Migrants on passage follow one another into thermals, and at times quite large parties roost together, although loners are at least as common. Most mid-winter encounters are with loners, and occasional records of two birds together (including at Fraser's Hill) may refer to residents.

MOVEMENTS. Barring occasional mid-winter parties on anomalous bearings, extreme passage dates are: southward, 10 September–21 December (but few before the last week of September); northward, 31 January–26 April (few after the first week of April) (BR 1978–79, SINGAV-1).

Even though birds regularly cross ridges up to 2000 m, migrations mostly follow lowland routes. In the north in autumn, thermal soaring is recorded over the Rap Ro hills (Chumphon) but the only large counts (1500 on 2 October 1992) have been made along the Ta Pi river (Surat Thani), out to the Nakhon Si Thammarat–Phatthalung plain via gaps in the E-central Range (BBCB-4, BCSTB-10). How many pass onto the eastern plain of Malaysia is unknown but no Honey-buzzards migrate along the E-coast fringe itself. In the west, heavy movements funnel onto the coastal plain via Satul and Songkhla (BR 1968, R. Gregory-Smith, MBR 1982–83). These exit for Indonesia mostly across the southern Melaka Straits, with no cross-water movements yet reported north of Cape Rachado (a major departure point). Relatively small numbers reach Singapore (crossed by converging western and eastern streams, the latter perhaps off the E-mainland plain), and leave via the S archipelago (Ollington and Loh 1992).

Routes in spring are the same, with regular passage over Singapore, some arrival over the southern Melaka Straits (observed in SW Johor), and a build-up at the latitude of Cape Rachado. Across the Thai border, high spring counts have been made over Satul, and the Ta Pi valley is again important, with large counts in late March (BCSTB-11, Hawkins and Howes 1986, J. Sunesen).

Oriental Honey-buzzards migrate by line-soaring between thermals, sometimes with several hundred rising in a column, to heights at which they can be found easily only against a background of bright cloud. Both track and countability are affected by local weather, and fixed-site counts need not be representative of what passes on a broader front. This is especially obvious in spring at W-coast landfall points, such as Cape Rachado. Low, flapping flight and open-billed panting show migrants are stressed by crossing the 40–50 km of sea from Sumatra on a tail-wind or in still air, but only under these conditions is this promontory attractive. E to NE winds produce no birds, but a wind backing westward over the mid-day period can draw birds within 10–20 minutes of the change becoming obvious on land. Evidently, some crossing takes place under most wind conditions but lift-supplying head-winds may allow longer, higher-soaring journeys more directly north to landfalls further up the coast. Detours via Rachado may occur only when up-draught is actively sought (MBR 1982–83).

Sea-crossings also pulse movements. On still or tail-wind days, birds reach Rachado 4–5 hours after dawn and numbers always peak over the first or second hour of passage, implying a build-up before departure from the opposite coast (cf. Ash 1993). This could explain why over Selangor, just north of the Cape, daily passage in spring peaks rather strongly in the afternoon while 200 km further north (and everywhere in autumn) it spreads more evenly through the day (BR 1964, BR 1980–81). In hot, dry weather on land, mass-starts occur as early as 0900 hours.

SURVIVAL. No information.

SOCIAL INTERACTIONS. Sky-dance display is given by loners flying at not above 30–40 m over clearings and forest canopy: a shallow up-swoop at the peak of which wings are stretched near-vertically above the back and winnowed shallowly 2–3 times before the bird drops back into level flight; the sequence repeated many times.

VOICE. Nothing recorded.

BREEDING. No nests or fledglings reported but sky-dance display, indicating breeding territories, seen on 23 February and 28 May.

MOULT. Little information. Among seven adult residents (from Nakhon Si Thammarat south to Selangor), four were in wing-moult in January (P1–2), late March (P2), and late August (P9–10, P8–9) while others dated September, December and early January showed none. Migrant *orientalis* dated October–March ranged from all-fresh to wing-tip (between P8 and 10) growing, commonly with the inner hand more worn (older) (BMNH, ZDUM, ZRCNUS). Gaps in the flight-feather row, suggesting moult, are still common during spring passage.

CONSERVATION. More information is needed on habitat requirements. Are residents really as scarce as they seem?

Bat Hawk; Yieo Khangkhao (Thai); Lang Malam (Malay)

Macheirhamphus alcinus Bonaparte 1850, *Revue et Magazin de Zoologie Pure et Appliquée*, series 2(2): 482. TL vicinity of Melaka.

Plate 18

GROUP RELATIONS. Free-standing.

GLOBAL RANGE. The Afrotropics and Madagascar; the Peninsula, Sumatra, Banka and Borneo; Sulawesi and New Guinea (CLBW, Oates 1883).

IDENTIFICATION/DESCRIPTION. Stocky; Peregrine Falcon-sized. The crest is held about horizontal and white throat and breast-centre are conspicuous only in views good enough also to reveal large yellow eye and white-feathered eyelids (versus superficially similar resident Peregrine's dark eye and yellow eyelids). There is no local description of a juvenile.

Falcon-like in shape, with proportionately rather short tail and broad-based, narrow-tipped wings. In all flight-modes, the wrist is part-flexed, with the arm inclined forward; especially noticeable at speed. Very rapid flight with much twisting and diving, on shallowly winnowed wings with tip drooped (Madoc 1950–51) could be some form of aerial display between pair-members. Cruises on relatively deep, deliberate wing-strokes, distinct from the shallow, winnowing beats of Peregrine in this flight mode.

Bill strongly compressed laterally, the high-arched culmen produced into a knife-ridge, but with mouth running back below the eye so that the gape is virtually the maximum width of the skull.

Bare-part colours. (Adult) iris golden yellow; bill and cere black; feet slaty blue.

Size (mm). (Skins: 2 males, 5 females; adult): wing 353, 364 and 380–385; tail 163, 173 and 179–189; bill from cere 18.6, 20.0 and 19.7–20.7; bill from mouth-corner 45.6–48.9 (sexes combined); tarsus 63.0, 65.0 and 64.4–66.9 (BMNH, ZRCNUS).

Weight. No data.

DISTRIBUTION. North to latitude 10°15'N. In the far south, sightings over the last ten years suggest a few may now be resident in Singapore. Historical summary: all divisions except *Chu, Pha, Phu, Pht, Son, Pat, Yal, Nar, Tru, Pra,* with other island records from Langkawi and (a specimen) Senang, Singapore.

GEOGRAPHICAL VARIATION. Nominate *alcinus* of SE Asia, eastern limits as yet unmapped.

STATUS AND POPULATION. Resident; local and uncommon but probably overlooked due to its mainly crepuscular habits. Sightings in various parts of Singapore suggests a few birds live in the main island's wooded central catchment area.

HABITATS AND ECOLOGY. Hunts in open spaces, and there are nest-records from parkland (the Kuala Lumpur Lake Gardens was in regular use until the 1950s), also from tall, relic timber standing clear of the edge of forest, particularly along rivers. The principal habitat-link is with forest itself, mature and disturbed (provided some tall cover remains), at plains level and on slopes, occasionally up to 1200 m (BMP5). Day-roosts usually high in the interior of a tree-crown.

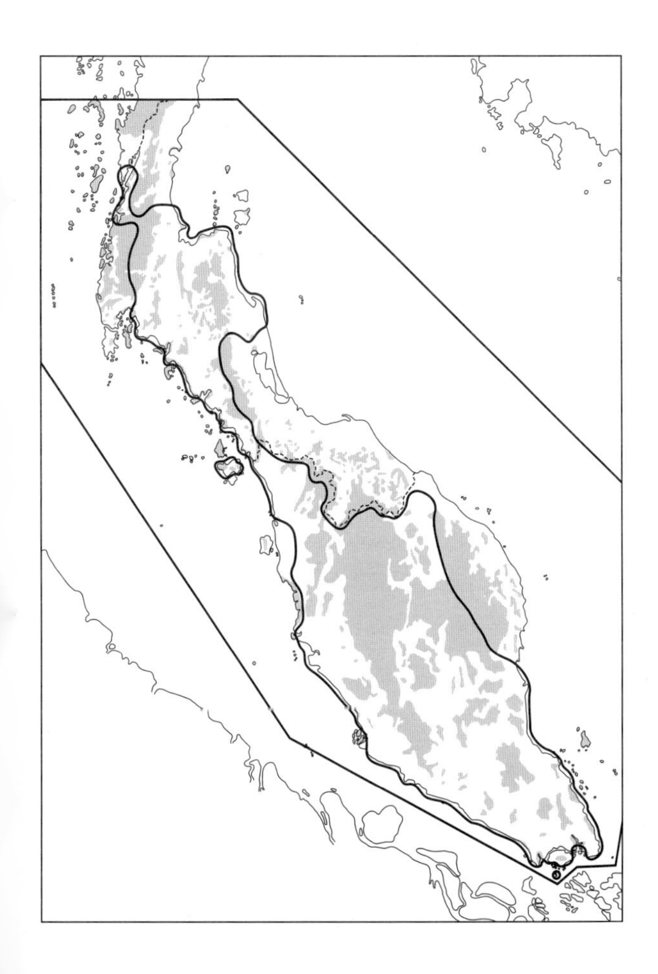

FORAGING AND FOOD. Hunts falcon-like by flying prey down in the open, from late evening (occasionally late afternoon in dull weather) until after dusk, and can operate at high speed in very dim light; also at dawn (Madoc 1950–51) but apparently not at night. This accords with roost-movements of the main prey: small bats, taken as they emerge from cave- and other colony-sites, and from flight-lines in clearings and along open stream-courses up to high above the forest canopy. Away from forest, seen working around suburban street-lighting and, in Taiping town (Perak), a bird captured bats emerging from under the eaves of a public building (BR 1980–81, MBR 1984–85, SINGAV-2). Prey are snatched in a foot and swallowed whole in flight (C.M. Francis, Sutari Supari). Four and eight animals (including *Rhinolophus* spp.) recovered from two stomachs (Gibson-Hill 1952, Riley 1938) imply hunting is intensive while it lasts.

A Sarawak observation of a high-quartering bird making dashes at swiftlets suggests occasional bird prey, but no attacks were successful and escaping targets (which free-fell with wings closed) were not pursued. In the Kerau wildlife reserve, Pahang, Bat Hawks chased nightjars (Lambert 1987a), and G.C. Madoc records a fledgling being fed a chicken poult.

SOCIAL ORGANIZATION. Hunts alone, although more than one may forage around particularly large bat colonies. The FMSM collector E. Seimund is said to have found two attended nests in adjacent, touching tree-crowns (Chasen 1939), but contents were not checked and such close proximity of breeding pairs seems unlikely.

MOVEMENTS. None recorded.

SURVIVAL. No information.

SOCIAL INTERACTIONS. Shows at least some activity during daytime, e.g., three birds (a family party?) chasing and diving at each other over Main Range forest in Perak at mid-morning on 19 April; and two in close and noisy pursuit, and attempting a talon-grapple, round the crowns of large forest trees by the Jelai river, Pahang, in early afternoon on 8 September (F. Parish).

VOICE. The frequent call of interacting pair-members, including after dark, is described as a high, petulant yelp, *kwik kwik kwik . . .*, repeated many times (Madoc 1950–51). A bird carrying a small bat gave a thin, high-pitched, two-note *enowk enoowk* (Sutari Supari). The call described in BMP5 has been reidentified as that of resident Peregrine Falcon, another twilight hunter.

BREEDING

Nest. Large, stick-built, in the high interior crown of a tall tree, but not described in detail. Seimund's nests were in large *Dipterocarpus crinitus* on a riverbank.

Eggs and brood. Not described from the Peninsula.

Cycle. Both parents feed young in the nest.

Seasonality. No clear pattern. Nest-building in December (Perak), display and copulation on 31 May (Johor), active nests during July–September (Surat Thani and Selangor), and a single young fledged from a nest at Kuala Lumpur on 25 October (Chasen 1939, G.C. Madoc, Madoc 1950–51, OBCB-23, Robinson 1914a, SINGAV-6).

MOULT. Replacement of primaries is regular-descendent. Adults dated April and July were moulting P7/8 and P2 respectively, and a third had suspended at P5 in mid August. Two others dated late January and May showed no moult, revealing no hint of seasonality (fresh plumage in January) (BMNH, ZRCNUS).

CONSERVATION. No special issues, other than that the bulk of the population appears tied to tall, plains-level forest, or its vicinity.

Black-winged Kite; Yieo Khao (Thai); Lang Tikus (Malay)

Elanus caeruleus (Desfontaines) 1789, *Histoire de l'Académie Royale des Sciences de Paris* 1787: 503. TL vicinity of Algiers.

Plate 18

GROUP RELATIONS. Lumped with American *leucurus* and Australian *notatus* (White-tailed and Black-shouldered Kites) by Parkes (1958) and Mees (1982), although Clark and Banks (1992) cite morphological and behavioural reasons for not adopting this arrangement.

GLOBAL RANGE. At its most inclusive, W USA to S America, Africa and S Iberia; the Indian subcontinent, Sri Lanka and Laccadives; China south of a line Zhejiang–Yunnan; SE Asia to the Greater Sunda islands, Bali and the Philippines; Sulawesi and southern outliers, the Lesser Sunda islands, eastern New Guinea and Australia.

IDENTIFICATION/DESCRIPTION. From male harriers in some of the same habitats by smaller size, all-pale head and upper surface of primaries, shorter tail, hunting behaviour and flight-modes. High over, from soaring adult Chinese Sparrowhawk by broad head, wing and tail proportions, and less obviously dark underside of primaries. Soars rather fast, and its habit of sailing along with wings held at a large dihedral angle (an obvious V) then flap-flying on flexed wings, with deep, elastic strokes that bounce the body, is distinctive even at long range. Often hovers when hunting, tail-down and with sweep of the wings nearer horizontal than vertical.

Immatures are separable by eye-colour, light brown mottling from hind-crown to mantle and white-fringed wing-coverts. Rarely, adults lack black in the wing: an apparently paired male noticed several times in 1989/90 at the Marina South wetland, Singapore (SINGAV-3), and in 1994 a bird at Sekinchan, Selangor.

Bare-part colours. Iris dull yellow (immature), blood-red (adult); bill black, cere pale yellow; feet peach-yellow.

Size (mm). (Live and skins: 3 males, 6 females; adult): wing 282–287 and 275–292; tail 125–130 and 125–131; bill from cere 17.0–17.7 and 17.4–18.2; tarsus 33.8–36.4 and 33.8–34.7 (BMNH, Kalai 1984, Mees 1982, ZRCNUS).

Weight (g). Selangor adults, 242–276 (n=6) (Kalai 1984).

DISTRIBUTION. As purely non-forest birds, Black-winged Kites are still expanding their range in the Peninsula. The E-coast plain from Pattani to Kelantan is a gap to be filled, even though much suitable-looking paddyland habitat in this area long predates the age of damaging pesticides. In the last 40 years small numbers have settled both Penang island and Singapore. Historical summary: all divisions except *Pak, Ran, Pat, Yal, Nar,* with other island records from Libong and Penang off the W coast; and Tekong and Sudong, Singapore.

GEOGRAPHICAL VARIATION. Mees (1982) found measurements from Perak and Melaka approached Indonesian *hypoleucus* Gould 1859 (TL Ujung Pandan district, Sulawesi), and proposed that the Peninsular population is either this subspecies or a *hypoleucus*/northern nominate *caeruleus* intergrade. Additional wing-lengths from Selangor are in the range of Sumatran *hypoleucus* and an observation at Cape Rachado opens the possibility of occasional direct exchange.

STATUS AND POPULATION. With most of the Peninsula occupied, a regular and uncommon to common resident. Established pairs are sedentary (an adult retrapped on site 44 months after ringing) but a part of the population moves, relatively quickly finding land newly opened for agriculture. Prior to mass use of herbicides, 2000 ha of paddyland in NW Selangor studied by A.R. Kalai (1984) held 12 breeding pairs, far from evenly dispersed, plus three non-breeders. Locally, this is the densest occupation so far

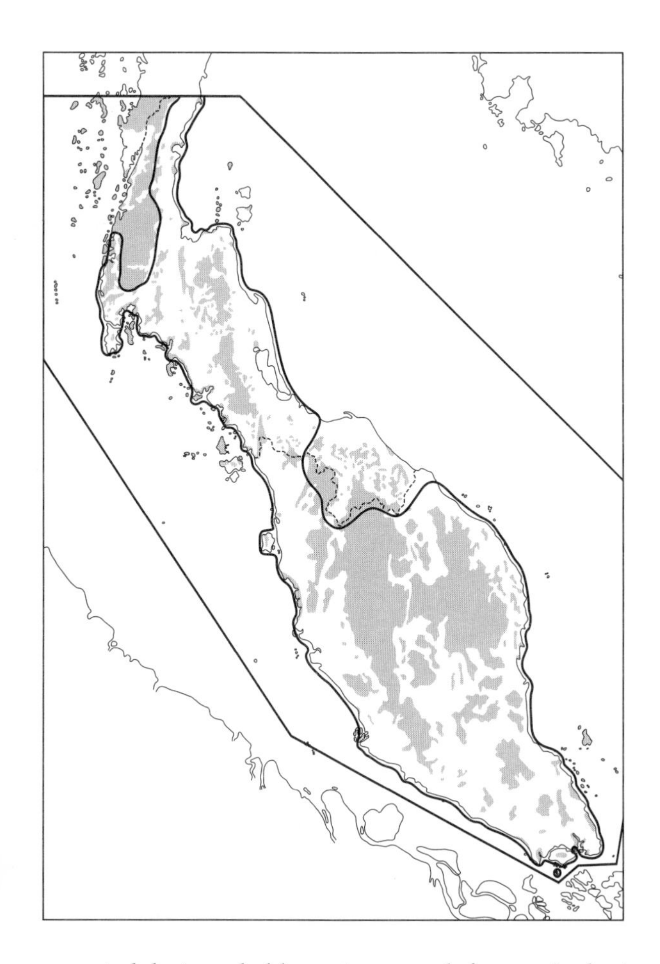

reported but probably not unusual for equivalent habitat at that time.

HABITATS AND ECOLOGY. Black-winged Kites occur in all kinds of open habitats, including the degraded landward edge of mangroves and dune scrub, and agriculture. They have benefited most from the spread of oil-palm and multi-crop paddy. Paddyland populations are probably still the densest, but in NW Selangor a sharp drop followed clearance of inter-planted palms and fruit trees (supplying most roost- and nest-sites) and the introduction of chemical weed-control. Herbicides are believed to have removed the fallow-season cover and food of kite prey – evident from the way in which remaining birds narrow their hunting-effort on to progressively shrinking patches of unsprayed fallow as the season develops (see also Greater Painted-snipe *Rostratula benghalensis*).

FORAGING AND FOOD. In paddyland, two time-budgeted adults spent 80 percent of daylight hours perched. This included time spent still-hunting from service-wires, pole-tops, projecting palm-fronds, etc. Up to one third of the day was spent hunting, from a perch or by aerial-quartering, starting before sunrise and with last kills at dusk.

Birds aerial-quarter 15–20 m above ground, hover to locate prey and, usually, parachute to one or more checks before a final drop with wings stretched vertically over the back. Still-hunters strike up to 140 m out from the perch, and still-hunting dominates through the day, versus quartering in the evening. Incidence is also affected by the weather (more perching during rain), and by stage of the breeding-cycle (males quarter more when feeding young). Aerial-quartering uses more energy but provides more chances and successes per unit time than still-hunting, which implies birds optimize their hunting behaviour (Kalai 1984). Over eight days of observations on Sekinchan paddy-fields (Selangor), quartering yielded 4–5 times as many kills as still-hunting.

Of 73 kills recorded at Sekinchan, 53 were rats, 19 water birds (rails or young bitterns) and one a lizard. The only invertebrates detected were insect fragments from one of six oral pellets analysed. All six contained rat bones, from animals estimated to have weighed up to 48 g. Numbers of mammals versus other items varied with the height of the rice crop: 100 percent rodents from bare ground to 50 cm stem-height; at full height, only 20 percent rodents versus 80 percent birds (and the lizard) (Kalai 1984). The only prey item recorded elsewhere is a bird, White-vented Myna *Acridotheres cinereus* (BIRDLINE 1993).

SOCIAL ORGANIZATION. At Sekinchan, the 12 paddyland pairs organized activity-spaces around nest- and roost-trees, in some instances defending all space against conspecifics (and one or two other species, notably Black Kites), in others only a part. The largest territories, of 40-plus ha, with non-contiguous boundaries, belonged to pairs in the first category. Other spaces were 15 ha or less. In two cases, these were hunting spaces only and the occupiers shared a nest-tree elsewhere (a dense-crowned mango with nests out of view of each other). Yet others had separated hunting and nest areas but roosted communally instead of in their nest-trees. Known unpaired birds used the same communal roost, and this may be regular non-breeding behaviour (Kalai 1984).

Not all space was hunted evenly. Regardless of crop-stage, the most consistently used areas tended to be those with the most perches (precisely what recent farming practice in the area has been removing). Hunting territories were defended at all times of day but with most encounters at mid-morning and in the evening, the latter also the time of most aerial-quartering (Kalai 1984).

MOVEMENTS. Apart from a pair of birds passing high over Cape Rachado during the raptor spring-passage season, none recorded.

SURVIVAL. No additional information.

SOCIAL INTERACTIONS. Some birds crossing through a foreign nest-territory have been described as dangling legs and flying with short, rapid strokes of sharply up-angled wings. One seen to stop this apparent submissive behaviour resumed immediately it was attacked by the owner. Adults tail-bob in a variety of stress situations, including when approached while still-hunting and prior to chasing an intruder out of a nest-territory (Kalai 1984).

Birds attacked in flight sometimes roll over and strike upward with their feet. Twice at Sekinchan two birds of a trio talon-grappled, spinning nearly down to the ground before separating (BR 1976–77, Kalai 1984) but, usually, encounters do not amount to physical contact.

Courtship includes mock dive-attacks by the male on his perched mate. Copulation, by the male landing directly on his mate's back, occurs mostly in tree and palm crowns, sometimes also on an exposed pole top. One breeding pair observed over eight days copulated 4–12 (mean 8) times daily, in bouts lasting 2–5 seconds (Kalai 1984). Presumed mates also share food, including away from the nest: in one instance a large rat carcass, passed on after having been one-third eaten (MBR 1982–83).

VOICE. Pair-members and flying young communicate with a thin, mewing whistle, *pieu*; also heard from a breeding male prior to chasing an intruder off a nest-territory. The more usual warning is a harsh, repeated scream, *ku-eekk* (Kalai 1984, G.C. Madoc).

BREEDING

Nest. Invariably in a tree or tall palm (coconut preferred), isolated or part of a small clump, with the nest near the top of a leafy crown or lodged well into a frond axil (one high in a bare tree), 6–46 m (usually not above 20) above ground. One measured 30 cm across × maximum 20 cm deep, built of sticks with a fine twig lining to the shallow cup. Twigs of a second were in the diameter range 0.7–6.3 mm (mean 2.2) and up to 24 cm long, the cup lined with paddy-straw and other grasses.

Eggs and brood. Egg glossless creamy white, heavily splashed all over with shades of brown to chocolate. Shape short elliptical. Size (mm): 38.4 × 31.8 (n=1). Full clutch three, in large, exclusive territories commonly with all young reared; but only one or two in small territories or marginal habitat. No data from north of Malaysia.

Cycle. Incubation and fledging periods not separately recorded but in one instance start of incubation to first flight of young took 71 days, with the whole brood on the wing by day 74. All incubation appears to have been by one bird (the presumed female). She was provisioned by the male, in the nest-tree but not at the nest, for five weeks and did not herself start hunting until day 35. Young were fed in the nest-tree until day 98 but left parental territory about one week later, roosting near its edge until day 113. This, and a second pair defending a large hunting space in paddyland, started incubating second clutches (one in a new nest in an adjacent palm) ten and 44 days after the first brood had departed (Kalai 1984). Black-winged Kite is the only diurnal raptor in the Peninsula shown to be multi-brooded.

Seasonality. Nest-building reported in March–May, November and December; active nests year-round; eggs in all months August–March; and nestlings in all months except August. Activity comes to no obvious seasonal peak, and in paddyland shows no clear link to stages in the agricultural cycle (F.G.H. Allen, BR 1974–75, Edgar 1933, Kalai 1984, MBR 1986–87, NRCS, SINGAV-3). The performance of individual pairs needs further study.

MOULT. Replacement of inner primaries is regular-descendant, with some evidence of precocious wing-tip moult (P9 or 10 simultaneous with P6). Adults showing bilateral wing-moult have been handled in early April–June and August–mid October, and the pattern is progressive (BMNH, BMP5, ZRCNUS).

CONSERVATION. The Black-winged Kite hunting day begins often within 30 minutes of Barns Owls being active on the same patch. Both take many pest rats yet steps to intensify rice agriculture have already seriously reduced the densest part of the kite breeding population in Malaysia. Birds achieve nothing like paddyland density in marginal and oil-palm habitats, but in plantations may benefit from the spread of biological rather than chemical means of controlling rodents.

Black Kite; Yieo Dam (Thai); Lang Bangkai (Malay)

Milvus migrans Boddaert 1783, *Table des Planches Enluminéez d'Histoire Naturelle*: 28. TL France.
Plate 19

GROUP RELATIONS. As one polytypic species, free-standing.

GLOBAL RANGE. Breeds through Africa, Madagascar and SW Arabia; temperate to low-arctic Eurasia from the Atlantic to Pacific Russia; the Indian subcontinent, Sri Lanka and the Andamans; Japan, Korea and China including Taiwan and Hainan; SE Asia to southern Burma, central Thailand and S Vietnam; then Sulawesi, E New Guinea and (mainly northern) Australia. Most northern populations migrate, wintering through and beyond the tropical breeding-range, in SE Asia to the Peninsula and Sumatra; vagrant in Palawan and Borneo. Intra-tropical movements also occur, but are nowhere well understood in Asia. Occasional Black Kites in the Moluccas and Lesser Sunda islands may be Australian (CLBW).

IDENTIFICATION/DESCRIPTION. From immature Brahminy Kite by larger size and more rakish appearance, with longer tail slightly to obviously forked (versus rounded) when closed, more or less straight-cut when fanned, and proportionately longer, more parallel-sided wings. Like Brahminy, soars with inner wing canted forward (from below, soaring dark-phase Booted Eagle has similar stance but its typically pale tail is never forked). Glides on arched wings, flexed at the wrist but with arm less strongly inclined forward than in Brahminy Kite.

Palaearctic migrants have a large, whitish patch over the lower base of the primaries (especially prominent in immatures) but in tropical breeders this is much restricted, sometimes not exposed at all. Seen perched, often on the ground, adult tropical migrants appear more uniformly brown, with chin and throat and belly to lower tail-coverts paler but distinctly brown whereas in Palaearctic birds these parts are dirty cream. Some tropical breeders show a small black patch behind the eye but not the all-black ear-coverts of Palaearctic birds. Immatures of both have chocolate-brown head, neck to upper mantle and breast to flanks striped white, broad and bright in Palaearctics, narrower in tropical birds. At all ages, the latter have a deeper tail-fork (mean 52 against 37 mm) (BMNH) but, in close view, the unmistakable difference is in bare-part colours (see below).

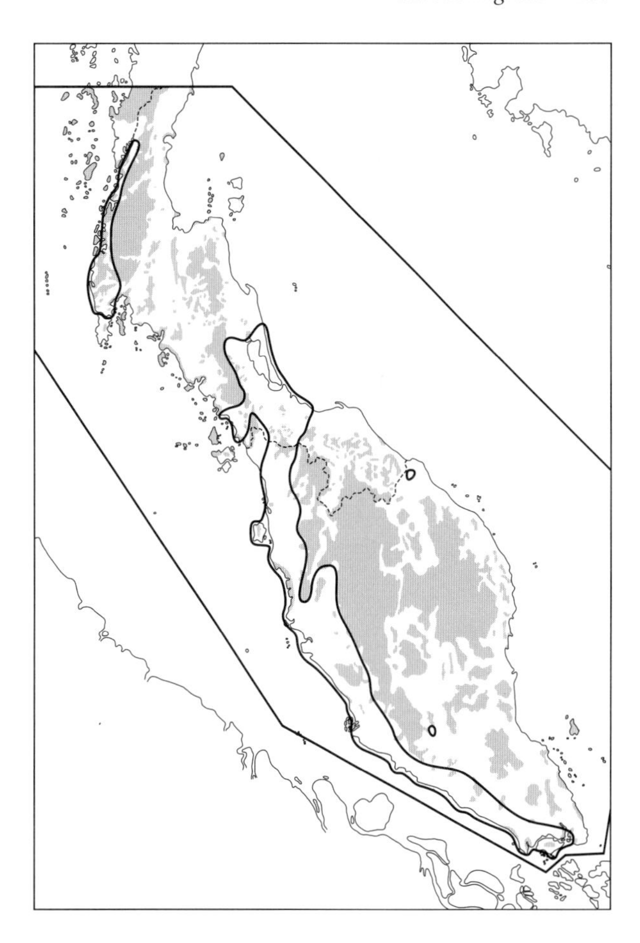

Bare-part colours. Iris yellow-brown; bill black; cere and feet bluish white (Palaearctic migrants), yellow (tropical migrants) (D.S. Melville).

Size (mm). (Skins: 3 females; immature): wing 447, 465, 495; tail 263 (one only, tail-fork 50); bill from cere 28.1 (one only); tarsus 56.5 (one only) (BMNH, BR 1970–71, ZRCNUS). Extremes from the E-Asian breeding-range (BMNH) are:

	(n)	Wing	Tail	Fork	Bill	Tarsus
Palaearctic ff	(12)	493–511	280–323	28–47	27.1–30.3	60–62
Palaearctic mm	(16)	458–486	259–295	30–50	25.7–30.9	59–65
Tropical ff	(12)	440–458	270–292	42–62	22.7–28.9	53–57
Tropical mm	(10)	412–436	258–289	44–70	24.4–27.1	51–57

Weight. No data.

DISTRIBUTION. Apart from two December records in NE Kelantan and a small party on passage over E Negeri Sembilan, none found east of the Main Range. Historical summary: *Ran, Pha, Pht, Son, Sat, Ked, Kel, Pra, Pek, Sel, Neg, Mel, Joh, Sin,* with additional island records from Penang off the W coast; and Tekong, Ubin, Kusu, St John's and Sentosa, Singapore.

GEOGRAPHICAL VARIATION. Yellow-skinned vagrants are tropical–subtropical S and SE Asian *govinda* Sykes 1832 (TL Deccan, India); whitish skinned regular migrants are *lineatus* J.E. Gray 1831 (TL China) of central/E Eurasia, north and east of *govinda*.

STATUS AND POPULATION. A local and uncommon to common non-breeding visitor, and sparse passage migrant onward to Indonesia (BR 1970–71, MBR 1986–87). Familiar in the Thalae Noi–Songkhla wetland more than half a century ago but at that time rare to vagrant further south (Gibson-Hill 1949b). Now an unremarkable sight in suitable habitat all the way to Singapore, but never in large numbers. The biggest spot-count has been 15, loafing at mid-day in a tall tree by the Sekinchan paddy-plain, NW Selangor, on 10 March 1989. Immatures consistently outnumber adults.

This change in status is due exclusively to expansion of Palaearctic migration within the last 25 years. If anything, tropical dispersants have declined, probably as breeding populations to the immediate north have collapsed (Round 1989). Recent reports of possible *govinda* include a small, unusually wary, yellowish footed bird lacking obvious white on the undersurface of the wing at Sekinchan on 8 March 1987; another attempting to enter but consistently ejected from the above-mentioned March roost; and a party of four in Singapore on 19 May 1990 (SINGAV-4), suspiciously late for Palaearctic migration.

HABITATS AND ECOLOGY. The Thalae Noi–Songkhla wetland is traditional wintering habitat. Extensive paddylands, especially through stubble and ploughing stages, feature prominently in Malaysia (although herbicides have had a negative impact).

Otherwise attracted to various open, part-swampy sites mainly near coasts, including rough grassland, patchy scrub and degraded back-mangroves. Sometimes with Brahminy Kites around harbours, but Palaearctic migrants are rural rather than urban scavengers. Most sightings far inland have been of passage birds only (BR 1978–79).

FORAGING AND FOOD. Black Kites aerial-quarter, typically 20–30 m up. They are strongly attracted to stubble and straw fires, perhaps for flushed live prey, but no active hunting has been reported and a major attraction of paddylands is carrion, including fish killed by pesticide run-off into irrigation channels and rats lying in the open after poison-baiting. They are also kleptoparasites, of one another and other raptors.

SOCIAL ORGANIZATION. Roost, and over the hottest mid-day hours, loaf socially. Commonly, 2–3 search in company, mutually attracted to good foraging patches.

MOVEMENTS. As in parts of Africa, Black Kites of Burma and Thailand breed in the dry season and move with the onset of summer rains (Madoc 1950, Smythies 1953). In early June, passage up the Sittaung valley is northward, but reports of the odd bird south to Singapore in May and July (BMP5, BR 1966, SINGAV-4) imply a few may also disperse in other directions. However, the only tropical kites actually collected in the Peninsula are dated November and January (BMNH, ZRCNUS), and both recent Sekinchan sightings were in early March. Such birds may have overshot their breeding-range while returning south, perhaps in the company of Palaearctic post-breeders.

Extreme dates of birds showing the bare-part colours of *lineatus* are 23 September (most records after mid October) and 15 April. The only actual migration witnessed has been of odd individuals making landfall over Cape Rachado (Negeri Sembilan) in early March, but a small party (with a Marsh Harrier) moving south over E Negeri Sembilan on 17 February also suggests mobility within the wintering period (BR 1970–71, 1978–79, MBR 1986–87).

SURVIVAL. No information.

SOCIAL INTERACTIONS. No additional information.

VOICE. Nothing recorded; migrants are generally silent.

BREEDING. No population.

MOULT. Migrant *govinda* dated November and January were in fairly fresh plumage, with no wing-moult. No *lineatus* checked.

CONSERVATION. The risk of secondary poisoning from zinc phosphide and anti-coagulants used against pest rats in the field is not known, but fall-off in usage of Malaysian paddylands coincided more closely with a move to large-scale, post-harvest application of herbicides.

Brahminy Kite; Yieo Daeng (Thai); Lang Merah (Malay)

Milvus indus (Boddaert) 1783, *Table des Planches Enluminéez d'Histoire Naturelle*: 25. TL Pondicherry, SE India.

Plate 19

GROUP RELATIONS. Free-standing. Shows close skeletal and chromosome similarities to other *Milvus* kites (Christidis and Boles 1994); a nostril-shape difference, used classically to separate a genus *Haliastur*, has recently been shown not hold in live birds (Amadon 1978, McAllan and Bruce 1988).

GLOBAL RANGE. Apart from its dry NW, the Indian subcontinent, Sri Lanka and Bay of Bengal islands; China south from the Changjiang valley; SE Asia; and Wallacea to New Guinea, the Solomons and (mainly northern) Australia. Vagrant in W Micronesia.

IDENTIFICATION/DESCRIPTION. The most often-seen medium-sized, resident raptor of non-forest habitats, providing a convenient standard of size-comparison with others. The rich chestnut upperparts, wings and tail, and white head of adults is a distinctive combination, detectable at long range as soaring birds turn in the sun. The more subtly coloured full juvenile resembles (larger) adult Black Kite, but in overhead flight a broad wedge of buff-white across the underside of the inner hand contrasts sharply with black wing-tip and solidly blackish secondaries (the latter obviously darker rather than the same as or lighter than lower wing-coverts). A pale band along the upper wing-coverts is reminiscent of (larger) Booted Eagle but the latter shows white upper tail-coverts and light rather than dark tail. Transitional moult produces bizarre intermediate patterns, especially on the wings. At all ages, tail rather round-ended (squarish in Booted Eagle, straight to forked in Black Kite), and appears longer relative to wing trailing-edge in juveniles than adults.

Glides on flexed but flat wings. Soars with inner wing canted both forward and up, and hand arched down and flexed out to slightly back, i.e., in the 'bent-sickle' posture of Black Kite but with arm angled still more forward. Bent-sickle glide-position of Oriental Honey-buzzard is flatter, and long, slender neck and patterned tail are unkite-like. Planes shallowly out of characteristic, closed-wing dives, which are not made in a hunting or aggressive context.

Bare-part colours. Iris dark hazel-brown; bill pale bluish horn, cere lead-blue (juvenile), pale clay-yellow (adult); feet pale clay-yellow.

Size (mm). (Skins: 11 adults, 13 immatures; none sexed): wing 383–412 and 377–409; tail 193–207 and 192–211; bill from cere 25.0–27.4 (adults only); tarsus 48.4–55.0 (adults only) (BMNH, ZRCNUS).

Weight. No data.

DISTRIBUTION. Uncommon more than a few kilometres inland of the coast and large estuaries. Historical summary: all divisions, and on most sizeable, wooded islands, including: Lanbyi, Hastings, the Surin and Similan groups, the Phangnga Bay archipelago, Phiphi, Libong, Tarutao, the Langkawi group, Penang, Pangkor, Jarak, the Kelang estuary islands, Pisang and Kukup off the W coast; Ang Thong, Phangan and Samui, the Redang group and the Pahang–Johor archipelago (Tioman, Aur, Sibu) off the E coast; and Tekong, Sajahat, Ubin, Ketam, Serangoon (a local gathering point), Seletar and most of the S archipelago, Singapore.

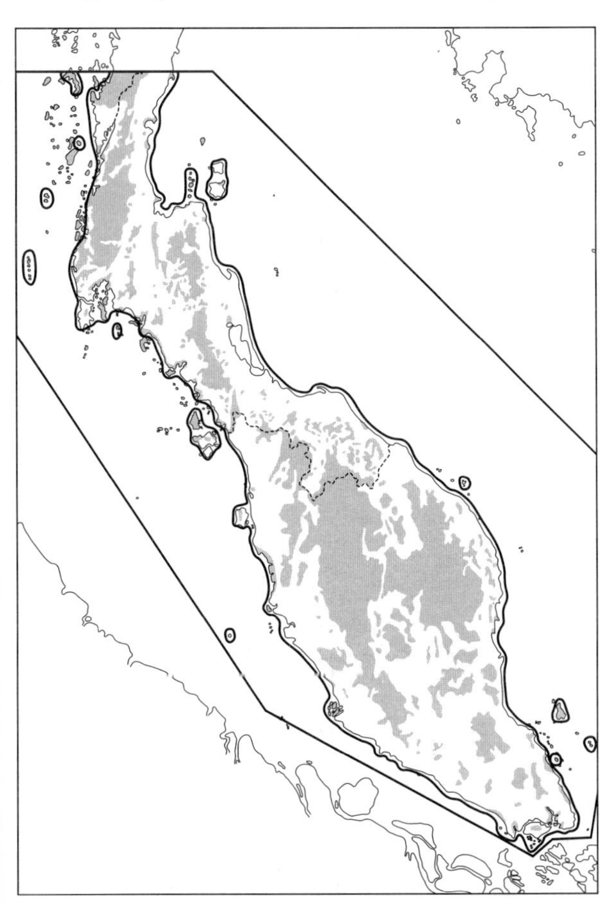

GEOGRAPHICAL VARIATION. Deignan (1963) recognized heavily marked continental *indus* along the NE coast south to Pattani, finer marked *intermedius* Blyth 1865 (TL Java) elsewhere. From individual variation in the strength of dark shaft-streaking on white parts of adults it seems better to treat the whole of the Peninsula as a zone of intergradation between these two.

STATUS AND POPULATION. Resident, declining due to loss of habitat overall, but still regular and common on mangrove coasts. The modern centre of distribution is the Melaka and Johor Straits and associated estuaries, south from Penang, with 3-figure roost-gatherings to be found, e.g., at Kapar (Selangor) and Serangoon island (Singapore) (ENGGANG-2, SINGAV-2). Much scarcer along most of the E coast, and population density is depressed everywhere in Thailand, where kites are more affected by hunting. Inland, regular in the Thalae Noi–Songkhla wetland; local or a wanderer elsewhere. A few pairs still haunt greater Kuala Lumpur, but with no recent reports of breeding success.

HABITATS AND ECOLOGY. Large estuaries and low-relief coasts with broad, muddy, mangrove-backed intertidal flats are prime Brahminy Kite habitat in the Peninsula. Within that zone, busy harbours, fish-processing sites, and waterside settlements attract, but dependence on wetlands has ensured they have not become urban scavengers. The larger expanses of subcoastal paddyland are also common foraging habitat, at all crop stages but especially between harvest and early flooding. Further inland, selects various open sites, from natural marshland to more widely available ex-dredge-mine land, and loafs in neighbouring trees (with a particular liking for tall casuarina and tembusu *Fagraea fragrans*). Where inland nesting occurs, these tree species are favoured, even in gardens; and on dry-land coasts they regularly substitute for mangroves.

FORAGING AND FOOD. Forages by quartering 20–50 m up over water, low-tide mudflats, emptying fish-ponds, wet ploughland, etc., and attracted to straw fires, taking easily-caught prey such as young birds (a Common Moorhen chick), amphibians, and carrion including floating or stranded fish and snakes, snatched in a skimming pass. One or more commonly patrol open-ground shorebird roosts on the look-out for weak birds, and have been seen to flush resting flocks, perhaps as a means of checking. Competes with other scavenging raptors for rat carcasses after poison-baiting of harvested paddyland, and is a kleptoparasite of conspecifics and other raptors, up to the size of White-bellied Fish Eagle (SINGAV-2). Food is often eaten directly, while soaring, which may reduce losses to other birds. Brahminy Kites also take swarming termites on the wing, snatched in the feet (BMP5, Edgar 1947, SINGAV-1).

SOCIAL ORGANIZATION. They do not share trees but two or more pairs may nest less than 100 m apart and in full view of one another, without hostilities. Roost-gatherings only exceptionally reach three figures but at Serangoon island, Singapore, up to 260 counted in late July (SINGAV-2).

MOVEMENTS. None recorded.

SURVIVAL. No information.

SOCIAL INTERACTIONS. See Breeding.

VOICE. A high, drawn-out mewing scream, *kyeeeer*, given mainly while soaring, and not in any well-understood context.

BREEDING

Nest. In mangrove forest, typically selects a living emergent, but within the regular tide-zone totally dead, virtually branchless relics (possibly traditional nest-trees) may continue in use as long as nest-supports remain. Where an isolated tree is used, height above ground varies with surroundings: in secure, swampy sites sometimes as low as 5–6 m, but on dry land rarely below 20–25 m. Within the tree, site varies from an interior fork in the leafiest part of the crown to a dead prong. First record of a non-tree site: in November 1993, a pair at Kapar (Selangor) built a nest on the flat summit of an electricity pylon. New nests are relatively slight but thicken as they are refurbished from season to season. Stick-built, they are 60–90 cm across, typically 15–30 cm deep, the cup often lined with a pan of dried mud, 10–15 cm across.

Eggs and brood. Eggs are chalky, glossless, dirty white, some with sparse, red-brown squiggles and dots. Shape elliptical. Size (mm): 52.0 × 40.6, 53.0 × 41.1 (n=2). Clutch two, and both chicks are raised, but incubation and fledging periods unrecorded.

Cycle. H.T. Pagden (BR 1963) described an early breeding-season 'building' activity on Penang island, in which a pair collected twigs and small branches (breaking some off a *Sterculia foetida* by diving on them), carried them in the bill to regular perches then dropped them into the sea, over a period of more than a month. Copulates (silently) by or on the nest.

Seasonality. Building, attendance at nests and copulation recorded during late October–March, mostly in November–December; eggs or incubation in December–March and mid June; chicks in all months January–mid August, but with most activity in the first half of the season (F.G.H. Allen, Edgar 1933, Madoc 1956a, NRCS, SINGAV-2, -4).

MOULT. Replacement of inner primaries regular-descendant, with evidence of mid-wing suspension or precocious moult of the wing-tip (P5–10 often newer than 1–4). Adults in wing-moult recorded in mid February (P1–2), May (P4–5), July (P8, 8–9) and mid September (P9–10). Eight others dated September–March had completed, suggesting seasonality (BMNH, G.W.H. Davison, ZRCNUS).

CONSERVATION. Brahminy Kites survive away from mangrove forests but their abundance is linked to the status of mangroves, and further area-losses are inevitable. In parts of Phangnga bay, water-villagers take young for pets and must be a factor behind the sparseness of the wild population in what is otherwise ideal habitat.

White-bellied Fish Eagle; Nok Awk (Thai); Lang Siput (Malay)

Haliaeetus leucogaster (Gmelin) 1788, *Systema Naturae* 13(1): 257. TL vicinity of Panaitan island, Sunda Straits.

Plate 20

GROUP RELATIONS. Placed in a superspecies with Solomon Islands endemic *H. sanfordi* (Sanford's Fish Eagle) (Stresemann and Amadon 1979) although the forest-canopy birds and mammals reported in the latter's diet (Mayr 1945) imply habits differ.

GLOBAL RANGE. SW and E coasts of the Indian subcontinent, Sri Lanka and Bay of Bengal islands; coastal S China from Fujian, including Hainan; and SE Asia and Wallacea to coasts of New Guinea and Australia, as far as Tasmania.

IDENTIFICATION/DESCRIPTION. Medium-large eagle with strongly wedge-shaped tail and proportionately broad inner wing, but hand narrowed by relatively short inner primaries. The distinctive soaring posture, with wings at a high (V-shaped) dihedral angle and prominently projecting neck and head appearing longer than tail, is identifiable at long range. The brown-bodied young juvenile resembles young Grey-headed Fish Eagle, but soaring posture and wing- and tail-shape are diagnostic. At all ages, dark flight-feathers contrast with paler lower wing-coverts. Head, body and wing-coverts lighten at successive moults, and the whitish wedge across the undersurface of the inner hand recedes. Moult into definitive adult plumage (grey-and-white body) inverts the tail-pattern to basal half black, the rest white.

Bare-part colours. (Adult) iris dark brown; bill slate-grey, darkest at tip, facial skin and cere paler greenish or bluish grey; feet dirty grey-white.

Size (mm). (Skins: 10 males, 10 females; adult): wing 525–547 and 552–597; tail 207–224 and 228–257; bill from cere 36.5–40.7 and 38.5–44.7; tarsus 83.2–100.0 and 90.8–102.3 (BMNH, UMZC, ZRCNUS).

Weight. No data.

DISTRIBUTION. All coasts, dispersing along the bigger rivers deep into the interior, where some have recently taken up residence on large, forest-backed reservoirs. Historical summary: all divisions except *Yal*, *Nar*, *Kel*, and on many additional islands, breeding where trees supply adequate sites, up to 65 km out, including: Lanbyi (*Pak*), the Surin and Similan groups, Phiphi, Maa, Libong and Tarutao, the Langkawi group, Penang, the Pangkor and Sembilan groups and Jarak (*Pek*), Tekukor, Angsa and the Kelang estuary islands (*Sel*) and Pisang (*Joh*) off the W coast; the Ang Thong group, Phangan and Samui, the Perhentian and Redang groups and Kapas (*Tru*), and the Pahang–Johor archipelago (Tulai, Tioman, Aur, Tinggi and Sibu) off the E coast; Sahajat, Ubin, Serangoon, Seletar, Lazarus, St John's, Sentosa, Senang, Pawai, Sudong, Salu and Air Merbau E–W through Singapore waters. However, most Singapore pairs breed on the main island, the only known offshore nest being on nearby Sentosa (SINGAV-3).

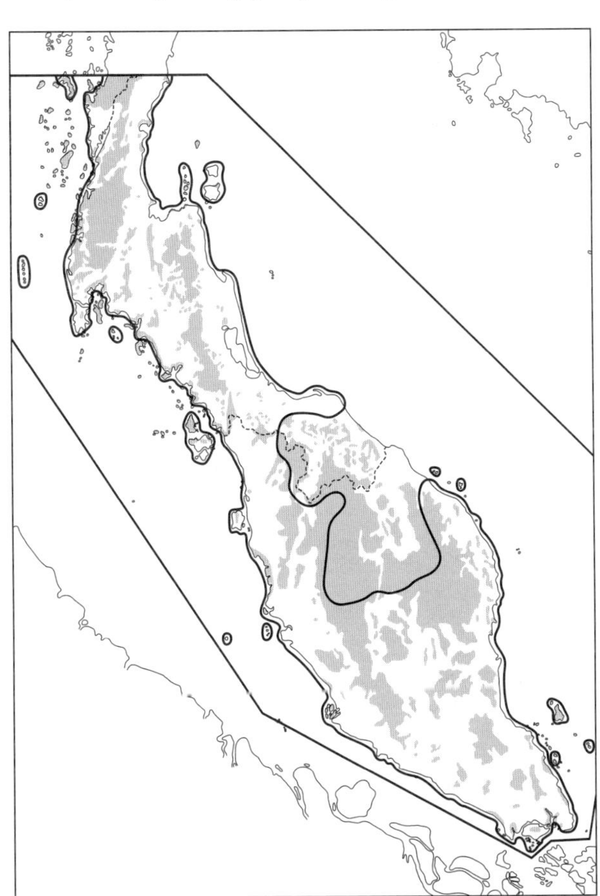

GEOGRAPHICAL VARIATION. None recognized.

STATUS AND POPULATION. Resident, regular and common although under some hunting pressure in Thailand. Immatures and unpaired adults wander but pairs settle in the vicinity of a secure nest-site year-round. Most breeders are on islands. F.L. Dunn's count of 13 birds day-roosting a mean 4.7 km apart round the coast of Tioman island in April 1962 (Medway 1966) did not specifically exclude immatures, but two of his sites were in the home ranges of known pairs and seven pairs occupying a total 60 km of coast would be a conservative guess. On Singapore main island (coastline about 120 km), ten nest-sites were reported used during 1987–1992, with up to five active in a given season. In 1992–93, two pairs bred on 55 km of the Selangor mainland coast between Kapar and Sekinchan, both at artificial sites, whereas three natural sites, active until the late 1980s (MBR 1986–87) and involving at least two other pairs, have been abandoned apparently because of tree-losses. Breeding density on this populated coast is now roughly as in Singapore.

HABITATS AND ECOLOGY. All kinds of shorelines and large estuaries are occupied, including low-relief coasts backed by mangrove and peatswamp forests, which are used for nesting where tall emergent timber remains (Edgar 1933, MBR 1986–87), but the preference is for availability of forested knolls or hills overlooking the shore or nearby lagoon, or a large reservoir. Extensive subcoastal paddyland is visited commonly but no hunting has been seen there, other than occasional kleptoparasitic attacks on other raptors (successful against Osprey and Brahminy Kite: SINGAV-1).

Wanderers are mainly coastal but also travel long distances inland, turning up irregularly over isolated water-bodies and intervening lowlands. In January 1971, several around the Kenarong confluence were over 330 km up the Perak river and about 120 km from the nearest point on the coast (BR 1970–71). By 1992–93, large reservoirs behind power dams on this upper stretch of the river had attracted residents, including on Kenering lake (Gerik district) in September 1992, a pair with a nest (R. Gregory-Smith, Sutari Supari 1992). A recent record of soaring over the ridge of the Larut Range opens up the possibility that birds from this area take short-cuts to the coast.

FORAGING AND FOOD. There are no records of feeding other than from water or, occasionally, low-tide flats, and even kleptoparasitic chases are typically over water. Hunts by low-level quartering, usually within a kilometre of the shore. Prey near the surface are gaffed by a powerful backward slash of both extended feet as the bird passes over (sending spray flying but with no Osprey-like plunge). If not destined for a nest, food is usually transferred to one foot and eaten directly, on the wing (Christmas Island Frigatebirds can take food from Fish Eagles: MBR 1982–83). Madoc (1956a) describes large crabs being dropped 30–40 m onto rocks, but this is unusual behaviour.

The main foods are fish and sea-snakes (Chasen 1939, Sebastian 1987), with many snake bones found around active nests (WFVZ).

SOCIAL ORGANIZATION. Only birds in full adult plumage have been found breeding, in apparently permanent pairs. It is not known how long young remain near the parents, nor how much space around the nest pairs typically defend as territory. No aggressive interactions have been reported and, outside the chick period at least, pairs tolerate both juveniles and older immatures (on 4 November, 11 of various ages soaring together with a pair of adults near a regular nest on Gelang headland, N Pahang coast: BMP5). Wanderers are otherwise typically solitary; rarely two together (BR 1964).

MOVEMENTS. Apart from the dispersal of non-breeders, none. Established pairs become sedentary.

SURVIVAL. No information.

SOCIAL INTERACTIONS. Aerial display by paired adults includes occasional talon-grappling (SINGAV-4). An attempted copulation involved the male landing directly on his mate's back as she perched near the nest, with much calling by him throughout. Possible display by one of a pair of immatures gliding side by side over Ampang reservoir, Kuala Lumpur: a series of corkscrew rolls, executed without losing height relative to its companion (BR 1964).

VOICE. The only call described is a powerful, clanging *hlank, hlank, hlank, hlank . . .*, freely given by both members of established pairs, perched or in the air near active nests. Such loud sounds, audible over 1 km away, could be important for advertising occupation of a breeding-site.

BREEDING

Nest. On steep, rocky islands, in the absence of tall timber, occasional nests are founded on a small tree projecting from a cliff. The major preference at all sites is for a big tree, either an emergent in swamp-forest or in a commanding position on a wooded knoll or headland. The typical position is in a main branch fork close to the trunk of a tall-boled, mature tree with free access through the open base of the canopy. Building-materials are dead branches (in one instance removed from an old nest), with fresh greenery in the cup. Nests, about 1.5 m across, are comparatively thin when new but are refurbished, certainly over decades and possibly by a succession of owners. The oldest can be over 1 m thick and become a considerable landmark. Nor are they abandoned when the tree dies, but continue to be repaired and used, completely exposed, as long as support remains.

Sites are typically 30 m or more up, and height is clearly attractive. Over many years at Mount Faber (Singapore) and Fort Melawati (Kuala Selangor), pairs have attempted to nest on high rest-platforms of communications pylons standing taller than any usable local tree. At Kuala Selangor, the building of a second, still taller pylon next to the occupied one caused the pair to shift to the new higher top (where fledging success has improved). In 1992, a second pair began nesting completely away from trees on the flat-frame summit of a pylon by Kapar power-station, 26 km to the south. It would not be a surprise if at least one pair-member was a pylon-orientated product of Kuala Selangor, in the process of establishing a new site tradition.

Eggs and brood. Eggs are plain white, glossless and chalky-textured. Size (mm): 73.6–66.7 × 54.8–51.1 (n=3). Clutch two and commonly both young fledge. There are no separate data on incubation and fledging periods. At Sime Road (Singapore) in 1988, birds behaving as though incubating or brooding in January were still feeding young in the nest on 3 May.

Cycle. Nest refurbishment continues well into the breeding cycle with, at Kuala Selangor, copulations noted only eight weeks before the fledging of a chick from the nest. Young return to the nest for at least two months after fledging.

Seasonality. Nest-building and refurbishing recorded during early September–late April, with a peak in number of pairs active in November–December. The only confirmed egg-months are December and January but incubation/brooding reported throughout mid October–early June, and young in the nest confirmed through December–early June (F.G.H. Allen, Chasen 1939, ENGGANG-2, G.C. Madoc, Madoc 1956a, Robinson 1927, SINGAV-2, WFVZ).

MOULT. Moult of inner primaries is regular-descendant to P5 or 6, but the wing-tip may moult precociously, out from P7 with P8 or 9 the last to grow. In so large a resident raptor, surprisingly, moult is both discontinuous and broadly seasonal. Eighteen adults showed steady progression from early, inner-hand moult (P2, P3–4) in February to completion in November (P9, P9–10), the earliest all-fresh bird dated 31 October (BMNH, UMZC, ZRCNUS), more or less congruent with the start of the nesting-season. One female broke this pattern, moulting P6 and 10 on 13 February, i.e., was close to finishing three months late.

CONSERVATION. Use of artificial nest-sites could expand breeding possibilities on the mainland, where suitable coastal trees will continue to be lost. White-bellied Fish Eagles are tolerant of human activity close to nests. With the bulk of the breeding population on islands, however, reaction to the spread of beach tourism needs monitoring.

Lesser Fish Eagle; Yieo Plaa Lek Hua Thao (Thai); Lang Kanguk (Malay)

Ichthyophaga humilis (Müller and Schlegel) 1841, *Verhandelingen over de Natuurlijke Geschiedenis der Nederlandsche Overzeesche Bezittingen. Zoologie, Aves*: 47 and plate 6. TL Sumatra.

Plate 20

GROUP RELATIONS. Free-standing.

GLOBAL RANGE. Foothills of the Himalayas and adjacent terai forest east from Kashmir; Hainan; SE Asia west of a line N Vietnam–Malay Peninsula, to Sumatra, Borneo and intervening islands; Sulawesi, Peleng and, possibly, Buru (Moluccas).

IDENTIFICATION/DESCRIPTION. Size of Brahminy Kite. Adult generally grey-brown, purer grey on the head and neck, with sharply demarcated white thighs, belly and lower tail-coverts. This pattern it shares with substantially larger, adult Grey-headed Fish Eagle. Both have all-dark underwing but are separated by tail-pattern, with only a hint of paler mottling towards the lower base in Lesser. Juveniles of both species are edged pale rufous above. Lesser has forehead, supercilium and underparts, including lower wing-surface, creamy, streaked pale brown to lower breast, and tail obscurely dark-barred.

The usual view is of flapping flight away under the canopy of riverside trees and quickly out of sight round a bend or up a side-stream. Soaring overhead, the wings are broad, with bulging inner-wing trailing-edge nipped-in against the body. White thighs and rear under-body are the only contrasting feature.

Sole-scales spiny; claws strong, very curved and oval (unflanged) in cross-section.

Bare-part colours. Iris pale brown (juvenile), yellow (adult); bill black (juvenile), slaty blue with upper mandible darker (adult); cere blue-grey; feet dirty white (juvenile), blue-grey (adult) (Chasen 1939).

Size (mm). (Skins: 10 adults, most not sexed): wing 352–384; tail 175–201; bill from cere 28.2–31.6; tarsus 70.5–74.7 (BMNH, ZDUM, ZRCNUS).

Weight. No data.

DISTRIBUTION. To S Johor. Historical summary: *Ran, Sur, Nak, Sat, Yal, Nar, Kel, Tru, Pek, Phg, Sel, Joh*, with a sighting at Air Hitam reservoir, Penang island. Occurrence on Ubin island, Singapore (SINGAV-3), needs confirmation.

GEOGRAPHICAL VARIATION. Nominate *humilis*, of the global range south and east from southern Burma; averages 20 percent smaller than northern *plumbea*.

STATUS AND POPULATION. Resident, local and uncommon to more or less common. 'Almost every reach . . . inhabited by a pair of these birds' is a past comment on the upper Tembeling and Tahan rivers of what is now the Pahang sector of Taman Negara (Chasen 1939). Still there, but not in such numbers. Elsewhere, occupies a rapidly shrinking habitat-type, and much former range has been lost.

HABITATS AND ECOLOGY. The neighbourhood of clear-flowing rivers and broad streams through tall, plains-level Lowland forest providing overhanging perches is the core habitat of Lesser Fish Eagle. Were forestry legislation affecting riparian cover enforced, a ramifying system of dispersal corridors would still exist, at the same time reducing siltation from logging and other disturbance. The clouding of rivers by silt is guessed to have negatively affected hunting, and even where backed by forest such rivers do not seem to hold Fish Eagles. Despite occasional presence along slope streams (to over 300 m) and ability to cross between catchments, pockets of population are being forced into nature reserves where,

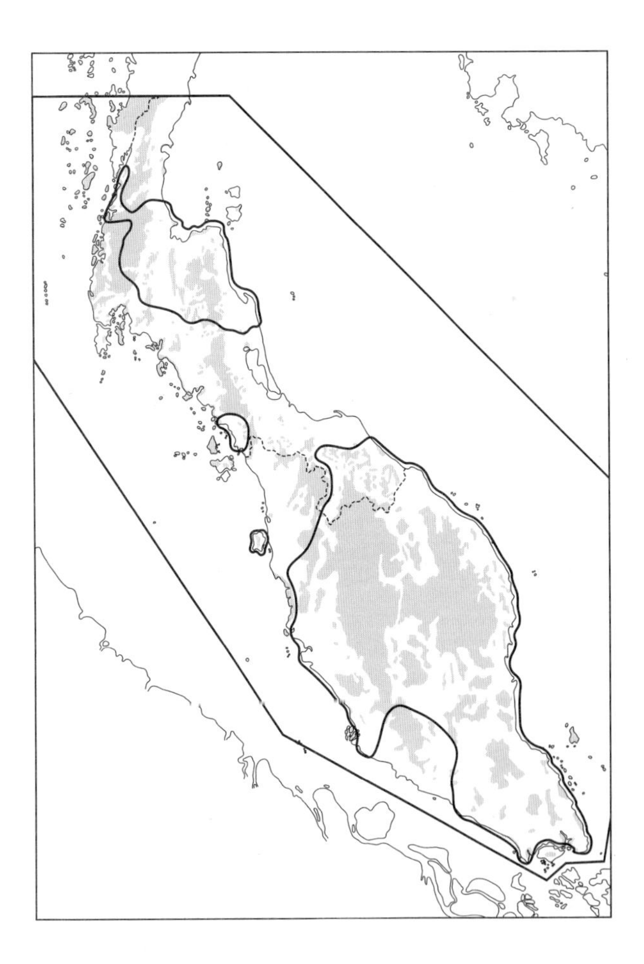

increasingly, the navigable streams carry tourist boat-traffic. One positive prospect is that forested re-entrants of some reservoirs will provide habitat, but this could only happen where tree-cover is retained down to the water's edge or substitute hunting perches are provided. Seen recently at forest-backed Air Hitam, Ampang and Panti reservoirs (Penang, Selangor and Johor).

FORAGING AND FOOD. Forages apparently exclusively by still-hunting from a perch typically several metres up, overhanging water. Sometimes snags or mid-stream rocks are used, but mostly branches under high, over-arching canopy such that birds may benefit from the water below them being in shade (rare at reservoirs in forest, where trees are usually cleared back from achieved shorelines). There is no local information on capture behaviour or prey, but puncture-wounds in the legs and feet of a dead juvenile imply it had attacked a (swimming?) snake (BR 1978–79).

SOCIAL ORGANIZATION. Solitary.

MOVEMENTS. None recorded.

SURVIVAL. No information.

SOCIAL INTERACTIONS. Far-carrying calls given while soaring well above canopy- level are presumed to advertise occupation of a territory.

VOICE. Inadequately described.

BREEDING. Large raptor nests are not uncommon in tall forest trees along rivers inhabited by Lesser Fish Eagles, but no occupation confirmed.

MOULT. Adults in wing-moult on 6 July (P7), 4 September (P9, with only 10 old) and 10 November (P9). Others dated May and June showed none (ZDUM, ZRCNUS).

CONSERVATION. Surveys are needed (a) of usage of forest-backed reservoirs, (b) of the effects of river siltation on distribution and hunting success. Globally near-threatened (BTW2).

Grey-headed Fish Eagle; Yieo Plaa Yai Hua Thao (Thai); Lang Kepala Kelabu (Malay)

Ichthyophaga ichthyaetus (Horsfield) 1821, *Transactions of the Linnean Society* 13(1): 136. TL Java.

Plate 20

GROUP RELATIONS. Free-standing.

GLOBAL RANGE. The Indian subcontinent (excluding the dry NW) and Sri Lanka; SE Asia south to the Greater Sunda islands and Philippines; and Sulawesi (Baltzer 1990).

IDENTIFICATION/DESCRIPTION. A medium-large eagle, much bigger than Lesser Fish Eagle but with similar colour-scheme; adult distinguished by bi-coloured tail, white with a blackish terminal band visible on both surfaces. Apart from size and likely habitat, immatures of these two species lack easy distinguishing characters, although at least some *ichthyaetus* show blackish lower primary and secondary wing-coverts, sharp against white flight-feather bases and other coverts (possibly only a moult-stage). Soars on flat wings held horizontal, and low gliding flight is interposed by wing-flicks, stiff-looking but surprisingly quick. Overhead, adults of both *Ichthyophaga* species show broad, dark wings with bulging inner trailing-edge nipped-in against the body, and white rear body, but the Grey-headed tail-pattern is conspicuous.

Spiny sole-scales and heavy, strongly curved claws, oval (unflanged) in cross-section, are characters of the genus.

Bare-part colours. (Adult) iris pale yellow (light brown in juvenile?); bill dark slate, paler bluish at lower base; cere dark slate; feet greenish white (G.C. Madoc, Riley 1938).

Size (mm). (Skins: 5 males, 5 females; adult): wing 430–454 and 458–493; tail 216–253 and 256–290; bill from cere 37.8–38.9 and 41.2–43.2; tarsus 38.1 (1 only) and 41.2–42.7 (BMNH, UMZC, ZRCNUS).

Weight. No data.

DISTRIBUTION. Historical summary: all divisions except *Chu*, *Ran*, *Nak*, *Pht*, *Son*, *Yal*, *Pes*, *Pra*, with island records from Rang (*Phu*), Tarutao and Langkawi off the W coast; Phangan and (tentatively) Redang (Kloss 1911b) off the E coast.

GEOGRAPHICAL VARIATION. Nominate *ichthyaetus*, of the global range except Sri Lanka.

STATUS AND POPULATION. Resident, local and uncommon to sparse. Formerly, commoner in the north than the south (at the turn of the century, 'very abundant' in strand woodland of the Pattani coast: Ogilvie-Grant 1906); now all but exterminated from Thailand, where the only recent records have been from sub-coastal swamp-forest in and around Chalerm Prakiat wildlife sanctuary, Narathiwat. Ousted from most original range south of the border as well, but a small and,

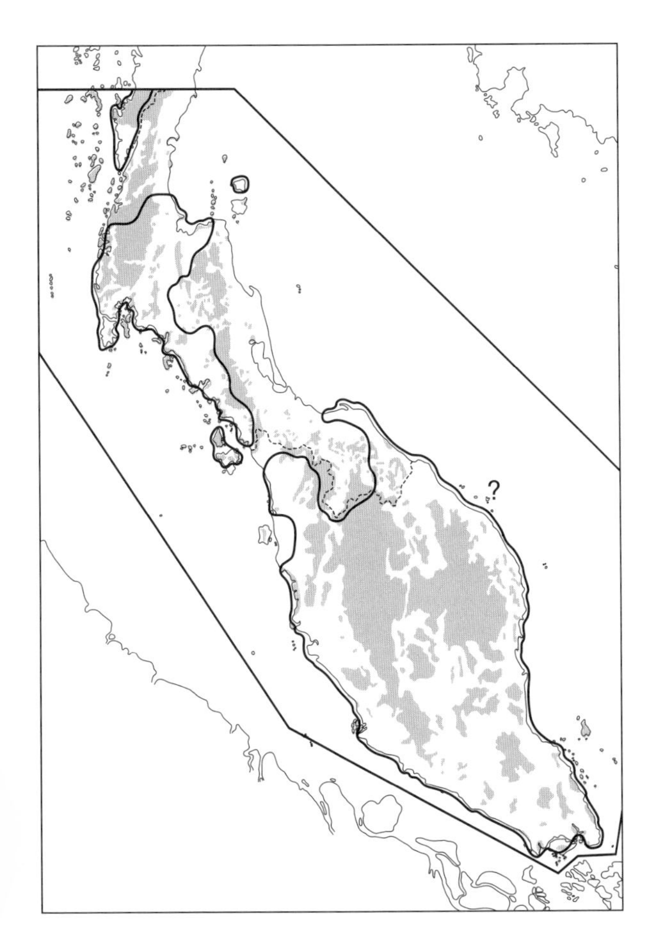

probably at the moment, growing remnant has colonized forest- and woodland-backed reservoirs, including power-dams of the interior. Mersing and Labung (Johor), Kenyir (Terengganu), Bukit Merah, Kenering and Temengor (Perak), and Pedu (Kedah) are on the list (R. Gregory-Smith, MBR 1984–85, 1986–87, SINGAV-6). In addition, the Singapore central catchment area has recently held at least two pairs, with records also from one of the new coastal embayments (Gibson-Hill 1950d, Ollington and Loh 1992, SINGAV-2). Nothing is yet known about likely attainable density in this new habitat, but 40 pairs would be a reasonable estimate of the current population of the Peninsula as a whole.

HABITATS AND ECOLOGY. Excluding reservoirs, known to have occurred from the coast (Pattani bay records in casuarina strand woodland) deep inland along the larger rivers, as far as the lower Tembeling in the Pahang drainage, hence overlapping Lesser Fish Eagle habitat. A few also inhabit Tasik Bera blackwater swamp on the Pahang/Negeri Sembilan border (ENGGANG-3). Original core habitat is likely to have been the lower, including tidal, reaches of large rivers backed by swamp-forest, and fast-shrinking relics of this ecosystem on the lower Perak river hold the best remaining pocket of population in a non-managed situation. Recent sightings in neighbouring Selangor have been at the edge of peatswamp forest, and Narathiwat birds are also in that habitat. No longer found in paddyland (cf. Chasen 1939).

FORAGING AND FOOD. Food includes quite large fish, but the hunting habits of both *Ichthyophaga* eagles need study, in particular, behaviour that might benefit this species over its smaller relative at reservoirs.

SOCIAL ORGANIZATION. Solitary forager, and roosts alone on tall trees near the edge of water.

MOVEMENTS. None known.

SURVIVAL. No information.

SOCIAL INTERACTIONS. Soaring and vocalizing by lone birds over and at the edge of forest are presumed to advertise territory.

VOICE. The advertising-call given while soaring is a rich, powerful bark, *kroi-ork*. In early September (start of the breeding season?), a bird roosting by Kenering reservoir gave this or a similar call at intervals throughout the night (SINGAV-6).

BREEDING

Nest. Only two described: massive stick structures, estimated 1.5 wide × 1 m deep, lined with leafy twigs; one 30 m up in an emergent, main-crown fork, about 20 m into forest from the edge of water, another 23 m up in a stand of dead paperbarks *Melaleuca cajiputi* on open swampland.

Eggs and brood. Eggs are rough-textured, plain glossless white. Shape ovate. Size (mm): 64.9 × 50.8 and 63.9 × 50.5 (n=2). Clutch two, and one record of a brood of two.

Cycle. A breeder collected off a nest in Kedah showed part-immature lower wing-coverts and tail, and had brownish rather than yellow eyes. No other information.

Seasonality. Eggs in Kedah and Singapore on 8 and 12 January, and nestlings in Narathiwat on 15 March (BCSTB-10, Gibson-Hill 1950d, G.C. Madoc).

MOULT. Adults replace primaries at up to two loci, with up to three inner feathers in overlapping growth, started between P1 and 3 (not always symmetrically between wings), and P10 dropped simultaneous with P6. Active wing-moult recorded in October, November, February and late May; non-moulters also in November and February (BMNH, UMZC, ZRCNUS).

CONSERVATION. Much depends on persuading governments that catchment forests need protection management, and that some reservoirs could have value other than as boating resorts. A late-stage rescue of the species could be foiled by insensitive tourism traffic, already intruding on some important sites. Globally near-threatened (BTW2).

White-rumped Vulture; Ee-raeng Thaa Lang Khao (Thai); Burung Hereng Tongkeng Putih (Malay)

Gyps bengalensis (Gmelin) 1788, *Systema Naturae* 13(1): 245. TL Bengal.
Plate 21

GROUP RELATIONS. Forms a superspecies with *G. africanus* (African White-rumped Vulture) (Stresemann and Amadon 1979).

GLOBAL RANGE. SE Iran, S Afghanistan and the Indian subcontinent from the Himalayan foothills; S and W Yunnan; and Burma, Laos and southern Vietnam to the Peninsula; with isolated sightings apparently of *Gyps* vultures that could have been this species in Brunei and N Sulawesi (CLBW, Mann 1987). Eastern populations are now much fragmented.

IDENTIFICATION/DESCRIPTION. A medium-sized vulture but very large bird by local raptor standards. On the ground, young immatures appear dark brown, grey-streaked below, with dark ruff, and head and neck covered in dark down; intermediate stages are light brown, streaked cream below, with dark-streaked whitish ruff and head and neck covered in whitish down; adults are uniform blackish with white rump, fluffy white ruff and head and neck more or less bare, blackish brown. Like other *Gyps* species, when soaring shows disproportionately small head, short but broad tail, and wings with straight leading-edge and slightly bulging inner trailing-edge, but is the only regional vulture holding wings in a shallow V rather than level. Non-juveniles have lower wing-coverts partly to, in adult, fully white, sharp against both underparts and flight-feathers (Boonsong and Round 1991, Grubh 1978, King *et al.* 1975).

Bare-part colours. Iris dark brown; cere black, bill dark horn with black tip (immature), all black with culmen-ridge horn (adult); skin of head and neck (beneath down) greenish yellow to brown with bluish tinge on lower hind-neck (immature stages), bald blackish brown (adult); feet black (Riley 1938, Robinson 1927).

Size (mm). (Skins: one intermediate male, one adult female): wing 507 and 553; tail 219 and 221; bill from cere 45.7 and 47.9; tarsus not measured (BMNH).

Weight. No data.

DISTRIBUTION. Believed to have occurred along the full length of the Peninsula in the nineteenth century (Chasen 1939), and in the 1870s common south at least to mid Perak (Kelham 1881–83). A further, temporary, expansion as far as Melaka during World-War Two is rumoured. Historical summary: *Ran, Sur, Phu, Tra, Pat, Sat, Yal, Ked, Kel, Tru, Pek, ?Mel, ?Joh, ?Sin,* with no other island records.

GEOGRAPHICAL VARIATION. None recognized.

STATUS AND POPULATION. Resident; widespread until early decades of this century, now very local and sparse. In the late 1930s, still a daily sight south to N Kedah and Kelantan, breeding in Kedah until 1950 (F.G.H. Allen, Bromley 1949) but by then scarce in Kelantan (Berwick 1952b). It is not known when the population in general collapsed but by about 1970 the only remaining pocket of regular presence was in Pattani and nearby Yala, including in the 1990s a maximum 20 birds living off the offal output of one or two old-fashioned Muslim slaughterhouses. In 1991, R.P. Jaensch found only adults, which suggests no recent breeding success. Elsewhere, now vagrant, including four near Ranong town in February 1974, one at Thung Thong reserve (Surat Thani) in October 1976 and one in Muang district (Satul) in June 1991 (BBCB-8, Holmes and Wells 1975, Storer 1978).

HABITATS AND ECOLOGY. A commensal of man exclusive to settlements (in 1919, many in and around

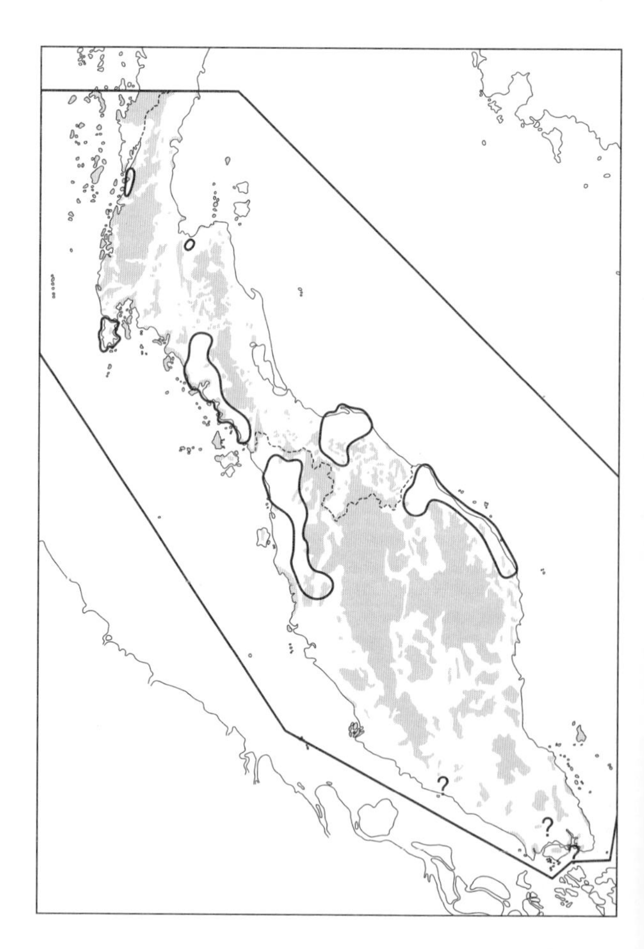

Phuket town: Robinson and Kloss 1921–24) and permanent agriculture, hence is likely to have had only a short recent history in the Peninsula, responding to ebb and flow of resources outside the limits of a typically more seasonal life-zone.

FORAGING AND FOOD. Kelham (1881–83) describes gatherings at water buffalo carcasses. Domestic stock can have been the only serious food-source, undermined progressively by improvements in animal husbandry. By the late 1930s, Kedah vultures were already concentrating on slaughter offal, and G.C. Madoc describes an instance of active, collaborative hunting: a group of about 15 landing around a paddyfield, slowly walking up, then rushing a flock of village ducks.

SOCIAL ORGANIZATION. Roosts and loafs communally, and bred in loose colonies, sometimes with nests in adjacent trees (G.C. Madoc). At carrion, said to be subordinate to Red-headed Vulture, but critical observations are lacking.

MOVEMENTS. Unknown.

SURVIVAL. No information.

SOCIAL INTERACTIONS. No information.

VOICE. No information.

BREEDING

Nest. Large, stick-built, with a fairly deep cup thickly but loosely lined with leafy twigs, including of *Ficus* species; 10-plus m up in a main crown fork of a tree. Localities in Kedah included woodland growing out of the steep side of Keriang hill, a limestone inselberg in the paddy-plain NW of Alor Setar, and tall, dead paperbark trees in swamp (long since cleared) at the edge of subcoastal paddyland, Kubang Pasu district.

Eggs and brood. Eggs have a pitted, chalky surface, unmarked white in one instance, with some reddish marks at the poles in another. Shape elliptical. Size (mm): 87.9 × 69.7 and 84.4 × 66.4 (n=2). Clutch one.

Cycle. No information.

Seasonality. At Keriang hill, nest-building during early October–late November; two single-egg clutches (slightly incubated and fresh) on 22 and 24 November; incubation in December; and still-active nests (stage unspecified) in February (F.G.H. Allen, G.C. Madoc).

MOULT. Replacement of inner primaries by an intermediate-stage immature regular-descendant, but wing-tip not in sequence: P1–5/6 new, 7 old/growing, 8–9 new unilaterally, rest old, on 2 November. Pattern multi-locus in an adult female dated 10 June: near-complete but with growth still at P2, 4 and 9–10 (BMNH).

CONSERVATION. Apparently, vulture populations have collapsed throughout Thailand and widely also in Burma. The management needed to avert extinction of breeders in the Peninsula is probably not practical. Globally near-threatened (BTW2).

Long-billed Vulture; Ee-raeng See Namtaan (Thai); Burung Hereng Paruh Panjang (Malay)

Gyps indicus (Scopoli) 1786, *Deliciae Florae et Faunae Insubricae* 2: 85. TL India.
Plate 21

GROUP RELATIONS. Free-standing.

GLOBAL RANGE. Except for the far SW, the Indian subcontinent from the Himalayan foothills; and SE Asia from Burma, Laos and southern Vietnam to the Peninsula.

IDENTIFICATION/DESCRIPTION. Slightly larger than White-rumped Vulture. At close range on the ground, by longer bill-base. Juveniles have head and neck pale, ruff brownish, upperparts including wing-coverts dark brown with lower back paler, and underparts pale-streaked. In intermediates, lower back and rump are contrastingly creamy white. Adults have head and neck blackish, ruff white, and body and wing-coverts all pale creamy- to clay-brown, contrasting with blackish flight-feathers. In flight, shape as White-rumped Vulture but soars on level rather than uptilted wings. Flight-feathers and tail are dark in both but lower wing-covert tone of Long-billed matches under-body at all stages. On colour-pattern, potentially more confusable with Himalayan Griffon.

Bare-part colours. Iris deep brown (adult); bill and cere blue-black (immature), rosy yellow (adult); head and neck beneath down pale grey (immature), bald brownish black (adult); feet blackish (Grubh 1978, Robinson 1927, P.D. Round).

Size (mm). (Skin: one intermediate-stage immature, not sexed): wing 610; tail 229; bill from cere 46.4; tarsus not measured (BMNH).

Weight. No data.

DISTRIBUTION. Robinson (1910) tentatively identified W.L. Abbott's 'large white vulture' apparently common in Trang and Penang at the end of the nineteenth century, as Egyptian Vulture *Neophron percnopterus*. Long-billed (adults all-pale except for head, flight-feathers and tail) is a more realistic option and Deignan (1963) accepted Trang apparently on that basis. The only actual specimen-records are a bird from Taiping (Perak) collected in the early 1890s, and an adult from Kuala Berang (Terengganu) dated June 1947, according to Gibson-Hill (1949b) produced in response to a request from the Raffles Museum for the head of the first vulture that could be collected easily. Other vultures were said to have been present in the area, but none confirmed to a species. A mid-nineteenth-century specimen in the Cantor collection (BMNH) is not reliably from 'Malacca' but may still have come from within the Peninsula. Historical summary: *Tra, Tru, Pek, ?Mel.*

GEOGRAPHICAL VARIATION. Subspecies *G.i. tenuirostris* G.R. Gray 1844 (TL Nepal), of the NE Indian subcontinent and SE Asia.

STATUS AND POPULATION. On the scant evidence available it has to be assumed this bird was never more than a non-breeding visitor to the Peninsula. With no records now for half a century it may also be assumed that the source-populations are either extinct or have changed their behaviour.

HABITATS AND ECOLOGY. Tied to the settled lowlands, and probably as dependant on carrion from domestic stock as White-rumped and Red-headed Vultures.

FORAGING AND FOOD. No definite information.

SOCIAL ORGANIZATION. No information.

MOVEMENTS. No information.

SURVIVAL. No data.

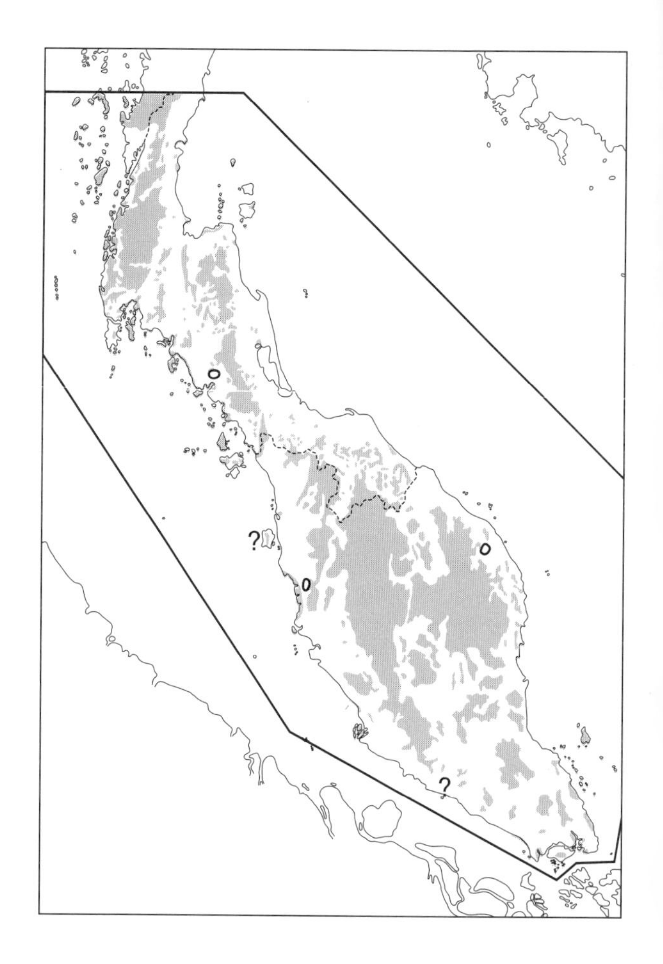

SOCIAL INTERACTIONS. No information.

VOICE. No information.

BREEDING. No population.

MOULT. Replacement of inner primaries by an undated immature, single-locus and regular-descendant: P1–4/5 new, P5/6 moulting, P6/7–10 old (BMNH).

CONSERVATION. No relevant local issues, but globally near-threatened (BTW2).

Himalayan Griffon; Ee-raeng See Namtaan Himalai (Thai); Burung Hereng Himalaya (Malay)

Gyps himalayensis Hume 1869, *My Scrapbook or Rough Notes on Indian Oology and Ornithology*: 12 and 15. TL Simla, W Himalayas.

Plate 21

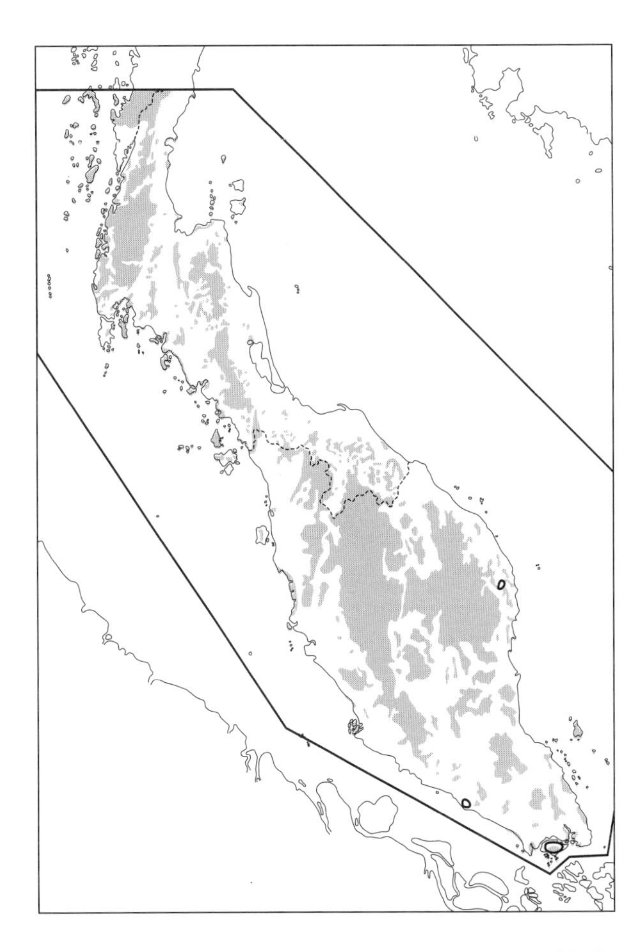

GROUP RELATIONS. Uncertain; close to *G. fulvus* (Eurasian Griffon) and S African *G. coprotheres* (Cape Griffon) (Stresemann and Amadon 1979).

GLOBAL RANGE. Breeds in (mostly) high-altitude central Asia from the Kirghiz and Altai ranges east to Inner Mongolia, south to the Pamirs, Tibet and Himalayas, and Gansu, Sichuan and W Yunnan. An altitudinal migrant.

IDENTIFICATION/DESCRIPTION. Huge; within the size-range of Cinereous Vulture but body and all wing-coverts uniform pale clay-brown (adult) or boldly white-striped dark khaki-brown (juvenile), with crop-patches, thighs and belly to lower-tail-coverts white (subadult), and tail and flight-feathers contrastingly blackish. Head and neck pale at all ages. Seen overhead, tail more wedge-shaped than in other regional *Gyps* species, but moult and wear affect its identification value.

Bare-part colours. (Immature) iris dark brown; head-skin showing through down and around eye pale, pink-tinged blue-grey; cere blackish, rest of bill purple-horn paling to yellow-horn on outer third of upper mandible, and with cutting-edge and tip black; feet pale flesh-pink.

Size (mm). (Live: approximate measurements of one immature, not sexed): wing 750; bill from cere 50, bill from skull 70; mid-toe plus claw 140 (Melaka Zoo).

Weight. No data.

DISTRIBUTION. *Tru, Joh, Sin.*

GEOGRAPHICAL VARIATION. None recognized.

STATUS AND POPULATION. Status uncertain, even though large griffons, probably Himalayan, have also been seen in continental Thailand (BBCB-7). Locally, only immatures have occurred: one captured exhausted by the Paka river (S Terengganu) on 24 June 1979 (PERHILITAN); four said to have occurred in SW Singapore island in December 1989 (but one of them taken into captivity at nearby Jurong Bird Park was still in immature plumage in March 1992); another group of nine, photographed at roost in the Bukit Timah nature reserve forest, Singapore, on 12–13 January 1992 (J. Smith, M. Strange); and one on the NW coast of Johor on about 20 January 1995, captured and transferred to Melaka Zoo after crashing, exhausted, off a roost-perch.

Himalayan Griffons are known to migrate altitudinally, but only in the general area of their breeding-range (HBI), and these tropical occurrences are unlikely enough to be suspect. Occasional vultures have appeared in the traditional medicine markets, e.g., of Hong Kong. Thus however bizarre, there is a chance that Griffons and perhaps other vultures are being shipped from remote areas for use or release in SE Asia (witness good details of an adult Egyptian Vulture soaring over NE Singapore in December 1982: C.J. Hails). In the meantime, those birds handled, and five separate individuals photographed at roost, appeared wound-free and clean, wing- and tail-tips, in particular, showing none of the dirt and wear expected of such big birds recently out of cages.

HABITATS AND ECOLOGY. No additional information.

FORAGING AND FOOD. No information.

SOCIAL ORGANIZATION. Two Singapore records have been of groups.

MOVEMENTS. No additional information. The nearest point of accepted regular range is roughly 3000 km north of Singapore.

SURVIVAL. No information.

SOCIAL INTERACTIONS. No information.

VOICE. No information.

BREEDING. No population.

MOULT. No data.

CONSERVATION. Capture on the ground of birds too starved to take off has been the circumstance of most recent vulture records. Large-mammal carrion is hardly available in open country and dispersants entering (or released in) the Peninsula are unlikely to leave unassisted.

Cinereous Vulture; Ee-raeng Dam Himalai (Thai); Burung Hereng Hitam (Malay)

Aegypius monachus (Linnaeus) 1766, *Systema Naturae* 12(1): 122. TL Arabia.
Plate 21

GROUP RELATIONS. Free-standing.

GLOBAL RANGE. Breeds in N Africa (Morocco), Eurasia from Spain, the Balkans and Black Sea east to Mongolia and N China; SW Asia; the Himalayas and Assam; and Sichuan. A few winter regularly to the Arabian peninsula, the northern Indian subcontinent, Japan, Korea, S China including Taiwan, and N Burma; vagrant further into continental SE Asia.

IDENTIFICATION/DESCRIPTION. Huge; the largest Eurasian raptor, with 2.5 m wingspan. Uniformly blackish brown or dull black except for bare pinkish neck, white patches around the ear (juvenile only), and sandy crown and nape (older stages only). In soaring flight, shows immense, more or less parallel-sided wings held level, proportionally small head and short, wedge-shaped tail. In a good view, pale feet contrast with wholly dark underparts (feet, thighs and entire rear under-body whitish in Himalayan Griffon).

Bare-part colours. Iris brown; bill black with grey to yellowish base, cere grey-pink; periorbital and other facial patches dirty pink, patches around juvenile ear-opening pearl-white; neck dirty pink; feet whitish (BWP, HBI).

Size. No data.

Weight. No data.

DISTRIBUTION. Recorded twice, near Kuantan, Pahang, on 14 August 1978 and in Khuan Kanun district, Phatthalung, on 7 December 1983, in both cases identification confirmed by live capture. Historical summary: *Pht*, *Phg*.

GEOGRAPHICAL VARIATION. None recognized.

STATUS AND POPULATION. Vagrant, a minimum 1500 km south of the regular winter range-limit

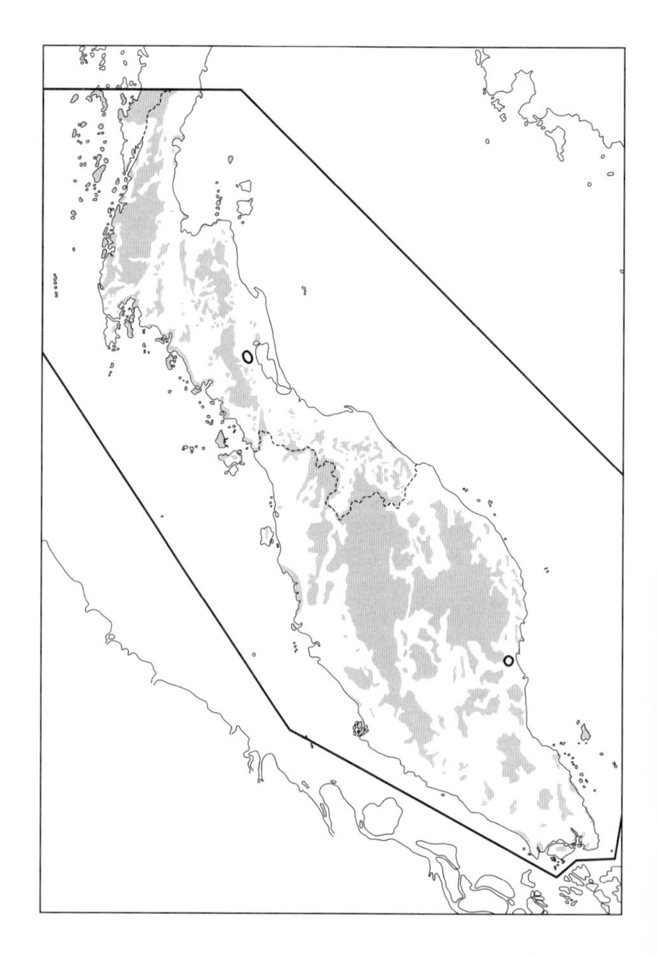

in E Asia. Both birds were immatures, the Kuantan individual identified from its head-pattern as second-year, and both apparently starved to exhaustion. One was chased out of a tree onto open ground from where it could not take off, the other captured in a paddy-field after being shot in the wing by a villager.

HABITATS AND ECOLOGY. Both birds were on open ground, but obviously out of regular habitat.

FORAGING AND FOOD. No information.

SOCIAL ORGANIZATION. Solitary.

MOVEMENTS. No information.

SURVIVAL. No information.

SOCIAL INTERACTIONS. No information.

VOICE. No information.

BREEDING. No population.

MOULT. No data.

CONSERVATION. No valid local issues, but globally near-threatened (BTW2).

Red-headed Vulture; Phaya Raeng (Thai); Burung Hereng Kepala Merah (Malay)

Sarcogyps calvus (Scopoli) 1786, *Deliciae Florae et Faunae Insubricae* 2: 85. TL Pondicherry, SE India.
Plate 21

GROUP RELATIONS. Free-standing.

GLOBAL RANGE. The Indian subcontinent from the Himalayan foothills; Yunnan; and SE Asia to the Peninsula.

IDENTIFICATION/DESCRIPTION. Larger than White-rumped and Long-billed Vultures, but with the latter's wing-length. The adult combination of red head, neck and feet, and mainly black body, wings and tail is unlike any other Asian vulture. Overhead, shows a white ruff, a white patch along the flank and, in close view, a narrow white line behind the leading-edge of the inner wing. From above, flank-patch visible along side of body, and base of the inner secondaries silvery grey. Immatures are mainly brown, with white flanks and rear under-body, and head and neck thinly covered in white down. In flight, hand proportionately narrower than in other vultures due to short inner primaries, more obvious in adults than immatures (Boonsong and Round 1991). Soars on slightly up-angled wings, shallowly flexed at the wrist, with proportionately small head projecting more prominently than short, wedge-shaped tail (Grubh 1978).

No specifically intermediate plumages have been described but birds in otherwise adult plumage with brown- versus grey-based inner secondaries may be a distinct age-class (BMNH).

Bare-part colours. (Adult) iris pale yellow; bill black, cere orange-red; head and neck orange-red with some yellow at base of neck-wattles; lateral patch on tibia orange-red, feet white to dull red (Oates 1883, Robinson 1927).

Size (mm). (Skins: one male, one female, both with with brown-based inner secondaries): wing 575 and 624; tail 233 and 252; bill from cere 53.7 and 57.4; tarsus not measured (BMNH).

Weight. No data.

DISTRIBUTION. Possibly as recently as the beginning of the century, south to Singapore, but no record exists of regular occurrence below mid Perak and Terengganu (e.g., none in nineteenth-century

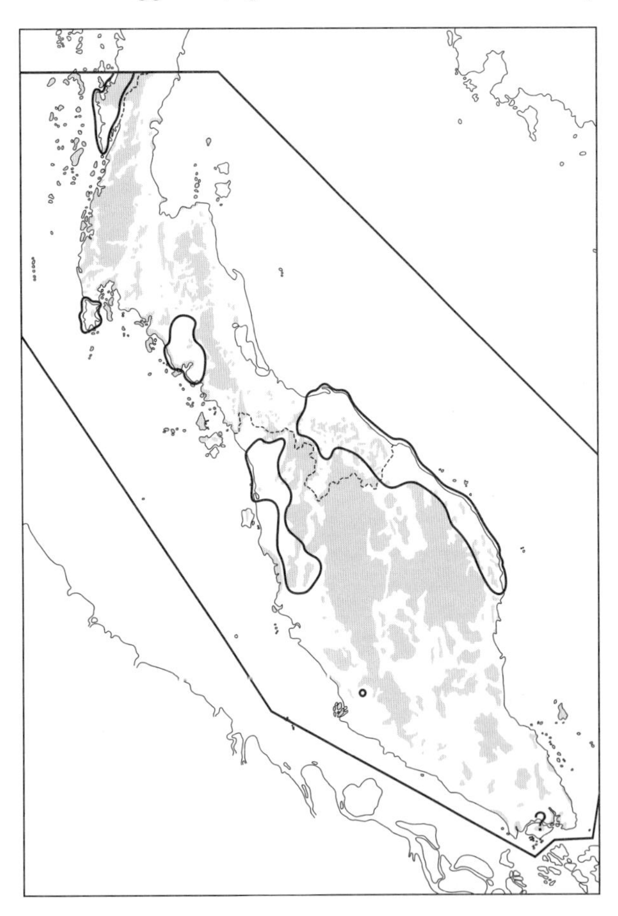

collections from Melaka, where more or less guaranteed had there been a significant presence in the south). Historical summary: *Pak, Phu, Tra, Pat, Yal, Nar, Ked, Kel, Tru, Pek, Sel, Sin.*

GEOGRAPHICAL VARIATION. None recognized.

STATUS AND POPULATION. Formerly present year-round, almost certainly resident, and locally common (Bromley 1949); now probably extinct, with no records anywhere in the last 25 years. During 1950–51, still plentiful in Kelantan and N Terengganu (Berwick 1952b), and not uncommon in Terengganu in 1956 but status evidently by then changing, with records only during September–early spring; all of adults (Lewin 1957). None found past 1968 (loners in September and October that year: BR 1970–71). In Kedah, findable almost daily up to the early 1940s (Bromley 1949, G.C. Madoc). It is not known when this NW Malaysian population collapsed, but gone by the early 1960s (last local record, a bird over the slope of Jerai peak on 24 February 1961: Nadchatram 1964). The last record anywhere in Malaysia: a wanderer passing over Ampang, Selangor, in February 1964 (BR 1964).

North of the border, 'abundant' in Yala and Pattani in 1901 when H.C. Robinson (Annandale and Robinson 1903, Robinson 1927) found a sizable roost in tall dipterocarp trees near the mouth of the Pattani river. Enquiries in 1991 suggested none had been seen in that area for 10–15 years (R.P. Jaensch).

HABITATS AND ECOLOGY. Like other vultures in the Peninsula, associated with agriculture and stock-raising, numbers in parts of the Thai provinces being said to have varied with incidence of cattle disease (Robinson 1927). However, this is the only vulture known to have been widespread in NE Malaysia, implying a possible ecological difference from *Gyps* species (it was perhaps more successful at finding food in natural gaps along the larger rivers, etc.).

SOCIAL ORGANIZATION. Apparently mainly solitary away from roosts. Lewin (1957) saw an occasional two, once three, soaring together in Terengganu, and five are recorded together at a carcass in Kedah (G.C. Madoc), but the typical attendance at carrion was only one or two Red-headed among a larger number of White-rumped Vultures.

MOVEMENTS. No information.

SURVIVAL. No information.

FORAGING AND FOOD. No information beyond domestic stock carrion.

SOCIAL INTERACTIONS. No information.

VOICE. No information.

BREEDING. No definite records, but in the 1930s a few Red-headed attended the White-rumped Vulture breeding-colony on Keriang outcrop, Kedah, and G.C. Madoc saw a bird there breaking off branches appropriate for nest-building.

MOULT. Replacement of the inner primaries of a male with brown-based secondaries, regular-descendant (P1–3 new, P4–5 growing), but multi-locus in a bird with grey-based secondaries (P3–4, 7 and 10 growing); both dated early August (BMNH).

CONSERVATION. Globally near-threatened (BTW2), but no further local issues. Reintroduction would require a fully managed feeding programme, impossible to guarantee long-term.

Short-toed Snake Eagle; Yieo Niw San (Thai); Lang Ular (Malay)

Circaetus gallicus (Gmelin) 1788, *Systema Naturae* 13(1): 259. TL France.
Plate 24

GROUP RELATIONS. Free-standing.

GLOBAL RANGE. Breeds through Africa, temperate Eurasia from SW Europe to Iran, Xinjiang and Mongolia; through the Indian subcontinent except the far NE; and in the Lesser Sunda islands east to Timor (Mees 1975, OBCB-11). Northern populations migrate, wintering in outer N-tropical Africa and SW Asia; the Indian subcontinent and, sparsely, SE Asia. A tentative identification of one on passage in Sumatra and a bird photographed in E Java (van Balen and Compost 1989) suggest transequatorial connections in this area might still be intact.

IDENTIFICATION/DESCRIPTION. Size of a medium *Aquila* eagle, with proportionately heavy head, conspicuous yellow eye, longish, bare tarsi and tail projecting not far beyond folded wing. Soars on long, broad, parallel-sided wings held more or less level, but with hand arched down when gliding (like Osprey but latter has narrower wings, more flexed at wrist, with an obviously dark carpal-patch). Underparts white, often conspicuously so against darker head to upper breast (but latter varies and local records so far have been of medium- to light-breasted birds), with dark spots and bars across breast extending variably to lower wing-coverts and inner flight-feathers. A bold terminal and two other distinct dark bars cross the square-ended tail. Some ?immature Oriental Honey-buzzards approach this general pattern but are smaller, have proportionately longer, rounder-ended tail, long, narrow versus distinctly broad head and neck, and lack the dark hood. Foragers often hover.

Bare-part colours. Nothing else from SE Asia.

Size. No data.

Weight. No data.

DISTRIBUTION. Historical summary: *Kra, Sel, Joh, Sin.*

GEOGRAPHICAL VARIATION. Presumed nominate *gallicus*, of Eurasia.

STATUS AND POPULATION. A sparse passage migrant and possible overwinterer (loners soaring over Krabi town on 1 January and on the Desaru coast, E Johor, on 27 February). The five other accepted records include two occurrences in lowland Selangor (a bird collected at Ampang: Butler 1899a) and, in Singapore, one at Serangoon and two instances of migrants on a common route for passage raptors crossing the W end of the island (BBCB-7, BMP5, BR 1978–79, MBR 1982–83, SINGAV-2, -4).

HABITATS AND ECOLOGY. Only one instance of a clear habitat association: a bird in Singapore at an open-ground grass-fire.

FORAGING AND FOOD. Apart from of hover-hunting at a grass-fire, no local information.

SOCIAL ORGANIZATION. Solitary.

MOVEMENTS. Loners on southward passage over Selangor and Singapore on 27 and 31 October and 11 December.

SURVIVAL. No information.

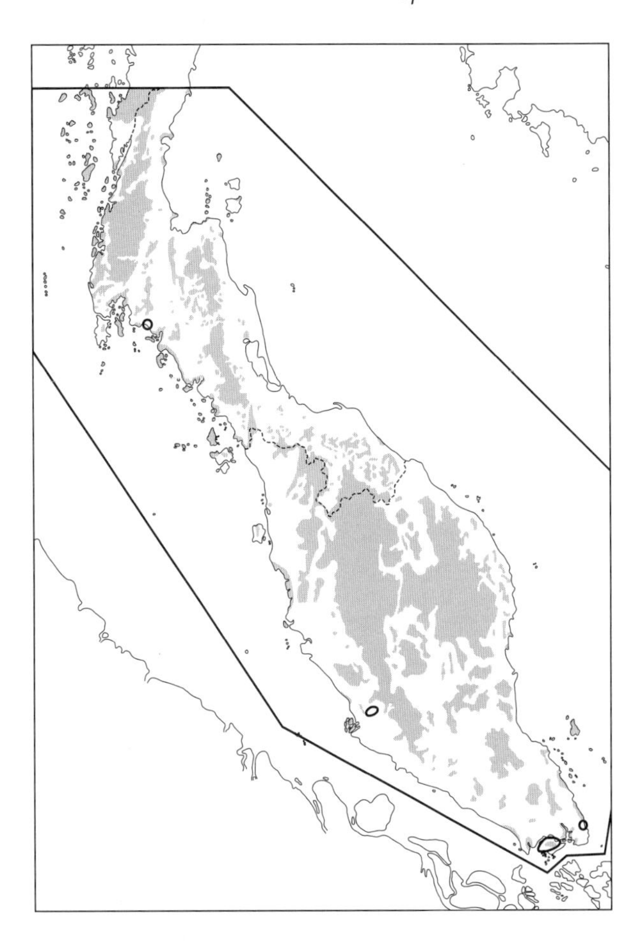

SOCIAL INTERACTIONS. No information.

VOICE. No information.

BREEDING. No population.

MOULT. No data.

CONSERVATION. No relevant issues.

Crested Serpent Eagle; Yieo Rung (Thai); Lang Kuik (Malay)

Spilornis cheela (Latham) 1790, *Index Ornithologicus* 1: 14. TL Lucknow, N India.
Plate 19

GROUP RELATIONS. *Spilornis* serpent eagles vary much in size (dwarfed on some Bay of Bengal islands), plumage-pattern and colour-intensity. Accepting only the fact of double colonization as adequate evidence of speciation, *cheela* can be taken to form a superspecies with *elgini* (Andaman Serpent Eagle) and Bornean *kinabaluensis* (Mountain Serpent Eagle), occupying distinct but adjacent habitats and, in the case of *kinabaluensis*, isolated also by vocalizations. This probably underestimates real diversity. Amadon (1974) lists seven other 'old', isolated Asian and Wallacean forms that may have reached the stage of being allospecies of *cheela*.

GLOBAL RANGE. The Indian subcontinent from the lower Himalayas, Sri Lanka and the Andamans; SE Tibet and China south from the Changjiang valley including Taiwan and Hainan (the S Nansei island form is a possible allospecies); SE Asia to the Greater Sunda islands, Bali and Palawan; possibly Lombok.

IDENTIFICATION/DESCRIPTION. A medium-sized eagle, bulkier but not longer-winged than Brahminy Kite, commonly perching more or less upright, with occasional side-to-side wags of the tail. The perched adult appears mainly dark brown with extensively bare, yellow lores; heavy, flat, white-flecked black crest; and vinous-brown, white-spotted lower breast and belly. Tail bi-coloured, with wide white sub-terminal and black terminal bands. In flight, broad, rounded, 'butterfly' wings show a pronounced trailing-edge bulge, nipped-in against the body, with a broad white band across the base of the flight-feathers, matching the tail. Soars with wings held slightly forward, up-angled in a distinct V, and with the hand swept shallowly back. During advertisement-display, closed tail and prominent head are also up-angled.

On present evidence, juveniles in this area fledge directly into an adult-like plumage, except that chin and throat are streaked rather than solidly brown, grey or blackish; the breast finely dark-barred; and crest black-flecked white (the inverse of adult, with only an apical wedge rather than the whole outer half of crest-feathers black). Dark tail-bars are relatively narrow and even-spaced. Juveniles also lack the white wing-bar of adults but show conspicuously pale-based primaries, narrow-barred.

Bare-part colours. (Adult) iris bright lemon- to chrome-yellow or orange; bill lead-blue, blackish on the culmen and tip; cere, lores and periorbital skin greenish yellow to clear yellow; feet dull greenish yellow to waxy yellow (BMNH).

Size (mm). (Skins: 43 adults, most not sexed): wing 348–414; tail 220–265; bill from cere 28.3–34.0; tarsus 74.8–97.0 (BMNH, UMZC, ZDUM, ZRCNUS).

Weight. No data.

DISTRIBUTION. Historical summary: all divisions, with additional island records from the Surins, Libong, Tarutao, Langkawi and Penang off the W coast; and Samui and Tioman off the E coast.

GEOGRAPHICAL VARIATION. Subspecies *malayensis* Kirke Swann 1920 (TL Raub, Pahang), of the Peninsula and mainland Sumatra (CLBS, Deignan 1963). N-S down the Peninsula, shows a shallow, uneven cline of decreasing size (including wing-length).

STATUS AND POPULATION. Resident, regular and more or less common; the most frequently seen large raptor in all natural and semi-natural wooded and forested habitats, except on mangrove coasts where outnumbered by Brahminy Kite. Now scarce in Singapore; a territory covering the city Botanical Gardens has not been occupied since 1982 (MBR 1982–83) and only 1–2 pairs persist in the central catchment area.

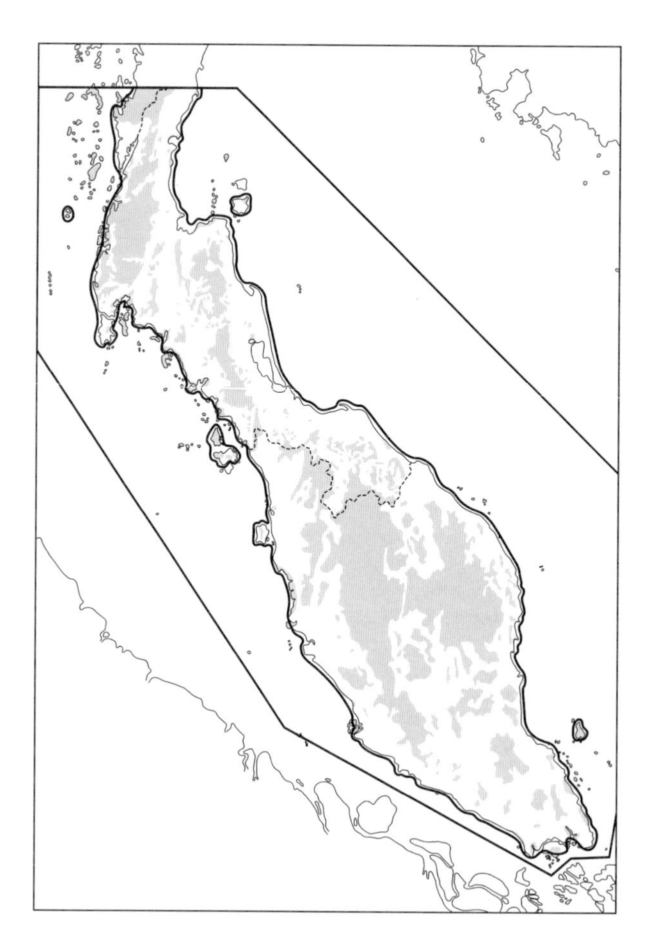

HABITATS AND ECOLOGY. Not able to persist where mixed woodland with tall trees has been entirely cleared or replaced, but tolerant of a quite high level of habitat disturbance and fragmentation, hunting in overgrown edge situations sometimes far into plantation and other agriculture. Often particularly common in mangroves, and uses all kinds of inland natural forests, regularly into the Montane zone, to an extreme 1900 m.

FORAGING AND FOOD. Still-hunts from a canopy-level perch both inside forest and in more open edge, dropping to prey on the ground or snatching from vegetation. Food includes snakes up to at least 1 m long (abundance in mangroves may relate to the easy low-tide availability of Dog-faced Water-snakes *Cerberus rhynchops*), lizards, amphibians (both frogs and toads recorded), apparently occasionally also small, grassland birds (weavers, munias, pipits) (Batchelor 1958). Larger birds tend not to show fear of it.

SOCIAL ORGANIZATION. Pairs often soar together but foragers are always solitary.

MOVEMENTS. Two 15-minute watches during a survey of raptor migration south over the coastal plain of Selangor on 20 October 1963 produced four and eight Serpent Eagles among numbers of genuinely migrating Oriental Honey-buzzards and

Japanese Sparrowhawks. No crossing of water-gaps has been reported and the assumption has been that these were local birds attracted to good soaring conditions, but that they would probably not have continued far.

SURVIVAL. No information.

SOCIAL INTERACTIONS. Soaring displays are nearly always accompanied by calling. The head-and-tail-up posture is common to lone soarers and pairs. Paired birds also dive at one another, and fly short, horizontal stretches on wings shallowly and rapidly winnowed while being held slightly below the horizontal.

VOICE. Loud and ringing. Soaring pairs often duet, one member giving a persistent *hurleeoo*, answered with a lower-pitched, variable-length *hurloo, (loo, loo)* by the second, circling often fairly high above its mate (sexes not distinguished). Advertising-calls by lone soarers range from the *hurleeoo, (loo)* phrase to a sustained, crescendo 'song': *ha'-ha'-ha'-ha' . . . hu-hu-hu-hu-hueeooleeoo*. Short calls are also given from perches in cover (BMP5).

BREEDING

Nest. Medium-sized (but no measurements available), stick-built, cup lined with fresh, leafy twigs. Sites include a relic mangrove tree, the lowest horizontal branch of a large durian tree at the edge of a small patch of forest, and the main crown fork of inland forest trees, in two instances leafless or dead trees in tall secondary-growth, 9–30 m above ground. However, the scarcity of records for so common a bird suggests none of these may be typical.

Eggs and brood. Not described. Elsewhere, the full clutch is one.

Cycle. Both pair-members nest-build, and are said to repair and re-use old nests, but an instance of an active nest alongside two older nests in the same crown suggests occasional fresh building.

Seasonality. Aerial display-soaring by pairs recorded during early September–early April; nest-building in January and March; occupied nests (contents unchecked) during February–May; recent fledglings in June and late September (BMP5, ENGGANG-2, G.C. Madoc, MBR 1986–87, NRCS).

MOULT. Replacement of inner primaries is regular-descendant, from P1 (rarely P2 before 1), but overridden by separate mid- and outer-hand moults starting mostly at P5 and between P8 and 10. Generally, not more than two loci are active together (BMNH, UMZC). Among 44 birds covering all months except November and December, 80 percent of those dated May–August were in active wing-moult, versus only eight percent of the September–April sample, showing moult occurs mostly outside the main aerial-display period. Only a few winter non-moulters had uniform-aged flight-feathers; the rest showed evidence of suspension or arrest, more or less at random. Evidently, few replace the whole wing at one moult.

CONSERVATION. Too familiar to be deemed at risk overall but locally rare, as now in Singapore, and total clearance of tall woodland has already eliminated breeders from large areas of the settled lowlands. Retention of a diversified rural landscape is essential.

Marsh Harrier; Yieo Thung (Thai); Lang Sawah (Malay)

Circus aeruginosus (Linnaeus) 1758, *Systema Naturae* 10(1): 91. TL Sweden.
Plate 22

GROUP RELATIONS. Forms a superspecies with southern African *C. ranivorus* (African Marsh Harrier); perhaps also with Australasian–Oceanian *C. approximans* (Swamp Harrier), which is sometimes regarded as conspecific (Nieboer 1973).

GLOBAL RANGE. Breeds on Malagasy islands, in N Africa, and temperate-zone Eurasia from the Atlantic to Pacific Russia and N Japan, south to Iraq, Afghanistan and far-N China; also in highland New Guinea. Northern populations migrate, wintering through Africa, SW Asia, the Indian subcontinent, Sri Lanka and Bay of Bengal islands; S Japan and China south from the Changjiang valley; and SE Asia to the Philippines and Greater Sunda islands, mainly north of the equator but a few reach Java and Bali (Ash 1993, M.J. Silvius, S. van Balen).

IDENTIFICATION/DESCRIPTION. All harriers have proportionately long tail and feet, and long, parallel-sided wings. They hunt by low quartering, alternating deliberate flapping with wrist flexed and a glide on wings angled up in a marked V, rocking from side to side as the bird steers along. Marsh is the largest, about the size of Brahminy Kite, with wings proportionately broader than in other species. Immatures are dark mahogany-brown, entirely, or creamy white on the head; wings plain or with a few shadow-bars across the underside of the tip; tail the same brown dorsally (birds with 5–6 narrow, darker bars may not be immature), paler below. Upper tail-coverts are as back or white-fringed.

Many adult females are also dark brown, and all show creamy white on the head. This varies from neatly demarcated, unmarked cap and lower face that may be separated by a dark band from bill through eye (perhaps the exclusive nominate *aeruginosus* pattern) to dark-streaked and extending back to the upper mantle, breast, inner leading-edge of the wing, and lower wing-coverts.

Another common morph is dark-streaked buff-white below and over the head, upper mantle and lesser wing-coverts; the rest of the upperparts including median wing-coverts dark brown, streaked buff, with upper tail-coverts dark-spotted white. Primaries are dark-tipped and variably dark-barred on both surfaces, and a pair of black bars crosses the upper primary coverts onto the outer secondaries; upper wing, including primary-coverts, otherwise grey. The tail is ash-grey shading to cinnamon laterally, plain or with 5–6 dark bars complete or on lateral feathers only, and uniformly narrow (other harriers show a wider apical bar). Such birds have been identified as a form or stage of male *spilonotus* (Boonsong and Round 1991, Sonobe and Washington 1982), but birds in this plumage have included some of the largest E-Palaearctic Marsh Harriers examined, wing up to 429 mm – which is a female measurement (BMNH, ZRCNUS).

Typical adult male *spilonotus* differ in their lack of brown or rufous, including any spotting on the upper tail-coverts, and are dark over head, neck, mantle and median wing-coverts, according to the extent these parts are white-fringed. The broader the white the more streaked and scalloped they appear, the narrower the more solidly black. At a distance, darkest individuals might pass for Pied Harrier, but always show a streaked collar and breast, and only the extreme leading-edge of the wing is fully white. A few show dark parts tinged brown, with feather-corners notched pale orange, underparts finely but fully brown-streaked, and flanks and trousers often marked rufous. These could be subadults or, perhaps, subspecific intergrades.

Adult male nominate *aeruginosus* is ginger-cream anteriorly, rich chestnut from the lower breast and sooty brown on the lower tail-coverts, boldly dark-streaked especially on the pale parts. Upper body and median wing-coverts are browner than in male *spilonotus*, and primary coverts lack the black banding. Upper tail-coverts are barred silver-grey rather than full white, concolorous with the tail which in both subspecies is pale grey, plain or with lateral barring. Both can also have white under-wings but in *aeruginosus* lower coverts are usually chestnut. Its primaries are only black-tipped, whereas all *spilonotus* show at least some additional barring.

Bare-part colours. Iris brown (immature), clear yellow (adult); bill black with slaty to greenish base, cere greenish yellow; feet rich yellow (BMNH).

Size (mm). *C.a. spilonotus* (Skins: 18 males, 7 pale females, 2 brown females; adult): wing 384–414, 404–429 and 405, 429; tail 218–239, 238–251 and 232, 248; bill from cere 21.7–25.1, 24.4–25.8 and 23.9, 24.1; tarsus 84.2–93.5, 89.7–96.9 and 86.4, 94.4. Nominate *aeruginosus* (Skins: 12 males, most from continental Thailand north of the Peninsula; adult): wing 380–408; tail 220–231; bill from cere 21.7–22.9; tarsus 83.2–88.2 (BMNH, ZRCNUS).

Weight. No data.

DISTRIBUTION. Nominate *aeruginosus* winters mainly west and north of the Peninsula, in SE Asia to the central plains of Thailand. The only definite local records are of two adult males collected together on the Pakchan estuary (*Ran*) and one from Taiping district (*Pek*) (BMNH, ZRCNUS). *C.a. spilonotus*, on the other hand, occurs throughout the north and the Malaysian W-coast plain south to Singapore. Historical summary: all divisions except *Pha, Kra, Yal, Nar, Pes, Kel, Tru, Phg*, with other island records from Langkawi and Penang.

GEOGRAPHICAL VARIATION. Where nominate *aeruginosus* and eastern *spilonotus* Kaup 1847 (TL Philippines) meet in W Mongolia and west of Lake Baikal, they are said to interbreed (Vaurie 1965). Nine apparently adult male *aeruginosus* from central Thailand vary in dorsal body to upper tail-covert tones and primary-covert pattern, and one has much white on thighs and belly (BMNH), suggestive of

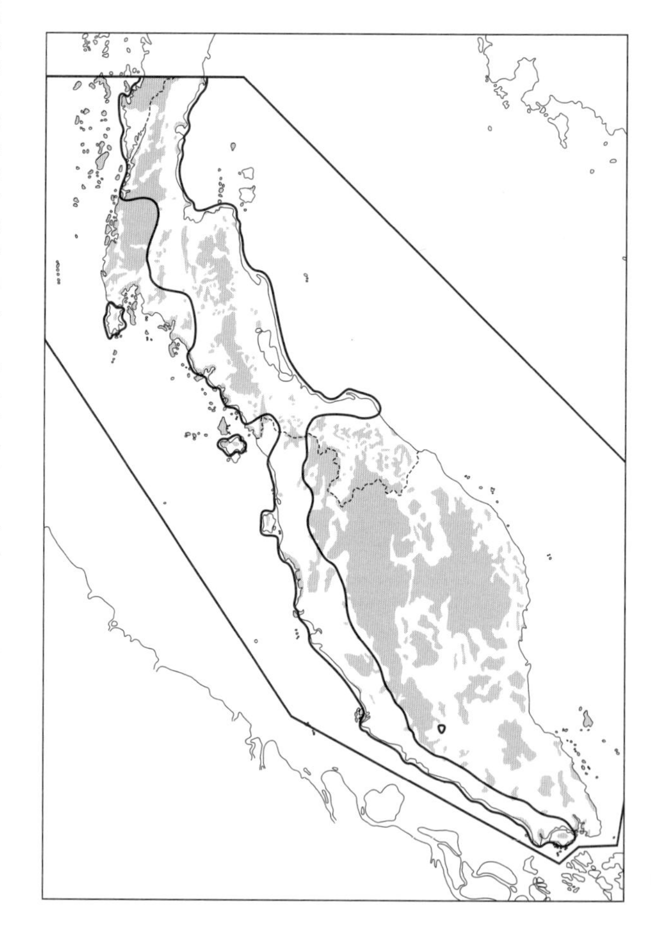

intergrades (that could easily have been overlooked also in the Peninsula). Replication of male *spilonotus*-type plumage in New Guinea, the Malagasy region and N Africa (BMNH, Vaurie 1965) supplies another reason for not recognising separate species.

STATUS AND POPULATION. A non-breeding visitor, more or less regular and uncommon to common, and an uncommon passage migrant. In most habitats, especially paddyland, the most numerous harrier by far. Typical mid-winter roosts are of ten or fewer but one found recently in S Perak held about 100 birds, including 30–40 grey adults.

HABITATS AND ECOLOGY. Natural marshland (the Thalae Noi–Songkhla system), swampy ex-dredge-mine land, rough grassland over coastal land-claims, etc., and extensive paddyland during tall-crop, harvest and fallow phases; all habitats shared variously with other harrier species. Roosts on the ground in bare fields or stubble, or perched in low bushes, the large group at Seberang Perak gathering in a young oil-palm plantation adjacent to paddyland. Where habitat persists, sites are re-used season by season.

FORAGING AND FOOD. Hunts almost exclusively during the early morning and evening, by slow-quartering a metre or so up and dropping on prey. Field margins are favoured and, post harvest, lines of remnant paddy or other tall grasses left uncut may be worked systematically, by a bird jumping into and rustling vegetation, then waiting motionless, apparently for prey to flush. Local diet unrecorded.

SOCIAL ORGANIZATION. Hunts individually, ignoring neighbours and apparently without defending space. From about one hour before dark up to last light birds converge over a radius of several kilometres to roost communally.

MOVEMENTS. Non-social. Migrates alone or only temporarily in the company of other raptors. Extreme dates are 12 September (NW Selangor) and 4 April (Singapore), 5 April (N Johor and central Selangor), with largest numbers of overwinterers present during November–March (BMP5, MBR 1986–87).

SURVIVAL. No information.

SOCIAL INTERACTIONS. No interactions noted between foragers, even though flight-paths may cross closely, but at a paddyland roost in Selangor arriving females displaced males and took over their places (Bakewell 1989).

VOICE. A single, kite-like mew, *keeau*, from a *spilonotus* closely passed by another while flying to roost.

BREEDING. No population.

MOULT. A late November female growing P9–10 and a February male suspended after renewing P1 and 6–10. Others dated November–February showed no wing-moult (BMNH, ZRCNUS).

CONSERVATION. The wintering population at Seberang Perak paddyland decreased abruptly following introduction of herbicides after harvest.

Hen Harrier; Yieo Thung Theb Neua (Thai); Lang Paya (Malay)

Circus cyaneus (Linnaeus) 1766, *Systema Naturae* 12(1): 126. TL vicinity of London, United Kingdom.

Plate 22

GROUP RELATIONS. Lumped with S American *cinereus* (Cinereous Harrier) as one free-standing species by Nieboer (1973). Mayr and Short (1970) treat *cinereus* and *cyaneus* as allospecies.

GLOBAL RANGE. At its most inclusive, breeds through southern S America, north along the Andes; and from mid-temperate to low-arctic latitudes around the N hemisphere, in Asia east to Anadyrland and Kamchatka, and south to the Tien Shan, N Mongolia, NE China, Ussuriland and Sakhalin. Northern (including apparently all Asian) populations migrate, wintering to Central America, the Mediterranean, SW Asia, the Himalayas, SE Tibet and the far-N Indian subcontinent; Japan; China south mainly from the Changjiang valley, including Taiwan; and northernmost SE Asia (NE Burma, N Vietnam), straggling to Thailand and the Peninsula.

IDENTIFICATION/DESCRIPTION. In-flight impression as Marsh Harrier but slighter and narrower-winged. Adult males are unstreaked pale grey, shading darker over the breast, with sharply demarcated white underparts and upper tail-coverts, and the outer half of the hand solidly black (smaller, slenderer male Pallid Harrier is white to the chin and has only a central wedge of longest primaries black); side of tail obscurely barred dark grey.

Other age/sex-classes are mid brown above, including wings (juveniles warmer throughout than adult female, but all ages more rufescent on the crown), with boldly white upper tail-coverts; head, neck and underparts buff-white boldly streaked black-brown, most densely over the breast. Periorbital marks creamy, and a ruff of short, curled feathers is complete around face up to ear-covert level, more obvious than in other local harriers. Outer half of tail light cinnamon, the rest as back, showing 3–4 full dark bars about the same width as intervening pale bars (except adult female has a wider apical dark bar). At all stages, the whole underside of the wing is boldly dark-barred.

Bare-part colours. (Adult) iris bright yellow (male), brown to amber or yellow (female); bill black, slaty at the base; cere greenish yellow to yellow; feet yellow to orange-yellow (BMNH, BWP).

Size (mm). (Skins: 15 males, 8 females, from China, Burma and the Peninsula; adult): wing 338–359 and 374–396; tail 212–227 and 240–261; bill from cere 14.8–17.4 and 18.1–19.1; tarsus 67.4–71.5 and 75.4–79.6 (BMNH, ZRCNUS).

Weight. No data.

DISTRIBUTION. Historical summary: *Pht, Sel, Mel, Sin.*

GEOGRAPHICAL VARIATION. Old-World nominate *cyaneus*.

STATUS AND POPULATION. Vagrant, recorded in all months November–March, but so much confusion has surrounded identification of harriers in the Peninsula that few records are totally above suspicion. Nor does it seem to have been recognized that, geographically, rather similar-looking Pallid Harrier *C. pallidus* is at least as likely to occur as Hen. The one specimen (adult male) was collected at the former Paya Lebar wetland, E end of Singapore island, in early January 1948 (ZRCNUS).

HABITATS AND ECOLOGY. Swampy, reclaimed mangrove-land, open freshwater marsh (Thalae Noi), ex-dredge-mine land, paddyland and rough, grassy scrub bordering an airfield (T. Axelson, BR 1963, 1965, 1968, 1972–73); all habitats likely to be used at times by other harrier species.

FORAGING AND FOOD. Hunts by low quartering, like other harriers but no specific information from the Peninsula.

SOCIAL ORGANIZATION. A pair together for about one month near Kuala Lumpur; other records all of loners.

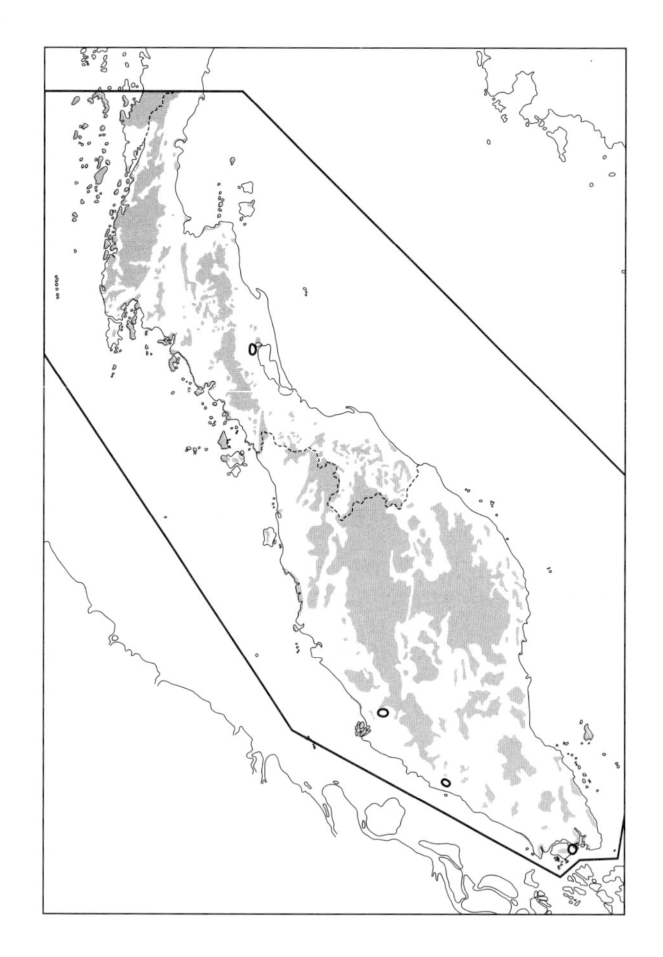

MOVEMENTS. Extreme dates are 3 November (Singapore) and 6 March (Selangor).

SURVIVAL. No information.

SOCIAL INTERACTIONS. No information.

VOICE. No information.

BREEDING. No population.

MOULT. An adult male in fairly fresh plumage in January (ZRCNUS).

CONSERVATION. Issues of wetland-loss and contamination pertaining to harriers generally; nothing specific.

Pied Harrier; Yieo Daang Dam Khao (Thai); Lang Tangling (Malay)

Circus melanoleucos (Pennant) 1769, *Indian Zoology*: 2 and plate 2. TL Sri Lanka.
Plate 22

GROUP RELATIONS. Free-standing (Nieboer 1973).

GLOBAL RANGE. Breeds in Pacific Russia, NE Mongolia, NE China (Heilongjiang) and N Korea, with apparent southern outliers in far-NE India, N Burma and N Philippines (Ripley 1982, Stanford 1936, van der Linde 1996). Over-summerers have also been recorded in Japan (Brazil 1991). Winters through the eastern Indian subcontinent and Sri Lanka; China south from the Changjiang valley and Sichuan; and in SE Asia to the Peninsula, northern Borneo and the Philippines.

IDENTIFICATION/DESCRIPTION. Smaller and proportionately narrower-winged than Marsh Harrier but with similar flight-postures and behaviour. Adult male from male *C.a. spilonotus* by head to back and breast, and median wing-coverts to alula, solidly black, sharply demarcated from white and grey parts (including fully white lesser wing-coverts), without streaking or scalloping.

Above, the adult female is dark-streaked over a brown crown and whitish collar and inner leading-edge of the wing. Alula, primary coverts and flight-feathers are silvery grey, with outer primaries tipped and all flight-feathers barred blackish on both surfaces. Rest of upperparts, including remaining wing-coverts, mid brown; upper tail-coverts variably dark-barred white. Underparts white, boldly dark-streaked over the breast; underwing white, with coverts sometimes rufous-streaked. Tail pale ash- to silvery grey with five complete dark bars (apical bar widest), in high contrast on the upper surface, shadowy below.

Juveniles resemble adult female but lack grey, are more rufescent generally, and uniform mahogany-chestnut below (including lower wing-coverts), with only the throat paler and some buff streaking on the breast. They resemble young Pallid Harrier whereas Hen Harrier is fully dark-streaked whitish below. The upper centre of the tail is darker than in adult female, hence its bars do not show as clearly (BMNH).

Claims that old females develop male colours are not supported by other morphology. A few specimens showing moult into black feathering from a partly female-type plumage were all male-sized, which suggests males pass through a female-type subadult phase (BMNH, ZRCNUS).

Bare-part colours. (Adult) iris bright yellow (conspicuous in black-headed male); bill black, cere greenish yellow; feet yellow to bright yellow (BMNH, Chasen 1939).

Size (mm). (Skins: 11 males, 6 females, including some from north of the Peninsula; adult): wing 340–363 and 362–373; tail 198–215 and 207–223; bill from cere 16.0–18.3 and 17.3–19.7; tarsus 70.9–79.1 and 77.6–83.0 (BMNH, ZRCNUS).

Weight. No data.

DISTRIBUTION. Few found east of the Main Range. Historical summary: all divisions except *Chu, Pha, Kra, Tra, Pat, Sat, Yal, Nar, Pes, Kel*, with no additional island records.

GEOGRAPHICAL VARIATION. None recognized.

STATUS AND POPULATION. A non-breeding visitor, rather local but said to be commoner in the north than the south, where juveniles are particularly scarce (Chasen 1939, ZRCNUS). Annual on the W-coast plain south to Selangor but over the last 25 years there has been only a handful of records from Singapore (SINGAV-3). Particularly in paddyland, outnumbered by Marsh Harrier (not more than four in the Seberang Perak harrier roost at mid winter 1990/91); less obviously so at drier sites.

HABITATS AND ECOLOGY. Uses more or less the Marsh Harrier range of open wetlands: natural marshland, paddyland from mid-crop to stubble and

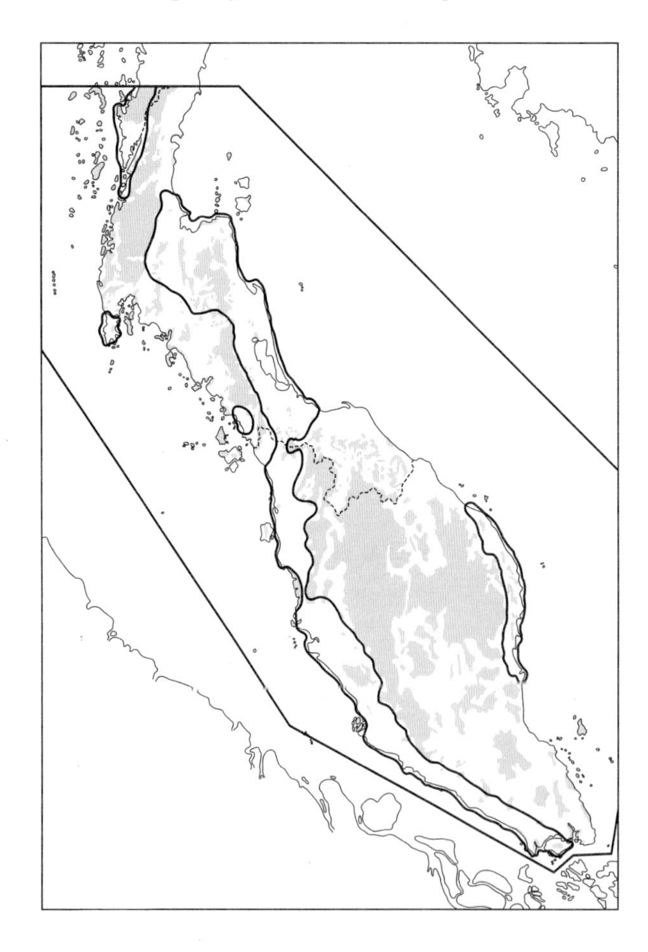

fallow stages, abandoned dredge-mine land, etc., but with greater use of drier sites, including young palm plantings and other low crops. Roosts form on bare ground, paddy-stubbles, etc., and at Seberang Perak a few joined Marsh Harriers in young oil-palms.

FORAGING AND FOOD. Forages like a Marsh Harrier, not infrequently over the same habitat-patches and at the same times of day, but no local information on diet.

SOCIAL ORGANIZATION. Hunts alone but, like other wintering harriers, evidently without defending any space. Neighbouring foragers are ignored but at dusk birds gather to roost communally with conspecifics and other harriers.

MOVEMENTS. Non-social on passage. Extreme dates are 13 October (Selangor) and 19 April (Negeri Sembilan), and overwinterers are commonest during November–March (BMP5).

SURVIVAL. No information.

SOCIAL INTERACTIONS. No information.

VOICE. Not recorded.

BREEDING. No population.

MOULT. A late-November adult male showed wing-tip (P6–10) fresher than P1–5. Other November–February birds gave no evidence of wing-moult (BMNH, ZRCNUS).

CONSERVATION. See Marsh Harrier for paddy-land issues; other Pied Harrier habitats are less contaminated, but on the decline from land-conversion.

Crested Goshawk; Yieo Nok Khao Ngawn (Thai); Lang Sikap (Malay)

Accipiter trivirgatus (Temminck) 1824, *Nouveau Recueil de Planches Coloriées d'Oiseaux* 51: plate 303. TL Sumatra.

Plate 23

GROUP RELATIONS. Forms a superspecies with *A. griseiceps* (Sulawesi Goshawk) (Mayr 1949, Wattel 1973). Juveniles are particularly similar.

GLOBAL RANGE. The W Ghats and Sri Lanka, and E-Himalayan foothills and far-NE Indian subcontinent; China south from Sichuan and Guangxi, plus Taiwan and Hainan; and SE Asia to the Greater Sunda islands and central and southern Philippines.

IDENTIFICATION/DESCRIPTION. Two-three times bulkier than commoner Japanese Sparrowhawk. At all stages, the crest is not more than a small, back-pointing, hind-crown spur. Perched, adults show dun-brown upperparts with upper tail-coverts broadly fringed white. Head grey, darkest on the crown and margined black at malar level; chin and throat sharply white, with bold black gular stripe. Remaining underparts, including underwing, white, with lateral breast-shields more or less solidly pink-rufous, strong dark streaking down centre of breast, and blackish barring over rear flanks and belly, obviously finer and denser on the trousers (not finer or denser in similar female Besra *A. virgatus*, which might occur in the far north). Lower tail-coverts plain white. All flight-feathers and both surfaces of the tail are obviously dark-barred, and lower wing-coverts dark-spotted. Soars and glides on straight and level wings, broad, blunt-tipped and with bulging inner trailing-edge.

Juveniles are pale-fringed brown above, developing broad, greyish supercilia that meet on the forehead (restricting the darker centre of the crown) and curve back to the ear-coverts. Below, creamy white with a dark gular stripe, short rows of small dark droplets radiating out from the chin, some big dark blobs on the flanks and fine dots on the lower tail-coverts. Dark barring of tail and flight-feathers narrower than in adults. It is not certain that trousers are barred in the first juvenile plumage.

Bare-part colours. Iris pale yellow (juvenile), orange-yellow (adult); bill slaty, black on the culmen, with base and cere greenish yellow and mouth-line yellow; feet bright yellow.

Size (mm). (Skins and live: 6 males, 5 females; adult): wing 209–222 and 231–246; tail 163–175 and 165–192; bill from cere 17.0–18.9 and 19.3–21.0; tarsus 60.0–64.0 and 63.6–69.4; mid-toe plus claw 47.8–54.8 and 53.2; longest crest feather 33.0–38.0 (sexes combined) (BMNH, UMBRP, ZRCNUS).

Weight (g). A Selangor female, 379.4 (UMBRP)

DISTRIBUTION. Historical summary: all divisions except *Son, Pat, Yal, Pes, Pra*, with additional island records from Lanbyi, the Similan group, Langkawi and Ubin (Singapore).

GEOGRAPHICAL VARIATION. Identified as subspecies *peninsulae* (BMP5, Deignan 1963) but surely

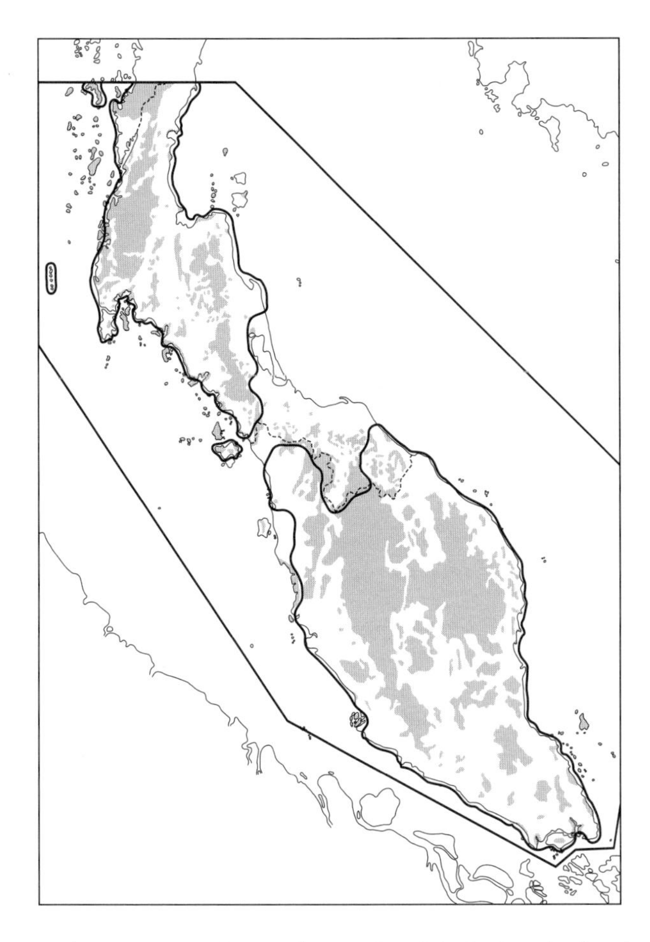

only convergently similar to this SW Indian isolate, and closer genetically to its northern neighbour *indicus* Hodgson 1836 (TL Nepal). Averaging smaller than *indicus*, and smaller in the south than the north (a Chumphon male and female wing 222 and 246 mm; not above 216 and 231 mm in Malaysia), the peninsular population is best treated as intergrading between *indicus* and small nominate *trivirgatus* of Sumatra (cf. Mayr 1949).

STATUS AND POPULATION. Resident and more or less regular but generally uncommon. Soars above the canopy less than most forest raptors, hence less often seen, but not rare in appropriate habitat.

HABITATS AND ECOLOGY. Occasional in mangroves (Parr 1988) but not confirmed from peatswamp forest; otherwise widespread in tall evergreen and semi-evergreen Lowland forest, mature and recovering from logging, at plains level and on hill-slopes to around 250 m elevation (BMP5). At least as frequent also in edge habitat, and occurs far into plantation agriculture, wherever stretches of old, overgrown rubber or other tall secondary-growth furnish retreats. Enters well wooded suburbia, e.g., is on the University of Malaya campus, Kuala Lumpur, and a Singapore pair has nested in the mid-city botanical gardens.

FORAGING AND FOOD. Still-hunts from perches in the lower canopy or mid-stratum of forest and in dense edge cover, taking prey from trees, the ground and at least occasionally in flight. Items identified include a munia, a woodpecker *Dinopium javanense* and a small squirrel *Sundasciurus tenuis*. Food brought to a female brooding young in Singapore included unidentified small mammals (C.M. Francis, MBR 1986–87, SINGAV-2).

SOCIAL ORGANIZATION. Usually solitary, but pairs soar together.

MOVEMENTS. Several sight-records of migrating Crested Goshawks (likewise of Besra) have been claimed, but none as yet accepted.

SURVIVAL. No information.

SOCIAL INTERACTIONS. Occasional loners, but mostly pairs, aerial-display at canopy height or over gaps and clearings. Regular gliding and soaring alternate with short, level passes on shallowly winnowing wings bowed below the horizontal, with extended neck and closed tail also held slightly depressed and white lower tail-coverts fluffed into a conspicuous blob either side of the tail-base (BR 1976–77). Recorded in June, October, December and January (R. Gregory-Smith, D.A. Holmes), it is given silently and is more likely to be a pair interaction than territorial advertisement.

VOICE. The only call recorded locally is a high-pitched, sunbird-like squeak, *chiup*, from an anxious captive adult.

BREEDING

Nest. Only four nests described, two of them at top-crown height, 18 and 20 m up bare-trunked, trackside *Horsfieldia* and *Dyera* trees, in one instance standing out from the forest edge. Stick-built, one was a large mass of small, dead twigs 77 cm across × 39 cm deep, the shallow, 20 cm-wide cup thickly lined with 'kelat' leaves (*Eugenia* sp.), those on top quite fresh at late-incubation stage.

Eggs and brood. Eggs plain, glossless white. Shape elliptical. Size (mm): 49.5 × 37.7 and 49.2 × 37.4 (n=2). Complete clutch two.

Cycle. After a failed (late?) attempt in July 1987, a pair in Singapore rebuilt and bred successfully during the next December–March.

Seasonality. Nest-building recorded in December, January and mid July; occupied nests (contents unchecked) in December–January, March–April and July; eggs (hard set) in mid January, and chicks in January and March (J.L. Gregory, G.C. Madoc, MBR 1986–87, NRCS, SINGAV-1, -2). 'Sparrowhawks' reported at nests in Perak in April and late May (Butler 1899b, Cairns 1963) are most likely to have been this species.

MOULT. Replacement of primaries is regular-descendant out to at least P8. Four July and early

October adults from Surat Thani to Selangor were growing P4, P6/7, P8 and P6/7; eight others dated November–January and March–early May showed no moult (and fresh plumage in November). Post-juvenile moult: P7 on 6 October, on an adult-type schedule (BMNH, BMP5, UMBRP, ZRCNUS).

CONSERVATION. As with Crested Serpent Eagle, survival in the settled lowlands depends on availability of secluded patches of well grown, at least semi-natural woodland in a diversified landscape.

Shikra; Yieo Nok Khao Chikra (Thai); Lang Cikra (Malay)

Accipiter badius (Gmelin) 1788, *Systema Naturae* 13(1): 280. TL Sri Lanka.
Plate 23

GROUP RELATIONS. Linked to *A. francesii* (Malagasy Sparrowhawk), Eurasian *brevipes* (Levant Sparrowhawk), *soloensis* (Chinese Sparrowhawk), and the small-island endemic *butleri* (Nicobar Sparrowhawk) at probably not above superspecies level (Wattel 1973).

GLOBAL RANGE. Breeds through sub-Saharan Africa, SW and S-central Asia; the Indian subcontinent and Sri Lanka; S China from Yunnan and Guizhou to Guangdong and Hainan; and SE Asia to SW Thailand and S Vietnam. Northern and some outer-tropical populations migrate, mainly within the gross breeding-range but in SE Asia reaching the Peninsula and northern Sumatra.

IDENTIFICATION/DESCRIPTION. Between Crested Goshawk and Japanese Sparrowhawk in size. Proportionately shorter-winged and larger but, when perched, can be confusingly similar to Chinese Sparrowhawk. Males of both lack barring on the upper side of the central tail-feathers, and adults that are finely pink-barred below can appear near-identical. Both species have a largely white underwing but the Shikra hand is proportionately broader and blunter, with all flight-feathers (female, juveniles) or just the wing-tip (male) dark-barred; tip never solidly black.

Juveniles resemble same-stage Chinese Sparrowhawk in being ginger-fringed brown above and white below, with blackish gular stripe (lost or faint in adults) and lines of large, mahogany-brown and rufous droplets down the breast. These widen on the flanks, whereas young Chinese Sparrowhawk has flanks and lower breast more fully dark-barred (white inter-bars broader).

Bare-part colours. (Adult) iris yellow or orange to (in older male) red; bill slaty with blackish tip; cere greenish or greenish yellow; feet yellow (Boonsong and Round 1991, Deignan 1945).

Size (mm). (Skins: 5 adults, 3 immatures; not sexed): wing 212–221 and 208–212; tail 154–172 and 154–166; bill from cere 14.7–16.0 and 13.7–16.1; tarsus 51.0–55.5 (60.8) and 52.1–53.9; mid-toe plus claw 46.4–48.3 (all) (BMNH, ZRCNUS).

Weight. No data.

DISTRIBUTION. Collected south to S Perak but with recent tentative sight identifications also in Johor, and has reached the equator in Sumatra (CLBS). Historical summary: *Pak, Chu, Ran, Sur, Pha, Phu, Kra, Tra, Son, Sat, Kel, Tru, Pek, ?Joh*, with additional island records from: Hastings, Yao Yai (*Pha*), Libong and Rembia off the W coast; and Tao (*Chu*) off the E coast.

GEOGRAPHICAL VARIATION. E Asian *poliopsis* Hume 1874 (TL Thayetmyo, S Burma).

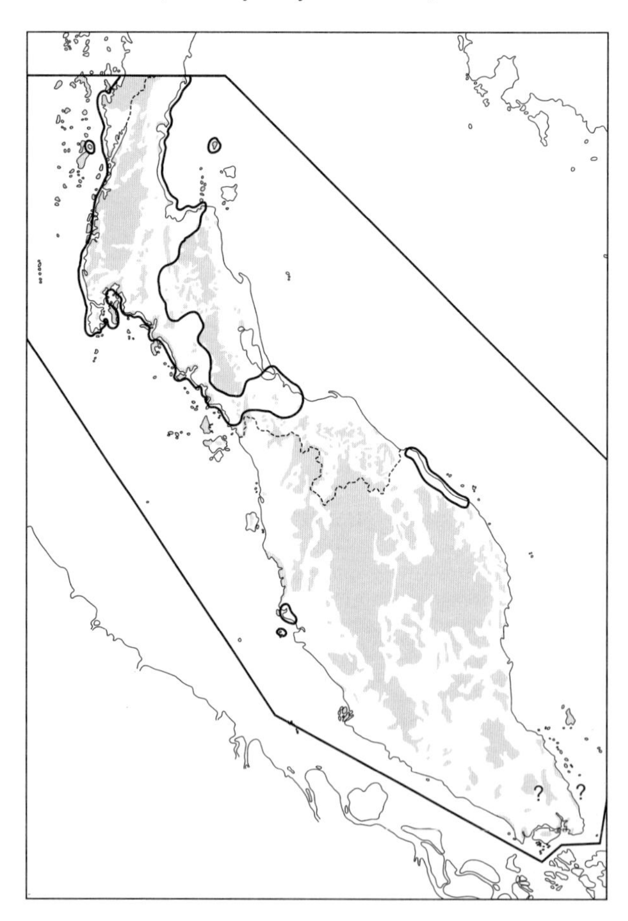

STATUS AND POPULATION. A non-breeding visitor, regular and uncommon to more or less common through Burma and the Thai provinces, sparse and erratic further south.

HABITATS AND ECOLOGY. Patchy scrub including coastal strand vegetation and semi-open agriculture, at plains level; avoids closed woodland but seen at the edge of mangroves on Libong island (Eve and Guigue 1982). The only other accipiter regular in such habitats is the smaller, more exclusively bird-hunting Japanese Sparrowhawk.

FORAGING AND FOOD. Still-hunts from concealed perches in trees, and elsewhere in SE Asia takes a mixed range of prey including a high proportion of insects and lizards. Birds are ambushed and flown down (Deignan 1945), and in Perak Edgar (1947) saw one take a Dollarbird.

SOCIAL ORGANIZATION. Solitary.

MOVEMENTS. Extreme dates 21 September and 8 March, and reported in all intervening months (BMP5, Riley 1938), which implies migrants are from a northern population. As dry-season breeders, inner-tropical Shikras would not be expected to be on the move over this period. However, a bird has been collected in N Sumatra on 18 June and two summer sightings in Johor identified at the time as out-of-season Chinese Sparrowhawks are at least as likely to have been Shikras: soaring over the slope of Panti ridge on 30 June 1979 and over the E coast at Sedili Kecil on 16 August 1986 (MBR 1986–87).

SURVIVAL. No information.

SOCIAL INTERACTIONS. No information.

VOICE. No information.

BREEDING. No population.

MOULT. Four January adults showed none and were relatively fresh. November and January juveniles had no new flight-feathers although one showed a little adult body-plumage (BMNH, ZRCNUS).

CONSERVATION. No relevant issues.

Chinese Sparrowhawk; Yieo Nok Khao Phan Jeen (Thai); Lang Rajawali (Malay)

Accipiter soloensis (Horsfield) 1821, *Transactions of the Linnean Society* 13(1): 137. TL Java.
Plate 23

GROUP RELATIONS. See Shikra, with which some breeding overlap may occur in S China (Cheng 1987).

GLOBAL RANGE. Breeds in S Ussuriland, Korea and China south and west to Sichuan and Guangxi. In autumn, migrants range from the Nicobar islands and Hainan through SE Asia, Wallacea and W Micronesia to western islands of New Guinea, over-wintering mainly in the south and east of this range.

IDENTIFICATION/DESCRIPTION. The sexes differ in tone: adult males bluer grey above and washed generally paler pink or pink-grey below; females more slaty above and averaging more russet-pink on the breast and trousers, some individuals finely barred. Perched, pale individuals are a near colour- and pattern-match for Shikra while darkest birds resemble the brightest of male Japanese Sparrowhawks, the latter separable by their combination of completely dark-barred upper tail-surface and greenish rather than orange-yellow cere. Older males of all three species have red eyes.

In overhead flight, adults are distinctively bi-coloured, black wing-tips sharp against otherwise immaculate white underparts (pink tones not detectable at a distance). The longer, more pointed hand of Chinese Sparrowhawk also gives it a slimmer, distinctly more rakish appearance than blunter-winged congeners, and a lighter, more agile flight-action.

Shape and size apart, juveniles differ from same-stage Shikra in averaging slightly sootier brown above (but with the same ginger fringing) and tending to be more fully barred across the lower breast and flanks, with narrow russet bars extending on to the trousers. The underwing pattern is as in adults except flight-feathers are not as pale (obvious in part-moulted birds), and in some the tip is dark-barred rather than solidly dark (BMNH).

Bare-part colours. (Adult) iris bright yellow (female), rich red (male); bill black, cere clear yellow to orange; feet orange yellow (Deignan 1945, Knystautas 1987).

Size (mm). (Skins: 5 adults, one juvenile; none sexed): wing 187–194 and 181; tail 128–131 and 123; bill from cere 11.7–12.7 and 12.6; tarsus 41.5–44.9 and 41.7 (BMNH, ZRCNUS).

Weight. No data.

DISTRIBUTION. Historical summary: *Kra, Tra, Son, Sat, Ked, Pek, Phg, Sel, Neg, Mel, Joh, Sin*, with additional island records from the Surins (*Ran*), Yao Yai (*Pha*), Langkawi, Rembia, Jarak and Pisang off the W coast; and Ubin and Sentosa, Singapore.

GEOGRAPHICAL VARIATION. None recognized.

STATUS AND POPULATION. On migration routes during passage, regular and more or less common. Claims of wintering in the Peninsula (BMP5) hang on a bird from Yao Yai island, Phangnga bay, collected on 26 January. All other evidence implies exclusively passage status, with many migrants at both seasons although in much smaller numbers than Japanese Sparrowhawk – by a factor of nine, calculated from sample day-counts over Singapore (Ollington and Loh 1992).

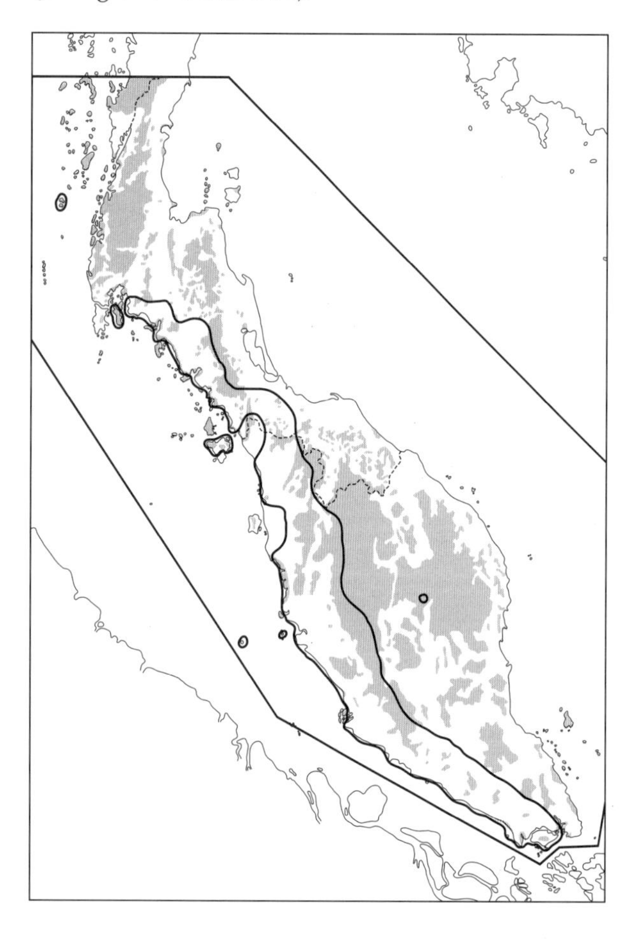

HABITATS AND ECOLOGY. The few records of birds not actively migrating have been from scrubby habitats with scattered tree-cover, including disturbed coastal strand woodland and abandoned rubber plantation.

FORAGING AND FOOD. No local information.

SOCIAL ORGANIZATION. Social on migration, typically in small, exclusive groups (maximum count seven: BBCB-6), but sometimes alone or with Japanese Sparrowhawks.

MOVEMENTS. Extreme dates are 26 and 28 September on the Kedah/Songkhla border and over Singapore, and 15 April at Cape Rachado, Negeri Sembilan. Records cover all intervening months but with none through the main part of January and obvious concentrations during October–November and March (BR 1974–75, R. Gregory-Smith, SINGAV-3, -4). Small-island records from the Melaka Straits imply southward movement continues to the beginning of January, and north-heading migrants have been seen over the Selangor plain as of 3 February (BR 1978–79, ZRCNUS).

There is regular passage across Singapore and in spring some birds make landfall at Cape Rachado (BR 1974–75), but records from Rembia and Jarak islands, well north of the narrow section of the Melaka Straits, imply routing is not constrained by big water-gaps. On the mainland, most records are from the W-coast plain, north to Krabi (U. Treesucon), but a migrant has also been seen over Taman Negara in the eastern lowlands, and shoulders of the Main Range are crossed to at least 1500 m altitude (BMP5, MBR 1982–83).

SURVIVAL. No information.

SOCIAL INTERACTIONS. No information.

VOICE. No information.

BREEDING. No population.

MOULT. Apart from an early November bird retaining an old P10, adults dated October–December showed all-fresh plumage, implying moult is mostly completed before autumn arrival. The slightly worn wing-tips of a November juvenile suggest a different schedule (BMNH, ZRCNUS).

CONSERVATION. No relevant issues.

Japanese Sparrowhawk; Yieo Nok Khao Phan Yeephun (Thai); **Lang Sewah** (Malay)

Accipiter gularis (Temminck and Schlegel) 1844, Siebold's *Fauna Japonica, Aves*: 5 and plate 2. TL Japan.

Plate 23

GROUP RELATIONS. Rejection of evidence for breeding sympatry with *A. virgatus* (Besra) in China re-opens the possibility of these sparrowhawks being conspecific. Less size- but more colour- and pattern-dimorphism between the sexes, shape-differences from *virgatus*, and greatest size-divergence between the two most closely-approaching (island) breeding populations of *gularis* and *virgatus*, indicate otherwise (Mees 1981). They are more likely to form a superspecies (Stresemann and Amadon 1979).

GLOBAL RANGE. Breeds in S Siberia east from the upper Ob drainage and on Sakhalin, also N Mongolia, NE China as far as the Yellow Sea, Korea and Japan including the Nansei islands. All except southern island populations migrate, wintering probably in the eastern Indian subcontinent and Bay of Bengal islands; perhaps far-S China (but only on passage at Hong Kong: Chalmers 1986); through SE Asia; in Sulawesi and the Lesser Sunda islands as far as Timor; and to W Micronesia.

IDENTIFICATION/DESCRIPTION. In all age/sex-groupings the tail is fully dark-barred on both surfaces (four bars show above) and the gular stripe hair-fine to absent. The adult male is slaty black above, with cheeks to sides of throat grey, chin, throat and lower tail-coverts white, the rest of the underparts narrowly and densely barred or washed pale pink-grey to rusty orange (see also Chinese Sparrowhawk). Adult females are dark, dun-brown above with white-streaked supercilium and greyish face. Below white, barred grey-brown except on lower tail-coverts. Juveniles are brighter, less sooty brown above than same-stage Chinese Sparrowhawk with lighter, brighter feather-fringing (cinnamon on back and wing-coverts, rufous-cream on inner secondaries and their coverts), and a more obviously white-streaked supercilium, back to the nape. Below, they are creamy with brown to dull cinnamon streaking over the breast giving way to bold, wide-spaced chevron marks and bars back to flanks and trousers.

At all ages, lower wing-coverts are creamy white, heavily dark-spotted, and flight-feathers fully barred shading to grey-brown apically but with no sharply defined dark wing-tip. The proportionately shorter tail and shorter, rounder hand give a more compact flight-shape than Chinese Sparrowhawk. When cruising fast, commonly alternates a few sharp wing-beats and a shooting glide but in sustained flight, including while migrating, flaps more continuously. As Chinese Sparrowhawk, climbs fast in thermals.

Bare-part colours. Iris light yellow (juvenile), rich yellow (adult female) or red (adult male), eyelid-rim pale greenish yellow; bill blue-grey, upper mandible tipped black; cere and mouth-line dirty green to yellowish green (*contra* Chinese Sparrowhawk); feet greenish yellow (immature) to bright yellow (adult).

Size (mm). (Skins: 11 males, 9 females; adult): wing 162–175 and 189–197 (210); tail 112–118 and 129–140 (148); bill from cere 10.9–11.7 and 11.5–13.1; tarsus 45.8–49.3 and 50.0–53.9; mid-toe plus claw 31.6–35.8 and 37.5–40.4. Juveniles range smaller on most measurements (wing down to 157 and 181) (BMNH, ZDUM, ZRCNUS).

Weight (g). Males, 84–101 (n=8); two females, 127, 133 (McClure 1964, PERHILI TAN, UMBRP, ZDUM).

DISTRIBUTION. Historical summary: all divisions except *Pak, Ran, Nak, Yal, Nar*, with additional, mostly passage-dated, island records from the Similan group,

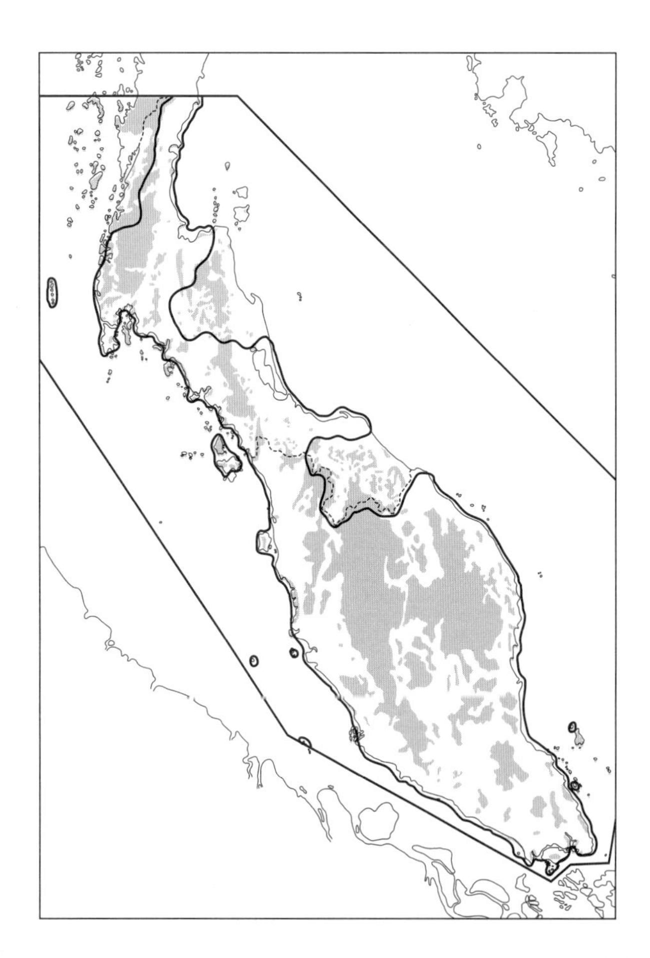

Phiphi, Libong, Tarutao, Langkawi, Penang, Rembia, Jarak and Pisang off the W coast; the Pahang–Johor archipelago (Tulai, Sibu) off the E coast; and Ubin, Seletar, St John's, Sentosa, Semakau, Pawai and Sudong around Singapore.

GEOGRAPHICAL VARIATION. Provisionally, only nominate *gularis* recognized but an exceptionally large, pale adult female from Singapore, wing 210, tail 148, bill from cere 11.5, tarsus 52.7 (ZRCNUS), could represent another population.

STATUS AND POPULATION. A passage migrant and non-breeding visitor, regular and uncommon to common. The mass of dated records, and all those in the north, are in passage months, with evidence of overwintering only south from Thalae Noi wetland, Phatthalung. Below latitude approximately 4°N, winterers are widespread.

Sampled along transects out to the coast, roughly 59 000 migrants are estimated to have crossed Selangor during the peak month of southward movement in the early–mid 1960s (BR 1963, 1964, 1965). This was a main route at that time, but lesser movements along the Malaysian E coast, inland including over the Main Range, and many records from islands in the Andaman Sea and northern Melaka Straits suggest broad-front passage probably involved much larger numbers overall. Since the 1970s, W-coast movements have been lighter, signalling a population decline or, perhaps, a dilution of the front as line-soaring conditions improved with forest clearance east of the Main Range (MBR 1982–83). Numbers exiting via Singapore (believed to draw from both coastal plains) have not altered much since that time, although passage there has never been heavy (hourly counts hardly ever above two figures) (BR 1963, 1964, Ollington and Loh 1992, SINGAV-1).

HABITATS AND ECOLOGY. Winterers are only occasionally found inside closed-canopy forest. Typical edge birds, they occur mostly along the margin of forest and in a variety of semi-open, agricultural and settled landscapes (even well-wooded suburban gardens), wherever open ground is interspersed with tree-cover, from the mangrove zone to at least 2000 m on the Main Range (Edgar 1947, McClure 1964). Extensive, clean plantation monocultures are sub-optimal habitat, perhaps because of their generally reduced densities of bird prey.

FORAGING AND FOOD. Hunting by surprise attacks from low-level flight in the open is common in the evening, including at visits made to gathering roosts of munias and swallows. At dusk, has also been seen chasing bats (Ollington and Loh 1992), and a male mobbed by swallows at last light appeared from its actions to be taking insects, though this was not confirmed. Suspected strategy-differences between the sexes in winter need research, but through the main part of the day males commonly ambush prey from a tree-crown, with a highly agile but relatively short chase through cover. During two recent winters at Fraser's Hill, possibly the same male regularly attended a Glossy Swiftlet colony, launching from a nearby tree-perch as birds emerged soon after dawn – but was never seen to make a capture (K.W. Scriven).

Only bird prey confirmed. Most captures are small passerines and the largest item I have seen a male grab (but fail to hold) was a Black-naped Oriole *Oriolus chinensis*. Females kill prey up to the size of Spotted Dove (130 g) (SINGAV-2). Other identifications have been of: domestic chick, Barn Swallow, Tree Sparrow, Scaly breasted- and White-headed Munias, Yellow-vented Bulbul, Common Myna, Zebra Dove, and among migrants on Melaka Straits islands in autumn: Chestnut-winged, Hodgson's Hawk and Drongo Cuckoos, Blue-winged Pitta and Crow-billed Drongo (Batchelor 1958, Robinson 1927, Spittle 1952). At certain seasons, exceptional feeding opportunities become available on remote islands, and some birds actually halt at sea; including several that spent the autumn of 1982 commuting between drilling-rigs in the Terengganu off-shore oil-field, harvesting especially the grounded Barn Swallows (MBR 1982–83, D.M. Simpson).

SOCIAL ORGANIZATION. On migration, solitary to strongly gregarious; in wintering habitat, nearly always solitary.

MOVEMENTS. Eleven first-arrival dates range evenly between 2 and 21 September, independant of latitude. Southward passage is fully established by the last quarter of September, reaches peak intensity in the second quarter of October (in the mid 1960s over Selangor at hourly rates of up to 1400 birds past a single observer), with lighter movements from late October until mid December – extreme date 21 December, in Singapore (MBR 1982–83, SINGAV-4).

The earliest return date is 15 February, a loner making landfall on Cape Rachado. Along the W-coast plain generally, spring passage is less intense than in autumn; heaviest in the third quarter of March and regular for a further month, tailing off into early May (extreme date 10 May) (BMP5, BR 1968).

At both seasons, most movement is by day, and definite records of overnight roosting involve some unusual situations (Kelham 1881–83, MBR 1982–83), including a party of seven on a barge being towed out of the E end of the Singapore Straits. A night-time strike on One-Fathom Bank lighthouse, Melaka Straits (Robinson and Kloss 1922), appears to be exceptional. To some extent, migration shifts in response to thermal activity, and in autumn large numbers of W-coast birds take the option of a short sea-crossing to Sumatra via Cape Rachado. At the same time, many more northerly island records ('a continuous stream' past the Arua group in November: Robinson 1927), and presence in the Terengganu oil-field, show migration is not inhibited by much larger water-gaps. Comparative scarcity at Cape Rachado in spring, even on days when many larger migrating raptors arrive there, is another indication of sparrowhawks being relatively independent of wind conditions over the sea (cf. Oriental Honey-buzzard and Black Baza).

SURVIVAL. No information.

SOCIAL INTERACTIONS. No information.

VOICE. Squealing by a male hunting at a swiftlet roost. A shrill, tinny *teeo-teeo-tutu-tee* is believed to be a call of this hawk, but needs confirmation.

BREEDING. No population.

MOULT. Replacement of primaries is regular-descendant, but interrupted by suspensions. Most adults arrive with up to two inner primaries already renewed. Moult continues directly, although a few pre-starters have been handled up to mid December, and some birds are still active in spring (P8 on 3 and 5 April). Twenty-eight first-winterers (both sexes) dated October–late January showed no wing-moult and slight tip-wear, on an evidently different schedule (BMNH, ZDUM, ZRCNUS).

CONSERVATION. This bird predator is high on the list of Asian raptors at risk of pesticide contamination via the winter food-chain.

Grey-faced Buzzard; Yieo Naa Thao (Thai); Lang Belalang (Malay)

Butastur indicus (Gmelin) 1788, *Systema Naturae* 13(1): 264. TL Java.

Plate 23

GROUP RELATIONS. Free-standing.

GLOBAL RANGE. Breeds in Pacific Russia from S Amurland, and in S Japan, Korea and NE China as far as the Yellow Sea. Winters in the Nansei islands and China south from the Changjiang valley including Taiwan and Hainan; SE Asia (mostly east of Burma) to the Greater Sunda islands, Bali and the Philippines; and N Wallacea to western islands of New Guinea. Main migration routes appear to lie east of the Peninsula.

IDENTIFICATION/DESCRIPTION. Half to two thirds the bulk of a Brahminy Kite. The most obvious features of perched birds are (1) their face-pattern: side dark grey, sharply demarcated from white chin and throat by black malar-streak; juveniles less grey but with a broad white supercilium from forehead to nape, broken above the eye (whereas adults retain it only on the forehead); (2) their regularly dark-barred tail. Upperparts otherwise pale vinous-brown, white fringes of upper tail-coverts often forming a band, conspicuous on take-off. Below, mostly clay-white, juveniles brown-streaked, adults plain vinous-brown on the upper breast, lower breast to belly and trousers dark-barred. All stages show a blackish gular stripe, bold in adults. Any resemblance to perched Crested Goshawk is quickly dispelled by the long, pointed wings, reaching close to the tail-tip.

In flight, wings appear long, parallel-edged and proportionately narrow, inner webs of the secondaries and inner primaries forming a pale cinnamon panel chequered by narrow barring, conspicuous during soaring. On the upper side, base of primaries rufous.

Bare-Part Colours. (Adult) iris chrome-yellow; bill-tip black, base and cere pale yellow to orange; feet pale yellow (BMNH, Hume and Davison 1878).

Size (mm). (Skins: 8 adults, most not sexed): wing 311–345 (smallest a male and no female below 325; four immatures 299–310); tail 174–192; bill from cere 18.9–20.3; tarsus 56.3–61.6 (BMNH, ZRCNUS).

Weight. No data.

DISTRIBUTION. Historical summary: all divisions except *Yal*, *Nar*, *Kel*, *Pra*, with additional island records from Langkawi and Penang off the W coast; Samui and (on passage) the Pahang–Johor archipel-

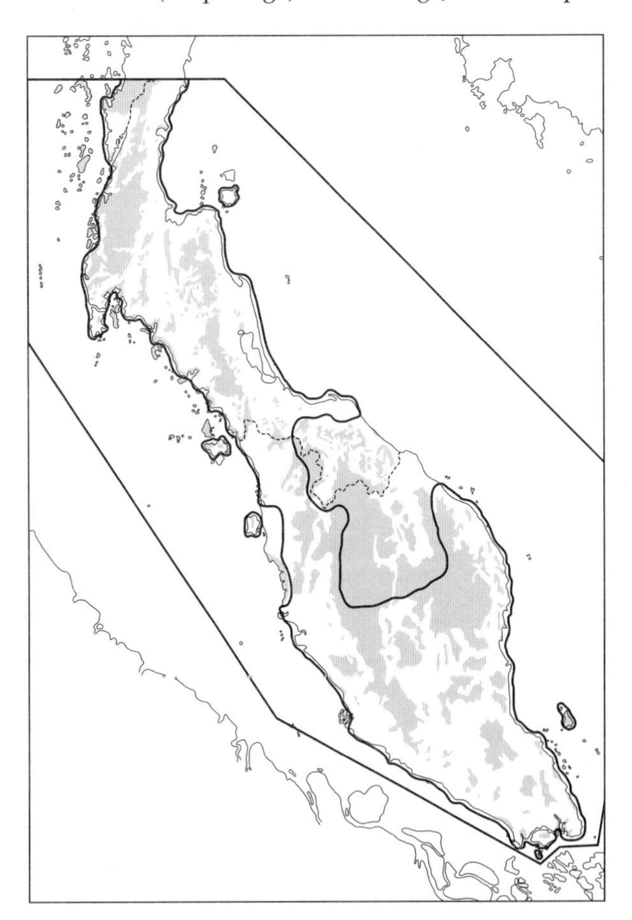

ago (Tulai, Tioman) off the E coast; and Tekong and Hantu, Singapore.

GEOGRAPHICAL VARIATION. None recognized. One report of the rare deep brown morph, from Tekong island, Singapore (SINGAV-6).

STATUS AND POPULATION. A passage migrant and non-breeding visitor. Winters throughout and fairly common in the north but local and uncommon to sparse in the south. Quite numerous at mid winter on Langkawi island (BR 1968) and dependably findable also on Penang, whereas overwintering in Singapore is exceptional.

HABITATS AND ECOLOGY. Winterers select open and semi-open situations, including large agricultural clearings where isolated trees remain and where the stumps of felled trees stand above cover-crops; also the interior of open woodland, such as rubber plantations. Natural closed-canopy forest, apparently of all kinds, is avoided.

FORAGING AND FOOD. Still-hunts from stump and mid-level tree perches, moving intermittently between search-patches. Edgar (1947) believed rats were taken, but lizards and orthopterans have been identified in stomach contents from Tenasserim (Hume and Davison 1878).

SOCIAL ORGANIZATION. Social on passage. Winterers are mostly solitary but where common 2–3 individuals may occur in the same clearing, hunting within 50–100 m of one another.

MOVEMENTS. Extreme dates of southward passage are 30 September and 6 December, with largest groups in late October–early November (counts of up to 23 on the Malaysian W coast, 33 on the E coast). Spring return reported between 20 February (Penang island) and 5 April (Terengganu).

Like other soaring raptors, thought to move only by day, waiting for morning thermals before leaving overnight roosts. In Malaysia, most migration records have been from the coastal plains, but crossings of the Main Range, e.g., at Fraser's Hill, show some birds pass inland, at least during autumn. Apparently, none leave via the Melaka Straits in autumn, and only a few returnees reach Cape Rachado in spring, during March (MBR 1982–83, 1986–87). At both seasons, substantially more occur along the SE coastline, hopping between headlands and, in spring, parties have also been watched moving between thermals over islands of the Pahang–Johor archipelago (north of which they face open sea). Absence of any obvious passage over Singapore implies this stream connects directly with the Riau archipelago (Indonesia) on a route east of the Republic.

SURVIVAL. No information.

SOCIAL INTERACTIONS. Apparent display-flights are reported from Langkawi island in mid March (BMP5).

VOICE. Described as a thin squeal (Edgar 1947), but winterers are mostly silent.

BREEDING. No population.

MOULT. Adults dated November–late February showed no more than slight wing-tip wear, and no moult; October and November-dated first-winterers retained all juvenile flight-feathers (BMNH, ZRCNUS).

CONSERVATION. No critical issues.

Common Buzzard; Yieo Thalae Sai (Thai); Lang Utara (Malay)

Buteo buteo (Linnaeus) 1758, *Systema Naturae* 10(1): 90. TL Sweden.
Plate 17

GROUP RELATIONS. Forms at most a superspecies with *jamaicensis* and *ventralis* (Red-tailed Hawk and S American Buzzard) of the Americas, Afrotropical *oreophilus* (Mountain Buzzard) and Madagascan *brachypterus* (Madagascar Buzzard) (Mayr and Short 1970, Voous 1960).

GLOBAL RANGE. Breeds across temperate to low-arctic Eurasia from N Atlantic islands to Sakhalin and Japan, south to Iran, Tien Shan, the Himalayas, NE China, and the Nansei and Bonin islands, and Marianas (Reichel *et al.* 1994). Most N-continental populations migrate, wintering in eastern Africa and SW Asia; the Indian subcontinent and Sri Lanka; Japan, Korea, China south from the Changjiang valley including Taiwan and Hainan; and continental SE Asia, straggling to Luzon, the Greater Sunda islands and Bali (Mann 1989, Mees 1971).

IDENTIFICATION/DESCRIPTION. About Brahminy Kite size. Perched birds lack easy identification marks: head and upperparts rufescent brown; underparts mostly buff-whitish, variably dark brown on trousers and belly, and dark-streaked on the breast; or all-rufescent brown. The local eagles (except distinctive Crested Serpent and very much larger Short-toed) have feathered tarsi, and larger Oriental Honey-buzzard and smaller immature

Jerdon's Baza and Grey-faced Buzzard, with bare tarsi, all have boldly patterned tails. Superficially, most like juvenile Brahminy Kite but, among various technical distinctions, bill contrasts with pale cere, lacks pale streaking on the anterior upperparts, and the distribution of white on the underwing is completely different.

In overhead flight, head short and wide, and wings proportionately broad, parallel-edged, and up-angled in a shallow V when soaring. Noticeably white flight-feathers have black tips forming a bold outer border (faint barring on the secondaries rarely visible in the field), and most individuals show a dark carpal-patch. The broad tail, often fanned, ranges from brown with variable narrow, dark barring (at a distance, not more than a blurred sub-apical bar noticeable) to plain cinnamon (overhead pale-tailed Booted Eagle has proportionately longer wings and tail, a different underwing pattern, and soars level-winged).

Bare-part colours. No local data. Range-wide, iris colour varies; bill black with bluish base and yellow cere; feet yellow.

Size (mm). (Skins: 2 males; adult): wing 364, 374; tail 193, 202; bill from cere 20.6, 22.0; tarsus 73.4, 69.6 (BMNH).

Weight. No data.

DISTRIBUTION. Historical summary: *Ran, Kra, Son, Pes, Pek, Phg, Sel, Neg, Joh, Sin,* with additional island records from Ubin, Sentosa and St John's, Singapore.

GEOGRAPHICAL VARIATION. Among only a handful of specimen-records, strength of tail-barring plus primary-emargination formula (BWP) have identified subspecies *vulpinus* Gloger 1833 (TL S Africa), *japonicus* Temminck and Schlegel 1844 (TL Japan), and apparent intergrades (BMNH, Mees 1971). A larger sample of sightings also suggests a mixed population, and the Siberian breeding-ranges of *vulpinus* and *japonicus* approach closest on roughly the longitude of the Peninsula (Vaurie 1965).

STATUS AND POPULATION. An uncommon to sparse non-breeding visitor and passage migrant, recorded in all months October–March, mostly in November and December (BR 1978–79, MBR 1982–83). Very local, and on well-watched Singapore island, where landbird migrants tend to concentrate, not more than two individuals have been found wintering in any one season (Ollington and Loh 1992, SINGAV-3).

HABITATS AND ECOLOGY. Likely overwinterers have been recorded on open marsh and rough grassland, in agriculture (including a harvested sugarcane plantation), and by a domestic waste dump in a clearing in mountain forest, from sea-level to 1500 m at Genting Highlands on the Main Range (Holmes and Wells 1975, MBR 1984–85).

FORAGING AND FOOD. One in Singapore attending a grassland fire (MBR 1982–83); no other local information.

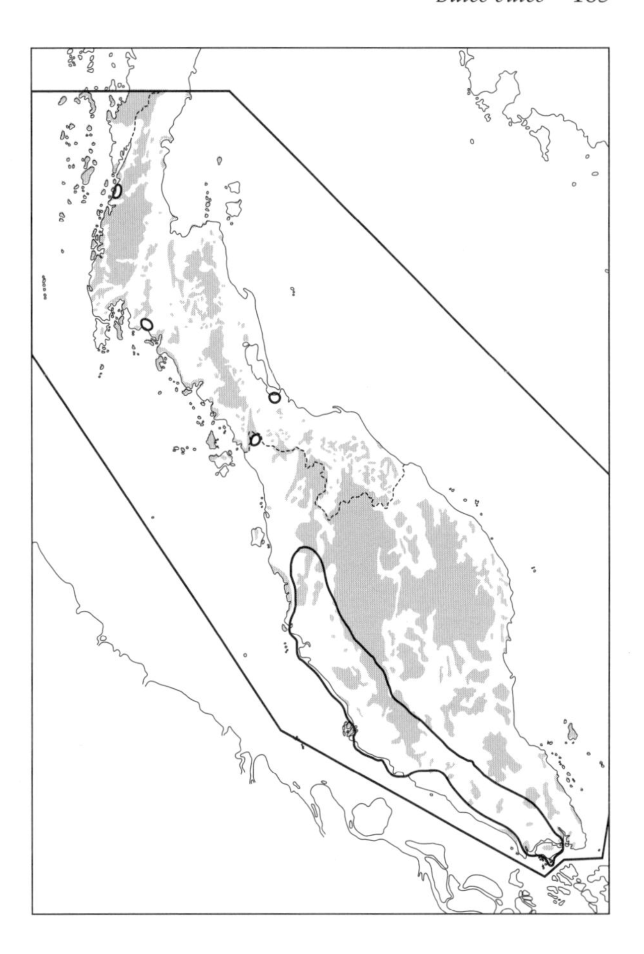

SOCIAL ORGANIZATION. Typically solitary in wintering habitat but on passage associates with other soaring raptors (including Oriental Honey-buzzard, Black Kite).

MOVEMENTS. Extreme dates are 14 October and 29 March, in Singapore and Ranong (Ollington and Loh 1992, SINGAV-4, G. Walbridge). A peak of records in November–December and small resurgence in March may reflect through-passage, confirmed by singles on 12 and 24 March making landfall over Cape Rachado in the Oriental Honey-buzzard stream crossing from Sumatra (BR 1978–79, MBR 1982–83). Birds over the S archipelago of Singapore in November–early December and late March (SINGAV-1, -4) imply some onward movement may also be routed via Riau.

SURVIVAL. No information.

SOCIAL INTERACTIONS. No information.

VOICE. No information.

BREEDING. No population.

MOULT. Undated specimens show none.

CONSERVATION. No relevant issues.

Black Eagle; Nok Insee Dam (Thai); Lang Hitam (Malay)

Ictinaetus malayensis (Temminck) 1822, *Nouveau Recueil de Planches Coloriées d'Oiseaux* 20: plate 117. TL Java.

Plate 17

GROUP RELATIONS. Free-standing. Believed not to be close to other booted eagle genera and, from juvenile plumage and other evidence, has been suspected of being related to milvine kites. However, its 'pot-hook' sky-dance display, like that of some *Hieraaetus* and *Aquila* eagles, has no recorded parallel in kites.

GLOBAL RANGE. Forested uplands of the Indian subcontinent and Sri Lanka; Fujian, Taiwan and Hainan; hill-tracts of SE Asia to the Greater Sunda islands and Bali; and Sulawesi and Halmahera.

IDENTIFICATION/DESCRIPTION. A medium-large eagle, all dark in most views and rarely seen perched. Soars and glides slowly (down to vegetation height when hunting) on level, proportionately very big wings, widest at the inner hand, and can show an impressive rack of splayed, up-swept primaries. Paleness at the extreme base of the primaries and pale barring on the tail are obvious only in good, overhead views. The juvenile has a dark crown but is otherwise very different: browner than adult above, with white upper tail-coverts; rest of head, underparts and lower wing-coverts dirty tawny-cream, boldly streaked dark brown, and dark-mottled on thighs and belly. Colours darken at successive moults, but immatures stay recognizable by their pale grey-brown tail and densely and narrowly dark-barred flight-feathers, with a tawny patch on the upper base of the primaries. Juvenile primaries do not appear as long relative to secondaries as in adults, reducing the impression of wing-size, but measurements are needed. Tarsi are feathered to base of toes, and outer toe and claw are reduced. At all ages yellow feet and cere show up conspicuously.

Bare-part colours. (Adults) iris dark brown; bill blackish, cere and mouth-line yellow; feet yellow.

Size (mm). (Skins: 2 males, 3 females; adult): wing 535, 536 and 552–592; tail 299, 316 and 316–322; bill from cere 27.1, 29.0 and 30.0–32.2; tarsus 76.7 (one male) and 78.2 (one female) (BMNH, ZRCNUS).

Weight. No data.

DISTRIBUTION. South to NW Johor. Historical summary: *Sur, Nak, Kra, Pht, Tra, Ked, Kel, Pek, Phg, Sel, Neg, Mel, Joh*, with no island records. The gap within ostensibly suitable habitat at the north end of the Peninsula is unlikely to be natural.

GEOGRAPHICAL VARIATION. Nominate *malayensis* of SE Asia. White on face and throat and contrasting black gular stripe, described from the

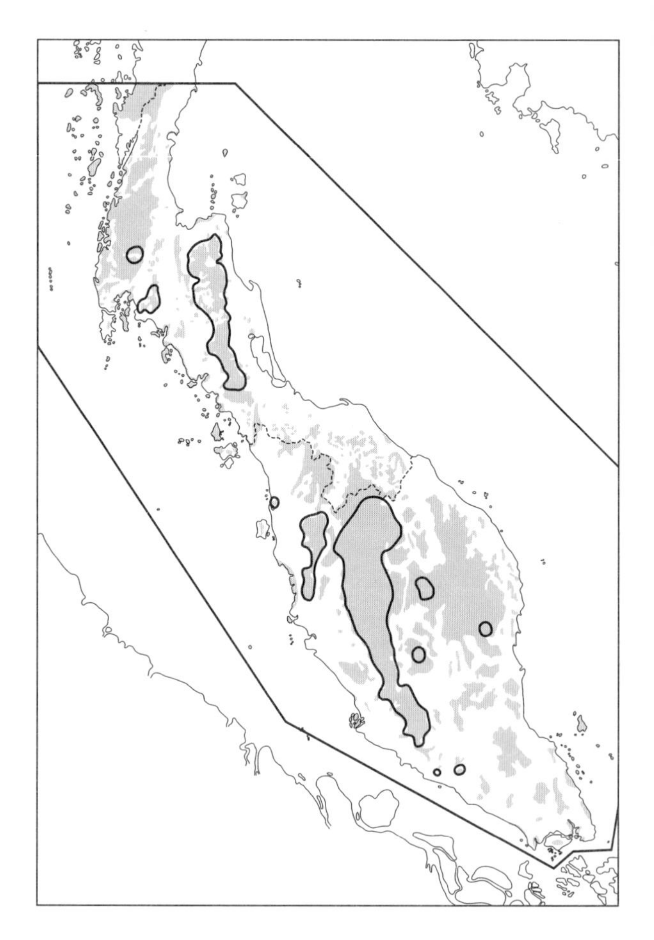

Indian subcontinent and N Thailand (Deignan 1945, HBI), have not been seen in the Peninsula.

STATUS AND POPULATION. Resident and more or less regular but uncommon, with pairs occupying an apparently very large home range. Recorded around Khao Sok (Surat Thani) and neighbouring Krabi-border outliers; along the E-central Range from Khao Luang to the Khao Pu and Khao Banthad sanctuaries (Trang/Phatthalung divide) (Robinson and Kloss 1910–11, 1923a, Round 1988); and on the Larut and Main Ranges and outliers: Jerai (Kedah) in the west; Ledang (NW Johor) in the south; Benom, Tahan and, more distantly, Tapis (Pahang) in the east (Batchelor 1958, BR 1972–73, Bromley 1949, R. Gregory-Smith, Madoc 1960, Medway 1972). No confirmation yet from the E-coast Range.

HABITATS AND ECOLOGY. Major slopes at all altitudes, with most sightings over Montane forest (up to the highest summits), and occasionally hunts over highland tea plantations. Found much less often in the lowlands, but ranges out on low, forested spurs, and in June 1985 several times seen around the vegetated summits of giant karst towers in the upper Sok valley. A sight-record of one quartering low over rubber plantation on the coastal plain of Melaka (ENGGANG-2) is exceptional.

FORAGING AND FOOD. None of the information from other parts of the range has been confirmed locally. Presumed foraging birds glide slowly, low over the relatively smooth surface of Upper Montane forest and between emergent crowns lower down. Natural evergreen forest excludes below-canopy hunting, but in N Sumatra I have watched a bird search over dense understorey vegetation while manoeuvring between tree-boles in a mature pine plantation.

SOCIAL ORGANIZATION. Solitary or occasionally hunts in pairs, and I have seen an adult noisily mantling what may have been prey in a tree-crown while another sat passively by. The largest free-flying social unit confirmed is a pair and one juvenile.

MOVEMENTS. Some wandering, but sightings at regular localities year-round imply established pairs are sedentary.

SURVIVAL. No information.

SOCIAL INTERACTIONS. 'Pot-hook' sky-dance display by a silent loner about 50 m above the canopy of Main Range Montane forest: three-quarter closure of the wings to flip into a steep, volplaning dive through a U-loop up to a near-vertical stall, then another dive, with many repeats over a short distance.

VOICE. G.C. Madoc describes a rather shrill yelp, *wee-a-kwek*, evidently more *Hieraaetus* than *Aquila*-like.

BREEDING. No nest reported. The only direct evidence of activity is aerial display in February and a bird carrying a large branch, flushed out of a tree-crown on the Main Range ridge near Fraser's Hill on 1 March (G.C. Madoc). A nest at Berastagi, N Sumatra, was a large, deep, stick-built structure in the crown-fork of a tall, clean-boled pine. Copulation took place on the nest, after the male landed directly on to the female's back.

MOULT. Two dated December and March showed none. On 2 September, a Perak male had shed P4, with P10 in remnants of its sheath, but showed no variation in the age of complete primaries. Undated birds growing P4 and P6 also showed no clear wear-differences among other feathers (BMNH, ZRCNUS). Order of replacement is unlikely to be simple.

CONSERVATION. Not exceptionally wary but seen progressively less often where disturbance and human traffic have regularly increased, as at Genting Highlands and Fraser's Hill on the Main Range.

Greater Spotted Eagle; Nok Insee Peek Lai (Thai); Lang Berbintik (Malay)

Aquila clanga Pallas 1811, *Zoographia Rosso-Asiatica* 1: 351. TL Russia.
Plate 24

GROUP RELATIONS. Probably free-standing.

GLOBAL RANGE. Breeds in mid temperate to low arctic Eurasia from E Europe to Ussuriland, south through NE China to the Yellow Sea, with outlying populations in Kazakhstan and the Altai, and the northern Indian subcontinent. Northern birds migrate, wintering in NE Africa and SW Asia; the Indian subcontinent; far-S China including Taiwan; and through SE Asia to subcoastal wetlands of SE Sumatra (Verheugt *et al.* 1993).

IDENTIFICATION/DESCRIPTION. Often on the ground or perched on a post, on which stance more upright, less horizontal than that of larger congeners. A medium-large eagle, roughly twice the bulk of Brahminy Kite. Full adults are dark brown (the rare clay-brown morph reported only once) whereas juveniles are richer, near-black with the following distribution of white: spots on the mantle and all upper wing-coverts (strongest on tips of greater coverts and scapulars), trailing-edge of secondaries and fringe to tail, horseshoe-shaped upper tail-covert band and centre-rump mark, streaks on legs, and belly to lower tail-coverts. Subadults commonly show dark trousers slashed with dirty buff streaks, sometimes also a short whitish 'sock' before the whole tarsus darkens. In isolation, some perched subadults are confusable with similar-stage Steppe Eagle (also showing pale spotting but never any on lesser wing-coverts, scapulars or body). Structural pointers are the narrowness of the trouser feathering, exposing most of the length of the tarsus (versus shaggy, concealing the tarsus in Steppe) and corner of the mouth anterior to the rear margin of the eye.

Soars on level wings with variably decurved hand, and looks bulky in flight: head proportionately broad and short; wings blunt-ended and broad to very broad, with straight or bulging inner trailing-edge; tail broad, depending on wing trailing-edge shape appearing rather short, round-ended to slightly wedge-shaped (but beware effects of moult and abrasion in other species). Lower wing-coverts are slightly to obviously darker than secondaries, and most birds show a pale base to both surfaces of the primaries. Greater Spotted never has a pale nape-patch, or a wedge of wholly pale inner primaries dividing the flight-feather row (cf. Inskipp and Inskipp 1985).

Bare-part colours. (All age-groups in the field) iris darkish brown; bill slaty black, cere and mouth-line conspicuously pale yellow; toes pale yellow (tarsus fully feathered).

Size (mm). (Skin: one first-winterer, not sexed): wing 525; tail 256; bill from cere 35.6; tarsus 95.5 (ZRCNUS).

Weight. No data.

DISTRIBUTION. Overlooked in the north and few records from Malaysia east of the Main Range. Historical summary: *Pht, Sat, ?Pes, Ked, Pra, Pek, Sel, Neg, Mel, Joh, Sin*, and on Sentosa island, Singapore.

GEOGRAPHICAL VARIATION. None recognized.

STATUS AND POPULATION. A non-breeding visitor, local and sparse to more or less common, and a sparse passage migrant. Apart from a young Greater Spotted collected in Singapore in autumn 1936 (Chasen 1939), *Aquila* eagles began to be noticed in the field only as of the early 1960s (some, probably including this species, in Perlis in 1962). As wide-ranging opportunists in winter, they are likely to have responded to environmental change favouring large, open-ground scavengers, although the few records of the first ten years were all on passage dates (including of ones and twos making spring landfall over the mid Melaka Straits coast: BMP5).

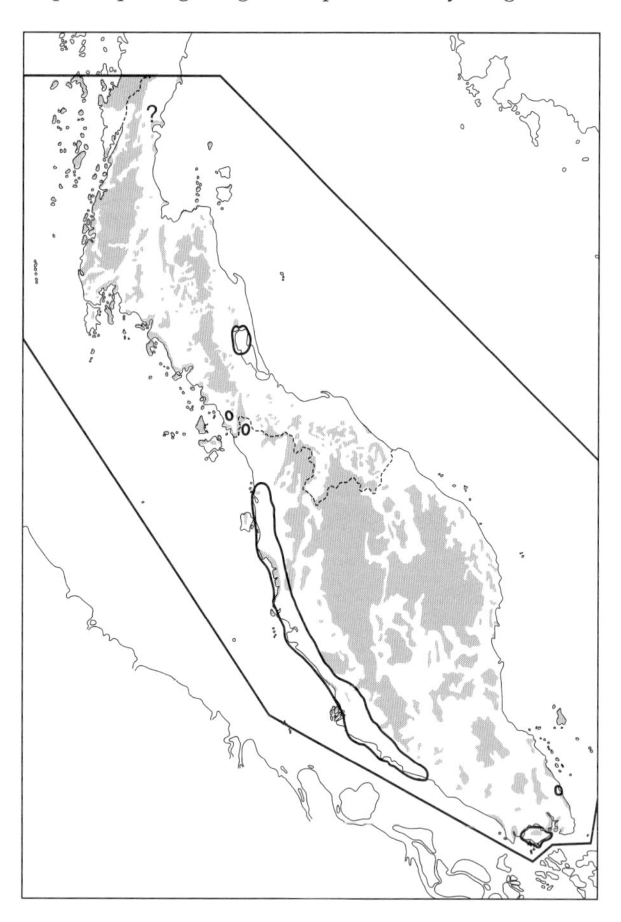

Typical natural habitat is extensive only in the Thalae Noi–Songkhla wetland, and surveys recorded winterers there through 1975/76 (Storer 1976). From the late 1970s, some wintered in Malaysian W-coast paddylands, with up to four birds also at a coastal site in Singapore (BR 1978–79). An upward trend through the 1980s produced peak counts of 10–13 on the Sekinchan paddy-plain (NW Selangor) in early March 1986 and eight on the Ponggol grassland (Singapore) in December 1989, with newly developed paddylands at Seberang Perak (S Perak) attracting attention over the same period. Three years later, it abruptly reversed, leaving hitherto dependable W-coast sites mostly abandoned and, since 1993, no reports at all from Singapore. Throughout, immatures have been the principal edge-of-range pioneers, strongly outnumbering adults.

HABITATS AND ECOLOGY. Open marsh, lake-margin, wet grazing and other rough grassland, vicinity of a large domestic waste dump (five birds at Serangoon dump in 1991), a cattle farm (BR 1978–79), and the largest tracts of open paddyland (free of interspersed orchards and housing) from harvest to the next cultivation phase, i.e., typically on bare, dry fields.

The paddyland attraction has been carrion, notably rats (mainly *Rattus argentiventer*), dead in large numbers on the surface after post-harvest control methods shifted from mechanical to mostly chemical, using zinc phosphide and super-warfarin baits. These might have caused some secondary poisoning (see Barn Owl) but evidence is lacking, and the main down-turn in eagle numbers coincided with a later trend away from poisons, back to modifying rat breeding-habitat and other biological control methods. A factor suggested for Singapore has been the end of pig-farming, former source of food in the favoured Ponggol area (R.F. Ollington).

FORAGING AND FOOD. In paddyland, takes rat and other small-animal carrion, including frogs and nestling waterbirds (rails, bitterns), etc., killed during harvest or harrowing of fallow cover. Much of the early part of the morning is spent loafing on posts or the ground, or walking about searching. Low soaring begins at mid morning, and in this way birds finding food quickly attract the attention of others. At Sekinchan, a kleptoparasitic attack by three on a flying Black Kite carrying food was successful (MBR 1986–87), but a pair that jostled a juvenile Steppe Eagle for the rat it was eating failed, and backed off when run at. On the hottest days, feeding ceases and birds either soar high or roost in shady tree-crowns.

SOCIAL ORGANIZATION. Roosts and loafs alone or in small groups, searches individually but also exploits others for food-finding and, where pickings are rich in paddyland, several may wait in a loose, apparently peaceful group around a field being worked by a tractor. Up to three seen in company on migration, including on sea-crossings (BMP5, MBR 1984–85, Ollington and Loh 1992).

MOVEMENTS. Extreme dates overall are 25 October and 5 May (MBR 1984–85, SINGAV-6). *Aquila* eagles over the Rap Ro hills (Chumphon) in the first two weeks of October 1987 (BBCB-4), earlier than any seen further south, were not identified to species. In spring, possible Melaka Straits crossings are dated February and March. However, mobility linked to the N–S staggering of the winter rice harvest makes it difficult to define true passage-seasons. Monitored in Singapore, some individuals may have settled on sites for up to four months, but many Singapore records were in November–December, i.e., before the onset of prime field conditions in Malaysia.

SURVIVAL. No information.

SOCIAL INTERACTIONS. One of a pair soaring together over Sekinchan paddyland on 10 March broke into 'pot-hook' displays, volplaning through shallow U-loops between sharp peaks.

VOICE. Ordinarily silent. Ringing barks during aerial display.

BREEDING. No population.

MOULT. No data.

CONSERVATION. Globally vulnerable (BTW2) but no certain local issues. If secondary poisoning on paddyland really has occurred, removal of the scavenging opportunity has to have been a good thing. Replacement of non-specific chemical rodenticides is just one step towards returning this important agricultural environment to biological usefulness in the Peninsula.

Steppe Eagle; (no Thai name); **Lang Gurun** (Malay)

Aquila nipalensis Hodgson 1833, *Asiatick Researches* 18(2): 13 and plate 1. TL Nepal.
Plate 24

GROUP RELATIONS. Widely accepted as distinct from the *A. rapax* (Tawny Eagle) complex of Africa and the Indian subcontinent (Amadon 1982, Clark 1992), but related at probably not above superspecies level.

GLOBAL RANGE. Breeds in mid temperate Eurasia, recently from the Black Sea to Mongolia, Transbaikalia and W and N China. Migratory, wintering through eastern Africa and parts of SW Asia; the Indian subcontinent except the south; far-S China including Hainan; and western SE Asia to the Peninsula, possibly also SE Sumatra (Verheugt *et al.* 1993).

IDENTIFICATION/DESCRIPTION. A very large eagle, over 1.5 times the bulk of Greater Spotted and about equal to Imperial Eagle. Like these, spends much time loafing on open ground or low perches such as field marker posts. Juveniles are plain *café-au-lait* with flight-feathers and tail mainly black and the following parts white: fringe of tail; a sharply defined, horseshoe-shaped upper tail-covert band; broad fringe to primary, median and greater wing-coverts; trailing-edge of secondaries; base and the upper surface (only) of a complete inner wedge of primaries; lower tail-coverts; and a wide, apical band along the full length of the lower wing-coverts (diagnostic).

Subadults turn dark, dun brown and progressively lose white, except at upper base of primaries and, for some time, a median streak on the rump (as also in some subadult Greater Spotted). Alone on the ground, structurally from Greater Spotted by shaggy trouser-feathering, concealing most tarsus, and mouth-corner opposite to well behind rear margin of eye. From perched subadult Imperial Eagle by bill colour and lack of any streaking or mottling. Adult from same-stage Imperial by being brown rather than blackish, with pale cap to nape-patch (if present) demarcated *above* face level, and no dark apical band on the tail.

Soars and glides on level wings with hand flat to slightly decurved. Long-necked like Imperial Eagle, and the tail appears longer, more square-cut than in Greater Spotted, but can wear down to a wedge (emphasized by growth of new central feathers). In flight, once the white underwing band has been lost, confusion is most likely with Greater Spotted. Head-posture, 'loose-handed' wing-shape, lower wing-coverts not darker than secondaries, and lower tail-coverts as dark as rest of under-body are pointers.

Bare-part colours. Iris brown; bill black with slaty lower base, cere and mouth-line bright yellow (cf. Imperial Eagle); toes bright yellow (tarsus fully feathered).

Size (mm). (Skins: 8 subadults and adults from NE India and Burma; most not sexed): wing 537–612; tail 265–303; bill from cere 38.0–44.3; tarsus not measured (BMNH).

Weight. No data.

DISTRIBUTION. Overlooked in the north and, in Malaysia, no records from east of the Main Range. Historical summary: *Phu, Pek, Sel, Sin*.

GEOGRAPHICAL VARIATION. Presumed nominate *nipalensis*, but none handled. Mouth-length relative to the eye varies, and needs investigating.

STATUS AND POPULATION. A non-breeding visitor and possible passage migrant, local and sparse to uncommon. Recorded in all months November–March, but the only Thai records have been on likely autumn-passage dates. Presence first detected in the mid 1970s: three large, dark eagles with narrow-barred wings and tail, migrating low over Perak island, mid-N Melaka Straits on 19 November 1976 (N.P.E. Langham). A decade later, in late February 1986, a juvenile appeared on paddy-stubbles at Sekinchan, NW Selangor, and the following winter a juvenile and two sub-adults at the beginning of February and five subadults and an adult during early March (MBR 1986–87). In every subsequent year on this coast, and also in the Ponggol–Serangoon area of Singapore, Steppe numbers approached or equalled those of Greater Spotted (R.F. Ollington, SINGAV-3, -6), until 1992, when the migration stopped (a last, lone juvenile moving across the W end of Singapore island on 1 November).

HABITATS AND ECOLOGY. Not observed to differ from Greater Spotted Eagle, and occurred alongside that species.

FORAGING AND FOOD. At Sekinchan, food found by low-soaring and, during cool hours of the day, by walking around on the ground. Took only carrion, mainly rats, eating them on the ground where found. One record of a failed attempt to rob a snake from a flying Brahminy Kite. When hunting alone on the ground, ignored nearby conspecifics, but competitive interactions took place with other *Aquila* species.

SOCIAL ORGANIZATION. Alone or, on passage, in small parties.

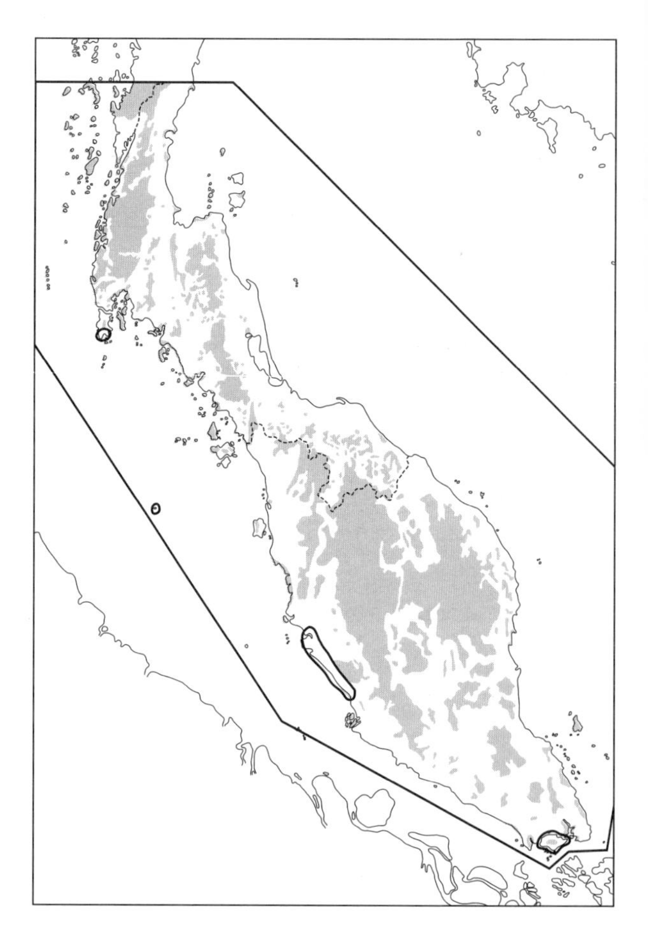

MOVEMENTS. Extreme dates 1 November and 10 March (SINGAV-6), with autumn passage continuing at least through November.

SURVIVAL. No information.

SOCIAL INTERACTIONS. No information.

VOICE. No information.

BREEDING. No population.

MOULT. No data.

CONSERVATION. See Greater Spotted Eagle.

Imperial Eagle; Nok Insee Hua Lai Khao (Thai); Lang Padang (Malay)

Aquila heliaca de Savigny 1809, *Description de l'Egypte &c. Histoire Naturelle, Système des Oiseaux de l'Egypte et de la Syrie*: 82 and plate 12. TL S Egypt.

Plate 24

GROUP RELATIONS. Free-standing.

GLOBAL RANGE. Breeds in Iberia and from central Europe and the E Mediterranean to the Tien Shan and Baikal. Resident in the far SW, migratory elsewhere, wintering in NE Africa and SW Asia; the northern Indian subcontinent; central and SE China, occasionally Korea and Japan; and in small numbers through mainland SE Asia as far as the Peninsula, possibly also SE Sumatra (Verheugt *et al.* 1993).

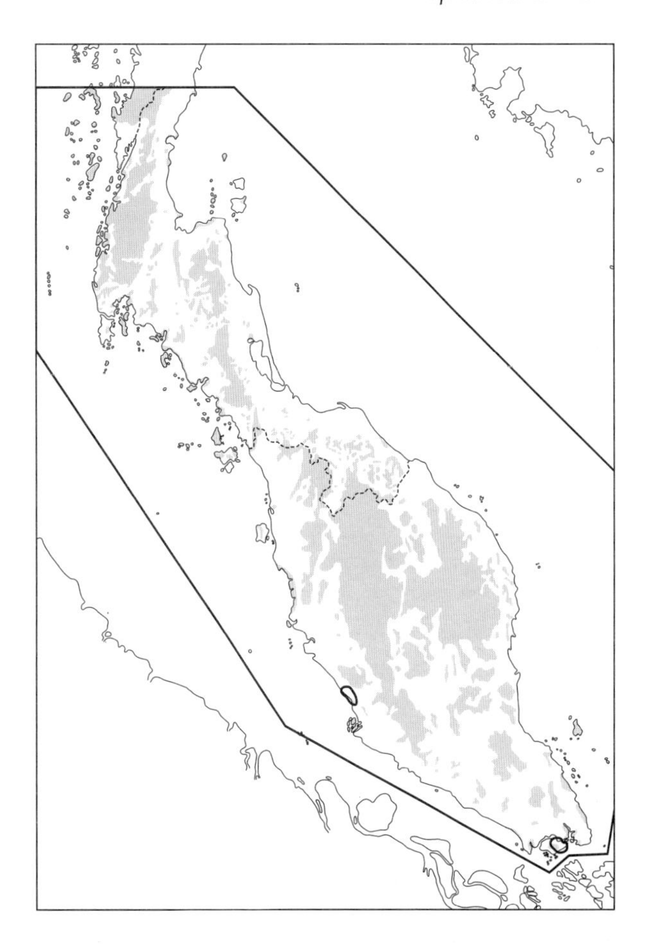

IDENTIFICATION/DESCRIPTION. Size-equivalent of Steppe Eagle. Like Steppe, stance when perched on a post, etc., more horizontal than Greater Spotted, and on the ground shaggy trouser-feathering more or less hides the tarsus. Immatures are the only local *Aquila* with cere and most of bill uniformly pale, non-contrasting.

Juvenile head, body and all wing-coverts mottled pale clay-yellow, shading to white on the rump and upper tail-coverts (a large, diffuse patch rather than the sharply delineated band of Steppe and Greater Spotted). Throat to upper belly finely but distinctly streaked dark, rear lower body plain buff-white. From above, juveniles show roughly the same pattern of white on the wing as same-stage Steppe, but a prominent wedge of whitish inner primaries divides the otherwise blackish feather-row on both surfaces. Dark flight-feathers and tail (with narrow, whitish fringe before wear) contrast with pale wing-lining, but at no stage do lower coverts show a white border.

Later-stage birds are mottled ginger-tawny, with dark ventral streaking also on the trousers, and little or no white left on the upper body. Thereafter, they darken to the blackness of young Greater Spotted, with lower wing-coverts becoming darker than flight-feathers but lower tail-coverts pale throughout (as in Greater Spotted but not in Steppe Eagle). Not all adults show the full, bi-coloured tail-pattern of pale to mottled base and broad, blackish apex, but buff-white of head-top to nape always extends down face to malar level, sharp against dark throat. Not so in Steppe, and no Greater Spotted ever shows a pale head.

In flight, neck prominent, tail full and rather square-ended, and wings parallel-sided, held level and flat when soaring, often conspicuously flexed when gliding.

Bare-part colours. Iris dark brown (juvenile) lightening to pale yellowish; cere and mouth-line pale yellowish green; bill as cere but with horn-black tip (juvenile), slate-blue with black tip (adult); toes yellow (tarsus fully feathered).

Size (mm). (Skins: 7 males, 3 females from S China; all ages): wing 557–585 and 606–629; tail 269–308 and 295–322; bill from cere 39.5–42.0 and 44.3–46.2; tarsus not measured (BMNH).

Weight. No data.

DISTRIBUTION. Evidently overlooked. Historical summary: *Sel, Sin.*

GEOGRAPHICAL VARIATION. Presumed nominate *heliaca*, but none handled.

STATUS AND POPULATION. Local and hardly more than vagrant in terms of number identified, but near-annual during the late 1980s–early 90s. Recorded in all months November–March, at the same sites in subcoastal Selangor and on Singapore island as other *Aquila* species. First detected in 1986, on the Sekinchan paddy-plain, NW Selangor: single juveniles (perhaps the same bird) there in February and March, and a subadult over the same period in 1987 (MBR 1986–87). In Singapore, a subadult photographed at Ponggol on 1 March 1987; singles there again in January and December 1989; apparently two, including the only recorded adult, in November 1990; and possibles in 1991 and on 1 January 1992 (R.F. Ollington, SINGAV-3, -4). None reported anywhere since.

HABITATS AND ECOLOGY. The same range of habitats, including fallow-season paddy-stubbles and, in Singapore, rough grassland, small wetlands and the vicinity of a large municipal tip, as Greater Spotted and Steppe Eagles; occurring alongside both. That a temporary advance of the winter range of all of these should have occurred over more or less the same timespan suggests some common controlling factor, perhaps in the local environment (see Greater Spotted Eagle).

FORAGING AND FOOD. Daily behaviour at wintering sites not distinguished from other *Aquila* species, but there are no records of actual food or feeding. At Sekinchan, a juvenile briefly chased Greater Spotted Eagles and inspected a passed Black-winged Kite, but none of these was carrying food at the time.

SOCIAL ORGANIZATION. Loners, in contact with wintering eagles of other species. A bird at Sekinchan displaced Steppe Eagles from field-post perches, and an aggressive encounter with a White-bellied Fish Eagle is reported from Ponggol, Singapore.

MOVEMENTS. Extreme dates: 3 November and 18 March at wintering sites, with no migration records.

SURVIVAL. No information.

SOCIAL INTERACTIONS. No information.

VOICE. No information.

BREEDING. No population.

MOULT. No data.

CONSERVATION. Probably as other *Aquila* species (see Greater Spotted). Globally vulnerable (BTW2).

Booted Eagle; Nok Insee Lek (Thai); Lang Tegap (Malay)

Hieraaetus pennatus (Gmelin) 1788, *Systema Naturae* 13(1): 272. TL France.
Plate 19

GROUP RELATIONS. May form a superspecies with African *H. ayresii* (Ayres' Eagle) and Australasian–E Wallacean *H. morphnoides* (Little Eagle) (cf. Amadon 1982).

GLOBAL RANGE. Breeds in far-S and far-NW Africa; temperate-zone Eurasia from Iberia to central Asia, the Tien Shan and W-central Himalayas; and from the Altai to N Mongolia and Transbaikalia. Northern populations migrate, wintering through sub-Saharan Africa; the Indian subcontinent and Sri Lanka; and western mainland SE Asia, with one record from Bali (Ash 1984).

IDENTIFICATION/DESCRIPTION. About Black Kite size but more compact. Generally *Aquila*-like when perched, with crestless head (yellow mouth-line conspicuous) and prominent tarsal trousers, but tail proportionately longer. Dark-morph birds are dark brown except for whitish lower tail-coverts, U-band on upper tail-coverts, spot at the base of the humerus (concealed by the folded wing but showing as a pair of 'headlights' in on-coming flight), and white-fringed, light brown rear scapulars and median wing-coverts forming a pale, angled band across the upper wing. Juvenile Brahminy Kite shows a similar band but lacks white on upper tail-coverts and has a strikingly different underwing pattern. Flight-feathers are blackish, greyer below and slightly paler than lower wing-coverts, especially at the base of the primaries. Tail dark above, pale cinnamon to silvery grey below, plain at a distance but in close, overhead view finely barred, with a heavier but obscure subterminal bar.

The light morph is similarly patterned but paler brown above, with crown streaked; underparts and lower wing-coverts white with variable streaking down to belly level.

In flight, head shows broad and short, and wings parallel-sided. Soaring shape similar to Black Kite except wings are held level rather than arched, and the tail lacks a fork. Glides with arm inclined shallowly forward, wrist flexed, hand slightly down-curved, and tail compressed – together with 'bullet' head in a shape recognizable at long range. Flying pale morph from pale Changeable Hawk Eagle by shape, lower wing-coverts sharply paler than secondaries and non-contrasting wing-tip. Like other *Hieraaetus* species, dives with wrist held clear of body, alula projecting and hand drawn tightly back on closed tail.

Bare-Part Colours. (From the field) iris brown; bill black with greyish base, cere and mouth-line yellow; toes yellow (tarsus fully feathered).

Size (mm). (Skins: 2 males, 1 female, from Burma and the Peninsula; adult): wing 372, 376 and 393; tail 202, 207 and 206; bill from cere 22.6, 22.7 and 24.0; tarsus 61.8, 62.5 (males only) (BMNH, ZRCNUS).

Weight. No data.

DISTRIBUTION. Confirmed only along the W-coast plain and in the far south. Historical summary: *Sat, Pek, Sel, Joh, Sin.* Three recorded in W.L. Abbott's Pakchan collection (Riley 1938) are Changeable Hawk Eagles.

GEOGRAPHICAL VARIATION. None recognized.

STATUS AND POPULATION. A non-breeding visitor and presumed occasional passage migrant, more or less annual but local and sparse. First recorded in 1899/1900 (singles collected in Singapore and at Kuala Lumpur). Confirmed again as of the early 1970s (BMP5), but with not more than 1–3 over-winterers, in total, located per season. Overall, dark morphs have predominated over light morphs in a ratio approximately 15 : 1.

HABITATS AND ECOLOGY. Paddylands (including at Seberang Perak and Sekinchan) and the cleared

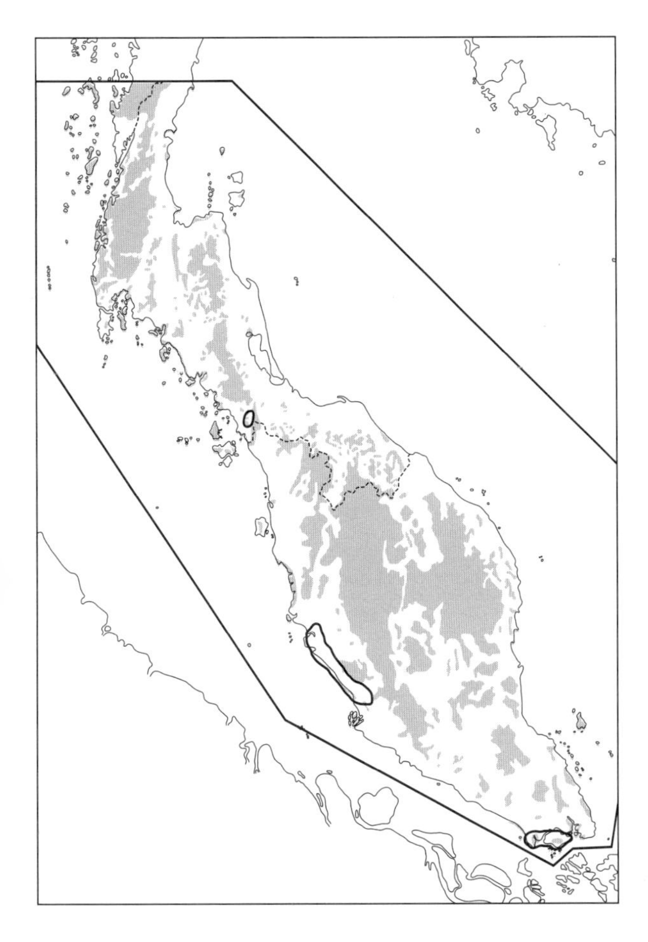

back-mangrove zone are the most regular but, evidently, not the only wintering habitats (BR 1972–73, 1976–77, 1978–79, 1980–81, MBR 1982–83, 1986–87). In Singapore in 1990, a bird spent several weeks of November and December on Mount Faber, a part-wooded suburban parkland (Ollington and Loh 1992, SINGAV-4).

Booted Eagles are occasionally harassed by resident Brahminy Kites, and persistently by pairs of Large-billed Crows *Corvus macrorhynchos*, but one wheeling over a straw fire at Sekinchan was ignored by a nearby pack of Black Kites.

FORAGING AND FOOD. At completely open sites, most of the day is spent patrolling a large area on the wing, soaring and gliding at low to medium heights, with only occasional perching on prominent look-outs such as service-pylons or cables; more rarely on the ground. The few pursuit-flights seen have been slanting dives from soaring height, in one instance a bird pulling up short in a heavy, 1–2 second hover before moving on. The only capture witnessed was of a newly ringed and released Common Redshank *Tringa totanus*, snatched as it stood resting, and plucked and eaten on the ground (BR 1972–73).

SOCIAL ORGANIZATION. Solitary. At overwintering sites never more than one individual present per season and, typically, they hunt away from the proximity of other raptors.

MOVEMENTS. Extreme dates: 28 October (a bird apparently already settled on a site in Selangor) and 17 April over Thaleban national park, Satul (BCSTB-10, BR 1980–81). In cleared back-mangrove habitat at Kuala Selangor, an overwinterer stayed put until at least 3 April (BR 1978–79).

SURVIVAL. No information.

SOCIAL INTERACTIONS. No information.

VOICE. A high-pitched *kik-kik*, at every close pass of mobbing Large-billed Crows, is the only call reported.

BREEDING. No population.

MOULT. No data.

CONSERVATION. No critical issues, except to note that rising use of pesticides, especially herbicides, on Malaysian W-coast paddylands has been marked by a large drop in numbers of most raptors using this habitat. Booted Eagle records have declined in the 1990s, but the situation needs further study.

Rufous-bellied Eagle; Yieo Thong Daeng (Thai); Lang Rimba (Malay)

Hieraaetus kienerii (E. Geoffroy Sainte-Hilaire) 1835, *Magazin de Zoologie, Paris, Aves* 5(2): text to plate 35. TL Himalayas.

Plate 25

GROUP RELATIONS. Free-standing.

GLOBAL RANGE. The W Ghats and Sri Lanka, E Himalayan foothills and far-NE Indian subcontinent; Hainan; SE Asia to the Greater Sunda islands, Bali and Philippines; and Wallacea east to the Moluccas and Flores (CLBW, Verhoeye and King 1990).

IDENTIFICATION/DESCRIPTION. A small, stocky eagle, adult in distant flight showing throat and chest white, sharp against dark face, lower body and lower wing-coverts; potentially confusable with Blyth's Hawk Eagle. They share black upperparts and 'resident peregrine' face-pattern but Rufous-bellied lacks barring on its underparts and has a different tail:

plain blackish above, pale grey with fine, even barring below. The juvenile is quite different: upperparts pale brown, cap sandy rufous, forehead and supercilium white, and a black mask through the eye; underparts unmarked white except for a brown mark on the side of the upper breast and distinctive dark brown patch on the upper flank, visible in both perched and flying birds; tail barred on both surfaces. It fairly closely resembles same-stage Blyth's and Wallace's Hawk Eagles *Spizaetus*, in shared forests, and their colour-patterns may have converged. No other *Hieraaetus* species shows such a difference between age-groups. At all ages, Rufous-bellied Eagle has a hind-crown crest, but not held as permanently cocked as in forest *Spizaetus* species.

In flight, wing proportionately longer than *Spizaetus* species but still with rounded inner trailing-edge nipped-in against the body. Soars on wings held level and flat, primary-tips often up-swept. When gliding (interspersed with a few rapid flaps), hand swept lightly back and tail held closed to slightly compressed (tapering). Adult lower wing-coverts are darker than flight-feathers, the base of the primaries showing whitish (above, rufous, in a patch conspicuous at all ages).

Bare-part colours. Iris dark brown; bill black with slaty base, cere and mouth-line yellow; toes yellow (tarsus fully feathered).

Size (mm). (Skins: 3 males, 4 females; all ages): wing 322–332 and 354–365; tail 175–184 and 193–207; bill from cere 21.4–22.0 and 23.0–24.3; tarsus 65.5–71.0 and 64.5–74.3; longest crest-feather 50–51 and 55–57 (BMNH, ZRCNUS). On wing-length, females average nine percent larger than males.

Weight. No data.

DISTRIBUTION. Historical summary: all divisions except *Pak, Sur, Phu, Son, Pat, Yal, Nar, Pes, Kel, Tru, Pra, Mel*, with other island records from Penang and Sentosa, Singapore.

GEOGRAPHICAL VARIATION. Accepted as eastern *formosae* Stresemann 1924 (TL N Sulawesi), but size-variation needs further study (two juvenile females from Singapore have unusually short wings).

STATUS AND POPULATION. Regular but uncommon. Reported associating with migrating sparrowhawks and honey-buzzards (BMP5, BR 1964, MBR 1982–83), but now known to occur year-round; at Fraser's Hill, a pair together in mid August. No nests have been reported, but juveniles in the company of adults and the patrolling of regular foraging routes during summer (BR 1980–81) point to local breeding.

HABITATS AND ECOLOGY. Many records of both adults and juveniles wandering over a variety of inland habitats, including several of a presumed non-breeding adult on and around a wooded hill in suburban Singapore that in a later year held a Booted Eagle (C.J. Hails, MBR 1982–83). The great majority are from

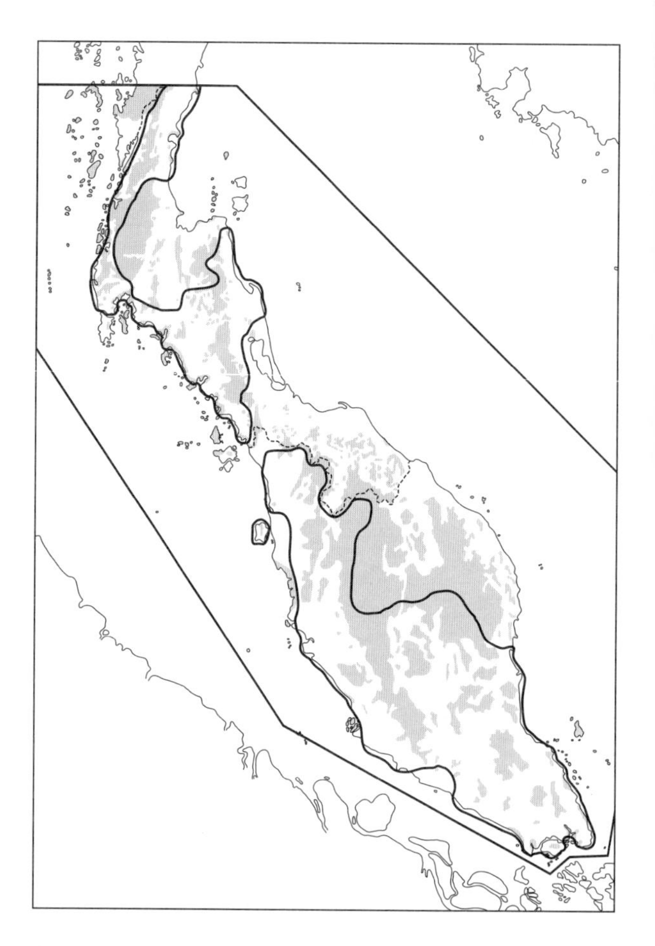

forest, mature to logged, at plains level and on slopes well into the Montane zone, recorded to 1400 m on the Main Range (BR 1968).

FORAGING AND FOOD. The long legs and toes are characteristic of a bird-hunter, and elsewhere in the range birds are said to form the main diet (HBI). Makes a classic, slanting, *Hieraaetus* stoop into forest from medium soaring height, and in Burma one seen to crash through foliage onto a party of canopy-feeding green pigeons (Cook 1911). Outside forest, some food is taken from the ground, with attacks recorded on Domestic Fowl, Town Pigeon, Pacific Golden Plover and Black-capped Kingfisher (Chasen 1939).

SOCIAL ORGANIZATION. Mostly solitary; rare records of pairs and, more frequently, of a single adult with a juvenile.

MOVEMENTS. None confirmed (cf. Crested Serpent Eagle).

SURVIVAL. No information.

SOCIAL INTERACTIONS. No information.

VOICE. A high-pitched *kliu* by a wandering adult being mobbed by Brahminy Kites (BMP5), and a shrill, screaming (but not certainly different) *tchiao*;

also a two-note *pruk-tchiao*, by an adult following a juvenile.

BREEDING. No record of a nest or of aerial display that might mark a nesting territory. Juveniles accompanied by adults (never more than one of each) recorded during early October–mid March, and lone juveniles from late February.

MOULT. Little known. A juvenile dated 19 January had all-fresh flight-feathers; others and an adult, undated, showed P5–10 much fresher than P1–4, implying precocious moult of the outer hand or mid-wing suspension. A February adult in this condition had re-started moult at P4 (BMNH, ZRCNUS).

CONSERVATION. Makes extensive use of steep terrain, hence not believed to be at serious risk from outright loss of habitat, but nothing is known about nesting requirements.

Changeable Hawk Eagle; Yieo Tang See (Thai); Lang Hindik (Malay)

Spizaetus cirrhatus (Gmelin) 1788, *Systema Naturae* 13(1): 274. TL India.
Plate 25

GROUP RELATIONS. Free-standing.

GLOBAL RANGE. The Indian subcontinent (except the NW), Sri Lanka and the Andamans; SE Asia from Burma, Laos and southern Vietnam to the Greater Sunda islands, Bali and central/S Philippines; and the Lesser Sunda islands (Sumbawa, Flores).

IDENTIFICATION/DESCRIPTION. A medium-sized eagle, 1.5-plus times the bulk of a Brahminy Kite. In all sex/age-classes, the crest merely squares the contour of the hind-crown, without projecting, and short tibial feathering gives a spindly-legged appearance. Apart from black mask-line through eye, the juvenile head and entire underparts are unmarked white, upperparts mid brown with narrow, whitish fringing, and tail grey-brown, narrowly and inconspicuously dark-barred on both surfaces. Adults are dimorphic rather than 'changeable'. Pale variants have a dark-streaked buff-brown to grey head, with a dark malar-stripe; upperparts mid brown with faint dark barring on the secondaries; underparts from chin buff-white with a black gular stripe, black streaks (varying between individuals from shaft-line only to 8 mm-wide droplets) over breast to upper belly, and narrow, pale rufous barring from thighs to lower tail-coverts. Tail as juvenile except bars are fewer (4–5 versus 5–7) and bolder, with sub-terminal pale and terminal dark bars broader than others. The dark morph is uniform dark chocolate-brown with all marks except the terminal tail-bar more or less obscured.

In flight, wings longer, less butterfly shaped than other *Spizaetus* eagles, but soaring birds still show an inner trailing-edge bulge, nipped-in against the body. Soars on level, flat wings with rather square hand (eased back when gliding), broad head jutting forward on thick neck, and longish, square-ended tail closed. Lower wing-covert colour follows the body (at close range, some light adults show dark barring) but seen from below flight-feathers are always more or less plain silvery grey, with rather sharply demarcated black wing-tip. In overhead view, therefore, coverts range from little different to darker than secondaries; never sharply lighter (cf. Booted Eagle).

Bare-part colours. Iris brown (juvenile and dark adult) to lemon-yellow (light adult); cere and bill slate-black; toes and extremity of tarsus yellow (rest of tarsus feathered).

Size (mm). (Skins: 13 males, 10 females; adult): wing 365–400 and (381) 405–421; tail 237–271 and 254–278; bill from cere 28.2–31.7 and 29.1–36.2; tarsus 95–117 and 105–124. Seven juveniles are within respective adult ranges (BMNH, ZRCNUS).

Weight. No data.

DISTRIBUTION. Few records from the far north. Historical summary: all divisions except *Chu, Ran, Pha, Nak, Pht, Pra*, with additional island records from Nakha Yai (*Phu*), Libong, Langkawi, Penang, Pangkor and Besar (*Mel*) off the W coast; Phangan off the E coast; and Tekong, Ubin and Berani, Singapore.

GEOGRAPHICAL VARIATION. Subspecies *limnaetus* Horsfield 1821 (TL Java), of the far-NE Indian subcontinent and SE Asia.

STATUS AND POPULATION. Resident, regular and uncommon to more or less common in Malaysia, sparser in most parts of Thailand, and only a few pairs persist in Singapore. In Malaysia, dark and light morphs are about equally common overall but the high frequency of mixed pairs suggests the ratio differs between the sexes; one of many points checkable by more nest-watching.

HABITATS AND ECOLOGY. Established pairs remain on nest-territories year-round. These may include much tall forest, from evergreen to near fully

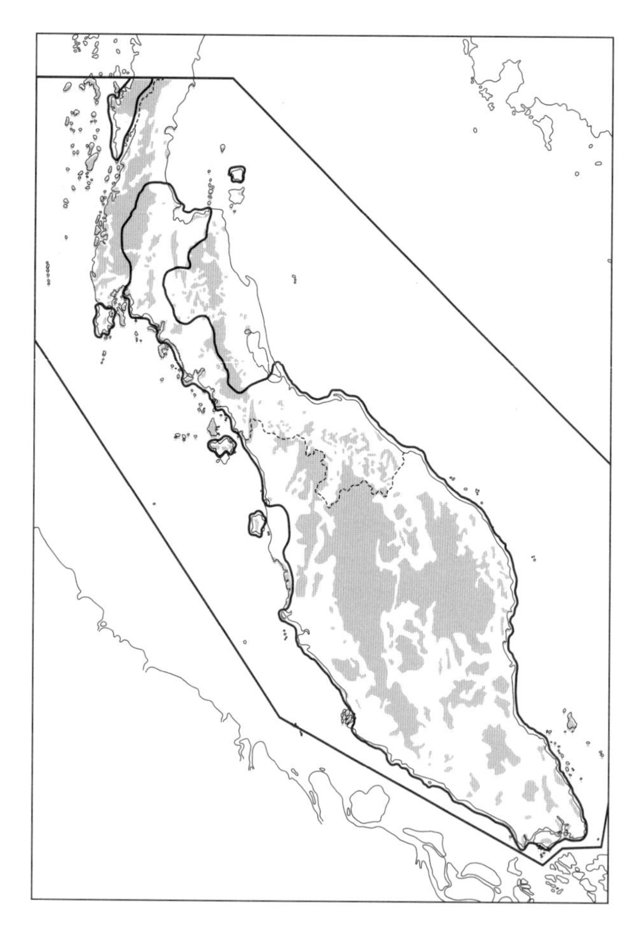

deciduous, mature to quite heavily logged; also peatswamp forest and, locally, the landward zone of mangroves. However, many birds occupy edge habitats, and are also able to use mixed agricultural landscapes where these include substantial and secluded patches of woodland, including old secondary-growth, with emergents tall enough for nest- and roost-sites. A single pair may own more than one such patch. Forested coastal promontories backed by settled country are another typical site, often shared long-term with White-bellied Fish Eagles (e.g., a pair of each on Cape Rachado, Negeri Sembilan, continuously since regular observations began there in the early 1960s). The bulk of the population lives at plains level but where slopes have been cultivated some nest to at least 800 m, and wander to 1200 m (BMP5).

FORAGING AND FOOD. Long periods may be spent immobile on an exposed perch at the edge of open ground, mostly high up but occasionally even on a field fence-post. May still-hunt from these, but believed to hunt mainly from concealment within tree-crowns. The taking of domestic poultry by diving out of cover has been reported many times (Robinson 1927, Ryves 1938, Spittle 1952). Wild prey includes squirrels (*Callosciurus prevosti* identified), birds (a Spotted Dove *Streptopelia chinensis*, presumably taken on the ground), snakes and lizards (a large agamid brought by a male to a forest nest in Perlis is likely to have been captured in the canopy) (K.D. Bishop, MBR 1982–83, 1986–87).

SOCIAL ORGANIZATION. Pairs soar together and roost and loaf close by, but hunt alone.

MOVEMENTS. No regular movements known, but immatures and displaced adults wander.

SURVIVAL. No information.

SOCIAL INTERACTIONS. Soars mainly during morning hours, alone or in pairs over parts of the home range regularly yielding best up-draught conditions, and advertises by calling persistently. Display-soars with head jutting forward and straight wings and closed tail canted up at a shallow angle.

VOICE. Contact-calls, by all age-groups including dependent young, are a sharp *hlit hlit*, or *hlit hlee*. The common soaring call is *hleee hlit* or *wheee whit*, with the full 'song' given by both loners and pairs a variable development of this: *hlit-hlit hleee*, or *hu-her-her hleee*, or *her-her hi hi (hi) hleee* (recalling Crested Serpent Eagle). Only one of the pair gives this call, the other answers at intervals with a single, squealing *hwii*.

BREEDING

Nest. Sited high (18–30 m) in a main-branch fork, usually close to the centre of the crown of a large tree, in forest or isolated (when usually tall-boled or in a swampy site difficult of access). *Shorea* species and *Intsia palembanica* are among those used in forest. Nest large, stick-built, with leafy twigs added to the cup-lining through most of the period of occupancy. One measured 76 cm across with cup 33 wide × 10 cm deep. Most are partly to well shaded, or even concealed from below by creeper foliage, but sometimes completely exposed on a dead emergent, perhaps through customary use of a tree before it died. Such sites may stay in use until support-branches finally give way.

Eggs and brood. The egg is plain, glossless white, sometimes with a few minute reddish brown speckles at the broad end, and with rough-textured surface. Shape short elliptical to ovate. Size (mm): 67.3–62.2 × 52.8–48.3 (n=3). Full clutch one. Incubation and fledging periods not recorded.

Cycle. While the downy chick is still small, some food is delivered by the male direct to the nest, but he stays only briefly. A juvenile that fledged in late May was still visiting the nest-tree in late November, close to the parents' next breeding attempt (egg in early January). Reports exist of the use of alternative nests in successive years.

Seasonality. Copulation recorded in late November–December, and egg- and chick-dates imply laying during December–February. Last fledglings are off the nest in late May (BMP5, Edgar 1933, R.P. Jaensch, G.C. Madoc, Ryves 1938, ZRCNUS).

MOULT. Post-juvenile replacement of at least the inner primaries is regular-descendant. The adult pattern is more complex, with active replacement at up to three loci, and suspensions apparently routine. P10 is invariably fresh in active moulters and must renew early. A sufficient number of non-moulters shows the process in adults is discontinuous, and dates of 11 active birds (May–July, September, November) suggest it is seasonal (BMNH, ZRCNUS).

CONSERVATION. In Malaysia, it is believed important numbers are supported in settled rural habitat that includes relic corners of tall woodland, original or otherwise. A trend in Malaysia towards total monocultures, without regard for landscape diversity, is doing this part of the population much damage. Artificially rare in most of Thailand, where large birds rarely survive long in contact with settlers.

Mountain Hawk Eagle; Yieo Phuu Khao (Thai); Lang Gunung (Malay)

Spizaetus nipalensis (Hodgson) 1836, *Journal of the Asiatic Society of Bengal* 5: 229 and plate 7. TL Nepal.

Plate 25

GROUP RELATIONS. An overlap of range with *S. alboniger* (Blyth's Hawk Eagle) in the north of the Peninsula (Boonsong and Round 1991) implies they are less related than *nipalensis* evidently is to certain island endemics, including *philippensis* (Philippine Hawk Eagle), the only other species with white-barred upper tail-coverts, and *bartelsi* (Javan Hawk Eagle) (cf. Amadon 1982). These three at least are likely to form a superspecies.

GLOBAL RANGE. SW India and Sri Lanka; the Himalayas and hill-tracts of far-NE India; Japan, China south of the Changjiang valley to Yunnan, including Taiwan and Hainan; and hill-tracts of continental SE Asia as far as the Peninsula; with some dispersal marginally beyond the breeding-range but no well-defined migrations.

IDENTIFICATION/DESCRIPTION. Slightly larger than Changeable Hawk Eagle and substantially larger than other long-crested species. Juveniles have upperparts pale-fringed brown, head and under-body plain rufous-buff (pale rusty barring on the legs may not be a first-plumage character); underwing creamy white with all flight-feathers except base of primaries boldly black-barred, narrower and more densely on the secondaries. Tail pale with up to seven uniform, evenly spaced dark bars, bolder on its upper surface, fainter below (in some, reduced to shadow marks). Adults are darker brown above with upper tail-coverts narrowly barred white; head streaked and pale-fringed, with a dark malar-stripe. Underparts from chin white, with blackish gular stripe, black-brown streaking over the upper breast, and brown barring from lower breast to tail-coverts, densest on the legs; underwing as in juvenile except coverts are dark-barred. Dark tail-bars (five show dorsally) broader than in juvenile, with apical bar about twice as broad as the rest but all pale bars uniform (and no age-group has them wider than dark bars); pattern clear on both surfaces but its strength varies individually. At all ages, a tall, wispy hind-crown crest, black with a white tip (as in Wallace's Hawk Eagle), is carried up-cocked.

In soaring flight, wings blunt and proportionately broad, with bulging inner trailing-edge nipped-in against the body. Head and thick neck jut well forward as in Changeable Hawk Eagle (G.E. Morris).

Bare-part colours. (Adult) iris orange; bill black with base and cere grey; toes yellow, tarsus fully feathered (ZRCNUS).

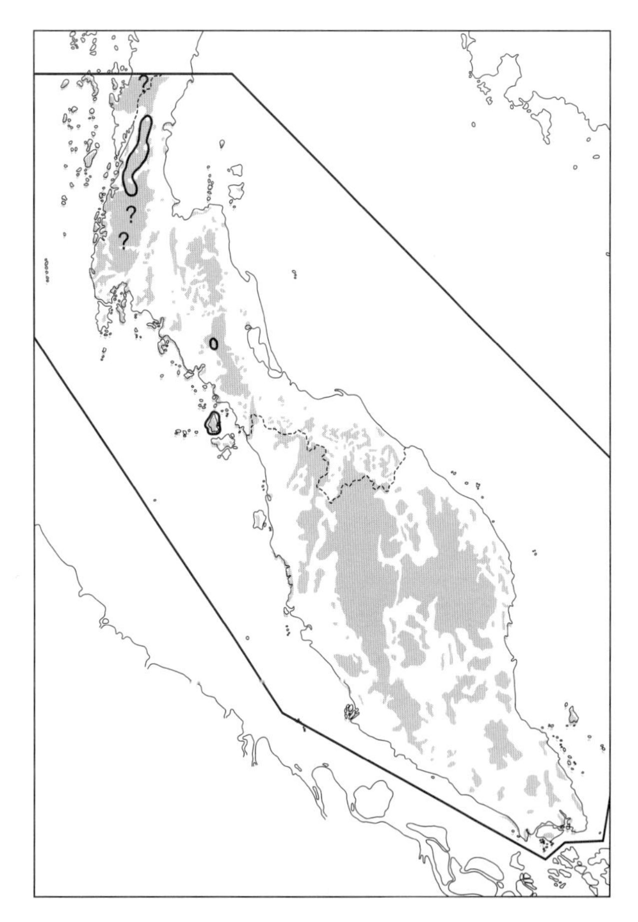

Size (mm). (Skins: 4 immatures and adults; none reliably sexed): wing 402–438; tail 255–305; bill from cere 31.9–36.2; tarsus 103–114; longest crest-feather 90–100 (ANSP, BMNH, ZRCNUS).

Weight. No data.

DISTRIBUTION. The NW Range, north from Surat Thani, dispersing to near the Malaysian border. Historical summary: *Chu*, *Ran*, *Sur*, *Tra*, including records from Tarutao island (*Sat*).

GEOGRAPHICAL VARIATION. Nominate *nipalensis* of the Himalayan, Chinese and SE Asian breeding-range.

STATUS AND POPULATION. Probably resident, though no nesting confirmed; local and sparse. Adults have been collected in the north (Ranong) in March and April, and presumed wandering immatures at Chong, foot of the E-central Range (Trang), and twice on Tarutao island, in October, November and March (ANSP, BLC, BMNH, Riley 1938, Robinson and Kloss 1921–24).

HABITATS AND ECOLOGY. Where specified, in forest on or close to steep land.

FORAGING AND FOOD. No local information. Congeners all still-hunt from mid to high perches in or at the edge of forest.

SOCIAL ORGANIZATION. No local information.

MOVEMENTS. No additional information.

SURVIVAL. No information.

SOCIAL INTERACTIONS. No information.

VOICE. A shrill trisyllable, *tlueet-weet-weet* (Boonsong and Round 1991).

BREEDING. No information.

MOULT. A March adult showed none, an immature dated 10 March none except one part-grown, adult-patterned central tail-feather (BMNH, ZRCNUS).

CONSERVATION. The Thai wildlife trade poses a direct threat to rare raptors from collection of nestlings.

Blyth's Hawk Eagle; Yieo Dam Thong Khao (Thai); Lang Hantu (Malay)

Spizaetus alboniger (Blyth) 1845, *Journal of the Asiatic Society of Bengal* 14: 173. TL Melaka.
Plate 25

GROUP RELATIONS. Uncertain; perhaps closest to *S. lanceolatus* (Sulawesi Hawk Eagle). Bills of both (and Wallace's Hawk Eagle) have a strongly convex upper mandibular cutting-edge, versus nearly straight in the *nipalensis* superspecies. The adult Blyth's tail-pattern is unique among Asian *Spizaetus*, whereas juveniles more closely resemble other species in their range.

GLOBAL RANGE. Borneo, Sumatra and the Peninsula.

IDENTIFICATION/DESCRIPTION. Young juveniles are white-fringed, mid brown above, with cap to nape sandy rufous, paling on face, a black mask-line back from the eye, and lores white. Underparts vary from plain buff-white to whitish with ochre-buff breast and flanks. Legs may be finely barred pale rufous but, as in young Mountain Hawk Eagle, the chronology of this character needs checking. Underwing white, with flight-feathers dark-barred. Tail narrowly and evenly dark-barred, four bars showing dorsally.

Plain underparts moult directly to a dark-barred pattern, apparently with no intermediate stage (cf. Wallace's Hawk Eagle). Black-and-white adults are distinctive: from dark adult Wallace's by sharply black 'resident peregrine' mask, versus dark-streaked tawny-rufous side of face, and ventral barring always black, never rufous. Only adults have a black gular stripe, but all age-groups show a tall, up-cocked, hind-crown crest (from Wallace's by lack of or with only a fine white tip).

In soaring flight, blunt, broad wings (with bulging trailing-edge nipped-in against the body), held level and canted slightly forward; hand eased back in the glide position. Adult lower wing-coverts are heavily black-barred and the whole flight-feather row shows four black bands, compressed on the secondaries. The broad black tip and wide, grey-white mid-section of the adult tail most closely resemble adult Crested Serpent Eagle (common in the same habitats), but the latter has quite different underparts and underwing. (See also Oriental Honey-buzzard and Rufous-bellied Eagle).

The downy chick is white.

Bare-part colours. Iris blue-grey, appearing dark at a distance (juvenile), orange-yellow (adult); bill slate-black, paler at the base of the lower mandible; cere slate-black; toes bright yellow (tarsus fully feathered).

Size (mm). (Skins: 4 males, 2 females, all ages): wing 321–333 and 343, 358; tail 218–237 and 230, 243; bill from cere 27.1–27.5 and 30.4, 31.9; tarsus 87–95 and 89 (one only); longest crest-feather 65–79 and 64, 65 (BMNH, ZRCNUS). Foot-size in this species is close to Mountain Hawk Eagle; much larger and heavier than in Wallace's (mid-toe minus claw up to 53, versus 38).

Weight. No data.

DISTRIBUTION. North to Ranong. Historical summary: all divisions except *Pak, Chu, Pht, Son, Pat, Nar, Pra, ?Sin,* with other island records from Penang and Pangkor off the W coast; and Tioman (R.P. Jaensch) off the E coast. Occurrence in Singapore is founded only on a specimen bought freshly stuffed (ZRCNUS).

GEOGRAPHICAL VARIATION. None recognized.

STATUS AND POPULATION. Resident, regular and uncommon to common on all the main hill-ranges and many large, forested outliers (south to the Muntahak–Panti ridge, E Johor), including on some large, hilly islands.

HABITATS AND ECOLOGY. The interior and edge of Lowland and Montane forest, mature and selectively logged, typically in steep country, from the hill-foot boundary to at least 1800 m (BMP5). Nests recorded on the Main Range have mostly been within about 400 m below the Montane ecotone to only just above it (Robinson and Seywald 1987), limited upwards, apparently, by the availability of large emergents. Wanders widely in the lowlands, including across habitat-gaps (I have flushed one from a small area of seaside heath forest in Terengganu), but few nesting territories have been found away from major hills (SINGAV-3). Soars often, at no great height above the forest canopy.

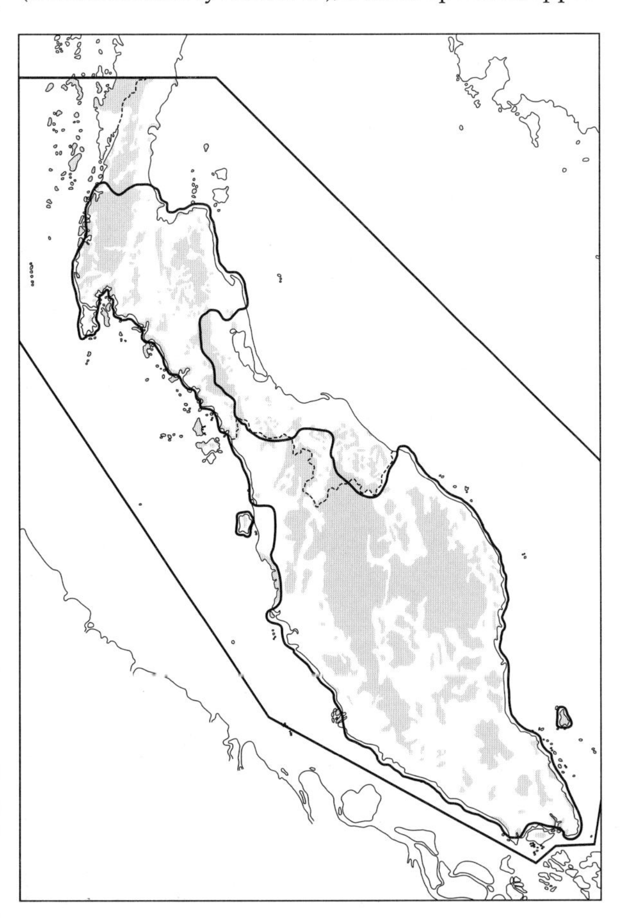

FORAGING AND FOOD. Still-hunts from shaded perches inside and at the edge of forest, at interior-canopy down to mid levels (sometimes only a few metres above the bank of a track or quiet forest road). Little is known about diet, but it includes lizards, and a subadult male shot in front of a cave in Nakhon Si Thammarat had eaten a leafnose bat *Rhinolophus affinis*, likely to have taken in flight (Robinson and Seywald 1987, TISTR). An association with forest-topped limestone karst-towers, containing many cave bat roosts, has been noticed in S Kelantan (BR 1976–77), and a population exists on the limestone Satul–Perlis border hills.

SOCIAL ORGANIZATION. Hunts alone, but established pairs appear to stay on their nest-territory year-round.

MOVEMENTS. Apart from non-breeder wandering, none known.

SURVIVAL. No information.

SOCIAL INTERACTIONS. The only display reported: a series of shallow dips while soaring near an active nest (R.P. Jaensch). Silent when soaring.

VOICE. Pre-flying young wait silently for hours but once on the wing become very noisy, calling incessantly from a canopy perch (where their shrill, pure-tone whistles are often hard to pin-point). The main phrase is *pik-wuee*, the second note rising slightly; less often, *pikpik-wuee*, with or without a terminal *pik*. The commonest adult calls are a shrill *pik-wuee* and *hleee-hlit* (similar to Changeable Hawk Eagle); occasionally a trisyllablic *kee-kew-kew* (Boonsong and Round 1991).

BREEDING

Nest. Invariably in a main-branch fork of a large emergent, often above the level of the surrounding canopy; a moderate-sized, thick platform of sticks with cup deep enough to conceal the body of the sitting parent when viewed at eye-level. Leafy branchlets are added to the lining to within a few days of the chick flying. Where available, north from mid Selangor, the dominant choice of site is the smooth-boled, giant legume *Koompassia excelsa*, tallest tree of the region and ranging up slopes to near the Montane ecotone.

Eggs and brood. Egg not described, but broods are uniformly of one. Incubation and fledging periods not separately measured. A bird incubating in mid November, with a small, downy chick on 21 December, fully fledged and out of the nest (hence within 1–2 weeks of flight) on 17 February, suggests a total development period of not more than four months.

Cycle. Favoured nest-trees, and specific branch positions, remain in use for long periods, even when logged about or close to a used road. One near the Gap, Selangor/Pahang boundary, discovered in 1968 was still active in 1995, the nest refurbished or replaced, but with only a few missed years, which implies no regular switch between alternative sites. A large nestling alternated long bouts of quiet perching with sessions of jumping and flapping exercise on and around the nest, then sleeping in the nest. During three hours, 0930–1230, it was visited twice and fed once, at noon.

Seasonality. Copulation recorded at the nest on 21 October, incubation from early November, and chicks during late December–late April (but in Selangor and Pahang no nests with young unfledged after the end of February have been shown to be successful) (BMP5, BR 1968, Robinson and Seywald 1987, P.D. Round, SINGAV-3).

MOULT. Replacement of the adult inner hand, out at least to P5, is regular-descendant. Birds dated 23 September and 3 November were growing P3 and P5, respectively, both with the outer hand still old (BMNH, ZRCNUS).

CONSERVATION. *K. excelsa* is not yet a sought-after timber species but selective removal of other tall emergents in logging operations must affect the supply of nest-sites, and remove some customary ones. The mainly hill-country range of this species suggests it is not otherwise seriously threatened.

Wallace's Hawk Eagle; Yieo Ngawn See Namtaan Thong Khao (Thai); Lang Hantu Kasturi (Malay)

Spizaetus nanus Wallace 1868, *Ibis* series 2(4): 14. TL Sarawak.
Plate 25

GROUP RELATIONS. Probably free-standing (see Blyth's Hawk Eagle).

GLOBAL RANGE. Borneo, Sumatra, the Peninsula and Tenasserim to latitude about 12°N.

IDENTIFICATION/DESCRIPTION. In the field, juveniles are hard to distinguish from same-stage Blyth's Hawk Eagle, and at least as variable. Upperparts white-fringed mid brown; cap to nape sandy rufous, with a variably developed black mask-line back from the eye; rest of face and underparts from chin, plus lower wing-coverts, all plain white or white with sharply demarcated cinnamon-buff breast, or all cinnamon-buff, slightly darker on the face (BMP5, BMNH, ZRCNUS). In a following plumage, all upperparts are brown, lighter on the neck and cap; underparts whitish to pale cinnamon, with a few dark streaks on the centre of the breast and rufous barring from lower breast to lower tail-coverts, including legs.

Definitive adult plumage, which from feather-wear variation appears not to develop all at one moult, is much darker: upperparts blackish brown, crown and lesser wing-coverts full black, contrasting with black-streaked, tawny-rufous side of face to hind-neck; below, white from chin, with strong black gular stripe, black-streaked upper breast, and black-barred lower breast to tail-coverts and legs. All age-groups show a tall, up-cocked, hind-crown crest, black with broad white tip (cf. Blyth's Hawk Eagle). From Jerdon's Baza by cere colour, feathered tarsus, foraging behaviour and vocalizations.

In overhead flight, shape as Blyth's Hawk Eagle. Underwing buff-white with cinnamon coverts plain to, in adult, fine-barred, and four dark bars along whole flight-feather row, compressed on the secondaries. The tail shows three dark bars, evenly narrow in juveniles, wider with apical dark and sub-apical pale bars widest in adults (but not to the extreme extent of Blyth's Hawk Eagle).

Bare-part colours. (From the field) iris dark (juvenile), yellow (adult); cere and bill slate-black, base of lower mandible paler; toes yellow (tarsus fully feathered).

Size (mm). (Skins: 13, all ages; most not sexed): wing 301–339; tail (226) 232–250; bill from cere 21.3–25.8; tarsus 85.0–92.7; longest crest-feather 47–64, maximum in short-winged, presumed adult males (not above 51 in immatures) (BMNH, ZRCNUS). The feet are small and delicate in comparison with Blyth's and Mountain Hawk Eagles.

Weight. No data.

DISTRIBUTION. Historical summary: *Pak, Chu, Kra, Tra, Son, Pek, Phg, Neg, Mel, Joh*, with no island records.

GEOGRAPHICAL VARIATION. Nominate *nanus*, of the global range except Nias island, W Sumatra.

STATUS AND POPULATION. Resident and uncommon to more or less common, but seriously reduced by habitat-loss; near to extinction in Thailand, where clearance of favoured plains-level

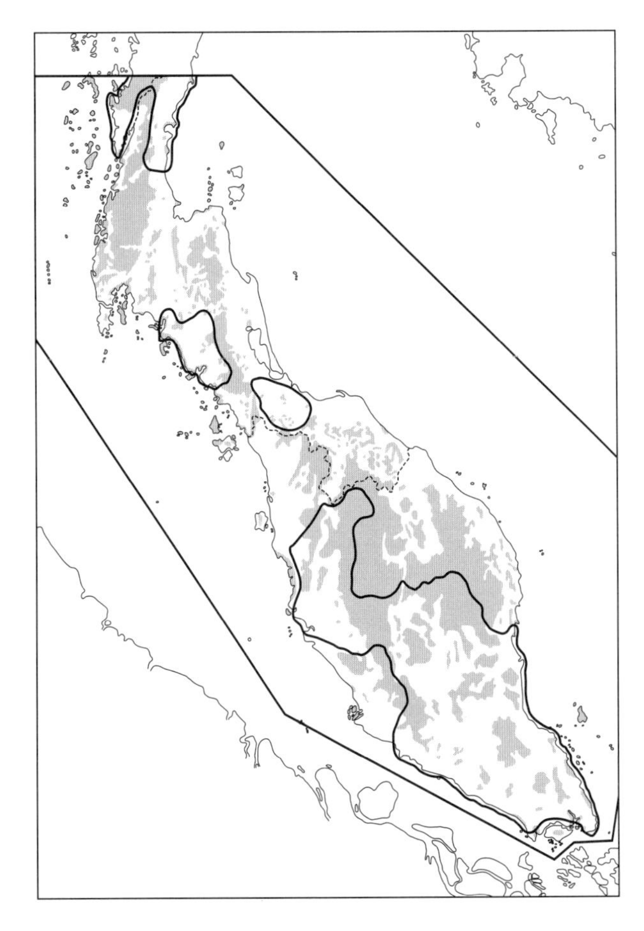

and river-terrace forest has run close to its full course. Modern records are from fragments left at only two sites: Chong and Khao Pra-Bang Khram (P.D. Round). In Malaysia, the lowlands of Taman Negara, Krau wildlife reserve and the Endau-Rompin conservation area hold what have become globally important numbers. The more general situation is typified by Pasoh research forest, Negeri Sembilan, whose uncut 600 ha flat-land core has for 25 years held only one breeding pair. This patch is now far removed from any equivalent habitat and, given that Wallace's Hawk Eagle seems not to leave the vicinity of forest (no records of dispersal comparable to Blyth's), survival of the young that regularly fledge there must be low.

HABITATS AND ECOLOGY. Exclusively dry-land evergreen and semi-evergreen Lowland forest, mature and logged; occasionally at quite heavily degraded sites but never without access to patches of continuous high canopy. The few nest records are all from tall forest in the level lowlands, and this is believed to be core habitat, although more checks are needed on ranging behaviour at the hill-foot boundary.

FORAGING AND FOOD. Still-hunts in and sometimes at the edge of forest, but hardly anything else is known about preferred perch-positions or where food is actually taken. Lizard parts were found in the stomach of a probable Wallace's (wing 310 mm) collected in Trang (Riley 1938), and one has been seen eating a lizard. At Pasoh, a bird was attracted in to the screams of a Greater Racket-tailed Drongo *Dicrurus paradiseus* being extracted from a mist-net (C.M. Francis).

SOCIAL ORGANIZATION. Established pairs stay on their nest-territory year-round and two birds have been seen loafing within a few metres of each other (SINGAV-1), but they hunt alone.

MOVEMENTS. None known.

SURVIVAL. No information.

SOCIAL INTERACTIONS. Some form of aerial display has been reported from near an active nest, but without details (MBR 1986–87).

VOICE. As with Blyth's Hawk Eagle, newly flying, still-dependent young are very noisy and may call from a perch for an hour or more: shrill single and double notes, *kliit* and *kliit-klee*, or *kliit-kleeik* with a slight upward slur. The last call is also made by adults.

BREEDING

Nest. Selects a branch fork at or near the base of a high crown, at main canopy level or (two records) in an emergent clear of the main canopy, 20–40 m up. Nest as Blyth's Hawk Eagle, a moderate-sized, thick platform with fresh, leafy branchlets added to the cup-lining until the chick is fully grown. Where available, giant *Koompassia excelsa* is the preferred tree species, but outside it range (as at Pasoh) large dipterocarps *Shorea* spp. are used. Most sites reported have been well within forest but a pair in Pahang continued to attend a nest in a tree left isolated in a new clearance, well out from the forest boundary.

Eggs and brood. Egg not described but the brood is routinely one.

Cycle. A flying juvenile being fed on a nest at Pasoh on 11 March was still roosting in the nest-tree on 18 April.

Seasonality. An active nest, contents unchecked, on 31 January, a nearly full-grown pre-flying young on 6 February, and a newly flying bird on 11 March (BMP5, J.E. Duckett, MBR 1986–87).

MOULT. December and March adults showed none. Post-juvenile replacement of the inner hand occurs before the start of body-moult and is regular-descendant out to at least P5 (BMNH).

CONSERVATION. One of a suite of species stenotopic in plains-level forest, naturally thinly distributed, and under serious threat from habitat-loss. Survival in the Peninsula is likely to depend on a few large Malaysian reserves not losing their complement of this forest. Globally vulnerable (BTW2).

Family FALCONIDAE

Falconets and falcons: five species

Black-thighed Falconet; Yieo Malaeng Paw Khaa Dam (Thai); Burung Falko Rajawali (Malay)

Microhierax fringillarius (Drapiez) 1824, Bory de Saint-Vincent's *Dictionnaire Classique d'Histoire Naturelle* 6: 412 and plate 59. TL Sumatra.
Plate 18

GROUP RELATIONS. Uncertain, but shows only minor overlap with *M. latifrons* (White-fronted Falconet) in northern Borneo, and isolated by habitat from deciduous forest-adapted *M. caerulescens* (Collared Falconet) in SW Thailand. Superspecies need a review.

GLOBAL RANGE. Borneo south of latitude about 5°N, Bali, Java, Sumatra, the Peninsula, and S Tenasserim and humid parts of SW Thailand to latitude 13°30'N (Phetchaburi).

IDENTIFICATION/DESCRIPTION. Very small, size of a Coppersmith Barbet *Megalaima haemacephala*, but chunky and broad-headed. At all ages, entire upperparts from cap to tail (excluding narrow forehead-band), side of body, posterior tibial trousers and lower tail-coverts black. Remaining underparts white, with a variable extent of rusty orange: at most from lower breast to anterior trousers and belly (a few also have pale rufous chin and throat); least in juveniles, and some of these show none. Forehead and narrow, connected supercilium (thinnest over the eye), curving down to cut off black face-patch, white in adults, rusty pink in juveniles. The latter also show fine, pale edging on the upperparts, especially upper tail-coverts. Often perches exposed on a dead snag, where head-bobbing and tail-pumping behaviour are characteristic. Flies direct on rapidly beaten, sharp-tipped wings, often gliding as it enters a tree-crown. From below, lower wing-coverts white, flight-feathers spotted white, and all tail-feathers except the central pair show four white, inner-web spots.

Bare-part colours. Iris dark red-brown, periorbital skin grey; bill and cere pinkish horn with black culmen (juvenile), all black (adult); feet black.

Size (mm). (Skins: 38 males, 37 females; adult): wing 88–96 and 97–107; tail 47–58 and 52–63; bill from cere 8.9–10.1 and 9.4–11.6; tarsus 18.0–20.1 and 19.9–23.7 (BMNH, UMZC, ZRCNUS). On wing-length, females average ten percent larger than males.

Weight (g). An adult female, 42.9 (UMBRP).

DISTRIBUTION. Historical summary: all divisions except *Ran*, with no additional island records.

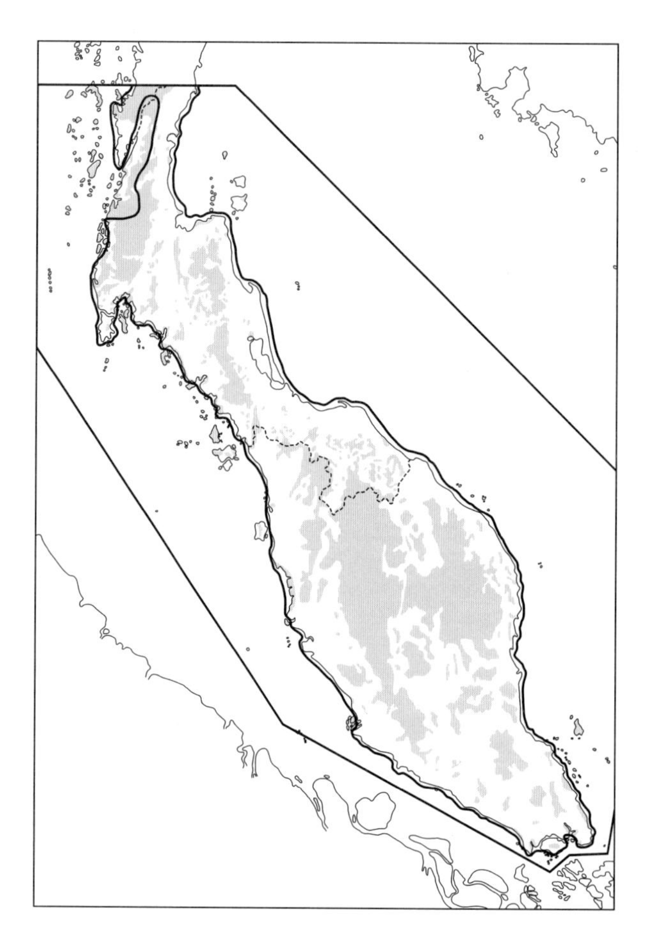

GEOGRAPHICAL VARIATION. None recognized, but 90 percent of mainland birds have the whole leading-edge of the tibial trousers white or rufous, whereas in Sunda-island populations it is distally black.

STATUS AND POPULATION. Resident and, except now on Singapore island where only a few remain, regular and common to latitude about 7°N, i.e., close to the Malaysian/Thai-Burmese Lowland forest-type divide (Whitmore 1984); uncommon further north.

HABITATS AND ECOLOGY. Die-backs, clearings and the edge of inland forest and secondary woodlands of all kinds, well out into part-wooded agriculture, parkland and large, wooded gardens; wherever tall, dead snags provide hunting perches and old woodpecker or barbet holes for roosting and nesting; from plains level to at least 1700 m (BMP5). Roost-holes are used by resident pairs year-round, including as rain-shelters (Molesworth 1955).

FORAGING AND FOOD. Hunts socially, in pairs or family-parties (of up to five birds), less often alone, flying individual sorties 100–200 m out from a favoured dead top, usually 5 m or more up with a clear view all round. Targets are mainly arthropods, including alate termites, butterflies and moths (one record of an atlas moth *Attacus*), dragonflies, carpenter-bees, beetles, mantids, large orthopterans (the grasshopper *Patanga succincta* identified) and cicadas; less often birds, including munias and sunbirds (Batchelor 1958, Kemp and Crowe 1994, Madoc 1956a, Molesworth 1955, Pagden 1955). Prey is snatched in free space at all levels, or in swerving dashes through a tree-crown; occasionally from surfaces, including the ground. Flowering crowns drawing various nectar-feeders are a particular attraction. Among 57 sorties, Kemp and Crowe (1994) observed 46 percent success (insect prey in all cases).

SOCIAL ORGANIZATION. Mostly pairs, or family-parties attended apparently by both parents. For at least two months after fledging, families return to roost together in the nest-hole. On the Kedah/Yala border, C.B. and D.W. Frith watched six birds enter a dead-tree hole, raising the possibility of social roosting by members of more than one brood.

MOVEMENTS. None recorded.

SURVIVAL. No information.

SOCIAL INTERACTIONS. Perched birds pump the tail as other individuals fly in to perch, and companions allopreen (Kemp and Crowe 1994).

VOICE. Hunting birds are often noisy, combining a whine and a shrill squeal, *kweer week*, with the tone of a paper party-whistle. One of a copulating pair kept up a loud chittering noise.

BREEDING

Nest. Adopts abandoned nest-holes of woodpeckers and larger barbets (Gold-whiskered Barbet identified: Molesworth 1955), mostly in dead and sometimes rotting wood, 15–20 m up. One nest-chamber was 25 cm below the entrance-hole, floored with wood fragments and beetle elytra (G.C. Madoc).

Eggs and brood. Eggs are rather thick-shelled, plain matt white. Shape short elliptical. Size (mm): 27.7–26.4 × 23.2–21.8 (n=4) (G.C. Madoc). Clutch four. Mostly only two young fledge, with no record of more than three, and direct evidence of mortality in the nest. One full-grown but pre-flying brood was heavily infested with mites and hippoboscid flies (Batchelor 1958).

Cycle. No information.

Seasonality. Copulation recorded in February and March; eggs in February; active nests, mostly not checked, in February–May and July (in E Johor, two large chicks on 13 July); with one apparently exceptional Perak record of adults carrying food to a hole on 17–18 December (Berwick 1952b, ENGGANG-2, P. and P. Heathcote, G.C. Madoc, MBR 1986-87, SINGAV-6).

MOULT. Replacement of primaries is regular-descendant. Among 108 adults from the length of the Peninsula and covering all months, 80 percent of those dated May–October showed active wing-moult versus only one individual of 49 dated November–April. Excluding this instance of P6 growing on 14 February, moults started during April–June and finished during August–late October (BMNH, UMZC), implying an average duration of around four months.

CONSERVATION. The total clearance of old tree-cover, including estate shelter-belts, etc., eliminates it from permanent agriculture. Otherwise no critical issues identified.

Common Kestrel; Yieo Khaes-trael (Thai); Burung Falko Padang (Malay)

Falco tinnunculus Linnaeus 1758, *Systema Naturae* 10(1): 90. TL Sweden.
Plate 26

GROUP RELATIONS. Forms a superspecies with *F. sparverius* (American Kestrel), Indian Ocean *araea, newtoni* and *punctatus* (Seychelles, Madagascar and Mauritius Kestrels), and Indonesian and Australian *moluccensis* and *cenchroides* (Spotted and Australian Kestrels) (Stresemann and Amadon 1979).

GLOBAL RANGE. Breeds through Africa, on E Atlantic islands, across temperate to low-arctic Eurasia from the Atlantic to the Sea of Okhotsk and central Japan; south to SW Asia, the Himalayas and far-NE India, with outlying populations in SW India and Sri Lanka; Guangdong and Yunnan; and possibly

NW Burma. Some northern continental populations migrate, wintering to sub-Saharan Africa; SW and S Asia to Sri Lanka and the Andaman islands; in S Japan, Korea and S China including Taiwan and Hainan; and SE Asia to the Peninsula, northern Sumatra, northern Borneo and the Philippines.

IDENTIFICATION/DESCRIPTION. Medium-small falcon. Upperparts of E Eurasian birds vary from cinnamon-ochre to rich rufous, streaked and droplet-spotted or barred dark brown from head to tail; marks generally but not invariably finer in pale birds, always heavier in richer ones (rufous reduced to narrow interstitial barring in darkest individuals). All show a narrow, dark moustachial stripe and bold, blackish subterminal band across both surfaces of the tail. Underparts pale buff to cinnamon-pink, finely to heavily streaked or spotted dark brown from upper breast to belly. All body-markings proportionately reduced in adult males, which also have head, upper tail-coverts and tail (other than distal band) plain blue-grey. Birds with just the tail-coverts grey are either immature male or adult female, but some of the latter also have a grey rather than rufous tail. Additional to the wide, distal bar, however, female and juvenile tails apparently always show multiple narrow bars (about ten dorsally). Underwing buff with coverts dark-barred.

When hunting, flight is mostly fairly leisurely, on shallowly beaten wings, but with intermittent, sustained hovers (see also Black-winged Kite).

Bare-part colours. (Adult) iris dark brown, periorbital skin greenish yellow; bill bluish- to greenish slate with black tip; mouth-line and cere greenish yellow; feet yellow to orange-yellow.

Size (mm). (Skins: one unsexed juvenile): wing 252; tail 172 (BMNH). Dark birds from Bangkok district (2 males, 2 females; adult): wing 246, 255 and 264, 274; tail 165, 172 and 168, 173; bill from cere 15.3, 15.8 and 15.4, 15.6; tarsus not measured (BMNH).

Weight. No data.

DISTRIBUTION. Historical summary: *Pak, Phu, Tra, Son, Pat, Pes, Ked, Phg, Sel, ?Neg, Joh, Sin*, with additional island records from Langkawi.

GEOGRAPHICAL VARIATION. Pale-toned nominate *tinnunculus* and richer, more heavily marked eastern *interstinctus* McClelland 1840 (TL Assam) have been collected around Bangkok and in SW Thailand. Both are expected in the Peninsula but only *interstinctus* has been confirmed there (BMNH, Riley 1938, Robinson 1907).

STATUS AND POPULATION. A non-breeding visitor; local and sparse. Overlooked in the far north, but the total record is less than annual and probably only a few enter the Peninsula each winter. Most recent reports have actually been from Singapore (well-watched and where south-moving open-country raptors have tended to concentrate), but even

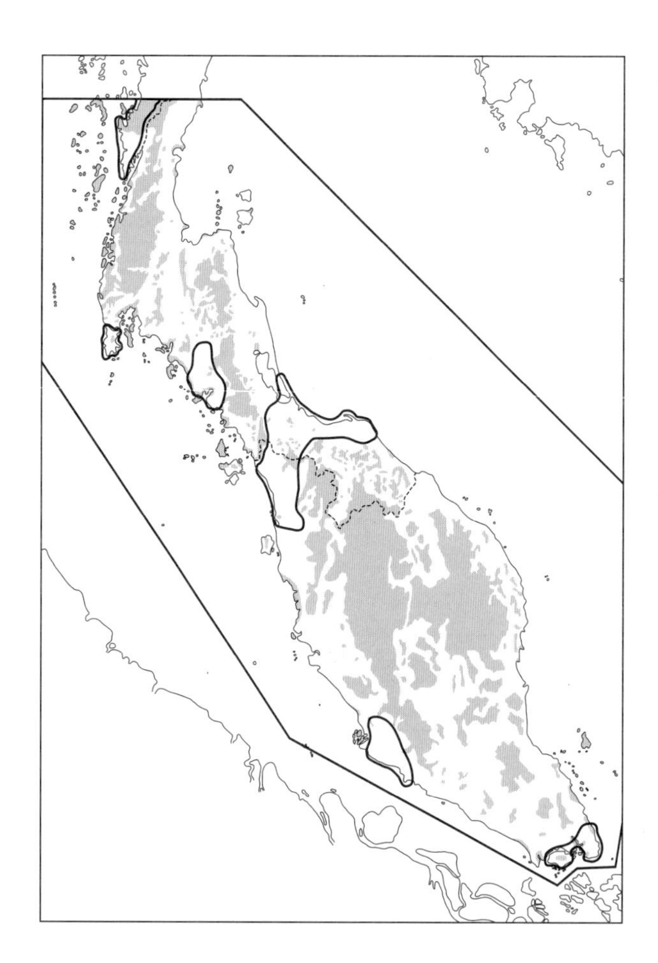

there in only eight of the last 25 seasons, with never more than three individuals recorded concurrently (BR 1978-79). Records cover all months November–April, most in December and January.

HABITATS AND ECOLOGY. Exclusively open country, including a large agricultural clearing newly opened out of forest, rough grassland of all kinds and, in Perlis, harvested sugarcane fields (BR 1970-71, MBR 198[illegible]-85). On passage, a record of a bird crossing the Main Range at Fraser's Hill (Gibson-Hill 1949b); otherwise at plains level. In their regular range, Kestrels usually elicit no mobbing response from small passerines but while hunting a Perlis bird was followed by a large pack of Yellow Wagtails.

FORAGING AND FOOD. Hover-scans 5–10 m up, with leisurely flight between search points. No local information on prey.

SOCIAL ORGANIZATION. Solitary.

MOVEMENTS. Extreme dates in wintering habitat are 25 November and 16 April, both in Singapore (BR 1974-75, 1978-79). A small falcon of Common Kestrel shape and flight-action (but identity not confirmed), arriving with other migrating raptors over Cape Rachado, Negeri Sembilan, on 4 March may have crossed the Melaka Straits from Sumatra.

SURVIVAL. No information.

SOCIAL INTERACTIONS. No information.

VOICE. No information.

BREEDING. No population.

MOULT. A juvenile dated 27 November showed none but had flight-feathers rather faded and tip-worn.

CONSERVATION. No relevant issues.

Eurasian Hobby; Yieo Hobee Yurop (Thai); Burung Falko Hobi Utara (Malay)

Falco subbuteo Linnaeus 1758, *Systema Naturae* 10(1): 89. TL Sweden.

Plate 26

GROUP RELATIONS. Likely to form a superspecies with *F. cuvieri* (African Hobby). Analaysis of feather keratins suggests other Asian and Australasian hobbies are not so closely related (Olson *et al.* 1989).

GLOBAL RANGE. Breeds in NW Africa and Eurasia north to low-arctic latitudes from the Atlantic to Kamchatka and N Japan, south to Iran, Afghanistan, the Himalayas east to Nepal and S China including Taiwan, but not confirmed anywhere in SE Asia. Possibly all populations migrate, wintering through eastern Africa, the N-central Indian subcontinent, extreme S China and continental SE Asia; vagrant in Java and the Lesser Sunda islands (Timor) (CLBW, Mees 1971).

IDENTIFICATION/DESCRIPTION. In a brief view, the perched immature could be confused with dark Eurasian Kestrel, but at all ages both local hobby species show a much bolder head-pattern. They are also proportionately shorter-tailed and longer-winged than a kestrel, primaries folding close to the tail-tip. At all ages, Eurasian told from Oriental Hobby by dark-moustached face with white cheek-patch; bold, dark ventral streaking against white rather than cinnamon underparts (rufous of Eurasian Hobby not forward of belly and trousers); and a pair of white 'windows' on the nape, obvious in rear views of a perched bird.

In a close view of overhead flight, the entire underwing appears densely dark-barred (solidly blackish at the extreme tip), and the tail may show narrow barring (unbarred dorsally). Fast and agile, with long sickle-shaped wings; in silhouette, some flight-postures suggest a large *Apus* swift.

Bare-part colours. Iris dark brown, periorbital skin greenish (juvenile), yellow (adult), bill slate-blue with blackish tip; cere and mouth-line greenish (juvenile), yellow (adult); feet pale yellow (juvenile), bright yellow (adult) (HBI).

Size (mm). (Skin: one unsexed juvenile): wing 264; tail 135; bill from cere 13.4; tarsus 34.2 (ZRCNUS).

Weight. No data.

DISTRIBUTION. Historical summary: *?Pek, ?Sel, ?Neg, Mel, ?Sin* and, provisionally, Perak island, N Melaka Straits.

GEOGRAPHICAL VARIATION. Timor and Javan specimens, and one labelled 'Singapore 1939' (ZRCNUS) are northern nominate *subbuteo* (BMP5, Bruce 1978, Mees 1971). Shorter-winged SE Palaearctic *streichi* has been identified south to central and E Burma (BMNH), but may not be a long-distance migrant.

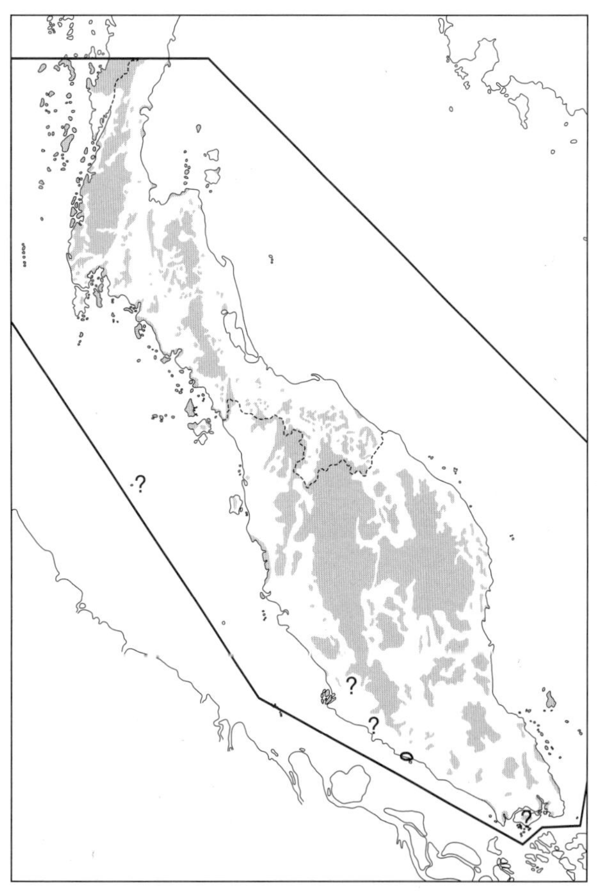

STATUS AND POPULATION. Local and sparse; records of hobbies likely to have been *subbuteo* carry this falcon just beyond the category of vagrant. Purchased as an already-prepared study-skin, the Singapore specimen cannot be guaranteed as local (BMP5), but a good description exists of a bird capturing and eating insects on the wing low over tidal mudflats at the Melaka town shore (MBR 1982-83). Likely *subbuteo* have also been reported over the open lowlands and coast of Perak, Selangor and Negeri Sembilan, and a hobby has been captured inside a Kuala Lumpur building, but escaped before key details could be collected (BMP5, BR 1978–79, J.E. Duckett, MBR 1986–87). Inclusive dates imply passage status, and from their active flight-behaviour two or more small, ventrally streaked falcons seen on Perak island, N Melaka Straits, on 19–20 November (Langham 1976) are now suspected of having been Eurasian Hobbies.

HABITATS AND ECOLOGY. Open mudflats and beach, a newly planted oil-palm estate, a dredge-mine lagoon reedbed, and suburbia with parkland, all at plains-level, are habitats in or over which definite or suspected Eurasian Hobbies have been noted on the mainland. Several sightings, including of hunting, have been in the late evening.

FORAGING AND FOOD. Apart from the observation of capturing and eating insects on the wing, no definite information.

SOCIAL ORGANIZATION. Solitary, apart from two possibles at Port Dickson (Negeri Sembilan), and the Perak island observations (BR 1978–79, Langham 1976).

MOVEMENTS. Inclusive dates in autumn are 13 September and 20 November, and 24 March in spring.

SURVIVAL. No information.

SOCIAL INTERACTIONS. No information.

VOICE. No information.

BREEDING. No population.

MOULT. No data.

CONSERVATION. No relevant issues.

Oriental Hobby; Yieo Hobee (Thai); Burung Falko Hobi Timur (Malay)

Falco severus Horsfield 1821, *Transactions of the Linnean Society* 13(1): 135. TL Java.
Plate 26

GROUP RELATIONS. Perhaps free-standing. External proportions differ from Eurasian Hobby.

GLOBAL RANGE. The Indian subcontinent from the Himalayan foothills; far-S China (Guangxi, Yunnan, Hainan); SE Asia to the Greater Sunda islands, Bali and the Philippines; Sulawesi and the Moluccas; and New Guinea, New Britain and the Solomons. Northernmost populations migrate, wintering as far as Sri Lanka and to uncertain limits in SE Asia (two mid-winter juveniles from Bangkok district are unlikely to have been local: BMNH).

IDENTIFICATION/DESCRIPTION. Shorter-winged and tailed than Eurasian Hobby, more stockily built and with a rather larger bill. Age for age, darker above, with nape all-black, lacking white 'windows'. Face fully black-masked, without a moustache-mark or white cheek,, and sharp against white chin and throat. Rest of underparts cinnamon to rufous-chestnut, the relatively pale juvenile dark-streaked from upper breast to tail-coverts, but not as boldly as in Eurasian Hobby. At all ages, underwing and under-tail barring as in Eurasian Hobby but on a tawny rather than white ground. Upper tail-surface laterally dark-barred rather than all-plain.

Bare-part colours. (Adult) iris dark brown, peri-orbital skin orange-yellow; bill dark slate with black tip, cere and mouth-line orange-yellow; feet orange-yellow (BMNH, Oates 1883).

Size (mm). (Skins: 3 males, 3 females, from SE Asia north of the Peninsula; adult): wing 216–224 and 236–246; tail 94–100 and 108–113; bill from cere 13.2–14.3 and 15.5–16.1; tarsus 32.2–32.8 and 33.8–35.9 (BMNH). On wing-length, females average nine percent larger than males (versus five percent in Eurasian Hobby).

Weight. No information.

DISTRIBUTION. Historical summary: adjacent parts of *Sur, Pha, Kra, Tra,* with no island records.

GEOGRAPHICAL VARIATION. Validity of subspecies has been questioned (CLBW). If recognized, Peninsular birds should be Asian nominate *severus*.

STATUS AND POPULATION. Assumed to be resident, with sightings (including of evident pairs) in March, May, August, September, November and December; but local and uncommon. All accepted records are clustered into 150 km of the NW mainland

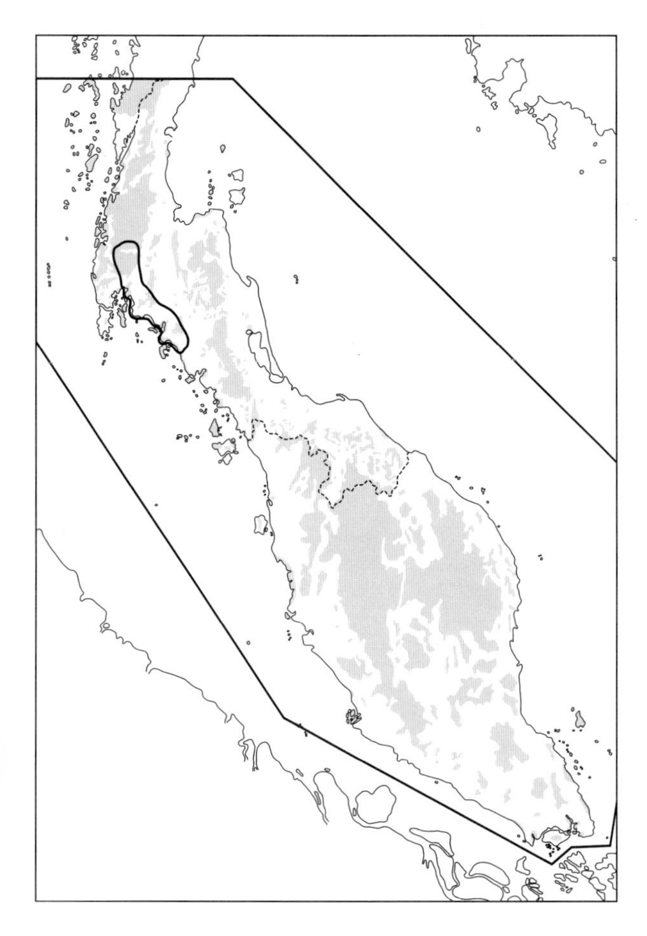

between the Trang/Krabi border and Khao Sok national park, W Surat Thani (BBCB-4, -9, BCSTB-13), in what may be an outlier of continental range to the north of the Peninsula. A July 1969 record from the Batu Caves limestone outcrop, Selangor, has since been revised in favour of small, dark, resident Peregrine Falcon, not then known to occur in the Peninsula (BMP5, BR 1969, MBR 1982–83).

HABITATS AND ECOLOGY. Lowland inland forest and forest-edge, secondary-growth and mangroves, typically in the neighbourhood of limestone cliffs. At Khao Sok, a bird has been seen diving away from a rock face, and juxtaposition of outcrop and forest may be important ecologically. Some NE Indian nests have been found in trees growing out of cliffs (HBI).

FORAGING AND FOOD. Little local information except that it is most active at dawn and dusk. On the Krabi coast, an Edible-nest Swiftlet *Aerodramus fuciphagus* seen captured in flight (U. Treesucon), and in Burma an Oriental Hobby was collected as it ate a small bird (BMNH).

SOCIAL ORGANIZATION. A pair together at Kok Kloy, Phangnga, on 7 September (B. King); other sightings have all been of loners.

MOVEMENTS. None known.

SURVIVAL. No information.

SOCIAL INTERACTIONS. No information.

VOICE. No information.

BREEDING. No information.

MOULT. No data.

CONSERVATION. No critical issues identified.

Peregrine Falcon; Yieo Phae-rae-grin (Thai); Burung Falko Peregrin (Malay)

Falco peregrinus Tunstall 1771, *Ornithologia Britannica*: 1. TL Northamptonshire, United Kingdom.
Plate 26

GROUP RELATIONS. The most conservative treatment recognizes one near-global species, of which Neotropical *F. deiroleucus* (Orange-breasted Falcon) could be a member (cf. Hickey and Anderson 1969, Mayr and Short 1970). The forest-living habits of *deiroleucus* are approached by some undoubted Peregrines in SE Asia.

GLOBAL RANGE. Breeds on all continents except Antarctica but avoids major desert regions and, except for a outlier in Fiji, shows a range-gap in Oceania. High-latitude northern populations migrate, wintering south to the southern tropics.

IDENTIFICATION/DESCRIPTION. Half to three-quarters the bulk of a Brahminy Kite, according to sex and subspecies; broad-headed and stocky, with broad-based but long, rather pointed wings folding close to the tail-tip. Juvenile upperparts are dark brown with buff-rufous fringing; adults vary from slaty-blue, darkest on the head, to (breeding residents) black with blue confined to lower back, rump and upper tail-coverts. Northern migrants also show a strong, dark brown to black moustache-mark and a white cheek-patch, residents a full black face without separate moustache-mark; in both cases sharp against white chin and throat. Remaining underparts of first-winter migrants (equivalent-stage resident not described) are heavily streaked dark brown on a buff-white ground. Adults are variably black-spotted or lined on upper breast, black-barred from lower breast to tibial trousers and tail-coverts (barring heaviest and densest in residents); on a whitish ground or, in residents, upper breast pink-grey shading to deep lavender-grey back from lower breast, dark enough for barred region to appear entirely black in the field, even at close range (resident).

In overhead flight, underwing densely barred on a ground-colour matching the under-body. Hence, apart from white bib (less conspicuous at a distance than yellow bare-parts), resident adult appears solidly black. Colour-scheme, habitat and crepuscular activity have caused much confusion with Bat Hawk. The latter is falcon-shaped but a little larger, wings very broad-based and hand acutely pointed but held more flexed in most flight-modes; in steady, cruising flight beaten quite deeply and deliberately rather than shallowly winnowed.

Bare-part colours. Iris dark brown, periorbital skin greenish grey to greenish yellow (juvenile), bright yellow (adult); bill slate-blue with black tip; mouth-line and cere greenish grey to greenish yellow (juvenile), bright yellow (adult); feet greenish to yellow (juvenile), bright yellow (adult).

Size (mm). (Skins: 7 male, 4 female northern migrants; all ages): wing 303–327 and 355–367; tail 138–161 and 166–189; bill from cere 19.4–21.1 and 22.6–24.0; tarsus 46.1–51.5 and 47.6–51.8 (BMNH, ZRCNUS). Residents are smaller, but none handled.

Weight. No data.

DISTRIBUTION. Historical summary (the species): all divisions except *Pak, Chu, Ran, Pha, Nak, Pat, Yal, Nar, Kel, Pra,* with additional island records from the Similan group, Phiphi Li and Poda (*Kra*), Libong, the Langkawi group, Perak, Penang, Rembia and Jarak off the W coast; Tioman off the E coast; and Ubin and Sentosa around Singapore. From dates, descriptions and behaviour, apparent residents occur south from Surat Thani (Khao Sok national park).

GEOGRAPHICAL VARIATION. Residents have not been identified formally but in the field appear close to subspecies *ernesti* Sharpe 1894 (TL Mount Dulit, Sarawak) of island SE Asia to New Guinea. Northward from the Peninsula, upperparts pale progressively, but individuals with some *ernesti* features (extensively black above, deep lavender below and with full black mask), have been collected as far as the Changjiang valley and west in the Himalayas to Sikkim (BMNH). Evidently, breeders in this area are not the same as those of the Indian subcontinent (though often identified as such).

Hickey and Anderson (1969) map five subspecies breeding in the NE Palaearctic. These have not been separated in winter quarters, where Ripley (1982) has lumped all as *japonensis* Gmelin 1788 (TL Japan). These large, pale birds vary in pattern and tone but have standard measurements (BMNH). Ventrally-rufous S Asian *P.p. peregrinator* Sundevall 1837 (TL at sea off the Nicobars) is suspected of reaching the Peninsula occasionally (MBR 1982-83), but this has yet to be confirmed.

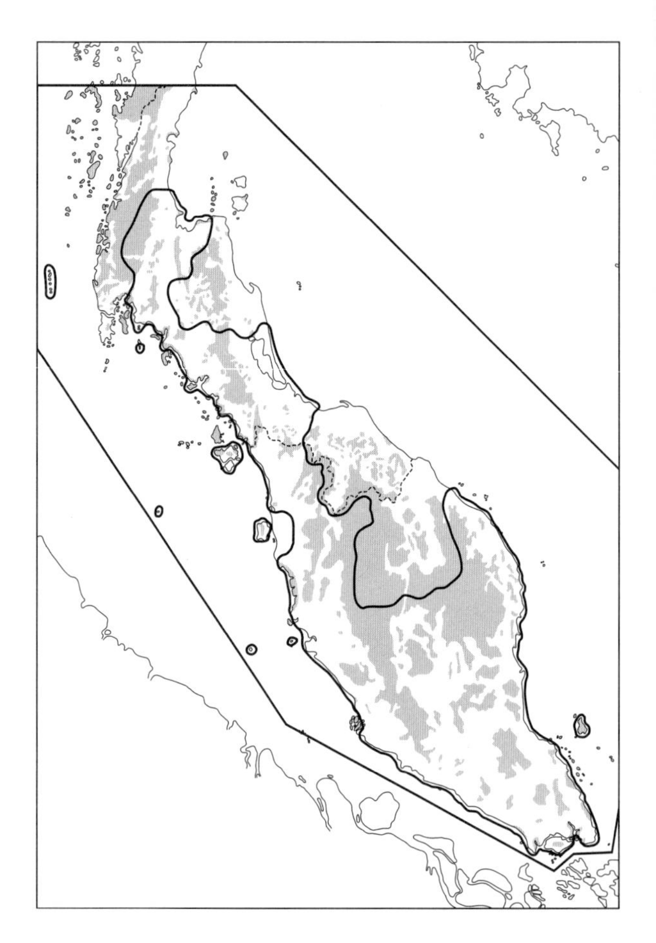

STATUS AND POPULATION. Regular but uncommon overall. Residents are local and uncommon but were confirmed only in the early 1980s (MBR 1982–83), hence confuse past estimates of the abundance of migrants. The general but no longer quantifiable impression is that migrants have declined over at least two decades. Certainly, they are not now seen more often than dark, presumed residents. The latter have not been censused but a habitat-based guess would be 20–50 pairs for the Peninsula as a whole. The limestone cliffs on which most seem to depend occur south to latitude 3°N, and dark birds as far afield as Johor and Singapore (mid-summer dates south to Desaru and Jason's Bay, SE Johor) are assumed to have been non-breeding wanderers.

HABITATS AND ECOLOGY. Tree-nesting reported from N Tenasserim (Hume and Davison 1878), but the only sites known in the Peninsula are tall, sheer, limestone-karst cliffs. Home outcrops appear to be tenanted year-round, although the best-known one, Takun outcrop in Selangor, is an exception. Birds there have had no recent breeding success and may not behave typically.

Most of the day is spent loafing in the shade on trees growing out of the cliff face, with routine use of just a few favoured perches. At Takun, a dead emergent 1 km away on a ridge overlooking both the nest-cliff and a wide sweep of surrounding forest is another, from which hunting sorties are flown. Most tenanted outcrops stand in or near extensive forest, and resident-type Peregrines have many times been recorded cruising over forest, from mangroves and subcoastal peatswamp to the summit ridge of the Main Range and other uplands, at 2000 m and above (MBR 1982–83, 1986–87, SINGAV-6). This is likely to be the main original hunting environment, but summer-dated reports have also come from an array of cleared habitats, including totally open, subcoastal paddy-land and the Thalae Noi marshes (BBCB-4). Recently, singles and pairs of dark birds have made casual use of high-rise buildings in the western suburbs of Kuala Lumpur, but with no sign yet of fixing on particular sites.

Palaearctic migrants occur widely in the open lowlands but settle into wintering sites mainly near coasts, particular around the feeding areas and larger high-tide roosts of shorebirds or where swifts or pigeons concentrate. Here, they adopt a regular high vantage-perch on a bare tree or structure such as a pylon or bridge-support. Some halt at, and a few may overwinter on, small islands, including Perak and the Phiphi group off the W coast, attracted presumably by pigeons, seabirds and passage migrants. During autumn in the S China Sea, over-water migration paths are exploited by using ships as feeding stations (Ellis *et al.* 1990, D.M. Simpson).

One sighting from Perak island is dated July (Langham 1976), but no islands have been confirmed to support breeding Peregrines, even though many in the NW have sea-cliffs.

FORAGING AND FOOD. Items brought to a nest included, apparently, birds up to drongo size. Otherwise, no summer prey recorded larger than a *Psittacula* parakeet or town pigeon (Ollington and Loh 1993). Residents become active towards dusk, and at Takun and Air Jernih (Perlis) outcrops, a bird left the home cliff at last light. Bats emerging from cave roosts may be a target, as they are in Borneo (C.M. Francis), and a falcon watched walking along a Krabi cliff ledge at dawn pulled a bat out of a crevice. The few food-deliveries witnessed have all been in the early morning or evening.

Food of winter migrants includes swifts, shorebirds and pigeons, and a freshly-picked Brown Booby carcass on Perak island could only have been a Peregrine kill.

No classic stoop-hunting is recorded, though it seems unlikely a booby could have been killed by any other method. An apparent resident skimming fast and low over paddy-stubbles flushed ground-feeding doves without following up, then attacked a Spotted Dove perched on power-wires, but left after several close passes failed to dislodge it. The only captures actually witnessed have been of prey flown down. Time-trials on a pair of migrants after House Swifts *Apus nipalensis* (eaten on the wing) showed the male more than twice as successful as the female, taking up to five in an evening hunt, at a mean rate of one per three attempts (W.M. Choy).

SOCIAL ORGANIZATION. Northern migrants winter mostly alone but a few records exist of interacting pairs (BR 1963, Madoc 1955), including one of a definite male and female. In the Arua islands (Melaka Straits), Madoc (1956) saw an apparent migrant attack a White-bellied Fish Eagle, and residents on home territory are aggressive towards other raptors. In the Sok valley, a pair combined to see off a Black Eagle passing their crag, and in response to a warning call by the sitting female at Takun her mate chased and dived repeatedly on a migrating Oriental Honey-buzzard, toppling it into the forest canopy (MBR 1984–85).

MOVEMENTS. Extreme dates of definite Palaearctic migrants are 17 October (Singapore) and 20 April (Jarak island) (SINGAV-4, ZRCNUS). A mid July record from Perak island may have been of a wandering resident, implying sea-gaps are no more of a barrier to summer dispersal than they are to migration.

SURVIVAL. No information.

SOCIAL INTERACTIONS. Mock diving attacks on other Peregrines (status uncertain) have been described from Perak island and the Negeri Sembilan coast, with both birds airborne or one perched, the attacker making close, high-speed passes and calling throughout (BR 1963, Madoc 1955). The Bukit Takun pair copulate on tree-perches; in one instance preceded by a food-transfer, in another by the male landing directly on the female's back, flapping and vocalizing throughout.

VOICE. By resident adults at their home outcrop, a rasping, *kech kech kech kech kech . . .*, the female distinctly deeper-toned than the male. Calling is mostly from perches, and the nest-ledge.

BREEDING

Nest. At Takun outcrop, a small, canopied recess in a sheer limestone face, deep enough to hide the sitting bird completely, except for a wing-tip raised as a sun-shade.

Eggs and brood. Not described.

Cycle. No information.

Seasonality. Copulations during late December–early February and an incubation started in the first half of February (MBR 1984-85).

MOULT. Replacement of primaries is regular-descendant. Northern migrant adults moult flight-feathers while wintering. The most advanced individual (female), growing P8 with only 9–10 old on 20 November, must have started well before arrival. Others dated 3 February and 20 April were at stage

P9–10 and P10, and two more April birds showed all-fresh wings. Apparent first-winterers dated December, February and April had not moulted and are likely to have left in more or less complete juvenile plumage.

CONSERVATION. Several observers have noted the small proportion of juveniles among recent Peregrine sightings, including of migrants. In Selangor, the Batu Caves outcrop is now heavily disturbed by development around its base and has been abandoned. A 1985 breeding attempt at nearby Takun failed after an abnormally long incubation period, and no young are known to have flown there in any subsequent year. Data are needed on productivity at more remote sites.

Order GRUIFORMES

Family GRUIDAE

Cranes: one species

Sarus Crane; Nok Gra-rian (Thai); Keria (Malay)

Grus antigone (Linnaeus) 1758, *Systema Naturae* 10(1): 142. TL India (rather than Hartert's 'Vorderindien', which historians would identify as covering the Burmese type locality of eastern *G.a. sharpii*).

Not illustrated in this volume

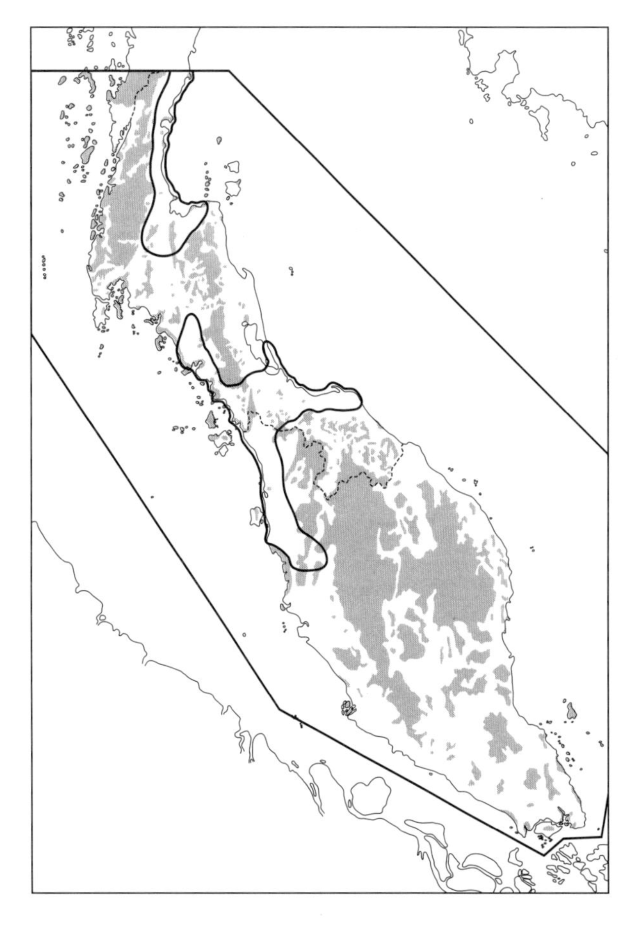

GROUP RELATIONS. Uncertain; perhaps closest to Australasian *G. rubicunda* (Brolga), but Australian populations occur entirely within the latter's breeding-range, and in the same habitats, hence these birds are presumed to have diverged past superspecies status.

GLOBAL RANGE. The Indian subcontinent south to the Godavari delta; occasional in SW Yunnan; lowland plains and great river valleys of continental SE Asia to the Peninsula, S Vietnam and Luzon; and northern Australia, which is the only part of the range where numbers may still be stable. Not reported from the Philippines since the mid 1970s, and gone also from most former range in mainland SE Asia, where pockets of population are believed to survive only in wetlands of S Vietnam and Cambodia (Archibald 1992, AWB); possibly also S Laos and E Burma.

IDENTIFICATION/DESCRIPTION. A huge bird, distinctively tall and sedate, uniformly grey with drooping secondaries and bald red head and upper neck (feathered ginger in juveniles). Flies with neck outstretched, unlike adjutant storks and large herons (but see Purple Heron).

Bare-part colours. No local details.

Size (mm). (Skins: 1 immature, 1 adult; not sexed): wings not measurable; tail 207 and 220; bill from rear edge nostril 101 and 108; tarsus 247 and 265 (BMNH).

Weight. No data.

DISTRIBUTION. Formerly, south to the NW Malaysian coastal plain. Historical summary: *Chu, ?Sur, Tra, Son, Pat, Sat, Pes, Ked, Pra, Pek,* with no island records (Cantor specimens labelled Penang show signs of having been captives, probably imported: BMNH).

GEOGRAPHICAL VARIATION. E Asian *sharpii* Blanford 1895 (TL Burma), with Australian populations, distinguished from western nominate *antigone* by lack of a white collar.

STATUS AND POPULATION. A former presumed resident, now extinct; there are no definite breeding records but tame captives seen by W.L. Abbott in Trang in the 1890s are likely to have been raised from local chicks. Said to have ranged south to Kuala Kangsar on the Perak river (Robinson and Chasen 1936), but not mentioned by Kelham (1881–83) who worked the Perak valley in the late 1870s so that it may only have been occasional there (the name of the rice-growing district immediately to the north, Kerian, is taken from a common swamp-forest tree *Eugenia pseudosubtilis*, not the crane). Locally common in Trang at the turn of the century (Riley 1938); London Zoo is said to have imported one live from

Kedah at about that time (AMNH); and some still present on the W-coast plain south to mainland Penang up to the 1920s, possibly even later (Hamilton 1923, Glenister 1951, Madoc 1950–51).

HABITATS AND ECOLOGY. Paddylands and, as a breeder, presumably also natural, open, freshwater wetlands.

FORAGING AND FOOD. No information.

SOCIAL ORGANIZATION. No information.

MOVEMENT. None recorded.

SURVIVAL. No information.

SOCIAL INTERACTIONS. No information.

VOICE. No local information.

BREEDING. No information.

MOULT. No data.

CONSERVATION. Globally near-threatened (BTW2). It is unlikely any present wetland reserve in the Peninsula has the capacity or security to sustain even captive-bred birds (U. Treesucon).

Family HELIORNITHIDAE

Finfoots: one species

Masked Finfoot; Nok Fin-fut (Thai); Burung Pedendang (Malay)

Heliopais personata (G.R. Gray) 1849, *Proceedings of the Zoological Society of London* 16: 90. TL Melaka.

Plate 7

GROUP RELATIONS. Free-standing.

GLOBAL RANGE. The extreme NE Indian subcontinent, Burma and NW Thailand south to Sumatra and (one record) W Java (Milton 1985), also SE Thailand, Cambodia and S Vietnam; still with no firm record of breeding south of the Irrawaddy delta.

IDENTIFICATION/DESCRIPTION. Size of a small duck, mostly grey-brown with large, yellow, dagger bill. Adult males show a full black mask with white at the base of the upper mandible, females a white bib with black surround. Towards its base, the mid-line of the culmen is produced into a narrow ridge, in males with a notch that supports a small, upstanding wattle. Swimming-lobes fringe both edges of the toes that face forwards; the rear toe is merely flattened (BMNH, UMZC).

Neck often held upright while swimming, and outstretched in flight. Flies low over the water surface on rather long, pointed wings (wing-tip P9), and tail that is obviously fuller and proportionately longer than in any local duck. On land, has dabbling-duck stance.

Bare-part colours. (Adult) iris reddish brown; bill and male wattle clear, bright yellow; feet bright sage-green with toe-lobes black, narrowly edged yellow (BMNH, Robinson and Kloss 1921–24).

Size (mm). (Skins: 2 males, 4 females; adult): wing 259 (one only) and 221–236; tail 114, 119 and 102–112; bill 51.6 and 43.0 (one each); tarsus 48, 49 and 44–48 (BMNH, UMZC, ZRCNUS).

Weight. No data.

DISTRIBUTION. Historical summary: all divisions except *Chu, Ran, Phu, Pht, Son, Pat, Nar, Pes, Tru, Pra, Neg, Joh, Sin,* with island records from Libong, Tarutao, Langkawi and the Kelang estuary group off the W coast; and Phangan off the E coast.

GEOGRAPHICAL VARIATION. None recognized.

STATUS AND POPULATION. Possibly more than one population occurs, but confirmed only as a non-breeding visitor; present in all months December–August. Local and uncommon, but more dependably findable than formerly supposed, especially in the W-coast mangrove zone. Visitor status is supported by an evident migrant flying into a school building in Melaka town (BR 1964), another mist-netted at flood-lights at Fraser's Hill, crest of the Main Range (BR 1976–77), and clearly seasonal appearances on isolated ponds far from forest cover. An unconfirmed report of an adult with three young in the Krabi mangroves in late May 1992 (BBCB-9) suggests migrants might augment a small resident population, but leaves hanging the question of what happens to supposed residents during August–November. Behaviour while moulting could be of relevance to this.

HABITATS AND ECOLOGY. Typically on lowland woodland waterways, ranging from relatively swiftly flowing, clear (including blackwater) rivers through forest far inland to subcoastal swamp, and creeks and

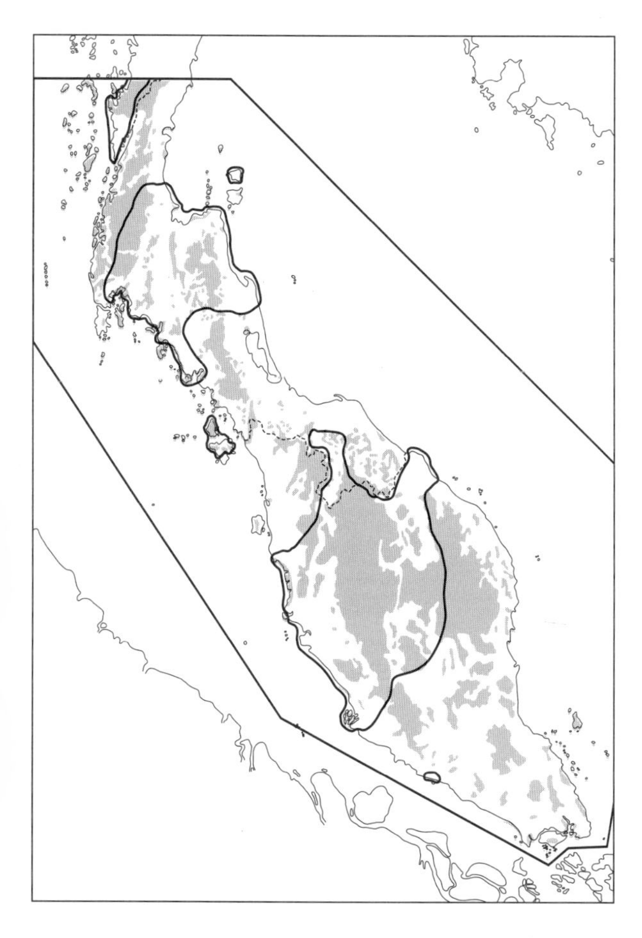

inlets in mangrove forest. Also on reservoirs, ponds and flooded mine-workings, far from forest (BBCB-3, -4, -5, -6, BR 1966, 1970–71, MBR 1986–87, Silvius *et al.* 1987). On the W-coast plain, some of these non-forest sites are occupied more or less annually, for much of the season.

Finfoots can dive but also move efficiently on land, and when disturbed, if no overhanging bank vegetation is available to hide in, leave the water and run into forest undergrowth (MBR 1986–87). Along the Tahan river, Taman Negara, they have learned to ignore tourist boat traffic, and this implies the same individuals occur there from year to year.

FORAGING AND FOOD. Diet varied. Invertebrates are snatched from overhanging branches and foliage, and a bird in the shallows of Ayer Keroh lake, Melaka, stirred bottom detritus with its feet for items that surfaced, one of 17 taken in 45 minutes being a small frog (Howes 1988a). They also dive, and fish are grabbed at the surface. On the Tahan river, a male took a 15 cm fish from a shoal, then scrambled up a tall, steep bank to kill and swallow it on shore (D.G. Gardner). In mangroves, watched picking small items from the surface and peering into burrows while walking over a low-tide mudflat; also dashing out of the water for small crabs on creekside mud (MBR 1986–87, P.D. Round).

SOCIAL ORGANIZATION. The occurrence of family parties has still to be confirmed. Records are otherwise of loners, occasionally two together.

MOVEMENTS. One taken at floodlights on Fraser's Hill on 27 December. Extreme daytime dates are 6 December and 15 August (Phangnga bay and Krabi mangroves), with an associating pair in Taman Negara on 10 July (BCSTB-12, K.D. Bishop, MBR 84–85) – still more or less compatible with wet-season breeding north of the Peninsula (HBI, Hopwood 1921) but more fieldwork is needed, especially at inland forest sites.

SURVIVAL. No information.

SOCIAL INTERACTIONS. Between preening bouts while perched on a floating bamboo in a forest river, a male pumped its tail and bobbed its head to and fro, but directed this action at no obvious target (Y.L. Mah).

VOICE. Call of a territorial male on the Kerau river, Pahang, in April and May: 'like a series of large bubbles blown under water, only the sound is deeper, changing to clucks with increasing tempo' (Y.L. Mah).

BREEDING. No proven population.

MOULT. None in specimens taken in January and February; a female from Yala dated 19 May was growing P1, with other primaries older (BMNH, UMZC).

CONSERVATION. The clouding of rivers by silt from logging operations is believed to have restricted inland foraging habitat, but more observations are needed. Globally vulnerable (BTW2).

Family RALLIDAE

Crakes, rails, swamphens and coots: 12 species

Red-legged Crake; Nok Anchan Paa Khaa Daeng (Thai); Burung Sintar Api (Malay)

Rallina fasciata (Raffles) 1822, *Transactions of the Linnean Society* 13(2): 328. TL Benkulen, SW Sumatra.
Plate 27

GROUP RELATIONS. Free-standing.

GLOBAL RANGE. The far-NE Indian subcontinent; Lanyu island (Taiwan); Burma, W Thailand and S Vietnam to the Greater Sunda islands and Philippines; the Lesser Sunda islands (Lombok, Flores, Kisar) and Moluccas. Limits of breeding uncertain, but they appear to include most of this range. Vagrant in W Micronesia (Palau) and Australia.

IDENTIFICATION/DESCRIPTION. From apparently much rarer Chinese Banded Crake by broader red eye-ring, uniformly orange head and neck, and extensive black-and-white banding and spotting on the wing-coverts and scapulars. Throat whitish in females, more uniform orange-rufous in males. Juveniles are dull olive-brown rather than rufous but have the adult wing and scapular pattern.

Bare-part colours. (Adult) iris bright red; fleshy eyelid-rim bright red; bill greenish horn with dark culmen and red base; legs and feet bright red.

Size (mm). (Live: a 3-figure sample of adults; most not sexed): wing 119–134 (no definite female above 129); tail 48–56; bill 20.2–22.5, from front edge nostril 10.9–13.0; tarsus 39–52; mid-toe plus claw 35.0–36.2 (UMBRP).

Weight (g). Passage migrants 68.8–107.5 (3-figure sample) (UMBRP).

DISTRIBUTION. Historical summary: all divisions except *Pak, Chu, Pha, Nak, Pht, Son, Nar, Pra, Neg*, with additional W-coast island records from the Similan group, Phiphi and Maa (*Kra*), Tarutao, Penang, and Pisang, all at typical passage dates, but calling in June on Lanta (BCSTB-12).

GEOGRAPHICAL VARIATION. None recognized.

STATUS AND POPULATION. Resident, non-breeding visitor and a passage migrant (records from the Melaka Straits, including at One-Fathom Bank lighthouse, imply onward journeys to Indonesia); local and sparse to uncommon. Reported in most months, and present probably year-round overall (cf. Lekagul and Round 1991), but hard to find when silent and the distribution of residents versus winterers is still uncertain. Breeding confirmed in Krabi, Trang and Singapore, and advertisement-calling or summer presence recorded in Surat Thani, Phuket, Krabi, Pahang and Selangor (BBCB-4, BMNH, MBR 1984–85, 1986–87, Riley 1938).

Best known as a nocturnal migrant, with numerous reports of strikes on lights inland and off the W coast and, since 1965, 150 captured for ringing at floodlights on Fraser's Hill, crest of the Main Range (PERHILITAN, UMBRP). Two of these were still just within the known spring migration period when retrapped in Terengganu and Perlis in May (BR 1970–71), hence need not have reached their breeding destinations.

HABITATS AND ECOLOGY. The above two birds are believed to have been recovered from paddyland,

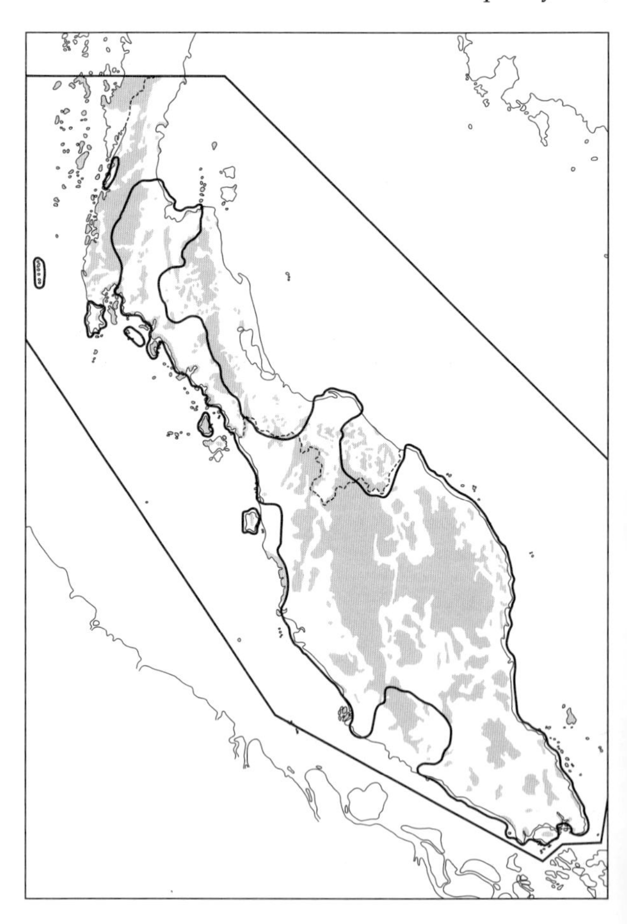

and presence of this rail in paddy crops is confirmed in autumn (October). Other winter sightings have been made in open swamps, including reedbeds (Cant 1957–58, SINGAV-4, Robinson 1913a), whereas all records of advertisement-calling and proven nesting, where the data exist, have been at the edge of, to actually in, scrub or closed woodland. The distinction could be between populations of different status, but at all seasons at least some use is made of open ground: during June–July in Surat Thani, Robinson (1914a) found birds at the edge of paddy-fields, and a pair in suburban Singapore made a habit of escorting a chick out to forage on a mown lawn (C.J. Hails, MBR 1986–87).

FORAGING AND FOOD. No additional information.

SOCIAL ORGANIZATION. Daytime field-encounters have been with loners, or single adults escorting downy chicks.

MOVEMENTS. On information from the Melaka Straits, Kedah and Kelantan, Chasen (1932) summarized passage-seasons as October–December and late April–June. Recent extreme dates of night-time interceptions at Fraser's hill, strikes on lighthouses, etc., are 11 October and 3 January (with heaviest passage at Fraser's Hill in November) and 16 April and 15 June (BR 1966, 1969, 1976–77, UMBRP). The latest spring bird had 7 mm testes (BMP5) but as a strike victim at Kuala Selangor lighthouse is likely still to have been on the move.

Orientation of movements has been assumed to be south in autumn, north in spring, but other patterns are possible (see Cinnamon Bittern). The only direct evidence is from the two ring-recoveries in May, both north of their migration position of the previous October and November (BR 1970–71).

SURVIVAL. No information.

SOCIAL INTERACTIONS. No information.

VOICE. Advertisement-calling is nocturnal: an explosive *pwek* given singly or in a steady, spaced series. A duetted call regularly heard at night from a known nest-territory in Singapore included this same sharp hiccup followed by shrill rattles reeling down scale over two-plus seconds.

BREEDING

Nest. Not described.

Eggs and brood. Eggs are plain, slightly glossy white. Shape short elliptical. Size (mm): 32.8–30.6 × 25.0–24.3 (n=11). Clutches of five and six eggs reported from Trang but broods of only one and three chicks in Singapore.

Cycle. No information.

Seasonality. Calling reported during May–August, eggs in July, and downy chicks with a parent over mid-summer and in January (BBCB-4, C.J. Hails, MBR 1984–85, 1986–87, Riley 1938, SINGAV-4), defining no very obvious season.

MOULT. No wing-moult found among nocturnal migrants at either season (BMP5), or in a male collected in likely breeding-habitat on 1 July (BMNH). At least some first-winterers arrive in juvenile plumage.

CONSERVATION. Little known, and no habitat issues identified.

Slaty-legged Crake; Nok Anchan Paa Khaa Thao (Thai); Burung Sintar Merah (Malay)

Rallina eurizonoides (Lafresnaye) 1845, *Revue Zoologique par la Société Cuvierienne*: 368. TL Philippines.

Plate 27

GROUP RELATIONS. Free-standing.

GLOBAL RANGE. The Indian subcontinent from the Himalayan foothills, and Sri Lanka, S Guangxi, Hainan, Hong Kong, Taiwan and the S Nansei islands; SE Asia to Sumatra, W Java and the Philippines; Sulawesi and the Sula islands; and W Micronesia (Palau). Northern continental populations migrate, wintering in NE India and SE Asia.

IDENTIFICATION/DESCRIPTION. From other bar-bellied crakes by dark rather than red legs and feet. Immatures are dull olive-brown rather than orange-rufous, and this is also a minority colour-phase among female adults (BR 1963).

Bare-part colours. (Adult) iris blood-red (orange in a juvenile) with inner ring olive-brown and eyelid-rim orange; bill greenish, culmen and tip dark grey-horn; legs and feet greenish slate (blackish in juvenile).

Size (mm). (Live and skins: 12 adults; most not sexed): wing 137–152 (confirmed females up to 142, juveniles down to 135); tail 60–70; bill 23.2–26.2, from front edge nostril 15.0–17.0; tarsus 42.0–48.6 (no confirmed female above 45.0); mid-toe plus claw 39.9–43.1 (BMNH, UMBRP, ZDUM, ZRCNUS).

Weight (g). One nocturnal migrant, 91.2 (UMBRP).

DISTRIBUTION. Historical summary: *Chu, Phu, Tra, Pat, Ked, Phg, Sel, Mel, Sin,* with additional (including mid winter-dated) W-coast island records from Rang (*Phu*), Langkawi, and Rembia (*Pek*).

GEOGRAPHICAL VARIATION. Subspecies *telmatophila* Hume 1878 (TL Melaka), of continental SE Asia and the Sunda region, similar to but longer-winged than the Indian subcontinent breeder (Wells and Medway 1976).

STATUS AND POPULATION. The limit of summering in western SE Asia has not been mapped, but strictly a non-breeding visitor and passage migrant in the Peninsula, recorded in all months November–April. Local and sparse; during 1965–90 only nine were captured at the Fraser's Hill floodlights (UMBRP). By their mid-season dates (BMNH, Robinson and Chasen 1936), evidently, some birds overwinter, whereas strikes on western lighthouses (One-Fathom Bank) plus shipboard captures in the Melaka Straits in November and May (BMNH, CLBS) show others must continue on to Indonesia.

HABITATS AND ECOLOGY. Most daytime records have been of birds trapped on the floor of secondary-growth and forest, in several cases close to streams; from plains-level to 1800 m in the Upper Montane zone of the Main Range (Beremban peak, Cameron Highlands). In Montane forest also on Jerai peak, Kedah (BMNH, BR 1963, Robinson and Chasen 1936, Robinson and Kloss 1916). A bird in a ditch across open grassland at Ponggol, Singapore, on 24 March (SINGAV-4) could already have been on passage by that date.

FORAGING AND FOOD. No information.

SOCIAL ORGANIZATION. Solitary.

MOVEMENTS. Extreme passage-dates, from night-time interceptions at floodlights and captures at sea: 11 and 22 November and, in spring, 12 April and 13 May (BMP5, BR 1976–77, Chasen and Hoogerwerf 1941).

SURVIVAL. No information.

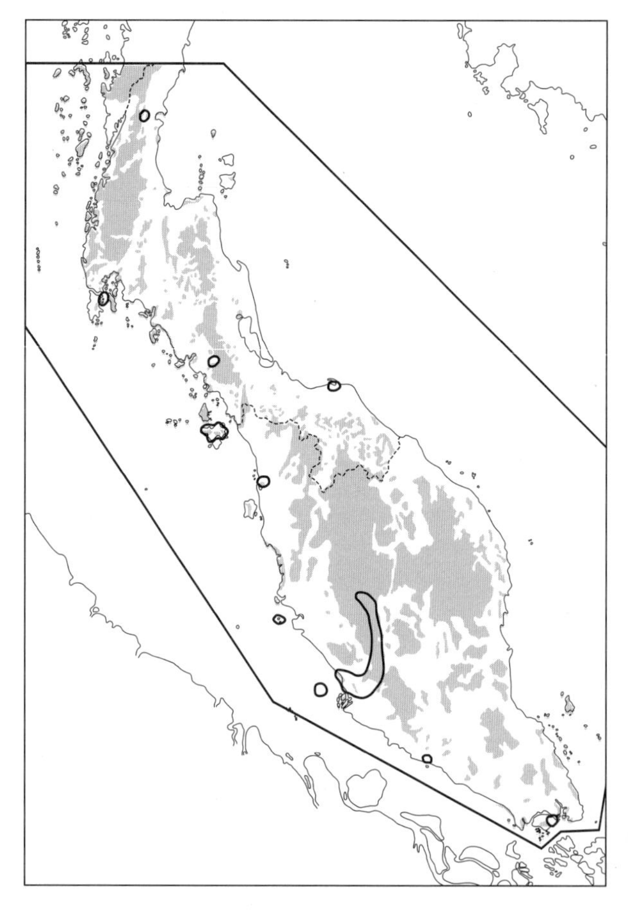

SOCIAL INTERACTIONS. No information.

VOICE. No information.

BREEDING. No population.

MOULT. None handled have shown any wing-moult, but November adults were in fresh plumage, suggesting completion of a moult before arrival. As with Red-legged Crake, some first-winterers arrive in full juvenile, others in part-adult plumage. No fully brown (rather than part-rufous) bird has been reported later than 12 December (BR 1963).

CONSERVATION. Not well-enough known for issues to be identified.

Slaty-breasted Rail; Nok Anchan Ok Thao (Thai); Burung Sintar Biasa (Malay)

Gallirallus striatus (Linnaeus) 1766, *Systema Naturae* 12(1): 262. TL Manila, Philippines.
Plate 27

GROUP RELATIONS. Free-standing. Considered by Olson (1973) to be partly convergent with *Rallus* species, within the structurally less specialized genus *Gallirallus*; but an opposite interpretation is possible.

GLOBAL RANGE. The Indian subcontinent (excluding the NW), and Sri Lanka and Bay of Bengal islands; S China from the Changjiang valley including Taiwan and Hainan; SE Asia to the Greater Sunda islands, Bali and the Philippines; and Sulawesi and the Lesser Sunda islands (Lombok, Sawu). Migratory in the northern part of its Chinese range and a large-scale dispersant in the N Philippines (McClure 1974).

IDENTIFICATION/DESCRIPTION. Longish bill partly pink to red, cap to hind-neck chestnut and upperparts and wings blackish, finely barred white. Juveniles lack chestnut and have upperparts streaky brown. A part-albino (with white cap) is on record (ZRCNUS).

Bare-part colours. (Adult) iris chestnut to yellow-brown; bill pink to red (pink in a male with 13 mm testes), tip and culmen grey-brown; legs and feet olive-grey.

Size (mm). (Skins and live: 11 males, 9 females; adult): wing 112–122 (129) and 111–118; tail 36–41 and 36–40; bill 32.4 (one only) and 27.6–33.5, from front edge nostril 18.7–21.9 and 16.9–21.6; tarsus 33.9–38.9 and 33.4–36.8; mid-toe plus claw 37.3–42.0 (sexes combined) (BMNH, ZRCNUS).

Weight (g). Two adults, 110, 111 (UMBRP).

DISTRIBUTION. Historical summary: *Sur, Nak, Phu, Kra, Son, Ked, Kel, Pra, Pek, Phg, Sel, Neg, Mel, Joh, Sin*, with additional islands records from Penang and Sentosa (Singapore).

GEOGRAPHICAL VARIATION. Needs study. The Peninsula may be a zone of intergradation between southern *gularis* Horsfield 1821 (TL Java) and larger, continental *albiventer* Swainson 1837 (TL India).

STATUS AND POPULATION. Resident (BBCB-4, P.D. Round), regular and more or less common, and a possible, occasional non-breeding visitor. Not taken at the Fraser's Hill floodlights or reported from lights elsewhere, but a long-winged (129 mm) male collected at the foot of Pulai peak, Johor, on 15 March (BMNH) is well out of the local size-range and could have been a migrant. It matches summer-dated birds of continental Thailand and Vietnam northwards.

HABITATS AND ECOLOGY. The landward edge of mangroves but, more typically, flooded paddy-fields and their dividing bunds; rough, wet grassland and reedbeds; and the edge of ditches, canals and flooded mine-workings. Occasionally drier sites, venturing into suburbia where suitable cover, ditches and quiet gardens are available, but much less common than White-breasted Waterhen in this habitat.

FORAGING AND FOOD. No information.

SOCIAL ORGANIZATION. One or both parents shepherd running chicks; otherwise typically solitary.

MOVEMENTS. None demonstrated, but see above.

SURVIVAL. No information.

SOCIAL INTERACTIONS. No information.

VOICE. No good description.

BREEDING

Nest. A shallowly concave pad of grass (including rice) stems, 14–20 cm across × 9 cm deep, concealed among grass and weeds; on the ground in dependably dry sites, but up to 30 cm above the general surface (on an earth clod, in a tussock or built into standing stems) in wetter ones.

Eggs and brood. Eggs are glossless pale stone-brown, sparsely spotted red-brown, with bold blotches of purple-grey, brown and chocolate over the broad end. Shape short elliptical. Size (mm): 34.5–31.1 × 25.7–24.1 (n=9). Full clutch 4–6.

Cycle. Apparently both parents escort chicks.

Seasonality. Egg- and downy chick-dates from Krabi south to Singapore indicate laying in all months except April and August, i.e., probably continuously overall, although not necessarily so at any one

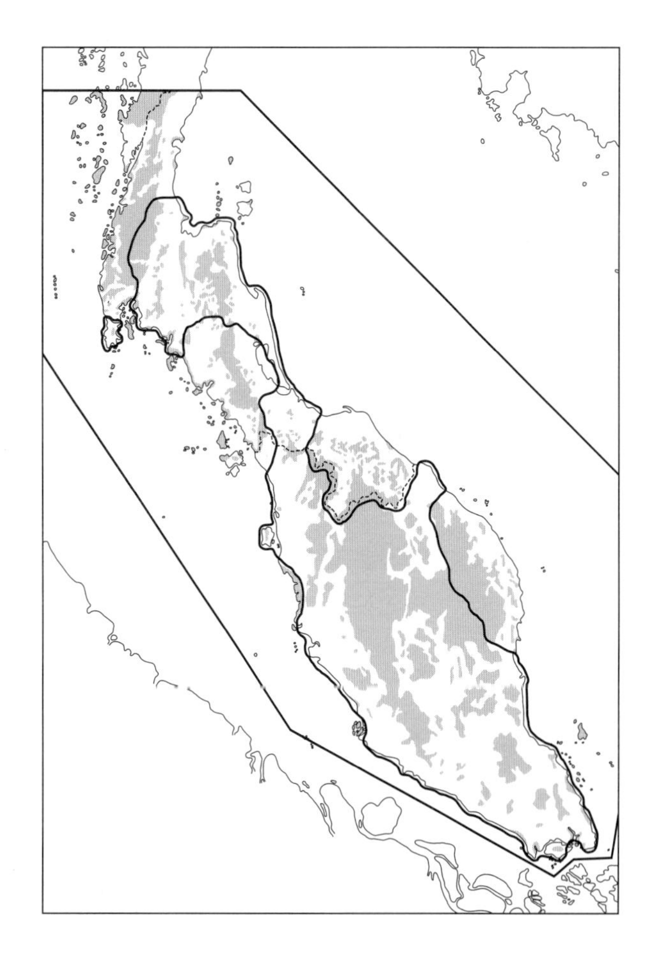

site/year (F.G.H. Allen, BBCB-4, Berwick 1952b, BMNH, BR 1974–75, Edgar 1933, ENGGANG-1, Madoc 1956a, MBR 1986–87, NRCS, P.D. Round, SINGAV-1, -2, -4, ZRCNUS).

MOULT. Among 17 from Selangor and Pahang south to Singapore collected in all months except February, April, July and November, only one showed wing-moult: P1 on 14 January (BMNH).

CONSERVATION. The Malaysian paddyland population is being hit by herbicides, and much other ground has been lost to the reclamation of open, dredge-mine land. Alternative habitats will hold a reduced population.

White-breasted Waterhen; Nok Gwak (Thai); Burung Ruak-ruak (Malay)

Amaurornis phoenicurus (Pennant) 1769, *Indian Zoology*: 10 and plate 9. TL Sri Lanka.
Plate 28

GROUP RELATIONS. Free-standing.

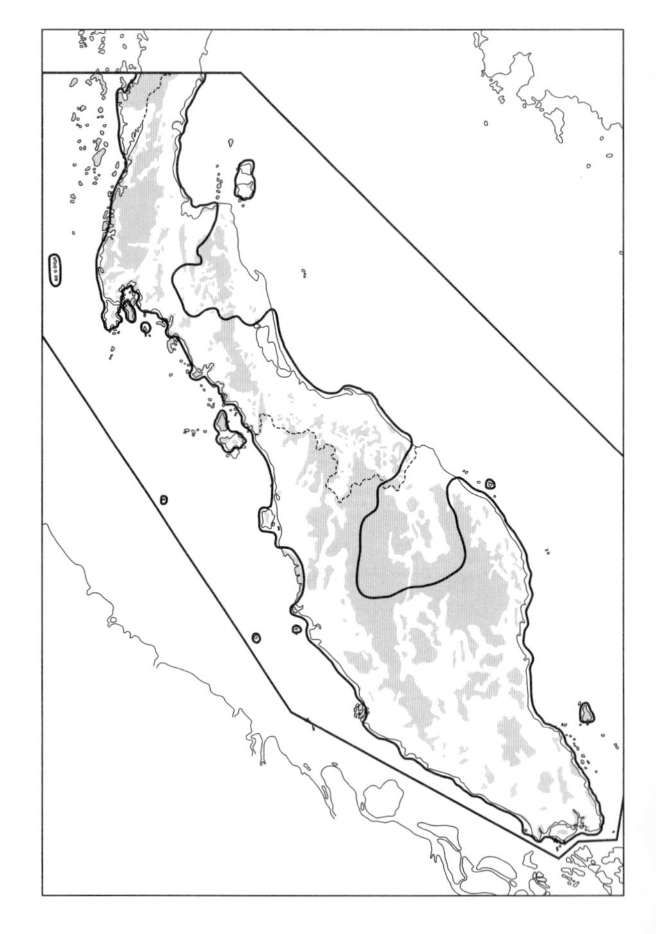

GLOBAL RANGE. The Indian subcontinent, Sri Lanka and Bay of Bengal islands; China south from latitude approximately 35°N, including Hainan and Taiwan, and invading Japan from the Nansei islands; SE Asia to the Greater Sunda islands, Bali and the Philippines; and Wallacea east to Damar (Lesser Sunda islands) and Buru (Moluccas).

IDENTIFICATION/DESCRIPTION. The pied pattern of juveniles is less clean-cut than in adults but all ages show orange-rufous lower tail-coverts beneath a cocked tail. A part albino, with the whole head, neck, mantle and tail white, reported from Singapore (MBR 1982–83).

Bare-part colours. Iris chrome-yellow to red-brown or red (basis of variation unknown); bill blackish (juvenile), yellow-green with culmen dark red and base of upper mandible red (adult); legs and feet dull wax-yellow (BMNH, UMBRP).

Size (mm). (Skins and live: 22 males, 15 females; adult): wing 143–182 and 141–175 (unsexed night-flying migrants not below 152); tail 53–73 and 52–70; bill 30.4–39.4 and 32.3–40.4; tarsus 49.8–56.8 and 51.7–57.5; mid-toe plus claw 64.5 (one, not sexed) (BMNH, TISTR, UMBRP, ZDUM, ZRCNUS).

Weight (g). Two (status unknown) from daytime habitat, 178 and 182; three nocturnal migrants, 157.5, 157.6 and 190.0 (UMBRP).

DISTRIBUTION. Historical summary: all divisions except *Nak*, *Kel*, and with additional island records from the Similan group, Yao Yai, Phiphi, Libong, Tarutao, Langkawi, Perak, Penang, Rembia, Jarak, Pangkor, Undan and Pisang off the W coast; Phangan, Samui, Redang and Tioman off the E coast; and Tekong, Ubin and Retan Laut around Singapore. No small-island date has been outside likely migration or wintering seasons, and none of the few island specimens seen has been small enough to confirm resident status.

GEOGRAPHICAL VARIATION. In need of revision. Variable nominate *phoenicurus* of continental Asia may be the only subspecies occurring (Ripley 1977). However, wing-lengths of summer-dated

(May–September) birds from Singapore north to Ban Kachon, Pakchan, are not above 149 mm (BMNH, UMBRP, ZRCNUS) and the Peninsula could be in a zone of intergradation with small, southern *javanicus* Horsfield 1821 (TL Java). From their size, migrants are *phoenicurus*.

STATUS AND POPULATION. Resident, a non-breeding visitor and apparent passage migrant; regular and common. Presumed northern migrants moving at night have been intercepted inland, including on the Main Range, and at Melaka Straits lighthouses south to Undan island, Melaka (B.D. Bond), but continue beyond the equator in Sumatra (CLBS) hence are likely to occur throughout.

HABITATS AND ECOLOGY. At all times, uses a wider range of habitats than other rails of the area, more tolerant of people, and correspondingly visible. Birds of unchecked status have been reported in agriculture on the Main Range at Cameron Highlands, at or above 1400 m (Berwick 1947). At plains level, reported from mangroves in winter (Edgar 1947); more typically around wet paddy-crops, reedbed margins, waterlogged scrub and other rank vegetation, by vegetated pools, waterways and drains, and in one instance (with young) at a salt-lick clearing well into mature forest (ENGGANG-2). Often ventures out to forage on the open, drier ground of mine-tailings, quiet road-verges, plantations, parks and gardens, provided suitable cover is within escape-flight range. Suburban birds regularly visit garden ponds, and escort chicks to drink there. Sometimes swims, and often climbs about in the dense crown-foliage of waterside bushes and small trees, perhaps roosting there.

FORAGING AND FOOD. No information.

SOCIAL ORGANIZATION. Solitary; less often in pairs, or shepherding chicks.

MOVEMENTS. In autumn, extreme dates of night-time interceptions, including at sea, are 1 and 26 November. In spring, a bird on Perak island, N Melaka Straits, on 4 March, and another taken at Fraser's Hill on 14 April (BMNH, BR 1970–71, 1972–73, 1974–75).

SURVIVAL. No information.

SOCIAL INTERACTIONS. Apart from duetting by pair-members, no information.

VOICE. Calls from cover, mostly at dawn and dusk, sometimes after dark. Pairs combine in a cacophony of howling and scolding: *kyurr kyurr kyurr kukaru-uk wuk wuk wuk*. . ., and variants. An insistent, repeated *u-wuk u-wuk u-wuk* . . . or *uark uark uark* . . . is given independently but has not been identified to a sex.

BREEDING

Nest. A pad of bent-over and interlaced stems and blades topped by a thin lining of dry grass and sometimes roofed by surrounding plants, typically 1–2 m above ground, held up in tall grass, reeds or scrub, in both wet and dry sites.

Eggs and brood. Eggs are glossless, pale, sandy grey, variably flecked and blotched all over with reddish brown and light lavender-grey. Shape elliptical to ovate. Size (mm): 43.3–39.7 × 29.5–28.5 (n=4). Full clutch 3–5.

Cycle. No information.

Seasonality. Eggs or downy chicks found on dates that imply laying in every month of the year (F.G.H. Allen, BMP5, BR 1974–75, Edgar 1933, Madoc 1956a, NRCS, Ryves 1938, SINGAV-3, Webber 1954).

MOULT. Rails collected by shooting are rarely in wing-moult. None of 35 adults from Pakchan to Singapore dated January–March, June, July, September, November and December, and none of the few passage migrants mist-netted, showed any (BMNH, UMBRP, ZDUM, ZRCNUS).

CONSERVATION. No critical issues. The habit of feeding along verges leads to many road-kills, guessed to be significant in suburban habitats, but effects can only be local.

Baillon's Crake; Nok Anchan Lek (Thai); Burung Sintar Kecil (Malay)

Porzana pusilla (Pallas) 1776, *Reise durch verschiedene Provinzen des russischen Reichs* 3: 700. TL Dauria, E Russia.

Plate 27

GROUP RELATIONS. The recently extinct Hawaiian *P. palmeri* (Laysan Crake) may have been an allospecies of *pusilla* (cf. Olson 1973).

GLOBAL RANGE. Breeds in southern and E Africa, and Madagascar; temperate Eurasia from the Atlantic to Japan, south to Iran, Kashmir, and China south from the Changjiang river; also New Guinea, parts of Australia, and New Zealand including the Chatham islands. Most Palaearctic populations migrate, wintering south through Africa, the Indian subcontinent, Sri Lanka and the Andamans, and SE Asia to the Greater

Sunda islands and N and central Philippines. The few Wallacean records may also be of northern migrants.

IDENTIFICATION/DESCRIPTION. Small size, brown-streaked upperparts, grey eyebrow and underparts, dark-and-white-barred lower tail-coverts, and short bill (distinct from juvenile Slaty-breasted Rail) are key features in the field. The leading-edge of the wing shows whitish in flight (Lekagul and Round 1991).

Bare-part colours. (Adult) iris red-brown to red; bill dull green with darker horn culmen and tip; legs and feet green.

Size (mm). (Live and skins: 8 adults; most not sexed): wing 86–93; tail 40–49; bill 15.3–18.1; tarsus 27.7–31.0; mid-toe plus claw 38.0 (one only) (BMNH, UMBRP, ZRCNUS).

Weight (g). Adults, 31.3–42.6 (48.2, 54.9) (n=6) (UMBRP).

DISTRIBUTION. Probably overlooked. Historical summary: *Pht, Pra, Pek, Sel, Sin,* with an additional island record from Chawaeng marsh, Samui (*Sur*), on 1 May 1990 (R.S.E. Swanquist).

GEOGRAPHICAL VARIATION. Chasen and Hoogerwerf (1941) assigned two Selangor specimens to a supposed tropical subspecies, *mira*, now regarded as within the range of variation of (migratory) nominate *pusilla*. There is no direct evidence of breeding in SE Asia.

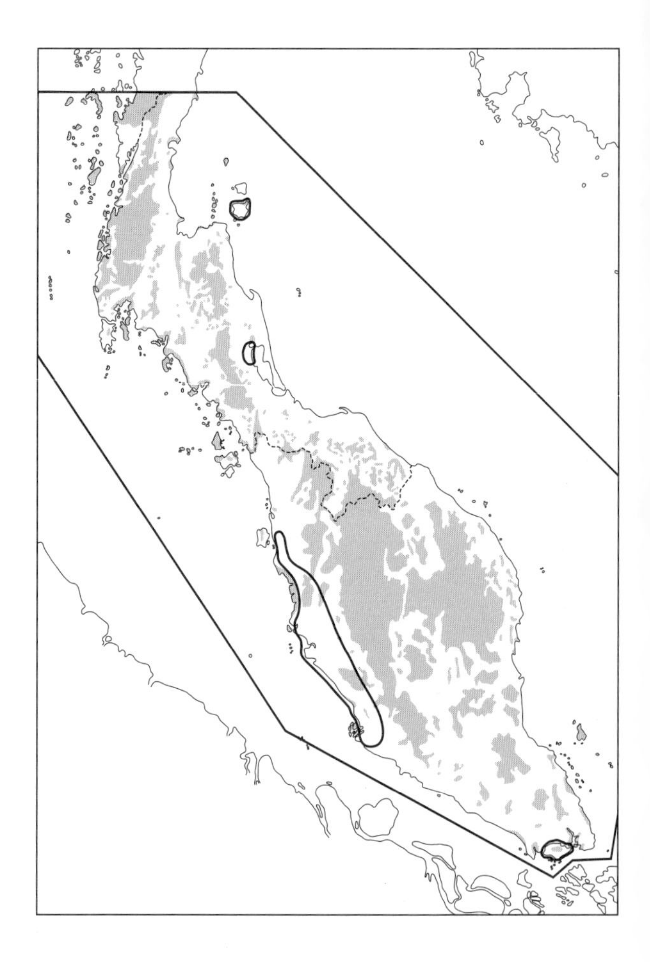

STATUS AND POPULATION. A non-breeding visitor, local and uncommon to more or less common, but with no record of a night-time interception at lights either inland or at sea (BMP5). Present in all months October–May.

HABITATS AND ECOLOGY. Like many birds of open, freshwater wetlands, except in the Thalae Noi–Songkhla system, depends on transient habitats, often unstable from year to year, and shrinking and declining in quality overall, e.g., in Malaysia with the decline of the dredge-mine industry and progressive dependance on chemical pesticides (especially winter herbicides) in paddy agriculture. Otherwise, selects sedge- and reedbeds and other rank, wet grassland, weed-choked channels, etc., wherever there is standing water (BIRDLINE 1993).

FORAGING AND FOOD. No information.

SOCIAL ORGANIZATION. Solitary.

MOVEMENTS. Extreme seasonal dates in the south of the Peninsula are 7 September and 17 May (BIRDLINE 1994, BR 1964, SINGAV-3).

SURVIVAL. No information.

SOCIAL INTERACTIONS. No information.

VOICE. No information.

BREEDING. No population.

MOULT. Unknown. None of nine adults covering all months January–May showed any active wing-moult, but an early April female from Phatthalung had P1–9 distinctly newer than P10 (BMNH, UMBRP, UMZC, ZDUM, ZRCNUS).

CONSERVATION. Faces loss of quality and area in some major habitats (see above), but also makes opportunistic use of marginal sites.

Ruddy-breasted Crake; Nok Nuu Daeng (Thai); Burung Sintar Belacan (Malay)

Porzana fusca (Linnaeus) 1766, *Systema Naturae* 12(1): 262. TL Philippines.
Plate 27

GROUP RELATIONS. Free-standing.

GLOBAL RANGE. The Indian subcontinent and Sri Lanka; Korea and Japan, and China south of a line Liaoning–Sichuan, including Taiwan; SE Asia to the Greater Sunda islands, Bali and the Philippines; and Sulawesi and the Lesser Sunda islands (Sumba and Flores). Vagrant on Christmas island, Indian Ocean (Chasen 1933). Some northern continental populations migrate, wintering within the gross breeding-range from an uncertain limit north of the equator.

IDENTIFICATION/DESCRIPTION. From other rufous-fronted, red-footed crakes by small size and unmarked, uniformly brown wings. Juveniles are all-dull, sooty brown with faint white barring on the underparts, from chin to tail-coverts.

Bare-part colours. (Adult) iris and eyelid-rim blood-red; bill greenish blue, culmen and base black; legs and feet coral-red.

Size (mm). (Skins and live: 28 adults, most not sexed): wing 85–101 (mean 92); tail 37–50; bill 19.8–23.4; tarsus 31.5–38.0; mid-toe plus claw 41.3–44.8 (BMNH, Meyer de Schauensee 1946, UMBRP, ZRCNUS).

Weight (g). From Selangor and Singapore, 51.5–63.7 (n=18).

DISTRIBUTION. Historical summary: *Sur, Kra, Pht, Tra, Pat, Ked, Kel, Pek, Sel, Sin*, with a December record from the Similan group (Phangnga) and one in May from Chawaeng marsh, Samui island.

GEOGRAPHICAL VARIATION. Deignan (1963) identified northern birds as continental *bakeri* Hartert 1917 (TL Kumaon, N India), implying *bakeri* grades into marginally smaller nominate *fusca* somewhere north of Selangor (UMBRP); but they are not recognised as separate by Ripley (1977).

STATUS AND POPULATION. On present evidence, exclusively resident (in Malaysia, summer-ringed adults retrapped on site up to 12 months later); regular and more or less common. It would be hard to prove migrants occur without direct interceptions and, so far, there has been none.

HABITATS AND ECOLOGY. Selects much the same freshwater habitats as Baillon's Crake: sedge- and reedbeds, paddy-crops, other rank grassland, and dense tangles standing in or at the edge of wetlands; but occasionally also brackish swamp (including in the Kuala Selangor nature park), and recorded on the floor of regularly tidal mangrove forest (MBR 1986–87).

FORAGING AND FOOD. No information.

SOCIAL ORGANIZATION. Solitary.

MOVEMENTS. None known.

SURVIVAL. No additional information.

SOCIAL INTERACTIONS. No information.

VOICE. A repeated, sharp and high-pitched *chep*, easily mistaken for a small frog, could be the call also described as like 'a guineafowl in miniature'. A high-pitched whistling, rising and falling, is also ascribed to this crake (G.C. Madoc), but more information needed.

BREEDING

Nest. A small pad of grass 10 cm across × 2–3 cm deep built about 30 cm up in reeds or the centre of a tussock on wet ground.

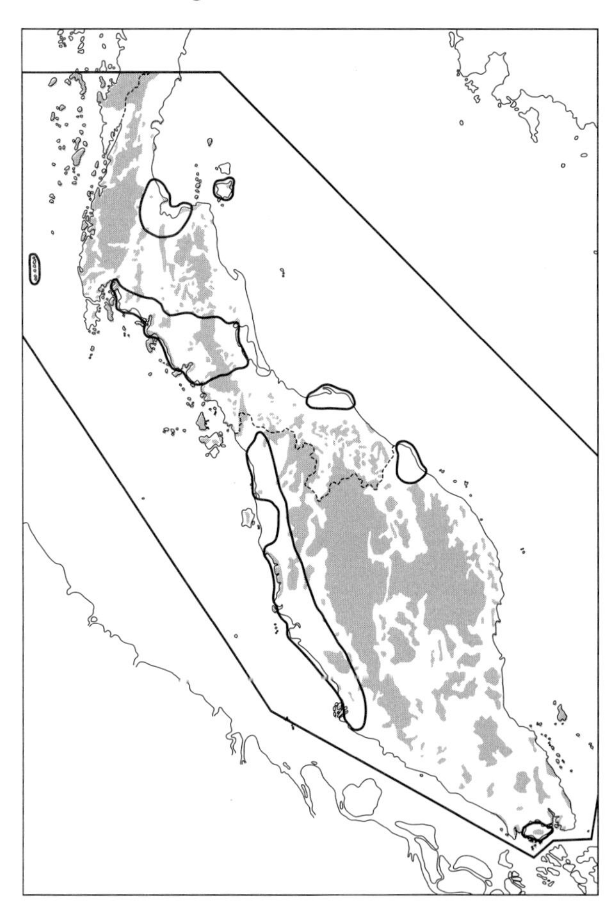

Eggs and brood. Eggs are faintly glossed, pale stone-brown, lightly and evenly freckled and blotched red-brown, and with underlying purple-grey marks mostly over the broad end. Shape elliptical to ovate. Size (mm): 29.7 × 22.8 (n=1). Full clutch unknown but up to three eggs recorded.

Cycle. No information.

Seasonality. In Perak, Selangor and Singapore, eggs and downy young on dates that imply laying in February, April and May; and at Sungai Way (Selangor) juveniles have been mist-netted during May–mid November (BMP5, BR 1965, Edgar 1933, NRCS).

MOULT. None of 23 adults from Selangor and Singapore handled in all months except February and April showed any wing-moult (BMNH, UMBRP). Typical of rails, they do not seem to be nettable or shootable during moult.

CONSERVATION. See Baillon's Crake. Herbicides are spoiling an important habitat in Malaysia.

Chinese Banded Crake; Nok Anchan Jeen (Thai); Burung Sintar Cina (Malay)

Porzana paykulli (Ljungh) 1813, *Konglige Vetenskaps Academiens Handlingar* 34: 258 and plate 5. TL Java and S Kalimantan.
Plate 27

GROUP RELATIONS. Free-standing.

GLOBAL RANGE. Breeds in the Amur and Ussuri valleys, probably also NE China south to N Henan. Winters in the Peninsula and Greater Sunda islands, with most records from Borneo and Java.

IDENTIFICATION/DESCRIPTION. Adult from Red-legged Crake by: white barring on the upper surface of the wing finer and confined to the coverts; crown to hind-neck dark brown, concolorous with the upperparts and sharp against orange-rufous of face and fore-neck; throat cleaner-cut white; and black bars dominant over white on flanks and lower tail-coverts. Juvenile like a large, same-stage Ruddy-breasted Crake, all dun-brown with obscure white barring up centre of breast and neck (BMNH).

Bare-part colours. (Adult) iris and eyelid-rim blood-red; bill grey-green, culmen brownish; legs and feet bright orange-red (Robinson and Chasen 1936).

Size (mm). (Skins: 3 males, 3 females; adult): wing 132–134 and 123–129; tail 44–54 and 49–54; bill 22.7–23.1 (female only); tarsus 38.8–42.1 and 37.7–39.4; mid-toe plus claw 43.4–45.8 and 41.7–47.4 (BMNH, ZDUM, ZRCNUS).

Weight (g). One autumn female, 84.8 (UMBRP).

DISTRIBUTION. Probably overlooked. Historical summary: *Pek, Phg, Sel, ?Mel* (a nineteenth-century specimen not necessarily of local origin), with no island records.

GEOGRAPHICAL VARIATION. None recognized.

STATUS AND POPULATION. A non-breeding visitor and likely passage migrant; local and sparse. Known from a lighthouse-strike at Kuala Selangor and night-interceptions at floodlights on Fraser's Hill; a handful of daytime records from the W-coast plain

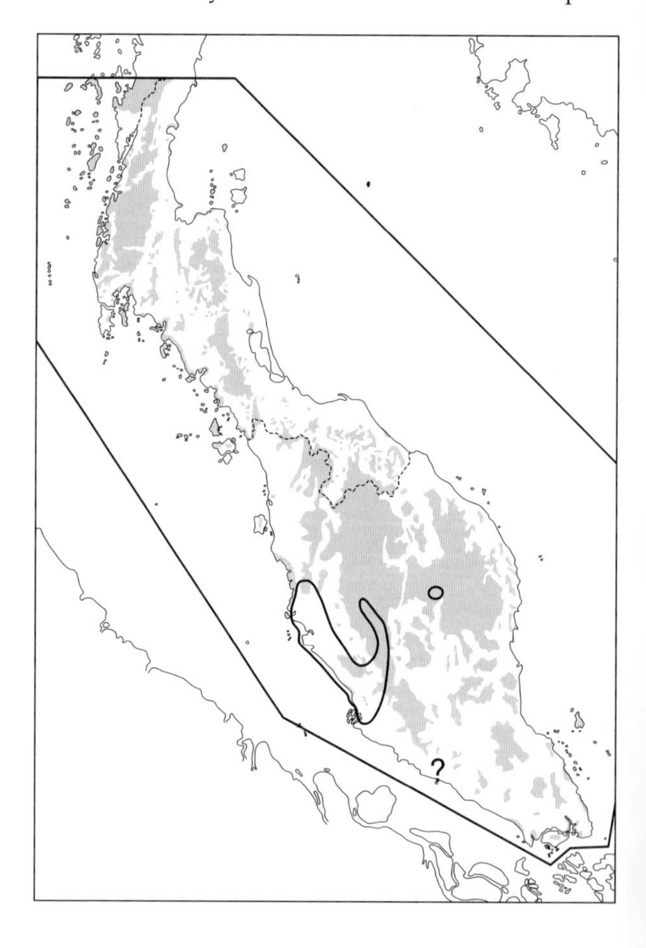

between mid Perak and mid Selangor; and, from east of the Main Range, sightings in late September 1987 at Kuala Tahan, Taman Negara (AMNH, BMNH, BR 1965, 1967, 1968, MBR 1986–87). Most have been on likely passage-dates, but two are from late December and early February.

HABITATS AND ECOLOGY. Recorded from paddyland in Java (Hume 1879), and on the W-coast plain appears to have been collected in open swamp (Robinson and Chasen 1936), but the Taman Negara sightings were of foragers (possibly just one individual) on the damp floor of Lowland forest (MBR 1986–87).

FORAGING AND FOOD. No information.

SOCIAL ORGANIZATION. Apparently solitary.

MOVEMENTS. Extreme passage-dates in autumn are 22 September and 20 November, with spring records on 30 April and 2 May (BR 1967, 1968, MBR 1986–87).

SURVIVAL. No information.

SOCIAL INTERACTIONS. No information.

VOICE. According to FMSM collector E. Seimund, gives a grating croak (Robinson and Chasen 1936). No better description available.

BREEDING. No population.

MOULT. None seen; a migrating adult dated 31 October was in fresh plumage, implying it had recently completed a moult. Wintering adults likewise have fairly fresh flight-feathers. Full juvenile plumage recorded to late December (BMNH, ZDUM, ZRCNUC).

CONSERVATION. Local habitat requirements are too little known. Globally, ranked near-threatened (BTW2).

White-browed Crake; Nok Anchan Khiw Khao (Thai); Burung Sintar Dahi Putih (Malay)

Porzana cinerea (Vieillot) 1819, *Nouveau Dictionnaire d'Histoire Naturelle* 28: 29. TL Java.
Plate 27

GROUP RELATIONS. Free-standing.

GLOBAL RANGE. Central Thailand, Cambodia and the Malay Peninsula to the Greater Sunda islands, Bali and the Philippines; Wallacea, New Guinea, northern Australia, and the tropical Pacific to Samoa.

IDENTIFICATION/DESCRIPTION. Generally pale grey and buff-brown, shading to cinnamon on lower tail-coverts, with black-and-white face-pattern prominent in adults.

Bare-part colours. (Adult) iris and eyelid-rim red: bill pale olive-green with red base; legs and feet clear sage-green (BMNH, UMBRP).

Size (mm). (Skins and live: 14 adults, most not sexed): wing 90–97; tail 44–50; bill 18.7–22.1; tarsus 32.3–36.6; mid-toe plus claw 41.2–46.4 (BMNH, UMBRP, ZDUM, ZRCNUS).

Weight (g). One unsexed adult, 49.0 (UMBRP).

DISTRIBUTION. Apparently not in the far north. Historical summary: *?Pha, ?Phu, Pht, Tra, Son, Sat, Ked, Pra, Pek, Sel, Mel, Joh, Sin,* with additional island records from Penang.

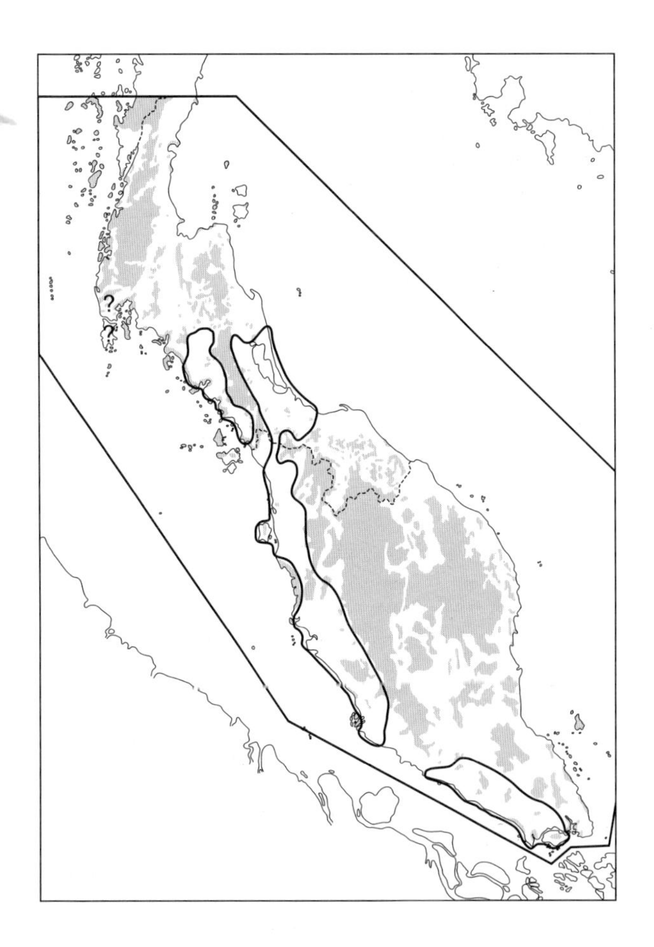

GEOGRAPHICAL VARIATION. Nominate *cinerea*, but the validity of subspecies has been questioned (Mees 1982).

STATUS AND POPULATION. Resident; at least in the south, regular and common. The habit of foraging out over floating vegetation-mats, where it is easily seen, gives a probably unjustified impression of abundance relative to other small crakes. Mostly dependant on transient, man-made habitat and, like some other open-wetland birds, affected in Malaysia by the decline of the dredge-mining industry.

HABITATS AND ECOLOGY. Water-hyacinth, lotus and waterlily beds, and other floating weed-mats are typical habitat (to which proportionately long toes are a good adaptation), plus the marshy fringes of still, fresh waters. Also enters flooded reedbeds and paddy-crops, and sometimes found at the margins of irrigation channels, but much less often than on vegetated ponds and lagoons.

FORAGING AND FOOD. In the Songkhla wetland, feeds around lotus and *Pistia* (water-lettuce) beds, taking arthropods from under leaves; sometimes also by wading among floating green algae. Large prey are carried onto big leaves and 'anvilled' (Anonymous 1981).

SOCIAL ORGANIZATION. Typically solitary.

MOVEMENTS. None recorded.

SURVIVAL. No information.

SOCIAL INTERACTIONS. No information.

VOICE. Not adequately described.

BREEDING

Nest. Not described.

Eggs and brood. Eggs are glossless stone-buff, evenly spotted purplish and yellow-brown. Shape elliptical to ovate. (mm): 31.8–29.0 × 22.6–22.0 (n=3). Full clutch unknown but no broods of more than four chicks on record.

Cycle. No information.

Seasonality. Eggs and escorted, downy chicks reported on dates that imply laying in January, February, July and August (BMP5, NRCS, Robinson and Chasen 1936, Silvius *et al.* 1987).

MOULT. A male dated 11 January growing all flight-feathers simultaneously, in the expected rallid manner. Fourteen other adults handled in February–April, July–September and December showed no wing-moult (BMNH, UMBRP, ZDUM, ZRCNUS).

CONSERVATION. No critical issues but, like most birds that are dependant on open freshwater swamp, destined to become rarer.

Watercock; Nok Ee-lum (Thai); Burung Ayam-ayam (Malay)

Gallicrex cinerea (Gmelin) 1789, *Systema Naturae* 13(2): 702. TL China.
Plate 28

GROUP RELATIONS. Free-standing.

GLOBAL RANGE. The Indian subcontinent, Sri Lanka and Andamans; possibly S Ussuriland; Japan, Korea, China south of a line Liaoning–Sichuan, including Taiwan and Hainan; SE Asia to the Greater Sunda islands, Bali and the Philippines; and Sulawesi. Vagrant in the Lesser Sunda islands (Flores). Many populations are migratory and in island SE Asia, apparently, only a non-breeder.

IDENTIFICATION/DESCRIPTION. The only large brown rallid, trailing its feet in flight. Males (mostly black in summer) approach Purple Swamphen in size; much larger than Common Moorhen. In flight, the blue-grey and white leading-edge of the wing is a useful identification-mark.

Bare-part colours. Iris pale grey-brown (juvenile) or deep brown (adult), eyelid-rim grey; upper mandible dusky olive, lower yellowish white to pale olive (in summer, male bill yellow, with base, shield and fleshy frontal horn of upper mandible, and spot on base of lower mandible, bright red); legs and feet grey-green or (summer male) red (BMNH, BMP5, Oates 1883, UMBRP).

Size (mm). (Skins and live: 12 males, 21 females; adult): wing 188–221 and 155–183; tail 66–88 and 57–72; bill from tip of frontal horn or shield 41.6–52.2 and 35.0–41.2; tarsus 63.9–78.6 and 55.2–69.4 (BMNH, UMBRP, UMZC, ZDUM, ZRCNUS).

Weight (g). Autumn migrants intercepted at Fraser's Hill: males, 326.5, 378.0; females, 206.7, 238.5, emphasizing the size-dimorphism of this rail.

DISTRIBUTION. Historical summary: all divisions except *Pak, Chu, Nak, Sat, Yal, Nar, Pes*, with passage migrants recorded from the following additional islands: the Surin and Similan groups, Perak, Penang, Angsa and Pisang off the W coast; and Tioman off the E coast.

GEOGRAPHICAL VARIATION. None recognized.

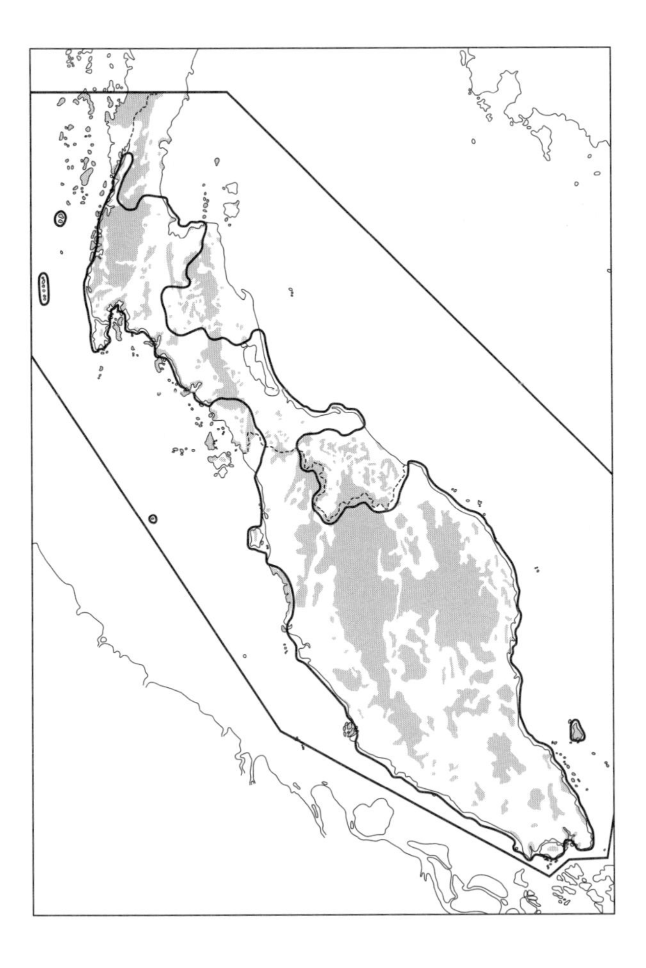

STATUS AND POPULATION. A local breeder (and possible resident), and regular and common non-breeding visitor and passage migrant throughout. Nesting recorded, so far, only in Kedah (Madoc 1956a). Elsewhere, south at least from Surat Thani (including the Thalae Noi–Songkhla wetland), present consistently during early November–early June (a male in near-full breeding-colours at Tanjung Karang, NW Selangor, on 5 June). The very few reported in the south during during July–October (including one at a forest salt-lick clearing in Taman Negara on 16 and 18 September) have been brown-plumaged, presumed non-breeders, although two Singapore males dated 26 September were half-moulted from black (Anonymous 1981, ENGGANG-2, Gibson-Hill 1949b, MBR 1982–83, MNC, SINGAV-2, -3, -4, Storer 1978).

HABITATS AND ECOLOGY. Wet paddyland and intersecting bunds where these are shaded by the crop, reedbeds (in which birds climb) and other open swampland, both freshwater and brackish. A couple of records are from salt-lick clearings in inland forest, and occasionally enters mangroves. A migrant on rocky Perak island foraged in the tidal splash-zone (BR 1972–73).

FORAGING AND FOOD. No additional information.

SOCIAL ORGANIZATION. Non-breeders are solitary but small, loose aggregrations can form during passage halts.

MOVEMENTS. Extreme passage dates, from interceptions at the Fraser's Hill floodlights, night-time strikes on Melaka Straits lighthouses and presence on islands lacking regular winter habitat are: 4 October and 19 December (peak movement in November), and 4 March and 12 June (the latest bird a female still with small gonads: BMP5). The spring peak is not defined but, in Singapore, unusual daytime aggregations have occurred in early May (BR 1966, 1967, 1968, 1970–71, 1972–73, Robinson and Chasen 1936, SINGAV-3, ZRCNUS).

SURVIVAL. No information.

SOCIAL INTERACTIONS. No information.

VOICE. A single low, gurgling growl followed by *kouk* notes (like the plucking of a slack cello string), starting weakly but gaining strength and timbre, to reach a crescendo of well-spaced, more clipped notes, *kow, kow, kow* ... (G.C. Madoc). Another call tentatively linked to Watercock (and the only one heard south of the breeding range) is a disyllabic *krex-aa*, the second note a hoarse exhaling sound.

BREEDING

Nest. Not described, but sited in reeds at the margin of small ponds.

Eggs and brood. Eggs not adequately described. Size (mm): 43.2 × 31.8 (average). Full clutch 4–5.

Cycle. No information.

Seasonality. Eggs in Kedah in May (Madoc 1956a). Records in other months lack confirmation.

MOULT. Passage migrants and winterers examined in all months October–March showed no wing-moult (BMNH, ZRCNUS, ZDUM). Freshness in early winter implies this is completed before arrival. Pre-breeding body-moult of males starts before spring departure, and in Selangor (south of the known breeding range) more or less fully black birds, with upstanding frontal horn, have been seen as of 17 March.

CONSERVATION. In Malaysia, affected by paddy-land pesticides, especially herbicides. It is unlikely the NW Malaysian paddy environment still provides breeding habitat.

Purple Swamphen; Nok Ee-gohng (Thai); Burung Pangling (Malay)

Porphyrio porphyrio (Linnaeus) 1758, *Systema Naturae* 10(1): 152. TL SW Europe.
Plate 28

GROUP RELATIONS. Free-standing.

GLOBAL RANGE. Madagascar, sub-Saharan Africa and locally around the Mediterranean to W Asia; through the Indian subcontinent, Sri Lanka and Bay of Bengal islands; Yunnan; SE Asia to Sumatra, S Borneo, Java, Bali and the Philippines; Wallacea east from Sulawesi and Sumba; and New Guinea, Australia and Oceania to Samoa and New Zealand.

IDENTIFICATION/DESCRIPTION. Large size, massive red bill and frontal shield, red legs and feet, and frequently flirted white lower tail-coverts are prominent in the field. Juveniles are more extensively grey than blue, and their bare-part colours are duller. In flight, feet trail conspicuously, like a Watercock, but wings are uniformly dark (no pale upper coverts).

Bare-part colours. (Adult) iris chestnut to blood-red; bill and frontal shield bright red; legs and feet bright red, joints browner (Allen 1948, Edgar 1947).

Size (mm). (Skins: 5 adults, none sexed): wing 245–255; tail 81–103; bill from top of frontal shield 63.0, 67.8 (two only); tarsus 86.0–91.3 (BMNH, TISTR, ZRCNUS).

Weight. No data.

DISTRIBUTION. Patchy. Historical summary: *Sur, Pht, Son, Sat, Pes, Ked, Pek, Sel, Mel, Sin*, with no island records.

GEOGRAPHICAL VARIATION. Subspecies *viridis* Begbie 1834 (TL Melaka), within the W and S Asian *poliocephalus* group, but individually variable. Some have mantle purple-blue (typical of *poliocephalus*) while in others it is green-shot. Extent of grey on head to upper neck also varies and, recently in Singapore, a few with distinctively dark heads resembled Greater Sunda island *indicus* (MBR 1986–87). Imported captives may have been released there, but the Peninsula could be a zone of natural *viridus-indicus* intergradation.

STATUS AND POPULATION. Resident; local, sparse to common, and centred on the permanent marshlands of Thalae Noi–Songkhla (up to 1200 estimated to have inhabited Thalae Noi in the late 1970s). Elsewhere, in numbers that fluctuate short-term with local hunting-pressure and transient habitat conditions. In Malaysia, the rise and decline of dredge-mining has been influential. As of the 1980s, reclamation of mining-land expelled them from most former habitat around Kuala Lumpur, whereas coastal polderization over the same period in Singapore had the opposite effect, allowing a population build-up (cf. BMP5). Curiously, unrecorded in neighbouring Johor state, so where recent Singapore colonists might have come from is unclear.

HABITATS AND ECOLOGY. Selects open, strictly freshwater wetlands usually with lagoons or channels of open water intersecting sedge- and reedbeds, and other wet, rank herbage. At Thalae Noi, frequents *Eleocharis dulcis* marsh and often forages along the water's edge (Storer 1976). In vegetation taller than their own stretching height, birds commonly rest on rough platforms formed by the bending back of stem-tops (G.C. Madoc). Not attracted to rice past the young tillering stage and, in contrast to Watercock, rarely found in this habitat.

FORAGING AND FOOD. Food at the Thalae Noi–Songkhla wetland includes: leaves of water-hyacinth and pith squeezed from *Eleocharis* by holding a stem in a foot and running it through the bill; rice tillers; *Salvinia* roots; young leaves and rhizomes of sedges and rushes (*Cyperus* and *Scirpus*); stems and

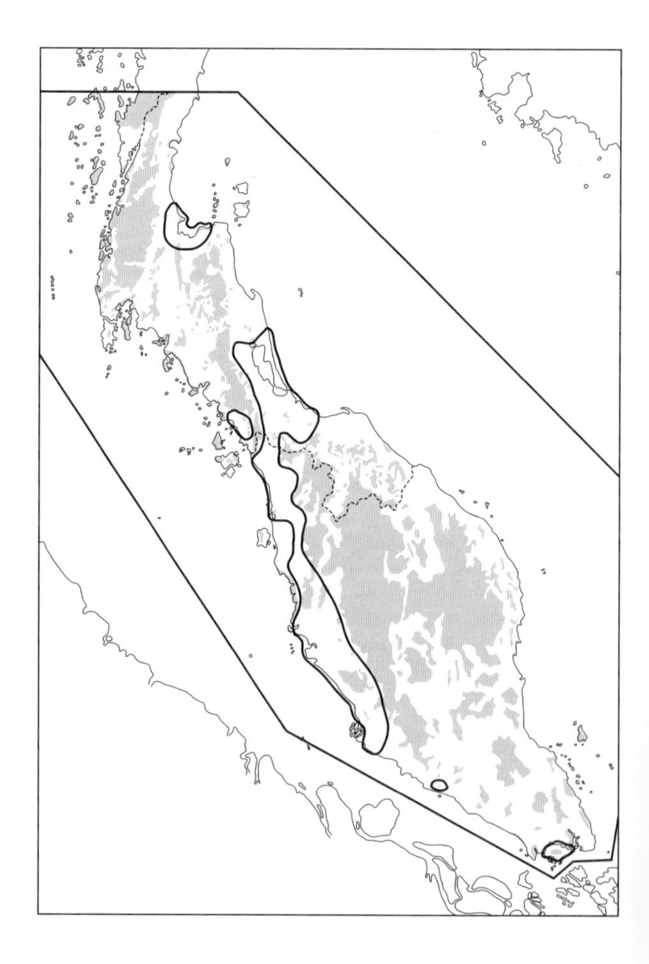

root-stocks of lotus, *Polygonum* and waterlilies, pulled out and cut up while being held in a foot; and flowers or seeds of lotus, water-hyacinth, sedges and *Eleocharis* (Anonymous 1981, Meeswat and Prentice 1984, Storer 1976). Some animal food (including large molluscs) is also processed while being held in a foot.

SOCIAL ORGANIZATION. Where undisturbed, becomes numerous and loosely gregarious (a count of 200 at Thalae Noi in early June 1992: R. Gregory-Smith). Young consort with parents until full-grown.

MOVEMENTS. None known.

SURVIVAL. No information.

SOCIAL INTERACTIONS. Persistent pumping of the tail flirts the white lower tail-coverts as a social signal.

VOICE. A 'whining cackle'; a loud, raucous *gaark, gaark, gaark . . .*; a creaking note, like a rusty hinge; and a loud *kwank* alarm-note from a full-grown juvenile (Allen 1948, Edgar 1947).

BREEDING

Nest. Sites include rank grass, *Eleocharis* marsh, a *Scirpus* sedge-bed, etc. Nests are built of water-plants and sedge stems, the cup variously lined, e.g., at Thalae Noi commonly with the waterweed *Ceratophyllum demersum*; one example shaded by stems pulled over and interwoven above the cup.

Eggs and brood. Eggs are pale olive-grey with light and dark cinnamon-brown blotches mostly over the broad half. Shape broad ovate. Size (mm): 54.0–49.0 × 36.1–35.9 (n=4). Full clutch commonly four but up to seven recorded (possibly due to dumping by other females). Incubation period 22–24 days.

Cycle. No information.

Seasonality. From Phatthalung to Perak, eggs and downy chicks found at dates that imply laying in November, January–March and May–July. In Perak and Selangor, juveniles occur through most of the rest of the year (Allen 1948, Anonymous 1981, R. Gregory-Smith, Storer 1976, P.D. Round, ZRCNUS).

MOULT. Four adults dated January, April and August showed none (BMNH, ZRCNUS).

CONSERVATION. Away from the Thalae Noi–Songkhla wetland, numbers will decline as transient, man-made habitats are converted faster than being renewed.

Common Moorhen; Nok Ee-lam (Thai); Tiong Air (Malay)

Gallinula chloropus (Linnaeus) 1758, *Systema Naturae* 10(1): 152. TL England.
Plate 28

GROUP RELATIONS. May form a superspecies with Australasian *G. tenebrosa* (Dusky Moorhen).

GLOBAL RANGE. Tropical to mid-temperate N and S America; Africa and Madagascar; N-Atlantic islands and Eurasia east to Ussuriland, Sakhalin and Japan; the Indian subcontinent, Sri Lanka and Andamans; Korea and China; SE Asia to the Greater Sunda islands, Bali and the Philippines; and Sulawesi and the Lesser Sunda islands east to Flores; also in the W-central Pacific. Some northern populations migrate, wintering as far as the tropics; in SE Asia to the Philippines (McClure 1974), possibly also Borneo and Thailand.

IDENTIFICATION/DESCRIPTION. Adult all blackish except for red frontal shield, white-bordered lower tail-coverts (flirted as in much larger Purple Swamphen) and, in adults, conspicuous white fringe to flanks. Juvenile duller, browner, with white on the underparts, similar to juvenile White-breasted Waterhen but lower tail-coverts white rather than cinnamon. Next to Common Coot, the most aquatic rallid, swimming in tail-high posture, with characteristic forward-bobbing of the head.

Bare-part colours. (Adult) iris red; frontal shield and basal half of bill red, apical half yellowish green; feet yellowish green, greener at the joints.

Size (mm). (Skins: 10 adults, most not sexed): wing 152–168; tail 59–67; bill from top of frontal shield 33.4–40.8; tarsus 44.4–51.2 (BMNH, ZRCNUS).

Weight. No data.

DISTRIBUTION. Few records from the far north or, in Malaysia, from east of the Main Range. Historical summary: *Ran, Kra, Pht, Son, Pat, Sat, Ked, Pra, Pek, Phg, Sel, Neg, Mel, Joh, Sin,* with other island records only from Penang.

GEOGRAPHICAL VARIATION. Subspecies *orientalis* Horsfield 1821 (TL Java) or *orientalis–chloropus* intergrades (showing a slightly more bronzy, less sooty back than in Indonesia), resident in the south. Thai birds have not been checked but if northern migrants occur they are likely to be nominate *chloropus*. The frontal shield of male *orientalis* extends to above the eyes and has a squarer-cut rear margin than in *chloropus* (HBI).

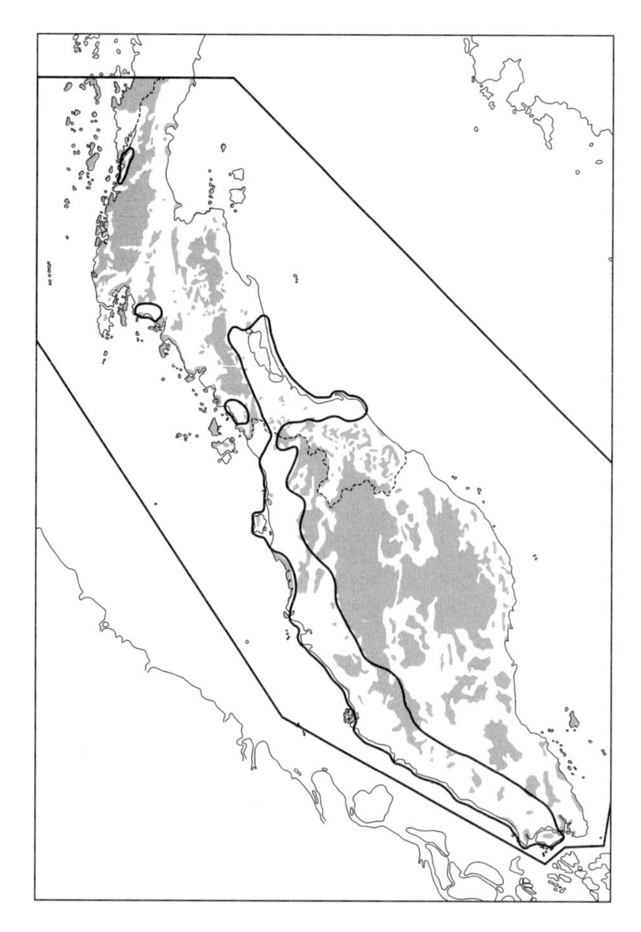

STATUS AND POPULATION. Resident and, at least in the north, probably also a non-breeding visitor (Boonsong and Round 1991); common but local. Like many other freshwater wetland birds, except in the Thalae Noi–Songkhla marshes and a few other northern sites, heavily dependent on man-made environments, including transient dredge-mine habitat. As a result, subject to big fluctuations in local abundance, but seems still to be expanding its range overall. From the late 1970s, has colonized the mainland south from Selangor and crossed the Main Range to W Pahang and E Negeri Sembilan (BMP5, BR 1978–79, 1980–81).

HABITATS AND ECOLOGY. Mostly in freshwater habitats but reaches brackish conditions on Thalae Songkhla. Commonest where open, still or slow-moving water with floating or emergent plants abuts reedbeds or other swamp herbage. Abandoned, vegetated dredge-mine lagoons are prime sites and, unlike Purple Swamphen, also makes extensive use of flooded paddy-crops. Follows overgrown channels, etc., and quickly discovers new sites as they develop.

FORAGING AND FOOD. Hunts on land, both in the open and among swamp vegetation; also while swimming, dipping and up-ending for submerged items. At Thalae Songkhla, takes waterplant parts (*Ceratophyllum, Jussiaea*), molluscs and arthropods (Meeswat and Prentice 1984).

SOCIAL ORGANIZATION. Local populations become dense where undisturbed, and loosely social when not nesting.

MOVEMENTS. None confirmed, but the speed with which residents find new, isolated sites implies active dispersal.

SURVIVAL. No information.

SOCIAL INTERACTIONS. No local observations.

VOICE. Calls include a loud, liquid *prroik*, given from cover, and a sharp, possible warning-note, *keek*.

BREEDING

Nest. Built mainly of twigs, with a leaf lining, about 15 cm wide × 10–15 cm deep, supported by stems 15–30 cm above water-level. On the Songkhla wetland, most nests are in beds of *Eleocharis*, or on wet meadows or floating vegetation mats. Elsewhere, often in tall, standing rice.

Eggs and brood. Eggs are creamy white with blood-red spots and scribbling, particularly over the broad end. Shape broad ovate. Size (mm): 41.9–39.2 × 30.7–29.6 (n=10); weight (g): 19.0–21.0. Clutch regularly up to six, once ten, but no reports of broods larger than five (up to four, mean 1.96, n=27, on Thalae Songkhla). Incubation period 19–22 days.

Cycle. Both sexes incubate.

Seasonality. Eggs or downy chicks reported on dates that imply laying in every month of the year, and at some good sites local populations may well breed continuously (F.G.H. Allen, Anonymous 1981, MBR 1986–87, Meeswat and Prentice 1984, NRCS, Phillips 1961, Robinson and Chasen 1936, SINGAV-1, -2, -3, -4).

MOULT. Ten adults dated January, February, April–June, September and October showed none (BMNH, ZRCNUS).

CONSERVATION. No critical issues but the recent population boom in Malaysia is likely to peak soon, with numbers destined to drop as the quality of paddyland declines and other transient habitat is no longer replaced.

Common Coot; Nok Khuut (Thai); **Burung Pangling Hitam** (Malay)

Fulica atra Linnaeus 1758, *Systema Naturae* 10(1): 152. TL Sweden.
Plate 28

GROUP RELATIONS. In a superspecies with *F. americana*, *leucoptera* and *caribaea* of N and S America and the W Indies (Mayr and Short 1970).

GLOBAL RANGE. Breeds on Atlantic islands, in N Africa, and across temperate to low-arctic Eurasia to N China and Japan; in the Indian subcontinent and Sri Lanka; and E Java, W New Guinea, Australia and New Zealand (found also in Bali, Sulawesi and Buru, Moluccas). Many northern populations are migratory, in Asia wintering as far as India and northern SE Asia (main terminus at about 16°N: Scott 1989), straggling to the Peninsula, Sabah, central Philippines and W Micronesia.

IDENTIFICATION/DESCRIPTION. A plump, black, aquatic rallid, with bill and frontal shield white. Larger and bulkier than Common Moorhen. Swims in tail-up posture and dives with a characteristic over-flip. To gain take-off momentum, runs grebe-like over the water-surface.

Bare-part colours. (Adult) iris red or red-brown; bill and frontal shield white; tibia dull orange, feet including swimming-lobes on toes greenish grey.

Size (mm). (Skin: 1 female; adult): wing 206; tail 50; bill from top of frontal shield 41.9; tarsus 53.2 (ZRCNUS).

Weight. No data.

DISTRIBUTION. Historical summary: *Son, Sin*.

GEOGRAPHICAL VARIATION. All records are presumed to have been of northern, nominate *atra*.

STATUS AND POPULATION. An overshooting migrant, local and hardly more than vagrant; since 1978, recorded spasmodically at Thalae Songkhla with 1–3 in September, December and January (Anonymous 1981, B.E. Bengtsson, R. Harwood); and in Singapore: one collected in January 1940, a loner on Poyan swamp, W end of the island, in early December 1983, and two at the same site during 1–17 January 1988 (BIRDLINE 1993, MBR 1982–83, SINGAV-2, ZRCNUS).

HABITATS AND ECOLOGY. Open wetlands with still or slow-flowing fresh water, a waterplant food supply, and reeds or other marginal cover.

FORAGING AND FOOD. Grazes on open ground and takes waterplant parts while swimming or, in deeper water, diving.

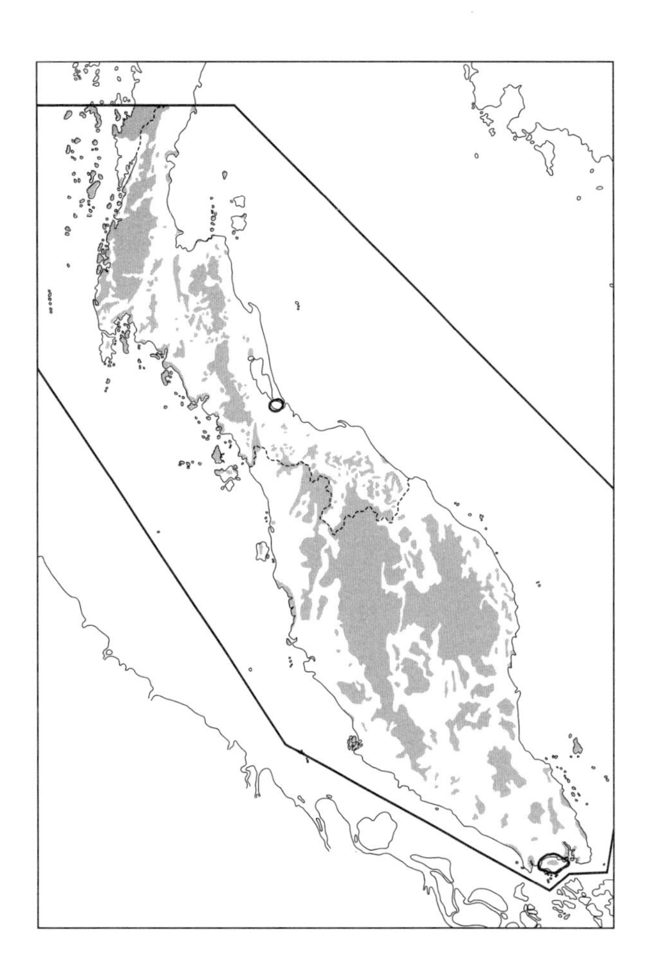

SOCIAL ORGANIZATION. In the main winter range, strongly gregarious.

MOVEMENTS. Extreme dates are 'September' and 17 January.

SURVIVAL. No information.

SOCIAL INTERACTIONS. No information.

VOICE. No local record.

BREEDING. No population.

MOULT. A January adult showed none (ZRCNUS).

CONSERVATION. No relevant issues.

Order TURNICIFORMES

Family TURNICIDAE

Buttonquails: two species.

Yellow-legged Buttonquail; Nok Khum Eud Yai (Thai); Burung Puyuh Kaki Kuning (Malay)

Turnix tanki Blyth 1843, *Journal of the Asiatic Society of Bengal* 12: 180. TL Bangladesh.

GROUP RELATIONS. May form a superspecies with Wallacean–Australasian *T. maculosa* (Red-backed Buttonquail) (cf. CLBW, Sutter 1955).

GLOBAL RANGE. Breeds through the Indian subcontinent and Bay of Bengal islands, to a global southern limit on Great Nicobar (ROM); far-E Russia, possibly north to Baikal and the Amur drainage, Korea, China east of a line Shanxi–Sichuan; and SE Asia to S Vietnam and the Peninsula. Northern populations migrate, wintering from the Changjiang valley to an unknown limit within the N tropics (straggler to Hong Kong: Chalmers 1986).

IDENTIFICATION/DESCRIPTION. Line drawing, page 211. Quail size and shape, and slightly larger than co-occurring Barred Buttonquail. Adult upper body freckled grey-brown, the female with a rufescent hind-collar. Upper wing-coverts and sides of the neck and breast studded with bold, round, black spots (the original 'button' of the family name). Below, rich buff, brightening to orange-rufous anteriorly. Feet chrome-yellow, as in Blue-breasted Quail. In flight, mainly sandy yellow wing-coverts contrast with brown flight-feathers. There are no local descriptions of downy chick or juvenile.

Bare-part colours. (Adult) iris white; upper mandible brown (base yellow in female), lower yellow; feet chrome-yellow.

Size (mm). (Skins: 3 males, 2 females; adult): wing 87–91 and 99 (1 only); tail 27 and 32 (1 each); bill 12.2–12.5 (sexes combined); tarsus 24.3–25.6 and 26.4 (1 only) (BMNH). As in all turnicids, females are larger than males.

Weight. No data.

DISTRIBUTION. Recorded south to latitude 10°09'N (Ban Kachon). Historical summary: *Pak, Chu, Ran.*

GEOGRAPHICAL VARIATION. All mainland populations east from NE India are subspecies *blanfordi* Blyth 1863 (TL Thayetmyo, Burma).

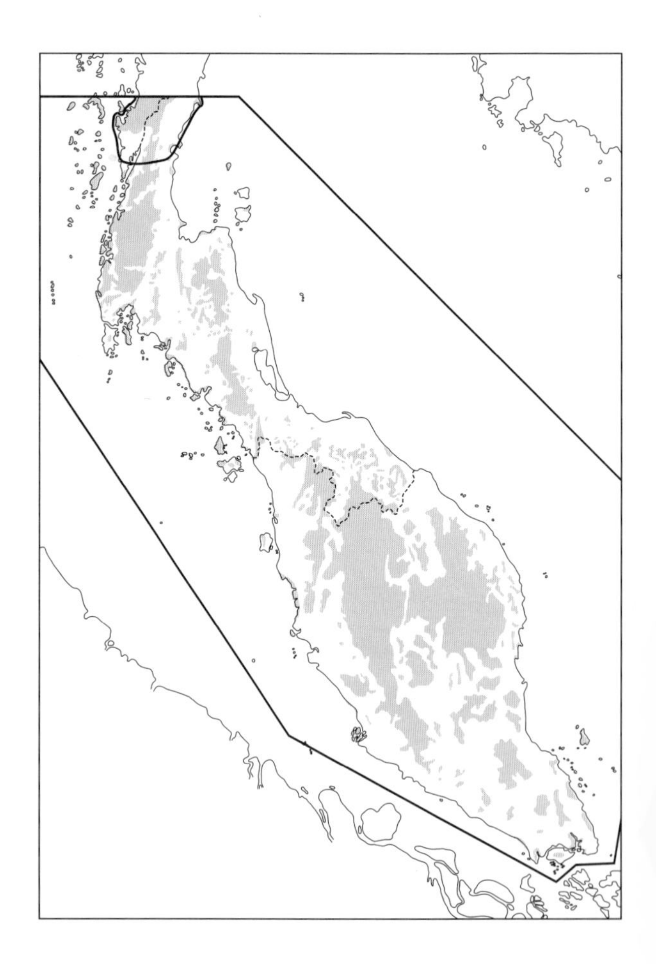

STATUS AND POPULATION. No breeding records but probably resident. During January–April in Chumphon, Robinson and Kloss (1921–24) found it regular and, apparently, more or less common.

HABITATS AND ECOLOGY. Open grassland and weedy cultivation, habitats that have much expanded in the north of the Peninsula since the above range-limit was defined, over 70 years ago. Experience elsewhere in Thailand suggests Yellow-legged selects damper habitat than Barred Buttonquail, but with

Yellow-legged Buttonquail

much overlap (P.D. Round). Hard to flush, quickly regaining cover after low escape-flight.

FORAGING AND FOOD. No information.

SOCIAL ORGANIZATION. Like other turnicids, solitary or in pairs, or a male with a brood.

MOVEMENTS. None known.

SURVIVAL. No information.

SOCIAL INTERACTIONS. No information.

VOICE. No local description.

BREEDING. Not recorded.

MOULT. None of four adults dated 30 January–22 April showed any (BMNH).

CONSERVATION. Not investigated.

Barred Buttonquail; Nok Khum Ok Lai (Thai); Burung Puyuh Tanah (Malay)

Turnix suscitator (Gmelin) 1789, *Systema Naturae* 13(2): 763. TL Java.
Plate 1

GROUP RELATIONS. Apparently free-standing.

GLOBAL RANGE. The Indian subcontinent below latitude 23°N, and Sri Lanka; the Nansei islands and S China from a line S Yunnan–Fujian, including Taiwan; SE Asia to the Greater Sunda islands, Bali and the Philippines; and Sulawesi and the Lesser Sunda islands as far as Alor.

IDENTIFICATION/DESCRIPTION. Quail size and shape. Adult head black-and-white-freckled; upper wing-coverts sandy buff, barred and spotted black; breast rufous-buff barred black, female with chin to centre breast solidly black; rear ventral body clear orange-buff. In flight, pale wing-coverts contrast with grey-brown flight-feathers, but less so than in Yellow-legged Buttonquail. Juvenile Blue-breasted Quail (in the same habitats) is black-barred dorsally but lacks ventral barring and rufescence, and has a different face-pattern and flight-mode.

The downy chick has a buff-white eyestripe, median dart of black from base of bill to mid-crown, and broad, mid-dorsal band of dark chocolate from cap to tail, edged black on the body and with a lateral spur behind the wings; the entire pattern frosted by fine, pale feather-tips. Side of face buff-white, rest of body peppered grey-brown, darkest at the sides (G.W.H. Davison).

Bare-part colours. (Adult) iris pearl-white to pale yellow (in one Pattani female, recorded as red), eyelid-rim lead-blue; upper mandible dark grey, lower lead-blue; feet lead-blue (dull pink in chick) (BMNH).

Size (mm). (Skins: 32 males, 23 females; adult): wing 75–87 (mean 83.4) and 87–95 (mean 91.0); tail not measured; bill 12.5–14.5 and 13.3–15.3; tarsus 21.9–25.2 and 23.5–27.3 (BMNH, UMZC, ZRCNUS). On wing-length, females average nine percent larger than males.

Weight. No data.

DISTRIBUTION. Historical summary: all divisions except *Son*, and with additional island records from Yao Yai, Langkawi and Pangkor off the W coast; Phangan and Samui off the E coast; and Tekong and Sentosa, Singapore.

GEOGRAPHICAL VARIATION. Endemic *atrogularis* Eyton 1839 (TL Melaka).

STATUS AND POPULATION. Resident, regular and more or less common. An adult female picked up dead at the Kuala Selangor lighthouse on 14 October 1969 (BR 1969) must have been active at night, but there is no independent evidence of migration.

HABITATS AND ECOLOGY. Habitats are mostly those of Yellow-legged Buttonquail, including rough

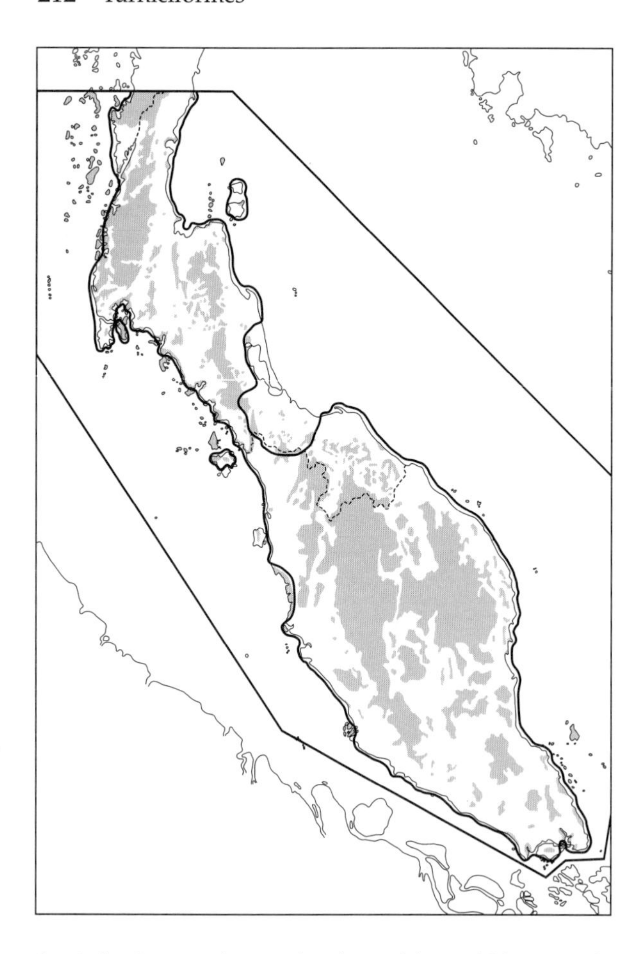

(mainly *Imperata*) grassland, paddy-stubble, weedy gardens; also recently burned ground and the bare earth of tracksides, at plains-level and following suitable habitat along hill roads to at least 600 m (G.C. Madoc). Once flushed, it drops quickly back into cover.

FORAGING AND FOOD. No local information.

SOCIAL ORGANIZATION. Loners, pairs, or a brood escorted by a male. Like other turnicids, polyandrous with reversed sex-roles, but its social system has not been studied locally.

MOVEMENTS. None confirmed.

SURVIVAL. The longest of few retrap-intervals on record is 18 months, at site of ringing near Melaka (UMBRP).

SOCIAL INTERACTIONS. No local information.

VOICE. The female advertising-call is a soft, deep hoot repeated at about half-second intervals (P.D. Round).

BREEDING

Nest. A slight scrape in the ground, lined sparsely with dry grass; on tilled earth, sometimes in the shelter of a clod. In grass, commonly close to a small bush or palm, thought to provide a marker but also likely to offer some shade at certain times of day. Grassland nests have surrounding stems interwoven with occasional extra material to form walls, and bent across at the top into a thin roof.

Eggs and brood. Eggs are grey-olive, densely spotted and blotched brown, uniformly or more heavily over the broad end. Shape broad near piriform. Size (mm): 23.8 × 20.5 (mean, n=16), exceptionally down to 22.3 × 19.2. The regular clutch is four but incubated clutches of 3–5 are on record.

Cycle. Not studied locally.

Seasonality. Egg-dates indicate laying in January–March, May–August and October, with downy chicks recorded in all months late January–early September; but in any one year and site the season is unlikely to be that long (F.G.H. Allen, Edgar 1933, Ryves 1938; G.C. Madoc, Madoc 1956a, Spittle 1949, ZRCNUS).

MOULT. Seventy-eight percent of birds in active wing-moult showed regular-descendant, single-locus replacement of primaries, 17 percent moult at two loci, and five percent at three. Sixty-nine adults from throughout the Peninsula, and covering all months, registered wing-moult in all except September and December, but with a hint of seasonality: single-locus inner-tract (early-stage) replacement only in April–June; single-locus outer-tract (late-stage) replacement only in late July–March. Moult at two-plus loci (following arrest?) seen in April, May and October (BMNH, UMZC).

CONSERVATION. Declining in cultivated habitats; it may be affected by the spread of herbicide-usage on fallow and marginal land.

Order CHARADRIIFORMES

Family SCOLOPACIDAE

Woodcocks, snipes, godwits, curlews, sandpipers, turnstones, dowitchers, stints, ruff and phalaropes: 36 species

Eurasian Woodcock; Nok Paak Som Dong (Thai); Burung Berkek Malam (Malay)

Scolopax rusticola Linnaeus 1758, *Systema Naturae* 10(1): 146. TL Sweden.
Plate 29

GROUP RELATIONS. Likely to form a superspecies with *S. mira* (Amami Woodcock of the central Nansei islands).

GLOBAL RANGE. Breeds on N Atlantic islands and across temperate-zone Eurasia east to Ussuriland, Sakhalin, Japan, and in pockets of northern China (south to Gansu); also the Himalayas and, possibly, hill-tracts of N Burma. Some higher-latitude populations migrate, in Asia wintering south to Sri Lanka and the Andamans, the Peninsula, NW Borneo and Luzon; but the main SE Asian terminus is continental, in W-central Thailand and S Vietnam.

IDENTIFICATION/DESCRIPTION. Extensively barred below and subtly mottled rufous-brown above, but larger than any local snipe, and lacks pale stripes on the upperparts. The long, sloping forecrown peaks rather sharply, with hind-crown ladder-barred rufous and blackish. Crepuscular, flighting from woody cover at dusk to feed at moist, often more open sites. In silhouette, from local snipe species by proportionately broader wing-shape. Dusk-flying Greater Painted-snipe is potentially confusable, although proportionately shorter-billed and much smaller.

Bare-part colours. (Adult) iris deep brown; bill dull pink shading to dark brown towards the tip; legs and feet grey-pink or brown-pink (Oates 1883).

Size (mm). (Skins: 9 adults from the Peninsula and continental SE Asia; most not sexed): wing 191–208 (2 males smallest, a female largest); tail 73–85; bill 73.8–82.7; tarsus 37.2–40.8 (BMNH, ZRCNUS).

Weight. No data.

DISTRIBUTION. Overlooked in the north. Historical summary: *Ran, Phu, Kra, Ked, Pra, Pek, Phg, Mel, Sin*, and Penang island.

GEOGRAPHICAL VARIATION. None recognized.

STATUS AND POPULATION. A non-breeding visitor, local and sparse, known from about twelve records, in November and January–March.

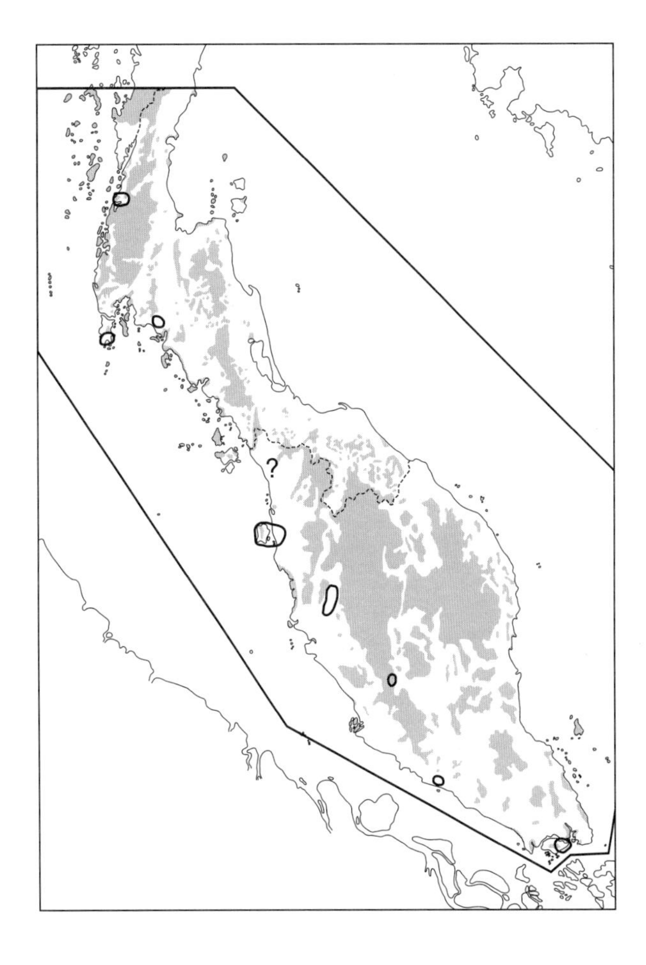

HABITATS AND ECOLOGY. At plains-level and on hills, to about 1250 m. Habitats range from coastal strand-scrub and rough, damp grassland to forest- and forest-edge stream-beds, including a bird flushed from a ditch by a small road through Lower Montane forest at Fraser's Hill (BR 1976–77, 1978–79, P.D. Round, Summers-Smith 1981).

FORAGING AND FOOD. No local information.

SOCIAL ORGANIZATION. Solitary.

MOVEMENTS. Extreme dates are 2 November and 29 March (BMP5, G. Walbridge).

SURVIVAL. No information.

SOCIAL INTERACTIONS. No information.

VOICE. No information.

BREEDING. No population.

MOULT. No data.

CONSERVATION. No relevant issues.

Pintail Snipe; Nok Paak Som Haang Khem (Thai); Burung Berkek Berbintik (Malay)

Gallinago stenura (Bonaparte) 1830, *Annali di Storia Naturale Bologna* 4(14): 335. TL Greater Sunda islands.

Plate 29

GROUP RELATIONS. Apparently free-standing.

GLOBAL RANGE. Breeds in mid-temperate to arctic Russia, from the Urals to the Sea of Okhotsk. Winters in the tropics: some to E Africa but most in Asia, in the Indian subcontinent, Sri Lanka and Bay of Bengal islands; far-S China including Taiwan; SE Asia to the Greater Sunda islands, and in smaller numbers also the Philippines and N and W Wallacea. A few reach NW Australia, and vagrant on Christmas island (Indian Ocean) (Chasen 1935).

IDENTIFICATION/DESCRIPTION. With practice and a clear view, the Pintail/Swinhoe's species-pair is separable from flying Common Snipe by indistinct versus clear white trailing-edge of secondaries and uniformly dark mottled, versus extensively white, lower wing-coverts. On the ground, they show pale supercilium obviously broader than dark loral line where these meet the bill, versus narrower than loral line in Common Snipe (Hayman *et al.* 1986). It has been claimed that the folded wing of Pintail reaches closer to the tail-tip than in Swinhoe's, but samples of foraging snipe watched in typical Pintail habitat in Selangor showed a distinct amount of free tail. This character may require direct comparison, and a dependable, independent identification method has still to be worked out. Calls and behaviour deserve more attention.

In the hand, the outer 6–9 of 12–14 tail-feathers per side are not above 2 mm wide, the outermost only 1 mm wide.

Bare-part colours. (Adult) iris dark brown; bill olive to grey-green with dark brown tip; legs and feet greyish olive to yellowish olive (BMNH, Hayman *et al.* 1986).

Size (mm). (Live and skins: 48, age/sex-classes not separated): wing 127–143; tail 40–51; bill 58.0–66.9; tarsus 31.0–35.9; mid-toe plus claw 35.3–39.2 (BMNH, UMBRP, ZDUM, ZRCNUS).

Weight (g). Mid-winter birds, age/sex-classes not separated, 92.6–123.8 (n=27) (UMBRP).

DISTRIBUTION. Historical summary: all divisions except *Pak, Chu, Ran, Son, Sat, Yal, Nar, Tru*, with additional island records from Yao Yai, Libong, Langkawi and Penang off the W coast; and Samui off the E coast.

GEOGRAPHICAL VARIATION. None recognized.

STATUS AND POPULATION. A non-breeding visitor and presumed passage migrant, though no obvious

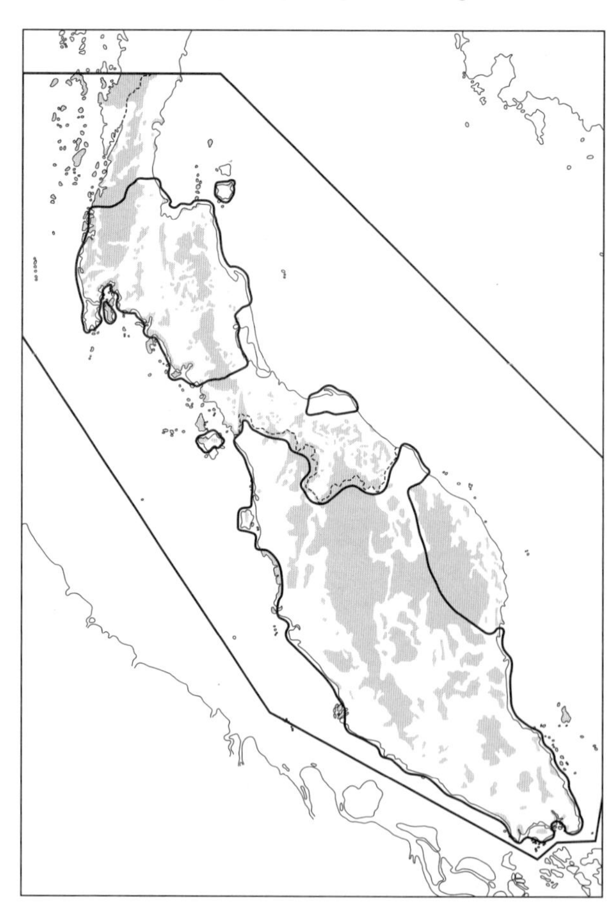

migration peaks have been reported; regular and common. On present evidence, the most numerous snipe by a wide margin (BMP5). There are no figures from north of Malaysia, but some hunting-bags from south of the border have been analysed (Ashby 1951, Gibson-Hill 1949, Kempe 1947). Four bags of 193 to several thousand birds, made from Kelantan and Perak to Singapore over periods of 3 months to 14 years, included 97.9–99.6 percent Pintails. Accuracy of identification and relative shootability of snipe species cannot be checked but are unlikely to have spoiled the general picture. A potentially more important source of error might be the partitioning of winter habitats between species, relative to those most often shot over. The impression from several parts of tropical Asia (HBI, Oates 1883) is that Pintail takes in drier, harder (i.e., more walkable) substrates than Common Snipe, and of 15 snipe mist-netted in waterlogged scrub (rather than open fields) by the edge of a lake near Kuala Lumpur, at least one (6.7 percent) was a Swinhoe's (BMP5). Overall, Common and Swinhoe's may both be commoner than indicated, but many more of one or the other relative to Pintail on typical shooting terrain elsewhere in SE Asia also implies some geographical partitioning. Pintail dominates in the Sunda Region, as in S India–Sri Lanka, and these areas appear to be where most winter (Gibson-Hill 1949).

Present in all months mid August–early May, with only a handful of records (marginally) outside that season, implying no over-summering by non-breeders.

HABITATS AND ECOLOGY. Winterers frequent open ground, mainly agricultural, especially paddy-land from stubble through to flooded, early-crop stages; also grassy bunds bordering wet fields, freshwater channels and ponds; damp areas on grazing-grounds, playing-fields and mine-tailings, river sand-bars, cleared and bunded mangrove-land, etc. They avoid high, dense, marsh vegetation, and rice taller than the standing bird.

FORAGING AND FOOD. No detailed observations.

SOCIAL ORGANIZATION. Several may forage in quite close proximity, but without obvious social behaviour.

MOVEMENTS. Night-flying migrants have been intercepted at floodlights on the Main Range and at western lighthouses (including One-Fathom Bank, off Selangor) during November, but daytime records show this is far into the passage season. At well-watched sites in Malaysia and Singapore, 22 first dates in autumn range fairly evenly between 10 August and 28 September, mainly in late August in Kelantan and Perak, not earlier than 20 August and mostly during September in Singapore. Records of loners near Kuala Kedah on 25 July and in S Perak on 2 August are exceptional. Spring departure starts in mid March, with local last dates during 30 March–13 May; none later than 22 April in Singapore (E.F. Allen 1951b, Bromley 1949, Gibson-Hill 1949, SINGAV-1, -2, -3, Young 1941).

SURVIVAL. The longest retrap-interval is 25 months, a bird back at site of ringing near Melaka (UMBRP).

SOCIAL INTERACTIONS. No information.

VOICE. Nothing published on snipe vocalizations has been adequately tested in the Peninsula, and flight-calls may yet be useful for identification.

BREEDING. No population.

MOULT. Replacement of primaries appears to be regular-descendant, but only four of 66 birds covering all months September–May showed wing-moult, at P7–8 to P9–10 between 18 September and 10 November. Adults appear to complete it rapidly, before arrival or, exceptionally, in early winter (cf. BWP). Other moult occurs later: six in November–January were growing tail-feathers (T1 or T2, in one case T5–10 on 20 January), and several January birds showed body-moult. Nothing is known of relative timing in different age-groups (B.D. Bond, BMNH, UMBRP, ZRCNUS).

CONSERVATION. The impact of agricultural chemicals, especially post-harvest herbicides, on snipe food in paddyland needs to be assessed.

Swinhoe's Snipe; Nok Paak Som Swinhoh (Thai); Burung Berkek Tiruk (Malay)

Gallinago megala Swinhoe 1861, *Ibis* 3: 343. TL Peiho river, Hebei, China

Plate 29

GROUP RELATIONS. Apparently free-standing.

GLOBAL RANGE. Breeds in high-temperate Siberia from the Ob valley to Baikal and Mongolia, and in S Ussuriland, possibly to Sakhalin. Winters in the eastern Indian subcontinent, Sri Lanka and the Andamans; the Nansei islands, Taiwan and far-S China; SE Asia to the Greater Sunda islands, Bali and the Philippines; Wallacea, W Micronesia and New Guinea, in small numbers as far as northern Australia. The main wintering-range is believed to lie east of the Sunda region.

IDENTIFICATION/DESCRIPTION. As yet, not safely separated in the field from Pintail Snipe (which see). In the hand, shows 9–13 (mostly ten) tail-feathers per side, the outer 6–7 narrow but all with distinct vanes and the outermost not narrower than 2.5 (mostly above 3.0) mm (UMBRP, ZRCNUS).

Among ZRCNUS specimens from Singapore is a dark bird with barring spread unusually far across the belly, identified by Gibson-Hill (1956a) as Wood Snipe *G. nemoricola*. Comparison with BMNH material has shown it to be a rare, rufescent variant of Swinhoe's, a possibility Gibson-Hill was aware of but he overlooked the short tail – only 54 mm (not below 63 in *nemoricola*: Hayman *et al.* 1986). The confirmed southern limit of Wood Snipe wintering is NW Thailand and Tenasserim, with a tentative sight-record of one in Pakchan (Hume and Davison 1878, Boonsong and Round 1991).

Bare-part colours. (Adult) iris dark brown; bill brown- to grey-olive with dark brown tip; legs and feet yellowish olive.

Size (mm). (Skins and live: 11, age/sex-classes not separated): wing 137–144; tail 47–58; bill 61.1–69.9; tarsus 32.6–36.8; mid-toe plus claw 37.8–41.9 (UMBRP, ZRCNUS).

Weight (g). A January bird, 130.6 (UMBRP).

DISTRIBUTION. Under-recorded. Historical summary: *Pek, Sel, Joh, Sin*, with no other island records.

GEOGRAPHICAL VARIATION. None recognized.

STATUS AND POPULATION. A non-breeding visitor and presumed passage migrant; local and uncommon. Little understood owing to problems of field identification and dependence on shooting or captures, but there are specimen-records for October–January, March and April. It has formed zero to 1.3 (mostly less than 0.5) percent of hunting-bags of 150 or more snipe taken over one or more years in typical plains-level Pintail Snipe habitat in Malaysia and Singapore (Gibson-Hill 1949, 1950d). On the other hand, certainly one (possibly two) of only 15 snipe mist-netted in waterlogged scrub by the University of Malaya lake, Kuala Lumpur, in January 1970 (BMP5) were Swinhoe's. Throughout SE Asia, the locally dominant snipe species appears to occupy one broad category of agricultural habitats, but the chance of a partial shift by rarer species into others not so regularly shot over cannot be overlooked.

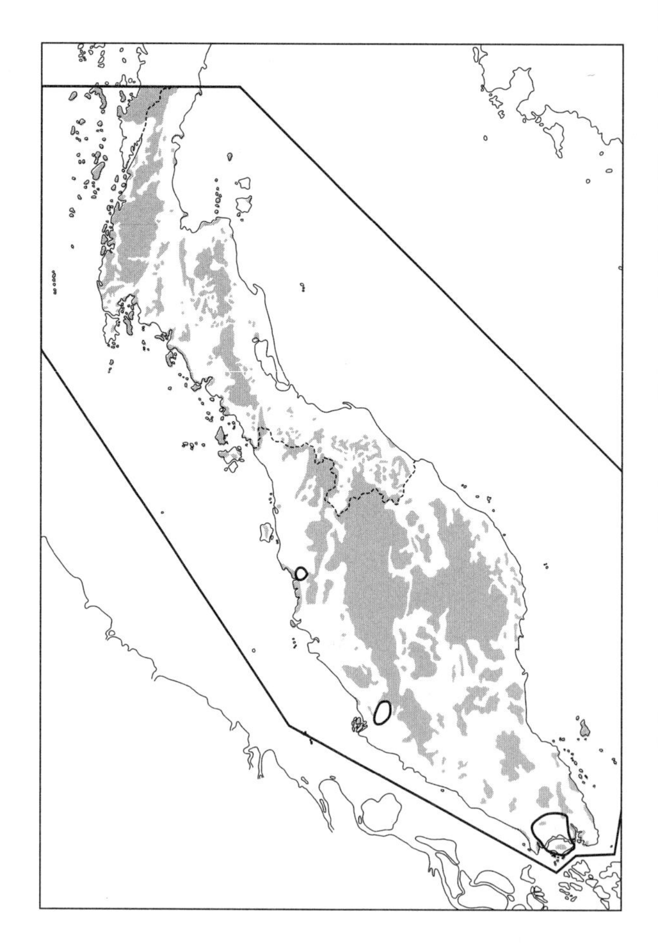

HABITATS AND ECOLOGY. Evidently, some of the ground used by Pintail Snipe is also used by Swinhoe's, but preferred habitats have still to be confirmed.

FORAGING AND FOOD. No observations.

SOCIAL ORGANIZATION. Not separated from other snipe species.

MOVEMENTS. Extreme dates are 1 October and 'April' (Gibson-Hill 1949, ZRCNUS).

SURVIVAL. No information.

SOCIAL INTERACTIONS. No information.

VOICE. No local information.

BREEDING. No population.

MOULT. Ten dated October–January, March and April showed none (UMBRP, ZRCNUS).

CONSERVATION. Issues not separated from those of other snipe species.

Common Snipe; Nok Paak Som Haang Phat (Thai); Burung Berkek Ekor Kapas (Malay)

Gallinago gallinago (Linnaeus) 1758, *Systema Naturae* 10(1): 147. TL Sweden.
Plate 29

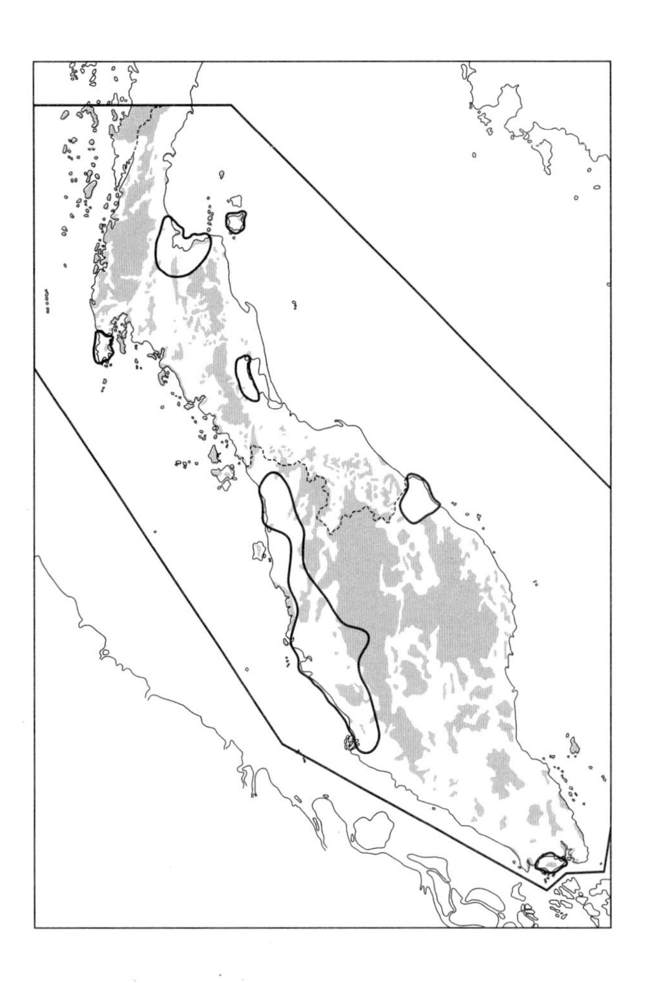

GROUP RELATIONS. The most conservative treatment includes Eurasian forms with American *delicata* and *paraguaiae*, and African *nigripennis* in one polytypic species; free-standing (BWP, Mayr and Short 1970).

GLOBAL RANGE. Breeds over most of S America, southern and eastern Africa and mid-temperate to arctic latitudes around the N hemisphere, in Asia east to Kamchatka and south to NW and NE China (Xinjiang and Heilongjiang), with an outlying population in the NW Himalayas. Most northern populations migrate, wintering from the mid N-temperate zone to the equator, in Asia in the Indian subcontinent, Sri Lanka and Andaman islands; Japan, Korea and China south from the Changjiang valley; and SE Asia (where the main migration terminus is continental) to the Greater Sunda islands and Philippines. Vagrant in the Moluccas and Oceania.

IDENTIFICATION/DESCRIPTION. Escape-flight is characteristically fast, jinking and steeply climbing. Plumage-features in the field include a distinct white trailing-edge to the secondaries and white-banded lower wing-coverts contrasting with dark underside of flight-feathers. Where they meet the bill-base, pale supercilium is narrower than dark loral line, versus broader in other Peninsular snipe species (Hayman *et al.* 1986).

In the hand, the tail shows 6–9 (mostly seven) feathers per side, all fully vaned and the outermost at least 9 mm wide (ZRCNUS).

Bare-part colours. (Adult) iris dark brown; bill horny brown, darker at tip; legs and feet grey- to yellow-olive (BMNH, Hayman *et al.* 1986).

Size (mm). (Skins: 9, age/sex-classes not separated): wing 129–139; tail 48–57; bill 59.9–69.8; tarsus 29.7–33.9; mid-toe plus claw 36.4–38.8 (BMNH, ZRCNUS).

Weight. No data.

DISTRIBUTION. Historical summary: *Sur, Phu, Pht, Ked, Kel, Pek, Phg, Sel, Sin,* with other island records from Samui.

GEOGRAPHICAL VARIATION. Nominate *gallinago* of Eurasia.

STATUS AND POPULATION. A non-breeding visitor and presumed passage migrant, local and apparently uncommon, but certainly overlooked. Recorded in all months August–April (Ashby 1951, BMNH, Bromley 1949, SINGAV-1, -2, -3, -4). Representation in hunting-bags of 150 or more birds from typical agricultural shooting grounds on the Malaysian coastal plains (Ashby 1951, Gibson-Hill 1949) ranges from zero to 2.1 percent, mostly less than 0.5 percent; much the same as Swinhoe's. On the other hand, Common are said to escape faster and steeper than other species, and are perhaps harder to shoot. Nothing obvious partitions Common from Pintail by habitat, although A.T. Edgar's only encounter with Common during 12 years' shooting in Perak was with a large party on dug land and wet thicket in a rubber estate 'in a place where we did not normally expect to see many snipe' (Gibson-Hill 1949). Improved field-identification now produces quite regular records, sometimes of parties, which may upwardly revise perceptions of abundance. Presumed to be commoner towards the north, e.g., a recent count of four against only 24 of other species at Thalae Noi (U. Treesucon).

HABITATS AND ECOLOGY. Preferred habitats little known. Localities imply agriculture, rough wet grassland, open freshwater marsh and waterside situations like those of Pintail; taking in bare tillage and short turf at one extreme, wet scrub at the other (Gibson-Hill 1949, SINGAV-2). These are predominantly lowland-plains environments, but snipe have also been recorded in agricultural areas of Cameron Highlands (1500–1900 m), including an injured Common identified in the hand (Berwick 1947).

FORAGING AND FOOD. No specific information.

SOCIAL ORGANIZATION. Solitary to weakly social, or mutually attracted by favourable habitat-patches.

MOVEMENTS. 18 August on Phuket island is the earliest reported arrival date. In Malaysia and Singapore, first and last dates per year fall between 19–27 September and 1–6 April (BMNH, Bromley 1949, Robinson and Chasen 1936, SINGAV-2, -4).

SURVIVAL. No information.

SOCIAL INTERACTIONS. No information.

VOICE. No local description.

BREEDING. No population.

MOULT. Eight dated August, October, December, January and April showed no wing-moult (BMNH, ZRCNUS).

CONSERVATION. See Pintail Snipe.

Black-tailed Godwit; Nok Paak En Haang Dam (Thai); Burung Kedidi Ekor Hitam (Malay)

Limosa limosa (Linnaeus) 1758, *Systema Naturae* 10(1): 147. TL Sweden.
Plate 30

GROUP RELATIONS. Widely accepted as forming a superspecies with American *L. haemastica* (Hudsonian Godwit), although the latter's bill and foot proportions more closely resemble Bar-tailed Godwit (Mayr and Short 1970).

GLOBAL RANGE. Breeds in Iceland and cool-temperate to low-arctic Eurasia east to longitude about 90°E, then in scattered populations from the Yenisey to the Pacific, south to Ussuriland and far-N China. Winters from the Mediterranean to N-tropical Africa and SW Asia; in the northern Indian subcontinent, straggling to Sri Lanka; SE Asia from S Burma (the Irrawaddy delta) and Thailand to an important likely terminus in SE Sumatra–N Java (Mundkur *et al.* 1992) and, farther east, to another major area in S New Guinea and (mainly N and W) Australia. A few reach Micronesia and New Zealand.

IDENTIFICATION/DESCRIPTION. A large wader. Both godwit species have a bi-coloured, basally pink bill that separates them from Asian Dowitcher; straight in Black-tailed. From winter Bar-tailed on the ground also by plain grey versus streaky upperparts and, in breeding-plumage, by dark-barred white, rather than red, belly. Autumn juveniles are generally cinnamon-buff. In flight, all ages show a bold, white band across the base of blackish flight-feathers and white upper tail-coverts and tail-base, sharp against broad, black tail-tip (these patterns hidden in the perched bird).

Bare-part colours. Iris dark brown; basal half of bill flesh-pink, apical half blackish; legs and feet dark grey.

Size (mm). (Skins and live: 12, age/sex-classes not separated): wing 180–189; tail 56–77; bill 70.0–83.5; tarsus 58.4–70.8 (Jørgensen 1949, UMBRP, ZRCNUS).

Weight (g). Second-winterers and adults, held overnight after ringing during late October–December, 179–236 (n=7) (UMBRP).

DISTRIBUTION. Heavily skewed to the coast of the Melaka Straits. Historical summary: *Nak, Kra, Tra, Pat, Ked, Kel, Pra, Pek, Phg, Sel, Mel, Joh, Sin,* with W-coast island records from Libong and Penang.

GEOGRAPHICAL VARIATION. NE Asian-breeding *melanuroides* Gould 1846 (TL Port Essington, far-N Australia), smaller and darker in all plumages than western forms.

STATUS AND POPULATION. A passage migrant and non-breeding visitor; local and sparse to abundant in winter, and a very few may over-summer although none recorded during the last two weeks of June. Over 95 percent of annual occurrence, and virtually all overwintering, is concentrated on the greatest expanses of soft-mud tide-flats along some 250 km of mainland Melaka Straits coastline in Perak and Selangor. During the early 1960s, autumn passage

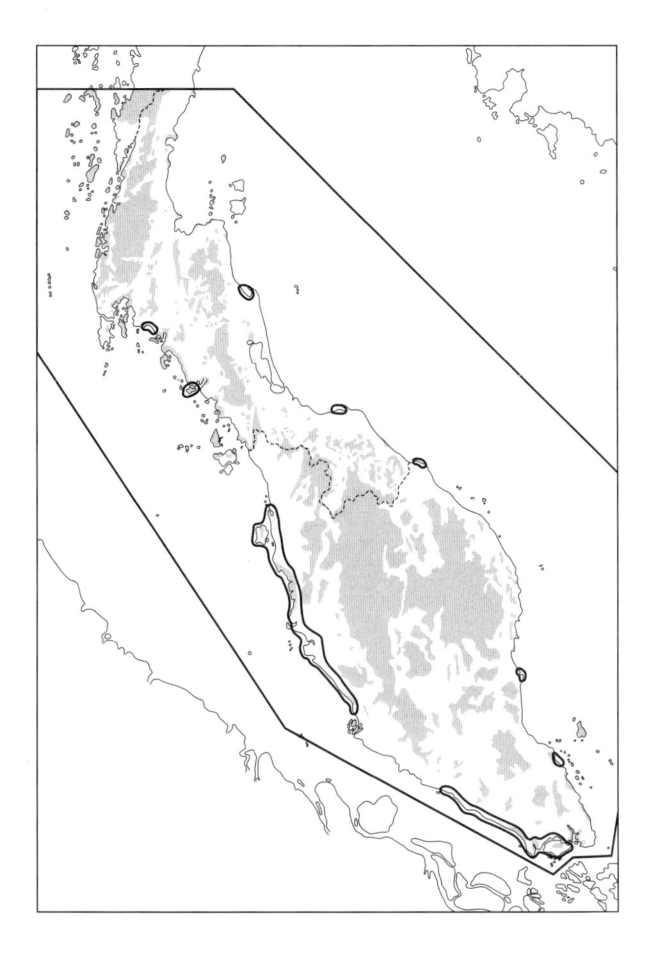

peaks of well over 4000 occurred on the Matang coast of Perak. From the mid-1970s, large flocks also began to halt in N Selangor and by the 1980s usage had spread evenly, perhaps as a result of long-shore erosion reducing some former Perak feeding-grounds (BR 1964, BR 1976–77). In the 1985/86 season, peak counts in Perak totalled 2875, versus 2617 in Selangor (Silvius *et al.* 1987), making this godwit one of the most numerous W-coast waders overall, though proportionately few stay past mid winter.

Only slight use is made of the Thai W coast, and peak counts at other sites, south to Singapore island, have not exceeded 50; mostly far fewer, and all during autumn (Eve and Guigue 1982, Parish and Wells 1984). In the NE, there is a late November record from Pak Phanang bay and a small autumn–early winter presence (50 in September), plus a few again in spring, at Pattani bay (Jørgensen 1949, Ruttanadakul and Ardseungnern 1987, Swennen *et al.* 1986). Over similar dates on the Malaysian E coast, one to a few have been seen in the Kelantan and Pahang river estuaries, and in Mersing bay (Johor) (Howes *et al.* 1986).

HABITATS AND ECOLOGY. Only marginal use is made of freshwater habitats, small numbers visiting flooded, subcoastal paddylands and wet grassland behind the beach, perhaps when pushed off traditional roosts by the highest tides. Large flocks far inland on the Pahang river in January (Robinson and Chasen 1936) may have been migrating, but there have been no repeat records.

Roosts in mangroves but prefers exposed beaches, and attracted to large openings in the mangrove forest, especially ones with pools.

FORAGING AND FOOD. Swennen and Marteijn (1985) found only six percent of foraging in fresh water, the rest strictly intertidal, and strongly linked to soft-mud sediments, as found on the N Selangor mainland coast but not on the vast flats of the outer Kelang estuary islands nearby, where Black-tailed is totally replaced by Bar-tailed Godwit (Silvius *et al.* 1987). The main coastal prey is bivalves, followed by polychaetes.

SOCIAL ORGANIZATION. Strongly gregarious throughout, and joins mixed-species roosts.

MOVEMENTS. Birds in full winter- to near-full breeding plumage on the Selangor coast in early–mid July were evidently on the move, but may not have migrated far. A first substantial wave of more probable post-breeders reaches the W coast at the end of July, with peak numbers in Perak by the first week of November. At Rasa Sayang beach, N Selangor, 2356 on 15 December sandwiched between counts of only 87 and 80 in the same month implies a major onward movement, perhaps after adults had finished their moult. In Riau, SE Sumatra, an actual southward departure of about 3000 birds has been witnessed on 20 November (BR 1964, 1976–77, 1978–79, Silvius *et al.* 1986).

At favoured spots, reduced numbers stay into the new year, but with few around anywhere by March and only light spring passage, passing uncertainly into over-summering in May–June. Most of the W-Indonesian wintering population either misses the Peninsula or overflies it in spring.

SURVIVAL. No information.

SOCIAL INTERACTIONS. No information.

VOICE. Mostly silent, but a July bird that had joined a small flock of Common Redshanks gave a persistent *tenk*, both in flight and when settled.

BREEDING. No population.

MOULT. The most advanced first-winterers begin body-moult in September (earliest record 16 September), whereas others are still fully juvenile at the end of the month. Nothing else is known about their moult-schedules. A dull-plumaged second-summerer showed heavy body-moult (into winter colours), with P1–2, P9–10 and all except central tail-feathers in growth, on 8 August. Only about 20 percent of a flock of 400 presumed returning migrants at Kuala Selangor was still in breeding colours on 31 July, indicating most adults start (and some may finish) post-breeding body-moult before arrival. Their wing-moult is little known: a suspension at P7 on 16 September and three complete (one with some tail-feathers still growing) on 29 October.

Substantial to full new breeding-plumage during

May–early July shows that spring body-moult of adults begins before departure and/or some non-migrating immatures acquire bright colours over the same period (BMP5, BR 1976–77, UMBRP).

CONSERVATION. Suffers some losses from hunting, monitored in Pattani bay (Ruttanadakul and Ardseungnern 1987), but not significant in the Melaka Straits. No other special issues have been identified but long-term plans to polderize the Malaysian W-coast intertidal zone, if implemented, would be disastrous for this and most other shoreline waders.

Bar-tailed Godwit; Nok Paak En Haang Lai (Thai); Burung Kedidi Berjalur-jalur (Malay)

Limosa lapponica (Linnaeus) 1758, *Systema Naturae* 10(1): 147. TL Lappland.
Plate 30

GROUP RELATIONS. Free-standing.

GLOBAL RANGE. Breeds in arctic tundra from Scandinavia to the Bering Strait and W Alaska. Winters from the N- to the S-temperate zones: round the coasts of Europe and Africa, east through SW Asia to the Indian subcontinent and Sri Lanka; S China (but perhaps mainly on passage there: Chalmers 1986); SE Asia to the Greater Sunda islands and Bali. Mainly on passage through the Philippines, Wallacea, New Guinea and Oceania, to further major wintering areas in Australia and New Zealand.

IDENTIFICATION/DESCRIPTION. In the field, not noticeably larger than Black-tailed Godwit, with the same long, pink-and-black bill, but slightly uptilted. Upperparts noticeably streaky in all age-groups. The summer-plumage red of adults extends to the belly and is unbarred. In flight, shows no obvious wing-bar; underwing variably dark mottled to plain white; and back to upper tail-coverts usually white, but in some sufficiently heavily marked to appear non-contrasting, more or less grey-brown.

Bare-part colours. Iris dark brown; base of bill flesh-pink, apical half blackish; legs and feet dark grey.

Size (mm). (Live and skins: 17 adults and second-winterers; none sexed): wing 191–238; tail 63 (1 only); bill 81.5–119.0; tarsus 51.5–59.5 (BMNH, UMBRP, ZRCNUS).

Weight (g). Small samples (all age-groups) in November–February, 208–335; in mid March–early April, 335–475 (AWB).

DISTRIBUTION. Heavily concentrated on the W coast. Historical summary: *Sur, Kra, Tra, Pat, Pes, Ked, Pek, Phg, Sel, Joh, Sin,* including on Libong, Penang and islands of the Kelang estuary (Tengah, Pintu Gedong).

GEOGRAPHICAL VARIATION. Dark-rumped, eastern-breeding *baueri* Naumann 1836 (TL Victoria, Australia) has been recorded from Bandon bay. In flight, W-coast birds (at Krabi and Tengah island) consistently show back and rump white, sharp against wings and mantle, but axillaries and underwing dark-barred. They appear to be *lapponica/baueri* intergrades (*'menzbieri'*?).

STATUS AND POPULATION. A non-breeding visitor and passage migrant, with evidence of some

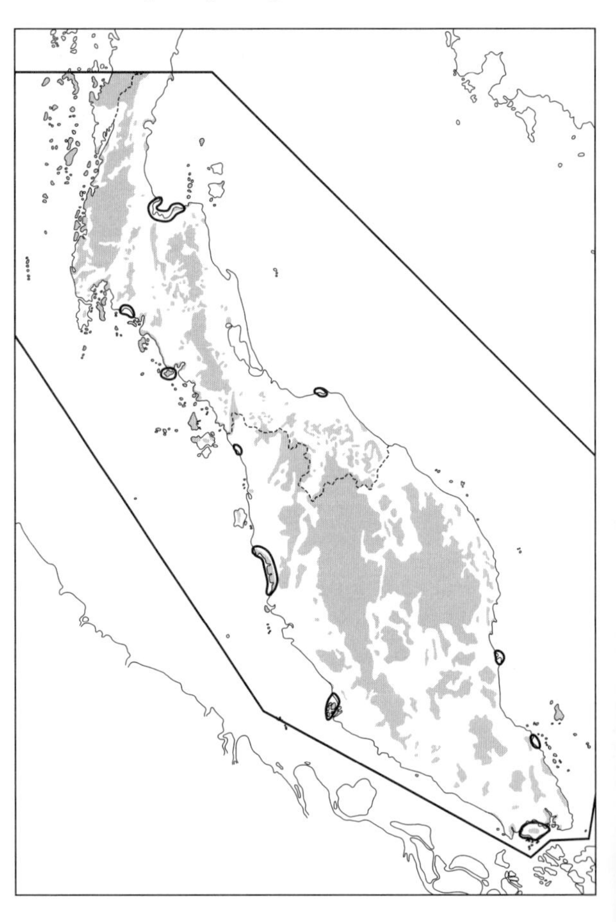

over-summering; local and sparse to abundant. Fewer overall than Black-tailed Godwit, and extremely few winter away from just three sites: Krabi bay, Libong island and Tengah island (outer Kelang estuary), each coupling relative remoteness with large expanses of the firm shell-sand/mud mix specifically favoured for foraging (Eve and Guigue 1982, P.D. Round, Silvius *et al.* 1987). Respective mid-winter numbers peak at around 200, 1200 and 1200, and at least Tengah is also a significant migration staging site.

Away from these concentrations and their high-tide roosts (and the handful that winters in Mersing bay, E Johor: BR 1980–81, Howes *et al.* 1986), strictly on passage, mainly in autumn. Only at Kuala Sanglang (Kedah/Perlis border) and Matang (Perak) in the west, and Pattani and Mersing bays in the east, do counts run to double figures (R. Gregory-Smith, OBCB-7, Parish 1985a, Ruttanadakul and Ardseungnern 1987).

HABITATS AND ECOLOGY. Strictly coastal, roosting in mangroves where necessary but prefering shoreline sandbars, and comes to large clearings in the mangrove forest where these butt directly on to the beach. The ash-collecting ponds of Kapar power-station, on former mangrove-land, have recently been the high-tide roost of a good part of the Tengah island population. A loner on tin-tailings 28 km inland in Selangor on 8 October (BR 1970–71) is completely exceptional, and presumed to have been on passage.

FORAGING AND FOOD. Swennen and Marteijn (1985) found all of several hundred feeding observations were on tidal flats dominated by a shell-sand/mud mix, distinct from the soft, unripe mud selected by Black-tailed Godwit. Polychaetes outstrip bivalves in the Bar-tail diet.

SOCIAL ORGANIZATION. Strongly gregarious at all times.

MOVEMENTS. The Libong and Tengah concentrations have not been monitored in late summer, and earliest passage dates are from elsewhere: 9 July (a loner on the move) in Singapore and 18 July in Krabi bay, with large waves of migrants there on 5–6 September (BCSTB-13, BIRDLINE 1992, J.R. Howes, MBR 1986–87, Ollington and Loh 1992). At Libong and Tengah, autumn peaks of 300–400 and over 500 occur in October, with further pulses to around 1200 in December–January, perhaps after the mid-winter finish of adult moult elsewhere. At Pattani bay and Singapore, etc., a trickle of passage likewise continues to about the end of the year (MBR 1986–87, Parish 1985, Ruttanadakul and Ardseungnern 1987, Silvius *et al.* 1987).

At Tengah, relatively low late-winter numbers surge to a spring peak in March/April (highest count in a 1992 survey, 1569 on 19 March), with evidence of through-passage from the changing proportion of birds in breeding-plumage (Sebastian *et al.* 1993). By 20 May that year, the population roosting at Kapar was exclusively of dull-plumaged immatures, presumed not to be returning to the arctic. How many over-summer locally is not known, but specimens of *baueri* have been collected in mid June in Surat Thani (Williamson 1916).

SURVIVAL. No information.

SOCIAL INTERACTIONS. No information.

VOICE. No good local description.

BREEDING. No population.

MOULT. The schedule of first-winterers is unknown. Regular-descendant replacement of primaries by adults includes up to four inner-tract feathers in overlapping growth. In Selangor, one still with 10 percent summer body-plumage was growing P2–5 on 24 September, and two more P4–5 on 2 November. Others had reached between P5–6 and P8–9 by late November, and one was at P10 on 25 January. Many adults show noticeable amounts of new red body-plumage by mid-February (AWB, ZRCNUS).

CONSERVATION. Feeding-grounds and the main roost at Libong are nominally protected within a non-hunting area. Tengah island is not protected and flights into a main roost at nearby Kapar are much shot-at. As the single most important location for migratory waders in the entire Peninsula, the Tengah system deserves special status.

Whimbrel; Nok Ee-goi Lek (Thai); **Burung Kedidi Pisau Raut** (Malay)

Numenius phaeopus (Linnaeus) 1758, *Systema Naturae* 10(1): 146. TL Sweden.
Plate 30

GROUP RELATIONS. Uncertain. Alaska-breeding *N. tahitiensis* (Bristle-thighed Curlew) and central-Palaearctic *N. tenuirostris* (Slender-billed Curlew) are probable close relatives (Mayr and Short 1970).

GLOBAL RANGE. Breeds in the subarctic and arctic from Iceland east across Eurasia discontinuously to the Pacific and in N Alaska and N-central Canada, to significantly below this zone only in Canada and the

SW Russian steppes. Winters in Central and S America, round sub-Saharan Africa and on Indian Ocean coasts to the Indian subcontinent, Sri Lanka and Bay of Bengal islands; the Nansei islands and China south from Taiwan; SE Asia; Wallacea; New Guinea, Australia and Oceania to New Zealand.

IDENTIFICATION/DESCRIPTION. A large brown wader standing two-thirds the height of, and usually more hunched than, Curlews. In isolation, from both local Curlew species by its flight-call and dark-and-light-striped crown-pattern. Back, rump and underwing vary from white to heavily dark-mottled, more or less concolorous with the rest of the body, according to breeding origin.

Bare-part colours. Iris dark brown; bill blackish brown with paler base, especially of the lower mandible; legs and feet dull blue-grey.

Size (mm). (Live: 37, age/sex-classes not separated): wing 224–260; tail 88–97; bill 73.2–93.5; tarsus 51–62 (AWB, UMBRP, ZRCNUS).

Weight (g). July–January birds (all age-groups), 300–395 (n=16); in early April, 440–530 (n=10) (AWB, UMBRP).

DISTRIBUTION. Historical range: all divisions except *Chu, Ran, Pha, Pht, Yal, Pra, Neg, Mel*, with additional island records from Lanbyi and Bada (*Pak*), Phiphi (spring), Lanta (summer), Libong, Langkawi (spring), Penang and the Kelang estuary group (Ketam, Tengah) off the W coast; Redang and Sibu (Johor) off the E coast; and Tekong, Ubin, Seletar, St John's, Sentosa and Sakeng around Singapore.

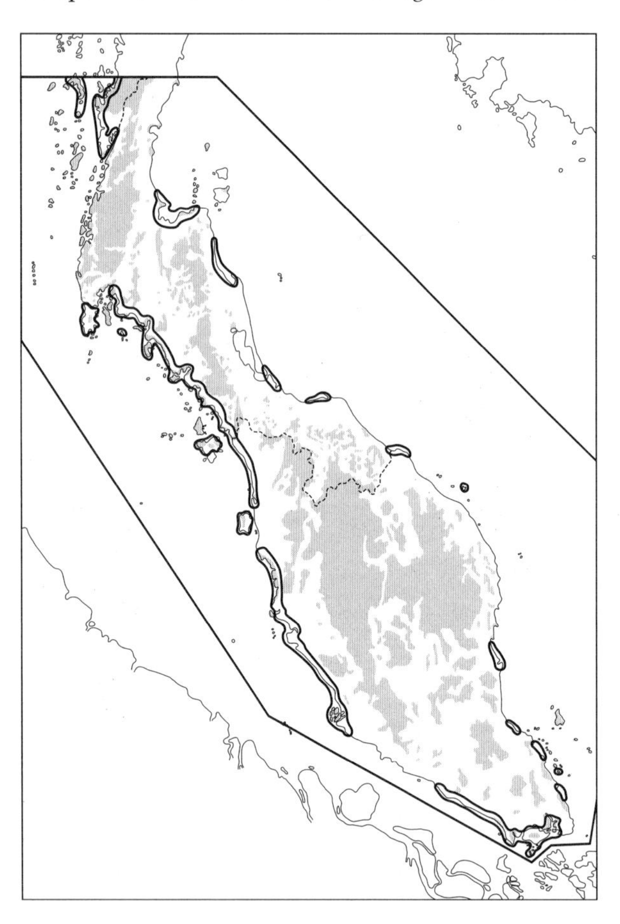

GEOGRAPHICAL VARIATION. W-coast Whimbrel are typically white on the back and rump (nominate *phaeopus*); only a few are dorsally all-dark, eastern *variegatus* Scopoli 1786 (TL Luzon, Philippines). Both are recorded in the NE (Deignan 1963), but representation there has not been analysed.

STATUS AND POPULATION. A non-breeding visitor and passage migrant, with some over-summering mostly, but not exclusively, in the south and west (BCSTB-12, BR 1963); regular, and uncommon to abundant. Few occur on the E coast, with peak site-counts (in Bandon, Pattani and Mersing bays) of mostly well below 50, even during passage-seasons (Howes *et al.* 1986, Parish 1985a, Ruttanadakul and Ardseungnern 1987, Swennen *et al.* 1986). By contrast, autumn surveys rank it seventh commonest wader along the W coast (as also in SE Sumatra), with particular concentrations at Krabi, Libong island (peak count 599), the Perak coast (950) and Selangor, including Kelang estuary islands (5000 at Tengah alone in late October) (ENGGANG-1, Mundkur *et al.* 1992, Parish 1985, Silvius *et al.* 1985, 1987). The far south and Singapore, including formerly important (reclaimed) Serangoon estuary, now support many fewer, with no recent site-counts past double figures (BIRDLINE 1992).

HABITATS AND ECOLOGY. Exclusively coastal. The rather wide W-coast distribution reflects use of both mud/shell-sand mixes and consolidated, pure mud (Swennen and Marteijn 1985), but soft, unripe muds are avoided. Roosts on exposed shoals, in the tops of mangrove trees (particularly dead ones), or in bare, preferably shallowly flooded clearings in the mangrove-zone large enough to give security – and usually only where these butt directly onto the sea (BMP5, Parish and Wells 1984).

FORAGING AND FOOD. Selects mixed and pure mud surfaces, in the ratio 75 to 25 percent preference. Burrowing crabs are the main prey item, and a smaller part of the diet is fish (Swennen and Marteijn 1985).

SOCIAL ORGANIZATION. Gregarious at roosts and when on the move; less obviously so while foraging.

MOVEMENTS. Along much of the W coast and in Singapore there are Whimbrel throughout the year. Groups of 20-odd in W Johor and Singapore as of mid July (ENGGANG-1, SINGAV-3) may be the vanguard of autumn migration but their age is unknown, and no large waves of migrants reach the Selangor coast until early September. Everywhere, including at E-coast sites, autumn numbers peak during September–November. In some but not all years,

Krabi bay, Libong and the Kelang-estuary islands maintain their populations until January or later (900 at Tengah on 24 January 1990), implying their vast mud/sand-flats have exceptional carrying-capacity (ENGGANG-3, Parish 1985). By the end of the year at E-coast sites such as Pattani bay, Whimbrels have entirely gone (Ruttanadakul and Ardseungnern 1987).

The spring influx begins by March (over 1500 at the Kapar, Selangor, roost on 7 March 1992) with high counts frequent to the first third of May (ENGGANG-2, Howes *et al.* 1986, Silvius *et al.* 1987), but it is not known when the last adults disappear.

SURVIVAL. No information.

SOCIAL INTERACTIONS. No information.

VOICE. A loud, clear, whinnying trill, given in flight.

BREEDING. No population.

MOULT. First-winterers in precocious wing-tip moult (P10) recorded in late February; and one showed only P10 new on 30 April. Apparent second-summerers were in progressive, regular-descendant wing-moult from early July (P1–3) to mid September (P8–10) or later (two suspended at P9 and P10 on 15 September), and one dated 21 September had completed. Other birds on a later schedule (between P1–2 and P6 in October, P6 and P7–8 in November, and at P9 in December/early January) are likely to have been adults (AWB, BMP5, SBNR, UMBRP, ZRCNUS).

CONSERVATION. The effect of seaward reclamation of mangroves and the bunding-off of freshwater and nutrient outflows from the land on the capacity of intertidal mudflats to support shorebirds, including Whimbrel, is of long-term concern. Hunting is an issue at some sites in the north, including Pattani bay where it is being countered by an education programme run from Prince of Songkhla University.

Eurasian Curlew; Nok Ee-goi Yai (Thai); Burung Kedidi Kendi (Malay)

Numenius arquata (Linnaeus) 1758, *Systema Naturae* 10(1): 145. TL Sweden.
Plate 30

GROUP RELATIONS. The three large curlews, *arquata, madagascariensis* (Eastern Curlew) and *americanus* (Long-billed Curlew) are either entirely allopatric or only marginally overlap in winter. They probably form a superspecies.

GLOBAL RANGE. Breeds in temperate-zone Eurasia, to the arctic circle in the far west, from Atlantic Europe east to Baikal, N Mongolia and adjacent NE China. Winters from the western breeding-range, around African and Indian Ocean coasts to the Indian subcontinent, Sri Lanka and Bay of Bengal islands; S Japan and S-coastal China; SE Asia to the Peninsula and Sumatra, and (in small numbers) Borneo, Java, Bali and the Philippines. Vagrant in Wallacea, W Micronesia and NW Australia.

IDENTIFICATION/DESCRIPTION. With Eastern Curlew, by far the largest wader, and from that species by generally paler tone and white back, rump and underwing. Both can have exceptionally long bills. In isolation, from Whimbrel by unstriped crown.

Bare-part colours. Iris dark brown; bill black-brown with lower mandible basally pinkish; legs and feet blue-grey.

Size (mm). (Live and skins: 5 adults; none sexed): wing 282–312; tail 100–115; bill 144.0–187.0; tarsus 80.8–92.0 (AWB, UMBRP, ZRCNUS).

Weight (g). December–January adults, 659–760 (n=4) (AWB, UMBRP).

DISTRIBUTION. Mostly in the north and west. Historical summary: *Pak, Sur, Nak, Phu, Kra, Tra, Pat, Pes, Ked, Pek, Sel, Neg, Joh, Sin,* with additional island records from Libong, Penang, Ketam and Tengah off the W coast; St John's, Busing, Hantu, Sudong and Sakeng around Singapore.

GEOGRAPHICAL VARIATION. Pale-toned *orientalis* Brehm 1831 (TL East Indies).

STATUS AND POPULATION. A non-breeding visitor and passage migrant, with no definite evidence of over-summering. Regular and more or less common to abundant. Bandon, Pak Phanang and Pattani bays are all used in autumn–early winter, and again in spring (Jørgensen 1949, Parish 1985, Ruttanadakul and Ardseungnern 1987, Swennen *et al.* 1986), but no Eurasian Curlews have been found elsewhere on the E coast. On the W coast, most occur between Krabi and Selangor, with up to 200 in autumn on Libong island (some of which overwinter: Eve and Guigue 1982, Swennen *et al.* 1986) and many more in Perak and Selangor (over 700 counted at the Kapar ash-ponds roost in January, most apparently from Tengah and Ketam islands, Kelang estuary). Southwards, recent counts have been single-figure but in Singapore these

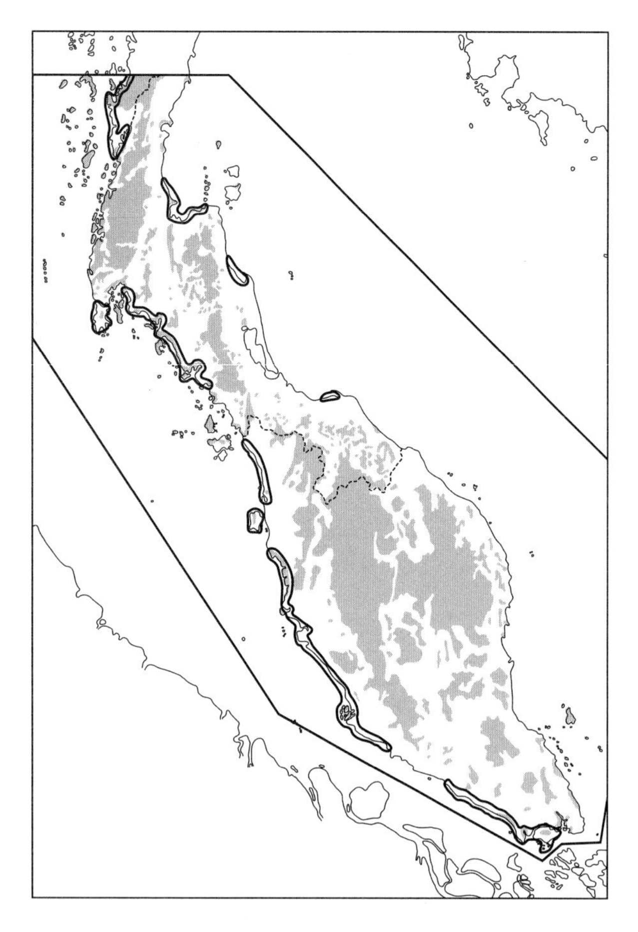

muds, both soft and consolidated (respectively 82, 12 and 6 percent of over 200 feeding-observations). Takes mainly crabs and bivalves (Swennen and Marteijn 1985).

SOCIAL ORGANIZATION. Strongly gregarious at roosts and when on the move; less so while foraging.

MOVEMENTS. A few on Libong in mid May, some at Tengah/Kapar (Selangor) to at least 20 May and a loner at Seletar (Singapore) on 3 July are the only evidence of possible over-summering (BMP5, Eve and Guigue 1982). First waves of presumed post-breeders arrive in Selangor and Singapore at the end of August (at Kapar, 251 on 31 August), with nett gains at all the more important W-coast sites through September and October. Subsequent declines indicate onward movement (BR 1964, ENGGANG-2). Unlike Whimbrel, Eurasian Curlew shows a proportionately small spring surge, although 1063 roosted at the Kapar ash-ponds on 7 March 1992. The returning SE-Sumatran concentration (AWB, Silvius *et al.* 1986) may miss or overfly the Peninsula.

SURVIVAL. No information.

SOCIAL INTERACTIONS. No information.

VOICE. The flight-call is a loud, musical *kour-lii*, not separated from that of Eastern Curlew.

BREEDING. No population.

MOULT. The first-winterer schedule is unknown. A bird moulting primaries at two loci (P3–4 and 8), plus T1, on 3 August is likely to have been a second-summerer, as are others at P8 on 25 October and two at P10 on 26 December. Apparent adults in Selangor follow a later schedule: no wing-moult in late September, P1–2 on 2 November and P1–2 and P1–3 on 2 December (AWB, UMBRP, ZRCNUS).

CONSERVATION. This wader would benefit greatly from the effective protection and management of Tengah island and satellite roost-sites.

extend to late January, implying a handful may over-winter there, too (Ollington and Loh 1992).

HABITATS AND ECOLOGY. Strictly the intertidal zone. Roosts on exposed bars when and where available, otherwise in and on mangroves and, like many coastal waders, attracted to clearings in this zone, especially flooded ones – but few visit sites not butting directly onto the sea.

FORAGING AND FOOD. Hunts mostly on mixed mud/shell-sand substrates, to a lesser extent on purer

Eastern Curlew; Nok Ee-goi Taphok Namtaan (Thai); Burung Kedidi Kendi Timur (Malay)

Numenius madagascariensis (Linnaeus) 1766, *Systema Naturae* 12(1): 242.
TL Manila, Philippines.
Plate 30

GROUP RELATIONS. See Eurasian Curlew.

GLOBAL RANGE. Breeds in Siberia from north of Baikal to the Seas of Japan and Okhotsk, and Kamchatka (Hayman *et al.* 1986), i.e., north and east of Eurasian Curlew. Most winter in SE Australia, others sparingly in S Japan, Taiwan, Philippines and the Sunda region. A few hundred in SE Sumatra (Silvius *et* *al.* 1985, 1986) have not yet been confirmed to stay through mid winter but are there again in March–April. On passage in W Micronesia, and vagrant as far as W Samoa and New Zealand.

IDENTIFICATION/DESCRIPTION. As big as Eurasian Curlew, some individuals with an even longer bill. Separated in flight by back and rump brown, uniform with rest of upperparts, more extensively brown underparts, and densely dark-barred (rather than plain white) underwing. In company on the ground, shows warmer brown all over, especially noticeable on the head where it highlights a white eye-ring. From *variegatus* Whimbrel by crown-pattern and much larger size.

Bare-part colours. Iris dark brown; bill black-brown, pink towards base of lower mandible; legs and feet blue-grey.

Size (mm). (Ranges for the species): wing 280–338; tail 100–129; bill 128–201; tarsus 77–96 (Hayman *et al.* 1986, UMBRP).

Weight (g). A November non-juvenile, 575 (UMBRP).

DISTRIBUTION. In the west and the far south. Historical summary: *Kra, Pek, Sel, Joh, Sin,* with additional island records from Libong (*Tra*) and Tengah off the W coast; and Sudong, Singapore.

GEOGRAPHICAL VARIATION. None recognized.

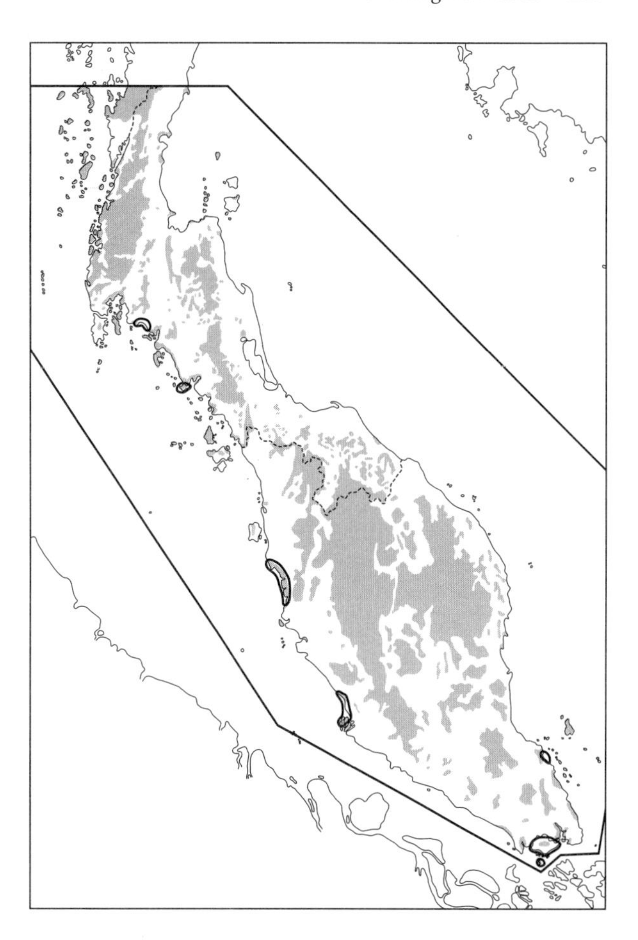

STATUS AND POPULATION. A passage migrant and non-breeding visitor, local and sparse to uncommon. In very small numbers on the W coast: at Krabi bay, Libong island, and in Perak and Selangor including on Tengah; occasional in Singapore (BBCB-6, -9, BMP5, Ollington and Loh 1992, Silvius *et al.* 1987, SINGAV-3); and once on the E coast, a pair of newly arrived migrants in Mersing bay, SE Johor, on 4 November 1982 (MBR 1982–83).

Most occur in autumn, with counts of 10–15 regular on the Perak mudflats during October–December in the 1960s, few to none seen there recently but more in Selangor, with an all-time high of 35 at Tengah island on 9–10 October 1985 (BMP5, Silvius *et al.* 1987). Elsewhere, not more than 2–3 at any one time, usually in the company of Eurasian Curlews. From the paucity of January–February records, evidently, only a handful actually overwinters.

HABITATS AND ECOLOGY. Nothing recorded that is specifically different from Eurasian Curlew, and usually seen together.

FORAGING AND FOOD. No information.

SOCIAL ORGANIZATION. At mixed-species roosts, joins Eurasian Curlews.

MOVEMENTS. Extreme dates on the Selangor coast are 31 August and 16 April (ENGGANG-2). At Tengah island, the autumn surge drops to single figures by November. Regular mid-winter (January) counts have never found more than six there, and intensive monitoring at the associated Kapar roost has shown no rise through March or April (Mundkur *et al.* 1992). As with Eurasian Curlew, spring migrants from further south may miss or overfly the Peninsula.

SURVIVAL. No information.

SOCIAL INTERACTIONS. No information.

VOICE. Not distinguished from Eurasian Curlew.

BREEDING. No population.

MOULT. One captured on 18 November had much-worn body plumage but fresh wings and tail, showing these phases of moult are separated in one-plus-year-olds.

CONSERVATION. See Eurasian Curlew. Globally near-threatened (BTW2).

Spotted Redshank; Nok Thalae Khaa Daeng Lai Juut (Thai); Burung Kedidi Berbintik (Malay)

Tringa erythropus (Pallas) 1764, Vroeg's *Beredeneerde Catalogus, Adumbratiunculae*: 6. TL The Netherlands.

Plate 31

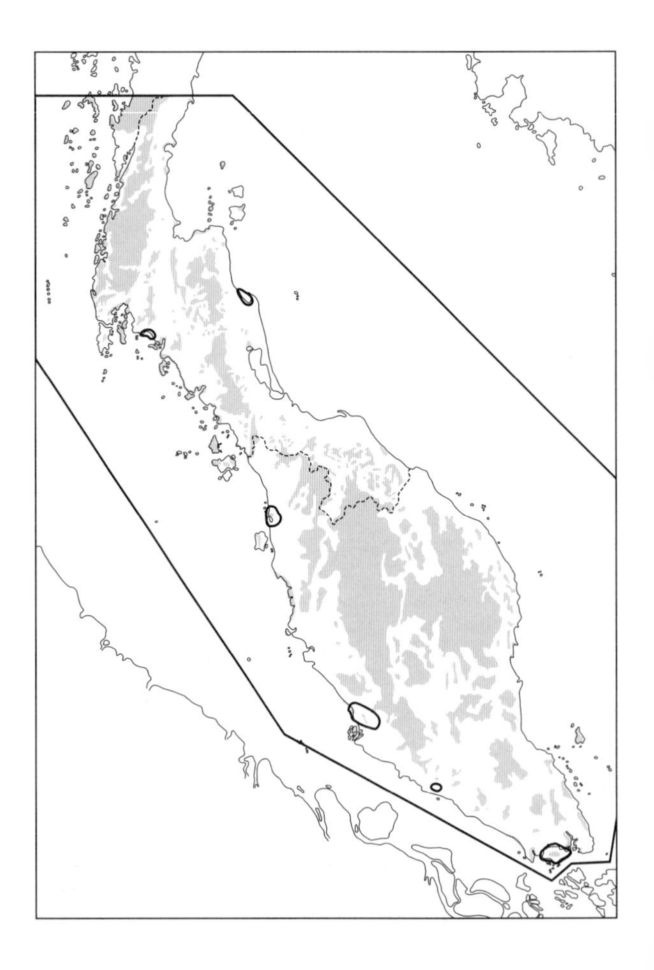

GROUP RELATIONS. Free-standing.

GLOBAL RANGE. Breeds mainly in the arctic, from Norway across Eurasia to Anadyrland. Winters in Atlantic Europe, the Mediterranean to tropical Africa (locally as far as the equator) and parts of SW Asia; the Indian subcontinent and Sri Lanka; S Japan and S China including Taiwan and Hainan; and SE Asia, in small numbers as far as N Borneo, the Peninsula and SE Sumatra. The main regional migration terminus is S Vietnam and wetlands of the Gulf of Bangkok. Vagrant in W Micronesia.

IDENTIFICATION/DESCRIPTION. White-speckled black summer body-plumage is distinctive. In winter, generally paler and greyer than Common Redshank, with a broad, white supercilium running from bill-base to behind eye, and red of proportionately longer, finer, slightly droop-tipped bill restricted to the base of the lower mandible. In flight, by upper surface of secondaries and inner primaries heavily dark-barred, versus contrastingly white; and by call.

Bare-part colours. Iris dark brown; bill blackish, base of lower mandible orange-red to deep red; legs and feet orange-red to bright red.

Size (mm). (Ranges for the species): wing 158–180; tail 60–69; bill 52–65; tarsus 52–64 (Hayman *et al.* 1986, HBI).

Weight. No data.

DISTRIBUTION. Historical summary: *Nak, Kra, Ked, Sel, Mel, Sin*, with no other island records.

GEOGRAPHICAL VARIATION. None recognized.

STATUS AND POPULATION. A non-breeding visitor, local and sparse. Reported less than annually, but in all months September–April, and recent surveys suggest it has been overlooked, particularly in the north (in Kedah over the 1992/93 winter, four records totalled some 26 birds). Flocks of 18 near the Merbok estuary (Kedah) on 30 September and 36 foraging on the muddy bed of an emptied fish-pond at Batu Berendam (Melaka) on 7 February are the only individual double-figure counts (BR 1972–73, R. Gregory-Smith). Pak Phanang bay is the only recorded E-coast site.

HABITATS AND ECOLOGY. Has occurred from the coast to 25 km inland, at open lagoon-sides, shallow pools in cleared back-mangrove areas and, especially, the soft-mud bed of recently emptied or part-emptied ponds, freshwater, brackish and tide-fed. Only a few records are from actual tide-flats (BR 1963, 1964, 1967, 1972–73, 1978–79, Cant 1957–58, Parish 1985).

FORAGING AND FOOD. A small group in Singapore showed well-known aquatic foraging behaviour, including picking from the water surface or submerging the head while wading belly-deep, and up-ending while swimming (BR 1963).

SOCIAL ORGANIZATION. Strongly gregarious in its main winter range, and there are local records of social foraging.

MOVEMENTS. Extreme dates are 2 September and 14 April (BR 1978–79), with largest counts at mid winter.

SURVIVAL. No information.

SOCIAL INTERACTIONS. No information.

VOICE. The flight-call is a single, ringing *kleuik*. Birds foraging in a group gave a short, abrupt note, *krut*, as they fed (BR 1972–73).

BREEDING. No population.

MOULT. None handled, but individuals at Serangoon (Singapore) on 8 and 14 April had nearly completed moult into summer body-plumage.

CONSERVATION. No specific issues.

Common Redshank; Nok Thalae Khaa Daeng Thammadaa (Thai); Burung Kedidi Kaki Merah (Malay)

Tringa totanus (Linnaeus) 1758, *Systema Naturae* 10(1): 145. TL Sweden.
Plate 31

GROUP RELATIONS. Probably free-standing. *T. flavipes* (Lesser Yellowlegs) occupies near-equivalent ecological space in N America (Voous 1960), but may not be closely related.

GLOBAL RANGE. Breeds in arctic Scandinavia; otherwise in the N-temperate zone from Iceland across Eurasia to Pacific Russia, south in Asia to the Caspian, Himalayas and W and N China. Winters from the Atlantic breeding-range (where some may be resident) to tropical W Africa, the Mediterranean and SW Asia; the Indian subcontinent, Sri Lanka and Bay of Bengal islands; China south from the Changjiang valley; and SE Asia to the Greater Sunda islands and Bali, with some in the Philippines. A few reach Sulawesi, the Lesser Sunda islands, W Micronesia and (mainly NW) Australia (Lane and Davis 1987).

IDENTIFICATION/DESCRIPTION. The bill and feet of first-winterers are dull, but nearly always red enough to confirm identification. On the ground in winter, large, grey individuals from Spotted Redshank by heavier neck- and breast-markings, and supercilium only anterior to the eye. In flight, all morphs at all ages told by conspicuous white secondaries; also by calls.

Bare-part colours. Iris dark brown; bill dark brown, basal third of the lower mandible putty-pink to bright red; legs and feet dull to bright red.

Size (mm). (Live: a 4-figure sample, most not aged or sexed): wing 150–171; tail 56–74; bill 39.5–50.4; tarsus 45–59 (UMBRP).

Weight (g). Total variation in a very large sample is 69–175. Except for minor upturns during autumn migration (August–September), from late July to early February half-monthly samples of body weights (n=20–188) sorted by 10 g classes peaked unimodally at 101–110 g, then at 91–100 g in early March. Late March and early April were not well represented but by late April/early May the pattern became multi-peaked as waves of fattening adults (at 131–140, 141–150 and 151–160 g) broke away from the continuing 101–110 g immature mode. In late May, the mid winter pattern was restored as young birds dominated the few, very heavy adults still to leave.

Stored fat shows under the skin at 120 g and above. A few such birds occur throughout, and may move onward (one in autumn put on 38 g in 17 days: Parish and Wells 1984). The heaviest (*eurhinus/ussuriensis* intergrades) exceed 170 g (maximum 175). Such birds have been recorded only during late April–late May and must be close to departure condition.

DISTRIBUTION. Historical summary: all divisions except *Chu*, *Pht*, *Sat*, *Yal*, and additional island records from Muk, Libong, Langkawi, Penang, Ketam and Tengah off the W coast; and Tekong, Singapore.

GEOGRAPHICAL VARIATION. Hale (1973) computer-matched the biometrics of Common Redshanks wintering in the Peninsula to populations breeding in the Himalayas and Tibet (subspecies *eurhinus* Oberholser 1900, TL Ladakh), ?Xinjiang (*craggi* Hale 1971, TL Tcha Tcheu oasis), NE China (*terrignotae* Meinertzhagen 1926, TL Koko Nor), and Mongolia and E Russia (*ussuriensis* Buturlin 1934, TL Sakhalin). All have since been identified from summer plumage as regular on the Melaka Straits coast in spring, together with incompletely moulting *eurhinus/ussuriensis* intergrades typical of the Tien Shan region (W.G. Hale). Past claims of nominate *totanus* (Scandinavia and SW Europe) refer to *eurhinus*, which differs from the dark morph of *totanus* only by its larger size (Hale 1971).

Summer-plumage features characterizing these subspecies are (a) mantle-feather colour: dark mud-brown without cinnamon edging (*eurhinus*), dark brown with cinnamon edging (*ussuriensis*), clear cinnamon-bay with centre third dark brown (*terrignotae*), clear cinnamon with dark brown shaft-streak (*craggi*); (b) breast-pattern (on a white ground): dark droplet spots (*eurhinus, terrignotae, craggi*), heavy streaks and spots (*ussuriensis*) (Hale 1971).

STATUS AND POPULATION. Passage migrant, non-breeding visitor, and with groups of up to 80 over mid summer in Singapore and along the W coast

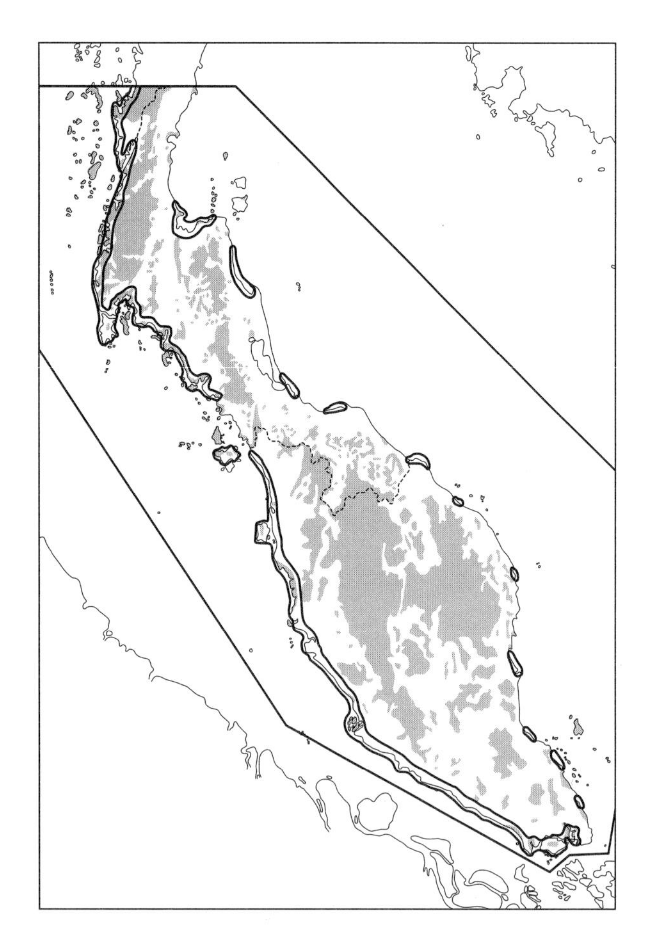

north at least to Krabi (BBCB-4, BR 1978–79, MBR 1986–87, SINGAV-1, -2), but not yet definitely recorded at this season on the E coast. Regular and common to abundant. Relatively few winter in the NW (a maximum 200 in December on Libong island: T. Lund) but estimates of 9300–14 600 between Perlis and NW Johor rank Common Redshank the most numerous wader of the Melaka Straits coast, probably year-round. Recent major gathering-points include: Kuala Sanglang (Perlis/Kedah border), Kuala Rubiah, Kalumpang and Kuala Larut (Perak), and Selangor south to the Kelang estuary islands (Parish and Wells 1984, Silvius *et al.* 1987).

Colour-dyed birds at Serangoon estuary, Singapore (Parish and Wells 1984), and recaptures among 3200 handled at Kuala Selangor during the 1970s demonstrate philopatry through the wintering period. Retraps of 64 ringed during 14 July–31 May were spread through every month, after intervals of up to nine months. Nine handled on 15 July 1979 included several juveniles of the previous winter, evidently due to remain year-round.

On the E coast, some Redshanks use Pak Phanang bay in November and December, but from a high peak in early autumn (pot-hunters trapped almost 2600 there in August–October 1986) very few remain in Pattani bay by December (Jørgensen 1949, Parish 1985, Swennen *et al.* 1986, Ruttanadakul and Ardseungnern 1987). South of the border, the only double-figure counts (maximum 40) have been in August and April (Howes *et al.* 1986), consistent with use of Kelantan, Terengganu and Pahang estuaries mainly, or perhaps only, on passage.

HABITATS AND ECOLOGY. With *T. guttifer*, the most marine 'shank', only occasionally visiting freshwater habitats such as paddyfields, probably when extreme tides submerge favoured coastal roosts. Commonly waits out high water perched in outer-zone mangrove trees, but much attracted to prawn-ponds and other largish openings in the mangrove forest, particularly where shallowly flooded. When tides are high after dark, flocks will stay overnight at such roosts, typically arriving late and leaving again before dawn.

FORAGING AND FOOD. On tidal flats, shows an 80-percent foraging preference for soft-mud substrates, versus only about 20-percent usage of mud/sand mixes. Behind the regular tide-zone, minor use is made of brackish, back-mangrove pools. The main prey are crabs, polychaetes and molluscs, according to availability. On the Selangor coast, young *Anadara* cockles can be prominent in stomach contents, whereas the NE-coast bays may be attractive staging sites because of their polychaete numbers (Swennen and Marteijn 1985, UMBRP).

SOCIAL ORGANIZATION. Strongly gregarious at roosts, less so when foraging. Among ringed one-year-olds handled at Kuala Selangor in July 1979, six had been trapped as couples on dates back to the previous October, which suggests that within the local wintering population they had been living in discrete social groups.

MOVEMENTS. A bird in full summer plumage and bright bare-parts at Kuala Selangor on 3 July, and a minimim five-year-old, ringed adult retrapped there on 16 July are presumed to have been early migrants from the temperate zone. First waves believed to include significant numbers of post-breeders arrive on the Melaka Straits coast as of 18 July, with mass presence by the end of the month (BR 1972–73, 1976–77). Earliest juveniles have been identified on 3 August but weight data suggest the first big influx is in the second half of August.

Generally, autumn numbers peak in September, but over the whole W coast and in Singapore locally high numbers occur, randomly, throughout the winter. Possible onward movement or switching between day-roosts might account for this, but neither is supported by the many on-site retraps of ringed birds. The E-coast pattern differs, and two ring-recoveries show Pattani bay is a staging post for migrants that reach Singapore by mid September (MBR 1984–85, 1986–87, Parish and Wells 1984).

Consistently high counts at favoured sites (including the Kapar power-station ash-pond roost, Selangor: Sebastian *et al.* 1993) show northward passage of adults starts by early March. Large waves pass to at least 20 May, but on 31 May only two of 34 birds examined at Kuala Selangor showed breeding plumage and pre-departure body-weight.

SURVIVAL. Only a few ringed birds have been retrapped or recovered more than one year on, the oldest 113 months (ten seasons) later, at its site of ringing at Kuala Selangor (MBR 1986–87, PERHILITAN).

SOCIAL INTERACTIONS. No information.

VOICE. Calls include a held and plaintive alarm, *tyuuuu*, and in flight a high, ringing *tyuu hu-hu*.

BREEDING. No population.

MOULT. The broadness of the schedule may be an artifact of pooling data from several different populations. It is also affected by suspensions and late restarts.

Most first-winterers moult the wing-tip precociously, starting anywhere between P5 and P9, with an earliest record (one feather already replaced) on 11 January. Complete wing-moult begins in March, or even earlier, and the latest pre-moulter (still with all-juvenile flight-feathers) is dated 31 May.

These two cycles of moult are often concurrent in second-summerers, although half of a mid-July sample had already completed. Degree of wing-tip wear (distinguishing them from adults) suggests latest birds are still active at the end of October.

Some adults must start wing-moult well before they reach W-coast wintering-sites (the most advanced growing P9 on 8 August), others not until after arrival (the last pre-moulter handled on 4 October). Since body-moult is not completed until after wing-moult starts, the latter still show some breeding plumage. Retrapping suggests uninterrupted replacement of primaries (regular-descendant, as in most adult waders) takes about 100 days (Parish and Wells 1984, UMBRP), with the number of adjacent feathers in overlapping growth reduced after mid moult (mean 3.0 at P4 and P5, 1.2 at P10). Most birds still moulting in January are close to completion and only a few continue into February–March (the latest growing P6 on 10 March, presumably after a suspension: UMBRP).

Earliest full summer plumage (in *craggi*) is dated 4 March and many birds of all races are at this stage by late March (UMBRP).

CONSERVATION. See Whimbrel. The large hunting-bag in Pattani bay is more or less in proportion to numbers occurring there, relative to other wader species. Loss of feeding-habitat through local foreshore reclamation is guessed to be having a more serious impact overall.

Marsh Sandpiper; Nok Chailaen Beung (Thai); Burung Kedidi Paya (Malay)

Tringa stagnatalis (Bechstein) 1803, *Ornithologisches Taschenbuch von und für Deutschland* 2: 292 and plate 29. TL Germany.

Plate 31

GROUP RELATIONS. Free-standing.

GLOBAL RANGE. Breeds in temperate-zone Eurasia north to latitude 57°N, from the E Baltic and Balkans to NE China and Ussuriland. Winters through sub-Saharan Africa, around the E Mediterranean and coastal SW Asia; in the Indian subcontinent and Sri Lanka; extreme S China including Hainan; SE Asia to the Greater Sunda islands, Bali and the Philippines; Wallacea; and W Micronesia to New Guinea and (mainly N) Australia. Vagrant in New Zealand.

IDENTIFICATION/DESCRIPTION. Medium-sized, smaller than Common Redshank, but proportionately tall and slender, with fine, straight, dark bill and long grey- to yellow-green legs. Before spring moult, conspicuously pale, with grey back and Common Greenshank-like dark shoulders. In flight, uniform upper wing-surface and long white V of rump and back resemble both Common and Nordmann's Greenshanks. Without a size-scale, long projection of feet beyond the tail is a good indicator.

Bare-part colours. Iris dark brown; bill blackish with paler base; legs and feet grey-green, becoming yellow-tinged in spring.

Size (mm). (Live: 35 adults, none sexed): wing 131–153; tail 52–59; bill 35.3–42.0; tarsus 46.2–56.5 (UMBRP, AWB).

Weight (g). Birds dated June and late September–mid March, 51–80 (n=85), 80 percent between 56–70 but with no clear connection to age or season. Premigratory fattening has not been monitored.

DISTRIBUTION. Mostly the W coast. Historical summary. *Sur, Nak, Kra, Tra, Pat, Pes, Ked, Pra, Pek, Sel, Mel, Joh, Sin*, with additional W-coast island records from Libong, Langkawi, Penang and Tengah.

GEOGRAPHICAL VARIATION. None recognized.

STATUS AND POPULATION. Passage migrant and a non-breeding visitor, with groups of up to 35 on the Melaka Straits coast also over mid summer. This is

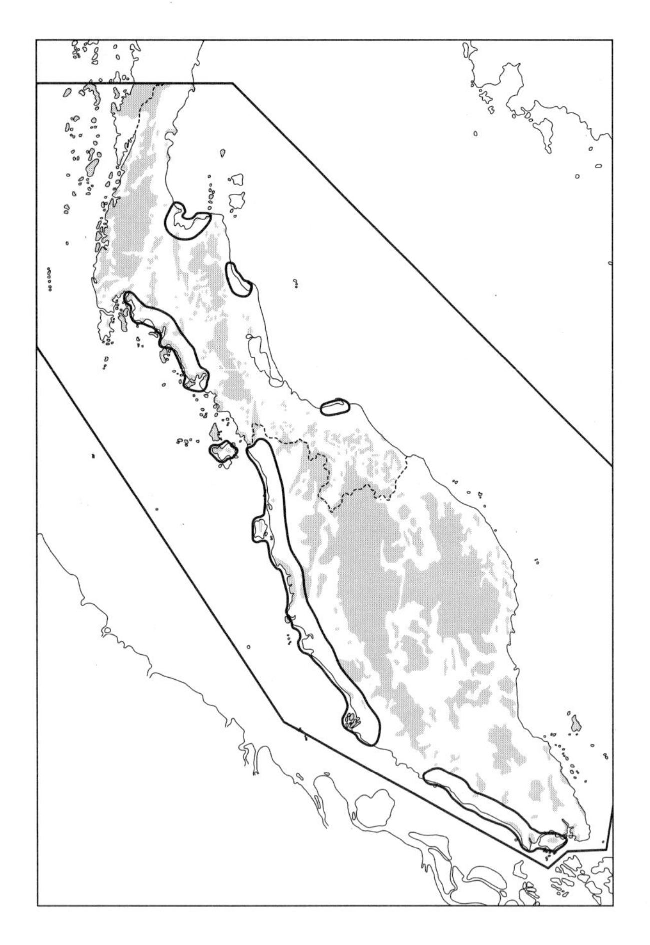

where most are found year-round, with an estimated 3000–3400 overwintering, mainly on soft-mud tideflats of the Perak and mainland Selangor coasts (BR 1978–79, Mundkur *et al.* 1992, Silvius *et al.* 1987). Island-wide mid-winter counts of 350–500 have been made around Singapore (SINGAV-3).

In the NW, a maximum 174 counted on Libong island but none after mid winter (Parish 1985). This may also be the pattern in the NE (Bandon and Pak Phanang bays), where isolated high counts during October–December could have been of passage migrants. Pattani bay numbers peaks at around 200 in December, but there some occur through the rest of the season, to as late as May (Parish 1985, Ruttanadakul and Ardseungnern 1987, Swennen *et al.* 1986). Unrecorded on the Malaysian E coast.

A few within-season retraps of ringed individuals at a roost at Kuala Selangor (October to January/ February and January to March) demonstrate winter philopatry, and retrapping of second-summerers on site in June suggests some immatures may have stayed year-round.

HABITATS AND ECOLOGY. Intertidal mudflats, lagoons within the mangrove forest and open, freshwater wetlands, especially paddylands at the irrigation and early-growth stages, up to 25 km inland. This is not one of the waders regularly roosting in mangrove trees, but strongly attracted to open clearings in the mangrove zone, especially with pools (in Selangor, up to 600 counted at the Kuala Selangor new-town clearing and nearly 400 on Kapar powerstation's seaside ashbeds: Parish 1985a, Sebastian *et al.* 1993).

FORAGING AND FOOD. On the coast, Swennen and Marteijn (1985) found a 63 percent preference for soft muds and 34 for shallow, brackish lagoons. This may account for relatively low numbers at the Libong and Tengah island wader sites, where stiffer mud/sand mixes predominate. The main prey are polychaetes, insect larvae and bivalves. Much foraging is done at the water-surface while wading, and lagoons deep within the Perak mangroves are important gathering points (Silvius *et al.* 1987).

SOCIAL ORGANIZATION. Strongly gregarious at roosts, and associates with Common Greenshanks.

MOVEMENTS. Arrives late and departs relatively early, with no significant influx anywhere before late September (250 on mudflats at Kuala Gula, Perak, and 100 at Jeram, Selangor, on 25–26 September). Thereafter, numbers at regular roosts oscillate between intermittent high counts until late November/early December, then slump before surging to a further peak in Singapore and the Melaka Straits in early/mid March (BR 1965, Parish 1985a). No such spring recovery occurs in the north, which may be overflown at that season.

About half of 30 scattered over Kuala Selangor saltpans on 26 April were in summer plumage but need not have been migratory adults (see below), leaving no reliable last date of adult departure.

One ringed as a chick on the Selenga river, SE side of Lake Baikal, on 15 June 1979 was retrapped six months later at Kuala Selangor (BR 1976–77), a longitude displacement only 5° off due south.

SURVIVAL. No information.

SOCIAL INTERACTIONS. No information.

VOICE. The flight-call is a loud *teu*, close in pitch to the last note of the Common Redshank flight-call (P.D. Round).

BREEDING. No population.

MOULT. Immatures moult the juvenile wing-tip out mostly from P8 (a few from 7 or 9), staggered over a minimum six months, from mid winter (freshly complete on 12 January) to mid summer (P9 on 19 June), with highest incidence in March. A second-summerer, also dated 19 June, had started complete wing-moult (P1) apparently without having renewed the wing-tip.

Since most second-summerers acquire part to full summer body-plumage, this is not a way of identifying returning adults; indeed, early autumn birds that from degree of wing-tip wear have been identified as adult are already in winter plumage. Apparently, most adult moult occurs before arrival. Some late-September/October adults show suspension of wing-moult at P9 or 10. Others are active between P7 and 10, but with only three instances of active moult on record past 1 November: P9 on 15 December and P10 on 14 January and 4 March, presumably after extra-long suspensions.

Earliest new summer feathers appear in mid January. Among adults, but not younger birds, body-moult is well ahead by early March, with full colours as of the second week of March.

CONSERVATION. Under pressure of herbicides, applied mostly post-harvest, it is doubtful if Malaysian paddyland now supports any Marsh Sandpipers independent of tide-flats.

Common Greenshank; Nok Thalae Khaa Khieo Thammadaa (Thai); Burung Kedidi Kaki Hijau (Malay)

Tringa nebularia (Gunnerus) 1767, Leem's *Beskrivelse over Finmarkens Lapper*: 251. TL Trondheim, Norway.

Plate 31

GROUP RELATIONS. May form a superspecies with American *T. melanoleuca* (Greater Yellowlegs) (Mayr and Short 1970).

GLOBAL RANGE. Breeds in cool-temperate and low-arctic Eurasia from Scotland and Scandinavia to Kamchatka and the Sea of Okhotsk, south in far-E Asia to the Amur valley. Winters in Atlantic Europe, from the Mediterranean through sub-Saharan Africa and SW Asia; in the Indian subcontinent, Sri Lanka and Bay of Bengal islands; China south from the Changjiang valley, including Taiwan and Hainan; SE Asia to the Greater Sunda islands, Bali and the Philippines; Wallacea; W Micronesia to New Guinea and Australia and, in small numbers, New Zealand.

IDENTIFICATION/DESCRIPTION. A medium-large wader, in winter white with grey-streaked nape and hind-neck, and dark grey upperparts shading to black on the lesser wing-coverts. In flight, as Marsh Sandpiper but larger and with lesser projection of foot (toes only) beyond tail. Flight-calls rather similar but Common Greenshank's are more powerful and mostly trisyllabic. From winter Nordmann's Greenshank by part-grey versus more nearly plain white head and neck, darker upperparts, more rakish shape with proportionately longer legs, toe-projection in flight, and leg colour. Only in a particularly clear view are bill-characters reliable.

Bare-part colours. Iris dark brown; basal half of bill grey-green, shading apically to blackish; legs and feet grey-green.

Size (mm). (Live: 16 adults; none sexed): wing 172–194; tail 75–85; bill 54.0–59.4; tarsus 57.9–65.0 (UMBRP).

Weight (g). Birds dated late July–mid May, 132–179 (n=19); most spread more or less evenly in the range 152–171. No demonstration of spring fattening.

DISTRIBUTION. Historical summary: all divisions except *Pak, Chu, Pht, Yal, Nar, Tru*, with other island records from Muk, Libong, Tarutao, Penang and Tengah off the W coast; Samui off the E coast; and Ubin and Seletar, Singapore.

GEOGRAPHICAL VARIATION. Clancey (1995) has proposed recognition of a large, pale eastern

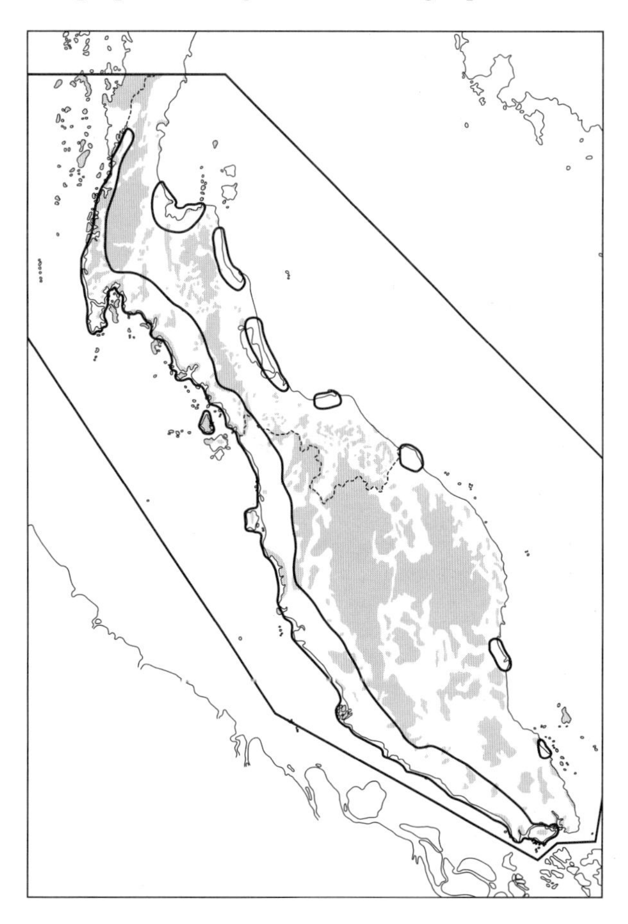

subspecies *glottoides* Vigors 1831 (TL E Himalayas). If accepted, it should be looked for in the Peninsula.

STATUS AND POPULATION. A non-breeding visitor, with some evidence of passage migration and, in Singapore and along the W coast north at least to Selangor, parties of up to 25 through mid summer (SINGAV-2). Apparently, most winter on the coast of Perak and mainland Selangor, but this 'shank' is found more widely than others, including at mid winter on the E coast: in Pak Phanang and Pattani bays (at Pattani, 200-plus in December), the Pahang estuary and Mersing bay (Howes *et al.* 1986, Parish 1985, Ruttanadakul and Ardseungnern 1987). Ability to use inland wetlands may assist, and this has made it difficult to determine total numbers. Three hundred has been suggested for the Melaka Straits coast in September but by mid winter in Selangor over twice this number has been counted at a single roost (AWB, ENGGANG-3, Silvius *et al.* 1987).

HABITATS AND ECOLOGY. Predominantly tide-flats but also in brackish and various open, brackish to freshwater wetlands, including back-mangrove creeks and pools, the margins of abandoned dredge-mine lagoons, shoals and fringes of large rivers and especially (but now decreasingly), paddyland.

At roost in mangroves, Common Greenshanks select stumps rather than the crown branches used by Redshanks, Whimbrels, etc. (Hawkins and Howes 1986), but like most waders cling to ground sites as long as these are exposed, and may retreat to wet fields some distance inland. They are strongly attracted to large, secluded clearings within the mangrove zone, especially where flooded, and safe sites can draw large numbers.

FORAGING AND FOOD. On the shore, shows a 60 percent preference for soft-mud substrates (perhaps because these retain more standing pools), against only 19 for firmer, freer-draining mud/shell-sand mixes and 17 for much rarer lagoon habitat within the mangrove forest (Swennen and Marteijn 1985). This could account for the proportionately high numbers wintering in Perak and mainland Selangor, versus rather low usage of the adjacent Kelang-estuary islands and sites such as Libong island (Trang), with their huge areas of mixed sand (Eve and Guigue 1982, Parish 1985, Silvius *et al.* 1987). On Tengah island, the few that occur forage mostly along or within the edge of the mangrove forest.

Main prey items are small fish and prawns (Swennen and Marteijn 1985).

SOCIAL ORGANIZATION. Strongly gregarious at high-tide roosts; alone or in only small parties elsewhere.

MOVEMENTS. Ringing shows there are adults on the W coast by 1 August but this is not obvious from counting, even at regular roosts. These remain at or near mid-summer numbers until early September, with none into three figures before early October, and oscillations that imply some onward movement until December. One hundred and eighty at Tengah island, Kelang estuary, on 9 October are presumed to have been passage migrants given that only 12–25 occurred there through the rest of the winter (Silvius *et al.* 1987). Evidently, the much higher mid-winter score at nearby Kapar power-station is drawn from the mainland.

Evidence of through-movement in spring includes small but significant surges in Mersing bay and the Pahang estuary during mid/late March, counts of over 800 at the Kapar roost during mid March–early April and, in the NW, a doubling of the small population on Libong island by 1 April (Howes *et al.* 1986, Parish 1985, Sebastian *et al.* 1993). It is still not clear when the last migratory adults leave.

SURVIVAL. No information.

SOCIAL INTERACTIONS. No information.

VOICE. The flight-call is a powerful, ringing *tyew tyew tyew*, often declining at the last note.

BREEDING. No population.

MOULT. Hard to mist-net, hence relatively few birds have been studied. First-winterers handled on 27 March and 31 May were in precocious moult of the wing-tip (both with P8 new, 9–10 growing), and a second-summerer dated 22 July had begun complete wing-moult (P3–5 growing). Another in 60 percent summer colours on the same day had already finished. Adults, identified by wing-tip wear, showed no wing-moult in August but one dated 21 September had suspended at P6, and all dated October–early December were active between P7 and P10. Others in the new year had all finished (UMBRP, AWB).

For a short period in late summer (August), adults retain substantial summer plumage. This is regained as of early March (one in heavy body-moult on 4 March).

CONSERVATION. See Whimbrel. Coastal reclamation is the most serious long-term issue.

Nordmann's Greenshank; Nok Thalae Khaa Khieo Lai Juut (Thai); Burung Kedidi Nordmann (Malay)

Tringa guttifer (von Nordmann) 1835, Erman's *Reise um die Erde durch Nord-Asien und die beiden Oceane in . . . 1828–30. Naturhistorischer Atlas*: 17. TL near Okhotsk, Pacific Russia.

Plate 31

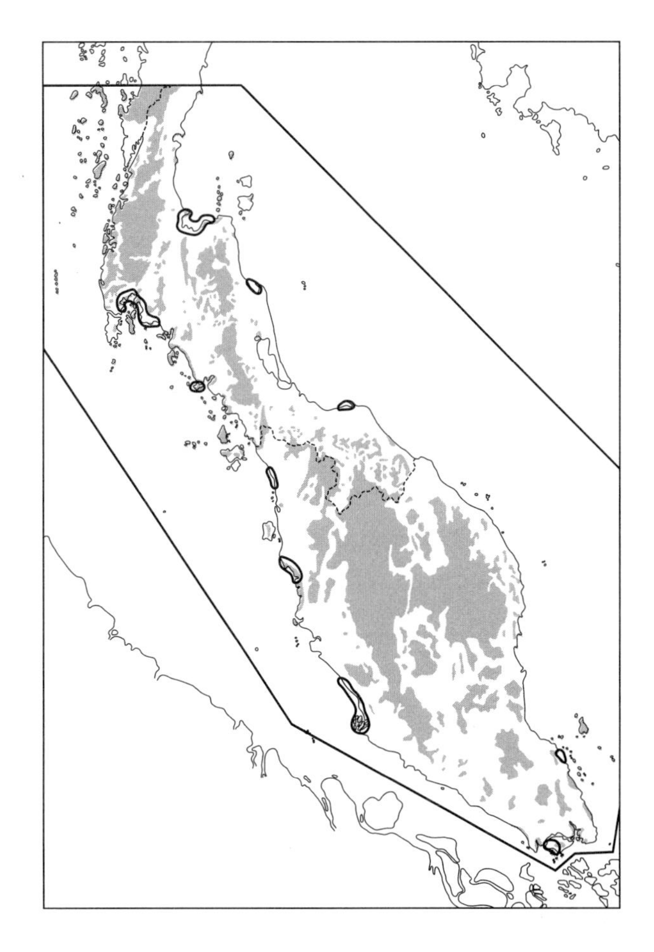

GROUP RELATIONS. Free-standing.

GLOBAL RANGE. Breeds on Sakhalin, possibly also Kamchatka, elsewhere on the mainland coast of the Sea of Okhotsk, and on islands in the Bering Sea. One wintering record from the Nansei islands; otherwise, on the Ganges–Brahmaputra delta (a mid-January 1988 count of 300 in the Meghna estuary: Scott 1989) and SE Asia from Burma and the Gulf of Thailand to SE Sumatra and Borneo, with a few records in N and central Philippines. Vagrant in Sri Lanka, Guam and, possibly, NW Australia (Lane and Davies 1987, OBCB-13).

IDENTIFICATION/DESCRIPTION. In winter, closest to Common Greenshank but head and neck all round are more nearly plain white, and upperparts are conspicuously paler grey. Proportionately rather wide bill and obviously shorter legs give a stockier appearance and, in flight, only tips of toes project beyond tail. Dull to rather bright yellow legs and feet are a more dependable marker than bi-coloured bill-pattern, which is clear only in good light.

The fresh, spring adult is distinctly black-and-white spotted and streaked on head and neck, with bold black dots from the base of the neck to the flanks, and white feather-edging on sooty black upperparts gives a spangled effect (BMNH). (In NE Asia, head and neck become sooty black, apparently as a result of early wear of pale fringing: Kennerley and Bakewell 1987).

Toes 2–3–4 are connected by narrow, fringing webs.

Bare-part colours. Iris dark brown; basal half of bill grey-green, apical half blackish; legs and feet dull- to clear yellow.

Size (mm). (Skins: 2 males, 3 females; adult): wing 171, 176 and 181–182; tail 63 and 68 (one of each); bill 53.8–55.5 (sexes combined); tarsus 43.9–47.0 (sexes combined) (BMNH, Jørgensen 1949, ZRCNUS).

Weight. No data.

DISTRIBUTION. Historical summary: *Sur, Pha, Nak, Kra, Pat, Ked, Pek, Sel, Joh, Sin*, with other island records from Libong (*Tra*) and Tengah (*Sel*).

GEOGRAPHICAL VARIATION. None recognized.

STATUS AND POPULATION. A passage migrant, and tiny numbers winter on the W coast between Phangnga bay and Selangor. Local, uncommon to sparse, and in general decline. Ninety-plus on tide-flats at Belanak headland, Perak, on 5 November 1964 is by far the highest score on record, and there has not been a double-figure count at this season since 1988 (19 on 23 December at the Tanjung Karang roost, N Selangor) (BR 1964, ENGGANG-2). Peak spring counts in Selangor have also fallen: from 29 at Kuala Selangor on 10 March 1978 to about 16 at Tanjung Karang on 16 April 1989, and only six on 20 March 1992 (during systematic monitoring of the Kapar power-station ash-bed wader roost) (BR 1978–79, ENGGANG-2, Sebastian *et al.* 1993). However, one week later, 22 were at Libong island (BBCB-9), and there has been a recent early March count of 20 at Krabi (BBCB-8). Elsewhere, old spring reports exist from Bandon and Pak Phanang bays in the NE (Jørgensen 1949).

Wintering trends are less clear. In the early 1960s, up to five were regular at the W end of Singapore island (BR 1963, 1964), but this nucleus either shifted range or died out, with no sighting anywhere in the

Republic since December 1981 (BR 1980–81). Recently, not more than 1–2 have been found in Selangor, but up to ten winter on Libong island and 3–5 at Krabi (P.D. Round), which seem now to be the most important sites in the Peninsula. A loner at Mersing on 10 January 1983 is the only mid-season record from the E coast (D. Diskin).

HABITATS AND ECOLOGY. Strictly intertidal, favouring firm, mixed sand/mud substrates with shallow tide-pools. Roosts with other, mainly medium-sized waders on secluded beaches and in clearings in the mangrove zone. At Krabi, regular use is also made of the support-stakes of permanent, offshore fish-traps (P.D. Round).

FORAGING AND FOOD. Seven of nine items identified at Libong were swimming crabs of carapace-width up to about 40 mm, dismembered and eaten piecemeal or, if small, swallowed whole. The others were small fish (see also Common Greenshank) (Howes and Lambert 1987).

SOCIAL ORGANIZATION. Gregarious on migration, but in mixed-species roosts shows no tendency to clump. Foragers space themselves individually (Howes and Lambert 1987).

MOVEMENTS. Encounters in Singapore during the 1960s covered all months early August–April. Most records are not earlier than November (implying an intermediate halt, perhaps to the north of the Peninsula), with evidence of onward passage until at least late December. Spring migration begins at the end of February and continues to at least mid April, with a few birds present into May. These are in winter-type plumage and may be second-summerers, perhaps not returning to the breeding-range. Extreme dates are 2 August and 18 May (BBCB-9, BMP5, ENGGANG-2).

SURVIVAL. No information.

SOCIAL INTERACTIONS. No information.

VOICE. Rather silent by *Tringa* standards. Birds flushed in a flock gave soft contact-calls: *wuk, wenk*. Loud, ringing or yapping notes, *wehk* or *chrieeuw* (likened to Black-tailed Godwit) are sometimes given just before and in flight (Bijlsma and de Roder 1986, Kennerley and Bakewell 1987, P.D. Round).

BREEDING. No population.

MOULT. Local data on wing-moult include only instances of suspension in W-coast non-juveniles dated 28 November (at P5) and 26 February (at P9) (BMNH, ZRCNUS). December and January specimens from Tenasserim also showed late-stage suspension. Apparently, summer plumage is lost before arrival, and most spring migrants are on the move before regaining it (or are not adult). The earliest record of renewal in an adult is 12 March, from Bandon bay (Jørgensen 1949).

CONSERVATION. Globally endangered; the world population may now be below 1000 (BTW2, Howes and Lambert 1987). Populations using the Peninsula continue to decline, due to factors operating probably mainly elsewhere.

Green Sandpiper; Nok Chailaen Khieo (Thai); Burung Kedidi Hijau (Malay)

Tringa ochropus Linnaeus 1758, *Systema Naturae* 10(1): 149. TL Sweden.
Plate 32

GROUP RELATIONS. Forms a superspecies with American *T. solitaria* (Solitary Sandpiper) (Mayr and Short 1970).

GLOBAL RANGE. Breeds at cool-temperate to low-arctic latitudes from Scandinavia and central Europe east to Amurland and the Sea of Okhotsk, with an outlier in the Tien Shan. Winters in Atlantic Europe, the Mediterranean, northern tropical Africa and SW Asia; the Indian subcontinent and Sri Lanka; S Japan and China south of about latitude 40° including Taiwan and Hainan; and SE Asia, in small numbers to the Greater Sunda islands and Philippines, but the main regional migration terminus is continental. Vagrant in New Guinea, possibly also N Australia.

IDENTIFICATION/DESCRIPTION. Wood Sandpiper-size but stockier (longer-winged and proportionately shorter-legged). White supercilium does not extend behind eye, upperparts are a shade darker than in Wood, and feet are darker, lacking a yellow tinge. In flight: no wing-bar; more showy white rump–upper tail-covert patch also includes tail-base; toe-tips barely project beyond tail; and blackish underwing contrasts with white belly (both whitish in Wood Sandpiper).

Bare-part colours. Iris dark brown; bill olive-green shading apically to blackish; legs and feet grey-green.

Size (mm). (Skin: 1 male, adult): wing 139; tail 57; bill 35.3; tarsus 32.9 (BMNH).

Weight (g). January birds, 64.6 and 69.0 (B.D. Bond).

DISTRIBUTION. Historical summary: *Pak, Pht, Sel, Mel, Joh, Sin*, with an island record from Samui (*Sur*).

GEOGRAPHICAL VARIATION. None recognized.

STATUS AND POPULATION. A non-breeding visitor, local and sparse; recorded overall in September and November–March (R.J. Banham, BIRDLINE 1993, BMP5, SINGAV-2, -4). Apparently, too few reach the Peninsula to be seen every year (and records from Nakhon Si Thammarat and Satul have been withdrawn on grounds of poor documentation and a confusion of localities; likewise a suspiciously large number reported from Pattani bay). South of the border, commoner in the 1960s when open wetlands associated with dredge-mining were more extensive along the W-coast plain than now, but a few still reach Singapore.

HABITATS AND ECOLOGY. Sites have included riversides, ditches, edges of shallow pools in open, freshwater wetlands left over from dredge-mining and land-clearance operations, wet grazing-land, and (once) paddy-fields (Parish 1985).

FORAGING AND FOOD. No specific information.

SOCIAL ORGANIZATION. Typically solitary; not more than three recorded together (BR 1969).

MOVEMENTS. Extreme dates are 26 September and 31 March (BMP5).

SURVIVAL. No information.

SOCIAL INTERACTIONS. No information.

VOICE. The flight-call is a loud, liquid *tlo-it* or *tlo-tluit*.

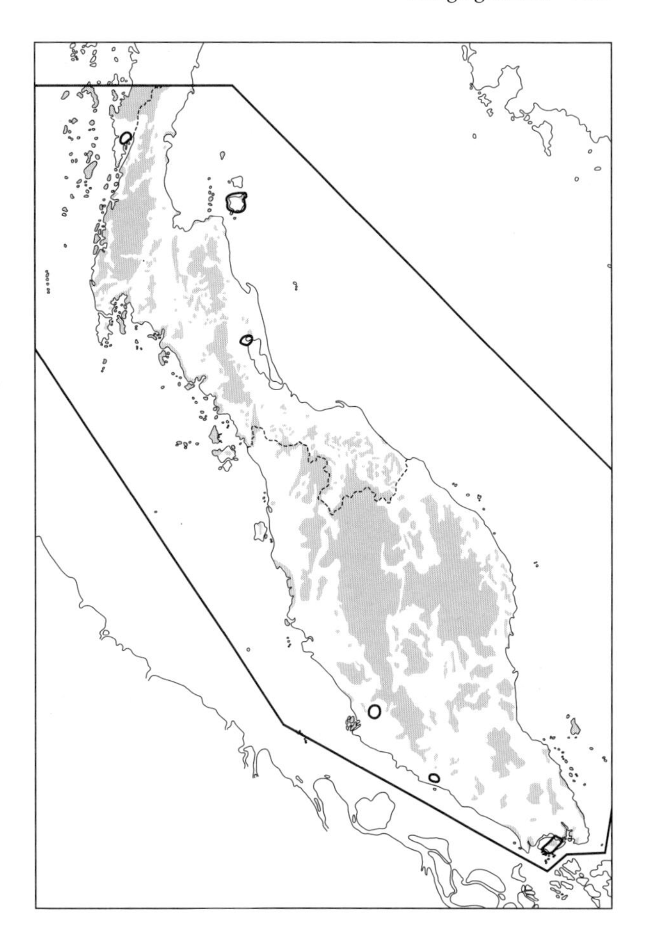

BREEDING. No population.

MOULT. One of two (age not recorded) mist-netted at Batu Berendam, Melaka, on 31 January was moulting the central tail-feathers (B.D. Bond).

CONSERVATION. No relevant issues.

Wood Sandpiper; Nok Chailaen Nam Jeud (Thai); Burung Kedidi Sawah (Malay)

Tringa glareola Linnaeus 1758, *Systema Naturae* 10(1): 149. TL Sweden.

Plate 32

GROUP RELATIONS. Probably free-standing.

GLOBAL RANGE. Breeds at cool-temperate to arctic latitudes from Scotland to Kamchatka, south in E Asia to NE China. Winters in sub-Saharan Africa and SW Asia; the Indian subcontinent, Sri Lanka and Bay of Bengal islands; S Japan and S China including Taiwan and Hainan; SE Asia to the Greater Sunda islands, Bali and the Philippines; and Wallacea, W Micronesia, New Guinea and Australia.

IDENTIFICATION/DESCRIPTION. A medium-small, elegant wader with whitish supercilium along whole length of head; grey-brown, white-freckled upperparts; neck and breast finely brown-streaked; and legs pale horn-yellow. In flight, rump and upper tail-coverts white; underwing pale, not in contrast with belly; and toes project beyond tail-tip. From Green Sandpiper in the hand by shaft of outermost large primary white (Hayman *et al.* 1986).

Bare-part colours. Iris dark brown; bill dull greenish with apical half blackish; legs and feet pale horn- or grey-yellow.

Size (mm). (Skins and live: 27 adults, most not sexed): wing 119–130; tail 45–55; bill 23.7–32.2; tarsus 30.0–35.8 (AWB, UMBRP, ZRCNUS).

Weight (g). One on 28 July, 70.0; others dated late July–early March, 45.8–64.0 (n=55). It is not known when or where spring fattening begins.

DISTRIBUTION. Historical summary: all divisions except *Pak, Chu, Kra, Yal, Nar*, with additional island records from Langkawi and Penang off the W coast; and Samui off the E coast.

GEOGRAPHICAL VARIATION. None recognized.

STATUS AND POPULATION. A non-breeding visitor and passage migrant, apparently not over-summering; regular and common. The most often-encountered wader in brackish and open freshwater wetlands, but these habitats are hard to census and overall numbers relative to strictly shoreline wader species remain unknown. Paddyland has been a key habitat but its usage by all waterbirds has plummeted as the rice industry deepens its dependence on chemical pesticides, especially broad-spectrum herbicides. With no clear shift of numbers to alternative habitats, it seems the carrying-capacity of at least the Malaysian part of the Peninsula for this species must be decreasing.

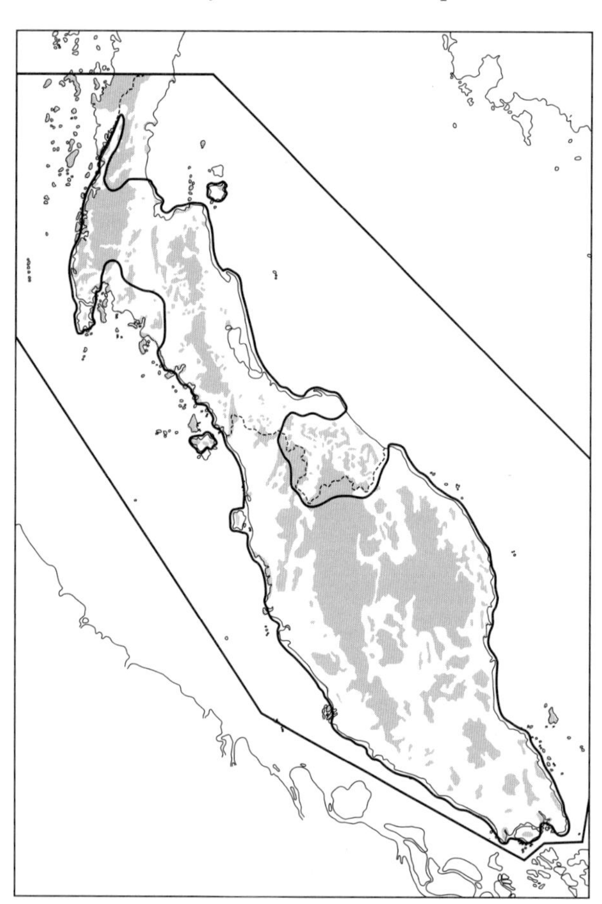

HABITATS AND ECOLOGY. As stated, formerly mainly in paddyland but only at the fallow and early (wet) cultivation stages when open ground and shallow water are available. Regular where these conditions are met in many other situations as well, including on wet grazing-land, margins of fish-ponds, wetlands left over from dredge-mining, etc.; also brackish pools and aquaculture pond-edges in cleared and bunded mangrove-land, but avoids the intertidal zone.

FORAGING AND FOOD. Forages alone or in small, loose groups. No local diet details available.

SOCIAL ORGANIZATION. Social, but not strongly gregarious.

MOVEMENTS. The earliest recorded arrival date is 18 July. First significant-sized groups reach Selangor a few days later, and Singapore by the end of the month, with waves of passage through August–September, a general influx in mid/late November and peak numbers everywhere during December–January. Departure begins in February and five-fold variation of daily counts in Singapore during late March reflects waves of spring passage, which continue into April. 5 May is the latest date on record, leaving a greater than two-month period of complete absence over mid summer (BMP5, BR 1964, 1968, 1976–77, 1978–79, ENGGANG-2, -3, Parish 1985, SINGAV-1, -2, -3, -4).

SURVIVAL. No information.

SOCIAL INTERACTIONS. No information.

VOICE. An alarm call, *fit*, and when flushed a shrieking *fii-fii-fiif* or *fii-fii-fii-fiif*.

BREEDING. No population.

MOULT. Autumn juveniles show no wing-moult; two first-winterers dated 4 and 5 March had replaced the wing-tip from P6 and P7, and one of these was still growing P10 (AWB, B.D. Bond, UMBRP). Apparent adults handled at Kuala Selangor on 28 July and 1 August had not started wing-moult. One on 16 September was growing P1–5 (with three adjacent feathers in pin, indicating rapid replacement at this stage). Eight during 28 October–5 November had reached between P7 and P10. One had finished by early December but others, perhaps from populations on different migration schedules, or after suspensions, were still growing P10 on dates in January, February and early March.

Partial summer plumage reported as of early March but the body-moult cycle needs study.

CONSERVATION. See above.

Terek Sandpiper; Nok Chailaen Paak En (Thai); Burung Kedidi Sereng (Malay)

Xenus cinereus (Güldenstaedt) 1774, *Novi Commentarii Academiae Scientiarum Imperialis Petropolitanae* 19: 473 and plate 19. TL vicinity of the Terek estuary, NW Caspian Sea.

Plate 31

GROUP RELATIONS. Free-standing.

GLOBAL RANGE. Breeds at cool-temperate to arctic latitudes from Finland to Anadyrland, south in far-E Asia possibly to the upper Amur, and with an outlier in SW Russia. Winters from S Africa and the Malagasy region round coasts of the Indian Ocean to the Indian subcontinent, Sri Lanka and Andamans; the Nansei islands; SE Asia to the Greater Sunda islands, Bali and the Philippines; Wallacea, W Micronesia, New Guinea, Australia and, in small numbers, New Zealand.

IDENTIFICATION/DESCRIPTION. A small wader with proportionately rather short, pale orange legs, steep forehead and long, orange-based, up-curved bill. Typically very active when foraging. In flight, dark wrist and white trailing-edge of the secondaries are pointers. Most show some black slash-marks along the scapulars but these are heavier and bolder in summer, when adult head and upperparts generally are more obviously dark-streaked than in winter.

Bare-part colours. Iris dark brown; bill blackish with small area of orange at base; legs and feet clear- to green-tinged orange.

Size (mm). (Live: 68, age/sex-classes mostly not separated): wing 131–147 (definite juveniles down to 126); tail 49–55; bill (33.5) 45.2–56.0; tarsus 29.0–32.0 (AWB, UMBRP).

Weight (g). All age-classes during early August–late February, 58.4–82.5 (n=47). In Selangor on 20 April, only three of 33 first-winterers were above 80, whereas only three of 36 adults were below 80 (the rest 84–105, probably close to departure weight). By May, virtually all birds are below 80 (AWB, UMBRP), implying fat migrants have already left.

DISTRIBUTION. Historical summary: all divisions except *Pak, Chu, Pht, Son, Yal, Tru, Pra, Neg*, with extra island records from Libong, Langkawi, Penang and Tengah off the W coast; and Ubin and Busing, Singapore.

GEOGRAPHICAL VARIATION. None recognized.

STATUS AND POPULATION. A non-breeding visitor and passage migrant, and numerous on the Selangor coast to the first week of June (a few to 13 June in Singapore), but none anywhere over mid summer (BR 1963, Silvius *et al.* 1987, SINGAV-1). Regular and common. From mist-net capture-rates and direct counting, ranked third or fourth most numerous wader on the Melaka Straits coast, with a peak total population of around 5000. Along the W coast as a whole, its chief locations are Krabi bay, Libong island, the Perak and N Selangor coasts (including Tengah island), and Benut (SW Johor) (BBCB-8, BR 1978–79, Hawkins and Howes 1986, MBR 1986–87, Parish 1985, Silvius *et al.* 1987). Smaller numbers (peak January count 100) winter around Singapore island (BIRDLINE 1992, SINGAV-2).

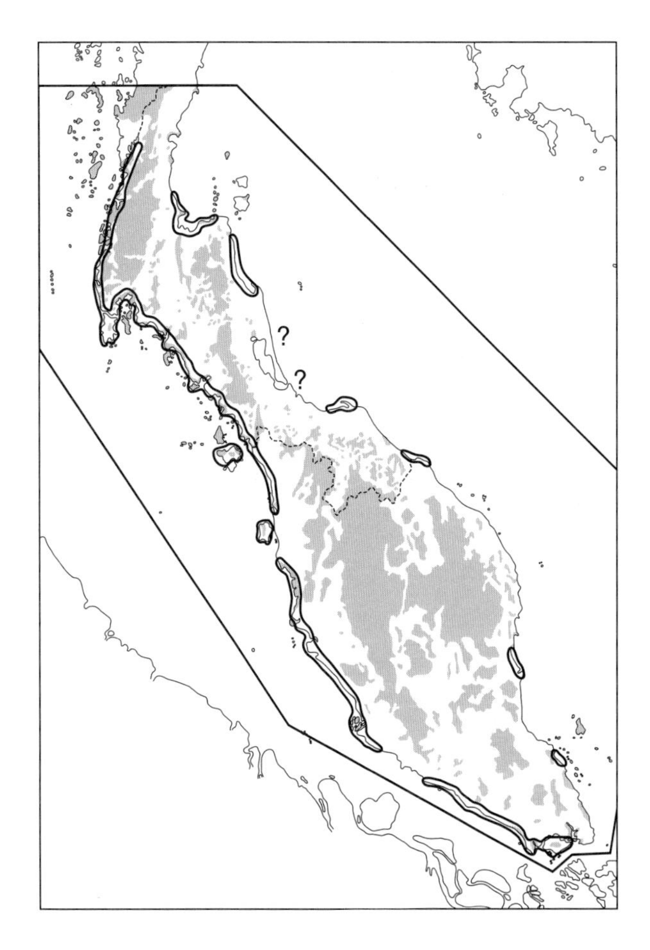

In the east, Bandon and Pak Phanang bays are used in autumn, and Pattani bay holds a remnant as late as mid January (Jørgensen 1949, Parish 1985, Ruttanadakul and Ardseungnern 1987, Swennen *et al.* 1986). Just over the border, a few have been seen on the Kelantan delta in spring and, southward, some actually winter around the Pahang estuary, Mersing bay, etc. (Howes *et al.* 1986), but in tiny numbers relative to W-coast populations.

HABITATS AND ECOLOGY. A shoreline species feeding strictly in the intertidal zone. Regularly roosts in mangrove trees, especially dead ones; also on fish-trap stakes (P.D. Round) and remote beaches. Attracted to the coastal clearings favoured by many other littoral waders, but mostly only on night tides. When forced off feeding-grounds in the evening, frequently kills time in off-shore flight until last light (the flock weaving to and fro, often in tight synchrony, low over the sea-surface) and leaves the roost again before dawn.

FORAGING AND FOOD. Shows a strong (91 percent) preference for soft muds, avoiding firmer substrates that are unsuited to its characteristic feeding-actions (but still numerous at Tengah island). The main prey items are small crabs and polychaetes (Swennen and Marteijn 1985), taken with recurved bill-tip sifting the surface layer as the bird runs, or by sideways scything.

SOCIAL ORGANIZATION. Forms quite large, close-knit flocks while on the move, including to roosts. Less social and usually well-scattered when foraging.

MOVEMENTS. A few small, apparently through-moving groups reach W and S coasts in late July, succeeded by a more general but still low-level presence as of mid August (BMP5, BR 1976–77, ENGGANG-2, SINGAV-2, -4). First large waves of migrants arrive everywhere at end August/early September (juveniles from late September), with irregular build-up to maximum numbers as of October (300-plus at Krabi, 2300 on Tengah island) (ENGGANG-2, Parr 1988, P.D. Round, Silvius *et al.* 1987). Local oscillations indicate through-movements continue until late January, when less than one-third of autumn numbers remains at Tengah, and the NE coast is entirely emptied.

Spring passage of returnees begins by mid March (300 at Krabi and 150 at Mersing, respectively, on 14 and 19 March) and, everywhere, numbers peak during mid–late April (up to 1000 at Libong island on 15 April) (ENGGANG-2, Howes *et al.* 1986, E.T. Myers, Parish 1985, Silvius *et al.* 1987, J.A. Wolstencroft). Extreme arrival and departure dates are 23 July and 13 June, but because of the difficulty of identifying summer plumage at a distance, it is not known when most adults leave.

Three recoveries of ringed birds north of the Peninsula identify spring and autumn staging points: an autumn adult from Singapore in Hangzou bay, latitude 30°47'N, China, on the following 1 May; a juvenile ringed in Deep bay, Hong Kong, on 12 October retrapped at Kuala Selangor 42 days later; and a late November bird from Kuala Selangor killed in Pattani bay in the following late August, on what is likely to have been its next journey south (MBR 1984–85, Siti Hawa Yatim 1990).

SURVIVAL. No information.

SOCIAL INTERACTIONS. No information.

VOICE. Not adequately described.

BREEDING. No population.

MOULT. First-winterers on the Selangor coast show no wing-moult until March or April (earliest 13 March), when many renew outer primaries from anywhere between P5 and P10; most from P8. They complete by May (lastest record 5 May) and a complete, second-summer wing-moult begins from P1 as of early July.

All early autumn non-juveniles are in more or less complete winter body-plumage and active wing-moult. Some, but not all, adults may start the latter before arrival (even with up to four inner primaries in overlapping growth, it is unlikely as many as six feathers could be renewed on the wintering grounds by early August). A few may finish sooner but the most advanced bird handled was growing P10 on 26 October. Others reach this stage between November and early February, perhaps after suspensions.

Full summer body-plumage has been identified in the hand as of early April, and at least some is acquired by all age-groups (AWB, UMBRP).

CONSERVATION. See Whimbrel.

Common Sandpiper; Nok Dao Din (Thai); Burung Kedidi Biasa (Malay)

Actitis hypoleucos (Linnaeus) 1758, *Systema Naturae* 10(1): 149. TL Sweden.
Plate 32

GROUP RELATIONS. Sometimes lumped with *A. macularia* (Spotted Sandpiper) of the Americas, but breeding-colours and voice-differences favour recognition of a superspecies.

GLOBAL RANGE. Breeds across northern Eurasia from the Atlantic to Anadyrland and Kamchatka, south to Iran, the Himalayas, W and N China, and central Japan. A few winter in Atlantic and Mediterranean Europe; most through sub-Saharan Africa, the Malagasy region and coastal SW Asia; the Indian subcontinent, Sri Lanka and Bay of Bengal islands; S Japan and China south from the Changjiang valley, including Taiwan and Hainan; SE Asia; and

Wallacea, New Guinea and Australia. Some reach Oceania, vagrant as far as New Zealand.

IDENTIFICATION/DESCRIPTION. Frequent bobbing ('teetering') of the rear body, and white kink behind the olive-grey patch on the side of the breast are distinctive. In short flights, often low over water, brief glides intersperse with rapid down-flicks of the wings, showing off the white bar along the flight-feathers. Sustained flight is by continuous flapping, as in other waders.

Bare-part colours. Iris dark brown; bill dark brown with dull olive-green base; legs and feet yellowish grey.

Size (mm). (Live: 72 non-juveniles; none sexed): wing 103–115; tail 48–60; bill 23.4–27.0; tarsus 23.6–28.0 (AWB, UMBRP).

Weight (g). An August–December sample, 33–58 (n=81); March–early April birds (n=84) the same. Except for one individual at 41, late April–early May birds were mostly heavier, at 56–73 (UMBRP).

DISTRIBUTION. Historical summary: all divisions except *Pak, Chu, Yal,* with many additional island records: from the Surins, Yao Yai, Phiphi, Libong, Muk, the Tarutao group (Ta Nga), the Langkawi group, Penang, Pangkor, Jarak, the Kelang estuary group and Pisang off the W coast; Tao, Samui, Lang Tengah, Redang, Bidung Laut, and the Pahang–Johor archipelago (Tulai, Tioman and Sibu) off the E coast: and Ubin, Seletar, St John's, Lazarus, Hantu, Sakeng and Sudong around Singapore.

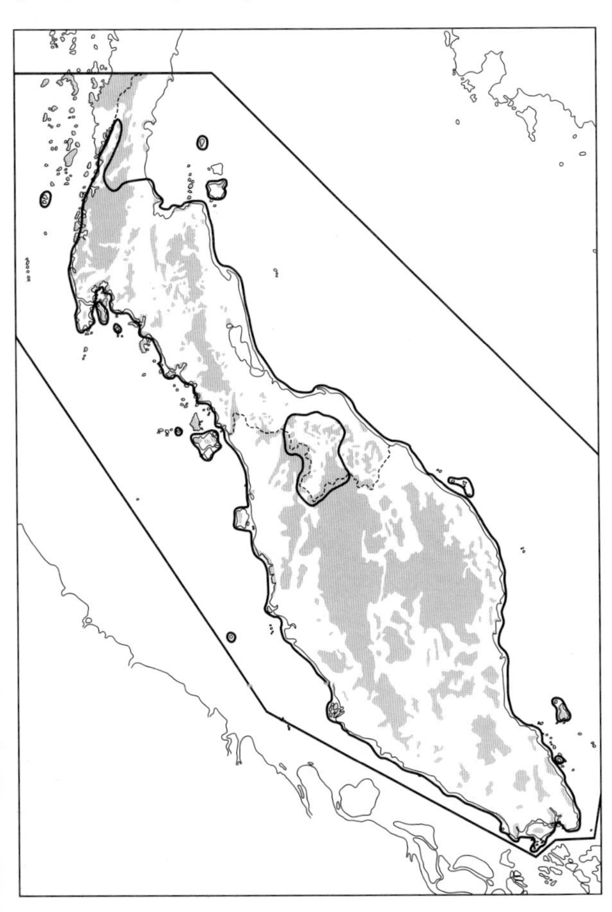

GEOGRAPHICAL VARIATION. None recognized.

STATUS AND POPULATION. A passage migrant and non-breeding visitor, with a few records at mid summer (BR 1964), but no definite over-summering. Regular and common. Likely to be among the most numerous of wintering waders overall, but no population estimates exist because of its dispersed distribution, from coasts to hills.

HABITATS AND ECOLOGY. Uses a wide variety of coastal and inland habitats offering firm mud, sandy, rocky or grassy surfaces, typically near open, often moving water: low-tide beaches, creeks through mangrove forest, pond-margins and river-edges and shoals, from plains level to the torrent zone, recorded as high as 1000 m along the Bertam river in Cameron Highlands (Berwick 1947). Roosts on secure snags, rocks or breakwaters, alone or in groups, locally of 60 or more (a record 300 in part-cleared mangroves at Rubiah river-mouth, Perak, during late August passage) but typically much smaller (Howes *et al.* 1986, Parish and Wells 1984, UMBRP).

FORAGING AND FOOD. Avoids contact with conspecifics while foraging, which fits a strategy of hunting invertebrates on the surface, visually. Explores crevices but does not probe, hence avoids soft muds. On sandy tide-flats, small, gregarious crabs are the main prey, taken in a quick dash, broken up and eaten piecemeal. Locally, exploits people for feeding opportunities, including along the Pahang river where winterers are recorded taking food-scraps from boat decks and riverside camp kitchens (A.M. Wells).

SOCIAL ORGANIZATION. Gregarious at roosts and while migrating; otherwise mostly solitary.

MOVEMENTS. Apart from a bird in Singapore on 29 June, extreme dates are 21 July and 21 May (BR 1963, 1964, Young 1941). From evidence of Melaka Straits roost-counts, autumn passage peaks during early September–mid October, with intermittent surges up to late January; spring passage during mid March–late April (ENGGANG-3, Parish and Wells 1984, Silvius *et al.* 1987, SINGAV-3).

SURVIVAL. Between-season retrap-intervals of up to 62 months, at sites of ringing near Melaka and Kuala Selangor (B.D. Bond, MBR 1982–83).

SOCIAL INTERACTIONS. No information.

VOICE. A shrill, piping, *pwee-wee-wee-wee*, as the flushed bird flies off, or when interacting with other individuals in low flight.

BREEDING. No population.

MOULT. Not well understood owing to problems of identifying year-groups. In Selangor, two definite adults on 1 August and 65 percent of a large, non-aged sample dated 22–24 August showed no wing-moult. The balance had reached between P2 and P5 (mostly not past P3). September birds included a minority of pre-starters, the rest in rapid moult of the inner primaries (up to five adjacent feathers growing), out to P6 by the end of the month. October–December samples showed a similar minority of pre-starters, many more suspended after P6 or 7, and a bird dated 22 December growing P9–10 (either a non-juvenile re-started or precocious wing-tip moult by a first-winterer). Only a few were still all-old by January; the rest divided about equally between continued suspension and active outer-hand moult. February is undersampled but March and early April birds were either growing outer primaries (between P6 and 10) or had completed. The few birds handled in late April–early May had all completed (UMBRP, AWB).

Many Selangor birds still moulting early in March (but none that had actually finished) showed a clear age-difference between inner and outer primaries, i.e., had either re-started after a longish suspension or were renewing the wing-tip precociously. A few apparent second-summerers caught in Singapore (AWB) had a new wing-tip and, in late August, were growing 1–5 inner primaries.

The early winter suspension of wing-moult in Selangor may have been local. Winterers on the Serangoon estuary, Singapore, in 1983 did not show it. Late October–November non-juveniles there were actively moulting (at P6 or beyond) and are likely to have completed before the end of the year.

CONSERVATION. No critical issues.

Grey-tailed Tattler; Nok Teen Leuang (Thai); Burung Kedidi Ekor Kelabu (Malay)

Heteroscelus brevipes (Vieillot) 1816, *Nouveau Dictionnaire d'Histoire Naturelle* 6: 410. TL Timor.
Plate 32

GROUP RELATIONS. Probably free-standing, overlapping the range of *H. incana* (Wandering Tattler) in the breeding season.

GLOBAL RANGE. Breeds in the uplands of NE Siberia from longitude about 88°E to Anadyrland, south possibly to Kamchatka. Winters in the Nansei islands, islands off Taiwan and on Hainan; in SE Asia to the Peninsula, Borneo, Java, Bali and the Philippines; Wallacea, New Guinea, Australia, and Oceania to New Zealand.

IDENTIFICATION/DESCRIPTION. A medium-sized wader with proportionately rather short, yellow legs. During winter, mostly ash-grey, with long white supercilium from above the bill to well behind the eye, and dark loral band. The summer adult is finely barred dark grey below, back to breast and flanks. In flight, whole upper surface uniform grey, with no wing or rear-body pattern, and grey underwing contrasts with white belly. In the hand, from as yet unrecorded Wandering Tattler *H. incanus* by nasal groove (not the nostril) extending to the mid point of the upper mandible.

Bare-part colours. Iris dark brown; bill blackish with base of lower mandible yellow; legs and feet clear yellow.

Size (mm). (Skins: 3 adults, not sexed): wing 164–168; tail 64–67; bill 37.8–40.9; tarsus 32.8–33.2 (Gibson-Hill 1956a, ZRCNUS).

Weight. No data.

DISTRIBUTION. Historical summary: *Ran, Pha, Pek, Sel, Joh, Sin,* with island records from Libong (*Tra*), Ketam (*Sel*) and Sultan shoal (*Sin*).

GEOGRAPHICAL VARIATION. None recognized.

STATUS AND POPULATION. A non-breeding visitor, local and sparse. Very small numbers occur more or less annually only on the far SE corner of the Peninsula: ones and twos from Mersing bay to the adjacent E end of Singapore island, in all months late August–May (BR 1967, 1969, 1980–81, BIRDLINE 1992, 1993, Gibson-Hill 1949b, Howes *et al.* 1986, Kidd 1961, MBR 1982–83, 1986–87, SINGAV-2, -3). Vagrant elsewhere in Singapore, also on Melaka Straits and Andaman Sea coasts, with a scatter of records from the Kelang estuary to Ranong (BLC, ENGGANG-2, Gibson-Hill 1956a, MBR 1984–85).

HABITATS AND ECOLOGY. Recorded on soft-mud to sandy tide-flats, and back-reef coral rubble (Gibson-Hill 1956a, Kidd 1961, Robinson and Chasen 1936). At least one W-coast sighting has been at a mixed-species roost on cleared mangrove-land.

FORAGING AND FOOD. A solitary forager; no other local information.

SOCIAL ORGANIZATION. No information.

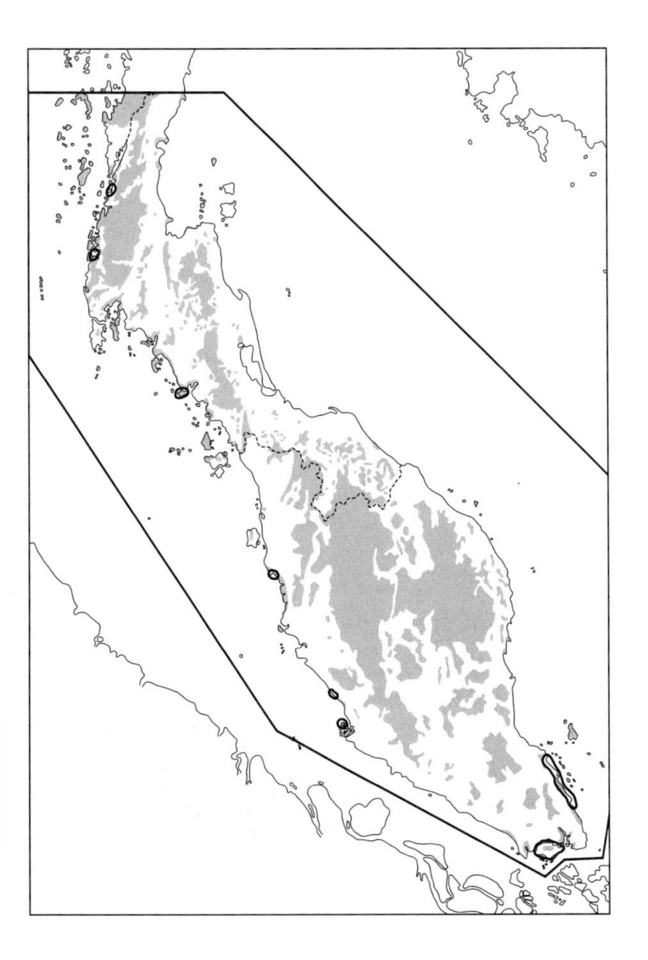

MOVEMENTS. Extreme dates are 20 August and 17 May, with no evidence of through-passage.

SURVIVAL. No information.

SOCIAL INTERACTIONS. No information.

VOICE. Flight-calls include a melodious *weet*, a two-note *chee-weet*, and longer *chee-wee-wee-weet*, sometimes running into a rapid trill (Kidd 1961). Elsewhere, double-note whistles have been described as up-slurred.

BREEDING. No population.

MOULT. Summer plumage recorded on 12 April, and two early September non-juveniles in mostly summer plumage showed no wing-moult. One definite adult dated 13 November was in full winter plumage and growing P7 (1–6 new, wing-tip old) (BCSTB-12, ZRCNUS).

CONSERVATION. No local issues.

Ruddy Turnstone; Nok Phlik Hin (Thai); Burung Kedidi Kerikil (Malay)

Arenaria interpres (Linnaeus) 1758, *Systema Naturae* 10(1): 148. TL Gotland island, Sweden.
Not illustrated in this volume

GROUP RELATIONS. Forms a superspecies with NW American *A. melanocephala* (Black Turnstone) (Mayr and Short 1970).

GLOBAL RANGE. Breeds on coasts and islands of the Arctic Ocean around the world, locally south to the high-temperate zone. Winters on coasts between latitudes about 40°N and S, in the Americas, Atlantic Europe, Africa, and around the Indian Ocean to the Indian subcontinent, Sri Lanka and Bay of Bengal islands; in the Nansei islands and China south from Fujian and Taiwan; SE Asia to the Greater Sunda islands, Bali and the Philippines; Wallacea, Australasia, and Oceania to New Zealand.

IDENTIFICATION/DESCRIPTION. A smallish, stocky wader with short bill, short, bright orange legs, and black chest-patches. Distinctive in summer plumage. The main features in flight are parallel centre and lateral stripes of white on an otherwise dark upper body, black-and-white tail, and bright white underwing.

Bare-part colours. Iris dark brown; bill black; legs and feet bright orange.

Size (mm). (Skins: 6 males, 4 females; adult): wing 147–152 and 155–158; tail 53–60 and 53–58; bill 20.7–25.5 and 21.8–24.4; tarsus 19.7–27.2 and 24.2–27.3 (BMNH, ZRCNUS).

Weight. No data.

DISTRIBUTION. Mainly the W coast. Historical summary: *Sur, Pha, Nak, Phu, Kra, Tra, Pat, Sat, Pek,*

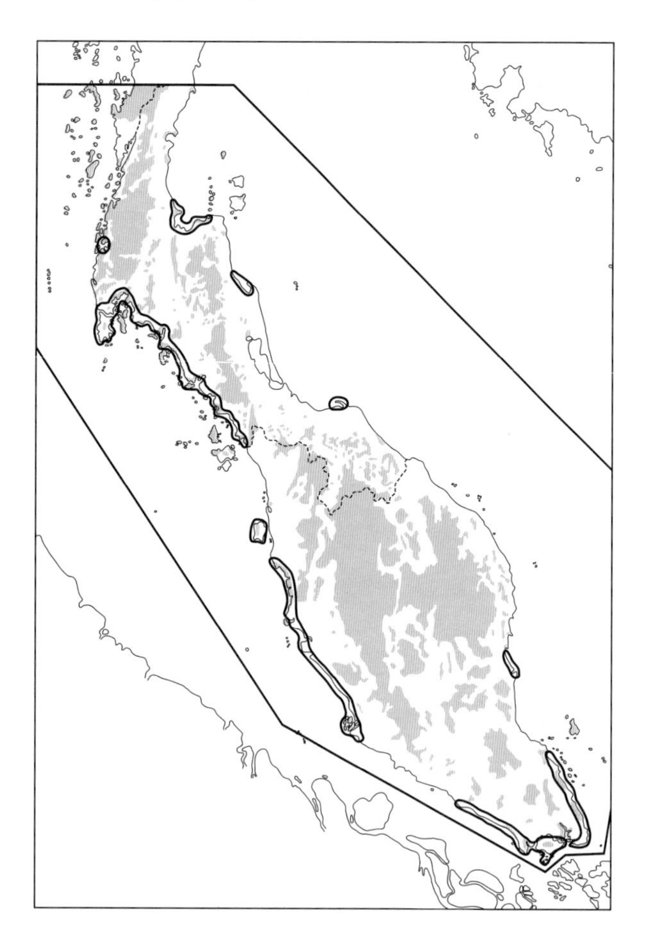

Phg, Sel, Joh, Sin, with additional island records from Muk, Libong, Penang and Tengah off the W coast; and Ubin, Sakeng and Penya shoal around Singapore.

GEOGRAPHICAL VARIATION. Nominate *interpres.*

STATUS AND POPULATION. A non-breeding visitor and passage migrant, with a small presence recorded through mid summer: including a few in Mersing bay during June and July, and ten at Kuala Selangor on 29 June (D. Diskin, MBR 1986–87). More or less common, but local. Overwinters along the W coast and in Singapore and E Johor, but only in N-central Selangor (the mainland coast rather than the islands) are mid-winter counts regularly into double figures (over 70 at Jeram beach in December, 60 at Tanjung Karang in January: ENGGANG-3, MBR 1984–85). Libong island (Trang) is a second key site, with December counts of up to 64 (Parish 1985).

On the E coast north of Johor, recorded only during passage, at one or both seasons, but some stay to December in Pattani bay (Howes *et al.* 1986, Jørgensen 1949, Parish 1985, Ruttanadakul and Ardseungnern 1987, Swennen *et al.* 1986).

HABITATS AND ECOLOGY. Strictly coastal, and typically small numbers attend mixed-species wader roosts on bare ground close to the sea.

FORAGING AND FOOD. Perhaps because they hunt visually rather than probe, Turnstones favour consolidated over soft surfaces, but with a 73 percent preference for mud against 27 for mixed mud/sands (Swennen and Marteijn 1985). The main winter prey is bivalves.

SOCIAL ORGANIZATION. Alone or in small parties; typically well-distributed in mixed-species roost-gatherings.

MOVEMENTS. Autumn surges are reported only from the north, with Pattani bay numbers at an annual peak during September and, on the opposite coast, 370 counted at Pakarang point, Phangnga, on 24 October (BCSTB-12, Ruttanadakul and Ardseungnern 1987). Southward, the general W-coast/Singapore picture is of small groups arriving in early August and escalating unevenly to a mid-winter maximum during late November–January.

Spring passage is sharply defined only on the Melaka Straits coast, possibly only in the Selangor area. Waves of migrants pass during early March–April, including counts of up to 266 at Kuala Selangor in April (MBR 1986–87, Silvius *et al.* 1987), declining to early May. Most of 20-plus birds at Tanjung Karang roost (N Selangor) on 2 May were in full summer plumage, whereas all at the Kapar roost on 20 May were in winter-type plumage, i.e., probable second-summerers not destined to move far.

SURVIVAL. No information.

SOCIAL INTERACTIONS. No information.

VOICE. No local information.

BREEDING. No population.

MOULT. Summer plumage well developed in late August–early September, and as of mid April (Jørgensen 1949, C.A. Rose, SINGAV-4). Adults dated 11 September and 6 October showed active wing-moult (P1–4 and P2–5 growing), and another non-juvenile had already renewed all but P10 by 24 September (BMNH, ZRCNUS).

CONSERVATION. See Whimbrel for issues pertaining to most coastal waders.

Short-billed/Long-billed Dowitcher; [no Thai name]/Nok Som Thalae Paak Yao (Thai); Burung Kedidi Dada Merah Amerika/Paruh Panjang (Malay)

Limnodromus griseus (Gmelin) 1789, *Systema Naturae* 13(2): 658. TL Long Island, New York.

Limnodromus scolopaceus (Say) 1823, Long's *Account of an expedition from Pittsburgh to the Rocky Mountains* 1: 170. TL vicinity of Council Bluffs, Iowa.

GROUP RELATIONS. These two similar-looking birds form a superspecies (Mayr and Short 1970).

GLOBAL RANGE. Short- and Long-billed Dowitchers breed allopatrically, from N Quebec to S Alaska, and W and N Alaska across the Bering Strait to Chukotka and Anadyrland. They winter from the S USA to S America. In the Pacific and down its western rim, Short-billed has been identified as vagrant and Long-billed probably annual, in very small numbers, as far as Hawaii and Japan, with a handful of records south to Thailand, the Peninsula, Borneo, Bali and New Guinea (Andrew 1992, BBCB-9, BMP5, Vowles and Vowles 1985).

IDENTIFICATION/DESCRIPTION. Line drawing, below. In the field, stocky, medium-sized waders, significantly smaller and shorter than Asian Dowitcher, with greenish or yellow-green rather than blackish legs, but sharing its long, straight, bulb-tipped bill-shape. In flight, both show much white up the body between uniformly dark wings, and are better separated by calls than morphology: a rapid, mellow *tu-tu-tu* by Short-billed and high, shrill *keek* or *keek-keek-keek . . .* by Long-billed (Colston and Burton 1988, Hayman *et al.* 1986, Wilds and Newlon 1983).

Bare-part colours. (One undiagnosed specimen) bill greenish brown, darker at the (swollen) tip; legs and feet dark greenish (Batchelor 1954).

Long-billed Dowitcher

Size. No local information; the wing-length of the one specimen (not identified to species) may not have been checked against moult.

Weight. No data.

DISTRIBUTION. Historical summary: *?Sel, Mel, Sin.*

GEOGRAPHICAL VARIATION. No local information.

STATUS AND POPULATION. One shot at an inland reservoir on the Melaka/Johor border on 22 November 1953 and a sighting at a tidal prawn-rearing pond in NE Singapore on 21 December 1991 (Batchelor 1954, 1955, Ollington and Loh 1992); neither confirmed to species. Most of the description of the Relau reservoir bird, including wing of 143 mm,

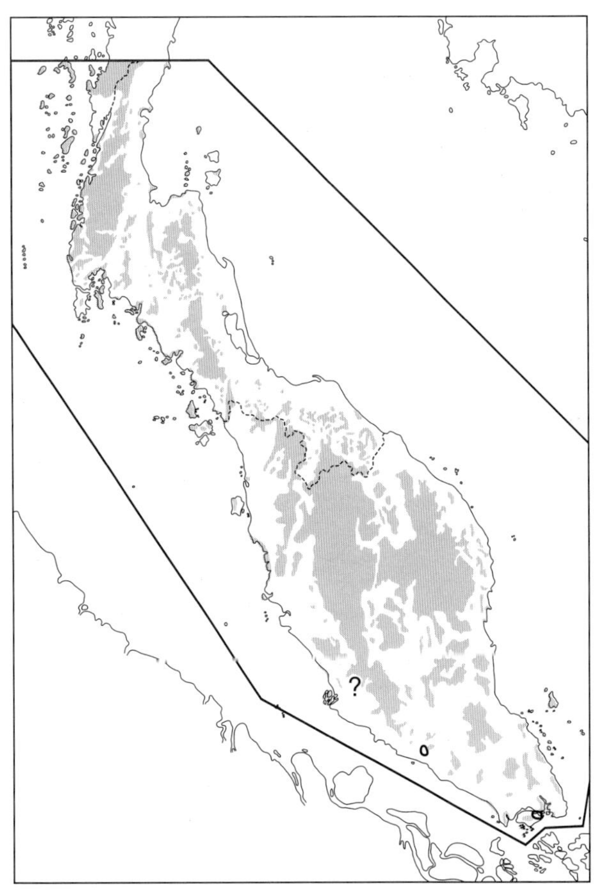

is equivocal but mantle-feathers dark brown marked with buff identify first-winter plumage, in which case scapulars merely edged buff (rather than tiger-striped) indicate Long-billed, as do dark-barred flanks. Predominantly white tail and finely dark-streaked breast, on the other hand, are more suggestive of Short-billed. The Singapore bird was in more difficult winter plumage but bill twice the length of the head, uniformly grey, poorly demarcated breast, bold dark barring on the flanks and predominantly dark tail all err on the side of Long-billed, the more likely of the two.

HABITATS AND ECOLOGY. In their main winter ranges, Short-billed Dowitcher selects intertidal flats whereas Long-billed prefers brackish and freshwater sites.

FORAGING AND FOOD. No information.

SOCIAL ORGANIZATION. No information.

MOVEMENTS. See above.

SURVIVAL. No information.

SOCIAL INTERACTIONS. No information.

VOICE. See above.

BREEDING. No population.

MOULT. No data.

CONSERVATION. No issues.

Asian Dowitcher; Nok Som Thalae Ok Daeng (Thai); Burung Kedidi Dada Merah Asia (Malay)

Limnodromus semipalmatus (Blyth) 1848, *Journal of the Asiatic Society of Bengal* 17(1): 252. TL Calcutta, NE India.

Plate 30

GROUP RELATIONS. Free-standing.

GLOBAL RANGE. Breeds patchily across temperate-zone Siberia east from longitude about 80°E to N Mongolia, far-N China and the Sea of Okhotsk. Recorded in winter along the E coast of the Indian subcontinent and in the Andaman islands (OBCB-11); in the Peninsula, the Greater Sunda islands, Bali and the Philippines; and S New Guinea and Australia. However, up to 13 000, believed to constitute most of the global population, converge on just one site, the Banyuasin delta in SE Sumatra (OBCB-9).

IDENTIFICATION/DESCRIPTION. About Common Greenshank size but shaped more like a Bar-tailed Godwit. From the latter by straight, relatively robust, bulb-tipped, all-black bill and, at all seasons, broad white supercilium from bill-base to hind-crown, sharp against dark (to blackish) lores and cap. In flight, colour-pattern resembles many Bar-tailed Godwits, except white extends less deeply up the back and the underwing is entirely plain white.

Bare-part colours. Iris dark brown; bill black; legs and feet slaty grey to blackish.

Size (mm). (Skins: 16 non-juveniles, most not sexed): wing 170–188; tail 60–71; bill 77.2–88.1; tarsus 45.2–54.7 (BMNH, UMBRP, ZRCNUS).

Weight (g). Two autumn adults, 138 and 140 (UMBRP, AWB).

DISTRIBUTION. Mostly the W coast. Historical summary: *Pha, Nak, Kra, Tra, Pat, Sat, Pek, Sel, Sin*, with island records from Libong, the Tarutao group (Ladang) and Ketam off the W coast; and Ubin, Singapore.

GEOGRAPHICAL VARIATION. None recognized.

STATUS AND POPULATION. A passage migrant and non-breeding visitor, local and sparse to uncommon, recorded along the W coast from Phangnga bay to Libong island (Trang) and in Perak and Selangor (BBCB-4, -5, BMP5, Parish 1985); in the NE at Pak Phanang and Pattani bays (Jørgensen 1949, Parish 1985, Ruttanadakul and Ardseungnern 1987); and around Singapore.

Occasional January and February records imply a very small number overwinters, south from Perak. Otherwise, makes a halt during autumn–early winter (with double-figure counts in Perak and, in late October, up to 75 at Libong island) (BR 1965, ENGGANG-3, MBR 1986–87, SINGAV-2, -3, Parish 1985). Spring occurrences are more restricted and erratic: only a few recorded in Krabi, Selangor and Singapore (MBR 1986–87), none reliably from any part of the E coast, but double-figure counts at three sites in Perak (64 at Kuala Gula on 15 March: ENGGANG-2). Counts in the Gulf of Bangkok during April (BBCB-6, Melville and Round 1982) far outweigh the known total population of the Peninsula at any season. On the assumption that Sumatran winterers are involved, it appears likely most overfly the Peninsula in spring,

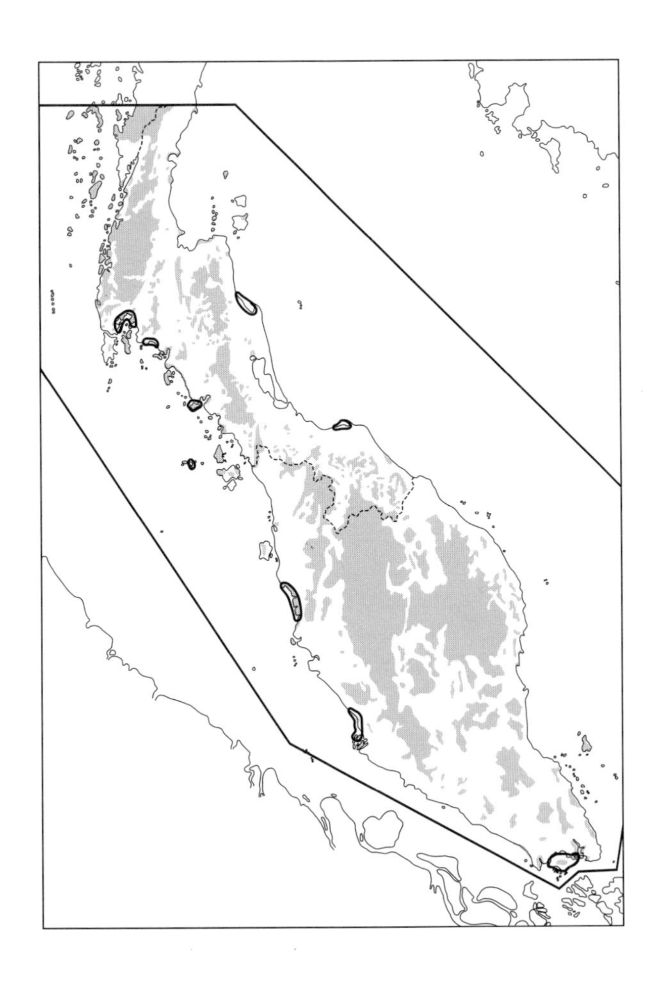

to refuel at the immediate southern edge of the continent.

HABITATS AND ECOLOGY. E. Seimund is said to have identified the heads of two shot inland near Kuala Lumpur (Robinson and Chasen 1936) but there is a possibility he saw Long-billed Dowitchers, of overlapping bill-length and known preference for fresh water. All confirmed records have been from intertidal flats, or prawn-ponds and lagoons within the mangrove zone. Roosts with other coastal waders on the ground in coastal clearings, particularly where shallow pools are available.

FORAGING AND FOOD. At Libong island, the strongly preferred substrate is muddy sand, with only 1 percent of foraging observed on softer, unripe mud (Swennen and Marteijn 1985). However, similar mud/sand mixes on Tengah island (Selangor) do not attract. Foragers hunt by jabbing the bill vertically down into the substrate every 2–3 paces (P.D. Round), sometimes under water into which birds will wade quite deeply. The main prey at Libong is polychaetes and bivalves.

SOCIAL ORGANIZATION. Strongly gregarious when on the move, loafing or roosting (Silvius *et al.* 1985). Disperses to feed.

MOVEMENTS. Reliable outside dates are 4 August and 23 April (BR 1964, Silvius *et al.* 1987). The general arrival period is late August, with highest autumn counts in late September–October and more or less regular presence to late November (late December in Perak). As noted, the spring halt is a S- and W-coast phenomenon only, and erratic except in Perak where numbers actually peak for the year in mid/late March.

SURVIVAL. No information.

SOCIAL INTERACTIONS. No information.

VOICE. Not definitely identified.

BREEDING. No population.

MOULT. On arrival, many adults still have much summer body-plumage, recorded up to early September, and some spring migrants show an advanced stage of renewal by late March (MBR 1986–87). The winter halt is a wing-moult stop. At Pak Phanang bay, four adults dated 29 August–27 September were all in inner-hand moult between P1–2 and P6 (with up to four adjacent feathers in overlapping growth). Nine more dated 22–26 November, i.e., close to departure, were at P9 or 10, or had recently finished.

September and November first-winterers from Pak Phanang bay and Selangor still had all-juvenile flight-feathers, and would have moulted on a later schedule (Jørgensen 1949, UMBRP, ZRCNUS).

CONSERVATION. Globally near-threatened (BTW2). Reliance on so few wintering and halting sites puts this species at special risk from coastal habitat-loss. Libong island has protected status, and a relevant part of the Perak coast is being considered for nature protection. Boundary-planning there must contend with the issue of long-shore drift, causing cycles of accretion and erosion of feeding-grounds.

Great Knot; Nok Not Yai (Thai); Burung Kedidi Dian Besar (Malay)

Calidris tenuirostris (Horsfield) 1821, *Transactions of the Linnean Society* 13(1): 192. TL Java.
Plate 32

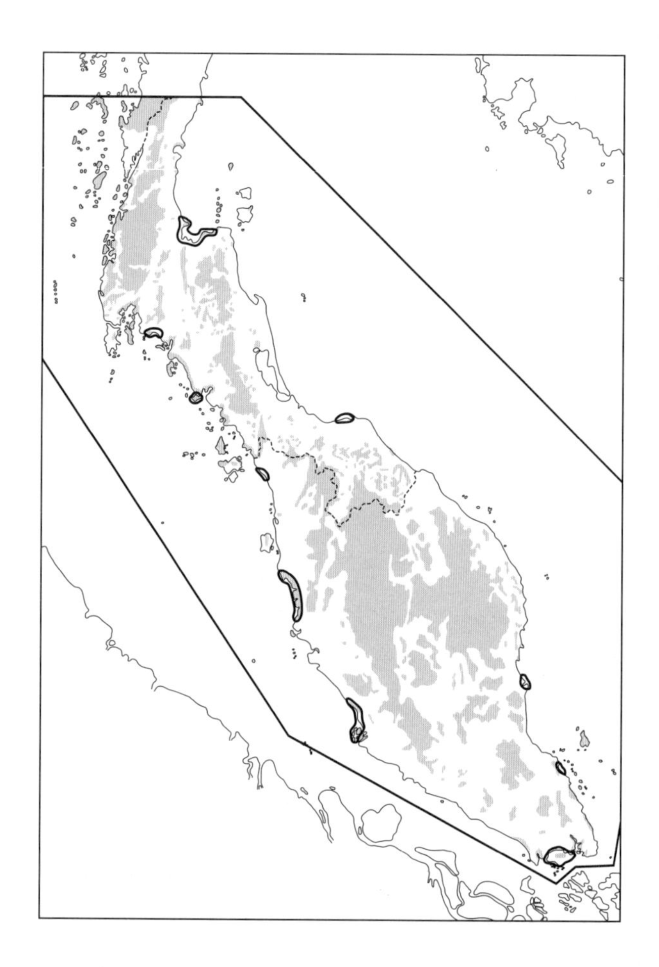

GROUP RELATIONS. Probably free-standing.

GLOBAL RANGE. Breeds in the highlands of far-NE Siberia, from longitude about 130°E to Anadyrland. Winters locally on the NW and E coasts of the Indian subcontinent and in the Andamans; in extreme S China including Hainan; and SE Asia to the Greater Sunda islands, Bali, the Philippines and Wallacea, but the bulk of the world's population converges on (mainly N) Australia. Sparse to W Micronesia and Oceania, as far as New Zealand.

IDENTIFICATION/DESCRIPTION. Redshank-plus sized but thick-set and relatively short-legged. Isolated, size is no distinction from winter Red Knot, but Great shows proportionately longer, more tapering bill and streakier head and upperparts. In flight, whiter upper tail-coverts contrast with dark tail, but has only a thin pale wing-bar.

Bare-part colours. Iris dark brown; bill blackish; legs and feet blackish, green-tinged in juveniles (Hayman *et al.* 1986).

Size (mm). (Live and skins: 15 non-juveniles, most not sexed): wing 171–198; tail 60–69; bill 39.6–47.6; tarsus 33.8–36.4 (AWB, BMNH, ZRCNUS).

Weight (g). All age/sex-classes during late September–late February (and immatures through to early May), 129–168. Adults in March, 178–210; the heaviest (on 13 March) in full summer colours, extremely fat and probably ready to leave (AWB).

DISTRIBUTION. Mostly the W coast. Historical summary: *Sur, Kra, Tra, Pat, Pes, Ked, Pek, Phg, Sel, Joh, Sin*, with island records only from Libong and Tengah, off the W coast.

GEOGRAPHICAL VARIATION. None recognized.

STATUS AND POPULATION. A non-breeding visitor and presumed passage migrant, with no evidence yet of any presence through summer. Concentrates almost completely at a few sites along the W coast: up to 350 at mid winter on Libong island (Trang), at least 420 and possibly as many as 800 around Kuala Sanglang (Kedah/Perlis border) and over 300 in N-central Selangor (mostly Tengah island), with double-figure counts also on the Krabi and Perak coasts (AWB, BBCB-8, -9, BR 1964, MBR 1986–87). Elsewhere, collected in March in Bandon bay and a very few winter in Pattani bay; perhaps also around the Pahang river-mouth, but not recorded there past mid February (Howes *et al.* 1986, Jørgensen 1949, Ruttanadakul and Ardseungnern 1987, Swennen *et al.* 1986). Southward and in Singapore, the odd few occur on autumn passage, with just one report in Singapore of a lone first-winterer remaining to January (BIRDLINE 1993, BR 1965, Howes *et al.* 1986, SINGAV-2, -3).

HABITATS AND ECOLOGY. Exclusively intertidal. Substrates around Kuala Sanglang have not been examined but elsewhere there is good correlation between wintering numbers and the availability of mud/sand mixes. Roosts in packs with other wader species on the bare ground of remote beaches, and attracted to big clearings in the mangrove zone where these open onto the sea. Use of fish-trap-support perches recorded in Krabi (P.D. Round).

FORAGING AND FOOD. Shows an 85 percent preference for mixed mud/sand surfaces, versus only 15 percent for soft muds. The main prey is bivalves (Swennen and Marteijn 1985).

SOCIAL ORGANIZATION. Strongly gregarious on the move and at roosts; more dispersed when foraging.

MOVEMENTS. Earliest date 31 July, in Singapore (BR 1965), but no double-figure counts reported anywhere before the end of August. Numbers on Libong and Tengah climb by October but with a significant dip (marking onward movement?) in November–December and further build-up as of mid/late January.

Scattered high peaks through February–early March (with nearly 400 at the Kapar, Selangor, roost on 6 March: Sebastian *et al.* 1993) indicate a complicated pattern of late winter movements leading to relatively early spring departure. Possibly all breeding adults have left by the end of March, with rather few birds of other age-groups remaining through April–early May (the latest record, a first-winterer ringed at Kapar on 5 May: AWB).

SURVIVAL. No information.

SOCIAL INTERACTIONS. No information.

VOICE. Calls include a low, soft *nyut nyut* and low-pitched but more carrying, presumed alarms (in flight, on release after ringing), *chak-chuka-chak* or *chaka-ruk-chak* (BR 1976–77).

BREEDING. No population.

MOULT. Among rather few handled, one Selangor first-winterer showed P10 newer than the rest of the wing on 7 April; others retained all-juvenile flight-feathers up to early May and are likely to have left to moult elsewhere. Among non-juveniles, a likely second-summerer had all-fresh primaries by 29 September while others (adults?) were still in active wing-moult three-plus months later: between P4–5 and P7 in January, at P10 in late February (AWB, UMBRP). The body-plumage cycle is not well known but adults are in advanced to full summer colours by time of departure.

CONSERVATION. At greater than average risk from habitat-deterioration through concentrating at only a few sites; would benefit long-term from the effective protection and management of Tengah island.

Red Knot; Nok Not Lek (Thai); Burung Kedidi Dian Kecil (Malay)

Calidris canutus (Linnaeus) 1758, *Systema Naturae* 10(1): 149. TL Sweden.
Plate 32

GROUP RELATIONS. Probably free-standing.

GLOBAL RANGE. Breeds on high-arctic barrens and tundra, and islands of the Arctic Ocean, in central to E Siberia, Alaska, Canada and Greenland. Winters from N- to S-temperate America, Atlantic Europe to W and southern Africa, in Sri Lanka (small numbers), and Australia and Oceania to New Zealand. Apparently mainly on passage through tropical E and SE Asia.

IDENTIFICATION/DESCRIPTION. Shape similar to Great Knot. From it in winter by smaller size (useful in direct comparison), proportionately shorter, thicker bill, and rump and upper tail-coverts heavily marked grey, near-uniform with grey tail. From Curlew Sandpiper in summer colours by superior size, more hunched stance, proportionately shorter, straight bill and, in flight, grey rather than contrastingly white upper tail-coverts.

Bare-part colours. Iris dark brown; bill black; legs and feet dull grey-green (BMP5).

Size (mm). (Skins and live: 1 male, 4 females; adult): wing 149 and 163–165; tail 49 (male only); bill 31.5–32.8 (sexes combined); tarsus 28.9 (male only) (AWB, ZRCNUS).

Weight (g). Two in August and January, 97 and 105; one in mid March (plumage 75 percent summer and perhaps already fattening for migration), 120 (AWB).

DISTRIBUTION. Historical summary: *Sur, Kra, Tra, Pat, Ked, Pek, Phg, Sel, Sin*, with W-coast island records from Libong and Tengah.

GEOGRAPHICAL VARIATION. Gibson-Hill (1949) identified a November first-winterer as nominate *canutus*, but all non-juvenile bills measured fall in the range of E-Siberian *rogersi* Mathews 1913 (TL Japan), shorter than *canutus* as seen in Europe (BWP). Summer-plumage variables have not been checked.

STATUS AND POPULATION. Passage migrant, absent during mid December–early February, and a possible occasional over-summerer; local and sparse to uncommon. Spring concentrations occur in SE Sumatra and the Gulf of Bangkok (BBCB-6, Silvius *et al.* 1987) but only a few stop in the Peninsula, on either journey. Highest individual counts have been ten and 33, at Kapar (Selangor) on 31 August and 19 March. Otherwise in ones and twos, scattered along the W coast between Krabi and Selangor (BBCB-8, BR 1978–79, ENGGANG-2, Sebastian *et al.* 1993), on the E coast at Bandon and Pattani bays and the Pahang estuary (Howes *et al.* 1986, Boonsong and Round 1991,

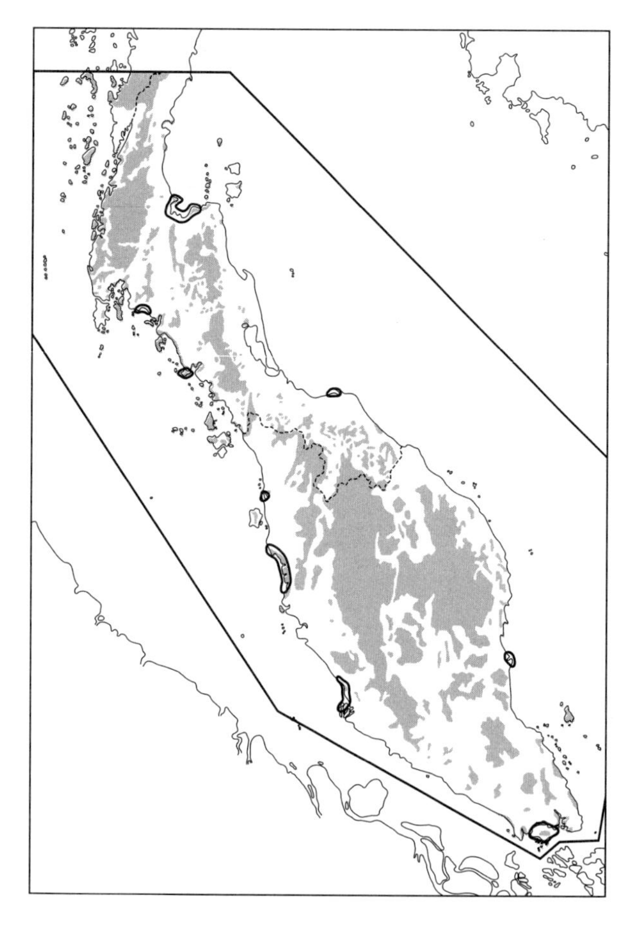

Ruttanadakul and Ardseungnern 1987), and in Singapore (Gibson-Hill 1949, BR 1980–81).

HABITATS AND ECOLOGY. Proportionately few sightings on Libong and Tengah islands imply Red and Great Knots may prefer different intertidal foraging substrates, but most records of Red have been at high-tide roosts and the point has not been checked directly. An early September loner at a fresh-water site in the Bujang valley, Kedah (R. Gregory-Smith), is exceptional and likely to have been migrating. Uses the same mixed-species roosts on remote beaches and in mangrove-zone clearings as Great Knot.

FORAGING AND FOOD. No information.

SOCIAL ORGANIZATION. No information.

MOVEMENTS. Extreme dates are 7 July and 13 May (AWB, BCSTB-13, MBR 1986–87), in Selangor and Krabi, which is where most Red Knot have been recorded. The July bird was a one-year-old and could have over-summered locally (there are comparable dates from the opposite Sumatran coast: CLBS).

SURVIVAL. No information.

SOCIAL INTERACTIONS. No information.

VOICE. A brief, low-pitched *nyut nyut*, repeated; rather like Great Knot.

BREEDING. No population.

MOULT. Relic summer plumage recorded to early September and, in spring, advanced adults have renewed to an late stage by early March (AWB, BR 1980–81, ZRCNUS). At Kapar, a second-summerer dated 7 July had renewed the wing-tip (P9–10) only, i.e., had not started complete wing-moult. A late August non-juvenile was growing P8–10 (P1–7 fresh), and another on 23 November had completed.

CONSERVATION. See Whimbrel for general issues.

Sanderling; Nok Khaw San Din Wai (Thai); Burung Kedidi Pesisir (Malay)

Calidris alba (Pallas) 1764, Vroeg's *Beredeneerde Catalogus, Adumbratiunculae*: 7. TL North Sea coasts.
Plate 34

GROUP RELATIONS. Free-standing.

GLOBAL RANGE. Breeds on coastal tundra and islands of the Arctic Ocean, to above latitude 80°N, in Spitzbergen, Siberia from Taimyr to the Lena delta, Alaska, Canada and N Greenland. Winters on coasts from the N- to the S-temperate zones around the world, in Asia in the Indian subcontinent and Sri Lanka; S Japan and China south from Fujian including Taiwan; SE Asia to the Greater Sunda islands, Bali and the Philippines; and Wallacea, Australia and Oceania, straggling to New Zealand.

IDENTIFICATION/DESCRIPTION. A small, actively running, in winter strikingly white wader, with pale, dove-grey upper body and noticeable black lesser wing-coverts. In flight, black leading-edge of wing contrasts with bold white bar across flight-feathers, and sides of rump to upper tail-coverts show white against a dark centre.

Bare-part colours. Iris dark brown; bill black; legs and feet black.

Size (mm). (Skins: 1 first-winterer, 1 adult; not sexed): wing 120, 124; tail 43, 47; bill 25.3, 25.4; tarsus 25.6, 25.4 (ZRCNUS).

Weight. No data.

DISTRIBUTION. Historical summary: *Ran, Pha, Kra, Tra, Son, Pat, Sat, Pek, Phg, Sel, Mel, Joh, Sin,* including Libong island and Hantu, Singapore.

GEOGRAPHICAL VARIATION. None recognized.

STATUS AND POPULATION. A passage migrant and non-breeding visitor, with no evidence yet of any over-summering; sparse to common but very local. The only recognized regular wintering-site is the sandy, in-filled coast of Changi promontory, E end of Singapore island, adopted in the late 1970s and recently supporting a mid-winter peak of 70-plus birds (BR 1978–79, SINGAV-6) – but unlikely to remain attractive for much longer. Thai Muang beach, Phangnga, with parties totalling about 75 on 18 February could be another, and a loner has occurred on Libong island in late January (BCSTB-13, Holmes and Wells 1975). Elsewhere, a thin scatter of passage migrants recorded along the W coast between Ranong and Melaka, and between Songkhla and Jason's bay (Johor) on the E coast, including peaks of 14 and 17 on Libong and at Pattani in November/December (Holmes and Wells 1975, MBR 1982–83, 1986–87, Parish 1985, Swennen *et al.* 1986).

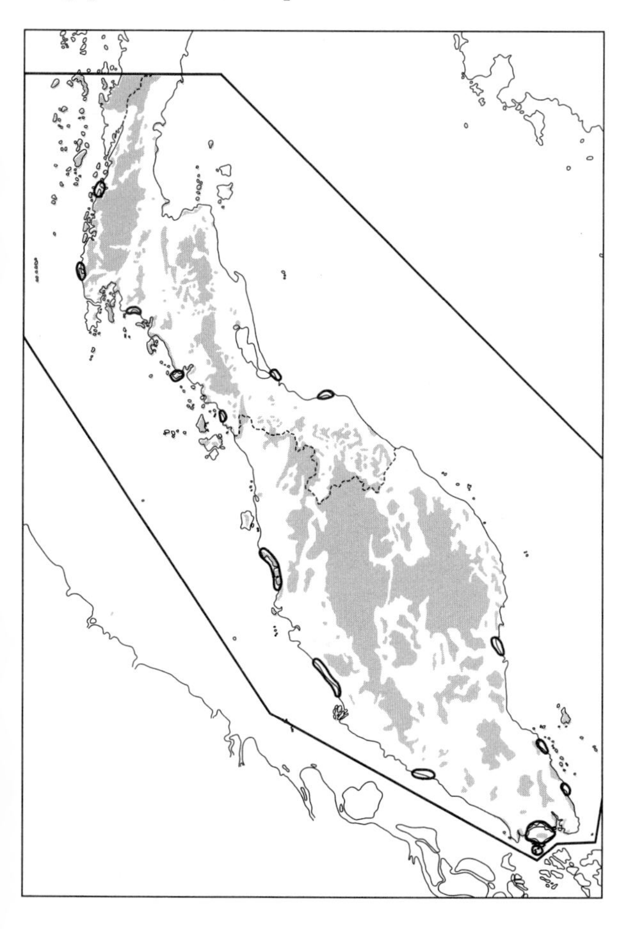

HABITATS AND ECOLOGY. A few records are from mudflats and tidal prawn-ponds (BMP5); most from beaches with high sand- or shell-content.

FORAGING AND FOOD. Food is located visually and picked from the surface while birds dash about actively, including at the edge of retreating surf.

SOCIAL ORGANIZATION. Where numerous, tends to forage in parties.

MOVEMENTS. 22 July at Changi (SINGAV-2) is the earliest date, with counts into double figures before the end of the month, rising irregularly to a peak presence in Singapore during January–March. Later spring records are sparse everywhere, up to 24 May at Melaka (MBR 1982–83).

SURVIVAL. No information.

SOCIAL INTERACTIONS. No information.

VOICE. No local information.

BREEDING. No population.

MOULT. Autumn activity not recorded. An adult dated 19 December had renewed seven primaries and was growing P8–9. Three presumed adults near Mersing and seven at Jason's bay (E Johor) on 2 and 3 May were all in full summer plumage, but an immature dated 8 April had not begun any moult (MBR 1986–87, ZRCNUS).

CONSERVATION. An opportunist. The Changi site became attractive as a result of large-scale filling. This process continues around the coast of Singapore and should ensure habitat in the medium term. The naturally sandy mainland E coast is perhaps too exposed to the NE monsoon to be attractive through the winter.

Little Stint; Nok Stint Lek (Thai); Burung Kedidi Kecil (Malay)

Calidris minuta (Leisler) 1812, *Nachträge zu Bechstein's Naturgeschichte Deutschlands*: 74. TL Hanau am Main, Germany.

Plate 33

GROUP RELATIONS. Probably free-standing. Assuming they actually are close relatives, extent of breeding overlap with *C. ruficollis* (Red-necked Stint) implies divergence past superspecies status.

GLOBAL RANGE. Breeds on coastal tundra and islands of the Arctic Ocean, from Scandinavia to approximately 140°E in NE Siberia. Winters through Africa and around the Indian Ocean to the Indian subcontinent, Sri Lanka and the Andamans; with a thin scatter of records through E and SE Asia to the Philippines, New Guinea, Australia, and Oceania as far as Hawaii.

IDENTIFICATION/DESCRIPTION. Small size. From winter Red-necked Stint by more finely tapering bill with slight decurvature of the lower margin, rather that thick and straight throughout; also by proportionately slightly longer legs. Head and neck are a shade browner, throwing pale supercilium into greater relief, and upperparts are mottled darker, less frosty grey. At close range, before autumn moult is complete, retained median and greater wing-coverts show a dark-brown centre and shaft and pale chestnut margin with white tip, whereas they are pale grey with just the shaft dark in Red-necked Stint (D.N. Bakewell; Veit and Jonsson 1987).

In the hand, two ratios separate from Red-necked Stint: wing/tarsus less than 4.9; and wing/bill-length from front edge of nostril less than 7.0 (data from fresh-plumaged Indian winterers) (Hayman *et al.* 1986, UMBRP, ZRCNUS).

Bare-part colours. Iris dark brown; bill black; legs and feet blackish.

Size (mm). (Live: 1 adult, not sexed): wing 98; tail not measured; bill 18.5; tarsus 22.0 (UMBRP). Ratios wing/tarsus and wing/bill-from-front-edge-nostril: 4.45 and 6.41.

Weight (g). The May adult, 30.0 (UMBRP).

DISTRIBUTION. Historical summary: *Sel*.

GEOGRAPHICAL VARIATION. None recognized.

STATUS AND POPULATION. Vagrant: a winter adult, passed over as *ruficollis* when ringed at Kuala Selangor on 17 November 1978, retrapped there in full summer plumage the following 3 May (BR 1978–79); another at the same site on 30 September–1 October 1987 (ENGGANG-1).

HABITATS AND ECOLOGY. Both captures were at a mixed-species roost on bare ground of a large

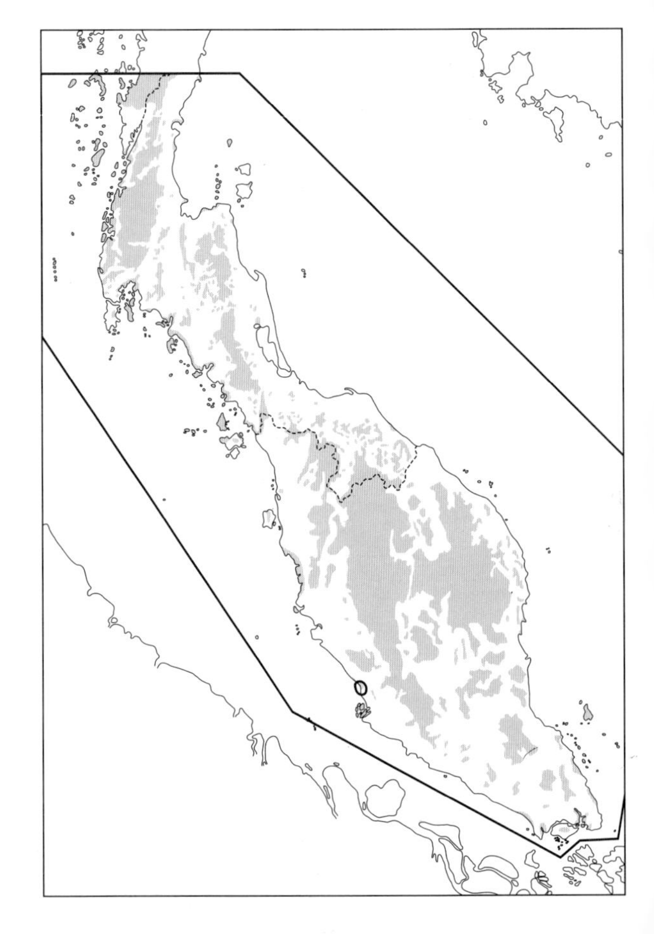

clearing in the mangrove zone, and the 1987 bird was foraging at a new scrape some 300 m in from the shoreline.

FORAGING AND FOOD. Picks from the surface during moderate-paced walking and while wading, into deeper water than used by Red-necked Stint (D.N. Bakewell).

SOCIAL ORGANIZATION. No information.

MOVEMENTS. No information.

SURVIVAL. No information.

SOCIAL INTERACTIONS. No information.

VOICE. Flight-call on release after ringing a soft, *sik sik sik sik . . .* (UMBRP).

BREEDING. No population.

MOULT. The September bird stood out from a number of accompanying Red-necked and Long-toed Stints as the only individual still showing part-summer colours (worn breast, scapulars, tertials and some wing-coverts (D.N. Bakewell). As stated, the May bird was already back in full summer plumage. There is no local information on flight-feather moult.

CONSERVATION. No specific issues.

Red-necked Stint; Nok Stint Khaw Daeng (Thai); Burung Kedidi Leher Merah (Malay)

Calidris ruficollis (Pallas) 1776, *Reise durch verschiedene Provinzen des Russischen Reichs* 3: 220 and 700. TL Kulusutay, far-E Russia.

Plate 33

GROUP RELATIONS. Probably free-standing (see Little Stint).

GLOBAL RANGE. Breeds in Siberian coastal tundra from Taimyr east to Chukotka, and in W Alaska. In winter, some reach the Bay of Bengal islands, S India and a few E Africa, but the main winter range covers S Japan, far-S China including Taiwan and Hainan; SE Asia; Wallacea, New Guinea, Australia (where, except in the north, it is the most numerous migratory wader), and Oceania as far as New Zealand.

IDENTIFICATION/DESCRIPTION. The rufous face and front of full summer plumage is distinctive. Half-moulted and in winter, confusable in the field with very much rarer Little Stint and, potentially, Spoon-billed Sandpiper (see both). From similar-sized winter Temminck's Stint by more mottled upperparts, white versus grey breast, black versus yellow-olive legs, and different vocalizations. In flight, all of these species show a blackish centre and white sides to the rump and upper tail-coverts, and narrow but obvious white wing-bar.

Bare-part colours. Iris dark brown; bill black; legs and feet black.

Size (mm). (Live: a 3-figure sample; age/sex-classes not separated): wing 93–108; tail 42–48; bill 16.3–19.6; tarsus 19.1–20.3. Ratios wing/tarsus and wing/bill-from-front-edge-nostril: 4.90–5.39 and 7.01–7.59 (AWB, UMBRP).

Weight (g). In Selangor and Singapore, 95 percent of weights taken year-round are in the range 18–31 (n=300), and monthly modal values vary only in the range 22–24. On the W coast, no regular weight-increase occurs in spring and most of this early-departing population is presumed to fatten elsewhere (AWB, UMBRP). However, a few individuals in samples for September, October, November and January reached 35–37, representing a part of the population evidently preparing to move on at mid season.

DISTRIBUTION. Historical summary: all divisions except *Pak, Chu, Pha, Pht, Son, Sat, Yal, Nar, Pes, Tru, Neg, Mel,* with additional island records from Libong, Penang and Tengah off the W coast; and Ubin, Singapore.

GEOGRAPHICAL VARIATION. None recognized.

STATUS AND POPULATION. Passage migrant and a non-breeding visitor; more or less regular, and

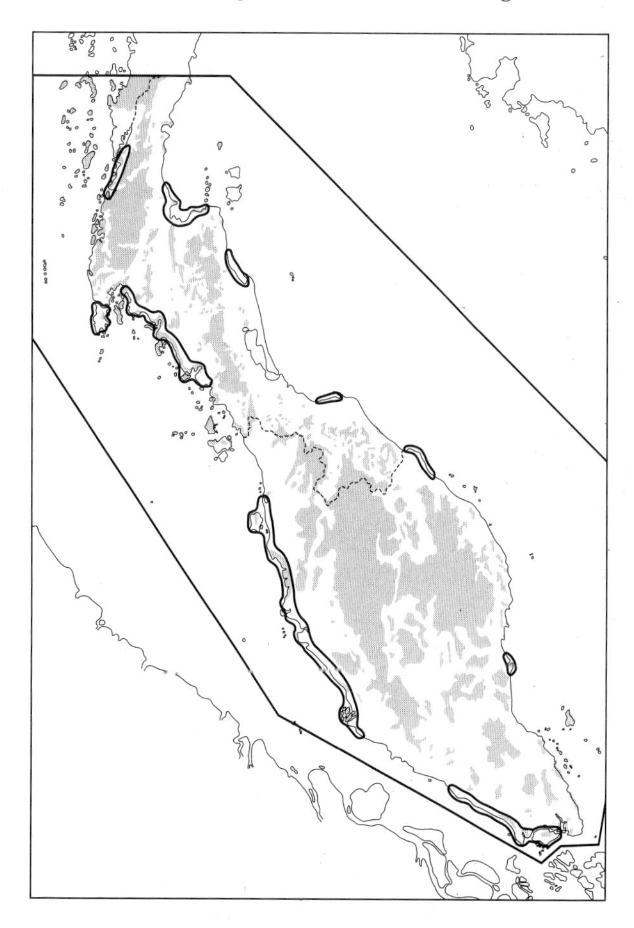

uncommon to very common, with some over-summering (counts of up to 170 on the mainland Selangor coast and smaller numbers at Pattani bay and Singapore). Few appear to use the NW at any time, but numerous in the NE. Up to 1350 counted in Pattani bay in autumn, and around half that number remain through winter, departing mainly in March (Ruttanadakul and Ardseungnern 1987). On the Melaka Straits coast, the winter build-up is postponed until November, but then common until spring, with high counts recorded south from mainland Penang (up to 800 at Perak sites, 400 in Selangor) (BR 1964, 1972–73, ENGGANG-2, MBR 1986–87, Silvius *et al.* 1987). No mid-season, E–W shift between coasts has actually been demonstrated, but relative trends make this is a possibility. Few winter in the far south, but some high passage-season counts (up to 800 in autumn) have been made in Singapore (Ollington and Loh 1992).

First-winterers appear in early September, become common in mist-netted samples in the third week and by the end of the month have constituted up to 40 percent of birds handled.

HABITATS AND ECOLOGY. Predominantly on intertidal flats, but visits tidal prawn-rearing ponds cut into the mangrove zone, and a few stop at open, freshwater wetlands, including the margins of old dredge-mine lagoons, part-flooded paddyland, etc., possibly mainly when pushed off regular habitat by high tides. Roosts on the ground and is attracted to shallow flooding in large clearings within the mangrove zone.

FORAGING AND FOOD. On the coast, shows a 76 percent preference for soft muds, against 20 for consolidated mud and only four for harder mud/sand mixes (Swennen and Marteijn 1985), which may account for scarcity around Krabi and Libong, and the small numbers using Tengah island relative to the nearby mainland coast (Silvius *et al.* 1987). Polychaetes appear to be the main prey, although no value has been put on small, unidentified items picked from the surface. Sludge-drying beds rich in dipteran larvae formerly attracted many to the Serangoon sewage treatment works, E end of Singapore (BR 1976–77).

SOCIAL ORGANIZATION. Gregarious on the move and at roosts, mixing with other, mainly small wader species; more dispersed when foraging.

MOVEMENTS. Autumn passage at Pattani bay and in Singapore runs from August through October, but with no evidence of a return halt at Pattani in spring. By April few birds remain there, whereas sizeable waves of migrants stop on E Singapore and Pahang coasts to late April or early May (BR 1976–77, Howes *et al.* 1986).

The W-coast pattern is different again, with no autumn peaking and most spring passage over in early April, which implies the Peninsula may be partitioned between populations on slightly different schedules. At Kuala Selangor, only 12 of 554 birds ringed during the 1970s were retrapped on site within the same season, most before November, which suggests that the mid-winter surge might be associated with onward movements (BR 1978–79). However, an early September bird retrapped in February and a March juvenile still present on 1 June showed that some birds stay long-term at this site.

SURVIVAL. The longest retrap-interval is 53 months, a bird back at site of ringing in Selangor (BR 1976–77).

SOCIAL INTERACTIONS. No information.

VOICE. The flight-call is a soft, repeated *prit*.

BREEDING. No population.

MOULT. First-winterers reach Selangor in part-juvenile plumage, body-moult suspended. It re-starts by October and most finish before the end of that month; none later than January. Identified by the odd retained median wing-covert, as of early January a few begin a complete wing-moult from P1. Most delay until at least early March then renew only the wing-tip, starting anywhere between P7 and 10, and some have not begun this even by late June. At the same time, many acquire partial summer colours – usually only a scattering of body-feathers (AWB, UMBRP).

Non-juveniles have lost most or all summer plumage by the time they arrive, and start to regain it in late winter. On the W coast, advanced birds are half-complete by early March, but year-classes have not been well-separated and some of the part-moulted birds around in April, giving the impression of departure before completion, may be first-winterers rather than adults.

Non-juveniles start a complete wing-moult in late summer (e.g., P3–4 growing on 10 August, at this stage often with all inner feathers in overlapping growth). Advanced birds are near to finishing (between P7 and 10) by mid September, and most have done so by late October. Mid-winter suspensions, noted during late October–late December, may account for a minority completing during late December–early March (AWB, UMBRP).

CONSERVATION. See Whimbrel for issues affecting shoreline waders generally.

Temminck's Stint; Nok Stint Ok Thao (Thai); **Burung Kedidi Temminck** (Malay)

Calidris temminckii (Leisler) 1812, *Nachträge zu Bechstein's Naturgeschichte Deutschlands*: 64. TL Hanau am Main, Germany.

Plate 33

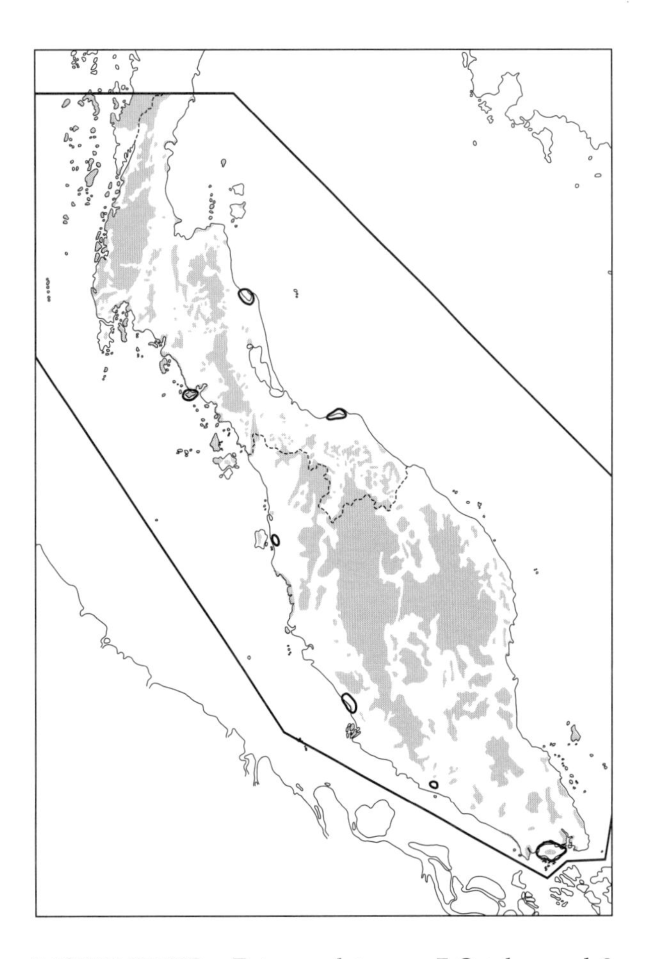

GROUP RELATIONS. Free-standing.

GLOBAL RANGE. Breeds in arctic and subarctic tundra and meadowland from Norway east to Anadyrland and Chukotka. Winters around the Mediterranean and in northern Africa and SW Asia; the Indian subcontinent, Sri Lanka and Andamans; S Japan and China south from Fujian including Taiwan; and SE Asia to the Peninsula, Borneo and the W Philippines, but the main eastern migration terminus is continental. Vagrant W Micronesia.

IDENTIFICATION/DESCRIPTION. Has the same horizontal, hunched stance as Little and Red-necked Stints, but leg-colour differs and, in winter, plainer upperparts and fairly sharply demarcated, unstreaked grey breast are characteristic. Independent of size, any resemblance to Common Sandpiper is dispelled by lack of teetering behaviour, flight-action (high-climbing escape and lack of wing-flicking), calls, and black-and-white upper tail-covert pattern. Outer tail-feathers are white, but this is not easily seen in the field.

Bare-part colours. Iris dark brown; bill black, some with a pale lower base; legs and feet dull yellowish green.

Size (mm). (Skin: 1 non-juvenile female): wing 95; tail 38; bill 17.4; tarsus 17.5 (ZRCNUS).

Weight. No data.

DISTRIBUTION. Historical summary: *Nak, Pat, Pra, Sel, Mel, Sin*, and on Libong island (*Tra*).

GEOGRAPHICAL VARIATION. None recognized.

STATUS AND POPULATION. A non-breeding visitor recorded in all months October–March and May, with no evidence of onward movements; local and uncommon to common (BR 1967, Gibson-Hill 1949b, MBR 1984–85). Mostly solitary, rarely more than 2–3 seen together, but a few larger counts have been made in the north, including eight at Libong island and 80 in Pattani bay, in December–January (Parish 1985).

HABITATS AND ECOLOGY. Wet grassland, paddyland channels, the margins of dredge-mine lagoons, freshwater fish-ponds and open-ground flood-pools, salt-marsh, and cleared areas of back-mangrove (BR 1978–79, Gibson-Hill 1949b, Parish 1985). A few records are from tide-flushed prawn-ponds but only one definitely from an intertidal flat (MBR 1984–85).

FORAGING AND FOOD. No information.

SOCIAL ORGANIZATION. No specific information.

MOVEMENTS. Extreme dates are 7 October and 8 May, in Selangor and Singapore (BR 1967, MBR 1984–85). Generally late autumn arrival compared with other wintering *Calidris* implies the Peninsula is a secondary destination, reached perhaps as favoured freshwater sites on the continent begin to dry out (see also Eurasian Woodcock, and Swinhoe's and Common Snipe).

SURVIVAL. No information.

SOCIAL INTERACTIONS. No information.

VOICE. The flight call is a persistent, high-pitched trill (BR 1978–79).

BREEDING. No population.

MOULT. A bird dated 13 March, age-group uncertain, had renewed P1–7 and was growing P8–9 (10 still old) (ZRCNUS).

CONSERVATION. No critical issues.

Long-toed Stint; Nok Stint Niw Yao (Thai); Burung Kedidi Jari Panjang (Malay)

Calidris subminuta (Middendorff) 1853, *Reise in den äussersten Norden und Osten Sibiriens* 2(2): 222 and plate 19. TL Uda river-mouth, Stanovoi Range, SE Russia.

Plate 33

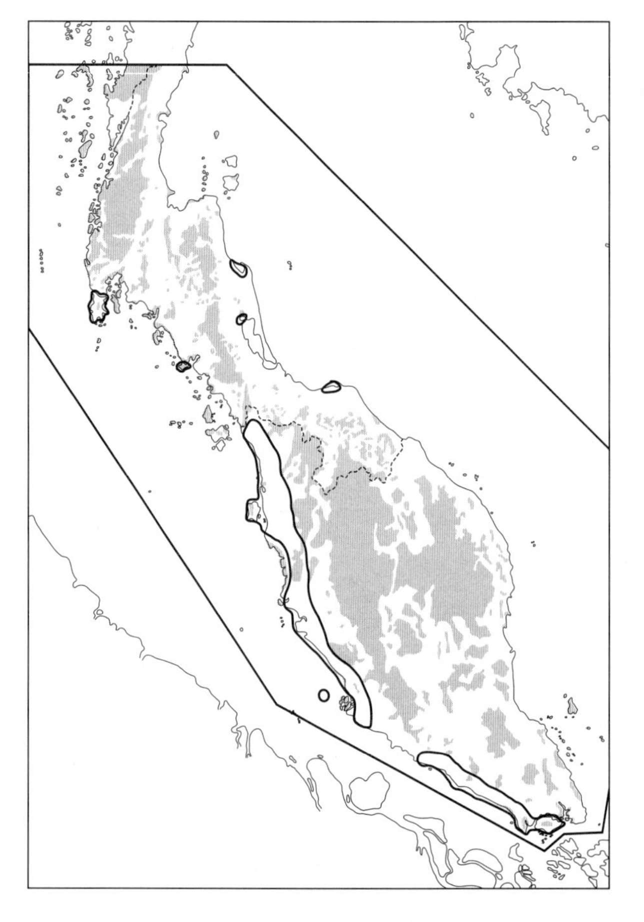

GROUP RELATIONS. Uncertain; closest to American *C. pusilla* (Least Sandpiper).

GLOBAL RANGE. Breeds in the boreal forest zone of Siberia from the Ob river to Anadyrland, south in the far east to Kamchatka and Amurland. Winters in the eastern Indian subcontinent, Sri Lanka and Andamans; S Japan and far-S China (Taiwan, Guangdong); SE Asia to the Greater Sunda islands, Bali and the Philippines; and small numbers reach Sulawesi, W Micronesia and (mainly W) Australia.

IDENTIFICATION/DESCRIPTION. From other local stints by its less hunched posture, often peering with upstretched neck like a *Tringa*, and in flight by narrower wing-bar. Pale supercilium contrasts with crown; neck and breast are finely but obviously streaked; and legs are dull yellowish (cf. Temminck's Stint). In the hand, uniquely among local *Calidris*, the mid-toe is longer than the tarsus.

Bare-part colours. Iris dark brown; bill black with paler lower base; legs and feet dull yellowish or greenish yellow.

Size (mm). (Live: a 3-figure sample of non-juveniles; none sexed): wing 86–98; tail 36–43; bill 16.9–19.4; tarsus 20.9–23.3; mid-toe plus claw 22.9–26.0 (UMBRP).

Weight (g). A large early September–early March sample, all age-classes, 18.3–28.1. Two non-juveniles in summer plumage on 29 April were slightly heavier: 31.5 and 35.0 (UMBRP), but this is the only evidence of pre-migratory fattening before departure.

DISTRIBUTION. Mostly the W-coast plain. Historical summary: *Nak, Phu, Pht, Pat, Pes, Ked, Pra, Pek, Sel, Mel, Joh, Sin,* including records from Libong (*Tra*) and Penang islands.

GEOGRAPHICAL VARIATION. None recognized.

STATUS AND POPULATION. A non-breeding visitor showing some evidence of passage migration (mid-season declines and a November strike on One-Fathom Bank lighthouse, Melaka Straits). Small numbers reported over the mid summer period in Singapore during the 1960s (BR 1964), but no summer records anywhere since. Regular, and uncommon to common. Some localized censusing has been carried out in parts of Singapore, but estimates of abundance elsewhere have generally been from small patches of foraging habitat that give no key to total numbers. Little known in the Thai provinces, except at Thalae Noi and around Pattani bay where mid-winter counts have reached 630 (Ruttanadakul and Ardseungnern 1987, U. Treesucon). South of the border, not yet reported east of the Main Range. On Malaysian W-coast paddylands generally accepted as common, but searches of Perak and Selangor during February–April 1993 found very few indeed, concentrated onto the odd field that had escaped post-harvest herbicide treatment. In this area at least, Long-toed Stint appears to have joined many resident paddyland waterbirds in needing conservation action. Recent numbers in Singapore are also far below former totals, following outright loss of habitat since the start of the national land-claim programme.

HABITATS AND ECOLOGY. Rare on intertidal flats. Good numbers formerly made regular use of tide-flushed prawn-ponds (now reclaimed) in Singapore (BR 1963, 1964), but the greater preference is for brackish to freshwater habitats, especially pool-margins in cleared back-mangrove areas, fallow to freshly cultivated paddyland, the open edges of old dredge-mine lagoons, fish-ponds, etc., and wet grazing-land – all essentially artificial habitats in the Peninsula. At Kuala Selangor in the 1970s, many roosted with other waders on shallow ponds in a large area of cleared mangroves.

FORAGING AND FOOD. In a recent survey, five percent of foraging preference was for bare, dry mud, six percent for pond-margins and 89 for open, wet fields, including paddyfields; emphasizing concern over the impact of agricultural chemicals. Food uninvestigated.

SOCIAL ORGANIZATION. Roosts gregariously, and daytime foragers associate loosely in small parties, probably partly as a function of the patchiness of prime feeding grounds.

MOVEMENTS. Extreme early arrival dates are 21 July (Senoko wetland, Singapore) and 23 July (Kuala Selangor), followed within a week at Kuala Selangor by the first substantial wave of returnees (BR 1976–77, SINGAV-4). Site-counts have reached three figures as of September/October, with a dip in the south by November but not before January around Pattani bay. On the Melaka Straits coast, numbers recover in March (Parish and Wells 1984, Silvius *et al.* 1987) and main departure is in April, but with flocks of up to 200 reported in Selangor as late as 26 April. Everywhere, only small numbers remain into May, the latest date in recent years being 17 May (a loner at Serangoon, Singapore) (BR 1972–73, Ruttanadakul and Ardseungnern 1987, SINGAV-2).

SURVIVAL. The longest retrap interval is 47 months, a bird back on its site of ringing at the Kuala Selangor wader roost (UMBRP).

SOCIAL INTERACTIONS. No information.

VOICE. The flight-call is a soft, purring *treep* or *treet*.

BREEDING. No population.

MOULT. Almost everything known about the winter cycle is based on 215 birds handled for ringing at Kuala Selangor in the 1970s (UMBRP).

First-winterers showed no body-moult before mid September but no definite juvenile plumage was seen later than 5 October. The only evidence this year-class may moult flight-feathers before spring departure is from a bird dated 30 April showing P1–8 older than 9–10.

Non-juveniles return in full summer plumage but are in heavy body-moult by late August, and by then virtually all also show wing-moult. One active at two loci (P1 and 8) on 2 September is likely to have been a second-summerer. Fifteen others on the same day had renewed at least P1–4, a few out to P8, and by 30 September advanced individuals had finished. Most of the rest were at finishing-point by mid October (a few still at P7 or 8 on 14 October) and no moult was seen later than this. For unknown reasons, Long-toed Stint rushes flight-feather replacement, regularly with five adjacent inner then as many as four outer primaries and up to six secondaries in overlapping growth, and commonly the full tail in moult – a performance unmatched by any other local wader. From retrapping of marked birds and dates of latest start and finish, individuals may renew all primaries in only 50–75 days.

In spring, first signs of renewal of breeding-colours are in early March and adults reach full plumage in April. At least some immatures also acquire partial breeding-colours (BR 1972–73, UMBRP).

CONSERVATION. The situation of this species in paddylands demands urgent attention.

Sharp-tailed/Pectoral Sandpiper; Nok Chailaen Gra-mawm Daeng (Thai)/(no Thai name); Burung Kedidi Ekor Tirus/Burung Kedidi Pektoral (Malay)

Calidris acuminata (Horsfield) 1821, *Transactions of the Linnean Society* 13(1): 192. TL Java.

Calidris melanotos (Vieillot) 1819, *Nouveau Dictionnaire d'Histoire Naturelle* 34: 462. TL Paraguay.

Plate 34

GROUP RELATIONS. Uncertain; even if closely related, no longer at superspecies level.

GLOBAL RANGE. Both breed in arctic tundra: Sharp-tailed in Siberia from the Lena delta east possibly to Chukotka; Pectoral over a wider range, from Taimyr to Chukotka and also in Alaska and Canada. Sharp-tailed winters in southern Australia and, in small numbers, New Zealand; is regular on passage west to Borneo and straggles as far as India and Sri Lanka. Pectoral winters mainly in S-hemisphere S America, reached via N America, and in small numbers in New Zealand and Australia. Some migrate though Oceania, but a separate Asian route has still to be confirmed.

IDENTIFICATION/DESCRIPTION. Medium-small waders of standard calidrine shape, and tricky to separate in winter; both with streaked breast and prominent white supercilium. The breast is either sharply demarcated against plain white underparts (Pectoral) or streaking continues onto flanks (Sharp-tail). The supercilium broadens behind the eye (Sharp-tail) or in front of it, bordered below by a distinct, black loral line and constricting the dark forecrown to a median stripe (Pectoral).

Bare-part colours. Iris dark brown in both; bill blackish, with yellow extreme base in Pectoral (R.P. Jaensch); legs and feet pale, dull yellowish or yellowish green in both.

Size. No data.

Weight. No data.

DISTRIBUTION. Historical summary: *Pat, Ked, Sel, Sin*, and on Penang island.

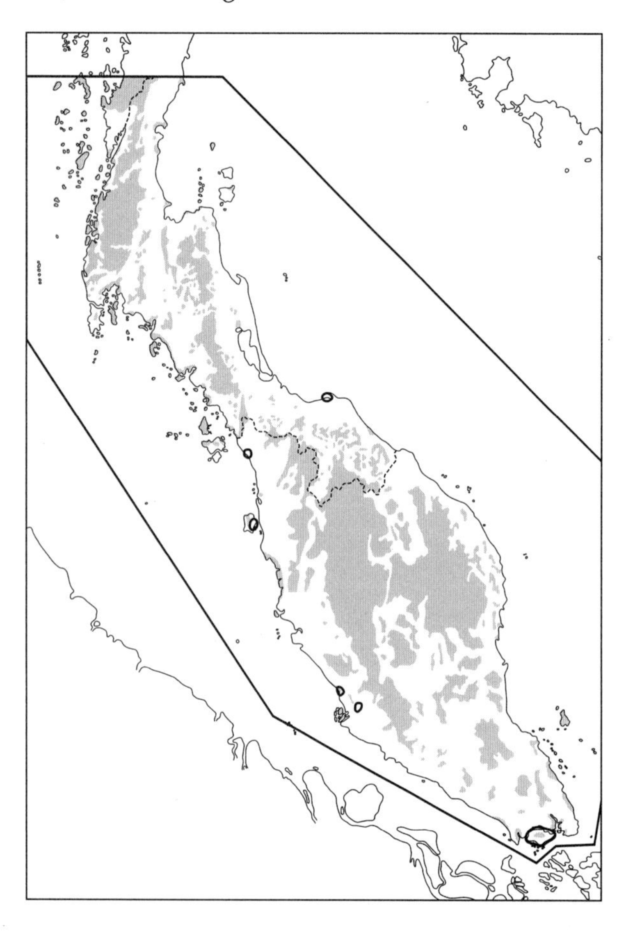

GEOGRAPHICAL VARIATION. None recognized.

STATUS AND POPULATION. Together, hardly more than vagrant, with only nine records (no specimens), from Pattani bay and the Kedah/Perlis border south to Singapore, in September–November, January, March and early May (BR 1972–73, 1980–81, MBR 1984–85, 1986–87), leaving open the possibility of occasional overwintering.

Three reports, up to January, cite a contrasting rufous cap typical of juvenile or summer-plumaged Sharp-tail, and an October bird in Singapore gave a Sharp-tail type of flight-call. Among others, two on intertidal mud at Georgetown (Penang) in March and sandflats behind the coastal bund at Kuala Selangor in May showed the underside pattern of Pectoral but not its bill and head details, which are believed to be diagnostic (R.P. Jaensch), hence identifications remain tentative. Finally, after comparison with the unique description by Kasprzyk *et al.* (1987), a buff-toned, Curlew Sandpiper-shaped bird with stint-like flight-pattern, probing in freshly exposed, tidal mud at Khatib Bongsu (Singapore) on 15 September 1991 has been proposed as a possible juvenile Cox's Sandpiper, the stable hybrid of Pectoral and Curlew Sandpiper (Ollington and Loh 1992).

HABITATS AND ECOLOGY. Sites include soft, intertidal mudflats, salt-marsh, an inland dredge-mine lagoon wetland and the bank of a Singapore reservoir.

FORAGING AND FOOD. No detailed information.

SOCIAL ORGANIZATION. In one case, two foraging together; all other records have been of loners.

MOVEMENTS. Extreme dates are 31 August and 1 May.

SURVIVAL. No information.

SOCIAL INTERACTIONS. No information.

VOICE. Locally described Sharp-tail-type flight-calls are a high-pitched, liquid *plip-plip* or *chu-weet*. Hayman *et al.* (1986) give the Pectoral equivalent as a loud, harsh, reedy *churk* or *trrit*, irregularly repeated.

BREEDING. No population.

MOULT. No data.

CONSERVATION. No relevant issues.

Dunlin; Nok Chailaen Thong Dam (Thai); Burung Kedidi Dunlin (Malay)

Calidris alpina (Linnaeus) 1758, *Systema Naturae* 10(1): 149. TL Lappland.
Plate 34

GROUP RELATIONS. Free-standing.

GLOBAL RANGE. Breeds in tundra and open moorland from the mid N-temperate zone to coasts and islands of the Arctic Ocean, in E Greenland and other N Atlantic islands, across Eurasia to Chukotka and in Alaska and N Canada. Winters in the N-temperate zone and outer N tropics around the world, in Asia south to northern coasts of the Indian subcontinent; and S Japan and China south from the Changjiang valley, including Taiwan and Hainan. Rare in S India and few enter SE Asia, straggling south to the Peninsula, Java, Borneo and Sulawesi. Occasional in the Pacific but reports as far as Australia are in doubt.

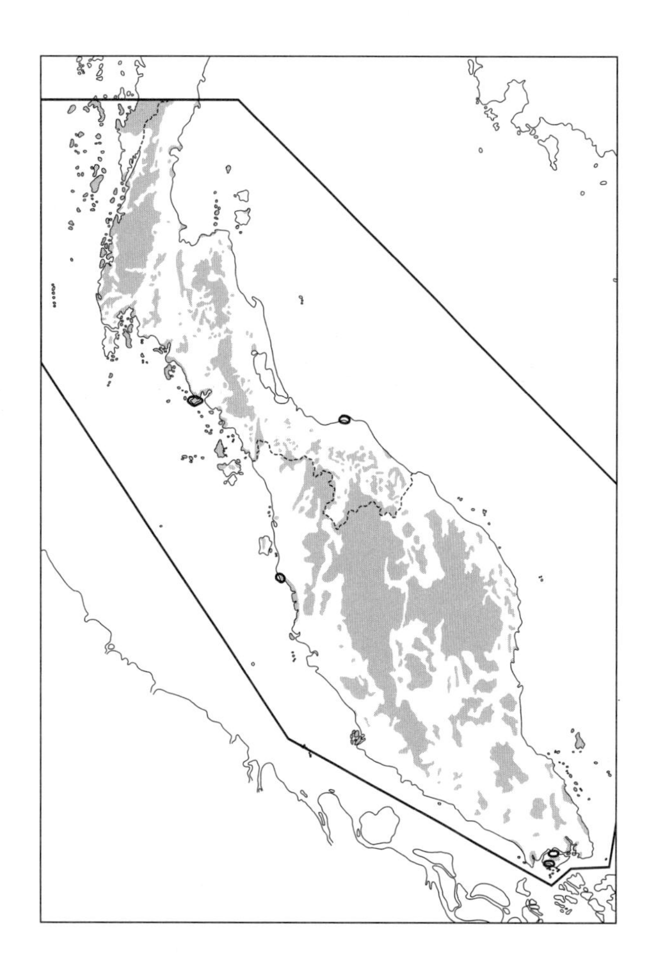

IDENTIFICATION/DESCRIPTION. A medium-small wader, about the size of Curlew Sandpiper but, seen on the ground, typically rather more hunched, proportionately slightly shorter in the leg and with bill droop-tipped rather than decurved (see also Broad-billed Sandpiper). The winter-plumage breast is darker grey, and more streaked than in Curlew Sandpiper, and supercilium less clear-cut. In flight, shows stint-like pattern of white wing-bar and upper tail-coverts black with white sides.

Bare-part colours. Iris dark brown; bill black; legs and feet black.

Size. No data.

Weight. No data.

DISTRIBUTION. Historical summary: *Pat, Pek, Sin,* including on Libong island (*Tra*).

GEOGRAPHICAL VARIATION. None handled or positively identified to subspecies.

STATUS AND POPULATION. Barely more than vagrant, and rarer than the Sharp-tailed/Pectoral Sandpiper pair, with only six records in the 30 years over which waders have been watched systematically. Apart from two birds on Libong island (Trang) on 15 April (J.A. Wolstencroft), all have been in autumn–early winter, including one associating with Broad-billed Sandpipers and Red-necked Stints in Pattani bay, one with Curlew Sandpipers at Belanak point, Perak, and in Singapore, one and four on tidal prawn-ponds (since reclaimed) at Jurong and a bird that stayed on the Senoko estuary for more than one month (BR 1964, 1968, 1969, 1980–81, Swennen *et al.* 1986).

HABITATS AND ECOLOGY. Strictly coastal, on low-tide mudflats and the exposed bed of tide-fed prawn-rearing ponds.

FORAGING AND FOOD. No local information.

SOCIAL ORGANIZATION. Strongly gregarious at loafing and roosting sites in the main winter range; up to four together locally.

MOVEMENTS. Extreme dates are 24 August and 15 April, with most records in November.

SURVIVAL. No information.

SOCIAL INTERACTIONS. No information.

VOICE. No local information.

BREEDING. No population.

MOULT. The birds at Senoko in September–early October and Pattani bay during early November were in full and part summer plumage (BR 1980–81, Swennen *et al.* 1986), hence not on the moult-schedule of the best-known eastern subspecies, *sakhalina*, which is said to complete body-moult before reaching its wintering area (BWP).

CONSERVATION. No relevant issues.

Curlew Sandpiper; Nok Chailaen Paak Gohng (Thai); Burung Kedidi Merah (Malay)

Calidris ferruginea (Pontoppidan) 1763, *Den danske Atlas eller Konge-riget Dannemark* 1: 624. TL Christiansø island, Denmark.

Plate 34

GROUP RELATIONS. Perhaps free-standing, but close enough to Pectoral Sandpiper, apparently, for occasional hybridization to occur (Mayr and Short 1970).

GLOBAL RANGE. Breeds on coasts and islands of the Arctic Ocean, in Siberia from the Yenisey to the Kolyma rivers and irregularly in N Alaska. Winters from the N tropics to 40°S, through Africa, the Malagasy region and around the Indian Ocean to the Indian subcontinent, Sri Lanka and Bay of Bengal islands; in extreme S China including Hainan; SE Asia to the Greater Sunda islands, Bali and the Philippines; Wallacea and W Micronesia to Australasia, with a few to New Zealand.

IDENTIFICATION/DESCRIPTION. A medium-small wader, proportionately longer-billed and longer-legged than other local calidrines, with posture typically more up-standing, less horizontal and hunched than, e.g., Broad-billed Sandpiper; bill decurved rather than merely droop-tipped. In summer colours, confusable only with same-stage Red Knot, which is brighter, larger, proportionately shorter-legged, with a shorter, straight bill. At all seasons, all-white rather than grey or dark-centred upper tail-coverts are distinctive in flight.

Bare-part colours. Iris dark brown; bill black; legs and feet black.

Size (mm). (Live: a 3-figure sample, age/sex-classes not separated): wing 122–136; tail 40–56; bill 32.0–44.5; tarsus 26.0–34.0 (UMBRP, AWB).

Weight (g). The year-round range among all age-groups in Selangor is 39–77. With data sorted by 5 g classes, modal values are not more than one rank above or below 51–55 in all months July–February. March shows a large group of first-winterers at 46–50 and smaller break-away peaks of older birds at 56–60 and 66–70 (maximum 72), evidently beginning the process of spring fattening. Too few have been caught in April–May to suggest typical spring departure weights from this coast, but a few July non-juveniles were at 70–80, newly arrived after fattening elsewhere and/or scheduled to move on (AWB, UMBRP). At 80-plus in Singapore, some autumn adults are likewise believed to have been ready to continue south (AWB, UMBRP).

DISTRIBUTION. Historical summary: all divisions except *Pak, Chu, Pha, Pht, Son, Sat, Yal, Nar, Tru, Neg*, with additional W-coast island records only from Libong, Penang, Tengah and Kukup (*Joh*).

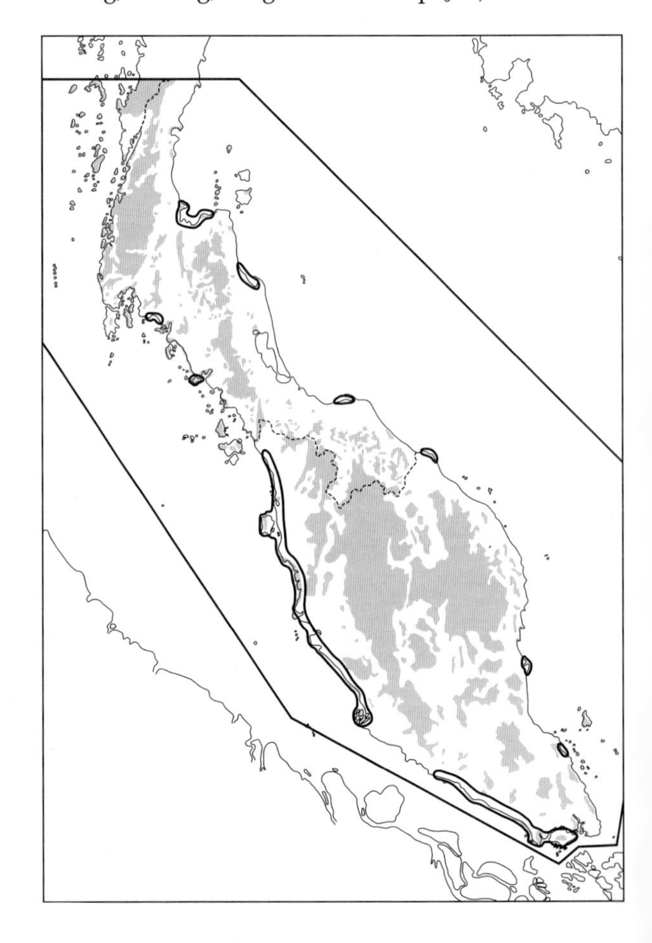

GEOGRAPHICAL VARIATION. None recognized.

STATUS AND POPULATION. A passage migrant and non-breeding visitor, with counts of up 250 over mid summer on the Selangor coast, in two figures at Pattani bay, and a single mid-June record from Bandon bay, but nowhere else at this season (MBR 1986–87, Robinson and Chasen 1936, Ruttanadakul and Ardseungnern 1987). Regular and uncommon to abundant.

Capture-rates at the Kuala Selangor roost during the 1970s (BR 1978–79) and direct, shoreline counting over the mid 1980s ranked Curlew Sandpiper second or third commonest wintering wader on the Melaka Straits coast, concentrated mainly between the Sanglang river (Perlis/Kedah border) and central Selangor, with 40-plus percent (up to 4000 in January) of an estimated 9000 total believed to overwinter at Tengah island, Kelang estuary (Parish and Wells 1984, Silvius *et al.* 1987). Up to 200 have occurred at Libong island (Trang) but few are there by mid winter (two-figure counts in December–January), and two birds at Krabi in late January are the only others recorded in the NW at that season (T. Lund, Parish 1985, P.D. Round). Use made of the far NE is still unclear. Pattani bay is occupied throughout but, again, holds very few by December (Parish 1985, Ruttanadakul and Ardseungnern 1987, Swennen *et al.* 1986). Along the Malaysian E coast, the only records are of a few birds on spring passage, with no more than a possibility of wintering around the Pahang river-mouth (57 roosting at Agas point on 11 February: Howes *et al.* 1986). Singapore shows a northern-type pattern, of relative abundance in autumn (before final loss of the Serangoon estuary, 800–1000 around the E end of the island in October) declining to near-zero by December, and no resurgence in spring (Ollington and Loh 1992, Parish and Wells 1984). Three-figure counts at Johor Straits sites (Senoko and Mandai) in January–February 1992 (SINGAV-6) imply an exceptional year.

Curlew Sandpipers are sexually dimorphic on bill-length, with only a narrow zone of overlap (Hayman *et al.* 1986). Taking 38.5 mm as the overlap mid-point, a distribution plot of 87 Selangor winterers identified 49 males and 38 females, suggesting a sex-ratio close to parity. The proportion of juveniles arriving in autumn has varied from 18 to 45 percent of mist-net catches (Parish and Wells 1984), presumed to reflect year-to-year fluctuations of breeding success in the arctic.

HABITATS AND ECOLOGY. Almost entirely intertidal, only occasionally visiting freshwater wetlands such as subcoastal paddyland and the margins of dredge-mine lagoons, perhaps when forced off regular grounds by extra-high tides. This is one of the wader species readily perching in mangrove trees, but open-ground sites are preferred and large numbers of Curlew Sandpipers join mixed-species roosts on remote beaches and bare clearings in the mangrove zone.

FORAGING AND FOOD. Swennen & Marteijn (1985) found an 89 percent preference for foraging on soft muds, against only 11 for consolidated substrates, which does not fit with the extent of firmer ground at the Tengah- and Libong-island concentration-points, and suggests a need for more studies. Polychaetes dominate over molluscs (both bivalves and gastropods) in the diet.

SOCIAL ORGANIZATION. Strongly gregarious on the move and at roosts, and sheer numbers of birds at Melaka Straits sites tend to overshadow other small species. Like many waders, more dispersed when foraging.

MOVEMENTS. Early moulting and/or fattening stops in the NW and NE may serve the Melaka Straits wintering area. This has not been confirmed, but ringing studies in Selangor and Singapore show the Peninsula hosts at least two populations, moving on different schedules.

Earliest autumn migrants are in Singapore as of 21 July, with site-counts in double figures by the end of the month and up to 550 by mid–late August. This is also the pattern of build-up in Pattani bay and the Melaka Straits, except that in the Straits numbers continue to rise through mid winter, merely dipping in February and resurging through March and April (Sebastian *et al.* 1993, Silvius *et al.* 1987). At Kuala Selangor, on-site retrapping of ringed birds has linked most months of the wintering period, as of late August. Second-summerers re-handled in early–mid July, after intervals of 6–9 months, may have stayed in the area year-round. In comparison, only two of over 200 birds plumage-dyed during August–September 1983 at Serangoon, Singapore, were spotted after release (as against regular sightings in and around the estuary of dyed Redshank, Black-tailed Godwit, etc.). They can only have moved away, and the proportion of non-moulting, unexpectedly heavy adults (a few over 80 g) implies many Curlew Sandpipers staging in Singapore are only part way through a much longer autumn migration. By early November that year, one dyed bird was at the Port Hedland saltworks, NW Australia, 3600 km away (MBR 1982–83, Parish and Wells 1984).

Other evidence that Curlew Sandpipers using parts of the Peninsula pass on to Australia comes from a late August Pattani bird recaptured in January in Westernport bay (Victoria), an October Serangoon bird recaptured in early March in Port Phillip bay (Victoria), and a February Victoria bird taken two months later back in Pattani bay (ABBBS, BR 1978–79, Mundkur *et al.* 1992). The Port Hedland region has been shown to be a regular staging area for this species, at least on the southward journey (Lane and Davis 1987).

Two recoveries of Selangor birds make northern connections. A January winterer recaptured in August, i.e., during its next southward migration, near the Kazakhstan/China border (76°05′E) and one in March ringed the previous autumn in Deep bay, Hong Kong (114°10′E) suggest complex routing through the temperate zone (BR 1980–81, Pook 1992).

SURVIVAL. The longest recovery-interval to date is 64 months (ABBBS). Among 1000 birds ringed at

Kuala Selangor during the 1970s, nine were retrapped on site in later seasons, including eight one year on and one three years on (interval 35 months) (UMBRP).

SOCIAL INTERACTIONS. New arrivals indulge in noisy group-chases, seen in Selangor at the end of July.

VOICE. In flight, a soft, rippling *cherrup*.

BREEDING. No population.

MOULT. First-winterers are identifiable from body-plumage until late October, and retain some inner median wing-coverts as late as early March. On the Selangor coast, first-winter wing-tip moult is universal, begins in early January, is general by early March and finishes during mid March–late May. One–six outer primaries are replaced but 50 percent of birds replace four, i.e., out from P7. This is the majority pattern also in Singapore but, unexpectedly, a small percentage of apparent second-year birds passing through Singapore in early autumn still showed all-juvenile flight-feathers (AWB, Parish and Wells 1984, UMBRP).

Some, but not all, juveniles acquire up to 30 percent summer body-plumage at a spring moult. As second-summerers, most lose this in August–September, when they also start a complete wing-moult (one growing P1–4 on 26 August), more or less on the schedule of adults. The latter arrive in various body-plumage states, up to near-full summer, but replace most of this by September. As of late August, they are also in wing-moult which, with up to five adjacent inner feathers in overlapping growth, is likely to start close to their arrival date. Records of stage P10 moult fall between 29 October and 7 February, which suggests some winterers suspend for a period; also that some southbound transients might not have finished wing-moult before they move on (Parish and Wells 1984).

In spring, adult body-moult back into summer colours can begin in late February but is not advanced until late March–April (AWB, BMP5).

CONSERVATION. See Whimbrel for issues also relevant to this species, especially along the Melaka Straits coast. Reclamation of the Serangoon estuary in Singapore deprived onward-moving, long-distance migrants of an important staging site, with unknown consequences for this population.

Spoon-billed Sandpiper; Nok Chailaen Paak Chawn (Thai); Burung Kedidi Paruh Sudu (Malay)

Eurynorhynchus pygmeus (Linnaeus) 1758, *Systema Naturae* 10(1): 140. TL E Asia.
Plate 33

GROUP RELATIONS. Free-standing. Excluded from *Calidris* only by its bill-shape.

GLOBAL RANGE. A world population of a few thousand breeds on the Chukot and Anadyr coasts of extreme NE Siberia and winters on the Ganges/Brahmaputra delta coast; perhaps far S China (but only a rare passage migrant through Hong Kong); and in SE Asia to the Peninsula. As yet, no winter concentrations have been found.

IDENTIFICATION/DESCRIPTION. About the size of Red-necked Stint, and with similar comportment. In winter, upperparts pale grey, darker on crown and sides of face; forehead, broad supercilium to well behind eye, and underparts purer white than in stints (BR 1963). The whole bill is laterally expanded (not obvious in side view), the tip widening abruptly into a rhomboidal spatula, at least as wide as long and broadest towards the rear.

Bare-part colours. Iris dark brown; bill black; legs and feet greenish black (BR 1963, Hayman *et al.* 1986).

Size (mm). (Live: 1 first-winterer, not sexed): wing 104; tail 38; bill from mouth-corner 24 (culmen range for the species 19–24); tarsus 22 (BR 1976–77, Hayman *et al.* 1986).

Weight (g). The November juvenile, 30.9 (BR 1976–77).

DISTRIBUTION. Probably overlooked. Historical summary: *Pat, Sel, Sin*.

GEOGRAPHICAL VARIATION. None recognized.

STATUS AND POPULATION. A non-breeding visitor, hardly more than vagrant, but so scarce globally that the Peninsula could still be a significant part of its winter range. Records in season order are: a party of 13 in Pattani bay on 15 October; one on a tidal prawn-pond at Jurong (Singapore) on 26 October; a first-winterer at Kuala Selangor on 7 November; and singles, presumably the same individual, seen regularly (and photographed) during 4 November–3 March 1978/79 on the Singapore W coast (BR 1963, 1976–77, 1978–79, MBR 1982–83, Parish 1985, PERHILITAN).

HABITATS AND ECOLOGY. Intertidal, but one recorded from an emptied, tide-fed prawn-rearing

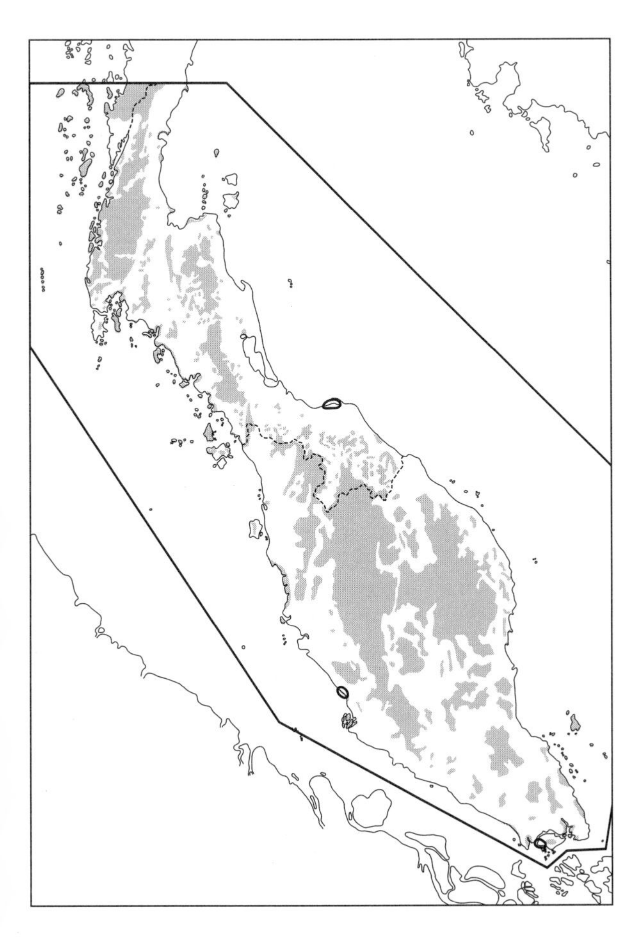

pond, and the bird at Kuala Selangor had been attracted to an overnight mixed-species roost on cleared and open back-mangrove-land (BR 1976–77).

FORAGING AND FOOD. The group at Pattani bay stayed exclusively on consolidated muds, foraging intensively in a small area, but the Jurong bird fed mostly in shallow pools or on soft mud. The main feeding action on soft surfaces is a rapid fore-and-aft vibration of the head, with slightly open bill inserted only to spatula-depth. Food has not been identified but items are evidently very small. The Jurong bird often fed amongst algae. Scything the bill from side to side appears to be a cleaning action (BR 1963, Swennen and Marteijn 1985, 1988).

SOCIAL ORGANIZATION. No other information.

MOVEMENTS. No information.

SURVIVAL. No information.

SOCIAL INTERACTIONS. No information.

VOICE. No information.

BREEDING. No population.

MOULT. A first-winterer dated 7 November was in mostly winter body-plumage but with crown and some scapular and mantle feathers buff-edged black, inner median and some lesser wing-coverts rufous-edged, and all-juvenile flight-feathers.

CONSERVATION. Globally vulnerable (BTW2). Since the Pattani bay observation was made, much mangrove forest has been removed to make way for aquaculture ponds at this site. Impacts on the mud-flats and wader food-supplies have not been fully assessed.

Broad-billed Sandpiper; Nok Chailaen Paak Gwaang (Thai); Burung Kedidi Paruh Tebal (Malay)

Limicola falcinellus (Pontoppidan) 1763, *Den danske Atlas eller Konge-riget Dannemark* 1: 623.
TL Denmark.

Plate 34

GROUP RELATIONS. Free-standing.

GLOBAL RANGE. Breeds in upland bogs and arctic tundra from Scandinavia, patchily across Eurasia possibly as far as Anadyrland. Winters in outer N tropical Africa and SW Asia; the Indian subcontinent, Sri Lanka and Bay of Bengal islands; Taiwan and Hainan; SE Asia to the Greater Sunda islands, Bali and the Philippines; and transient though W Micronesia and Wallacea to New Guinea and northern Australia.

IDENTIFICATION/DESCRIPTION. A short-legged, stocky, stint-like wader with hunched, horizontal stance; a little larger than Red-necked Stint, with proportionately longer, uniformly broad, droop-tipped bill, and inner leading-edge of wing dark, conspicuous in pale winter plumage. Has a double supercilium, the upper stripe less conspicuous than the lower, especially in winter plumage. In flight, upperparts show a stint-like pattern with dark centre to rump and upper tail-coverts.

Bare-part colours. Iris dark brown; bill black, in some yellowish at the extreme base; legs and feet blackish, a yellowish to greenish tinge seen elsewhere not reported from the Peninsula.

Size (mm). (Live and skins: 60, age/sex-classes not separated): wing 100–110; tail 35–40; bill 27.0–35.5; tarsus 20.9–23.0 (AWB, UMBRP, ZRCNUS).

Weight (g). A September–March sample, all age-groups, 20.0–48.5. Six (including first-winterers) above 40 are dated September and December (UMBRP), and may have been preparing to move on at mid season.

DISTRIBUTION. Historical summary: *Nak, Phu, Pat, Ked, Pek, Phg, Sel, Mel, Joh, Sin*, with additional island records from Penang and Tengah off the W coast; and Ubin, Singapore.

GEOGRAPHICAL VARIATION. Deignan (1963) lists nominate *falcinellus* from the Gulf of Bangkok but the the only subspecies identified in the Peninsula is eastern-breeding *sibirica* Dresser 1876 (TL China), in summer with brighter rufous fringing above; below whiter, streaked mostly only on the breast.

STATUS AND POPULATION. Passage migrant and to a smaller extent a non-breeding visitor, with no evidence yet of over-summering; local and uncommon to common. Hardly known in the NW but regular on the Melaka Straits coast south from Kedah, also around Singapore (BR 1963, 1964, Ollington and Loh 1992, Parish 1985a, Silvius *et al.* 1987, UMBRP). Along the E coast, uses Pak Phanang and Pattani bays in the north, and a few occur at the Pahang river-mouth (Howes *et al.* 1986, Jørgensen 1949, Parish 1985, Ruttanadakul and Ardseungnern 1987).

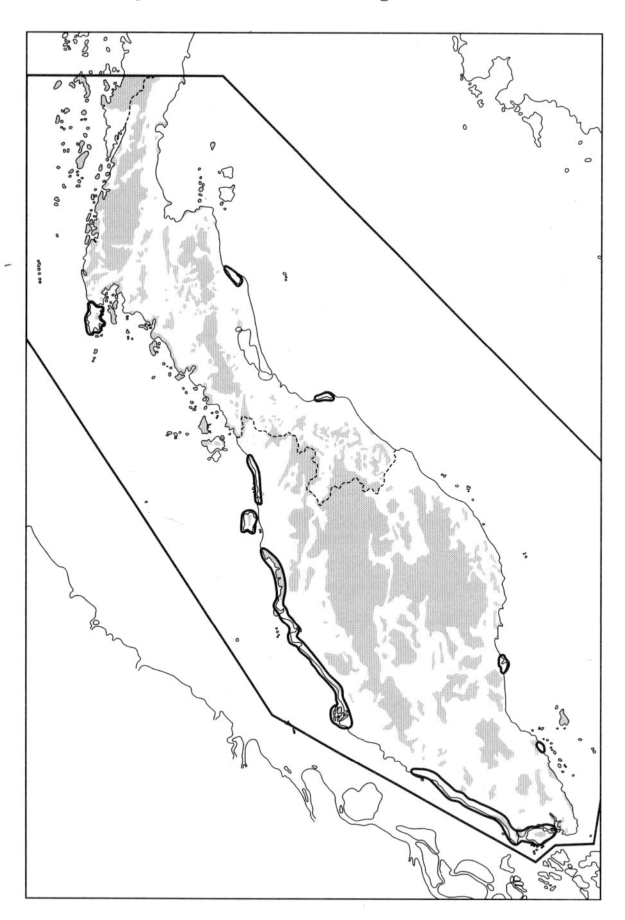

Pending more complete surveys in the north, the most important recent site is Pattani bay, where counts of 200-plus and 300 have been made in October and November, with close to 100 still present in mid January (Parish 1985). Most then move out, with few left by February, but a halt this long would more than cover adult moult. Elsewhere, peak autumn counts are smaller and numbers decline sooner, but within-season retrapping of ringed birds on the Selangor coast suggests individual stays to as late as early December (UMBRP). Early October counts of up to 300 are on record from the E end of Singapore (Mueller and Hails 1985), where a recent large decrease in the volume of passage has been linked to loss of key halting sites, including the Serangoon estuary (Ollington and Loh 1992).

HABITATS AND ECOLOGY. Intertidal, and recorded at tide-fed prawn-ponds. Attends mixed-species roosts on the ground in clearings in the mangrove zone.

FORAGING AND FOOD. Selects exclusively soft-mud substrates. The typical feeding action is a rather rapid, vertical jabbing ('stitching') of the bill into mud, and the only prey identified in the field has been polychaetes (Swennen and Marteijn 1985).

SOCIAL ORGANIZATION. Little known, but a dispersed forager and roosts well-scattered through the company of other small wader species, with no sign of clumping.

MOVEMENTS. The first few reach all sectors in August (extreme early date 19 August, at Pasir Ris, Singapore: BIRDLINE 1993), with double-figure counts from mid September (regular mist-netting at the Kuala Selangor roost caught a high proportion of juveniles as of 21 September), and peak autumn numbers during mid October–early November. The only convincing spring surge recorded has been in Selangor, with a peak 150 at Tengah island, Kelang estuary, on 7 April (Silvius *et al.* 1987). The latest spring date anywhere is 1 May, at a high-tide roost at Tanjung Karang, N Selangor (ENGGANG-2).

SURVIVAL. No information.

SOCIAL INTERACTIONS. No information.

VOICE. Flight-call a distinctive, harsh *brzink* (P.D. Round).

BREEDING. No information.

MOULT. Most information is from 110 birds caught for ringing at the Kuala Selangor wader-roost during the 1970s (UMBRP). First-winterers arrive in dark, all-juvenile plumage, start body-moult as of late September and complete by late December at the latest, except for a few wing-coverts, retained by some to early March. Wing-tip moult, started between P6 and P8, mainly at P7, is recorded from late December to mid March (no handlings after 13 March), the most advanced individual growing P10 on 24 January.

Non-juveniles return with body-moult suspended and a scatter of summer feathers, retained by some to late November, well after wing-moult has begun. An apparent second-winterer had renewed five inner primaries by 8 September. Adults, identified from wing-tip wear, may not start until after arrival. Respectively, three dated 2 September showed no moult, and P1 and P1–3 growing. P5 is the most advanced stage recorded by end of September, P8 by late October, and P9 by late November. Two at Sungai Buloh nature reserve, Singapore, still growing P9–10 and P10 on 24 January and 13 March, had probably suffered suspensions (noted in Selangor as of mid September).

Moult of adults back into summer body-colours begins in mid March (AWB).

CONSERVATION. See Whimbrel for relevant issues.

Ruff; Nok Raf (Thai); **Burung Kedidi Ropol** (Malay)

Philomachus pugnax (Linnaeus) 1758, *Systema Naturae* 10(1): 148. TL Sweden.
Plates 29 and 32

GROUP RELATIONS. Free-standing; its nearest living relative is likely to be American *Tryngites subruficollis* (Buff-breasted Sandpiper) (van Rhijn 1991).

GLOBAL RANGE. Breeds on wet meadow and tundra of the mid N-temperate zone to coasts and inner islands of the Arctic Ocean, from Britain east to Anadyrland. Winters through Africa, with a main global concentration in outer tropical W Africa; in SW Asia and the Indian subcontinent (mainly NW and NE) and Sri Lanka; sparingly eastwards in S Japan, China south from Fujian including Taiwan and Hainan; SE Asia to the Greater Sunda islands, Bali and the Philippines; and a few reach Wallacea, New Guinea and Australia.

IDENTIFICATION/DESCRIPTION. Males are the largest calidrine sandpiper, bulkier than Common Redshank. Fairly long-legged and stout-bodied, with typically upstanding posture showing off proportionately small head and shortish, very slightly droop-tipped bill. Juveniles are conspicuously buff. Older birds have a mottled, grey-brown chest, white throat and eyering, and white around the base of the bill. In flight, no obvious wing-bar, but a large oval of white borders the brown centre of the upper tail-coverts.

Bare-part colours. Iris dark brown; bill black with purple-red tinge to base of lower mandible; legs and feet dark grey-green or clear orange-pink, said to be the difference between first winter and older birds, but there is some doubt about the consistency of the change-over (a female identified as second-winter-plus still had them green).

Size (mm). (Live: 6 females; non-juvenile): wing 150–159; tail 55–60; bill 29, 30.7 (two only); bill from mouth-corner 31.5–33.0; tarsus 43.0–45.0 (PERHILITAN, UMBRP).

Weight (g). January females, 92.5–102.5 (n=5) (PERHILITAN, UMBRP).

DISTRIBUTION. Mostly the W-coast plain. Historical summary: *Son, Sel, Mel, Sin,* with island records from Libong (*Tra*).

GEOGRAPHICAL VARIATION. None recognized.

STATUS AND POPULATION. A winter visitor in small and variable numbers; local and sparse to uncommon; the concentration of records in Selangor and Singapore is probably a function of observer activity. Not recorded every year but in all months August–April, with most records and highest counts during mid winter, giving no evidence of onward migration. Most are of loners but double-figure counts (up to 26) were being made in NW Selangor paddylands in the mid 1970s, before pesticide loads in the area became excessive (BR 1976–77). Very few have occurred there recently and the incidence of Ruffs has fallen away generally.

Seven out of eight captured at the Kuala Selangor wader roost were female, and females predominated in the largest daytime parties observed, which fits the behavioural bias noted in Europe–Africa, where females make longer migration journeys to winter, on average, further south than males (van Rhijn 1991).

HABITATS AND ECOLOGY. A few records are from intertidal mudflats and, before they were reclaimed, tide-fed prawn-rearing ponds were quite regular habitat in Singapore (Mueller and Hails 1985, Parish 1985, Silvius *et al.* 1987). Much greater use is made of freshwater wetlands, predominantly paddyland at the early cultivation stage. The captures for ringing at Kuala Selangor were all made at

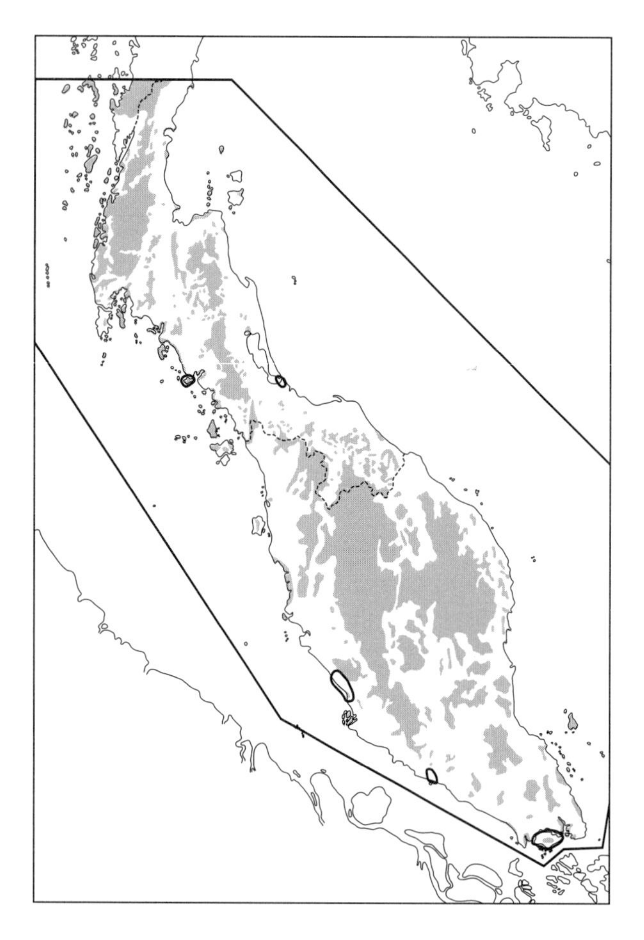

night at a mixed-species roost on cleared back-mangrove land.

FORAGING AND FOOD. No information.

SOCIAL ORGANIZATION. Where numerous, foragers on paddyland form loose parties.

MOVEMENTS. Extreme early and late dates are 14 August and 23 April, in Singapore and Selangor (MBR 1986–87, Parish and Wells 1984).

SURVIVAL. No information.

SOCIAL INTERACTIONS. No information.

VOICE. No local record.

BREEDING. No population.

MOULT. Among eight birds dated 7–12 January, one first-winterer with some buff-edged, juvenile median wing-coverts was in wing-tip moult out from P8 (P8–9 growing). Of non-juveniles, some were in rather worn, generally greyish winter plumage (tertials and tail unpatterned). Two apparently more advanced individuals showed partial summer plumage, including broadly white-fringed neck and breast feathers, and prominently dark-patterned tertials, central upper tail-coverts and central tail-feathers. Unexpectedly, some of these feathers were fresh, others abraded, suggesting direct replacement of one generation by the next, where post-breeding moult appears not to have been complete. All non-juveniles had either completed a wing-moult or were at stage P9 or 10.

CONSERVATION. As indicated, a developing southward extension of winter range into the Peninsula appears to have been cut off by the deteriorating quality of Malaysian paddyland as wildlife habitat. South of Thailand, little suitable, unpolluted habitat is now on offer.

Red-necked Phalarope; Nok Lai Thalae Khaw Daeng (Thai); Burung Kedidi Laut (Malay)

Phalaropus lobatus (Linnaeus) 1758, *Systema Naturae* 10(1): 148. TL Hudson's Bay, NE Canada.
Plate 8

GROUP RELATIONS. Free-standing.

GLOBAL RANGE. Breeds on bogs and tundra at cold-temperate and arctic latitudes around the world, in E Asia south to Kamchatka and the Commander islands. Winters at sea in three regions of tropical marine upwelling: off Peru, in the N Arabian Sea to western India, and from Melanesia/New Guinea south to Australia and west through Wallacea to the S Philippines, Borneo and Bali. On passage through SE Asia, strays west to Thailand and the Melaka Straits.

IDENTIFICATION/DESCRIPTION. A small, dainty wader with dark, needle-thin bill, foraging mainly by picking from the surface while swimming buoyantly, and often spins about after active prey. In winter, white with white-fringed, pale grey back, and black patches on hind-crown and face. Summer plumage is extensively dark grey, with a pale orange (male) or brick-red (female), oblique slash down side of neck. When flushed, shows a conspicuous, white wing-bar and mainly dark rump and upper tail-coverts. In the hand, note flat swimming-lobes along the outside margins of inner and outer toes.

Bare-part colours. Iris brown; bill all-black; legs and feet slaty black.

Size. No data.

Weight. No data.

DISTRIBUTION. Historical summary: *Sur, Sel, Sin.*

GEOGRAPHICAL VARIATION. None recognized.

STATUS AND POPULATION. Vagrant during passage seasons; recorded four times between 1982 and 1994. In season order: two birds flushed from under the bow a ship east of the Pahang–Johor archipelago on 7 October; at sea between Ang Thong and Samui islands (Surat Thani) on 13 October; one at Tuas, W end of Singapore island, on 16–18 November; and a party of 14, including one female already in summer plumage, off Tengah island (Selangor) on 8 April (S. Cohen, MBR 1982–83, Silvius *et al.* 1987, SINGAV-8, -9). Migration encompasses Borneo (Smythies 1981) but how far the Peninsula is west of regular routing over the S China Sea has not been discovered.

HABITATS AND ECOLOGY. On passage, stops at freshwater wetlands (flooded grassland at Tuas, Singapore), but more typically marine.

FORAGING AND FOOD. Picks small invertebrates from the water-surface while swimming.

SOCIAL ORGANIZATION. At sea in the main wintering areas, gregarious, forming close-knit rafts.

MOVEMENTS. Through-passage in both directions; see above.

SURVIVAL. No information.

SOCIAL INTERACTIONS. No information.

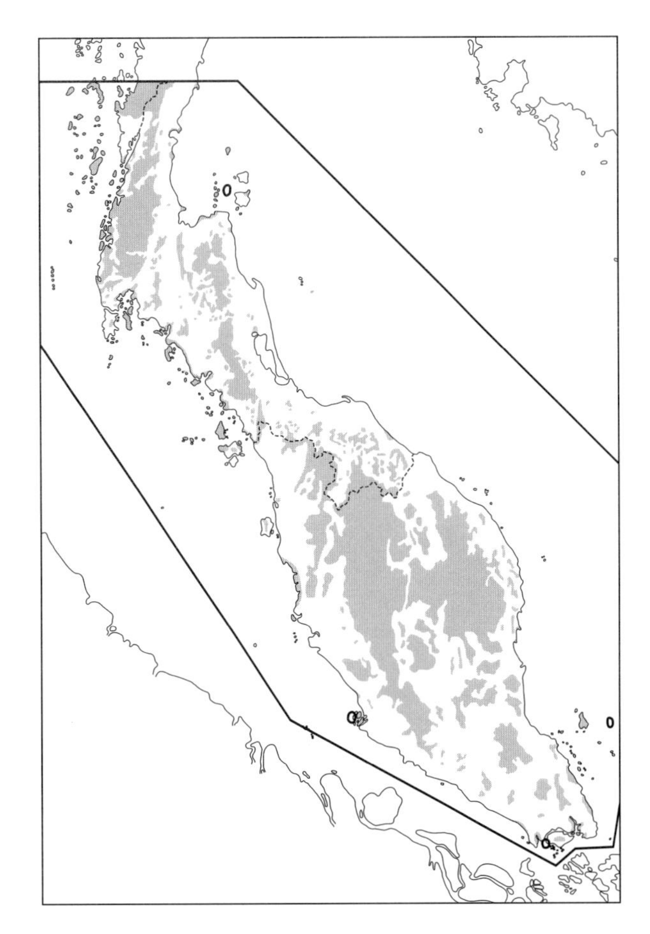

VOICE. No information.

BREEDING. No population.

MOULT. No data.

CONSERVATION. No relevant issues.

Family ROSTRATULIDAE
Painted-snipe: one species

Greater Painted-snipe; Nok Pong Wid (Thai); Burung Meragi (Malay)
Rostratula benghalensis (Linnaeus) 1758, *Systema Naturae* 10(1): 153. TL Asia.
Plates 29 and 35

GROUP RELATIONS. Free-standing.

GLOBAL RANGE. The Nile delta, sub-Saharan Africa and Madagascar; the Indian subcontinent and Sri Lanka; S Japan and China south of a line Liaoning–Shaanxi–Sichuan, including Taiwan and Hainan; SE Asia to the Greater Sunda islands, Bali and the Philippines; and the Lesser Sunda islands and Australia. Outer-latitude populations migrate, or disperse long distances.

IDENTIFICATION/DESCRIPTION. Appears and behaves like a cross between a snipe and a rail and, in flight, broad, rounded wings are particularly rail-like.

On the ground, long, droop-tipped bill, and bold white to buff postorbital streak and ring round large dark eye are obvious. When flushed into flight, shows Ruff-like oval white patch either side of otherwise dark upper tail-coverts, and white 'braces' converging down the back. In the hand, juveniles from dull-coloured adult male by hind-neck and mantle light russet with fine white fringing, versus darker vinous-grey without the white.

The downy chick is pale buff-grey with a broad, blackish mid-dorsal stripe from forehead to nape and along the body, on which it is split by a mesial stripe of orange running back to the tail. From the lores, a second blackish line runs through the eye, down the side of the neck and dorsolaterally along the body. The outer thigh has a diffuse dark spot. Bill already longish, blunt, and with down-tilted tip.

Bare-part colours. Iris dark brown; bill greenish at the base, shading to pale orange-pink (at least in breeders); legs and feet yellowish- to grey-olive.

Size (mm). (Skins and live: 5 males, 10 females; adult): wing 127–132 and 135–145; tail 36–41 and 36–44; bill 43.8–46.9 and 46.7–51.9; tarsus 40.6–47.1 and 44.7–51.9 (AWB, BMNH, UMBRP, ZRCNUS).

Weight (g). Adult males, 108, 131; adult females, 143, 150.

DISTRIBUTION. Historical summary: *Sur, Pha, Pht, Pat, Ked, Pra, Pek, Sel, Neg, Mel, Joh, Sin*, with additional island records from Langkawi and Penang (R. Gregory-Smith).

GEOGRAPHICAL VARIATION. Nominate *benghalensis*, of the global range except Australia.

STATUS AND POPULATION. Resident; heavily dependent on man-made, often transient wetlands, hence likely to be dispersive although no movement has actually been intercepted. Regular and uncommon to common.

HABITATS AND ECOLOGY. Seeks open freshwater wetlands, boggy but not necessarily with standing surface water, including weedy, fallow paddyland, old dredge-mine lagoon swamp overgrown with yams, water-hyacinth, reed-mace, etc., wet grazing land, vegetated edges of irrigation canals, even well-shaded concrete drains. Most such habitat is at plains level but on Jerai peak recorded in scrub at 900 m, probing in the wet-earth rootlings of wild pigs (Bromley 1949).

Most active at dawn and dusk, and mist-netting shows it is also on the wing at night.

FORAGING AND FOOD. Probing in soft earth is a common behaviour. No local information on diet.

SOCIAL ORGANIZATION. The largest (strictly transient) adult social units are the pair and an adult with chicks. Foragers are generally solitary. However,

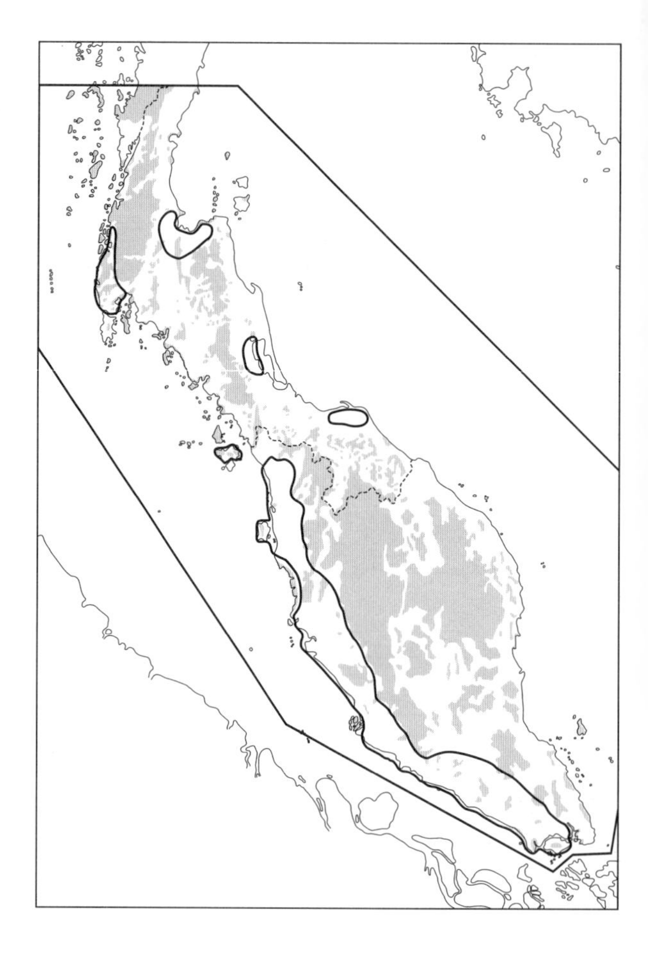

where fallow paddyland is reduced by ploughing, up to 20 birds have been found on residual plots of no more than 1–2 ha, showing no obvious aggression even while some were still mating and egg-laying (BR 1974–75, C.A. Rose). At such gatherings, birds in male-type plumage (presumably including immatures) heavily outnumber adult females.

Reversal of the sex-roles permits females to lay clutches for several successive mates, but connected social behaviour has not been studied in this area.

MOVEMENTS. No information.

SURVIVAL. No information.

SOCIAL INTERACTIONS. Some of the display-ritual recorded elsewhere (BWP) has been seen in the Peninsula, including frontal fanning of wings and tail by a courting female (Cairns 1940) and unilateral wing-raising (flagging) by both pair-members (MBR 1986–87). At dusk, courting birds indulge in low, roding flights over open spaces (including a pair struck by an aircraft landing at Penang airport, placing Greater Painted-snipe on the official list of hazard species: A.C. Sebastian).

VOICE. A low but carrying *koo-u, koo-u, koo-u . . .* constantly repeated by a female displaying to a male (Cairns 1940), is the only vocalization reported.

BREEDING

Nest. A pad with shallow central depression, built of immediately available dry blades and stems, on or close to the ground in the base of a clump of grass in low, boggy to part-flooded herbage; one nest 1.5 m from the edge of a shallow pool.

Eggs and brood. Eggs are warm clay-brown boldly and more or less regularly blotched with black-brown overlaying mostly smaller, irregular dots of grey. Shape broad near-piriform. Size (mm): 36.1–33.9 × 25.2–24.7 (n=6). Full clutch four.

Cycle. Only males have been flushed from nests with full clutches, and males tend chicks. The regular post-laying role of the female has not been studied locally. However, a female put up very close to an already-sitting male might have been continuing to mate-guard, and there is one record of a female escorting chicks.

Seasonality. Egg- and downy chick-dates extrapolate to laying in April–August (BMP5, ENGGANG-2, MBR 1986–87, NRCS, C.A. Rose, UMBRP).

MOULT. Juveniles moult flight-feathers simultaneously (ZRCNUS) whereas adults renew at least the inner primaries descendantly. Active early-stage primary moult of non-juveniles (out to P4 and precocious P10) is recorded in late August, October and November (AWB, ZRCNUS).

CONSERVATION. A significant part of the population has depended on paddyland and, in Malaysia, is under pressure from intensification of rice production. Reduction of the fallow period has reached a stage of barely allowing completion of a breeding attempt before ploughing, and post-harvest herbicide treatment now altogether eliminates fallow cover. At Sekinchan (Selangor), C.A. Rose watched a small aggregration being sprayed as it laid and incubated, with nests ploughed in on the same day. Breeding success in this formerly important habitat is not now believed to be high.

Family JACANIDAE

Jacanas: two species

Pheasant-tailed Jacana; Nok Ee-jaew (Thai); Burung Teratai Sayap Putih (Malay)

Hydrophasianus chirurgus (Scopoli) 1786, *Deliciae Florae et Faunae Insubricae* 2: 92. TL Luzon, Philippines.

Plate 35

GROUP RELATIONS. Free-standing.

GLOBAL RANGE. Breeds from the Himalayan foothills through the Indian subcontinent and Sri Lanka; S Japan (occasionally); China south from the Changjiang valley including Taiwan and Hainan; and SE Asia to Burma, central Thailand, the Mekong delta and the Philippines. Some northern populations migrate, wintering within and beyond the breeding-range west as far as Yemen and to the Greater Sunda islands. Straggles to Bali, and vagrant in Australia (Christidis and Boles 1994, Indrawan 1991). A claim of breeding in SE Borneo (Smythies 1981) has not been confirmed.

IDENTIFICATION/DESCRIPTION. Moorhen-plus sized, and no other jacana species show seasonally alternating plumages. In winter, inconspicuously clay-brown until extensively white wings flash on take-off (cf. winter Pond Herons *Ardeola* spp.). Extravagant summer plumage decorations include the long tail, carried arched, and delicate, lanceolate rackets, quick to abraid, at the tips of primaries 8–10. A sharp, white carpal spur matches wing-covert colour. In flight, the long legs and toes with enormously elongated, straight claws trail behind. Sexes alike, year-round.

Bare-part colours. Iris brown; bill brown with yellowish base, in summer slaty blue with yellow tip; legs and feet pale blue-grey.

Size (mm). (Skins: 1 male, 3 females; winter adults): wing (minus spur but with rackets) 188 and 207–228; tail 73 and 85 116; bill 26.0 and 28.9–30.4; tarsus 51.1 and 54.5–59.0 (ZRCNUS).

Weight. No data.

DISTRIBUTION. Historical summary: *Sur, Pht, Tra, Son, Sat, Kel, Pek, Phg, Sel, Mel, Joh, Sin*, with an additional (spring passage-dated) island record from Redang (*Tru*).

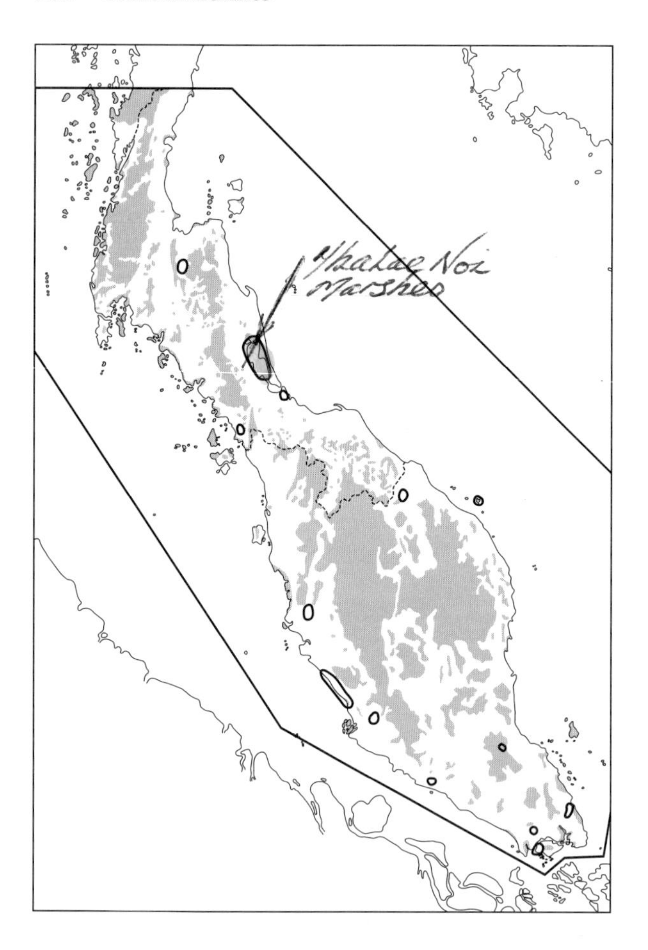

GEOGRAPHICAL VARIATION. None recognized.

STATUS AND POPULATION. A non-breeding visitor and passage migrant, recorded in all months October–June; local and uncommon to common. Many winter on the Thalae Noi marshes (BMP5). Much less common south of Thailand and usually solitary, but in January–February small groups gather at favoured sites, including To' Uban lake, N Kelantan, flooded mine-workings around Batu Gajah, Perak, and Poyan reservoir, Singapore, where up to seven are regular (A.C. Sebastian, Phillipps 1961, SINGAV-2).

HABITATS AND ECOLOGY. Winters in freshwater wetlands with floating macrophyte cover, particularly water-hyacinth and waterlilies, including natural, open marshland, disused dredge-mine lagoons, low-lying reservoirs, and large fish-ponds in open country; only occasionally paddyland, where prime conditions are never more than transient. Reported on rivers through inland and mangrove forests, but only while migrating (BR 1965, 1970–71, ENGGANG-2).

FORAGING AND FOOD. Picks from the water-surface, probes algal masses and searches by lifting over aquatic plants, mostly while slow-walking on floating vegetation; sometimes while wading or swimming. Diet not described.

SOCIAL ORGANIZATION. Morning and evening flighting by up to 50 individuals at Thalae Noi (Storer 1976) suggests winterers may roost gregariously where they are common, but this has not been confirmed. Loosely social also during migration, and some phase of gregariousness during the non-breeding season might have had a bearing on the evolution of the dull, eclipse plumage in winter, unique among jacanas. At no stage is foraging obviously social. In early spring at Thalae Noi, P.J. Storer saw aggressive chases, and a bird on a lily-pool behaving as though defending individual space.

MOVEMENTS. This is the only jacana species known to migrate long distances. Extreme dates in autumn: 13 October at Thalae Noi, 20 October in Satul and 7 November in Singapore (Holmes and Wells 1975, SINGAV-2, Storer 1976); and in spring, 13 June at Batu Gajah, Perak, and 25 June at Thalae Noi (BCSTB-12, Phillips 1961). Duration of autumn passage is unknown, but transients in tidal and river habitats, where the species does not winter, show spring passage runs from late April and peaks in early May (over 40 jacanas counted along tidal reaches of the Sedili Kecil river, SE Johor, on 9 May 1970). The June records are isolated and seem not to be typical (BMP5, BR 1976–77, Phillips 1960).

SURVIVAL. No information.

SOCIAL INTERACTIONS. Apart from spacing behaviour at Thalae Noi, no information. The functional significance of the flight-feather rackets is a particular mystery.

VOICE. A nasal *jiew* (P.D. Round). Chases at Thalae Noi in late March were noisy (Storer 1976), but winter foragers are normally silent.

BREEDING. No known population, but given that nesting is regular in Gulf of Bangkok wetlands (BBCB-8) occasional breeding attempts may occur in the north.

MOULT. Hardly any have been handled, but autumn birds in eclipse colours are presumed to have moulted at least body and tail before arrival. Adults dated November–January showed no wing-moult and it is not known when new ornamented flight-feathers are acquired. Spring moult begins before/during return passage, and from late April most show at least part-summer colours and tail-growth (complete in a June bird) (BMP5, BR 1970–71).

CONSERVATION. Much depends on integrating the ecology of the main wintering site, the Thalae Noi lake/marsh system, into engineering plans for the entire Phatthalung/Songkhla wetland complex.

Bronze-winged Jacana; Nok Phrik (Thai); **Burung Teratai Hitam** (Malay)

Metopidius indicus (Latham) 1790, *Index Ornithologicus* 2: 765. TL India.
Plate 35

GROUP RELATIONS. Free-standing.

GLOBAL RANGE. The Indian subcontinent except the dry NW; S Yunnan; and continental SE Asia to the Peninsula, S Sumatra and Java (where now rare).

IDENTIFICATION/DESCRIPTION. Moorhen-plus sized and adults are similarly dark, but are longer-legged (with the enormous toes and claws of the family). They lack any white on flanks or rear, but show a bold white postorbital stripe curving round the side of the nape. In flight, long feet and straight claws trail behind. The carpal spur is blunt and dark, matching wing-colour. Juveniles have a rufous cap with short white supercilium, bronze-brown upper-parts, and are white below washed buff from chin to breast.

Bare-part colours. Iris brown; relatively large bill yellow-green, base of culmen and frontal wattle lying against forehead bright red, tip bright yellow; legs and feet dark green.

Size (mm). (Skin: 1 male; adult): wing unmeasurable; tail 42; bill (excluding upstanding wattle) 43.1; tarsus 65.3 (ZRCNUS).

Weight. No data.

DISTRIBUTION. Mainly the northeast. Historical summary: *Sur, Pht, Son, Pek.*

GEOGRAPHICAL VARIATION. None recognized.

STATUS AND POPULATION. Resident; very local, and uncommon to common, recorded from the Thung Thong wetland, Surat Thani (Chasen 1935, Storer 1978), Thalae Noi marshes (where it is numerous) and once near Asam Kumbang, Taiping, Perak (one of a pair collected on 14 December 1911: BMP5).

HABITATS AND ECOLOGY. At Thalae Noi, selects mostly lotus and waterlily pools, less often on water-hyacinth rafts. By their locality, the Perak vagrants are likely to have been on swamp in a tin-mine.

FORAGING AND FOOD. Lifts small mats of water-weeds and tosses them aside as it searches for food while slow-walking over floating vegetation (P.D. Round). Adults have been seen to eat fragments of water-hyacinth leaf (Storer 1976).

SOCIAL ORGANIZATION. Typically solitary and defends a feeding territory, warning off intruders with shrill calls.

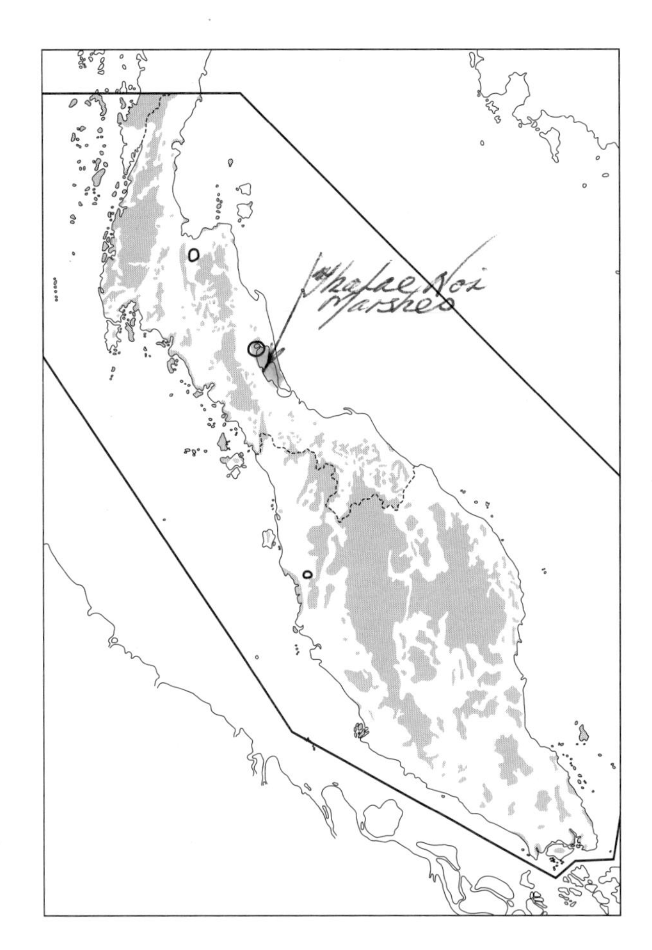

MOVEMENTS. None known.

SURVIVAL. No information.

SOCIAL INTERACTIONS. No information.

VOICE. Not adequately described.

BREEDING

Nest. Floating, at Thalae Noi built by piling up waterweed (*Salvinia cucullata* identified).

Eggs and brood. Eggs glossy, light brown, with reticulate pattern of black scrawls, bolder at broad end. Shape near-piriform. Full clutch four, but at Thalae Noi adults recorded shepherding broods of not more than three chicks.

Cycle. Not described. Among jacanas generally, sex-roles are reversed for incubation and brood-rearing.

Seasonality. At Thalae Noi, active nests in November, December and June and young chicks during December and March–October, suggesting no clear pattern (Anonymous 1981, BMP5, R. Gregory-Smith, K. Komolphalin, Storer 1976).

MOULT. None recorded; the Perak male had extraordinarily worn primaries and could hardly have been able to fly (ZRCNUS).

CONSERVATION. Survival in the Peninsula depends heavily on maintaining the ecological integrity of the Thalae Noi wetland system, mainly against interference with its natural cycle of water-level changes.

Family BURHINIDAE

Thick-knees: two species

Eurasian Thick-knee; Nok Gratae Phee Lek (Thai); Burung Pasir Padang (Malay)

Burhinus oedicnemus (Linnaeus) 1758, *Systema Naturae* 10(1): 151. TL England.
Plate 37

GROUP RELATIONS. Likely to form a superspecies with African *B. senegalensis* (Senegal Thick-knee). They overlap in N Africa but in the area of contact are said to occupy different habitats.

GLOBAL RANGE. Breeds from S Britain across W-central Eurasia, south to the Canary islands, N Sahara and SW Asia; then through the Indian subcontinent, Sri Lanka, and continental SE Asia from Burma to Thailand, Cambodia and central Vietnam. Most non-tropical populations migrate, wintering within and beyond the gross breeding-range to W and E Africa, and SW Asia. Movements in S and SE Asia are little-known but guessed only to be dispersive.

IDENTIFICATION/DESCRIPTION. A large, heavily brown-streaked 'wader' that never wades; with stout bill, big yellow eye and long, pale yellowish legs, but difficult to see against typical bare-soil backgrounds. When forced to fly by day, shows pale median wing-coverts and black flight-feathers with two white patches on the primaries.

Bare-part colours. No exact information.

Size. No data.

Weight. No data.

DISTRIBUTION. Historical summary: *Pht*.

GEOGRAPHICAL VARIATION. None handled, but likely to be tropical-Asian-breeding *indicus* Salvadori 1865 (TL Mussoorie district, N India).

STATUS AND POPULATION. Recently found breeding in dry agriculture in SE Thailand, and parties of possible residents recorded in winter in SW Thailand (BBCB-7). Vagrant in the Peninsula, the only record being of a party of seven presumed dry-season

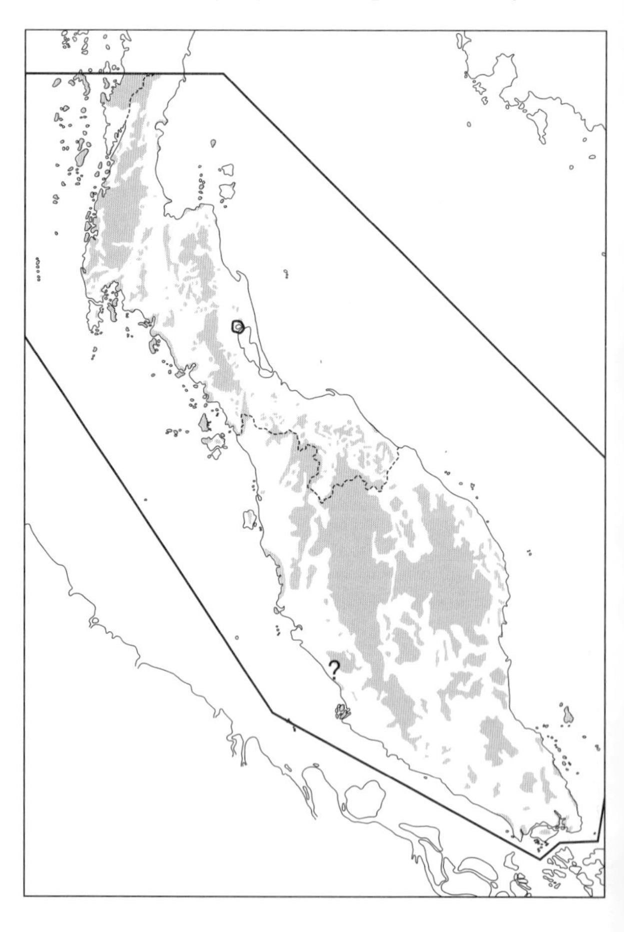

dispersants at the Thalae Noi wetland on 27 January 1989 (BBCB-6). Further south, a bird giving a typical wail-call glimpsed flying over dry, bare paddyland at Sekinchan (Selangor) at dusk on 21 February 1986 (R.V. Lansdown) was evidently a thick-knee and could have been this species.

HABITATS AND ECOLOGY. In SE Asia, as elsewhere, this bird of dry savanna and river sandbanks has adapted to agriculture. Those at Thalae Noi were on dredge-spoil piled along the bank of a watercourse (P.D. Round). Active mainly at dusk, and at least partly nocturnal.

FORAGING AND FOOD. No local information.

SOCIAL ORGANIZATION. Non-breeders are solitary or form small parties.

MOVEMENTS. No definite information.

SURVIVAL. No information.

SOCIAL INTERACTIONS. No information.

VOICE. The flight-call is a loud, wailing disyllable, *kour-lee* (Boonsong and Round 1991).

BREEDING. No known population.

MOULT. No data.

CONSERVATION. No relevant issues.

Beach Thick-knee; Nok Gratae Phee Chai Haad (Thai); Burung Pasir Terumbu (Malay)

Esacus neglectus Mathews 1912, *Novitates Zoologicae* 18: 226. TL Lewis island, W Australia.
Plate 37

GROUP RELATIONS. Forms a probable superspecies with continental S and SE Asian *E. recurvirostris* (Great Thick-knee) (CLBW). A sinking of *Esacus* into *Burhinus* by Meinertzhagen (1924) has had repercussions on the validity of the more familiar specific name '*magnirostris*', with further upsets in store should separate southern and northern species be erected on the basis of chick colour-patterns (Condon 1975, Inskipp *et al.* 1996).

GLOBAL RANGE. The Andamans and Mergui archipelago to the Greater Sunda islands, Bali and the Philippines; and Wallacea to New Guinea, northern Australia, the Solomons and New Caledonia. In the NW of its Asian range, confined more or less exclusively to small islands.

IDENTIFICATION/DESCRIPTION. Stands as high as a Curlew. Massive, black-and-yellow, dagger bill, black head with white face-markings, big yellow eye, long yellow-green legs and rectangular grey patch dorsally edged black-and-white in the closed wing are the key characters on the ground (BR 1978–79). In flight, shows all-white inner primaries and a white flash on the black outer primaries. The white underwing lacks the dark carpal-patch of northern *recurvirostris* (Hayman *et al.* 1986).

Bare-part colours. (Adults) iris clear yellow; bill black with yellow patch at base of upper and yellow band across base of lower mandible; legs and feet dull, greenish yellow.

Size. No data from this area.

Weight. No data.

DISTRIBUTION. Islands of the NW, and Singapore's S archipelago. Historical summary: *Pak, Ran, Pha, ?Tra, Sat, Sel, Sin.*

GEOGRAPHICAL VARIATION. None recognized.

STATUS AND POPULATION. Resident, local, and sparse. In the NW, reported from: Lanbyi, St Luke's, Phayam, the Surins (several pairs in November and April 1975/76, and a bird there in November 1993), and Ladang in what is now Tarutao national park (Brockelman and Nadee 1977, Dickinson 1966, Riley 1938, Robinson and Kloss 1921–24, E. Stuart). In early December 1991, a presumed transient was identified from a description taken by villagers on Libong island, Trang (BBCB-9). Together, these records fall in the period 3 November–22 April, but no movement is suspected beyond possible inter-island exchange. In the far south, lone adults reported on neighbouring Salu, Hantu, Sudong and Busing islands, S archipelago of Singapore, during March 1978–September 1992 (BR 1978–79, SINGAV-1, -3, -6) may have referred to just one individual.

Esacus thicknees, presumably this species, seen on one of the rocky islets off Jeram, Selangor, in June 1878 (Hornaday 1885) supply the only evidence of former presence in the modern range-gap. There have never been any E-coast records.

HABITATS AND ECOLOGY. Strictly beaches and back-reef flats exposed at low tide. Must forage mainly according to the tide-cycle but also said to be

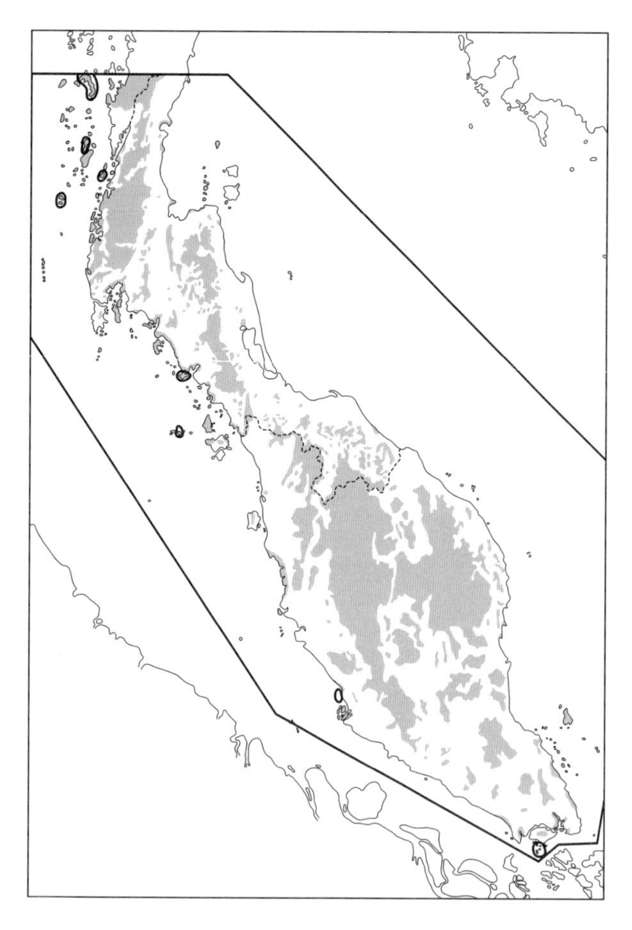

most active at night, or at least at dusk and dawn. During the daytime, the Singapore bird is invariably found quietly at rest. There has been no record of a nest but likely sites would be open ground close to the shoreline.

FORAGING AND FOOD. No local information.

SOCIAL ORGANIZATION. Alone or in pairs.

MOVEMENTS. Inter-island dispersal.

SURVIVAL. See above for a possible minimum survival interval.

SOCIAL INTERACTIONS. No information.

VOICE. No information.

BREEDING. No information.

MOULT. No data.

CONSERVATION. Everywhere, highly vulnerable to incidental disturbance of beach habitat. Breeding-sites must be found and protected strictly if the species is to be maintained. Sudong island, the Singapore bird's most recent locality, has been taken over as a military training ground. This cuts off public access without necessarily reducing the area's conservation value (although much of the S archipelago is slated for reclamation in the foreseeable future). Other restricted-access islands in the neighbourhood might hold a few more individuals, but this bird's failure to acquire a mate implies no viable population has been present. Formerly present in the Riau archipelago (Indonesia), across the Singapore Straits (Chasen 1935), but none reported recently.

Family HAEMATOPODIDAE

Oystercatchers: one species

Eurasian Oystercatcher; (no Thai name); **Burung Tetiram** (Malay)

Haematopus ostralegus Linnaeus 1758, *Systema Naturae* 10(1): 152. TL Öland island, Sweden. Plate 37

GROUP RELATIONS. Red-eyed *longirostris* and *finschi* of Australia and New Zealand are likely to be part of an *ostralegus* superspecies, if not conspecific.

GLOBAL RANGE. Breeds between latitude about 37°N and the arctic coast, in Iceland and from Atlantic Europe east to longitude about 90°E, then from Kamchatka and Amurland to the Yellow Sea. Winters from the European breeding range to S Africa and SW Asia; on W and NE coasts of the Indian subcontinent, and Sri Lanka; and coastal China from the Changjiang river to Taiwan. Vagrant in far-south China, W Micronesia and the Peninsula.

IDENTIFICATION/DESCRIPTION. A medium-large, stocky shorebird, conspicuously black-and-white, with long, straight, orange bill. From Australasian counterparts by having at least some white showing on the upper surface of the primaries and, in winter, by its white throat-band (Hayman *et al.* 1986).

Bare-part colours. Iris red-brown to red; bill orange; legs and feet grey to pink (Hayman *et al.* 1986).

Size. No data.

Weight. No data.

DISTRIBUTION. Historical summary: *Sel*.

GEOGRAPHICAL VARIATION. Good views of the distribution of white on the primaries identified W Asia-breeding *longipes* Buturlin 1910 (TL Zmeinogorsk district, W Siberia). This calls into question the assumption that oystercatchers seen in Bangladesh and Burma are necessarily all far-eastern *osculans* (Ripley 1982, Smythies 1953).

STATUS AND POPULATION. Vagrant; known from probably one individual that may have wintered on the Selangor coast during 1992/93. At various times, it roosted with other waders at the Kapar power-station ash-ponds.

HABITATS AND ECOLOGY. No additional information.

FORAGING AND FOOD. No information.

SOCIAL ORGANIZATION. No information.

MOVEMENTS. Extreme dates are 29 August and the first week of April (A. Ponnambalam, C.A. Rose).

SURVIVAL. No information.

SOCIAL INTERACTIONS. No information.

VOICE. No information.

BREEDING. No population.

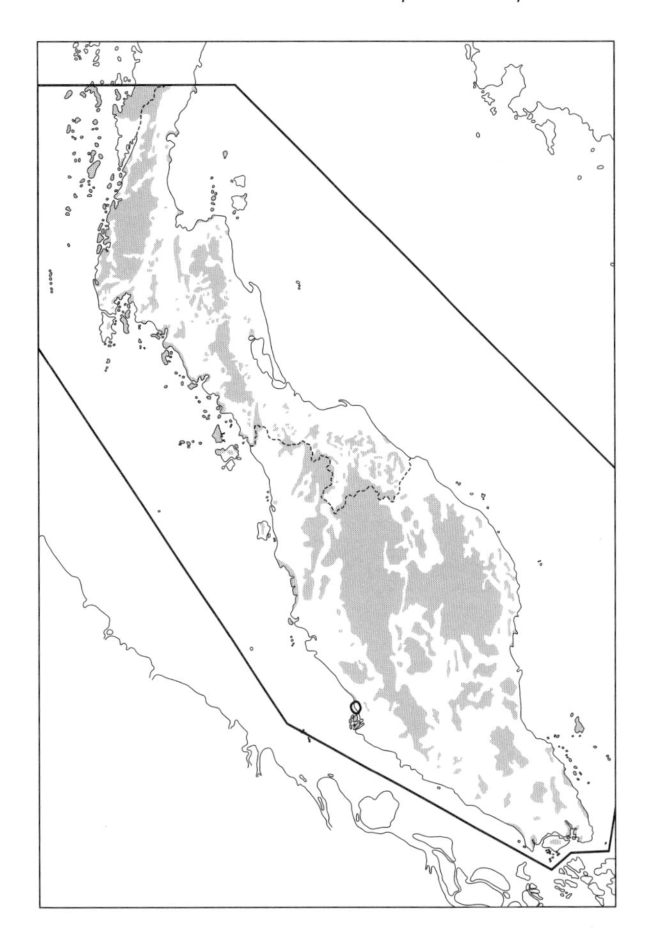

MOULT. The white throat-band of autumn had moulted out by April.

CONSERVATION. No relevant issues.

Family RECURVIROSTRIDAE

Stilts: one species

Black-winged Stilt; Nok Teen Thian (Thai); Burung Stilt (Malay)

Himantopus himantopus (Linnaeus) 1758, *Systema Naturae* 10(1): 151. TL S Europe.

Plate 37

GROUP RELATIONS. Uncertain. Recent immigrants to New Zealand interbreed freely with endemic *H. novaezealandiae* (Black Stilt). Hybrids are fertile, but parent stocks are distinct morphologically.

GLOBAL RANGE. The USA through to S America; Africa and Madagascar; Eurasia south of latitude about 50°N, from the Atlantic to China; the Indian subcontinent and Sri Lanka; SE Asia to the Greater Sunda islands, Bali and the Philippines; and Sulawesi and the Lesser Sunda islands to New Guinea, Australia and New Zealand; also Hawaii. Many populations migrate or disperse, in eastern Asia reaching S China and equatorial SE Asia.

IDENTIFICATION/DESCRIPTION. A medium-sized wader, mainly white with upperparts grey or black, on extremely long, pink legs (whole tarsus projecting beyond tail in flight).

Bare-part colours. Iris yellow-brown (juvenile), red (adult); bill black; legs and feet dull putty-pink (juvenile), rose-pink (adult).

Size. No data.

Weight. No data.

DISTRIBUTION. Historical summary: *Nak, Kra, Pht, Son, Ked, Pek, Mel, Joh, Sin*, also Penang island.

GEOGRAPHICAL VARIATION. Most records away from breeding-sites have been of indeterminate juveniles. Breeders and other adults have all been nominate *himantopus*, of Eurasia.

STATUS AND POPULATION. Resident, non-breeding visitor and a possible passage migrant; local and sparse to common. Breeds, and recorded more or less year-round, only on the Thalae Noi–Songkhla wetland where in the late 1970s the population is believed to have peaked in spring at around 600–1000 birds (Anonymous 1981). At Kukut reserve, Thalae Sap, about 70 birds (some nesting) were present in late June 1984 and 140 in late February 1993 (R. Gregory-Smith, J. Scharringa). Otherwise, small numbers of non-breeders collect at only two other regular sites: Pak Phanang bay (Nakhon Si Thammarat) during late September–early December, including 28 with other waders on a part-drained prawn-pond on 8 December (BMP5, Parish 1985); and Singapore island, where first recorded in 1918 (Robinson and Chasen 1936) and on which small groups (recently of up to seven: BIRDLINE 1992) are now annual, mainly in autumn and during February–March. Elsewhere, known from odd transients at likely passage-dates on both coastal plains (BR 1976–77, ENGGANG-2, MBR 1984–85, P.D. Round).

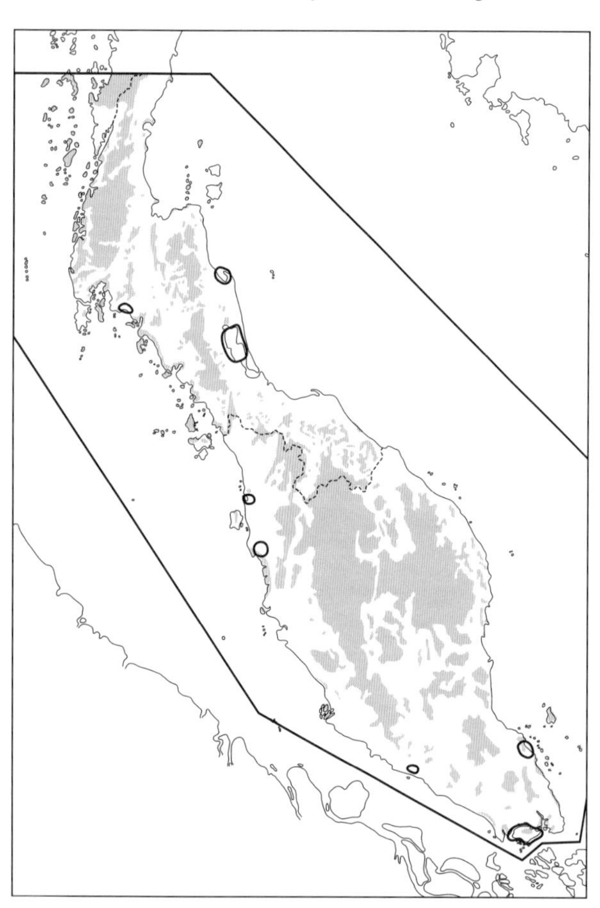

HABITATS AND ECOLOGY. Breeders occupy wet meadows and open lake-edge mud (R. Gregory-Smith, Holmes and Wells 1975, J. Scharringa, Storer 1976). Records elsewhere are from open brackish to freshwater stream- and pond-margins, and young paddy (BR 1976–77), with a few on intertidal flats, tide-fed prawn-ponds and in clearings in mangrove forest (BR 1978–79, ENGGANG-2, Parish 1985).

FORAGING AND FOOD. No information.

SOCIAL ORGANIZATION. Around Kukut, breeds in loose colonies.

MOVEMENTS. Away from concentration points, outside dates are 27 October-–16 December and 14 March, suggestive of through-passage. Records in Singapore imply occasional overwintering but timing of arrival and departure, and individual stays, show much variation year to year. Extreme dates there are 19 July and 10 May (Ollington and Loh 1993).

SURVIVAL. No information.

SOCIAL INTERACTIONS. No information.

VOICE. No information.

BREEDING

Nest. Around Kukut, nests in meadowland and on dried mud during low-water conditions, with one record from floating vegetation in a mid-lake sedge-bed. In colonies, nests are typically 5–7 m apart.

Eggs and brood. Eggs not described locally. One clutch of two is unlikely to have been complete, and brood-sizes have not been reported.

Cycle. Distraction display recorded, and both parents escort chicks.

Seasonality. Active nests in April–June, eggs on 22 June, and several pairs with chicks on 22–23 June (Anonymous 1981, P.D. Round, J. Scharringa).

MOULT. No data.

CONSERVATION. Breeders depend on access to water-level grassland and exposed lake-edge for foraging. Any engineering of the Thalae Noi–Songkhla wetland that materially alters its hydrology will affect these habitats.

Family CHARADRIIDAE

Plovers: 14 species

Pacific Golden Plover; Nok Hua Toh Lang Juut See Thong (Thai); Burung Rapang Kerinyut (Malay)

Pluvialis fulva (Gmelin) 1789, *Systema Naturae* 13(2): 687. TL Tahiti.
Plate 29

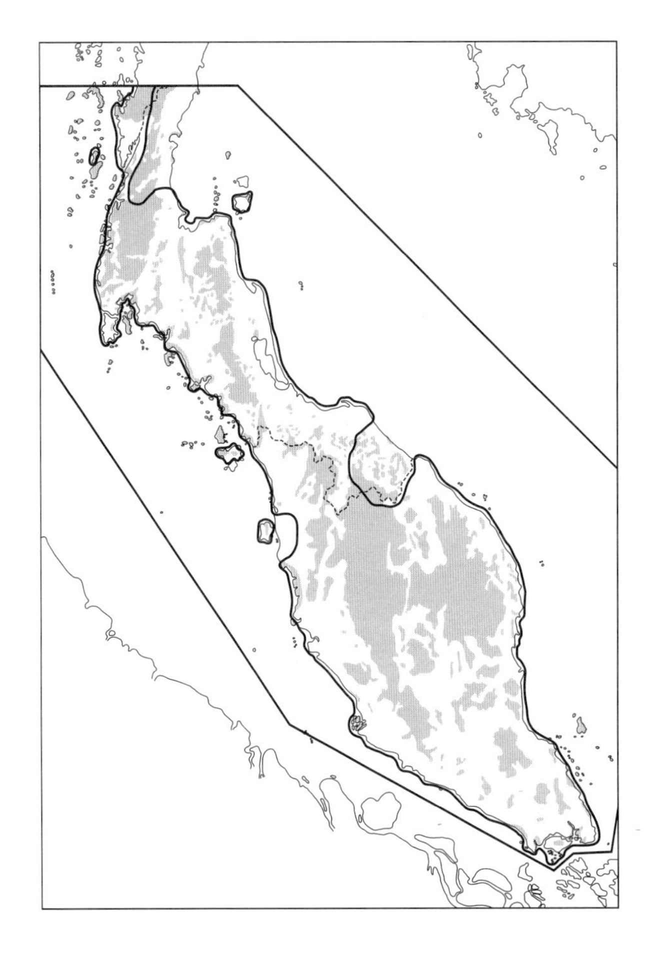

GROUP RELATIONS. Uncertain. Given some breeding overlap, perhaps no longer in a superspecies with western *P. apricaria* or New World *P. dominica* (Greater and American Golden Plovers) (cf. Connors *et al.* 1993).

GLOBAL RANGE. Breeds in Siberian tundra from the Yamal Peninsula at longitude about 70°E to Chukotka, and in W Alaska. Winters from E Africa around the Indian Ocean to SW Asia, the Indian subcontinent, Sri Lanka and the Bay of Bengal islands; in the Nansei islands and far-S China including Taiwan and Hainan; SE Asia; Wallacea; and New Guinea, Australia and Oceania south to New Zealand. Some also in SW USA.

IDENTIFICATION/DESCRIPTION. Against a variegated soil background, often tries to avoid detection by standing motionless. Larger than other common waders found inland, with rounded head and large, dark eye, generally yellow-brown tone, spangled pattern on the upperparts, and sedate movements (see also Grey Plover). Very much rarer first-winter Oriental Plover is superficially similar but smaller, more slender and elegant, on proportionately longer, yellow legs; and has different feeding actions. In flight, both show uniformly dark upperparts.

Bare-part colours. Iris black-brown; bill black; legs and feet slate-grey.

Size (mm). (Live: 60 non-juveniles; none sexed): wing 160–179; tail 54–63; bill 20.8–28.1; tarsus 37.0–48.5 (AWB, UMBRP).

Weight (g). All age/sex-classes at mid-winter, 102–138 (n=116). Two adults fattening in March and April, 146 and 181 (AWB, UMBRP).

DISTRIBUTION. Historical summary: all divisions except *Chu, Nar, Pra,* with additional island records from St Luke's, Libong, Langkawi, Penang, Tengah and Kukup off the W coast; Samui off the E coast; and Ubin, Seletar, St John's, Salu, Sudong, Sakeng and Merlimau around Singapore.

GEOGRAPHICAL VARIATION. None recognized.

STATUS AND POPULATION. A winter visitor and probable passage migrant, with a small mid-summer presence in the far south and SW as far as Selangor (BR 1978–79, ENGGANG-1, SINGAV-1, -2, -4). Shoreline counts rank this plover tenth commonest wintering wader along the Melaka Straits coast (MBR 1986–87). Less is known about its status elsewhere, and especially about the contribution made by those using inland habitats. It has been assumed birds shift their foraging between habitats, including the coast, but this has still to be confirmed. Monitoring of favoured inland sites, such as Subang airfield, 25 km inland from the Selangor coast, has shown consistent presence during September–April, with a peak in November–December (A.C. Sebastian), but no over-summering. Summer groups, typically of 20 or less, appear to be strictly coastal.

HABITATS AND ECOLOGY. The largest aggregations, and probably most birds overall, forage in the intertidal zone. Counts of up to 800 have been made during passage seasons in the south (SINGAV-4), although typical foraging-groups are in the range 5–50, and only at top-quality sites do more than this gather inland. The favoured inland substrate is a broad expanse of short, preferably damp grassland, such as found on stocklands, playing-field complexes and the outlying parts of airfields (making this species a prime bird-strike hazard). Large expanses of paddyland at stubble, plough and early-growth stages are also favoured, but have been negatively affected by post-harvest application of pesticides, and pesticide loads keep most birds off the ever-growing supply of golf courses. Some enclosed sites are used at night but daytime visits inland are only to large, open ones, giving long views all round.

Sand-fill and cleared, dry back-mangrove areas are typical high-tide loafing habitat on the coast, but regular nocturnal activity keeps most birds away from overnight mixed-species roosts at such sites.

FORAGING AND FOOD. On the shore, estimates of substrate-preference have ranged from entirely soft mud to 40 percent mud, 36 percent sand/mud mixes and 24 percent sand, suggesting a fairly wide tolerance. Molluscs, mainly bivalves, form most of the coastal diet, and the main prey item in the Melaka Straits is *Orbicularia orbiculata*, eaten whole up to a shell-length of about 12 mm (Howes *et al.* 1986, Swennen and Marteijn 1985).

SOCIAL ORGANIZATION. Foragers scatter individually, but form cohesive parties when on the move.

MOVEMENTS. Little known in the north. South of the Thai border, no three-figure counts have been made before the end of August and none regularly before mid/late September. In general, numbers increase through October–November but on the Melaka Straits coastal plain and in Singapore then fall again quite sharply, with few counts above ten by mid December. Recovery begins in mid/late January, with high counts everywhere through February–March. Pre-migratory fattening has started by early March, migrants have left the far south by April, and in Selangor no three-figure counts have been reported past 10 April (Silvius *et al.* 1987).

SURVIVAL. No information.

SOCIAL INTERACTIONS. No information.

VOICE. The main communication-call, most often given by birds flying at night, is a lilting, up-inflected *kyew-eek*.

BREEDING. No population.

MOULT. First-winterers not studied. By early May, most immatures carry a light scatter of breeding-type body-feathers. As at 1 June, all those handled had also started a regular-descendant, complete wing-moult, and two dated 21 August were close to completing (at P9 and 9–10). With up to five inner primaries in overlapping growth, even the most advanced adults (two on 24 August and 14 September suspended at P4 and 5) are unlikely to have started before arrival. By end September, adults were active between P1 and P7 (mostly beyond P3), and 49 dated 10 October–3 November were between P5 and P9. By the end of this period a few had completed, and the last moulter handled was at P10 on 24 January.

First traces of adult summer body-plumage appear in early March (AWB, UMBRP).

CONSERVATION. Though able to exploit a wide range of habitats, this is a shy bird permanently ousted from an inland site by even small increases of regular human activity.

Grey Plover; Nok Hua Toh See Thaw (Thai); Burung Rapang Kelabu (Malay)

Pluvialis squatarola (Linnaeus) 1758, *Systema Naturae* 10(1): 149. TL Sweden.
Plate 29

GROUP RELATIONS. Free-standing.

GLOBAL RANGE. Breeds on the arctic coastal plain from the White Sea to Chukotka, and in Alaska and Canada. Winters from the N- to the S-temperate zones, in the Americas; Atlantic Europe, Africa, the Malagasy region and coasts of the Indian Ocean to the Indian subcontinent, Sri Lanka and the Andamans; S Japan and China south from the Changjiang river including Taiwan and Hainan; SE Asia; and Wallacea to New Guinea and Australia, with a few to Oceania as far as New Zealand (Lane and Davis 1987).

IDENTIFICATION/DESCRIPTION. A medium-large wader, and largest local shoreline plover. From Pacific Golden Plover on the ground, by heavier build, more hunched stance, lack of any brown tone in the plumage and absolutely and proportionately larger bill. In flight, white wing-bar, conspicuous white rump, black axillaries sharp against white underwing and distinctive call are a diagnostic combination.

Bare-part colours. Iris blackish brown; bill entirely black or with basal cutting-edge and mouth-angle pink-yellow (an age factor?); legs and feet grey-black.

Size (mm). (Live and skins: 15 non-juveniles, none sexed): wing 187–213; tail 70, 75 (2 only); bill 29.7–35.0; tarsus 45.5, 46.2 (2 only) (AWB, UMBRP, ZRCNUS).

Weight (g). Variation during July–February, 190–231 (n=6, age/sex-classes not separated); fattening adults during 13 March–7 April, 240–293 (n=5) (AWB, UMBRP).

DISTRIBUTION. Historical summary: all divisions except *Pak, Chu, Ran, Pha, Pht, Son, Yal, Nar, Pra, Mel,* with additional island records from Muk, Libong, Penang, Ketam and Tengah off the W coast; and Tekong, Ubin and Semakau, Singapore.

GEOGRAPHICAL VARIATION. None recognized.

STATUS AND POPULATION. A non-breeding visitor and probable passage migrant, with a small summer presence (parties of ten or less) in Pattani and Mersing bays and Singapore, and a potentially much larger one in Selangor (700 dull-plumaged, evident immatures counted at roost on the Kapar power-station ash-ponds on 20 May) (MBR 1982–83, Ollington and Loh 1993, Ruttanadakul and Ardseungnern 1987, Silvius *et al.* 1987, SINGAV-2, UMBRP). At mid winter, recorded from all sectors but heavily concentrated in Selangor where more than 90 percent of the Peninsula's Grey Plovers may over-winter at just one site, Tengah island in the outer Kelang estuary. Up to 1200 have been counted there in late January (ENGGANG-3) and approximately that number has roosted at nearby Kapar in early March (Sebastian *et al.* 1993). In the NW, Libong island (Trang) holds over 100 at mid winter (Parish 1985) and up to 200 in spring, with a maximum 150 in Krabi bay (P.D. Round). No counts above 60 reported at any time of year from Singapore, or 30 at the few regular E-coast localities.

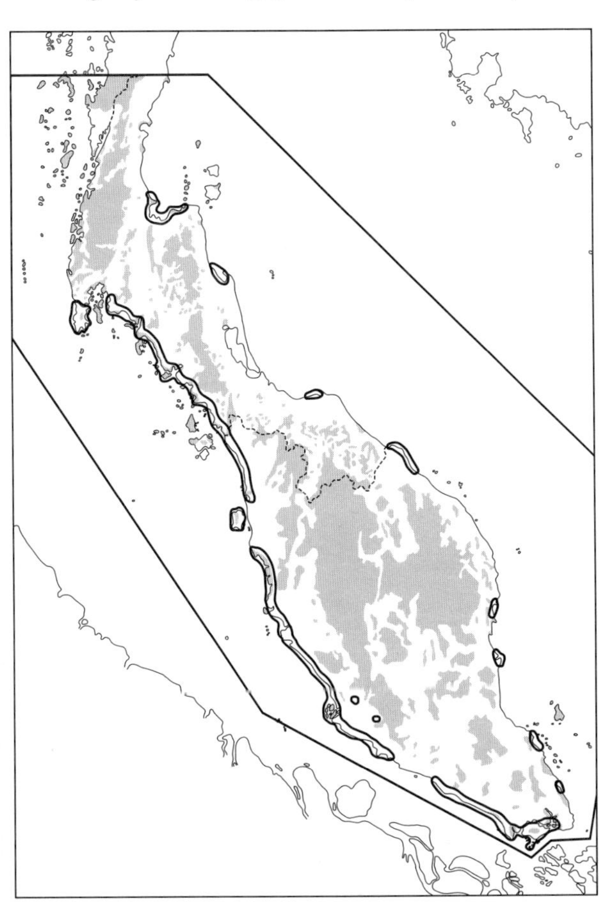

HABITATS AND ECOLOGY. Records away from the intertidal zone or adjacent roost-sites are exceptional. Parties at dredge-mine lagoons near Kuala Lumpur and Seremban (Negeri Sembilan) in late November/December are likely to have been migrating (BMP5). Grey are unusual among plovers in sometimes waiting out high tides perched on mangrove snags or fish-trap pilings (P.D. Round), but prefer the ground on remote beaches, and over highest tides join other waders at mixed-species roosts in coastal clearings (Sebastian *et al.* 1993).

FORAGING AND FOOD. On the shore, Grey Plovers show a strong (91 percent) preference for mixed mud/sand surfaces (Swennen and Marteijn 1985), such as dominate the Tengah and Libong island habitats. General avoidance of others (only nine percent of feeding records on soft muds) may help to isolate Grey from shore-feeding Pacific Golden Plovers. These relatives tend not to concentrate at the same sites, and Tengah and Libong are hardly used by Golden Plovers. Takes more polychaetes than bivalves, another difference from Pacific Golden Plover.

SOCIAL ORGANIZATION. Scatters to forage; otherwise strongly gregarious, particularly during roost movements.

MOVEMENTS. In Singapore, noticeable dips in November and February suggest waves of onward movement, and spring passage reaches a peak in mid April. Numbers in Selangor build up more or less steadily from the end of July to mid/late January, at Tengah island with the same large dip in February and recovery by early March. On this coast, intermittent high counts continue through late May, but without a record of exactly when most adults depart (see above). Spring passage has also been observed at Libong island, but with no monitoring past early April (Parish 1985). Elsewhere, a few spring migrants halt in the SE (Howes *et al.* 1986) but, apparently, not in the NE.

SURVIVAL. No information.

SOCIAL INTERACTIONS. No information.

VOICE. The flight-call is a light, slurred but musical trisyllable, *tlee-o-ee.*

BREEDING. No population.

MOULT. First-winterers not studied. A complete, regular-descendant second-summer wing-moult starts post late April, with a bird active at P5–6 on 4 July and another at P7–8 on 14 August. A late-December adult had suspended at P8 and another on 18 January was growing P10. Adults develop extensive to complete summer body-plumage before departure; the most advanced birds 50 percent moulted by mid March (AWB, UMBRP).

CONSERVATION. The key wintering-site for the species is not yet protected and the current major roost-site of this concentration is regularly shot-over. Both lie close to areas of expanding economic activity, and require decisive conservation action.

Common Ringed Plover; (no Thai name); Burung Rapang Kerikil (Malay)

Charadrius hiaticula Linnaeus 1758, *Systema Naturae* 10(1): 150. TL Sweden.
Plate 36

GROUP RELATIONS. Related to American *C. semipalmatus* (Semipalmated Plover), probably at superspecies level.

GLOBAL RANGE. Breeds at subarctic to arctic latitudes from NE Canada, Greenland and Iceland across Eurasia to Anadyrland and Chukotka, south into the temperate-zone in W Europe. Winters from the W-European breeding-range and Mediterranean to Africa and SW Asia; in small numbers in the western Indian subcontinent and Sri Lanka; sparsely in Japan, Korea, China, and SE Asia as far as the Peninsula, N Borneo and Palawan; with a few records also from New Guinea, Australia and New Zealand.

IDENTIFICATION/DESCRIPTION. Larger and deeper-bodied than Little Ringed Plover, without the latter's pale eyelid-rim and with legs usually brighter orange. Winter supercilium and forehead are buff rather than white, and face-mask brown rather than black. In flight, from Little Ringed and Long-billed Plovers by conspicuous white wing-bar and flashes along the base of the primaries.

Bare-part colours. Iris deep brown; bill black, dull orange at the base, with basal two thirds clear orange in summer adults; legs and feet dull to bright yellow-orange.

Size. No local data.

Weight. No data.

DISTRIBUTION. Undoubtedly overlooked. Historical summary: *Sel*, *Sin* and Penang island.

GEOGRAPHICAL VARIATION. No handlings, but certain to be Old World arctic-breeding *tundrae* Lowe 1915 (TL Yenisey valley, central Siberia).

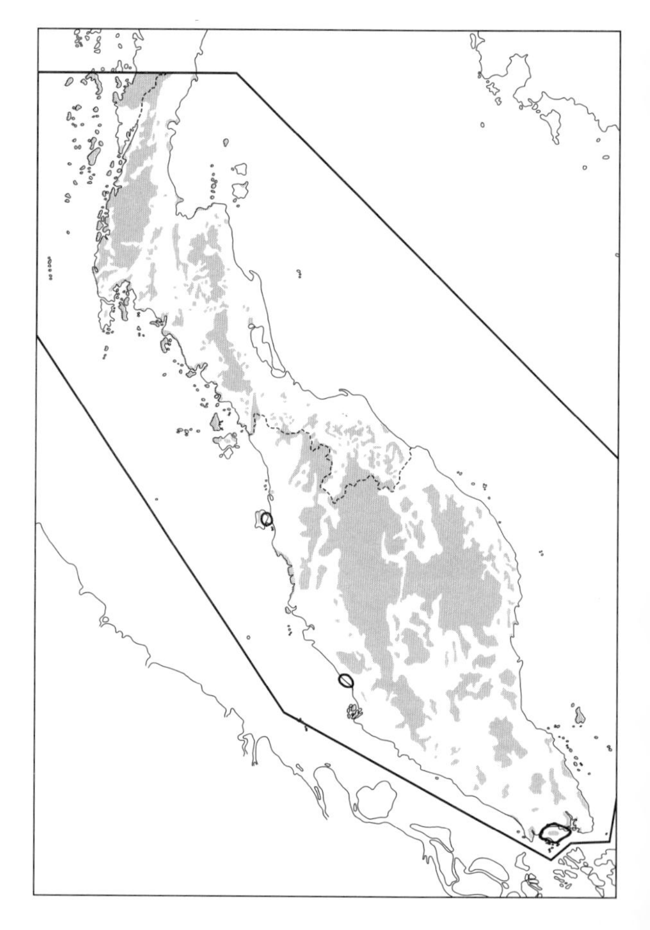

STATUS AND POPULATION. A non-breeding visitor, local and sparse, but which vigilance in Singapore shows to be annual, at a rate of 1–4 individuals recorded per season (Ollington and Loh 1992). The only records away from Singapore island are of a bird identified by flight-call in a group of Little

Ringed Plovers over shore habitat near Georgetown, Penang island, on 25 March 1984, and one on sand-flats at Kuala Selangor on 6 February 1988 (MBR 1984–85, A.J. Richards).

HABITATS AND ECOLOGY. The margins of tide-flushed prawn-ponds and low-tide mudflats are habitats used in Singapore (BMP5, Ollington and Loh 1993).

FORAGING AND FOOD. No information.

SOCIAL ORGANIZATION. No information.

MOVEMENTS. Found in all months from 11 September to 25 March, with a small peak of records in October suggestive of some through-passage, but not matched anywhere in spring (MBR 1982–83, 1984–85).

SURVIVAL. No information.

SOCIAL INTERACTIONS. No information.

VOICE. The flight-call is a mellow, up-inflected whistle, *too-lii* or *tu-weep* (BR 1964).

BREEDING. No population.

MOULT. None handled, but birds in substantial amounts of summer plumage reported up to 21 October, and again on 2 March (SINGAV-3, -4).

CONSERVATION. No relevant issues.

Long-billed Plover; Nok Hua Toh Paak Yao (Thai); Burung Rapang Paruh Panjang (Malay)

Charadrius placidus G.R. Gray 1863, J.E. Gray's *Catalogue of the specimens and drawings of mammals, birds, reptiles, and fishes of Nepal and Tibet, presented by B.H. Hodgson, Esq., to the British Museum* (second edition): 70. TL Nepal.

Plate 36

GROUP RELATIONS. Uncertain.

GLOBAL RANGE. Breeds from the Amur valley to Japan, and NE China as far as the Changjiang valley. Winters in S Japan and China south of the Changjiang, including Taiwan; the NE Indian subcontinent west to Nepal; and SE Asia to N Burma, NW Thailand, Laos and central Vietnam. Vagrant in Sri Lanka, the Peninsula, NW Borneo and Bali.

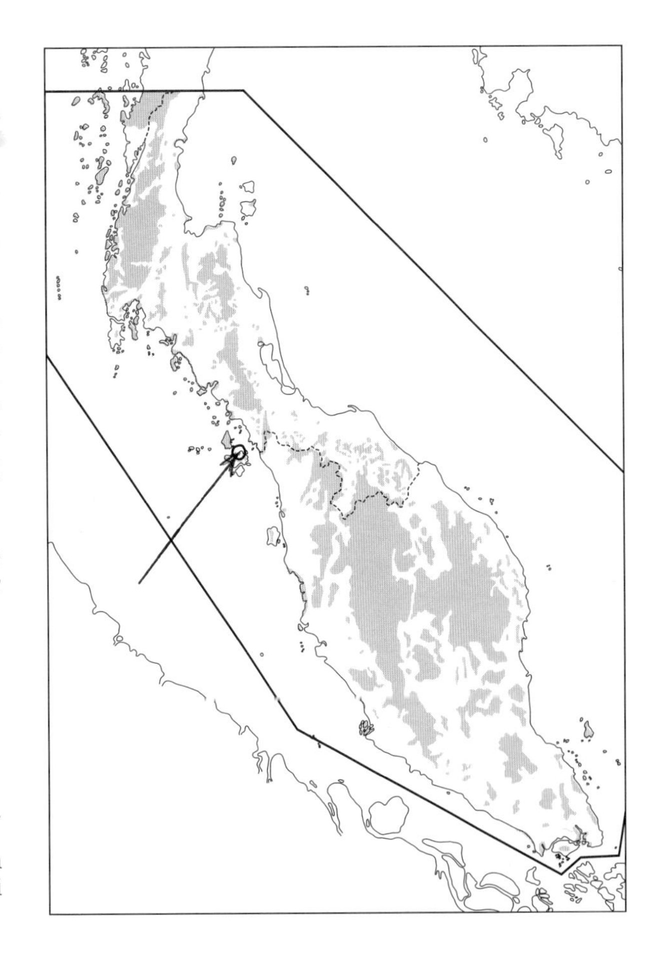

IDENTIFICATION/DESCRIPTION. About the size of a Mongolian Plover but slenderer, with proportionately long bill and tail. In winter, forecrown and collar are brown and, as in Common Ringed Plover, forehead and supercilium buff rather than white. Eyelid-rim and legs are pale yellow, as in Little Ringed Plover. In flight, narrow white wing-bar crosses only the secondaries.

Bare-part colours. Iris deep brown, eyelid-rim pale yellow; bill black with some dull orange on lower base; legs and feet pale yellow (Hayman *et al.* 1986).

Size. No data.

Weight. No data.

DISTRIBUTION. Historical summary: *Ked.*

GEOGRAPHICAL VARIATION. None recognized.

STATUS AND POPULATION. Vagrant. Known from a single occurrence at Tanjung Ru, Langkawi island, on 19 March 1968 (BR 1968).

HABITATS AND ECOLOGY. On a sandy beach.

FORAGING AND FOOD. No information.

SOCIAL ORGANIZATION. No information.

MOVEMENTS. No information.

SURVIVAL. No information.

SOCIAL INTERACTIONS. No information.

VOICE. Calls include a shrill, clear, up-inflected *piwee* and musical *tudulu* (BR 1968, Hayman *et al.* 1986).

BREEDING. No population.

MOULT. No data.

CONSERVATION. Globally near-threatened (BTW2), but no local issues.

Little Ringed Plover; Nok Hua Toh Lek Khaa Leuang (Thai); Burung Rapang Biji Nangka (Malay)

Charadrius dubius Scopoli 1786, *Deliciae Florae et Faunae Insubricae* 2: 93. TL Luzon, Philippines.
Plate 36

GROUP RELATIONS. Probably free-standing.

GLOBAL RANGE. Breeds across temperate–low arctic Eurasia from the Atlantic to Japan, south to N Africa and SW Asia; in the Indian subcontinent and Sri Lanka; China east to a line Yunnan–Shandong (i.e. not in the SE); continental SE Asia south to about 15°N (including SW Thailand) (BBCB-8), and N and central Philippines; also New Guinea. Northern populations migrate, wintering within and beyond the breeding-range as far as N-tropical Africa, Sri Lanka and the Andamans; China south from Fujian including Taiwan and Hainan; SE Asia; Wallacea, W Micronesia and, in small numbers, New Guinea and Australia.

IDENTIFICATION/DESCRIPTION. Dark breast-band complete, and dark eye-mask contrasts with pale eyelid-rim. In flight, shows virtually no wing-bar. From Long-billed Plover by small size and bill-proportions, brighter eyelid, proportionately broader breast-band and, in summer adult, black rather than brown mask.

Bare-part colours. Iris deep brown, eyelid-rim yellow; bill black with slight spot of yellow at base of lower mandible; legs and feet pale yellow to pale pinkish.

Size (mm). (Live and skins: 22 adults; none sexed): wing 111–119; tail 51–62; bill 11.8–14.4; tarsus 23.2–26.2 (UMBRP, ZRCNUS).

Weight (g). All age/sex-classes during August–March, 29.0–38.3 (UMBRP).

DISTRIBUTION. Historical summary: all divisions except *Chu, Kra, Tra, Nar,* with additional island records from the Similan group, Penang and Tengah off the W coast; and Ubin, Singapore.

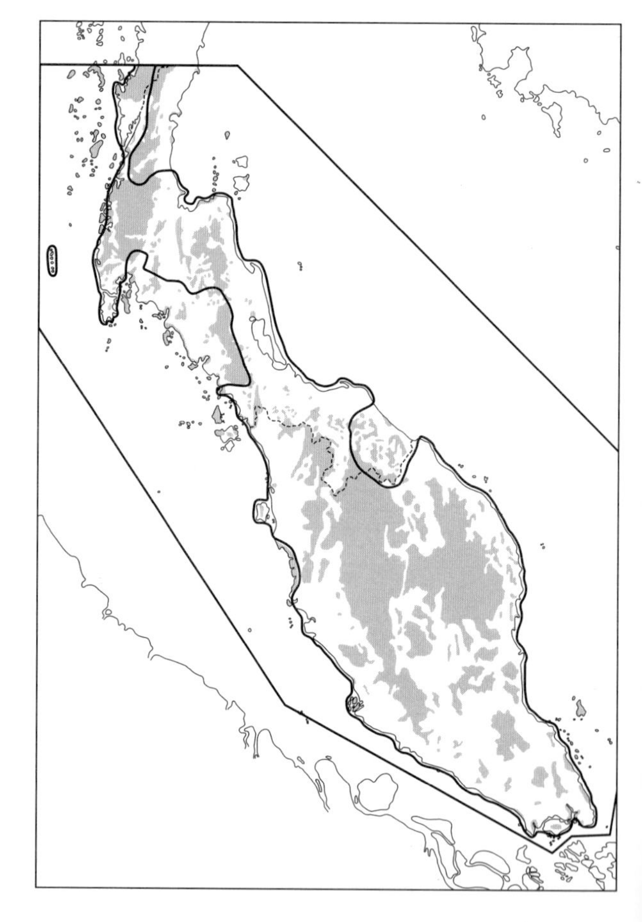

GEOGRAPHICAL VARIATION. A specimen-record of tropical-Asian-breeding *jerdoni* Legge 1880 (TL Sri Lanka) from inland Pahang, identified on the basis of its short wing (BMP5), is rejected. The wing-tip (P10) is in moult, and a 13.0 mm bill is just out of the range of *jerdoni* but within that of northern migrants. Probably, only Palaearctic *curonicus* Gmelin 1789 (TL Kurland, Latvia) occurs.

STATUS AND POPULATION. A non-breeding visitor and passage migrant, not recorded at mid summer, although one in Singapore on 31 May is seven weeks on from the next-latest spring record (BR 1964). Regular and common, this non-shoreline plover is widely distributed through open-ground habitats, but of unknown real abundance. On abandoned salt-pans at Kuala Selangor during the 1970s it was the eleventh most often mist-netted wader (BR 1978–79), but in tiny numbers compared with front-runners such as Mongolian Plover.

HABITATS AND ECOLOGY. Selects open expanses of short grass or bare soil, commonly near shallow flood-pools, on grazing-land, airfields, large playing-fields, river-shoals, mine-tailings, fill, and cleared and bunded mangrove-land; also ploughland, both dry and part-irrigated. A progressive switch from transplanting to dry-seeding of rice, lengthening the bare-soil period, could favour this plover. However, numbers using paddyland have actually declined, it is thought in response to pesticide loads, especially herbicides used to kill fallow-stage cover before seed-set. Sewage-farm sludge-drying beds rich in dipteran larvae were favoured habitat before conversion of the Serangoon plant, Singapore. Found much less often on sandy beaches and only exceptionally on intertidal mud (Young 1941), although attracted to the margins and exposed beds of aquaculture ponds in the mangrove-zone.

FORAGING AND FOOD. No additional information.

SOCIAL ORGANIZATION. Birds scatter to forage but form coherent flocks on the move.

MOVEMENTS. Extreme dates, from Singapore, are 21 July and 9 April, with an isolated record on 31 May (BR 1964, SINGAV-4). The largest count in July is 12, with none over 50 anywhere before the last week of August. Trends then differ by region. In the NE (Ruttanadakul and Ardseungnern 1987), numbers around Pattani bay rise steadily to peak at over 400 in December but drop by half from January, and most leave in March – the best April count, 20. On the Selangor plain, peaks by late September (1300 at the Sekinchan paddyland on 30 September 1984: Parish 1985a) and oscillates through to November–December before the same January decline. Only in Singapore has a minor recovery been recorded in March, presumably due to halting of passage migrants from further south.

SURVIVAL. No information.

SOCIAL INTERACTIONS. No information.

VOICE. The flight-call is a light but carrying *pee-oo.*

BREEDING. No population.

MOULT. The few first-winterers handled up to early March showed no wing-moult. Among non-juveniles (year-classes not separated), one on 1 August still had all-old primaries while a second dated 23 August was growing P1–3. Others dated early September–early November were active between P7 and 10, and one on 26 November had completed. Instances of late-stage suspension (after P7 to P9) occurred over the same period. Spring body-moult starts as of early January, can be heavy by late January, and is complete by early–mid March (AWB, UMBRP).

CONSERVATION. An opportunist. Various other inland habitats may absorb some of the displacement from Malaysian paddyland.

Kentish Plover; Nok Hua Toh Khaa Dam (Thai); Burung Rapang Pantai (Malay)

Charadrius alexandrinus Linnaeus 1758, *Systema Naturae* 10(1): 150. TL Egypt.
Plate 36

GROUP RELATIONS. Relatives spread an '*alexandrinus* complex' over most of the southern continents. Some are entirely allopatric, others share range with non-breeding Kentish Plover. Recently, at least African *marginalis* (White-fronted Plover), SE Asian *peronii* (Malaysian Plover) and Australian *ruficapillus* (Red-capped Plover) have been proposed as members of an *alexandrinus* superspecies (BWP). Grounds for assuming Indonesian *javanicus* has reached species level are not as well founded.

GLOBAL RANGE. Breeds from mid-temperate to outer-tropical latitudes in N and S America, Eurasia from the Atlantic to Japan, south to N Africa and SW Asia; the northern Indian subcontinent; and coastal China to Vietnam (OBCB-22); with outliers in S India and Sri Lanka, and Java to the Kangean islands (Java Sea) (Hoogerwerf 1967). Northern populations migrate, wintering to the tropics around the world, including the Indian subcontinent and Sri Lanka; China from the Changjiang valley plus Taiwan and

Hainan; SE Asia to the Greater Sunda islands, Bali and the Philippines; and Sulawesi. Vagrant in the Moluccas, W Micronesia and Australia.

IDENTIFICATION/DESCRIPTION. Little Ringed Plover-sized but generally whiter-looking, dark-legged and, in flight, shows a distinct white wing-bar. From Malaysian Plover (which see), with care, by proportions, less sandy-toned upperparts (but they bleach pale), and absence of black hind-collar in adult male or a rust-orange lateral breast-patch in other age/sex-classes. Some individuals can be tricky: a November-dated first-winterer with typical measurements had its white collar broken mid-dorsally and an almost-complete, brown breast-band rather than just side-marks (UMBRP). Dark rather than yellow or pink-tinged legs and feet is typical but, perhaps, not diagnostic.

Bare-part colours. Iris deep brown; bill blackish; legs and feet dark grey.

Size (mm). (Live and skins: 15 non-juveniles; none sexed): wing 104–114; tail 45–51; bill 16.2–18.5; tarsus 28.0–29.0 (UMBRP, UMZC).

Weight (g). Age/sex-classes not separated, 32.5–45.0 (n=14), birds 40-plus recorded only in early September and as of early February (UMBRP).

DISTRIBUTION. Historical summary: all divisions except *Pak, Chu, Pht, Son, Yal, Nar, Pes, Pra, Neg*, with additional island records from the Surins, Libong, Langkawi, Penang and Tengah off the W coast; and Bidung Laut (*Tru*) off the E coast.

GEOGRAPHICAL VARIATION. Long bills (in most cases 17 mm-plus) identify the Peninsular population as E Eurasian *dealbatus* Swinhoe 1870 (TL S China). One with all-white instead of typically black lores, sketched by C.A. Rose at the Kapar power-station roost in March 1993, may not have been this subspecies.

STATUS AND POPULATION. A non-breeding visitor and apparent spring passage migrant, showing no evidence of over-summering. Regular and more or less common. One of few migratory waders for which the E is nearly as important as the W coast, with some eastern spring stop-over points (Mersing and Pattani bays) among the most important in the Peninsula (Howes *et al.* 1986, Ruttanadakul and Ardseungnern 1987). In the west, comparable counts have been made only at Tanjung Karang and on Tengah island, Selangor (ENGGANG-2, -3). At highest tides, some join other waders at mixed-species roosts behind the beach or on cleared mangrove-land, etc., but tend to avoid dense packs of birds.

HABITATS AND ECOLOGY. Strictly coastal, with a strong preference for firm sand or mixed mud/sand substrates; much less often on pure mud and usually then only where the surface has caked (Howes *et al.* 1986, Swennen and Marteijn 1985).

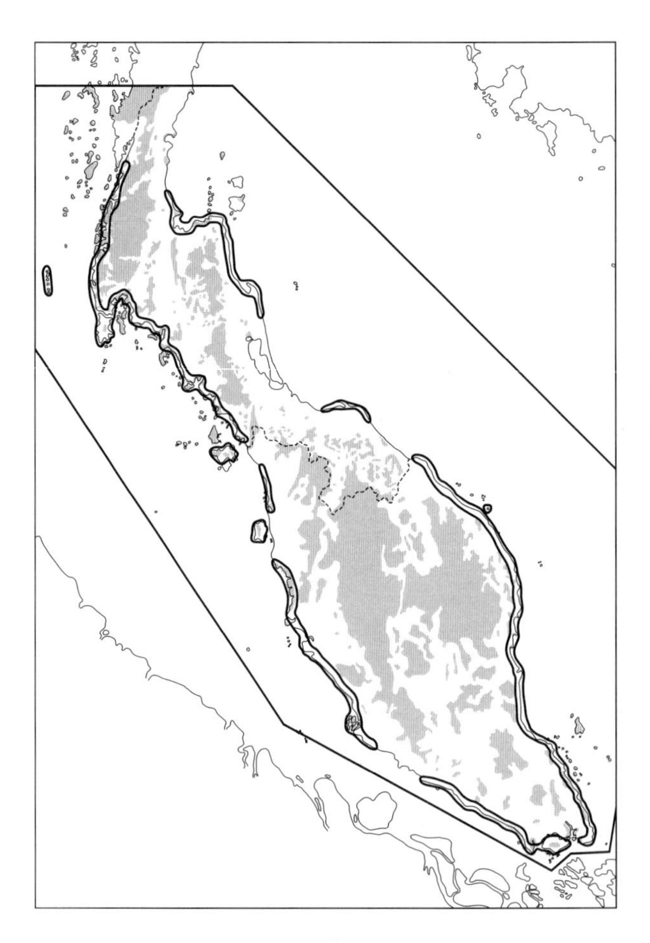

FORAGING AND FOOD. Like other small plovers (Little Ringed, Malaysian), forages mainly by fast-running with sudden pauses to pick from the surface. No local data on prey.

SOCIAL ORGANIZATION. As Little Ringed Plover.

MOVEMENTS. Extreme dates are 5 August (at Changi, E Singapore) and 1 May (in Mersing bay, E Johor) (BIRDLINE 1993, Howes *et al.* 1986). The pattern everywhere is one of low-level presence through autumn, double-figure counts only as of October (earliest on Libong island: Parish 1985) and no further build-up before mid–late January. From early February to the start of April counts occasionally reach three figures (maximum 150 at Mersing). This covers spring passage, and numbers drop abruptly (maximum count ten) as of the second week of April.

A bird ringed at Kuala Selangor in late March 1988 was recovered from hunters near Hai Phong, N Vietnam, on 12 September 1992; perhaps on passage at that date.

SURVIVAL. The longest ring recovery-interval is 53 months.

SOCIAL INTERACTIONS. No information.

VOICE. The flight-call is a brief, soft *pwit*.

BREEDING. No population.

MOULT. Kentish Plovers are relatively hard to mist-net, hence little is known. None of 18 (all age-groups) handled on both E and W coasts of Malaysia in all months early September–early April showed any wing-moult (B.D. Bond, UMBRP, UMZC). Degree of wear implies this is completed before arrival, although an exceptional adult male dated 12 February appeared too fresh-looking to have had flight-feathers six months old.

Renewal of adult summer body-plumage begins early, is complete in some by early February and universal by March (Howes *et al.* 1986, UMBRP). First-winterers handled in Selangor up to early April were still in winter-type plumage (with buff-edged, juvenile inner median wing-coverts), and may leave in this condition.

CONSERVATION. No specific issues.

Malaysian Plover; Nok Hua Toh Malayu (Thai); Burung Rapang Malaysia (Malay)

Charadrius peronii Schlegel 1865, *Muséum d'Histoire Naturelle des Pays-Bas* 4(29): 33. TL Samau island, W Timor.

Plate 36

GROUP RELATIONS. See Kentish Plover, but breeders may meet in S Vietnam (OBCB-22), and Hoogerwerf (1967) implied both might breed in the Kangean archipelago, E Java Sea.

GLOBAL RANGE. Coastal SE Asia from the NW Malay Peninsula, Gulf of Bangkok and S Vietnam to the Greater Sunda islands (but no breeding records from mainland Java), Bali and the Philippines; and Sulawesi and the Lesser Sunda islands to Timor.

IDENTIFICATION/DESCRIPTION. From Kentish Plover by finely patterned, sandier upperparts (but in late winter check bleached young Kentish); black hind-collar and ear-covert patch (isolated from eye) in adult male; orange-brown mask and side-marks on breast in young and most females. Compared directly with Kentish, Malaysian appears larger-headed, and longer-legged (relative to its shorter folded wing) (C.A. Rose, P.D. Round).

Bare-part colours. Iris deep brown; bill black; legs and feet yellow- or pink-tinged grey to dark grey (sexual or possible cyclic variation needs more study).

Size (mm). (Skins: 7 males, 5 females; adult): wing 94–103 and 100–101; tail 38–42 and 37–40; bill 15.1–16.9 and 15.4–17.3; tarsus 28.0–30.3 and 27.8–29.9 (BMNH, ZRCNUS).

Weight. No data.

DISTRIBUTION. Historical summary: all divisions except *Pak, Chu, Pht, Sat, Yal, Pes, Kel, Pra, Pek, Mel,* with additional island records from Libong, Langkawi and Tengah off the W coast; and Phangan, Samui and the Pahang–Johor archipelago (Tioman, Tinggi) off the E coast. Not confirmed from any Singapore satellite but military take-over of Tekong island has isolated some likely habitat (BIRDLINE 1993).

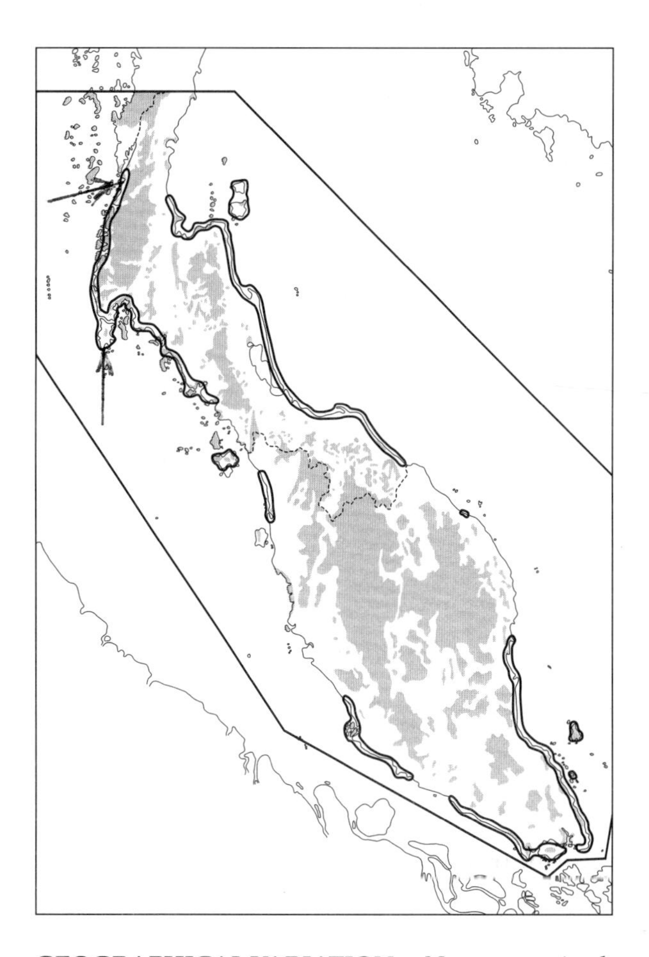

GEOGRAPHICAL VARIATION. None recognized.

STATUS AND POPULATION. Resident, and present year-round in breeding habitat. However, birds thinly scattered along the SW coast, mostly during the local non-breeding season (and where no breeding has been recorded) must be at least medium-distance dispersants (BR 1963, 1964). Local, and sparse to more or less common. Other than in Kelantan and Terengganu (a single record at Setiu Baru: Howes *et al.* 1986), recorded widely along the sandy E coast, south to Singapore, and this is the principal breeding-range. Much less prime nesting habitat is available elsewhere and the only W-coast breeding records are from Ranong, Phuket and the Langkawi islands (NRCS, P.D. Round, Summers-Smith 1981). Breeders in Singapore have colonized new coastal sand-fill, but as this stabilizes and becomes vegetated it is unlikely to retain its attractiveness.

Breeding pairs are often widely spaced, although clutches only about 75 m apart have been found at Changi, Singapore. Mean density in a linear habitat at Changi has recently been estimated at four pairs per km (BIRDLINE 1993), which is above anything reported from further north, including pairs 1 km apart on Phuket and 2 km apart in Jason's bay, E Johor (Howes *et al.* 1986, Summers-Smith 1981).

HABITATS AND ECOLOGY. Breeds on sandy beaches, dunes, and artificial coastal sand-fill, with no more than low, creeping vegetation (mostly *Ipomoea*), foraging among tide-wrack or on the adjacent exposed flat, often close to the water's edge (Madoc 1956a). Melaka Straits birds make some use of mud-flats, although most sightings there have been at high-tide roosts (ENGGANG-3). Records from mine-tailings inland in Selangor during September–October (Cant 1957–58, G.C. Madoc) have not been recognized, although the only reasonable alternative, Kentish Plover, is equally unlikely. A link may exist with dispersal to the SW coast.

FORAGING AND FOOD. See Kentish Plover.

SOCIAL ORGANIZATION. In breeding habitat, mostly alone or in pairs. Parties typically comprise just the pair plus fledged brood but, outside the breeding season, more social roosting can occur (up to 27 counted on a sea-wall site at Changi: Ollington and Loh 1993).

MOVEMENTS. None confirmed.

SURVIVAL. No information.

SOCIAL INTERACTIONS. No information.

VOICE. Not adequately described.

BREEDING

Nest. Typically sited near the top of the beach, sometimes near low plant-cover: a shallow depression about 8 cm across in bare, coarse, often shelly sand, unlined (though, where present, shell fragments tend to gather in the cup). Coarse, shelly sand is actually a better match for the egg-pattern than uniformly fine sand.

Eggs and brood. Eggs are glossless creamy to pale stone with profuse dots and squiggles of black, brown and lavender-grey. Shape broad near-piriform. Size (mm): 30.6 × 22.6 and 31.5 × 23.6 (means of two small series). Full clutch two or three, predominantly three.

Cycle. Breeders at the egg stage do not tolerate a close approach and loaf a few to 50-plus m away from the nest, calling quietly. Their time to returning varies with frequency of disturbance. The Langkawi pair and a bird on Prapad beach, Ranong, returned to a single egg immediately, in one case standing over and shading it. Chicks crouch in the presence of an intruder and are extremely hard to find; rather easier with a flashlight at night when they do not show this response.

Seasonality. Eggs from 19 March (the start of a clutch) to 31 July, chicks from 16 March (implying laying by February) to 17 June, with most records in April and May (BIRDLINE 1993, Howes *et al.* 1986, G.C. Madoc, NRCS, P.D. Round, Summers-Smith 1981).

MOULT. Among handlings from Chumphon south to Johor, two June males and a mid-July female showed early/mid-stage wing-moult (respectively at P1, P4 and P2–3), and a female dated 9 September had reached P8–9. Other adults dated January and April–June showed none (BMNH, UMBRP, ZRC-NUS). No data on post-juvenile moult.

CONSERVATION. Globally near-threatened (BTW2). Opportunistic within its narrow habitat-range, exploiting new ground as this becomes available but equally quick to abandon in the face of incidental disturbance (identified as the prime cause of nest-failure in Singapore). Everywhere, more and more sandy coastline is coming into regular use, especially from beach tourism, and the grassing- and building-over of coastal fill are developments paying no attention to conservation-needs at the shoreline. Elimination has already occurred, e.g., from Samui island (P.D. Round), and some former prime localities in Malaysia are now overrun by resorts. The situation must be faced if this species is to be retained and, for a start, demands a comprehensive population survey.

Mongolian Plover; Nok Hua Toh Sai Lek (Thai); Burung Rapang Mongolia (Malay)

Charadrius mongolus Pallas 1776, *Reise durch verschiedene Provinzen des Russischen Reichs* 3: 700. TL Kulusutay, far-E Russia.

Plate 36

GROUP RELATIONS. Free-standing; probably close to *C. leschenaultii* (Large Sand Plover). Where ranges overlap, they select breeding-sites at different elevations (BWP), and seek out different intertidal substrates for foraging in winter.

GLOBAL RANGE. Breeds at high altitude in Chukotka, Kamchatka and the Commander islands, locally in Pacific Russia and Mongolia, and in central Asia from the Tien Shan, neighbouring Xinjiang and the Pamirs south to Ladakh, then east across S Tibet into China, as far as Gansu. Winters around the Indian Ocean from S and E Africa and SW Asia to the Indian subcontinent, Sri Lanka and Bay of Bengal islands; in the Nansei islands and Taiwan; and through SE Asia and Wallacea to New Guinea, Australia and (sparingly) Oceania as far as New Zealand.

IDENTIFICATION/DESCRIPTION. A medium-small wader, but in isolation size does not help separate it from Large Sand Plover. Otherwise, shows a rounded rather than flattish forehead profile (Hayman *et al.* 1986) and blackish rather than yellow-grey feet. The dominant local wintering form has the mean longest bill of the species, hence this is not an easy character although, proportionately, Large Sand Plover bills are always deeper and more powerful. In summer plumage, the largest white forehead-windows of local Mongolian Plovers still leave a substantial black, median divider, whereas this is typically quite fine in Large Sand Plover.

Bare-part colours. Iris deep brown; bill black; legs and feet dark grey.

Size (mm). (Live: a 3-figure sample of non-juveniles; none sexed): wing 121–136, with peaks at 126–128 and 131–133; tail 49–53; bill 17.4–23.1, mostly in the range 18–20; tarsus 30.0–38.0 (AWB, UMBRP).

Weight (g). On the Selangor coast, age/sex-classes not separated, 39.3–79.0; birds 66-plus recorded in August–October and March–May. With data grouped by 5 g units, monthly modal values fell from 56–60 in August/September to 46–50 in October then rose to 51–55 during November–February. March values diverged at 51–55 and 61–65 as adults, and a few immatures, fattened before migration (but no obviously very fat birds encountered). Later samples are small but by May (with immatures dominant) had lapsed back to 51–55.

DISTRIBUTION. Historical summary: all divisions except *Pak, Chu, Pha, Pht, Son, Yal, Nar*, with additional island records from the Surins and Lao (*Ran*), Muk, Libong, Tarutao, Langkawi, Penang, Ketam and Tengah off the W coast; Phangan and Redang off the E coast; and Tekong, Ubin, Sudong and Sakeng in Singapore waters.

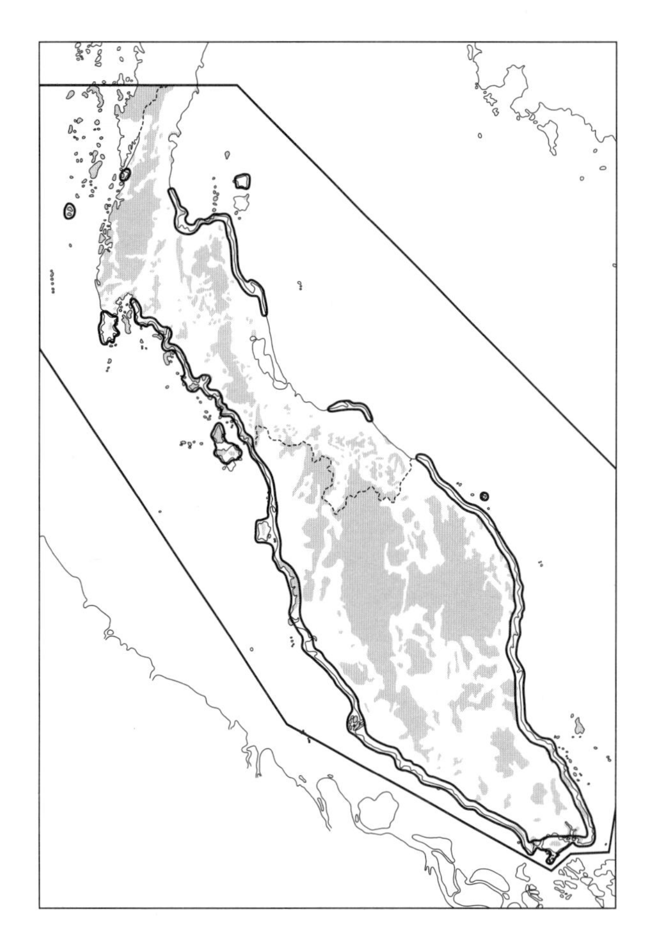

GEOGRAPHICAL VARIATION. Ninety-two percent of bill-lengths 18 mm or over, 86 percent of bill-length/depth ratios over 4.2 (AWB, UMBRP) and at least a little white feathering (often quite conspicuous 'windows') on the otherwise black summer-plumage forehead identify subspecies *schaeferi* Meyer de Schauensee 1937 (TL Qinghai, W China), from the SE end of the breeding-range, as dominant.

STATUS AND POPULATION. Regular and common to abundant. A non-breeding visitor and passage migrant, with groups of up to 75 intermittent over mid summer in Singapore and up to 40 in the NE (Pattani bay) (BR 1964, Ruttanadakul and Ardseungnern 1987).

Along the W coast, a six-week gap through June–early July is unexpected given the numbers of young birds roosting at Selangor sites until at least 20 May.

On W and E coasts of Malaysia, respectively, it has been ranked third and sixth commonest wader (Howes *et al.* 1986, Silvius *et al.* 1987), but in all sectors concentrates at a few key locations. Possibly as many as 5000 winter on the W coast, up to 30 percent of them in Selangor, most on the mainland but 400–700 at Tengah island (Silvius *et al.* 1987). Other high counts are recorded from Krabi bay, Libong island, and coasts of the Perlis/Kedah border and Perak (Parr 1988, Parish 1985, Parish and Wells 1984, Silvius *et al.* 1987, Swennen *et al.* 1986). On the E coast, nearly half the waders present in Bandon bay during late October were Mongolian Plovers (Swennen *et al.* 1986), and Pattani and Mersing bays are other important sites – as was the E end of Singapore before loss of Serangoon estuary.

Fifteen of 56 local retraps among 1000-plus birds ringed at the Kuala Selangor night-roost during the 1970s (BR 1978–79) were between seasons, at dates implying return to an overwintering site or, in a few cases, faithfulness to a passage halt. Within-season retraps, made 1–8 months after ringing and in every month September–May, showed interesting variation in autumn. Whereas half of those retrapped after ringing in late September were not seen beyond October and could have moved on, all five dating from August wintered locally (PERHILITAN, UMBRP). The proportion of juveniles in the population rises sharply in September (Parish and Wells 1984) and this difference in philopatry could be age-related.

HABITATS AND ECOLOGY. Mongolian Plovers depend on the intertidal zone and have only occasionally been recorded inland, typically transient on dredge-mine lagoon-margins, etc. (BMP5). They show a different foraging-substrate preference but often mingle with similar-looking Large Sand Plovers while loafing on quiet beaches during the day. Instances have also been reported of the use of off-shore fish-traps support-stakes as rest perches (Hawkins and Howes 1986). Regular, mixed-species, overnight roosts on land behind the beach attract large numbers, but usually only during phases of nocturnal high tides (Sebastian *et al.* 1993).

FORAGING AND FOOD. From large sets of observations, 85 percent of foraging preference is for soft muds versus 15 for firmer mud/sand mixes; distinct from Large Sand Plover, and reflecting a diet mainly of polychaetes and bivalves, especially the siphons of *Orbicularia orbiculata* (Swennen and Marteijn 1985).

SOCIAL ORGANIZATION. Scatter while foraging but highly gregarious when on the move and at roost.

MOVEMENTS. On the W coast, extreme arrival and departure dates are 12 July and 1 June (BR 1974–75, 1978–79). First likely long-distance migrants (identified by plumage) appear in the third week of July, but with no counts into three figures anywhere until August (earlier in Singapore than on the W coast). Changing retrap-rates and, in Singapore, monitoring of plumage-dyed birds (Parish and Wells 1984) give evidence of continued onward movement, but generally high numbers develop from August, peaking everywhere as of September–October. Except at certain key sites (Pattani bay, Tengah island, and elsewhere in Selangor), they dip from December to a relatively low level by March. Small surges are widespread during mid March–early April, but only in the NW (Libong island) has substantial spring passage been reported (Parish 1985). Most of the rest of the Peninsula may be overflown at this season. On Malaysian coasts, minor peaks in late April–May (Howes *et al.* 1986) are mainly of winter-plumaged birds presumed to be second-summerers that may not be moving far.

Distant recoveries show Pattani bay is an autumn-staging and/or over-summering ground for Selangor-coast winterers: two birds ringed at Kuala Selangor in December and February killed there in the following August (Siti Hawa Yatim 1990).

SURVIVAL. Longest ring retrap-intervals are 73 and 137 months, back at the Selangor wintering-site seven and 11 seasons on (MBR 1986–87).

SOCIAL INTERACTIONS. No information.

VOICE. The flight-call is a short, soft *chi-tik*.

BREEDING. No population.

MOULT. Arriving as of the second week of August (mainly later), some first-winterers are already in heavy body-moult. Most complete before mid October and no trace of the buff, juvenile chest-band has been seen after 30 October. On the Selangor coast, about seven percent moult the wing-tip precociously, starting between P4 and P9. The rest moult the whole hand, from P1, with up to five inner feathers in overlapping growth (in all age-groups, moult intensity peaks at stage P5). This complete moult occupies a long, staggered season beginning between January (possibly December; an advanced bird at P4–5 on 5 February) and May, and finishing during early March–August (one with all-new flight-feathers, moulting into a further winter-type body-plumage on 10 March; another at P9–10 on 10 August). Asymmetry and temporary suspensions (identified by feather-wear) are common. Second-summerers start their new complete wing-moult in July/August, at or before completion of juvenile moult, and finish during mid September–December.

Adults arrive in near-full summer plumage, but have replaced it by early October at the latest. Four dated 14 August showed all-old flight-feathers but three of five at the end of the month had started a wing-moult (P1–3). Most complete in October (one record of suspension at P10 on 25 November). Renewal of summer body-plumage starts in February/March, the most advanced individuals near-complete by mid March (AWB, PERHILITAN, UMBRP).

CONSERVATION. See Whimbrel for long-term issues affecting this species. Impacts of intertidal land-fill and reclamation are already clear in Singapore.

Large Sand Plover; Nok Hua Toh Sai Yai (Thai); Burung Rapang Pasir (Malay)

Charadrius leschenaultii Lesson 1826, Levrault's *Dictionnaire des Sciences Naturelles* 42: 36. TL Pondicherry, SE India.

Plate 36

GROUP RELATIONS. Probably free-standing, but see Mongolian Plover.

GLOBAL RANGE. Breeds from Turkey, the Black Sea and E Mediterranean across mid-temperate-zone Asia as far as Mongolia and NW China (claims from NE Africa, Arabia and Iran unconfirmed: Vaurie 1964). Winters around the Indian Ocean from S and E Africa and the Malagasy region to the Indian subcontinent, Sri Lanka and Bay of Bengal islands; in the Nansei islands and Taiwan; through SE Asia; Wallacea to New Guinea and Australia and, sparingly, Oceania as far as New Zealand.

IDENTIFICATION/DESCRIPTION. From Mongolian Plover (which see) by size only when they are viewable together. In isolation in winter, by head-shape, leg colour, and longer-tipped, proportionately heavier bill. In summer plumage, also by larger, more finely separated, white 'windows' on the forehead, narrower breast-band and more extensive orange above the eye-mask.

Bare-part colours. Iris deep brown; bill black; legs and feet yellowish to greenish grey, not dark as in Mongolian Plover.

Size (mm). (Live and skins: 22 non-juveniles; none sexed): wing 133–150; tail 48–55; bill 23.4–26.2; tarsus 35.9–40.0 (AWB, UMBRP, ZDUM, ZRCNUS).

Weight (g). Overall, sex/age-classes not separated, 61–95. Birds 90 or over include a second-summerer in mid July and adults (one in full summer plumage) in mid March.

DISTRIBUTION. Historical summary: all divisions except *Pak, Chu, Pht, Sat, Yal, Nar, Pra*, with additional island records from Loughborough, Lao, the Surins, Lanta, Libong, Langkawi, Penang and the Kelang estuary group (Ketam, Babi and Tengah) off the W coast; Tioman off the E coast; and Tekong, Ubin, Sakeng and Semakau around Singapore.

GEOGRAPHICAL VARIATION. The E-Asian winterer is nominate *leschenaultii*, with the heaviest, but not the longest, bill of the species (Hayman *et al.* 1986).

STATUS AND POPULATION. A non-breeding visitor and passage migrant, with a small presence over probably the whole mid-summer period noted in Singapore and Selangor (BR 1964). More or less regular, and uncommon to abundant. Though almost as widely found as Mongolian Plover, 70 percent or more

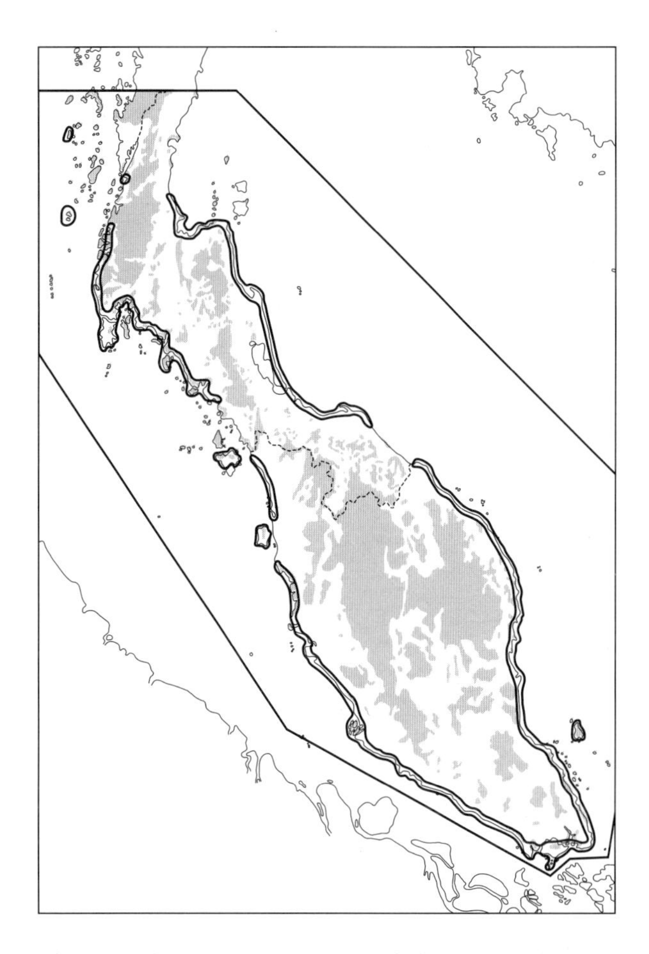

of the mid-winter population of the Peninsula may depend on just one site: Tengah island in the Kelang estuary (Selangor), where up to 4000 occur in late January (ENGGANG-3). The next-highest counts are about 900 at Krabi (P.D. Round) and, in autumn, 600 on Libong island but with no more than 250 there by January (Parish 1985, Swennen *et al.* 1986). Otherwise, three-figure counts have been made only at a few sites on the mainland coasts of Selangor and E Johor (ENGGANG-2, Silvius *et al.* 1987), all during passage periods.

Large Sand Plover is the most numerous wader along the Malaysian E coast (34 percent of all identifications), including substantial numbers in the Kelantan estuary (at least on passage), but it hardly occurs in nearby Pattani bay and only a few have been found in the far NE (Howes *et al.* 1986, Parish 1985, Ruttanadakul and Ardseungnern 1987, Swennen *et al.* 1986). Along the rest of the W coast and in Singapore (where it seems to have declined in the last 30 years: BR 1964), counts above 25 are unusual.

HABITATS AND ECOLOGY. Its skewed distribution reflects mainly the need for solid foraging substrates, and avoidance of soft, unripe muds. Casual observations indicate mangrove trees could be a high-tide retreat, which might account for the disproportionately low numbers from Tengah island visiting regularly watched, mixed-species roosts on open ground of the neighbouring Selangor mainland.

FORAGING AND FOOD. Swennen and Marteijn (1985) found 42 and 58 percent preference for foraging over consolidated mud and mud/sand mixes, but purer sands can also be important, accounting for 61 percent of feeding observations made along the Malaysian E coast (Howes *et al.* 1986). The prey is small crabs, for which this plover's proportionately heavy bill is a characteristic adaptation among waders.

SOCIAL ORGANIZATION. As Mongolian Plover.

MOVEMENTS. Old records from Singapore (BR 1963) show a first, sharp wave of arrivals on 29 July. Recently, summer-plumaged, presumed adults have been seen there as of 9 August (SINGAV-4) but lower counts throughout imply Singapore may no longer be important either as a wintering or a staging area. Extreme dates along the E coast are 3 September (Jørgensen 1949) and 1 May, with high counts only as of March. On the W coast, small surges of migrants occur by early/mid July, but no counts have been made on Tengah or Libong islands before late October, when numbers are already at or close to maximum. At both, they dip by November/December, with a further surge in late January then, at Tengah, a second dip in February before general spring passage during early March–mid April (Parish 1985, Silvius *et al.* 1987, Swennen *et al.* 1986). The meaning of the mid-winter oscillations is not understood, and no ringed Large Sand Plovers have been recovered at a distance.

SURVIVAL. No information.

SOCIAL INTERACTIONS. No information.

VOICE. The flight-call is a brief, soft trill, *trrri*.

BREEDING. No population.

MOULT. The only evidence some Large Sand Plovers renew the juvenile wing-tip precociously is from a bird captured in July that had moulted out from P8 and suspended at P10. Typical first-winter wing-moult is complete, begun between November/December (a bird growing P3/5 on 14 January) and early March (P1–2 on 9 March), and finished during mid March–late July (P9 on 18 July). At population level, its later stages are overlapped by the start of a complete second-summer wing-moult, recorded as of early July (P2 on 5 July).

Identified from body-plumage, adults handled during 11 September–21 November were in wing-moult between P7–8 and P10. It is not known when they start relative to arrival, but all non-juveniles have all-fresh wings by January. Advanced individuals complete moult back into summer body-plumage as early as mid March (AWB, PERHILITAN, UMBRP, ZRC-NUS).

CONSERVATION. Comments under Grey Plover relating to Tengah island apply to this species.

Oriental Plover; Nok Hua Toh Khaa Yao (Thai); Burung Rapang Timur (Malay)

Charadrius veredus Gould 1848, *Proceedings of the Zoological Society of London* 16: 38. TL northern Australia.

Plate 29

GROUP RELATIONS. Related to allopatric Caspian Plover *C. asiaticus* at not below superspecies level. Vaurie (1964) lists colour and plumage-sequence differences, and their size-difference would be unique for wader subspecies.

GLOBAL RANGE. Breeds in Mongolia east across the Russian and Chinese borders as far as Liaoning, NE China. Migrates across E China, eastern SE Asia, Wallacea and W Micronesia to winter mainly in northern Australia, small numbers reaching New Zealand (Lane and Davis 1987). Occasional on (mainly spring) passage west to Thailand, the Peninsula, Sumatra, the Andamans and Sri Lanka.

IDENTIFICATION/DESCRIPTION. About Large Sand Plover bulk but slender and long-winged, with rather long, graduated tail. Legs are proportionately long, and obviously yellow at all ages and seasons. Round head on erect neck recalls a small, slender Pacific Golden Plover. First-winterers are superficially like this bird, with mottled back, golden-buff face, neck and breast, darker cap and rusty-brown ear-covert patch, large black eye, bill noticeably dark against pale surround and, in flight, featureless, all-dark upperparts. Leg-proportions and foraging action are quite different from Pacific Golden Plover. In adults, the white collar of summer-plumage is obvious as birds stand up to peer.

Bare-part colours. Iris deep brown; bill black; legs and feet yellow to orange-yellow.

Size (mm). (Skins: 2 adults, neither sexed): wing 164, 165; tail 57, 62; bill 23.0 (1 only); tarsus 46.5, 47.6 (BMNH, ZRCNUS).

Weight. No data.

DISTRIBUTION. Historical summary: *Sel, Sin,* reflecting observer effort.

GEOGRAPHICAL VARIATION. None recognized.

STATUS AND POPULATION. Oriental Plover 'years' are erratic and when they do occur involve only a handful of records. Two birds collected on Singapore island in April 1898 are the only specimens (Gibson-Hill 1949b). Otherwise known from two on wet grazing-land near Kuala Lumpur in mid May 1957; at least two on nearby mine-tailings during late January–early February 1964; and a bird at Changi (Singapore) on 17 November 1985, with singles there again on 16 and 22 February 1986. In the same spring, at least two occurred on dry ploughland at Sekinchan (Selangor) on 8–9 March and another, with Pacific Golden Plovers, on a Kuala Lumpur playing-field on 10–11 March (BR 1964, Cant 1957–58, C.J Hails, MBR 1984–85, 1986–87). Two to four on bare landfill at Tuas, Singapore, during 29 October–9 November 1993 (BIRDLINE 1993) are the most recent finds reported. The preferred inland habitats are not among those regularly watched by wader enthusiasts, and Oriental Plovers may pass through more often than realized.

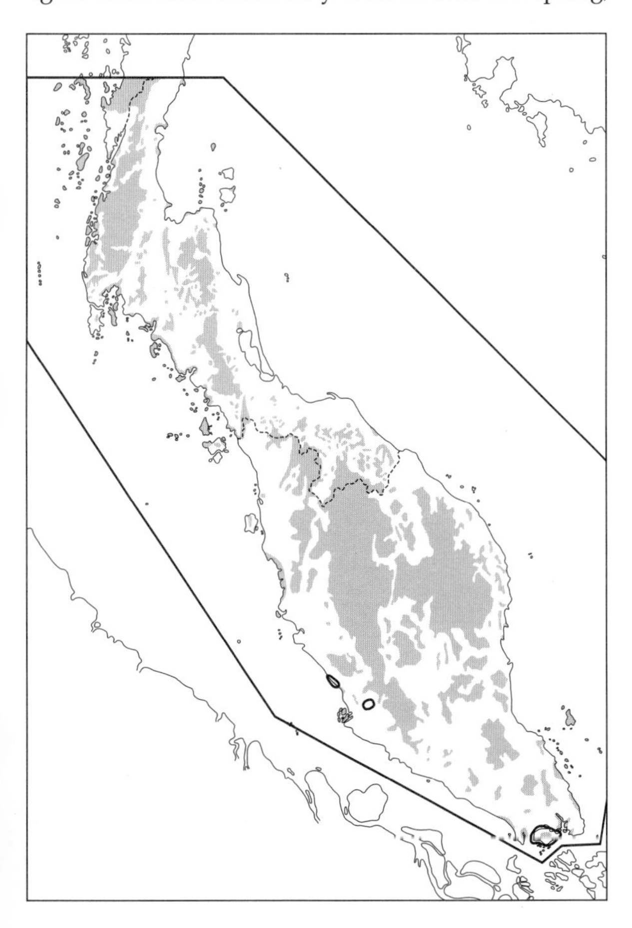

HABITATS AND ECOLOGY. The only coastal records are from sand-fill, above the high-tide mark (C.J. Hails). More typical habitats are short-cropped grassland and open expanses of bare soil and sand inland, as stated, including fields, mine-tailings and ploughland.

FORAGING AND FOOD. This proportionately tall plover hunts visually, making short, swift runs with an abrupt halt and stiff-legged but deft pick from the surface. No local prey data but stomach contents from Borneo included mostly small terrestrial arthropods, consistent with this feeding method (Smythies 1981).

SOCIAL ORGANIZATION. Mostly solitary; not above two confirmed together.

MOVEMENTS. November is a regular passage-month further east in SE Asia. Apart from the two Singapore occurrences, however, all local records have been in spring. 27 January may seem early for return migration but there is no doubt the birds involved were on the move. Given that moult into summer plumage can be well-advanced by mid February (MBR 1986–87), departure from regular wintering grounds may begin sooner than generally realized. Extreme dates of local spring passage are accepted as 27 January and mid May (BR 1964, Cant 1957–58).

SURVIVAL. No information.

SOCIAL INTERACTIONS. No information.

VOICE. The flight-call is a brief, high-pitched *hweet*, or *tip* by a bird forced to flush (BR 1964).

BREEDING. No population.

MOULT. A good proportion of records have been of early to full summer plumage, i.e., of likely adults, starting with birds half-moulted in mid–late February. Winter-type plumage has been seen in November and January–early March, and in spring may involve immatures (BR 1964, C.J. Hails, MBR 1986–87).

CONSERVATION. No relevant issues.

Yellow-wattled Lapwing; (no Thai name); Burung Rapang Malabar (Malay)

Vanellus malarbaricus (Boddaert) 1783, *Table des Planches Enluminéez d'Histoire Naturelle*: 53. TL Kerala, SW India.

Not illustrated in this volume

GROUP RELATIONS. Apparently free-standing.

GLOBAL RANGE. The Indian subcontinent south and east from the Indus valley, and Sri Lanka; vagrant in central Burma and the Peninsula (Johns and Thorpe 1981, Oates 1883).

IDENTIFICATION/DESCRIPTION. Slightly smaller than Red-wattled Lapwing but stands taller than Pacific Golden Plover. Cap black (brown in juveniles), margined by a white band from the rear edge of the eye round the nape; rest of face, neck, upperparts and upper breast sandy brown, coming to a darker line against the white of remaining underparts. In flight, tail white with a bold black subterminal bar across its centre, and black flight-feathers show a white bar across the base of the secondaries.

Bare-part colours. Iris pale yellow; bill black with a yellow base; eyelid and conjoined, pendant, loral wattle yellow; legs and feet yellow.

Size. No data.

Weight. No data.

DISTRIBUTION. Historical summary: *Sel*.

GEOGRAPHICAL VARIATION. None recognized.

STATUS AND POPULATION. Vagrant; one in the company of Pacific Golden Plovers on grassy playing-fields and open ground of the Malaysian Agricultural University campus, Serdang, Selangor, during 8 December–April 1979/80 (BR 1978–79). This is only the second reported in SE Asia, after one collected more than a century ago at Theyetmyo on the Irrawaddy river, S Burma (Oates 1883).

HABITATS AND ECOLOGY. In its regular range, a dry-land plover moving locally away from the wet of the SW monsoon, and in some areas occurring only as a dry-season (northern winter) visitor (HBI).

FORAGING AND FOOD. No information.

SOCIAL ORGANIZATION. No information.

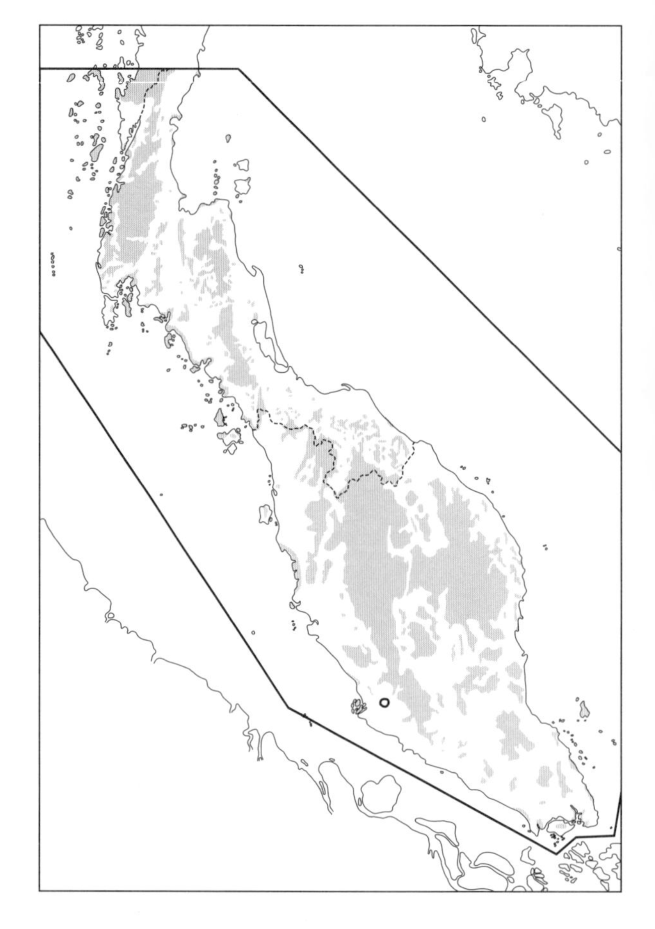

MOVEMENTS. No information.

SURVIVAL. No information.

SOCIAL INTERACTIONS. No information.

VOICE. No information.

BREEDING. No population.

MOULT. No data.

CONSERVATION. No relevant issues.

River Lapwing; Nok Gratae Haad (Thai); Burung Rapang Sungai (Malay)

Vanellus duvaucelii (Lesson) 1826, Levrault's *Dictionnaire des Sciences Naturelles* 42: 38. TL Calcutta, NE India.

Plate 35

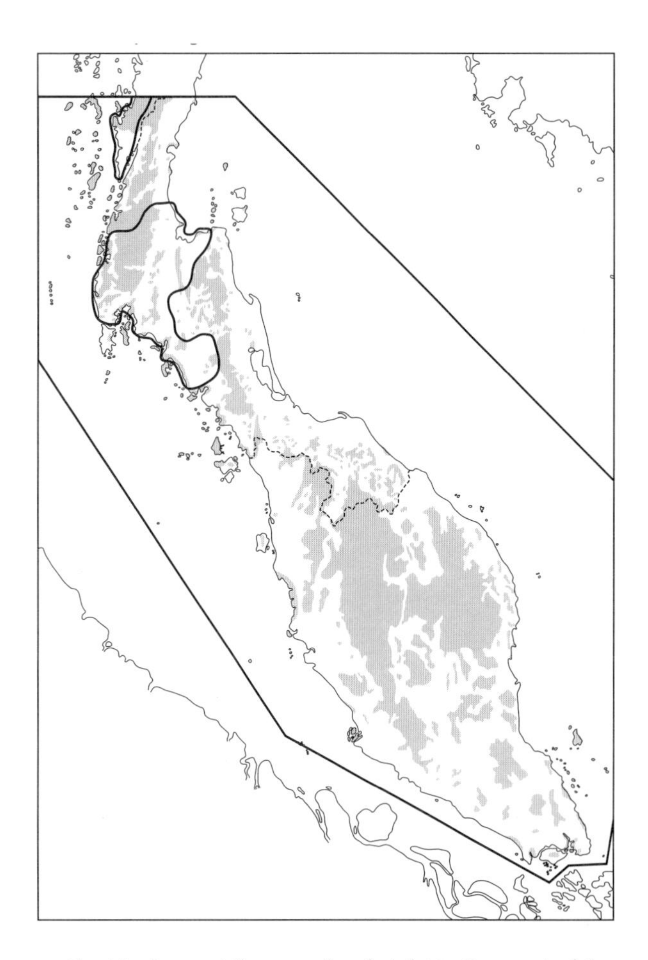

GROUP RELATIONS. Forms a superspecies with western *V. spinosus* (Spur-winged Plover). The pattern of plumage-parts used in display is different enough to suggest these allopatric birds would be reproductively isolated.

GLOBAL RANGE. The eastern Indian subcontinent from the Himalayan foothills; W and S Yunnan and Hainan; and continental SE Asia to the Peninsula.

IDENTIFICATION/DESCRIPTION. Slightly shorter-legged than Red-wattled Lapwing, and no other local wader has bib, anterior face, crown and drooping crest black. In flight, upper tail-coverts and tail show white with a wide, black terminal bar; the black of the flight-feathers is bisected by a bold white bar slanting inwards across the wing from the wrist. Local juveniles not described.

Bare-part colours. Iris deep reddish brown; bill black; carpal spur black; legs and feet black.

Size (mm). (Skin: 1 male; adult): wing 204; tail 93; bill from front edge nostril 17.8; tarsus 68.3; recurved carpal spur 11.9 (BMNH).

Weight. No data.

DISTRIBUTION. Not south of latitude 8°N. Historical summary: *Pak, Sur, Pha, Kra, Tra.*

GEOGRAPHICAL VARIATION. None recognized.

STATUS AND POPULATION. Resident, local, and sparse to more or less common. Recorded south to NW and possibly central Trang (BMNH, Holmes and Wells 1975, Jørgensen 1949, Riley 1938, Robinson and Kloss 1910–11) but, since the 1980s, only in Phangnga and Krabi: including nine and 11 counted on random sorties along about 400 m of river-bank in the middle Li valley in mid July and late August; over 30 on downstream shingle banks on 20 October; and a loner by a rubber-estate pond at Ao Luk, Krabi, on 9 November (BCSTB-12, S. Sheridan-Johnson).

HABITATS AND ECOLOGY. Relatively common where the Li river meanders past rubber gardens, rough grazing-land and seasonal paddy-fields on its middle and lower flood-plain. Typically a waterside lapwing but also recorded in paddyland, and in Trang W.L. Abbott collected two from what appears to have been an open, inland marsh (AMNH, Riley 1938). Along the Li river, found only on bare, sandy and gravelly flats and shoals. High water must force them out but in August the grassland right to the crest of the bank was held exclusively by Red-wattled Lapwings, suggestive of partitioning by habitat.

FORAGING AND FOOD. No information.

SOCIAL ORGANIZATION. Solitary, in pairs and, on the Li river from August, evident post-breeding parties in double figures.

MOVEMENTS. No information, but the Ao Luk bird had gone by the following day and is likely to have been a dispersant.

SURVIVAL. No information.

SOCIAL INTERACTIONS. No information.

VOICE. No local record. In Burma, an insistent, repeated *dip* and four-note *did did do weet*, similar to Red-wattled Lapwing but less shrill (Smythies 1953).

BREEDING. Not reported.

MOULT. An adult from Pakchan dated 20 January showed none and was in fairly fresh plumage (BMNH).

CONSERVATION. The largest risk must be to eggs and chicks, from casual hunting. At the moment, the Li valley is only lightly populated, with low-intensity agriculture that includes stock-grazing essential to the maintaining of open grassland. This benign regime is unlikely to last, and needs study.

Grey-headed Lapwing; Nok Gratae Hua Thao (Thai); Burung Rapang Kepala Kelabu (Malay)

Vanellus cinereus (Blyth) 1842, *Journal of the Asiatic Society of Bengal* 11: 587. TL Calcutta, NE India.
Plate 35

GROUP RELATIONS. Apparently free-standing.

GLOBAL RANGE. Breeds in central Japan and NE China south to the Yellow Sea; also in the Changjiang delta and, possibly, Fujian. Continental populations migrate, wintering in far-S China (Yunnan and Guangdong); the NE Indian subcontinent west to Nepal; and SE Asia to the Peninsula and N Philippines. Vagrant to S Andaman island, NW Borneo and N Sulawesi.

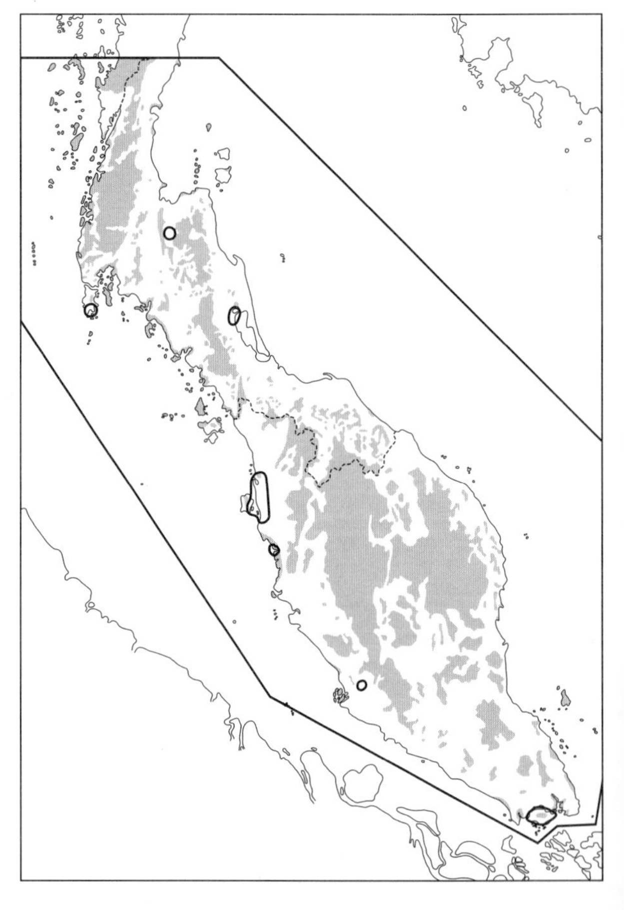

IDENTIFICATION/DESCRIPTION. Biggest lapwing of the area, standing at least as tall as Red-wattled and, apart from wattle and close-range impression of a lighter eyebrow, the only one with entirely plain grey-brown head and neck. Juveniles lack the dark pectoral line between grey breast and white belly, and have buff-fringed upperparts. On take-off, the dorsal pattern breaks into a set of colour triangles: grey-brown head, back and wing-coverts; black primaries and their coverts; white wrist, secondary coverts and secondaries; and white upper tail-coverts and fanned tail (with bold, black terminal bar) (MBR 1982–83).

Bare-part colours. Iris red; eyelid rim and small, upstanding loral wattle yellow; bill yellow with a black tip; legs and feet yellow.

Size (mm). (Skins: 11 males, 5 females, from the Chinese breeding-range; adult): wing 230–251 and 230–245; tail 94–107 and 96–104; bill 34.0–40.0 (sexes combined); tarsus 71.9–81.8 and 72.0–78.4 (BMNH).

Weight. No data.

DISTRIBUTION. Historical summary: *Sur, Phu, Pht, Ked, Pra, Pek, Sel, Sin,* also Penang island.

GEOGRAPHICAL VARIATION. None recognized.

STATUS AND POPULATION. A non-breeding visitor; local and uncommon to sparse. It has recently been shown that small numbers occur annually south to the NW coastal plain of Malaysia, with records in all months mid September–late January and March, April (mainly October–mid December). South of mainland Penang, known from four strays: on the Kuala Gula coast (Perak), at Sungai Way (Selangor) and twice in Singapore, including on the Senoko wetland, collectively during 15 September–20 December (BIRDLINE 1993, BR 1980–81, Cant 1957–58, A. Jeyarajasingam). Most northern records have been of parties of five or fewer but include 15 on Phuket island, 16 in the Thalae Noi wetland, 15 and 24 in successive years in the Merbok valley, S Kedah, and 47 and eight in Seberang Prai district, mainland Penang (BBCB-7, -8, BCSTB-12, Choy Wai Mun, R. Gregory-Smith, MBR 1982–83). Kedah flocks stayed until their buffalo-pasture began to dry out in mid December, then moved on.

HABITATS AND ECOLOGY. Habitats have included muddy stream-banks, sandy landfill, wet grass-marsh, grazing-land, and paddy-fields, both operated and abandoned (MBR 1982–83). What becomes of dispersants as their grounds dry off is not known but records later than December have been from more permanently available wetland, including at Thalae Noi and Thung Thong (Surat Thani), on Phuket and in Penang territory.

FORAGING AND FOOD. No information.

SOCIAL ORGANIZATION. Gregarious in the main winter range.

MOVEMENTS. Extreme dates are 15 September in Singapore and 14 April at Thalae Noi (BBCB-7, BR 1980–81).

SURVIVAL. No information.

SOCIAL INTERACTIONS. No information.

VOICE. Mostly silent but flying birds give an occasional sharp *kik* (Boonsong and Round 1991). A rasping 3-note alarm-call, *did-all-eet*, has been reported elsewhere in winter (HBI).

BREEDING. No population.

MOULT. Unchecked locally but a series from N China shows that adults start moult of at least flight-feathers during May–June (from gonad data, apparently while still breeding). They finish possibly before migration begins (BMNH).

CONSERVATION. Globally near-threatened (BTW2). No specific local issues but the spread of pesticide-usage on paddyland must eventually affect it in this area.

Red-wattled Lapwing; Nok Gratae Tae Waet (Thai); Burung Rapang Duit (Malay)

Vanellus indicus (Boddaert) 1783, *Table des Planches Enluminéez d'Histoire Naturelle*: 150. TL Goa, W India.

Plate 35

GROUP RELATIONS. Free-standing.

GLOBAL RANGE. The Euphrates–Tigris valley and Persian Gulf to Turkmenia and Afghanistan; the Indian subcontinent and Sri Lanka; W Yunnan; and SE Asia to the Peninsula and N Sumatra.

IDENTIFICATION/DESCRIPTION. A combination of black, white and red head-colours is distinctive, and the white neck-patch stands out at a distance, even against backgrounds that camouflage the rest of the bird. Juveniles have head much duller than adult, and chin and throat whitish rather than black (Hayman *et al.* 1986). At all ages, flight-feathers are black, with a relatively narrow bar of white across only the secondary coverts (see also vagrant Yellow-wattled Lapwing). The white tail has a bold, black subterminal bar.

Bare-part colours. Iris red; eyelid rim, bare lores and small loral wattle red; bill red with a black tip; legs and feet pale lemon-yellow. Both sexes have a small, grey carpal spur, mostly concealed within the wrist-plumage.

Size (mm). (Skins: 18 males, 14 females; adult): wing 209–221 and 193–213; tail 99–113 and 90–109; bill 31.0–35.3 and 33.0–36.3; tarsus 76.8–89.2 and 72.9–80.9 (BMNH, ZRCNUS).

Weight (g). One unsexed adult, 194.1 (UMBRP).

DISTRIBUTION. Historical summary: all divisions except *Chu, Yal, Pes, Pra*, with additional island records from Yao Yai, Libong, Tarutao, Langkawi and Penang off the W coast; and Phangan and Samui off the E coast.

GEOGRAPHICAL VARIATION. Subspecies *atronuchalis* Jerdon 1842 (TL Burma) of the SE Asian range; darker than western forms, with white on the side of the neck restricted to an isolated patch, and a narrow white hind-collar behind the black of the neck.

STATUS AND POPULATION. Resident, local and uncommon to common. Numerous now only in what remains of traditional, low-intensity wetland agriculture, but most of the historical range is still occupied, year-round except on the W-coast plain below latitude 5°30′N, where only occasional non-breeding dispersants occur (recorded in September, October, December and February: BMNH, BR 1970–71, 1976–77, MBR 1984–85). In general, commoner north

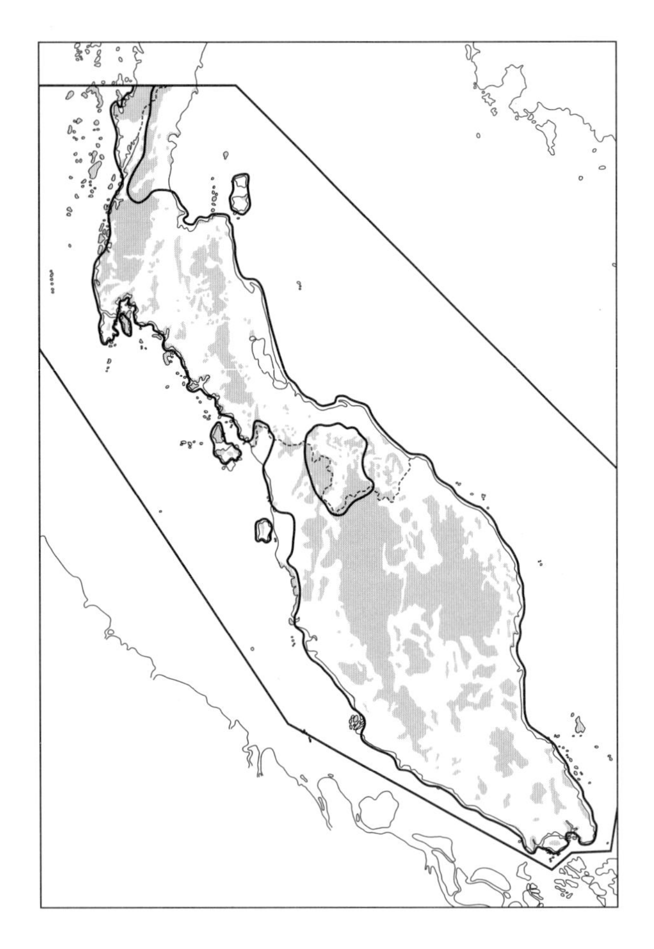

of Malaysia but increasingly numerous also in the far south. Pockets of single-crop paddy-farming with water buffaloes along the SE coast are important, but small and scattered. By the mid 1980s, however, dispersants in S Pahang and Johor were also breeding in extensive new habitat on cattle ranches and a golf course cut out of coastal forest. Shortly thereafter (and after a long interval), the species reappeared in Singapore, mainly on marshland around Poyan reservoir, W end of the island, including (for the first time in 1993) several birds present through the breeding-season (BIRDLINE 1993, SINGAV-2). Some also exist along large southern rivers, including the Pahang river upstream as far as Jerantut (A.M. Wells).

HABITATS AND ECOLOGY. The most intensively used habitat in the Peninsula is open, actively grazed pasture interspersed with wallows and marshes (and where cattle and water buffalo dung supports invertebrate prey), such as found along the middle Li river, Phangnga. Others are paddyland, farmed traditionally using animal-power (not where pesticide-usage is heavy or multi-cropping has truncated the fallow-season); low-lying golf courses and secure corners of grassy airfields; short-grass beach strand; cleared and burned, temporary field-sites; and banks, bars and shoals of large rivers except, apparently, where River Lapwing occurs.

FORAGING AND FOOD. Hunts visually by walking and picking from the surface, but diet unrecorded in this area.

SOCIAL ORGANIZATION. Pairs space out when breeding, but neighbours are attracted to a source of disturbance and they mob communally (MBR 1986–87). Foragers disperse individually but, after the breeding-season, isolated sites may attract small aggregations, including ten birds (age-class unrecorded) on a burned, roadside clearance in Terengganu in late June (BR 1982–83). It is not known whether such parties move together between sites.

MOVEMENTS. No definite information.

SURVIVAL. No information.

SOCIAL INTERACTIONS. No information.

VOICE. Noisy, with a shrieking alarm, *di-di-do-it*, given in flight or by a breeder on guard on some prominence such as a field bund-top. Excited birds monitoring the movements of an intruder often increase the *di* notes to three or four and occasionally insert an extra syllable: *di-di-di-dare-do-it*.

BREEDING

Nest. An unlined scrape in short grass, sand or other soil, with one recorded on the charcoal remains of a burned tree trunk; typically fully exposed and away from obstacles, giving uninterrupted all-round vision for the sitting bird.

Eggs and brood. Eggs are glossless stone-brown to pale olive-brown, marked with irregular blotches of lavender and dark brown, the latter densest over the broad end. Shape near-piriform. Size (mm): 42.6 × 29.5 and 40.8 × 30.8 (n=2). Full clutch three.

Cycle. No information.

Seasonality. Eggs and downy chicks found on dates that indicate laying in all months January–May (G.C. Madoc, Madoc 1956a, MBR 1986–87, Riley 1938, ZRC-NUS). A pair on fallow paddyland at Penor, SE Pahang, on 7 August behaved as though it had running young, but none was found.

MOULT. A May adult from Pahang showed regular-descendant moult of the inner primaries, and was growing P5. No moult in others of both sexes dated mid October and December–May implies a definite seasonality (BMNH, ZRCNUS).

CONSERVATION. A small population of lapwings persists on Langkawi island, site of a storm of tourism development in recent years (R. Subaraj). If, for tourism reasons, cultivation of the island's paddylands by customary methods is deemed to be worth preserving it could persist, and the situation provides an interesting test-case. Safety of nesting sites and presence of water buffaloes could be critical. In Singapore, the Poyan reservoir marshland is temporary habitat, but sits next to a large, live-firing artillery range that could supply a secure and permanent alternative.

Family GLAREOLIDAE

Crab-plover and pratincoles: three species

Crab-plover; Nok Hua Toh Gin Puu (Thai); Burung Rapang Ketam (Malay)

Dromas ardeola Paykull 1805, *Konglige Vetenskaps Academiens Handlingar* 26: 182 and plate 8. TL India.

Plate 37

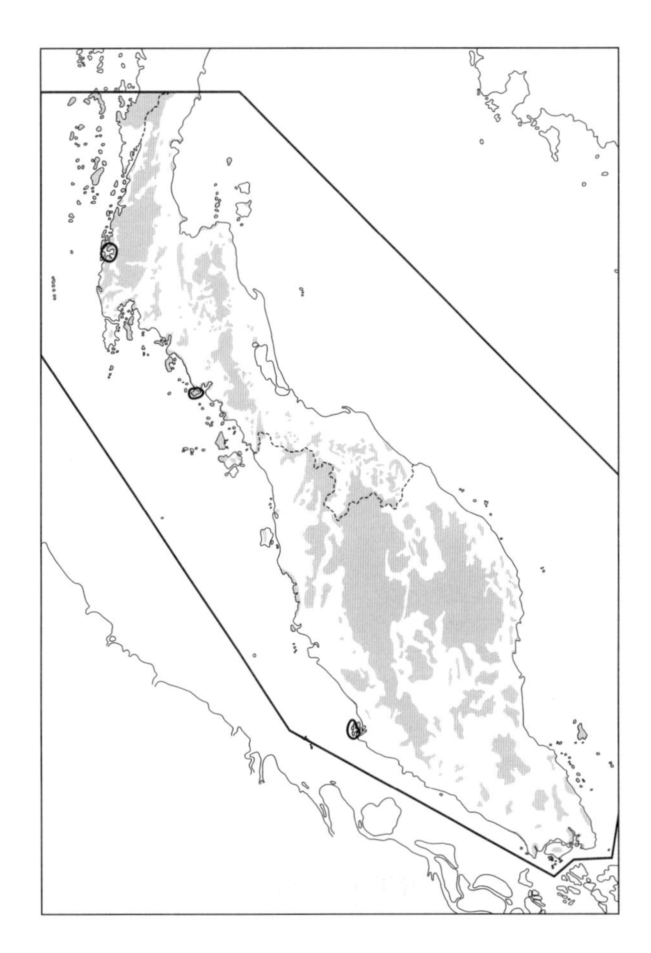

GROUP RELATIONS. Free-standing, with no near relatives.

GLOBAL RANGE. Breeds on coasts and islands of the S Red Sea, Gulf of Aden and Gulf of Oman; almost certainly also far-NW India and N Sri Lanka. Non-breeders range south and east around coasts of the Indian Ocean as far as S Africa, the Malagasy region, the Indian subcontinent, Sri Lanka and Bay of Bengal islands, and the Malay Peninsula.

IDENTIFICATION/DESCRIPTION. A large wader, proportionately very long-legged and with massive black bill. Juveniles appear buff-tinged on the nape, neck and upper wing-coverts, with mantle light grey rather than black. In flight, the entire underparts are white, and feet project well past the tail-tip (Hayman *et al.* 1986).

Bare-part colours. Iris deep brown; bill black; legs and feet blue-grey.

Size (mm). (Skins: 1 male; non-juvenile): wing 218; tail 58; bill 63.1; tarsus 99.5 (ZRCNUS).

Weight. No data.

DISTRIBUTION. Pakarang point, Phangnga, and W-coast islands Libong and the Kelang estuary group (Pintu Gedong, Tengah).

GEOGRAPHICAL VARIATION. None recognized.

STATUS AND POPULATION. A non-breeding visitor; very local and sparse. Libong island is its only consistent location. Ten were discovered there in late December 1980 (P. Poonswad) and fluctuating but generally dwindling numbers of both adults and juveniles reappear annually (BBCB-4, -5, -7, -9, Eve and Guigue 1982, Parish 1985, Swennen *et al.* 1986). Not more than four have occurred since 1988, and in 1993 only one returned. A regular few may have gone to local hunters but it is also possible migrants to the Peninsula are under pressure at their breeding-site, wherever that may prove to be.

Elsewhere, known from two records on mangrove islands in the Kelang estuary: a flock of six (two adults and a juvenile collected) on the mudflats of Pintu Gedong on 24 September 1912 plus a lone juvenile at neighbouring Tengah island on 24 January 1990; and in April 1995 a loner at Pakarang, Phangnga (BCSTB-12, ENGGANG-3, Robinson 1913).

HABITATS AND ECOLOGY. Known only from tidal flats, with a consistent preference for consolidated, mixed mud/sand substrates.

FORAGING AND FOOD. Crab-plovers on the Libong coast foraged territorially, walking and stopping to scan, and selected only crabs of carapace-width about 1–7 cm (grapsid species and *Portunus pelagicus* identified). A monitored bird stayed exclusively on muddy sand (Swennen and Marteijn 1985), but some foraging also occurs while wading tarsus-deep in tide-pools (Eve and Guigue 1982).

SOCIAL ORGANIZATION. Spaced while foraging but at other times social.

MOVEMENTS. Extreme dates are 24 September and 6 May, with records in all intervening months (Eve and Guigue 1982, Robinson 1913).

SURVIVAL. No information.

SOCIAL INTERACTIONS. No information.

VOICE. No information.

BREEDING. No population.

MOULT. A presumed pre-adult, grey on nape, wing-coverts and scapulars, was in regular-descendant wing-moult on 24 September: P1–5 new, 6–7 growing, tip old (ZRCNUS). Apparent juvenile body-plumage has been identified in the field to early February (Eve and Guigue 1982).

CONSERVATION. Apparently too late for local measures.

Oriental Pratincole; Nok En-thung Yai (Thai); Burung Lelayang Padang (Malay)

Glareola maldivarum J.R. Forster 1795, *Faunula Indica*: 11. TL at sea near the Maldive islands.
Plate 37

GROUP RELATIONS. Split from western *G. pratincola* (Collared Pratincole) on the basis of a breeding overlap claimed in Sind, Pakistan (HBI). Different morphology independently suggests they have reached superspecies status, perhaps together with western *G. nordmanni* (Black-winged Pratincole) (CLBW).

GLOBAL RANGE. Breeds opportunistically through the Indian subcontinent east from Sind, and in Sri Lanka; NE Mongolia to NE and E China as far as Fujian; S Japan, Taiwan and Hainan; and SE Asia as far as Peninsula and Luzon. Possibly all populations wander or migrate, wintering in India and (mainly northern) Australia, with a scattered presence also through SE Asia.

IDENTIFICATION/DESCRIPTION. Hard to spot against an earth background but shape distinctive and the rear dorsum (rump, upper tail-coverts and tail-base), sharply white against all-dark back and wings, are immediately obvious on take-off. In high, overhead silhouette, the only possible confusion would be with a tern. Only summer-plumaged adults show the characteristic dark necklace and pink-buff chin, throat and lower breast. In winter, necklace replaced by a zone of dark streaking. Before autumn moult, juveniles are heavily fringed dark and buff dorsally, and mottled on the neck and breast.

Bare-part colours. Iris deep brown; bill blackish with lower base and mouth-line orange-red (no red in juvenile); legs and feet brownish black.

Size (mm). (Skins: 19 adults; none sexed): wing 172–199; tail 65–84, tail-fork 17.0–29.3; bill 16.1–21.8; tarsus 31.5–35.5 (BMNH, UMZC, ZRCNUS).

Weight (g). Non-juvenile migrants in November–December, 64.0–74.3 (91.1) (n=6) (B.D. Bond). Fattening has not been checked.

DISTRIBUTION. Overlooked in the far north. Historical summary: all divisions except *Pak, Chu, Ran, Pha, Kra, Yal, Nar*, with additional island records from Penang and (on spring-passage dates) Tioman.

GEOGRAPHICAL VARIATION. None recognized.

STATUS AND POPULATION. A breeding visitor and passage migrant (when regular and more or less common), with a small, erratic presence over mid winter. Except for late spring stragglers over the Selangor coast (BR 1978–79, ENGGANG-2), found during May–July only north of latitude 4°N. A recent observation of distraction-display by about 20 pairs in a Little Tern nest-colony near Kuantan port, Pahang, suggests they were breeding this far south (T. Mundkur). Elsewhere on the E-coast plain, suspected of breeding also in N and central Terengganu (BR 1968, MBR 1982–83, A.C. Sebastian), and present through August on the Songkhla wetland (Meeswat and Prentice 1984). In the west, a flock at Chenderong Bali, lower Perak river, on 19 July (E.F. Allen 1951b) could already have been migrating, and on this coast no breeding has been confirmed south of Perlis (BR 1970–71). However, present through the likely season in N Kedah, from early March to July (Bonhote 1901, Bromley 1949, MBR 1986–87).

The only convincing overwintering records are from Kelantan during 1950/51 (Berwick 1952b), and a series of single-figure counts made through January 1989 in Singapore (SINGAV-3); both, perhaps, exceptional years. Typically, the Peninsula empties at mid winter, but only for a few weeks.

Plate Section

Plate 1 (G.W.H. Davison): *Turnix suscitator* (Barred Buttonquail) ad. female (1); ad. male (2). *Coturnix chinensis* (Blue-breasted Quail) ad. female (3); ad. male (4). *Argusianus argus* (Great Argus) chick (5). *Pavo muticus* (Green Peafowl) chick (6). *Rheinardia ocellata* (Crested Argus) chick (7). *Polyplectron malacense* (Malayan Peacock Pheasant) chick (8). *Rollulus rouloul* (Roulroul) chick (9). *Melanoperdix nigra* (Black Partridge) six-week poult (10). *Gallus gallus* (Red Junglefowl) chick (11). *Lophura erythrophthalma* (Crestless Fireback) chick (12). *Lophura ignita* (Crested Fireback) 2.5-week poult (13); chick (14). *Coturnix chinensis* (Blue-breasted Quail) chick (15). *Turnix suscitator* (Barred Buttonquail) chick (16).

Plate 2 (G.W.H. Davison): *Caloperdix oculea* (Ferruginous Partridge) ad. male (1). *Arborophila orientalis* (Grey-breasted Partridge) ad. (2). *Arborophila charltonii* (Chestnut-necklaced Partridge) ad. (3). *Melanoperdix nigra* (Black Partridge) ad. male (4); ad. female (5). *Rollulus rouloul* (Roulroul) ad. male (6); ad. female (7).

Plate 3 (G.W.H. Davison): *Rhizothera longirostris* (Long-billed Partridge) ad. male (1); ad. female (2). *Gallus gallus* (Red Junglefowl) ad. male (3); ad. female (4). *Lophura erythrophthalma* (Crestless Fireback) ad. female (5); ad. male (6). *Lophura ignita* (Crested Fireback) ad. male (7); ad. female (8).

Plate 4 (G.W.H. Davison): *Polyplectron inopinatum* (Mountain Peacock Pheasant) ad. female (1); ad. male (2). *Polyplectron malacense* (Malayan Peacock Pheasant) ad. female (3); ad. male (4); ad. male frontal display (5). *Polyplectron inopinatum* (Mountain Peacock Pheasant) ad. male frontal display (6). *Rheinardia ocellata* (Crested Argus) ad. female (7); ad. male display (8). *Argusianus argus* (Great Argus) ad. male frontal display (9). *Pavo muticus* (Green Peafowl) ad. male display (10).

Plate 5 (G.W.H. Davison): *Rheinardia ocellata* (Crested Argus) ad. female (1); ad. male (2). *Argusianus argus* (Great Argus) ad. female (3); ad. male (4). *Pavo muticus* (Green Peafowl) ad. male (5); ad. female (6).

Plate 6 (David Quinn): *Cairina scutulata* (White-winged Wood Duck) ad. (1). *Dendrocygna javanica* (Lesser Whistling Duck) ad. (2). *Nettapus coromandelianus* (Asian Pigmy-goose) ad. male (3); ad. female (4). *Anas crecca* (Common Teal) ad. female (5). *Anas querquedula* (Garganey) ad. female (6); ad. male (7). *Anas penelope* (Eurasian Wigeon) ad. female (8). *Anas acuta* (Northern Pintail) ad. female (9). *Anas strepera* (Gadwall) ad. female (10). *Anas clypeata* (Northern Shoveler) ad. female (11).

Plate 7 (David Quinn): *Tachybaptus ruficollis* (Little Grebe) ad. (1); juv. (2). *Aythya baeri* (Baer's Pochard) ad. female (3). *Aythya fuligula* (Tufted Duck) ad. female (4). *Heliopais personata* (Masked Finfoot) ad. male (5). *Microcarbo niger* (Little Cormorant) ad. nbr. (6); juv. (7). *Phalacrocorax carbo* (Great Cormorant) ad. br. (8); ad. nbr. (9). *Anhinga melanogaster* (Darter) ad. (10).

Plate 8 (Ian Lewington): *Puffinus pacificus* (Wedge-tailed Shearwater) ad. (1, 2). *Puffinus tenuirostris* (Short-tailed Shearwater) ad. (3, 4). *Calonectris leucomelas* (Streaked Shearwater) ad. (5, 6). *Oceanites oceanicus* (Wilson's Storm-petrel) ad. (7). *Oceanodroma monorhis* (Swinhoe's Storm-Petrel) ad. (8). *Bulweria bulwerii* (Bulwer's Petrel) ad. (9). *Anous stolidus* (Brown Noddy) juv. (10); ad. (11). *Phalaropus lobatus* (Red-necked Phalarope) fw. (12, 13); ad. female br. (14).

Plate 9 (Ian Lewington): *Sula dactylatra* (Masked Booby) juv. (1); ad. (2). *Sula sula* (Red-footed Booby) juv. (3); ad. (4). *Sula leucogaster* (Brown Booby) juv. (5); ad. (6). *Fregata ariel* (Lesser Frigatebird) ad. male (7); ad. female (8); juv. (9). *Fregata andrewsi* (Christmas Island Frigatebird) ad. male (10); ad. female (11); juv. (12). *Fregata minor* (Great Frigatebird) ad. male (13); ad. female (14); juv. (15).

Plate 10 (R. David Digby): *Ardea cinerea* (Grey Heron) ad. br. (1); juv. (2). *Ardea purpurea* (Purple Heron) juv. (3); ad. (4). *Egretta sacra* (Reef Egret) dark phase ad. br. (5); ad. nbr. (6). *Ardea sumatrana* (Great-billed Heron) ad. (7); juv. (8).

Plate 11 (R. David Digby): *Casmerodius albus* (Great Egret) ad. br. (1); ad. nbr. (2). *Egretta eulophotes* (Chinese Egret) ad. br. (3); ad. nbr. (4). *Egretta garzetta* (Little Egret) ad. br. (5); ad. nbr. (6). *Egretta sacra* (Reef Egret) white phase ad. br. (7); ad. nbr. (8). *Mesophoyx intermedia* (Intermediate Egret) ad. br. (9); ad. nbr. (10).

Plate 12 (R. David Digby): *Nycticorax nycticorax* (Black-crowned Night Heron) juv. (1); ad. (2). *Gorsachius melanolophus* (Malayan Night Heron) ad. (3); juv. (4). *Bubulcus ibis* (Cattle Egret) ad. br. (5); ad. nbr. (6). *Ardeola speciosa* (Javan Pond Heron) ad. br. (7). *Ardeola bacchus* (Chinese Pond Heron) ad. nbr. (8); ad. br. (9).

Plate 13 (R. David Digby): *Ixobrychus cinnamomeus* (Cinnamon Bittern) ad. female (1); ad. male (2). *Ixobrychus eurhythmus* (Von Schrenck's Bittern) ad. female (3); ad. male (4). *Ixobrychus sinensis* (Yellow Bittern) ad. female (5); ad. male (6). *Ixobrychus flavicollis* (Black Bittern) ad. male (7); ad. female (8). *Butorides striatus* (Little Heron) ad. br. (9); juv. (10).

Plate 14 (David Quinn): *Threskiornis melanocephalus* (Black-headed Ibis) ad. (1). *Plegadis falcinellus* (Glossy Ibis) ad. (2). *Pseudibis davisoni* (White-shouldered Ibis) ad. (3). *Thaumatibis gigantea* (Giant Ibis) ad. (4).

Plate 15 (David Quinn): *Ephippiorhynchus asiaticus* (Black-necked Stork) ad. female (1). *Anastomus oscitans* (Asian Openbill) ad. (2). *Ciconia episcopus* (Woolly-necked Stork) ad. (3). *Ciconia stormi* (Storm's Stork) ad. female (4). *Platalea minor* (Black-faced Spoonbill) ad. (5).

Plate 16 (David Quinn): *Leptoptilos dubius* (Greater Adjutant) ad. (1). *Leptoptilos javanicus* (Lesser Adjutant) ad. (2). *Mycteria cinerea* (Milky Stork) ad. (3). *Mycteria leucocephala* (Painted Stork) ad. (4).

Plate 17 (Peter Hayman): *Pernis ptilorhyncus* (Oriental Honey-buzzard) ad. male (1, 5); ad. female (2-4); imm. (6) (NB. colour-phases are not sex-linked). *Aviceda jerdoni* (Jerdon's Baza) imm. (7); ad. (8). *Buteo buteo* (Common Buzzard) ad. *vulpinus* (9); ad. *japonensis* (10). *Ictinaetus malayensis* (Black Eagle) ad. (11); juv. (12).

Plate 18 (R. David Digby): *Elanus caeruleus* (Black-winged Kite) ad. (1, 2); juv. (3). *Macheirhamphus alcinus* (Bat Hawk) ad. (4). *Aviceda leuphotes* (Black Baza) ad. pattern morphs (5, 6). *Microhierax fringillarius* (Black-thighed Falconet) ad. (7); juv. (8); ad. to scale of rest of plate (9).

Plate 19 (R. David Digby): *Spilornis cheela* (Crested Serpent Eagle) juv. (1); ad. (2). *Milvus indus* (Brahminy Kite) ad. (3); juv. (4). *Hieraaetus pennatus* (Booted Eagle) dark phase ad. (5). *Milvus migrans* (Black Kite) juv. (6); ad. (7).

Plate 20 (R. David Digby): *Ichthyophaga ichthyaetus* (Grey-headed Fish Eagle) juv. (1); ad. (2). *Haliaeetus leucogaster* (White-bellied Fish Eagle) juv. (3); ad. (4). *Pandion haliaetus* (Osprey) ad. (5). *Ichthyophaga humilis* (Lesser Fish Eagle) ad. (6); juv. (7).

Plate 21 (Peter Hayman): *Aegypius monachus* (Cinereous Vulture) imm. (1). *Sarcogyps calvus* (Red-headed Vulture) ad. (2); juv. (3). *Gyps indicus* (Long-billed Vulture) ad. (4); juv. (5). *Gyps bengalensis* (White-backed Vulture) ad. (6); juv. (7). *Gyps himalayensis* (Himalayan Griffon) subad. (8); juv. (9).

Plate 22 (Peter Hayman): *Circus cyaneus* (Hen Harrier) ad. male (1, 3) ; ad. female (2, 4). *Circus melanoleucos* (Pied Harrier) ad. male (5, 8); ad.female (6, 10, 11); juv. (7, 9). *Circus aeruginosus* (Marsh Harrier) ad. male *spilonotus* (12, 17); ad. male *aeruginosus* (15, 16): ad. female *spilonotus* (14, 19); ad. female *aeruginosus* (13, 18); juv. *spilonotus* (male 21, female 22); juv. *aeruginosus* (20).

Plate 23 (R. David Digby): *Accipiter soloensis* (Chinese Sparrowhawk) ad. (1); juv. (2). *Accipiter gularis* (Japanese Sparrowhawk) ad. male (3); juv. (4). *Accipiter badius* (Shikra) ad. (5); juv. (6). *Butastur indicus* (Grey-faced Buzzard) juv. (7); ad. (8). *Accipiter trivirgatus* (Crested Goshawk) juv. (9); ad. (10).

Plate 24 (R. David Digby): *Aquila heliaca* (Imperial Eagle) ad. (1); juv. (2). *Aquila clanga* (Greater Spotted Eagle) ad. (3); juv. (4). *Aquila nipalensis* (Steppe Eagle) subad. (5); juv. (6). *Circaetus gallicus* (Short-toed Eagle) ad. (7).

Plate 25 (R. David Digby): *Spizaetus nipalensis* (Mountain Hawk Eagle) ad. (1). *Spizaetus alboniger* (Blyth's Hawk Eagle) juv. (2); ad. (3). *Hieraaetus kienerii* (Rufous-bellied Eagle) ad. (4); juv. (5). *Spizaetus cirrhatus* (Changeable Hawk Eagle) light phase ad. (6); juv. (7); dark phase ad. (8). *Spizaetus nanus* (Wallace's Hawk Eagle) ad. (9); juv. (10).

Plate 26 (R. David Digby): *Falco severus* (Oriental Hobby) ad. (1); juv. (2). *Falco peregrinus* (Peregrine Falcon) ad. migrant (3); ad. resident (4). *Falco subbuteo* (Eurasian Hobby) ad. (5); juv. (6). *Falco tinnunculus* (Common Kestrel) ad. male (7); ad. female (8).

Plate 27 (David Quinn): *Gallirallus striatus* (Slaty-breasted Rail) ad. (1). *Rallina fasciata* (Red-legged Crake) ad. (2). *Rallina eurizonoides* (Slaty-legged Crake) ad. (3). *Porzana paykulli* (Chinese Banded Crake) ad. (4). *Porzana fusca* (Ruddy-breasted Crake) ad. (5). *Porzana pusilla* (Baillon's Crake) ad. (6). *Porzana cinerea* (White-browed Crake) ad. (7).

Plate 28 (David Quinn): *Amaurornis phoenicurus* (White-breasted Waterhen) ad. (1); juv. (2). *Gallinula chloropus* (Common Moorhen) ad. (3); juv. (4). *Gallicrex cinerea* (Watercock) ad. male br. (5); ad. male moulting (6); ad. male nbr. (7). *Porphyrio porphyrio* (Purple Swamphen) ad. *viridis* (8); ad. *indicus* (9). *Fulica atra* (Common Coot) ad. (10).

Plate 29 (Chris Rose): *Pluvialis fulva* (Pacific Golden Plover) ad. nbr. (1); ad. br. (2). *Pluvialis squatarola* (Grey Plover) ad. nbr. (3); ad. br. (4). *Charadrius veredus* (Oriental Plover) ad. br. (5); ad. nbr. (6). *Philomachus pugnax* (Ruff) ad. male nbr. (7). *Scolopax rusticola* (Eurasian Woodcock) ad. (8). *Rostratula benghalensis* (Greater Painted-snipe) ad. male (9); ad. female (10). *Gallinago gallinago* (Common Snipe) ad. (11). *Gallinago megala* (Swinhoe's Snipe) ad. (12). *Gallinago stenura* (Pintail Snipe) ad. (13).

Plate 30 (Chris Rose): *Numenius phaeopus* (Whimbrel) ad. (1); flight (2). *Numenius arquata* (Eurasian Curlew) ad. (3); three in flight (4, 5). *Numenius madagascariensis* (Eastern Curlew) ad. (6); two in flight (7). *Limosa limosa* (Black-tailed Godwit) flight (8); ad. nbr. (9); ad. br. (10). *Limnodromus semipalmatus* (Asian Dowitcher) ad. br. (11, 12). *Limosa lapponica* (Bar-tailed Godwit) ad. br. (13); ad. nbr. (14); two in flight (15).

Plate 31 (Chris Rose): *Xenus cinereus* (Terek Sandpiper) ad. (1). *Tringa totanus* (Common Redshank) ad. br. *craggi* (2); ad. br. *ussuriensis* (3); nbr. (4). *Tringa erythropus* (Spotted Redshank) ad. nbr. (5); ad. br. (6). *Tringa guttifer* (Nordmann's Greenshank) ad. nbr. (7, 9); ad. br. (8). *Tringa nebularia* (Common Greenshank) ad. nbr. (10, 12); ad. br. (11). *Tringa stagnatalis* (Marsh Sandpiper) ad. br. (13); ad. nbr. (14, 15).

Plate 32 (Chris Rose): *Tringa glareola* (Wood Sandpiper) ad. (1). *Tringa ochropus* (Green Sandpiper) ad. (2). *Actitis hypoleucos* (Common Sandpiper) ad. (3). *Heteroscelus brevipes* (Grey-tailed Tattler) ad. nbr. (4). *Philomachus pugnax* (Ruff) ad. female (5). *Calidris canutus* (Red Knot) ad. nbr. (6); ad. br. (7). *Calidris tenuirostris* (Great Knot) ad. nbr. (8); ad. br. (9).

Plate 33 (Chris Rose): *Eurynorhynchus pygmeus* (Spoon-billed Sandpiper), ad. nbr. (1); ad. br. (2). *Calidris ruficollis* (Red-necked Stint) ad. nbr. (3); ad. br. (4). *Calidris minuta* (Little Stint) ad. nbr. (5); ad. br. (6). *Calidris temminckii* (Temminck's Stint) ad. nbr. (7); ad. br. (8). *Calidris subminuta* (Long-toed Stint) ad. nbr. (9); ad. br. (10).

Plate 34 (Chris Rose): *Calidris acuminata* (Sharp-tailed Sandpiper) ad. br. (1). *Calidris melanotos* (Pectoral Sandpiper) fw. (2). *Calidris alpina* (Dunlin) ad. br. (3); ad. nbr. (4). *Calidris alba* (Sanderling) ad. nbr. (5); ad. br. (6). *Calidris ferruginea* (Curlew Sandpiper) ad. nbr. (7); ad. br. (8). *Limicola falcinellus* (Broad-billed Sandpiper) ad. nbr. (9); ad. br. (10).

Plate 35 (R. David Digby): *Hydrophasianus chirurgus* (Pheasant-tailed Jacana) ad. br. (1, 2); ad. nbr. (3); *Metopidius indicus* (Bronze-winged Jacana) juv. (4); ad. (5). *Vanellus indicus* (Red-wattled Lapwing) ad. (6). *Vanellus duvaucelii* (River Lapwing) ad. (7). *Vanellus cinereus* (Grey-headed Lapwing) ad. (8). *Rostratula benghalensis* (Greater Painted-snipe) ad. female (9); ad. male (10).

Plate 36 (Chris Rose): *Charadrius placidus* (Long-billed Plover) ad. nbr. (1); ad. br. (2). *Charadrius dubius* (Little Ringed Plover) ad. nbr. (3); ad. br. (4). *Charadrius hiaticula* (Common Ringed Plover) ad. nbr. (5); ad. br. (6). *Charadrius peronii* (Malaysian Plover) ad. male (7); chick (8); ad. female (9). *Charadrius alexandrinus* (Kentish Plover) ad. male br. (10); ad. nbr. (11). *Charadrius mongolus* (Mongolian Plover) ad. br. (12); ad. nbr. (13). *Charadrius leschenaultii* (Large Sand Plover) ad. br. (14); ad. nbr. (15).

Plate 37 (Chris Rose): *Esacus neglectus* (Beach Thick-knee) ad. (1). *Dromas ardeola* (Crab-plover) ad. (2). *Burhinus oedicnemus* (Eurasian Thick-knee) ad. (3). *Himantopus himantopus* (Black-winged Stilt) ad. nbr. (4); ad. br. (5); juv. (6). *Haematopus ostralegus* (Eurasian Oystercatcher) ad. br. (7). *Glareola maldivarum* (Oriental Pratincole) ad. br. (8); juv. (9); two in flight (10). *Glareola lactea* (Small Pratincole) ad. nbr. (11); two in flight (12).

Plate 38 (Ian Lewington): *Stercorarius longicaudus* (Long-tailed Skua) dark-phase juv. (1); barred-phase juv. (2, 3); ad. br, (4, 5); ad. nbr. (6). *Stercorarius parasiticus* (Arctic Skua) dark-phase ad. br. (7); light-phase ad. br. (8, 9); ad. nbr. (10); juv. (11, 12). *Stercorarius pomarinus* (Pomarine Skua) dark-phase ad. br. (13); light-phase ad. br. (14, 15); ad. nbr. (16); juv. (17, 18). *Catharacta maccormicki* (South-polar Skua) intermediate-phase ad. nbr. (19, 20); dark-phase ad. nbr. (21); light-phase ad. nbr. (22).

Plate 39 (Ian Lewington): *Phaethon lepturus* (White-tailed Tropicbird) juv. (1); ad. *lepturus* (2). *Phaethon rubricauda* (Red-tailed Tropicbird) juv. (3); ad. (4). *Larus brunnicephalus* (Brown-headed Gull) ad. br. (5); fw. (6); ad. nbr. (7). *Sterna caspia* (Caspian Tern) ad. br. (8); ad. nbr. (9). *Larus heuglini* (Heuglin's Gull) ad. br. *taimyrensis* (10); fw. (11); ad. nbr. (12). *Larus ridibundus* (Common Black-headed Gull) ad. br. (13): fw. (14); ad. nbr. (15).

Plate 40 (Ian Lewington): *Chlidonias leucopterus* (White-winged Black Tern) ad. br. (1, 2); ad. nbr. (3); fw. (4, 5). *Chlidonias hybridus* (Whiskered Tern) ad. br. (6, 7); ad. nbr. (8); juv. (9, 10). *Sterna hirundo* (Common Tern) ad. br. (11, 12); ad. nbr. (13). *Sterna dougallii* (Roseate Tern) ad. br. (14, 15); juv. (16). *Sterna sumatrana* (Black-naped Tern) ad. (17, 18); juv. (19). *Sterna albifrons* (Little Tern) ad. br. (20, 21); ad. nbr. (22); juv. (23).

Plate 41 (Ian Lewington): *Sterna anaethetus* (Bridled Tern) ad. (1, 2); juv. (3). *Sterna fuscata* (Sooty Tern) ad. (4, 5); juv. (6). *Sterna nilotica* (Gull-billed Tern) ad. br. (7); ad. nbr. (8). *Sterna bernsteini* (Chinese Crested Tern) ad. br. (9, 10); ad. nbr. (11). *Sterna bengalensis* (Lesser Crested Tern) ad. br. (12, 13); ad. nbr. (14). *Sterna bergii* (Great Crested Tern) ad. br. (15, 16); ad. nbr. (17); juv. (18).

Plate 42 (Dana Gardner): *Macropygia unchall* (Barred Cuckoo Dove) ad. male (1); ad. female (2). *Macropygia ruficeps* (Little Cuckoo Dove) ad. female (3); ad. male (4). *Streptopelia chinensis* (Spotted Dove) ad. (5). *Columba livia* (Town Pigeon) wild-type ad. (6); rufous-phase ad. (7). *Streptopelia tranquebarica* (Red Collared Dove) ad. female (8); ad. male (9). *Geopelia striata* (Zebra Dove) ad. (10). *Chalcophaps indica* (Emerald Dove) ad. female (11); ad. male (12).

Plate 43 (Dana Gardner): *Ducula badia* (Mountain Imperial Pigeon) ad. (1). *Ducula aenea* (Green Imperial Pigeon) ad. (2). *Columba argentina* (Silvery Wood Pigeon) ad. (3). *Ducula bicolor* (Pied Imperial Pigeon) ad. (4). *Columba punicea* (Pale-capped Pigeon) ad. (5). *Caloenas nicobarica* (Nicobar Pigeon) ad. (6).

Plate 44 (Dana Gardner): *Treron capellei* (Large Green Pigeon) ad. female (1); ad. male (2). *Treron seimundi* (Yellow-vented Green Pigeon) ad. male (3); ad. female (4). *Treron curvirostra* (Thick-billed Green Pigeon) ad. male (5); ad. female (6). *Treron sphenura* (Wedge-tailed Green Pigeon) ad. male (7); ad. female (8).

Plate 45 (Dana Gardner): *Ptilinopus jambu* (Jambu Fruit Dove) ad. male (1); ad. female (2). *Treron olax* (Little Green Pigeon) ad. female (3); ad. male (4). *Treron vernans* (Pink-necked Green Pigeon) ad. female (5); ad. male (6). *Treron bicincta* (Orange-breasted Green Pigeon) ad. male (7); ad. female (8). *Treron fulvicollis* (Cinnamon-headed Green Pigeon) ad. male (9); ad. female (10).

Plate 46 (R. David Digby): *Psittacula alexandri* (Red-breasted Parakeet) ad. male (1); ad. female (2). *Psittacula longicauda* (Long-tailed Parakeet) ad. male (3); ad. female (4). *Psittinus cyanurus* (Blue-rumped Parrot) ad. female (5); ad. male (6). *Loriculus vernalis* (Vernal Hanging Parrot) ad. female (7); ad. male (8). *Loriculus galgulus* (Blue-crowned Hanging Parrot) ad. female (9); ad. male (10).

Plate 47 (Dana Gardner): *Eudynamys scolopacea* (Koel) ad. female *malayanus* (1); ad. male (2). *Clamator coromandus* (Chestnut-winged Cuckoo) ad. (3). *Centropus bengalensis* (Lesser Coucal) juv. (4); ad. (5). *Centropus rectunguis* (Short-toed Coucal) ad. (6). *Centropus sinensis* (Greater Coucal) juv. (7); ad. (8).

Plate 48 (Dana Gardner): *Cuculus fugax* (Hodgson's Hawk Cuckoo) ad. *fugax* (1); ad. *nisicolor* (2). *Cuculus vagans* (Moustached Hawk Cuckoo) ad. (3). *Cuculus micropterus* (Indian Cuckoo) ad. (4). *Cuculus saturatus* (Oriental Cuckoo) grey-phase ad. migrant (5). *Cuculus sparverioides* (Large Hawk Cuckoo) ad. *bocki* (6); subad. *bocki* (7); ad. *sparverioides* (8).

Plate 49 (Dana Gardner): *Cacomantis merulinus* (Plaintive Cuckoo) grey-phase ad. (1); rufous-phase ad. (2); juv. (3). *Cacomantis sepulchralis* (Rusty-breasted Cuckoo) grey-phase ad. (4); rufous-phase ad. (5); juv. (6). *Cacomantis sonnerati* (Banded Bay Cuckoo) ad. (7). *Surniculus lugubris* (Drongo Cuckoo) ad. (8); juv. (9).

Plate 50 (Dana Gardner): *Chrysococcyx maculatus* (Asian Emerald Cuckoo) ad. male (1); ad. female (2). *Chrysococcyx basalis* (Horsfield's Bronze Cuckoo) ad. (3). *Chrysococcyx minutillus* (Little Bronze Cuckoo) ad. male (4); ad. female (5). *Chrysococcyx xanthorhynchus* (Violet Cuckoo) ad. male (6); ad. female (7).

Plate 51 (Dana Gardner): *Phaenicophaeus tristis* (Green-billed Malkoha) ad. (1). *Phaenicophaeus chlorophaeus* (Raffles's Malkoha) ad. male (2); ad. female (3). *Phaenicophaeus javanicus* (Red-billed Malkoha) ad. (4). *Phaenicophaeus sumatranus* (Chestnut-bellied Malkoha) ad. (5). *Phaenicophaeus diardi* (Black-bellied Malkoha) ad. (6). *Phaenicophaeus curvirostris* (Chestnut-breasted Malkoha) ad. male (7).

Plate 52 (Dana Gardner): *Glaucidium brodiei* (Collared Owlet) ad. (1, 2). *Otus sp.* (Small-island Scops Owl) ad. (3). *Otus rufescens* (Reddish Scops Owl) ad. (4). *Otus sunia* (Oriental Scops Owl) rufous-phase ad. (5); grey-phase ad. (6). *Otus bakkamoena* (Collared Scops Owl) ad. (7). *Otus spilocephalus* (Mountain Scops Owl) ad. (8). *Otus sagittatus* (White-fronted Scops Owl) ad. (9).

Plate 53 (Dana Gardner): *Bubo sumatranus* (Barred Eagle Owl) ad. (1). *Strix leptogrammica* (Brown Wood Owl) ad. (2). *Strix seloputo* (Spotted Wood Owl) ad. (3). *Bubo coromandus* (Dusky Eagle Owl) ad. (4). *Ketupa zeylonensis* (Brown Fish Owl) ad. (5). *Ketupa ketupu* (Buffy Fish Owl) ad. (6).

Plate 54 (Dana Gardner): *Batrachostomus auritus* (Large Frogmouth) ad. (1). *Batrachostomus stellatus* (Gould's Frogmouth) ad. (2). *Batrachostomus javensis* (Javan Frogmouth) ad. male (3); ad. female (4). *Tyto alba* (Barn Owl) ad. male (5). *Phodilus badius* (Oriental Bay Owl) ad. (6). *Ninox scutulata* (Brown Boobook) ad. (7). *Asio flammeus* (Short-eared Owl) ad. (8).

Plate 55 (Dana Gardner): *Caprimulgus affinis* (Savanna Nightjar) ad. male (1); ad. female (2). *Caprimulgus indicus* (Grey Nightjar) ad. male (3); ad. female (4). *Caprimulgus macrurus* (Large-tailed Nightjar) ad. male (5); ad. female (6). *Eurostopodus temminckii* (Malaysian Eared Nightjar) ad. (7). *Eurostopodus macrotis* (Great Eared Nightjar) ad. (8).

Plate 56 (Chris Rose): *Hydrochous gigas* (Waterfall Swift) ad. at nest (1). *Aerodramus maximus* (Black-nest Swiftlet) ad. at nest (2). *Collocalia esculenta* (Glossy Swiftlet) ad. at nest (3, 4). *Aerodramus fuciphagus* (Edible-nest Swiftlet) ad. *amechana* at nest (5, 6). *Cypsiurus balasiensis* (Asian Palm Swift) ad. (7, 8). *Rhaphidura leucopygialis* (Silver-rumped Spinetail) ad. (9-11).

Plate 57 (Chris Rose): *Hirundapus cochinchinensis* (Silver-backed Needletail) (1-3). *Hirundapus caudacutus* (White-throated Needletail) (4-6). *Hirundapus giganteus* (Brown-backed Needletail) (7-9). *Apus nipalensis* (House Swift) (10-15). *Apus pacificus* (Pacific Swift) (16-20). *Hemiprocne longipennis* (Grey-rumped Treeswift) (21-25); ad. male (25). *Hemiprocne comata* (Whiskered Treeswift) (26-29); ad. male (27); ad. female (28).

Plate 58 (Dana Gardner): *Harpactes duvaucelii* (Scarlet-rumped Trogon) ad. male (1); ad. female (2). *Harpactes orrhophaeus* (Cinnamon-rumped Trogon) ad. female (3); ad. male (4). *Harpactes oreskios* (Orange-breasted Trogon) ad. male (5); ad. female (6). *Harpactes diardii* (Diard's Trogon) ad. female (7); ad. male (8). *Harpactes erythrocephalus* (Red-headed Trogon) ad. male (9); ad. female (10). *Harpactes kasumba* (Red-naped Trogon) ad. female (11); ad. male (12).

Plate 59 (Dana Gardner): *Anthracoceros malayanus* (Black Hornbill) pale-browed ad. male (1); ad. female (2); dark-browed ad. male (3, 4). *Anorrhinus galeritus* (Bushy-crested Hornbill) ad. male (5, 7); ad. female (6). *Anthracoceros albirostris* (Oriental Pied Hornbill) ad. female (8); ad. male (9, 10). *Upupa epops* (Common Hoopoe) ad. (11).

Plate 60 (Dana Gardner): *Buceros vigil* (Helmeted Hornbill) ad. female (1); juv. (2); ad. male (3). *Buceros bicornis* (Great Hornbill) ad. female (4); ad. male (5). *Buceros rhinoceros* (Rhinoceros Hornbill) ad. female (6); ad. male (7); juv. (8).

Plate 61 (Dana Gardner): *Aceros corrugatus* (Wrinkled Hornbill) ad. male (1, 3); ad. female (2). *Berenicornis comatus* (White-crowned Hornbill) ad. male (4, 6); ad. female (5). *Aceros undulatus* (Wreathed Hornbill) ad. male (7, 8); ad. female (9). *Aceros subruficollis* (Tenasserim Hornbill) ad. female (10); ad. male (11, 12).

Plate 62 (Philip Burton): *Halcyon capensis* (Stork-billed Kingfisher) ad. (1); juv. (2); ad. pair (3). *Halcyon amauroptera* (Brown-winged Kingfisher) ad. (4); juv. (5). *Halcyon smyrnensis* (White-throated Kingfisher) ad. (6); juv. (7). *Halcyon coromanda* (Ruddy Kingfisher) ad. *coromanda* (8); juv. (9). *Halcyon pileata* (Black-capped Kingfisher) ad. (10). *Halcyon chloris* (Collared Kingfisher) ad. (11). *Actenoides concretus* (Chestnut-collared Kingfisher) ad. female (12); ad. male (13).

Plate 63 (Philip Burton): *Lacedo pulchella* (Banded Kingfisher) ad. male (1); ad. female (2). *Alcedo euryzona* (Blue-banded Kingfisher) ad. male (3); ad. female (4). *Alcedo atthis* (Common Kingfisher) ad. male (5); juv. (6). *Alcedo meninting* (Blue-eared Kingfisher) ad. male (7); subad. female (8). *Ceyx erithacus* (Oriental Dwarf Kingfisher) ad. *erithacus* (9); juv. *erithacus* (10); ad. *rufidorsum* (11); juv. *rufidorsum* (12).

Plate 64 (Philip Burton): *Coracias benghalensis* (Indian Roller) ad. (1, 2). *Eurystomus orientalis* (Dollarbird) ad. (3, 5); juv. (4). *Merops leschenaulti* (Bay-headed Bee-eater) ad. (6); juv. (7). *Nyctyornis amictus* (Red-bearded Bee-eater) ad. male (8); juv. (9). *Merops viridis* (Blue-throated Bee-eater) ad. (10); juv. (11). *Merops superciliosus* (Blue-tailed Bee-eater) ad. (12).

Plate 65 (Dana Gardner): *Picumnus innominatus* (Speckled Piculet) ad. male (1). *Sasia ochracea* (White-browed Piculet) ad. male (2). *Sasia abnormis* (Rufous Piculet) ad. male (3); ad. female (4); juv. (5). *Hemicircus concretus* (Grey-and-buff Woodpecker) ad. male (6). *Meiglyptes tukki* (Buff-necked Woodpecker) ad. male (7). *Meiglyptes tristis* (Buff-rumped Woodpecker) ad. male (8). *Picoides moluccensis* (Brown-capped Woodpecker) ad. (9). *Picoides canicapillus* (Grey-capped Woodpecker) ad. (10).

Plate 66 (Dana Gardner): *Picus puniceus* (Crimson-winged Yellownape) ad. male (1). *Picus mineaceus* (Banded Yellownape) ad. male (2). *Picus chlorolophus* (Lesser Yellownape) ad. male (3). *Picus mentalis* (Chequer-throated Yellownape) ad. female (4); ad. male (5). *Picus flavinucha* (Greater Yellownape) ad. male (6); ad. female (7). *Celeus brachyurus* (Rufous Woodpecker) ad. male (8). *Blythipicus rubiginosus* (Maroon Woodpecker) ad. male (9). *Blythipicus pyrrhotis* (Bay Woodpecker) ad. male (10).

Plate 67 (Dana Gardner): *Chrysocolaptes lucidus* (Greater Flameback) ad. male (1); ad. female (2). *Dinopium javanense* (Common Flameback) ad. male (3); ad. female (4). *Dinopium rafflesii* (Olive-backed Woodpecker) ad. female (5); ad. male (6). *Dryocopus javensis* (White-bellied Woodpecker) ad. male (7). *Reinwardtipicus validus* (Orange-backed Woodpecker) ad. male (8); ad. female (9). *Mulleripicus pulverulentus* (Great Slaty Woodpecker) ad. male (10).

Plate 68 (Dana Gardner): *Megalaima lineata* (Lineated Barbet) ad. (1). *Megalaima haemacephala* (Coppersmith Barbet) ad. (2). *Calorhampus fuliginosus* (Brown Barbet) ad. male (3). *Indicator archipelagicus* (Malaysian Honeyguide) ad. male (4). *Gecinulus viridis* (Bamboo Woodpecker) ad. female (5); ad. male (6). *Picus vittatus* (Laced Woodpecker) ad. male (7); ad. female (8). *Picus viridanus* (Streaked-breasted Woodpecker) ad. male (9). *Picus canus* (Grey-faced Woodpecker) ad. male (10).

Plate 69 (Dana Gardner): *Psilopogon pyrolophus* (Fire-tufted Barbet) ad. (1). *Megalaima rafflesii* (Red-crowned Barbet) ad. (2). *Megalaima chrysopogon* (Gold-whiskered Barbet) ad. (3). *Megalaima henricii* (Yellow-crowned Barbet) ad. (4). *Megalaima asiatica* (Blue-throated Barbet) ad. (5). *Megalaima oorti* (Black-browed Barbet) ad. (6). *Megalaima franklinii* (Golden-throated Barbet) ad. (7). *Megalaima mystacophanos* (Red-throated Barbet) ad. male (8); ad. female (9). *Megalaima australis* (Blue-eared Barbet) ad. (10).

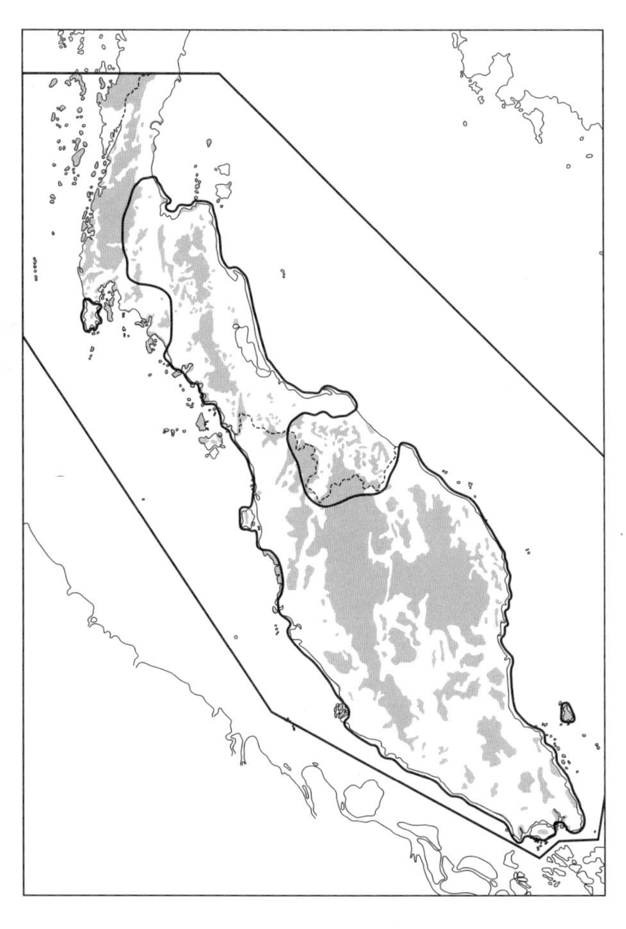

Passage-flocks are mostly of 60 or fewer, occasionally much larger and, up to the early 1980s, during September–October and March, favoured sites in Selangor attracted resting concentrations of one or more thousands. The impression since has been of a large drop in numbers. At Subang airfield, Selangor, a peak March count of only 245 in 1991 compares with 1500 in 1967 (BMP5, Parish 1985a, A.C. Sebastian).

HABITATS AND ECOLOGY. Breeders are attracted to bare earth, including paddyland after spring stubble- and straw-burning, and large earth scrapes. With progressive shortening of the fallow period in irrigated rice agriculture and widespread, post-harvest application of pesticides, this opportunistic capacity to switch to other, temporary, sites could be an advantage. Post-breeders and migrants loaf and roost on open paddylands, especially where dry-ploughed, also on the short grass of large pastures, airfields, remote beach strand, old mine-tailings, etc. Flocks on the move commonly soar in thermals.

FORAGING AND FOOD. An aerial insectivore. At all seasons, foragers concentrate especially over wetlands, brackish to freshwater, including sometimes open water. They are also the only common waders attending termite swarms.

SOCIAL ORGANIZATION. A colonial nester and gregarious throughout, especially on migration.

MOVEMENTS. Along the Malaysian E coast, passage reported during 10 October–8 November and 11 February–6 April (Howes *et al.* 1986, MBR 1982–83, Medway 1966, Swennen *et al.* 1986). At both seasons, sight-records from oil-rigs 200 km off the Terengganu coast imply possible direct overflights of the Gulf of Thailand (MBR 1982–83).

Apart from May stragglers in Selangor (ENGGANG-2), broadly similar spring dates apply also in the south and west. In autumn, movement across Singapore regularly continues through at least the first week of December, and on the Melaka Straits coast shows an altogether greater spread: from early August (substantial flocks in Kedah and Selangor) to 25 December (ENGGANG-2, MBR 1982–83). Moves mostly by day, with some thermal soaring, but in Selangor in September has also been heard passing over after dark.

SURVIVAL. No information.

SOCIAL INTERACTIONS. No information.

VOICE. The flight-call is a rather high-pitched, grating *tir-rek* or *tirrk*.

BREEDING

Nest. The only one seen was a small, unlined depression on the bare ground of a dry, burned-off paddyfield.

Eggs and brood. Eggs are khaki-brown heavily marked with irregular blotches of pale grey-brown and rich, deep brown. Full clutch apparently two.

Cycle. On being approached, the whole nesting colony flies circling round uttering plaintive distress-calls. At Kangar, the sitting parent left the nest at about 10 m range and gave broken-wing displays on the ground until the eggs were handled, whereafter both pair-members returned to circling and calling.

Seasonality. The only eggs found, dated 30 March, were an apparently early clutch in a colony of a few pairs. On the Malaysian E coast, behaviour implying presence of eggs or chicks has been reported in April, May and June (BR 1968, 1970–71, MBR 1982–83, T. Mundkur).

MOULT. Stripe-throated (juvenile and non-breeding) plumage is recorded during June–mid January, with replacement among evident adults starting as early as October (one in part-breeding plumage on 29 October), i.e. during southward migration. Adult wing-moult is by then either already complete (one dated 24 September showed primaries 1–9 new, P10 growing) or has suspended (between P6 and P9). It is not known when it resumes but ten spring migrants collected in Selangor on 4 March all had fully renewed wings. One late-migrating or possibly overwintering W-coast juvenile dated 10 January was growing P2–3, on an evidently later schedule (BMNH, UMBRP, ZRC-NUS).

CONSERVATION. There is no recent information on breeding success in paddyland. Impacts of irrigation, shortening of the fallow period and spread of pesticide-usage in multi-cropped areas all need investigating. At a major migration halt near Ceribon, N Java, on a likely route to and from the Peninsula, pratincoles have been the core species of a vast trade in bird meat to restaurants (Milton and Marhadi 1989).

Small Pratincole; Nok En-thung Lek (Thai); Burung Lelayang Kecil (Malay)

Glareola lactea Temminck 1820, *Manuel d'Ornithologie* 2: 503. TL Bengal.
Plate 37

GROUP RELATIONS. Ecological representative of W-central African *G. cinerea* (Grey Pratincole); they are a probable superspecies (Snow 1978).

GLOBAL RANGE. The Indian subcontinent from the Indus valley, SE Afghanistan and Himalayan foothills, and Sri Lanka; S Yunnan; and larger rivers and other open wetlands of SE Asia to Tenasserim, central Thailand and the Mekong as far as Cambodia. Dispersants reach SW Thailand and, occasionally, the Peninsula.

IDENTIFICATION/DESCRIPTION. On the ground, pale sand-grey body (tinged peach-buff across cheeks, throat and centre breast) blends well with bare-soil background. A dark loral line disappears during moult (Hayman *et al.* 1986) and a bird without it in early December showed a whitish line from the eye to below the beak; also a small white half-ring round the rear of the eye (MBR 1986–87). Flight-feathers and lower wing-coverts are black, with a bold white, chevron-shaped bar across the base of the secondaries and innermost primaries, showing on both surfaces. The shallowly forked white tail has a chevron-shaped, black tip.

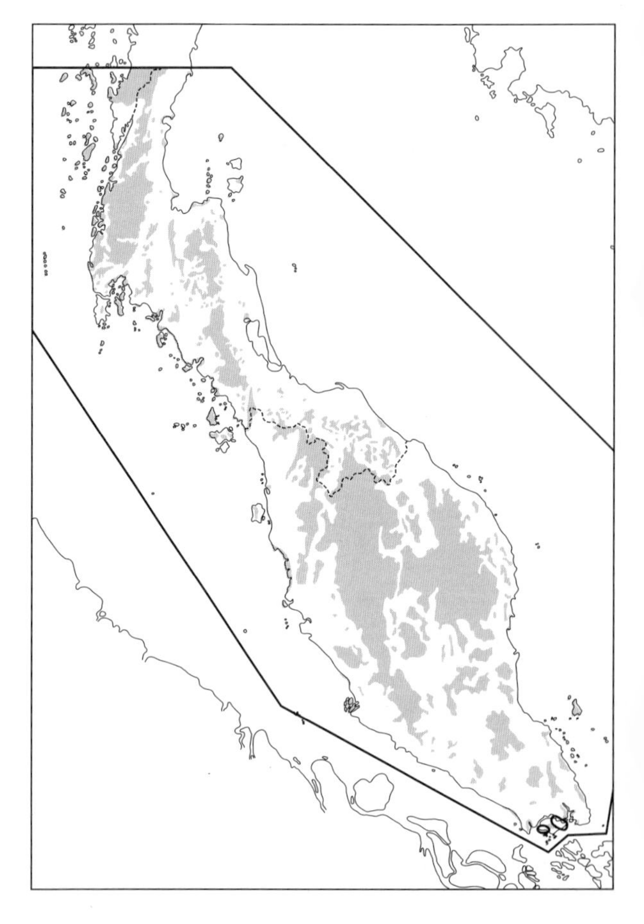

Bare-part colours. (Adults) iris dark brown; bill black with mouth-line and small patch at base orange-red; legs and feet dark olive-brown.

Size (mm). (Skins: 2 males from the Gulf of Bangkok; adult): wing 154, 154; tail 50, 50, with tail-fork 5.5, 6.4; bill 11.2, 11.9; tarsus 20.9, 22.2 (BMNH).

Weight. No data.

DISTRIBUTION. Historical summary: *Sin.*

GEOGRAPHICAL VARIATION. None recognized.

STATUS AND POPULATION. Vagrant. Overlooked on the mainland but odd individuals, thought to have dropped out of south-moving flocks of Oriental Pratincoles, have wintered in Singapore: recorded at Jurong during mid November–early January 1964/65, on the coast at Changi during early December–late January 1987/88 and at Serangoon on 7 January 1989 (BR 1964, SINGAV-1, -2, -3).

HABITATS AND ECOLOGY. Sites on Singapore have included the margins of tide-flushed prawn-ponds in the mangrove zone, and bare, coastal sand-fill at the E end of the island. The 1964 bird consorted with Oriental Pratincoles; others were alone or roosted with mixed wader groups.

FORAGING AND FOOD. Aerial insect-hunting. Long-winged Small outflies foraging Oriental

Pratincole, with faster beats and frequent upward swoops (BR 1964).

SOCIAL ORGANIZATION. No information.

MOVEMENTS. Extreme dates are 16 November and 24 January.

SURVIVAL. No information.

SOCIAL INTERACTIONS. No information.

VOICE. No information.

BREEDING. No population.

MOULT. No data.

CONSERVATION. No relevant issues.

Family LARIDAE

Skuas, gulls and terns: 22 species

(?South-polar) Skua; (no Thai name); Burung Pelangi Antartik (Malay)

Catharacta maccormicki (Saunders) 1893, *Bulletin of the British Ornithologists' Club* 3: 12. TL Possession island, Antarctica.

Plate 38

GROUP RELATIONS. Marginally sympatric with breeding *C. skua loennbergi* (Great Skua) in the S Shetland islands (Devillers 1977) but, perhaps, they are still treatable as a superspecies, together with *C. chilensis* (Chilean Skua).

GLOBAL RANGE. Breeds on antarctic coasts, moving into northern oceans during the austral winter. Identified north to Greenland in the Atlantic and regular as far as the cool N-temperate zone of the Pacific. In the Indian Ocean, confirmed north to Sri Lanka and the Gulf of Aden.

IDENTIFICATION/DESCRIPTION. Smallest of the *Catharacta* species; approached in size by some Pomarine Skuas. Light-phase adults have head, neck and underparts pink-brown to near-white; in dark-phase birds these parts are dark brown. Wings, scapulars and tail are near-black, and (at least by late northern summer) both phases show golden hackles on the nape. Juveniles have head and body grey, and lack nape-hackles (Devillers 1977). In flight, white flash at base of primaries, showing on both surfaces, is larger and bolder than in *Stercorarius* species, and wings and wedge-shaped tail are proportionately broader.

Bare-part colours. Bill bluish with a black tip (juvenile), all-black (adult); feet bluish (juvenile), black (adult) (Devillers 1977).

Size. No data.

Weight. No data.

DISTRIBUTION. Off both Thai coasts.

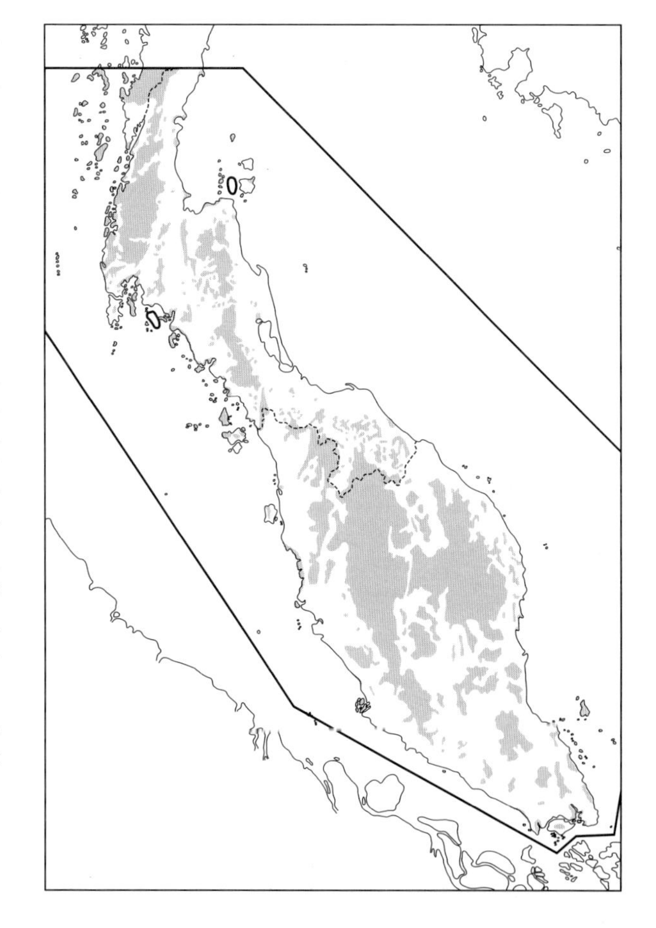

GEOGRAPHICAL VARIATION. None handled.

STATUS AND POPULATION. Vagrant. Local sight-identifications have not been past the level of genus, but on the basis that *maccormicki* is a regular transequatorial migrant whereas Indo-Pacific *skua* has only once been confirmed beyond S-temperate-zone waters (in SW India) (Devillers 1977), they are most likely to have been of South-polar Skuas. Recorded twice: five at sea between the Krabi mainland and Phiphi island, entrance to Phangnga bay, on 13 April 1989 and, off the opposite coast, four near Samui island on 29 December of the same year (BBCB-6, -7). Mid April is consistent with northward migration but December implies 'over-summering' by non-breeders, perhaps immatures (which are said not to return to breeding-colonies before their third year). Other Sunda-Shelf sightings include a bird off Belawan, NW Melaka Straits, in mid May and several between the W Sabah coast and Tiga island on 17 February, another potential 'over-summering' date (CLBS, OBCB-15).

HABITAT AND ECOLOGY. Open sea, including continental-shelf waters.

FORAGING AND FOOD. No information.

SOCIAL ORGANIZATION. Solitary, or small parties travel together.

MOVEMENTS. No other information.

SURVIVAL. No information.

SOCIAL INTERACTIONS. No information.

VOICE. No information.

BREEDING. No population.

MOULT. No data.

CONSERVATION. No relevant issues.

Pomarine Skua; Nok Skua Haang Chawn (Thai); Burung Pelangi Pomarin (Malay)

Stercorarius pomarinus (Temminck) 1815, *Manuel d'Ornithologie*: 514. TL arctic Europe.
Plate 38

GROUP RELATIONS. Free-standing.

GLOBAL RANGE. Breeds on the arctic coastal plain and islands from the White Sea to Chukotka, and Alaska to W Greenland. Main wintering areas are in the N-tropical Atlantic, the NW Indian Ocean, the NW Pacific, and off N New Guinea and E Australia (Barton 1982). Some Sunda shelf records are winter-dated, concentrated off NW Borneo, and Pomarine Skuas are said to gather in the Gulf of Bangkok (where birds unidentified to species have also been seen during summer: D.M. Simpson).

IDENTIFICATION/DESCRIPTION. Less chunky than a *Catharacta* skua, with narrower hand and tail, but not very much smaller than *C. maccormicki*. Most lack the diagnostic, projecting, spatulate central tail-feathers and are then best told from Arctic Skua by shape and flight-mode. Pomarine has a big bill, full body, and proportionately wide-based wings. Deep and deliberate wing-strokes do not bounce the body in level flight, and turning and gliding on the wind is relatively slow. Both species show a white flash at the base of the primaries (both surfaces), have all-dark brown or barred juveniles and two colour-phases of adult, the light phase with a black cap, whitish underparts and a dark pectoral band, generally stronger in Pomarine than in Arctic (BWP, Malling Olsen 1989).

Bare-part colours. No local information.

Size. No data.

Weight. No data.

DISTRIBUTION. Off the length of both coasts.

GEOGRAPHICAL VARIATION. None recognized.

STATUS AND POPULATION. A sparse passage migrant, mainly in spring off the W coast; also in autumn (and some may overwinter) off the E coast. Most W-coast sightings, from Phangnga south to Singapore, have been during 23 March–7 June. Two off Phuket during 19–22 November are the only opposite-season records in the west (BBCB-5, -6, BCSTB-11, -12, BR 1963, Eve and Guigue 1982, Kiørboe 1991, MBR 1982–83, R.F. Ollington, A.C. Sebastian). Equivalent passage-dates in the S China Sea are 3–15 May (between Chumphon and Songkhla, including around Samui island), and 5 and 23 October (one and three birds in the Terengganu off-shore oil-field). Others seen off the E coast during the northern winter, include groups between Samui island and the mainland on 29 December and 3 January, individuals in Mersing bay (Johor) on 7 and 21 January and (most probably this species) a raft of 12 off the E end of the

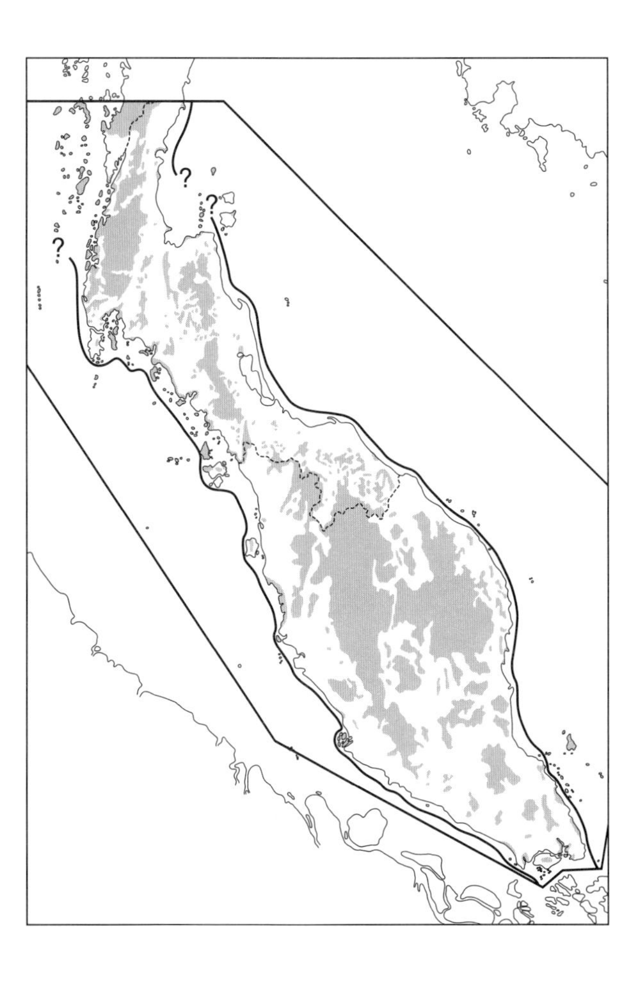

Singapore Straits on 6 February (BBCB-7, MBR 1982–83, D.M. Simpson).

HABITATS AND ECOLOGY. Open sea, including continental-shelf waters.

FORAGING AND FOOD. No information.

SOCIAL ORGANIZATION. Travels less often alone than in pairs or small parties.

MOVEMENTS. No other information.

SURVIVAL. No information.

SOCIAL INTERACTIONS. No information.

VOICE. No information.

BREEDING. No population.

MOULT. Ten off the NE coast in May all showed full tail-streamers (BCSTB-13).

CONSERVATION. No relevant issues.

Arctic Skua; Nok Skua Lohk Neua (Thai); Burung Pelangi Artik (Malay)

Stercorarius parasiticus (Linnaeus) 1758, *Systema Naturae* 10(1): 136. TL Sweden.
Plate 38

GROUP RELATIONS. Free-standing.

GLOBAL RANGE. Breeds on coasts and islands at high-temperate to high-arctic latitudes across Eurasia and from Alaska to Greenland, south in far-east Asia to Kamchatka, the Sea of Okhotsk, and the Commander and Aleutian islands. A mainly trans-equatorial migrant, to chief wintering areas in the SW and SE Atlantic, SE Pacific and off E Australia.

IDENTIFICATION/DESCRIPTION. Smaller, more slender-bodied than Pomarine Skua, with narrower-based wings. Flight lighter, more floating, with agile gliding and turning, but shows the same extent of white over the base of the primaries, visible on both wing surfaces. Light-phase adult has cap and face sharply darker than grey-yellow nape, a dark pectoral band, greyish belly, grey and dark lower tail-coverts. In some, rump, upper tail-coverts and base of proportionately rather long, wedge-shaped tail are white, contrasting sharply with blackish tip of tail. Not all birds have central tail-feathers pointed and projecting.

A combination of bi-coloured tail and graceful flight indicates Arctic rather than Pomarine Skua (Harrison 1985, Malling Olsen 1989).

Bare-part colours. No information.

Size. No data.

Weight. No data.

DISTRIBUTION. Confirmed only off the E coast (Pahang).

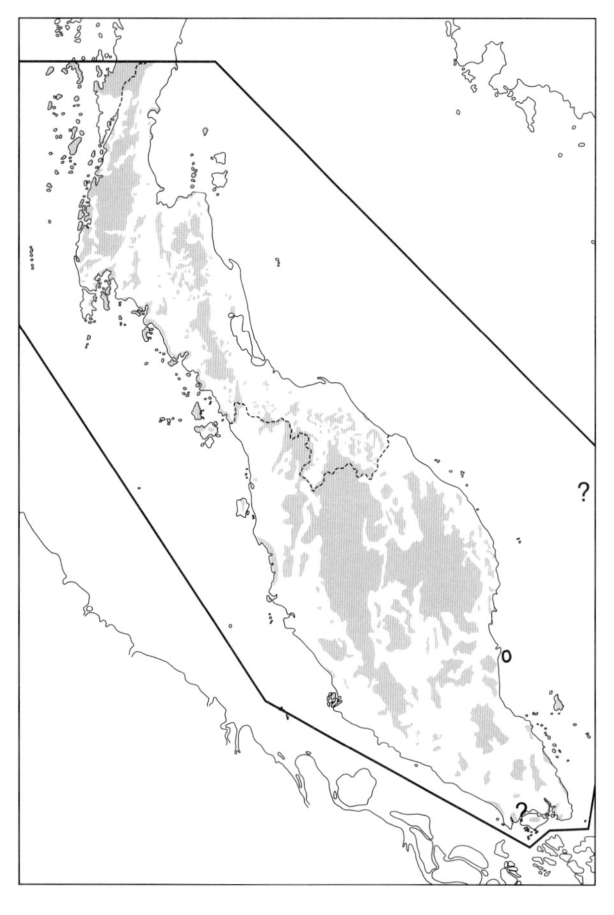

GEOGRAPHICAL VARIATION. None recognized.

STATUS AND POPULATION. Apparently only vagrant, with the provisos that some local reports of skuas have not been confirmed to species and that quite a number of claims of Arctic Skua on spring and autumn passage have been made from Bali, Java and the Sunda Straits (van Balen 1991). The one firm identification is of a pale-phase bird 4 km SE of Agas point, Pahang, on 29 April 1986 (Howes *et al.* 1986). Other likely but inconclusive sightings are of a lightly built, pale-phase individual in the Terengganu oil-field on 19 October 1982 and a bird over the NW coast of Singapore island on 25 September 1988 (MBR 1982–83, D.M. Simpson, SINGAV-2).

HABITATS AND ECOLOGY. Open sea, including continental-shelf waters.

FORAGING AND FOOD. No information.

SOCIAL ORGANIZATION. The only records to date have been of loners.

MOVEMENTS. No information.

SURVIVAL. No information.

SOCIAL INTERACTIONS. No information.

VOICE. No information.

BREEDING. No population.

MOULT. No data.

CONSERVATION. No relevant issues.

Long-tailed Skua; Nok Skua Haang Yao (Thai); Burung Pelangi Ekor Panjang (Malay)

Stercorarius longicaudus Vieillot 1819, *Nouveau Dictionnaire d'Histoire Naturelle* 32: 157. TL N Europe.

Plate 38

GROUP RELATIONS. Free-standing.

GLOBAL RANGE. Breeds on the Scandinavian mountains, and arctic coasts and islands across Eurasia and from Alaska to Greenland, south in far-east Asia to Kamchatka and the Sea of Okhotsk. A transequatorial migrant, wintering mainly in the S Atlantic, S Pacific and Tasman Sea. The few SE Asian and Wallacean records (van Balen 1991) have been on likely migration dates.

IDENTIFICATION/DESCRIPTION. From other skuas by smaller size, proportionately rather small head, no clear white flash or bar (too small to be obvious) on the flight-feathers, and upper wing-coverts paler than flight-feathers. All adults show a neat black cap contrasting strongly with yellowish nape and sides of face; chin to breast bright white and belly dusky grey, with no interposed pectoral band; and medium/long tail-streamers. Wing-pattern and lack of the pectoral band are an apparently diagnostic combination in this age-group (Malling Olsen 1989), whereas only the plain wing applies in darker, streamerless juveniles.

Bare-part colours. No information.

Size. No data.

Weight. No data.

DISTRIBUTION. The Andaman Sea and E coast.

GEOGRAPHICAL VARIATION. None recognized.

STATUS AND POPULATION. Hardly more than vagrant, on passage: an adult off the SE coast near Tioman island, Pahang, on 5 May 1986; one, two and three adults at sea between Krabi and Phiphi island, entrance to Phangnga bay during 13–16 April 1988; and one and three there again on 13 April 1989 and 3 April 1990 (BBCB-6, Howes *et al.* 1986, MBR 1986–87, P.D. Round), presumably all on spring passage. W-coast records are particularly surprising as Long-tailed Skua is hardly known in the eastern Indian Ocean.

HABITATS AND ECOLOGY. Open sea, including continental-shelf waters.

FORAGING AND FOOD. No information.

SOCIAL ORGANIZATION. No information.

MOVEMENTS. No further information.

SURVIVAL. No information.

SOCIAL INTERACTIONS. No information.

VOICE. No information.

BREEDING. No population.

MOULT. No data.

CONSERVATION. No relevant issues.

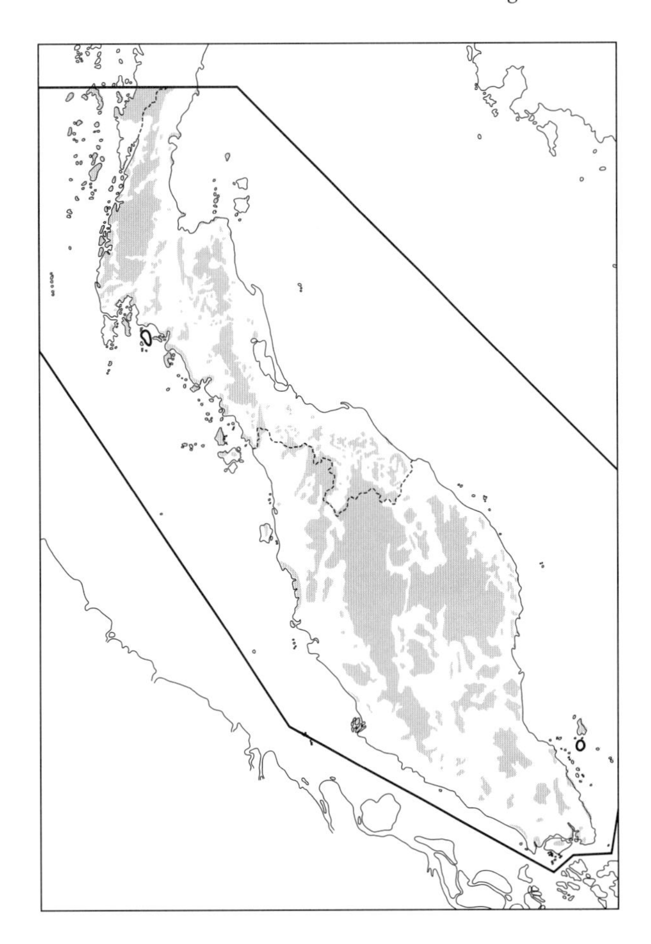

(?Heuglin's) Gull; (no Thai name); Burung Camar Heuglin (Malay)

Larus heuglini Bree 1876, *History of the Birds of Europe* 5: 58. TL Zeyla, Somalia.
Plate 39

GROUP RELATIONS. Reviewed by Kennerley *et al.* (1995). A dark backed, yellow-legged gull widely considered to represent either *Larus argentatus* (Herring Gull) or *L. fuscus* (Lesser Black-backed Gull), *heuglini* overlaps both in NW Siberia, apparently without interbreeding. Eastward, it is believed to incorporate medium to dark grey-backed, yellow- to orange-legged *taimyrensis* Buturlin 1911 (TL Gulf of Yenisey, N Russia).

GLOBAL RANGE. Breeds in arctic Siberia from the Kola to the Taimyr peninsulas, including the lower Yenisey valley. Winters from E Africa and the Arabian peninsula apparently to the Indian subcontinent (birds of this type seen south to Cape Comorin: D.S. Melville), and *taimyrensis* has recently been identified as the commonest of the large gulls wintering in Hong Kong (Kennerley *et al.* 1995, J. Palfrey). 'Herring' gulls needing further research regularly reach the Gulf of Bangkok and SW Thailand, and dark-backed forms are vagrant in Luzon and the Peninsula.

IDENTIFICATION/DESCRIPTION. Features of a bird at Changi, Singapore: on the ground, three times bulkier than nearby Grey Plovers; head, neck, underparts and tail all pure white except for brown flecking on the nape and hind-neck; upperparts charcoal-grey; legs and feet (against sand background) orange-yellow, other bare-part colours not recorded. In flight, trailing-edge of wing white, outer primaries black against rest of upper wing and showing rather little white subterminally (i.e., perhaps subadult). Identified by elimination: the grey-backed populations of Lesser Black-backed Gull, of far-W Eurasia, migrate mainly southwestwards, hence are geographically remote, while adult far-NE Asian Slaty-backed Gull *L. schistisagus* shows an unusually broad white trailing-edge to the wing, plus has legs and feet consistently pink.

Bare-part colours. No additional information.

Size. No data.

Weight. No data.

DISTRIBUTION. Historical summary: *Sin*. A large, immature gull with all-pale wings in Penang harbour on 17 November 1976 (N.P.E. Langham) was not conclusively identified.

GEOGRAPHICAL VARIATION. No appropriate information.

STATUS AND POPULATION. Known from a single adult or near-adult seen on a sandspit at Changi, E coast of Singapore island, on 7 January 1986 (after ten days of strong NE winds), and not found subsequently (C.J. Hails, MBR 1986–87). Nothing comparable has been reported in Thailand, where most 'Herring Gull' records have been of immatures.

HABITATS AND ECOLOGY. Coasts.

FORAGING AND FOOD. No information.

SOCIAL ORGANIZATION. No information.

MOVEMENTS. No information.

SURVIVAL. No information.

SOCIAL INTERACTIONS. No information.

VOICE. No information.

BREEDING. No population.

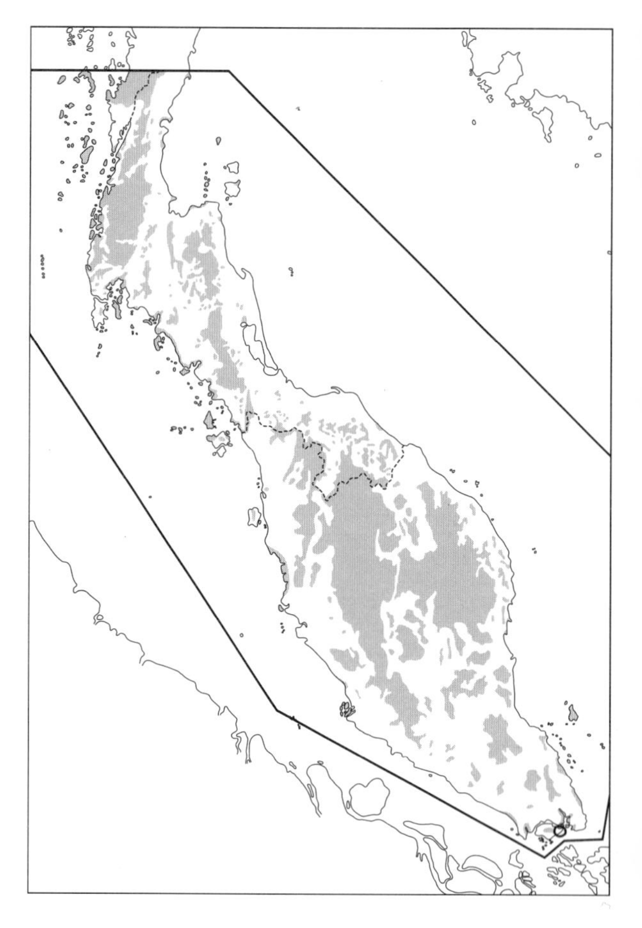

MOULT. No data.

CONSERVATION. No relevant issues.

Brown-headed Gull; Nok Nangnual Thammadaa (Thai); Burung Camar Kepala Coklat (Malay)

Larus brunnicephalus Jerdon 1840, *Madras Journal of Literature and Science* 12: 225. TL W coast of the Indian subcontinent.

Plate 39

GROUP RELATIONS. Uncertain.

GLOBAL RANGE. Breeds by upland lakes and rivers from the Pamirs east across Xinjiang and Qinghai and south to Tibet and Ladakh. Winters on coasts and larger inland waters of the Indian subcontinent and Sri Lanka; W Yunnan and, in small numbers, the S China coast (Chalmers 1986); and SE Asia from Burma and Laos to the lower Mekong, Gulf of Thailand and Peninsula; perhaps also E Sumatra.

IDENTIFICATION/DESCRIPTION. On the ground, from winter-plumaged Common Black-headed Gull by heavier bill, and birds with white eyes are Brown-headed Gulls. In flight, by a triangular black wing-tip with, in adults, subterminal white 'windows' on the two longest primaries. First-winterers show a solidly dark trailing-edge to whole wing, and immatures of both species have a black tail-band.

Bare-part colours. Iris brown (immature), yellowish white with red eyelid-rim (adult); bill dull to pinkish orange with dusky tip (immature), blood-red, with dusky tip in winter (adult); legs and feet dirty pink to red.

Size (mm). (Skins: 7 adults, 10 immatures, from SW and central Thailand; none sexed): wing 325–350 and 305–330; tail 113–122 and 96–120; bill 38.6–39.9 (age-classes combined); tarsus 45.7–53.9 (age-classes combined) (BMNH, ZRCNUS).

Weight. No data.

DISTRIBUTION. NW and far NE coasts; vagrant south of Perak. Historical summary: *Sur, Phu, Pes, Ked, Pek, Sel, Joh, Sin*, with additional W-coast island records from Ra (*Pha*), Tarutao (*Sat*), Penang and Tengah (*Sel*).

GEOGRAPHICAL VARIATION. None recognized.

STATUS AND POPULATION. A non-breeding visitor and possible passage migrant; local and sparse to common. The main SE Asian migration of Brown-headed Gulls terminates on the Gulf of Bangkok (BBCB-6). Only small numbers enter the Peninsula, sparsely in the NE (Bandon bay in October) and perhaps not overwintering. Along the W coast, recorded only a few times between Phangnga and Satul but present annually from Perlis to the Matang coast, Perak (BMNH, BMP5, Hume and Davison 1878, MBR 1986–87, P.D. Round). Typical overwintering group-sizes there are 25 or less, and a count of 200-plus on mudflats of Belanak point, Matang, in December 1964 has proved to be exceptional. This was also a winter of early arrival and unusually late departure. South of Perak, loners have been reported twice in Selangor, twice in the Johor Straits, and once at Kranji dam, Singapore, in November–December and late March (BR 1964, 1965, C.J. Hails, MBR 1984–85).

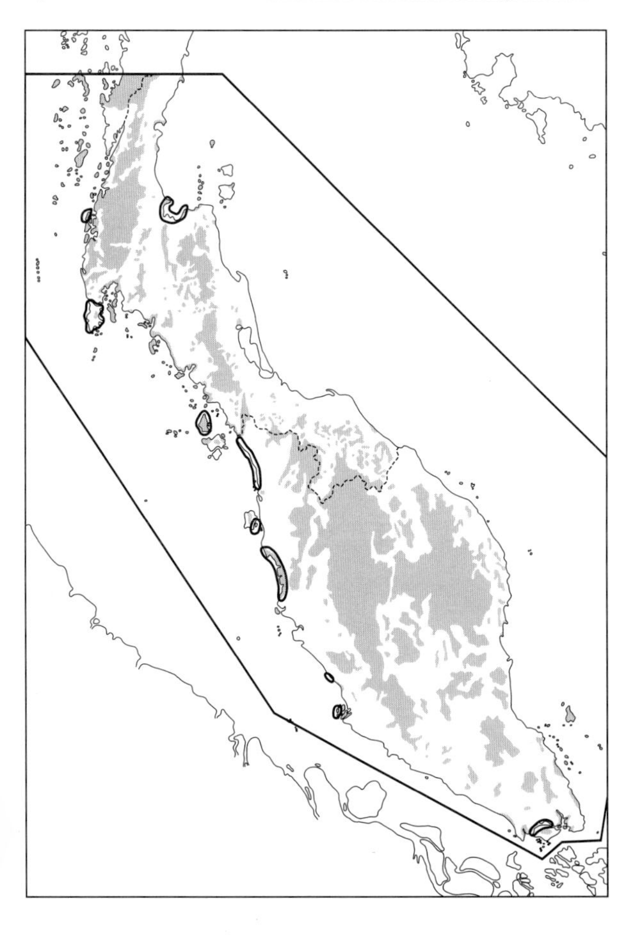

HABITATS AND ECOLOGY. Except for a passage-flock moving through Penang harbour (BR 1964), there have been no records away from intertidal mudflats.

FORAGING AND FOOD. No details, but observed to steal food from egrets foraging on the same beaches (A. J. Helbig).

SOCIAL ORGANIZATION. In the main winter range, travels and loafs gregariously.

MOVEMENTS. Successive counts on the Matang coast suggest a small build-up through the latter half of March (MBR 1986–87, Silvius *et al.* 1987). A flock of about 200, guessed to have been mostly this species, in the S approach to Penang harbour on 30 March 1963 (Etchécopar and Hüe 1966), represents more birds than normally winter in the southern Peninsula and might have come partly from further afield. Extreme dates are 5 November and 2 May, in Perak (BMP5).

SURVIVAL. No information.

SOCIAL INTERACTIONS. No information.

VOICE. No information.

BREEDING. No population.

MOULT. About half of a count of 55 at Kuala Gula, Perak, on 23 March were in summer plumage.

CONSERVATION. Polderization of Melaka Straits mudflat wintering habitat is the chief long-term issue.

Common Black-headed Gull; Nok Nangnual Khob Peek Khao (Thai); Burung Camar Kepala Hitam (Malay)

Larus ridibundus Linnaeus 1766, *Systema Naturae* 12(1): 225. TL European seas.
Plate 39

GROUP RELATIONS. Uncertain. Related to Afrotropical–S American *L. cirrocephalus* and *L. maculipennis* (Grey-headed and S American Brown-hooded Gulls) (BWP).

GLOBAL RANGE. Breeds on N Atlantic islands, to S Greenland and Iceland, across Eurasia to Kamchatka and Sakhalin, and south to NE China. Migrants winter south to SE USA, coasts and large inland waters of W and NE Africa; SW Asia and the northern Indian subcontinent, straggling to Sri Lanka (Phillips 1978); in Japan, China south of the Huang Ho including Taiwan and Hainan; N Vietnam and, in small numbers, through the rest of SE Asia to the Peninsula, N Borneo and Philippines; sparsely also to Wallacea, W Micronesia, New Guinea, the Solomons and NW Australia (Argeloo 1993).

IDENTIFICATION/DESCRIPTION. See Brown-headed Gull. In flight, the long wedge of white along the front of the hand extends to the wing-tip, adult primaries showing only a narrow fringe of black. Juvenile primaries have outer webs mostly black, forming narrow rays in the extended wing. At all ages, the lower surface of the hand is uniformly dusky, versus white-streaked in Brown-headed Gull.

Bare-part colours. Iris deep brown, eyelid-rim dark red; bill dull to yellowish pink with a dark tip (immature), dark red, dusky tipped in winter (adult); legs and feet dark red.

Size (mm). (Skins: 2 subadults; not sexed): wing 290, 298; tail 92, 96; bill 32.3, 32.7; tarsus 41.4, 45.1 (ZRC-NUS).

Weight. No data.

DISTRIBUTION. Regular only in the far SE. Historical summary: *Pat, Pek, Sel, Joh, Sin*, including Penang and Tengah islands off the W coast; and Ubin, Singapore.

GEOGRAPHICAL VARIATION. None recognized.

STATUS AND POPULATION. A non-breeding visitor, perhaps overlooked north of Malaysia, with just one sighting of an immature off Pattani spit (Ogilvie-Grant 1906). Southward, small numbers occurred among Brown-headed Gulls on the Perak coast in winter 1964/65 and again in 1990, with scattered records in other years between Penang and the Kelang estuary, Selangor. The only area of proven regular occurrence (perhaps reached over the S China Sea rather than via the mainland) is the extreme SE, from

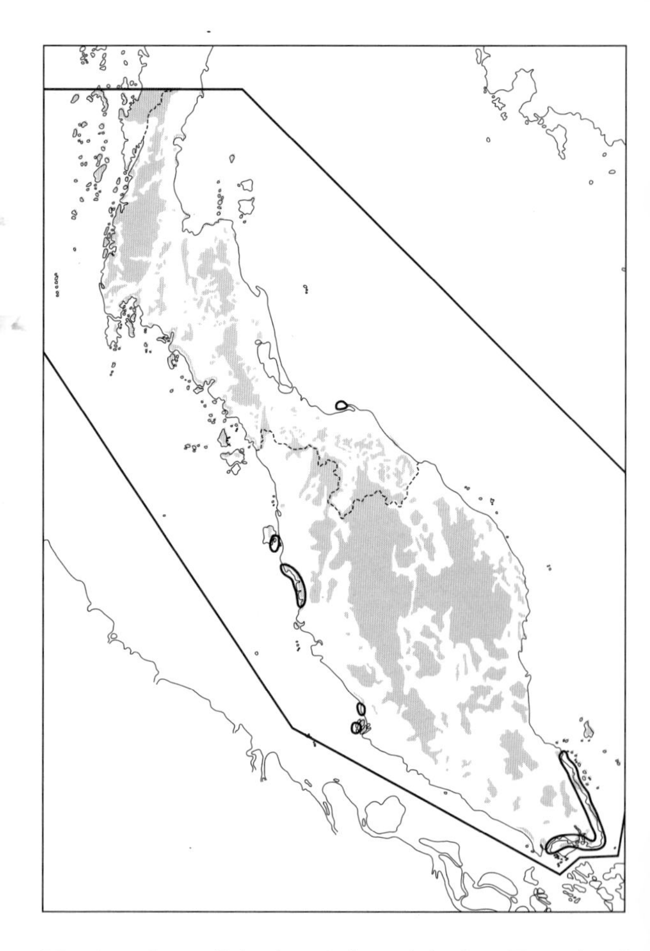

Mersing bay (Johor) to (mostly) the E end of Singapore island (BMP5, BR 1964, 1970–71, 1972–73, 1980–81, ENGGANG-3, MBR 1982–83, Sebastian *et al.* 1993, SINGAV-4). Typical groups there are five or less, but 13 counted at roost on fish-trap supports near Ubin island (SINGAV-6). A flock of 55 small gulls off nearby Seletar estuary (since shown to be a key site) in October 1964 (BR 1965) is unlikely to have been of any other species.

HABITATS AND ECOLOGY. Like Brown-headed Gull, depends on low-tide mudflats, with single records from a freshwater wetland (Kranji impoundment, Singapore) and, on Penang island, an open refuse-dump; both close to the shore (BR 1972–73, MBR 1986–87).

FORAGING AND FOOD. No information.

SOCIAL ORGANIZATION. Travels, loafs and roosts mainly in parties.

MOVEMENTS. Extreme dates are 'October' and 4 March (BR 1965, SINGAV-1), with most records in December–January.

SURVIVAL. No information.

SOCIAL INTERACTIONS. No information.

VOICE. No information.

BREEDING. No population.

MOULT. Two subadults dated 16 December and 2 February showed none (ZRCNUS).

CONSERVATION. Remaining wintering sites in Singapore are under direct threat from coastal land-claim projects.

Gull-billed Tern; Nok Nangnual Gleb Paak Naa (Thai); Burung Camar Ketam (Malay)

Sterna nilotica Gmelin 1789, *Systema Naturae* 13(2): 606. TL Egypt.
Plate 41

GROUP RELATIONS. Free-standing. On molecular evidence (Hackett 1989), closest to S American *S. (Phaetusa) simplex* (Large-billed Tern).

GLOBAL RANGE. Breeds in scattered colonies from low-temperate USA to about the equator in the Americas; from Atlantic Europe to coastal Mauritania, east to SW Asia and the Kazakhstan/China border; the northern Indian subcontinent; the upper Amur and China coast from the Yellow Sea to Guangdong, including Taiwan; and widely also in Australia. N-hemisphere populations winter from the breeding range to southern S America, northern tropical Africa and SW Asia; through the Indian subcontinent to Sri Lanka and the Andamans; in SE Asia to the Greater Sunda islands and Philippines; and Wallacea to N Australia. S-hemisphere birds range as far as the SW Philippines.

IDENTIFICATION/DESCRIPTION. A largish, stocky tern with shoreline feeding habits. Pale enough dorsally to appear all white in winter except for inconspicuous black fringe round primaries, stout black bill and variable black smudge or, in first-winterers, band behind eye (in some, the band continues forward as a black spot immediately in front of the eye). First-winterers also show extensive brown streaking over hind-crown and nape, and sooty brown chevron-marks subterminally on long scapulars and tail.

Bare-part colours. Iris dark brown; bill black; legs and feet black, dusky flesh in some first-autumn juveniles.

Size (mm). (Skins and live: 14 non-juveniles; none sexed): wing 270–315; tail 98–126, tail-fork 33–44; bill 32.9–40.0 and bill-depth at gonys 9.3–10.5; tarsus 27.5–31.9 (BMNH, UMBRP, ZRCNUS).

Weight. No data.

DISTRIBUTION. Mostly on the W coast. Historical summary: *Sur, Nak, Kra, Tra, Son, Pat, Sat, Pes, Ked, Kel, Pek, Phg, Sel, Mel, Sin*, and on or near W-coast islands: Phiphi, Libong, Ladang (*Sat*), Penang and the Kelang estuary group (Tengah).

GEOGRAPHICAL VARIATION. E China-breeding *affinis* Horsfield 1821 (TL Java). Deignan (1963) listed slightly longer-winged nominate *nilotica* from Nakhon Si Thammarat but the only specimens seen

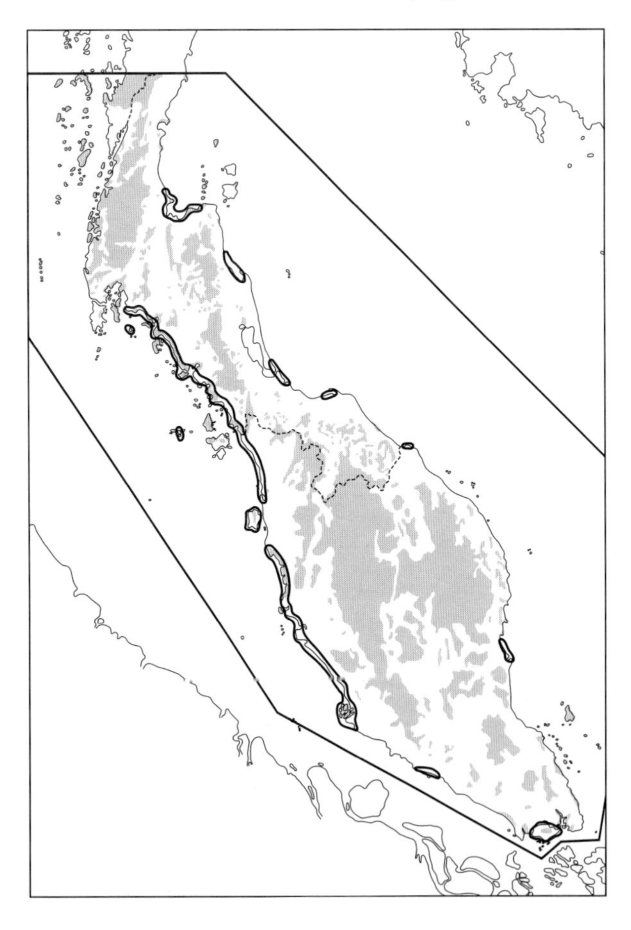

(BMNH) fit within the subspecies size-overlap range (BWP).

STATUS AND POPULATION. A passage migrant and non-breeding visitor; local and uncommon to common. Barring a loner in summer plumage near Ubin island, Singapore, on 12 June (SINGAV-2), absent overall for about one month. Overwinters more or less exclusively on the Melaka Straits coast, on mudflats mainly of Selangor and Perak, where loafing flocks of 50–250 are regular (Silvius *et al.* 1987), and with up to 2000 present on Tengah island in mid January. This is also an important migration staging area. In the NW, a few occur between Penang and Krabi (P.D. Round) but, except at Libong island where roost-counts in late January are in double figures (Eve and Guigue 1982), only on autumn and spring passage. In Singapore and along the E coast, primarily an autumn migrant, and uncommon, recorded mostly in the bays and estuaries of the NE, from Bandon to Tumpat lagoon (Kelantan) (BMNH, Holmes and Wells 1975, Swennen *et al.* 1986, Young 1941).

HABITATS AND ECOLOGY. This tern's distribution in the Peninsula fits that of the widest intertidal mudflats.

FORAGING AND FOOD. Differs from other local terns in quartering more over wet mud than open water, snatching crabs and small fish in flying passes (Swennen and Marteijn 1985).

SOCIAL ORGANIZATION. Roosts and loafs gregariously.

MOVEMENTS. In Selangor, groups of up to 30 recorded as of 29 June (BR 1976–77, MBR 1986–87) are not known to have summered locally, but larger numbers become regular only at the end of August. Limits of autumn passage are obscure on this coast but small numbers fly past Singapore, perhaps out of the Melaka Straits, during mid August–mid September, with a few records up to mid November (BR 1964, SINGAV-1). Autumn records at Libong and on the E coast also run to late October/November.

Spring numbers roosting on the Selangor mainland are not greater than those wintering at Tengah island, but oscillate through March–early April, with big counts at unusual sites as of the first week of March (MBR 1986–87, UMBRP). An early March surge also occurs at Libong (Parish 1985). Only a few (age unknown) remain anywhere after mid April, recorded to 31 May (BR 1964, G. Speight).

SURVIVAL. No information.

SOCIAL INTERACTIONS. No information.

VOICE. No information.

BREEDING. No population.

MOULT. In autumn, occasional caps remain extensively black until early September, and many presumed adults have renewed by early March. Birds have been handled only during September–January. A first-winterer showing signs of wing-moult during this period had renewed P1–3 by 14 January. Two non-juveniles were in single-locus moult (P7) in mid October, and six at P7 or 8 during November had also started a second bout, out to P5 by the end of the month. Nothing is known of the cycle of definite adults, except that a black-capped bird dated 2 September had not begun (MNC, UMBRP, ZRCNUS).

CONSERVATION. See Brown-headed Gull. Protected status for Tengah island (Kelang estuary) would be a positive move.

Caspian Tern; Nok Nangnual Gleb Khespian (Thai); Burung Camar Kaspia (Malay)

Sterna caspia Pallas 1770, *Novi Commentarii Academiae Scientiarum Imperialis Petropolitaniae* 14: 582 and plate 22. TL Caspian Sea.

Plate 39

GROUP RELATIONS. Free-standing.

GLOBAL RANGE. Breeds patchily from the S-temperate zone to the arctic circle: through N America, mainly coastal Africa and the Malagasy region; Eurasia from the Baltic to Ussuriland; SW Asia to the NW Indian subcontinent, and Sri Lanka; coastal China south from the Yellow Sea, including Hainan; and Australia and New Zealand. Many N-hemisphere populations migrate, wintering to the Caribbean, Africa and coasts of the Indian Ocean; S China; and SE Asia to the Peninsula and SE Sumatra. Vagrant in Luzon and the central Pacific (Hawaii).

IDENTIFICATION/DESCRIPTION. A giant tern, with dark-streaked or fully black cap and impressively large, heavy bill intensely blood-red (entirely in black-capped spring adult, otherwise shaded dark at the extreme tip). Seen overhead, the outer hand shows dark.

Bare-part colours. No additional information.

Size. No data.

Weight. No data.

DISTRIBUTION. The W coast and Singapore. Historical summary: *Phu, Kra, Ked, Sel, Sin,* including Tengah island (Kelang estuary).

GEOGRAPHICAL VARIATION. None recognized.

STATUS AND POPULATION. A non-breeding visitor; local and sparse to uncommon. First recorded in 1980 and in small, fluctuating but generally increasing numbers since, implying the regional wintering-range is on a cycle of expansion past a previous southern limit in Burma (Smythies 1953). Not recorded on the E coast and irregular in Singapore (a few around the E end of the island in 1980, 1981 and 1987) but annual since 1985 on the Selangor coast (BR 1980–81, MBR 1984–85, 1986–87, SINGAV-1). The outer Kelang estuary is an important foraging area, and nearby Kapar power-station ash-ponds a regular roost, with up to ten birds attending in 1990/91, double that number in 1993/94 (a peak 22 in late January) (AWB, Sebastian *et al.* 1993). Northward, more scattered records include five birds at the Krabi river-mouth on 4 February 1989 (P. Svenson).

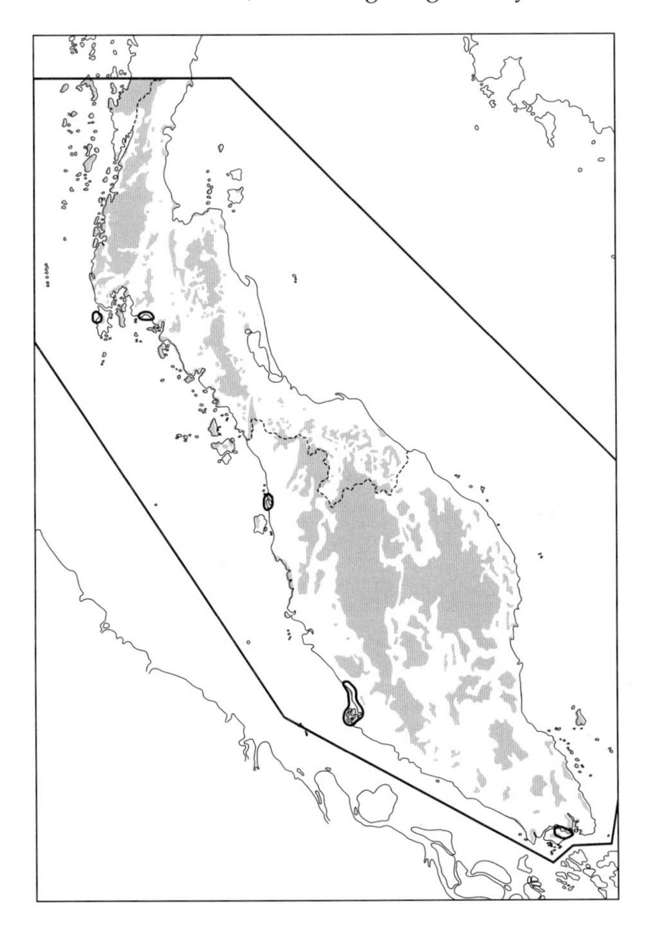

HABITATS AND ECOLOGY. Little-observed away from roosts but most records are from muddy coasts. One of the few tern species regularly attracted to mixed-species wader roosts in clearings in the mangrove zone.

FORAGING AND FOOD. No information.

SOCIAL ORGANIZATION. Roosting birds space themselves out within packs of waders and other, smaller terns.

MOVEMENTS. A bird on 19 July in Singapore; thence in all months from 4 September to 2 May (when five were still high-tide roosting at Kapar) (AWB, BR 1980–81, MBR 1984–85). The range of dates assumes a N-hemisphere breeding origin; Australian Caspian Terns have not been recorded past Timor (CLBW).

SURVIVAL. No information.

SOCIAL INTERACTIONS. No information.

VOICE. A deep, harsh *kerruch,* from two birds circling a roost at Kuala Selangor (MBR 1986–87).

BREEDING. No population.

MOULT. No data.

CONSERVATION. No critical issues, but reinforces the argument for protection and sustainable management of Tengah island, Kelang estuary.

Lesser Crested Tern; Nok Nangnual Gleb Ngawn Lek (Thai); Burung Camar Berjambul Kecil (Malay)

Sterna bengalensis Lesson 1831, *Traité d'Ornithologie* 8: 621. TL coasts of India.
Plate 41

GROUP RELATIONS. Forms a superspecies with *S. bernsteini* (Chinese Crested Tern), American–W Eurasian *S. sandvichensis* (Sandwich Tern) and W-central American *S. elegans* (Elegant Tern); allopatric in their breeding-ranges.

GLOBAL RANGE. Breeding proven only locally within a vast tropical–subtropical Old World range: in the S Mediterranean, Red Sea and Persian Gulf, N Australia, E New Guinea and (formerly?) off N Sulawesi. Non-breeders extend round NW Africa, the Indian Ocean coastline from S Africa and the Malagasy region to the Indian subcontinent, Sri Lanka and Bay of Bengal islands; extreme S China; SE Asia to the Greater Sunda islands; and Wallacea, New Guinea, the Solomons and N Australia.

IDENTIFICATION/DESCRIPTION. About the size of a Gull-billed Tern, and the long, wholly orange bill is diagnostic. At all ages, paler, more silvery grey above than Great Crested Tern, with old, outer primaries less contrastingly dark. Summer adults lack the conspicuous white forehead of Great Crested.

Bare-part colours. Iris dark brown; bill orange; legs and feet yellowish (juvenile), changing to black (BWP).

Size (mm). (Live and skins: 14 non-juveniles; none sexed): wing 280–310; tail 116–150, tail-fork 40–63; bill 48.5–57.9; tarsus 25.0–26.9 (AWB, BMNH, Nadee 1982).

Weight. No data.

DISTRIBUTION. Historical summary: *Pha, Phu, Kra, Tra, Pes, Pek, Sel, Mel, Joh, Sin*, including on or around Yao Yai, Libong, Penang, Tengah and Jarak islands off the W coast; and Ubin, Singapore.

GEOGRAPHICAL VARIATION. No information.

STATUS AND POPULATION. A non-breeding visitor and possible passage migrant, local and uncommon to common on the W coast and around Singapore, with some present through summer in the Melaka Straits (June records are lacking from Singapore waters). Most have been found at Phangnga bay and Krabi (counts of 200-plus), Libong island (a peak 189), on the Matang–Larut (Perak) coast and off the Kelang estuary, Selangor (up to 1000 at mid winter on Tengah island) (BBCB-8, BCSTB-10, -13, T.D. Christensen, ENGGANG-3, Nadee 1982, Ollington and Loh 1992, 1993, P.D. Round, Silvius *et al.* 1987). Unknown in E-coast waters.

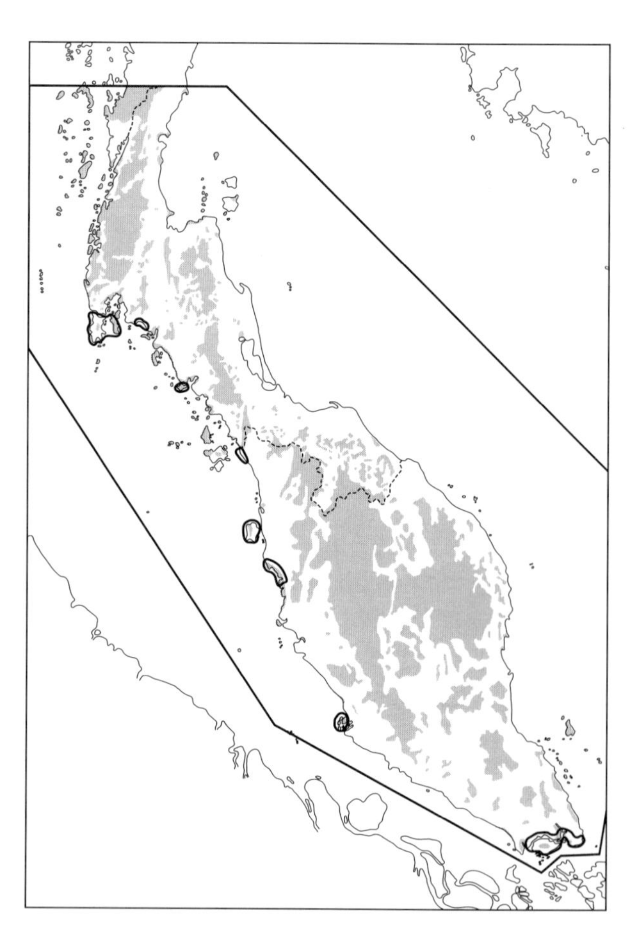

Peak numbers during November–early March suggest a northern source, but a party of eight at Seletar dam, Singapore, on 17 November 1988 included a juvenile that repeatedly begged and was fed by an adult (SINGAV-2). It seems unlikely this still-dependent bird would have made the journey from any of the known northern breeding-stations.

HABITATS AND ECOLOGY. Casual observations in the Melaka Straits suggest winter foragers select inshore waters, but keep mainly to inaccessible mangrove coastlines and islands with large tide-flats. They loaf and roost with other tern species on isolated banks and rocks (AWB, Nadee 1982, P.D. Round), avoiding mainland sites (only two individuals recorded during month-long monitoring of the Kapar power-station ash-pond roost in March 1991, despite its proximity to important feeding areas: Sebastian *et al.* 1993).

FORAGING AND FOOD. No information.

SOCIAL ORGANIZATION. Strongly gregarious at roosts.

MOVEMENTS. Small numbers are involved in an eastward movement of terns through the Singapore Straits, recorded during mid August–mid September (BR 1964) and suggesting migration; but no return movement has been reported.

SURVIVAL. No information.

SOCIAL INTERACTIONS. Apart from the feeding of a juvenile, no observations.

VOICE. No information.

BREEDING. No population.

MOULT. First-winterers with all-juvenile flight-feathers have been handled up to mid December. It is not known when post-juvenile replacement starts but two apparent juveniles had reached P6 and P7 (wing-tip still old) in mid April and early May, and a third (still with some dark-patterned, juvenile-type secondaries) growing P9–10 on 24 July had starting a second complete wing-moult (P1–2 new). Non-juveniles dated 21 November had moulted out to P5 or 6; to P7–8 in mid December; and P9–10 in January/early February. As of December, this age-group starts a further moult, out to P3 by January/February.

CONSERVATION. See Caspian Tern.

Chinese Crested Tern; Nok Nangnual Gleb Ngawn Jeen (Thai); Burung Camar Berjambul Cina (Malay)

Sterna bernsteini Schlegel 1863, *Muséum d'Histoire Naturelle des Pays-Bas* 6(24): 9. TL Halmahera, Moluccas.

Plate 41

GROUP RELATIONS. See Lesser Crested Tern.

GLOBAL RANGE. Breeds, or bred, on islands off the Shandong Peninsula, Yellow Sea, and known to have wintered in coastal waters of SE Asia as far as the Peninsula, NW Borneo, Philippines and N Wallacea (Mees 1975a). Among several claimed recent sightings, ones giving reasonable hope this tern may yet survive are of small parties on the Yellow Sea coast in March 1978 and September 1991, and a bird at Bali in March 1983 (C.F. Mann, OBCB-15).

IDENTIFICATION/DESCRIPTION. Palest of the Asian crested terns, with upperparts likely to appear white in the field. Old, unmoulted outer primaries appear quite black, in sharp contrast to the rest of the wing. Long bill yellow with sharply defined subterminal band or whole tip black. The winter cap is a black mask from just in front of the eye, widening round the nape, with white crown streaked grey (BMNH).

Bare-part colours. No additional information.

Size (mm). (Skins: 3 adults, none sexed): wing 299–309 (but all tips abraded); tail 129–150, tail-fork 55–75; bill 60–64; tarsus 26.6–27.9 (BMNH, Hall 1956).

Weight. No data.

DISTRIBUTION. NE coast.

GEOGRAPHICAL VARIATION. None recognized.

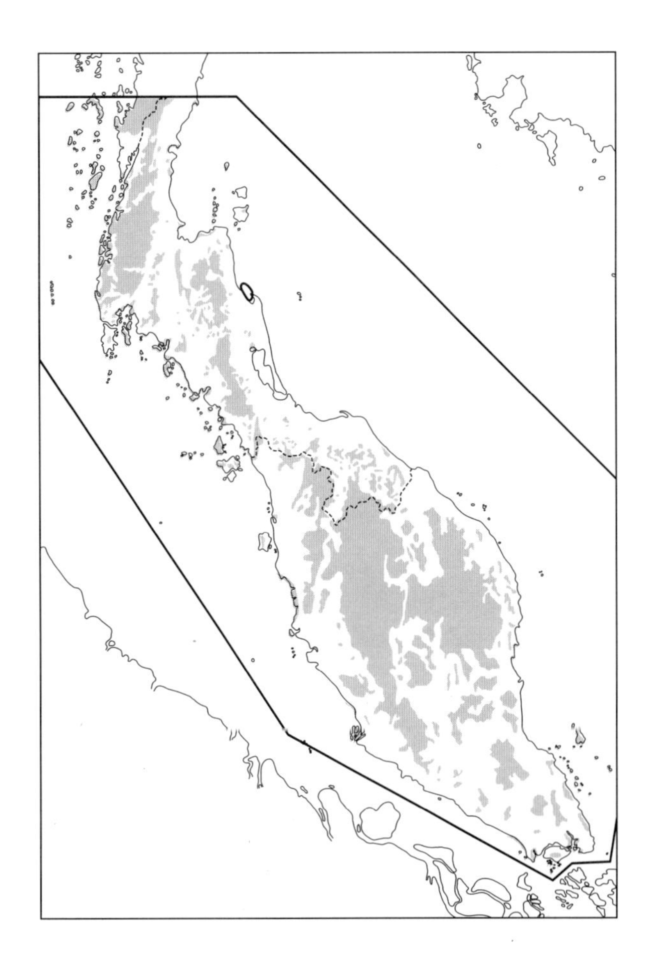

STATUS AND POPULATION. Vagrant or former non-breeding visitor. Known from three adults collected on 22 November 1923 on the coast of Nakhon Si Thammarat (probably in Pak Phanang bay) (BMNH, Hall 1956).

HABITATS AND ECOLOGY. No information. It is curious that the bays and estuaries of the E coast should be so empty of Lesser Crested Terns. Perhaps these two species once partitioned winter range.

FORAGING AND FOOD. No information.

SOCIAL ORGANIZATION. No information.

MOVEMENTS. No information.

SURVIVAL. No information.

SOCIAL INTERACTIONS. No information.

VOICE. No information.

BREEDING. No population.

MOULT. All three specimens show post-breeding wing-moult, with P1–6 new and, in two cases, P7 growing, but no sign of a following spring wing-moult (cf. W-coast Lesser Crested Tern).

CONSERVATION. Globally critical (BTW2). Too little is known of this bird to define local issues, should any remain relevant, but E-coast waters deserve a continuing watch.

Great Crested Tern; Nok Nangnual Gleb Ngawn Yai (Thai); Burung Camar Berjambul Besar (Malay)

Sterna bergii Lichtenstein 1823, *Verzeichniss der Doubletten des zoologisches Museums der Konigl. Universität zu Berlin*: 80. TL Cape province, S Africa.

Plate 41

GROUP RELATIONS. May form a superspecies with Central American–W African *S. maxima* (Royal Tern) (BWP).

GLOBAL RANGE. Breeds round S Africa and on coasts and islands of the Indian Ocean to the Red Sea, SW Asia, the Indian subcontinent and Sri Lanka; the S Nansei islands and China south from Fujian, including Taiwan and Hainan; SE Asia; Wallacea, New Guinea and Australia, and Oceania to the Tuamotus. Migrates or disperses within this gross range.

IDENTIFICATION/DESCRIPTION. Large size, and from other crested terns by pale bill, white forehead year-round, and comparatively dark upperparts. Immature wing shows leading-edge, outer hand and band across secondaries dark, leaving inner primaries as a wedge of white. Occasionally, pale lemon-yellow bill has extreme tip dusky – source of some dubious Chinese Crested Tern records?

Bare-part colours. Iris dark brown; bill pale lemon-yellow, entirely or with extreme tip dusky; legs and feet dull yellowish (autumn juvenile), turning black.

Size (mm). (Skins: 6 males, 11 females; adult): wing 331–351 and 326–356; tail 141–190 and 130–170, tail-fork 72–104 and 71–81; bill 56.0–63.8 and 57.4–64.0; tarsus 28.1–31.0 and 26.5–31.3 (BMNH, ZRCNUS).

Weight. No data.

DISTRIBUTION. Historical summary: all divisions except *Pak, Chu, Pht, Son, Yal, Nar, Pra, Neg, Mel*, and to at least 50 km off shore (near the Surin islands, *Ran*: Brockelman and Nadee 1977).

GEOGRAPHICAL VARIATION. Subspecies *cristata* Stephens 1826 (TL China). Some atypically dark-backed W-coast birds, it has been suggested, might be S–SW Asian *velox* Cretzschmar 1827 (TL Red Sea coasts), but none of the specimens examined has been large enough to be convincing (*velox* not below wing 365, tail 188, bill 65, tarsus 30: BWP).

STATUS AND POPULATION. A non-breeding visitor and probable passage migrant, but present year-round overall; regular and common at appropriate seasons. Off the E coast, in substantial numbers (3-figure flock-counts) from mid July to at least the end of January; off the W coast, mainly during early September–November but in the NW also in early April (Parish 1985), implying passage movements. Only a few occur anywhere in the west during May–August. Nearest nesting-colonies are reported from the Burma coast north of the Irradwaddy delta (a Tenasserim locality unconfirmed) (Smythies 1953) and, eastward, at Spratly island and Layang-layang (Swallow) Reef, off the continental shelf WNW of Sabah (Haile 1964, Noramly and Noramly 1985, Wells 1991). Formerly bred in the Gulf of Bangkok but no nesting demonstrated there since the 1920s, and only one, never definitely confirmed, record exists from Peninsular waters: two eggs dated 14 May 1913 in the E.G. Herbert collection (BMNH) said to have come from Samui island, Surat Thani (Herbert 1923–26). A claim of breeding on islets in Phangnga bay (Scott

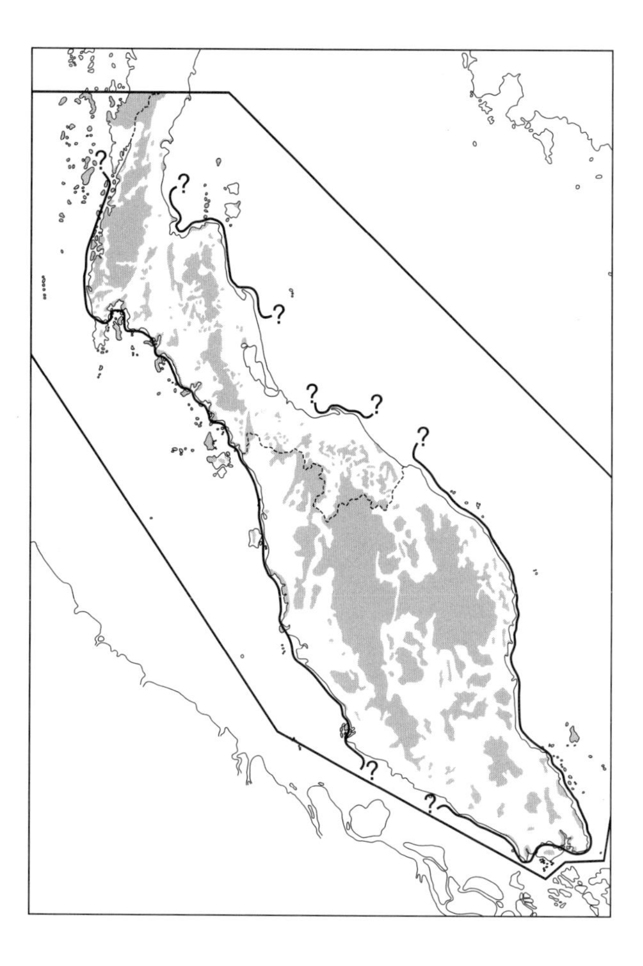

1989) is likewise unsubstantiated. Juveniles in E-coast waters as of the first week of May (Howes *et al.* 1986) may come from further east in the S China Sea, where breeders on Layang-layang reef have eggs by March.

HABITATS AND ECOLOGY. Forages at sea (Swennen and Marteijn 1985), mostly within just a few kilometres from the coast, but on migration or dispersal must move over a much wider sea area. Not attracted to mixed-species wader and tern roosts on mainland beaches, and loafs and roosts almost entirely on islets, fish-trap supports, etc., well off shore.

FORAGING AND FOOD. No more information.

SOCIAL ORGANIZATION. Often gregarious at roost.

MOVEMENTS. No more specific information.

SURVIVAL. No information.

SOCIAL INTERACTIONS. No information.

VOICE. The only vocalization recorded is a deep *kurr-agh* or *kirreak*, repeated several times (G.C. Madoc, P.D. Round).

BREEDING. No known population.

MOULT. Little understood. Progress of juvenile wing-moult has not been followed, but birds still only half complete by April and recently finished or with only an outermost old primary remaining in late August/September may have been second-summerers. Some of these had started a further complete moult, the most advanced out to P3–4 by early September. Among evident adults, regular-descendant replacement of obviously old flight-feathers is complete by late December, with a further moult starting from P1 as of November, but poorly synchronized among, perhaps, mixed populations (BMNH, ZRCNUS).

CONSERVATION. No critical issues.

Roseate Tern; Nok Nangnual Gleb See Gulaab (Thai); Burung Camar Molek (Malay)

Sterna dougallii Montagu 1813, *Ornithological Dictionary; or Alphabetical Synopsis of British Birds*, Supplement. TL Cumbrae islands, Firth of Clyde, Scotland.
Plate 40

GROUP RELATIONS. Apparently free-standing.

GLOBAL RANGE. Breeds on coasts and islands of both sides of the N-temperate Atlantic; S and E Africa and the Malagasy region; SW Asia, the western Indian subcontinent, Sri Lanka and the Andamans; the Nansei islands and China south from Zhejiang, including Taiwan; SE Asia from Tenasserim and the Gulf of Thailand to the Greater Sunda islands and NW Philippines; the Moluccas, New Guinea and Australia, and Oceania as far as New Caledonia. Northern (including Chinese) populations migrate, wintering to the tropics.

IDENTIFICATION/DESCRIPTION. Shorter-winged but appears more slender than otherwise similar-sized Common Tern, the full tail-streamers of adults longer, finer and entirely white. At all ages, paler-winged than Common, with black confined to the fringe of the outer primaries, though immatures (first-winterers) of both show a dark wrist and inner wing leading-edge. Slightly larger than Black-naped Tern, not as slender, and all age-classes show more extensive black on the cap. Young juveniles of both are scaled dark brown on the upper body, contrasting with pale wings and near-white rump to tail.

Bare-part colours. Iris dark brown; bill black with greyish tip (juvenile), all-black, black with some red at base, or fully bright red (adults showing individual or possibly cyclic variation); legs and feet brownish (juvenile and non-breeding adult), bright red (breeding adult).

Size (mm). (Skins: 7 males, 2 females; adult): wing 210–232 and 213, 214; tail 114–150 and 114, 154, tail-fork 64–86 and 57, 87; bill 34.0–37.4 and 31.9 (1 only); tarsus 18.9–21.4 and 17.3 (1 only) (BMNH, ZRCNUS).

Weight. No data.

DISTRIBUTION. Historical summary: *Sur, Pha, Kra, Tra, Pat, Sat, Pes, Tru, Phg, Sel, Joh*, including island breeding-stations listed below.

GEOGRAPHICAL VARIATION. Gibson-Hill (1949) identified E-coast breeders as subspecies *bangsi* Mathews 1912 (TL Fuchow, SE China), paler and larger; Melaka Straits breeders as NE Indian Ocean *korustes* Hume 1874 (TL Andaman islands), dorsally greyer, wing and bill not above 224 and 37. Re-checking the same series, I cannot confirm a difference. A wider comparison is needed. Four October migrants/dispersants collected at sea off the SE coast are all short-winged: 210–211 mm (ZRCNUS).

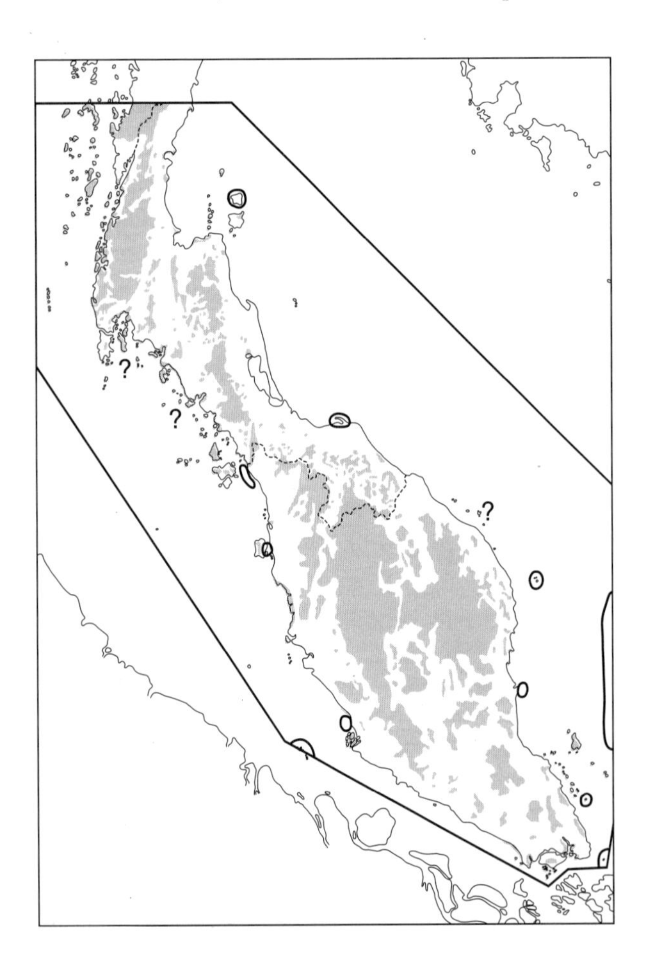

STATUS AND POPULATION. Local and uncommon. During mid August–early October 1982, D.M. Simpson saw small parties at sea between Terengganu and Singapore, on routes well east of the Pahang–Johor archipelago. Specimens from Horsburgh lighthouse, E end of the Singapore Straits, are dated 11–13 October (BMNH, ZRCNUS) and birds are reported from Pattani bay during the first half of November (Swennen *et al.* 1986). In the Melaka Straits, R. Gregory-Smith saw small parties of migrants/dispersants, including juveniles, passing along the Perlis coast on 22 September and 16 November.

All other records have been at potential/proven breeding-sites, mainly off the E coast: near Phangan island (Surat Thani); up to 80 birds at Tokong Burung rocks near Tenggol island, 28 km off Terengganu; and 150 at Yu island, S end of the Pahang–Johor archipelago (Gibson-Hill 1950c, 1956, G.C. Madoc, Robinson 1914b), collectively during late May–late August. However, none of these sites has been checked (or further serious searches made) since the 1950s. Off the W coast, Robinson (1906) found many in the Arua group, central Melaka Straits, in early August, but none seen there on later visits, up to 1952 (G.C. Madoc). It is not known if this site has been used recently. The only other Melaka Straits records are of a single bird off Jeram, Selangor, in July 1969 and, in late December 1973, one at Tanjung Tokong, close to a reputed former breeding-station (Tikus islet, since reclaimed), N Penang harbour (BR 1972–73, Cairns 1953a, 1955a). With sporadic records north to Phangnga, the situation in the NW needs exploring.

HABITATS AND ECOLOGY. A predominantly open-sea tern, coming to small, remote islands. The only in-shore records are those from Perlis and Penang harbour, and a June-dated, apparent non-breeder at Agas point, Pahang estuary (BMNH). The Jeram (Selangor) bird occurred during a westerly squall that could have brought it in from further out to sea.

FORAGING AND FOOD. No information.

SOCIAL ORGANIZATION. Nests in association with Black-naped and Bridled Terns, but in discrete sub-colonies, often of only a few pairs.

MOVEMENTS. No additional information, or clear evidence that northern migrants reach this area.

SURVIVAL. No information.

SOCIAL INTERACTIONS. No information.

VOICE. No information.

BREEDING

Nest. Selects flat to sloping, bare rock where the surface is broken into ruts and pockets deep enough to conceal the sitting bird, and lays on dry grass or pandan leaf fragments.

Eggs and brood. Eggs from Yu island are vinous-buff to biscuit-brown, boldly spotted and blotched with grey and sepia. Size (mm): 38.9 × 28.1 (mean, n=8). Full clutch two.

Cycle. Cairns (1953a) states Roseate Terns bred at Tikus islet only in occasional years, which may explain apparent disappearance from infrequently checked sites, such as the Arua islands. On the other hand, off the E coast, birds were present at every summer visit to Tokong Burung and Yu islands made over eight years between 1938 and 1959.

Seasonality. In different years at Tokong Burung and Yu, eggs found during 20 June–29 July; once in late August, possibly a re-laying after an egging raid by fishermen (Gibson-Hill 1950c, 1956, G.C. Madoc).

MOULT. May adults from Phangan island were in full, fresh breeding-plumage. August birds from the Arua group were still fully black-capped but more worn, and a male dated 2 August was moulting P1. Among non-breeders collected off the E coast, a June bird (age uncertain) moulting P6 had outer primaries already fairly fresh. Others in October were all in regular-descendant moult between P2 and P6, and one has started a concurrent second bout at P1 (BMNH, ZRCNUS).

CONSERVATION. Tern populations throughout SE Asia are held artifically low by intensive egging. No breeding-colonies are beyond regular reach and nearly all are well known to the fishing community (de Korte 1991, Wells 1991). Their attachment to a limited array of typically easy sites makes Roseates particularly vulnerable. A fresh census is overdue.

Black-naped Tern; Nok Nangnual Gleb Thai-thoi Dam (Thai); Burung Camar Sumatera (Malay)

Sterna sumatrana Raffles 1822, *Transactions of the Linnean Society* 13(2): 329. TL Sumatra.
Plate 40

GROUP RELATIONS. Free-standing.

GLOBAL RANGE. Islands of the tropical Indian Ocean from Aldabra to the Bay of Bengal; the Nansei islands and coastal China south from Hebei, including Taiwan and Hainan; SE Asia to the Greater Sunda islands, Bali and the western Philippines; Wallacea to New Guinea, N Australia, and tropical Oceania to the Cook group. Migrates/disperses within the gross breeding-range.

IDENTIFICATION/DESCRIPTION. A medium-small, dainty, narrow-winged tern with long-pointed, deeply forked tail. Apart from narrow nape-band, adults are strikingly white all over, and separable from adult Roseate Tern in flight by cap-pattern, dorsal whiteness and wing-shape. Like Roseate, young juveniles are scaled dark brown on back and wing-coverts. Flight and other behavioural differences between these two need further study.

Bare-part colours. Iris deep brown; bill black, with greyish tip in juveniles; legs and feet black.

Size (mm). (Skins: 6 males, 10 females; adult): wing 221–230 and 220–232; tail 127–147 and 129–162, tail-fork 59–92 (sexes combined); bill 32.6–36.5 and 31.4–35.8; tarsus 17.1–18.6 and 18.3–19.8 (BMNH, ZRCNUS).

Weight. No data.

DISTRIBUTION. Historical summary: all divisions except *Pak, Pht, Pat, Yal, Nar, Pes, Kel, Pra*, and on many small islands.

GEOGRAPHICAL VARIATION. Short-billed, nominate *sumatrana* of the E hemisphere.

STATUS AND POPULATION. Resident, more or less regular and more or less common, but heavily pressured while breeding and in general decline. Local populations focus on communal nesting and loafing/roosting-stations, of which Gibson-Hill (1950c) identified three types. The commonest is a low outcrop of mainly bald, granite boulders, typically from a few to not more than a few hundred metres away from a larger landmass, holding rarely more than six pairs. Such colonies occur along all coasts, but sparingly in the Melaka Straits where long stretches of muddy shoreline completely lack outcrops. Similar to slightly larger breeding-groups associate with Bridled Terns on sea-stacks, but such sites are comparatively few, and localized. The only colonies with 50 or more

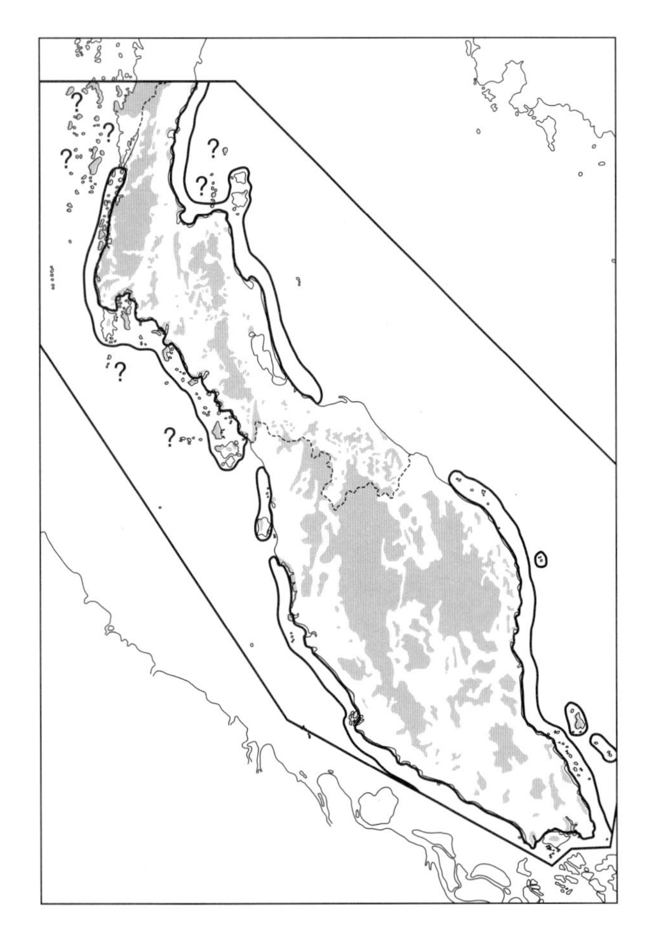

pairs reported are on intermediate structures, stacks that have weathered too low to be very attractive to Bridled Terns but provide the bare, shelving surfaces that Black-napes particularly favour. Five (in the Lima and Sri Buat groups, and Yu and Jahat) have been identified in the Pahang–Johor archipelago, and Tokong Burung near Tenggol (Terengganu) is the remotest known breeding-site in any category. Tekukur (Selangor) and White and Fairway rocks in the Sembilan group (Perak estuary) are (or were) possible Melaka Straits examples (Allen and Berwick 1950, Gibson-Hill 1950c) – none checked in recent years. The situation on both NW and NE coasts needs exploring. Some in the Phiphi and Lanta island groups, and a few pairs on an islet off Songkhla town beach (BBCB-4, BCSTB-12, Holmes and Wells 1975) are the only northern colonies identified recently.

HABITATS AND ECOLOGY. The favoured boulder-islet habitat is an in-shore/archipelago feature, and Black-naped Terns are scarce in remote sea. Thus, none reported during regular watches in and around the Terengganu oil-field, 200 km out (D.M. Simpson) or from the vicinity of such distant W-coast islands as the Similans and Jarak, and only a single, non-breeding-season record from Perak island, 140 km off Kedah (Madoc and Allen 1956). Roosts and loafs on off-shore boulders, marker-buoys, etc.; never attracted to mixed wader/tern roosts on beaches.

FORAGING AND FOOD. Hunts exclusively at sea (Swennen and Marteijn 1985), with no use made of intertidal flats.

SOCIAL ORGANIZATION. No additional information.

MOVEMENTS. None recorded.

SURVIVAL. The only return reported is of a bird ringed as a chick on Tekukur island in July 1967, picked up dead there twelve months later (BMP5).

SOCIAL INTERACTIONS. No information.

VOICE. No information.

BREEDING

Nest. Unlike Roseate and Bridled Terns, Black-napes select completely exposed rock surfaces with enough irregularity only to stabilize the egg, rarely to conceal the sitting adult.

Eggs and brood. Eggs are whitish to light buff or stone-coloured, variously blotched with mauve, dark grey, dark chestnut and occasionally black. Size (mm): 40.0–36.0 × 28.8–26.0 (mean 38.2 × 28.2, n=20 from Yu); 40.5–38.5 × 28.5–27.0 (mean 39.3 × 27.8, n=8 from Tenggol); 40.7–36.0 × 27.8–27.1 (n=5 from Selangor). Full clutch 1–2. Along the Malaysian E coast, single-egg clutches predominated over two eggs in the ratio 1.4 : 1 (n=100), and at Tekukur (Selangor) in early July, 1.9 : 1 (n=17). Better control for the effects of date and re-laying is needed in making such calculations.

Cycle. No information.

Seasonality. Extreme egg-dates are 18 May (Redang group, Terengganu) and 14 August. A fledgling at a colony in the Phiphi group on 24 May, a small chick at a Singapore site on 28 May and one from Redang island dated 15 October imply the very earliest and latest clutches must be laid in April and September (BBCB-4, BMNH, BMP5, Gibson-Hill 1950c, SINGAV-2).

MOULT. Among 39 handlings during April–October (i.e., including the breeding-season), the only non-moulters were an adult male dated 18 April and two fresh-plumaged October juveniles. All others, from both coasts, were active at 1–3 loci in the primary row. Year-group differences and seasonality need further work (BMNH, ZRCNUS).

CONSERVATION. Less vulnerable than Roseate Tern in that breeders occupy a wide scatter of small sites, but still under heavy pressure from eggers. There is no doubt the population overall is artificially depressed, and declining.

Common Tern; Nok Nangnual Gleb Thammadaa (Thai); Burung Camar Siput (Malay)

Sterna hirundo Linnaeus 1758, *Systema Naturae* 10(1): 137. TL Sweden.
Plate 40

GROUP RELATIONS. Molecular (allo-enzyme) studies (Hackett 1989) imply *hirundo* and *S. vittata* (Antarctic Tern) are still treatable as a superspecies, related to Arctic and S-hemisphere Kerguelen and South American Terns (Mayr and Short 1970).

GLOBAL RANGE. Breeds in the N-temperate zone, including central-E Canada and islands and both coasts of the Atlantic, across Eurasia to Anadyrland, Kamchatka and the Sea of Okhotsk, patchily south to the Caribbean and W Africa, Iran, Afghanistan, the outer Himalayas (Ladakh) and, in China, to Shandong and Sichuan. Winters in Central and S America, Africa and the Malagasy region and around the Indian Ocean to the Indian subcontinent and Sri Lanka; SE Asia from the Gulf of Thailand to the Greater Sunda islands, Bali and SW Philippines; Wallacea, New Guinea and N and E Australia; sparsely in Oceania.

IDENTIFICATION/DESCRIPTION. A medium-sized tern, confusable with Roseate and, in isolation in winter, Whiskered Tern. Immatures of all three show a dark inner leading-edge to the wing, but Common is absolutely and proportionately longer-winged than the others. From Roseate, by darker grey upperparts, primaries more extensively tipped and margined blackish (on both surfaces), and tail-points laterally margined black (and never reaching the tip of the closed wing). Common Tern is also always extensively black from hind-crown to nape, whereas many Whiskered have little black on the head. Best separated by predominant plunge-dive hunting behaviour, versus Whiskered Tern's dip to the surface.

Bare-part colours. Iris dark brown; bill all-black or with base of lower mandible or whole basal half bright coral-red to deep red; legs and feet blackish or coral-red to deep red.

Size (mm). (Live and skins: 14 males, 5 females; adult): wing 251–280 and 245–281 (immatures down to 240); tail 123–162 and 113–130, tail-fork 46–62 (sexes combined); bill 30.8–37.0 (39.9) and 30.9–35.4; tarsus 18.7–20.8 and 18.7–20.2 (AWB, UMBRP, ZRCNUS).

Weight (g). November-dated non-juveniles, 77–125 (mean 107, n=7); and two spring adults, 127.2 and 128.7. April-dated immatures, 79.4–115.9 (mean 94.1, n=18) (UMBRP).

DISTRIBUTION. Most on the W coast. Historical summary: *Nak, Phu, Kra, Pht, Tra, Son, Pat, Sat, Pes, Ked, Tru, Pek, Sel, Mel, Joh, Sin,* including around

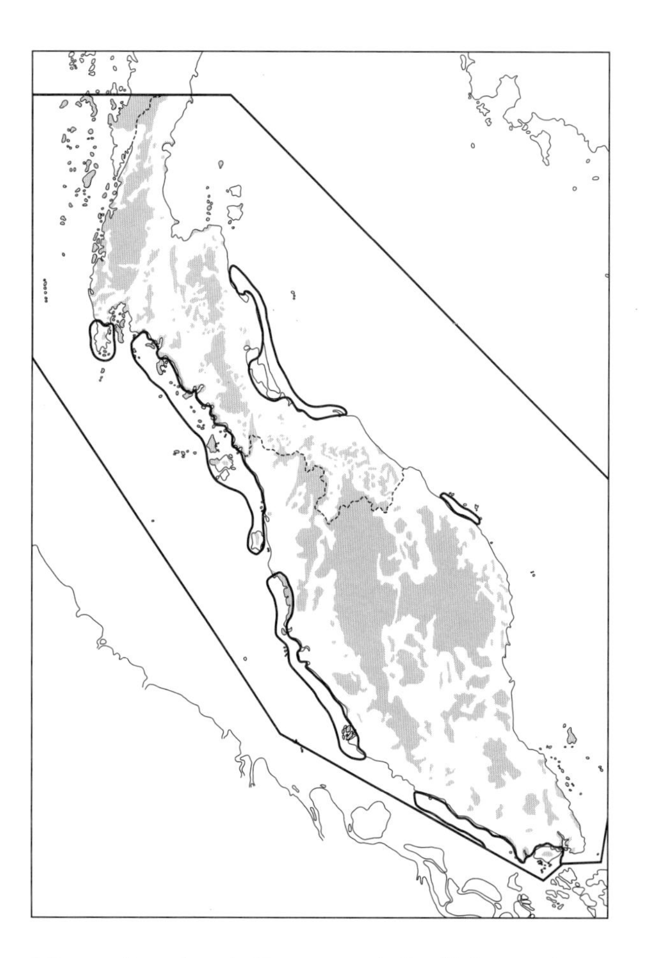

Libong, Langkawi, Penang and the Kelang estuary islands.

GEOGRAPHICAL VARIATION. Most winterers are immature, impossible to identify to subspecies in the field. Among non-juveniles, the range of bill and foot colours indicates a mix of populations (Deignan 1963, Gibson-Hill 1949b). Strikingly grey-bodied adults with contrastingly white rump and tail, and black bill and feet (noted in autumn and spring), are likely to be subspecies *longipennis* Nordmann 1835 (TL Kutchui estuary, Sea of Okhotsk). Paler, merely grey-washed birds with feet and basal half of the bill dark red may be central-Asian *tibetana* Saunders 1876 (TL Tibet). At times in the Melaka Straits, apparently white-bodied birds with all-dark bill and feet predominate. These have been identified tentatively as N-central Eurasian nominate *hirundo/longipennis* intergrades (*'minussensis'*). Overall, too few live birds have been described in the hand and the situation needs clarifying.

STATUS AND POPULATION. A passage migrant and non-breeding visitor, with a small presence in the south and along the W coast through most of the summer – but no records in June. More or less regular and uncommon to common; most in the west. On the E coast, the only large counts (over 1000 during early November) have been in Pattani bay (Swennen *et al.* 1986). Also recorded close to the Terengganu coast, but D.M. Simpson saw none in the Terengganu offshore oil-field or on sea journeys between there and Singapore.

Along the W coast, flocks of up to 40 are widespread, with peak winter counts around the mangrove islands of the Kelang estuary (900 on Ketam in mid November; 1000 on Tengah in late January: ENGGANG-3, Silvius *et al.* 1987). In the NW, highest counts (230, 60) at Libong island (Trang) have been in late October and early March (Parish 1985, Swennen *et al.* 1986), perhaps during passage migration. Singapore numbers are consistently low, with no winter counts above about 30 (at roost on a fish-trap near Ubin island in February: SINGAV-6).

HABITATS AND ECOLOGY. Found well out to sea while on passage (Gibson-Hill 1950e) but winters inshore, including in estuaries. Fondness for muddy coastlines extends to loafing socially on tide-flats, shell-banks, etc., but when forced off by high tides Common Terns typically resort to rocks or secure structures off-shore. Where sites butt directly onto the beach, a few visit mixed wader/tern roosts on cleared mangrove-land, and at Kapar (Selangor) some joined the coastal power-station ash-pond roost, although never as many as could regularly be counted fishing at high water off the same beach (Sebastian *et al.* 1993).

FORAGING AND FOOD. Foraging is exclusively over water, divided between coastal sea and the larger river-mouths, with a few records from flooded, subcoastal paddyland.

SOCIAL ORGANIZATION. Travels and roosts gregariously.

MOVEMENTS. Migration periods are not well defined, but Common forms a small proportion of the tern passage east through the Singapore Straits during mid August–late September (BR 1964, SINGAV-2, -3). Extreme arrival and departure dates of adults in full summer colours are 17 September and 18 May (UMBRP).

SURVIVAL. The only recovery is of a bird ringed in its first winter on Langkawi island on 5 April 1970, and killed in the Terong estuary, Perak, on 17 October 1971 (BR 1970–71). At these dates, both sites could have been migration stages.

SOCIAL INTERACTIONS. No information.

VOICE. No information.

BREEDING. No population.

MOULT. Replacement of primaries is regular-descendant. Two November first-winterers showed no sign of wing-moult, whereas 17 trapped at a Langkawi roost in early April were all active between P3 and 8 (most at P5). Ten May- and July-dated, presumed second-summerers at the same site had reached P10 or finished, and started a second complete wing-moult, out to an extreme P4–5 by late July. Degree of wing-tip wear and remains of breeding-plumage identified some birds in single-locus moult in September as likely returning adults. At Tengah island during 17–21 November, 13 non-juveniles were all still active between P3 and 10, most at P5 or 6. Two early April adults had both completed (AWB, BMNH, UMBRP, ZRCNUS).

Some adults renew summer body-plumage by the end of March, and some second-summerers acquire partial summer colours (UMBRP).

CONSERVATION. See Brown-headed Gull for issues in the Melaka Straits wintering area.

Little Tern; Nok Nangnual Gleb Lek (Thai); Burung Camar Kecil (Malay)

Sterna albifrons Pallas 1764, Vroeg's *Beredeneerde Catalogus, Adumbratiunculae*: 6. TL Holland.
Plate 40

GROUP RELATIONS. *S. albifrons*, N American *antillarum* (Least Tern), S American *lorata* and *superciliaris* (Peruvian and Yellow-billed Terns), S Asian *saundersi* (Saunders's Tern) and W and S Australian *nereis* (Fairy Tern) replace each other geographically and form a superspecies (BWP, Mayr and Short 1970).

GLOBAL RANGE. Breeds on coasts and major rivers of W Africa, Eurasia east to the Kazakhstan/NW China border; SW Asia, the Indian subcontinent and Sri Lanka; then Amurland, Japan and China east of a line NE provinces–Sichuan, including Taiwan and Hainan; SE Asia to the Peninsula,

Java, Bali and the Philippines; Wallacea; and New Guinea, the Solomons and N and E Australia. Migrates/disperses within the gross breeding-range, and to northern S America, S Africa and New Zealand.

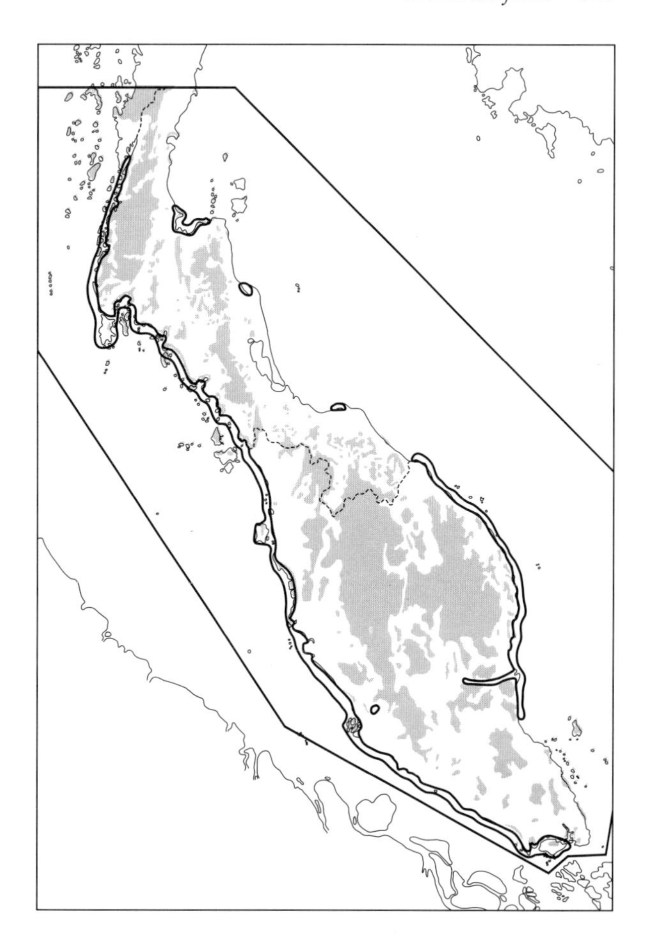

IDENTIFICATION/DESCRIPTION. Uniquely small and slender. The next-sized local tern, White-winged Black, has a different head-pattern at all ages/seasons, slower flight on proportionately broad wings and quite different foraging behaviour. Light, darting flight on narrow, rapidly beating wings is distinctive. As in some larger relatives, first-winterers show a prominent dark wrist and inner leading-edge to the wing.

Bare-part colours. Iris deep brown; bill all-black (juveniles and wintering adults), or clear yellow with apical third black (summer adults); legs and feet brown-yellow, bright yellow or dusky orange (BMNH). Population-differences have not been researched in this area.

Size (mm). (Skins: 15 males, 11 females; adult): wing 163–186 and 152–178; tail 65–90 and 67–78; bill 27.1–32.1 and 26.0–31.6; tarsus 16.0–18.1 and 15.5–17.3 (BMNH, ZRCNUS).

Weight. No data.

DISTRIBUTION. Historical summary: all divisions except *Pak, Chu, Son, Yal, Nar*, including around Penang and the Kelang estuary islands.

GEOGRAPHICAL VARIATION. All breeders and most migrants are subspecies *sinensis* Gmelin 1789 (TL China), with shafts of the outer hand white. Off the W coast, migrants with a variable number of dark (tawny to blackish) outer-hand shafts are also common. Some have been identified as *S. saundersi* but, as pointed out by Junge (1948), length and colour-pattern of wings fall within the range of variation of Asian-breeding nominate *albifrons*. Lack of confirmation from summer plumage leaves no good reason yet for including *saundersi* on the Peninsular list (MBR 1984–85). Twenty-two pure *sinensis* and 15 *albifrons* and intergrades are in wing-length ranges 152–186 and 160–179 mm (BMNH, ZRCNUS).

STATUS AND POPULATION. Resident and a non-breeding visitor, also showing evidence of through-passage; regular and common. Residents are believed to occur in Phangnga bay (Scott 1989) but the only confirmed nesting is along the E coast: in Kelantan (colonies on the Kelantan delta and Kemasin estuary); Terengganu (Setiu and Kerteh estuaries); Pahang (Kuantan port and Pahang Tua and Bebar estuaries) (Berwick 1952b, Gibson-Hill 1950c); and on Singapore island where, since 1987, groups have made opportunistic use of coastal sand-fill at Changi, Seletar and Tuas (BIRDLINE 1993, R.F. Ollington, SINGAV-1). Small numbers have also been found nesting on sand-bars over the lower 160 km of the Pahang river, inland as far as the Bera confluence (Madoc 1936) but, oddly, on no other river system. Most colonies are of only a few pairs but possibly up to 100 bred on the Seletar land-claim (Singapore) in 1992, and 80 on a large scrape near Kuantan port in 1993 (BIRDLINE 1992, T. Mundkur).

The only non-breeding-season records of Little Terns on the E coast have been of a large flock at sea in Bandon bay (Surat Thani) on 22 October, two collected in Nakhon Si Thammarat in late November and a few in Pattani bay in early November (BMNH, Swennen *et al.* 1986). Winter numbers around Singapore are also fairly low, with only occasional 3-figure counts (200-plus off Changi on 13 December: Ollington and Loh 1993). Apart from migrating White-winged Black, however, this is the most widespread and numerous winter tern along the W coast, where largest mid-season concentrations occur at Krabi (300), Sanglang on the Kedah/Perlis border (300) and Tengah island, Kelang estuary (400–750) (P.D. Round, Silvius *et al.* 1987).

What becomes of local breeders during winter is not clear and the status of the occasional yellow-billed bird as late as November and December (BMNH, R.F. Ollington) is unknown (seasonal bare-part colour-change of residents has not been investigated).

HABITATS AND ECOLOGY. Breeders seek expanses of completely bare, flattish ground near water, including sand-islands of large rivers, remote dunes, sand-fill and large scrapes (such as prepared for developments) close to the sea (Gibson-Hill 1950c, Madoc 1956a, T. Mundkur, SINGAV-1). Migrants on passage visit dredge-mine lagoons, paddyland irrigation canals, reservoirs, etc., sometimes far inland, but winter exclusively on coasts and large estuaries, staying mainly close in shore. Two November birds from One-Fathom Bank lighthouse, 42 km off Selangor (Robinson and Kloss 1922) are the most remote sea records. Unlike breeders, winterers favour muddy shorelines, loaf gregariously on tide-flats alongside Common and Gull-billed Terns, and routinely join mixed shorebird roosts on areas of cleared mangroveland that open directly to the sea.

FORAGING AND FOOD. Groups hunt by scanning with bill typically down-pointed as they quarter 2–3 m above water, hover often and splash-dive vertically. G.C. Madoc describes an exceptional alternative method: a lone bird standing in apparent ambush over a small crab-burrow.

SOCIAL ORGANIZATION. Occasional pairs breed alone but most in loose colonies, with nests a few to a few tens of metres apart. At rich food-sources, foragers hunt socially, and they are gregarious at roost.

MOVEMENTS. Largest numbers occur at mid winter, but counts at Singapore and W-coast sites suggest post-breeding passage runs from August to at least early December (125 over Batu mine-lagoons, Kuala Lumpur, on 5 December, evidently still on the move). Spring passage runs from late February to early May, 363 high-tide-loafing at the Kapar power-station ashponds (Selangor) on 2 May and five over minelagoons near Kuala Lumpur on 5 May being the latest records (AWB, BMP5, ENGGANG-1, -2, MBR 1984–85, R.F. Ollington, SINGAV-1).

Specimens of both *sinensis* and *albifrons* collected around Angsa island, Selangor, during 24–29 July (BMNH, ZRCNUS) are most likely to have been early-arriving migrants but leave open the possibility of a small over-summering presence by non-breeders from the north.

SURVIVAL. No information.

SOCIAL INTERACTIONS. Adults are bold and noisy in aerial, mobbing defence of running young.

VOICE. Calls not adequately described in this area.

BREEDING

Nest. A slight scrape with a rim, or in a pre-existing hollow (footprint, etc.), on bare, sandy ground. On beach sand, scrapes are often lined with shell fragments, likely to have worked to the surface as a result of the birds' movements.

Eggs and brood. Eggs are matt olive- to stone-buff (one bluish), variably spotted lavender, grey, pinkgrey, dark chestnut and black. Shape elliptical. Size (mm): 34.0–31.0 × 24.5–22.5 (mean 32.6 × 23.9, n=20) from the E coast, 33.5–31.0 × 24.6–23.6 (mean 32.3 × 23.9, n=4) from the Pahang river. Full clutch three.

Cycle. Young runners shelter in tufts of grass, etc., sometimes in the entrance to small burrows.

Seasonality. Eggs and young chicks found on dates that imply laying in May–July, with flying juveniles still being fed by adults in Singapore in mid September (Berwick 1952b, BIRDLINE 1993, Gibson-Hill 1950c, Madoc 1936, R.F. Ollington, SINGAV-2, -4).

MOULT. Among 34 birds (status unknown) covering all months except February, April, May and December, only eight were not in active wing-moult. Order of replacement is regular-descendant but, as in other terns, successive moults overlap, and halts (mostly a failure to replace P10) are not uncommon. Among non-juveniles, single-locus moult prevailed from June to November, between P1–2 and P8, but with instances of suspension or arrest and no obvious seasonal progression. Double-locus moult predominated in January and March samples, the second moult out to P5. Population-differences have not been investigated.

Fifteen out of 100 Little Terns at Changi (Singapore) on 15 February showed summer colours, and in W-coast flocks these are widespread by early/mid March (BR 1976–77, MBR 1982–83).

CONSERVATION. Mobility and opportunism are plus factors for breeders. On-going coastal reclamation is set to provide much habitat in the medium term, but fewer and fewer sites of any kind will be safe from disturbance (cf. Malaysian Plover).

Bridled Tern; Nok Nangnual Gleb Khiw Khao (Thai); Burung Camar Batu (Malay)

Sterna anaethetus Scopoli 1786, *Deliciae Florae et Faunae Insubricae* 2: 92. TL Panay, Philippines.

Plate 41

GROUP RELATIONS. Forms a superspecies with central-Pacific *S. lunata* (Grey-backed Tern). They meet only marginally and are fully allopatric in their breeding-ranges (King 1967).

GLOBAL RANGE. Breeds in the Caribbean and on both sides of the tropical Atlantic, coasts and islands of the tropical Indian Ocean to SW Asia and the western Indian subcontinent; in the S Nansei islands and China south from Fujian including Taiwan and Hainan; SE Asia from the Andaman Sea and Vietnam to the Greater Sunda islands, Bali and the Philippines; and Wallacea, New Guinea, the Solomons and tropical Australia. Some large-scale dispersal/migration occurs within this total range.

IDENTIFICATION/DESCRIPTION. A medium-large, pied tern with long tail-points. From adult Sooty Tern by white eyebrow, narrower white forehead and, in a clear view, cap blacker than, and more or less separated from, back. Juveniles of both are sooty brown, freckled with white above, but Bridled always has white underparts and forehead.

Downy chicks are off-white below and vary dorsally from silvery to buff-grey or drab grey, always mottled with dark brown (Gibson-Hill 1950c).

Bare-part colours. Iris deep brown; bill black; legs and feet black.

Size (mm). (Skins: 6 males; adult): wing 266–270 (unsexed immatures down to 241); tail 178–183, tail-fork 97 (1 only); bill 36.7–41.9; tarsus 19.2–22.3 (BMNH, ZRCNUS).

Weight. No data.

DISTRIBUTION. Historical summary: *Chu, Pha, Phu, Kra, Son, Sat, Pes, Ked, Kel, Tru, Pek, Phg, Sel, Mel, Joh, Sin*, including around Penang island.

GEOGRAPHICAL VARIATION. Dark-backed nominate *anaethetus*, of the Pacific, Australasia and SE Asia.

STATUS AND POPULATION. A breeder and passage migrant. More or less regular and sparse to common. Off the W coast, present year-round only south of about latitude 6°N, i.e., within the mouth of the Melaka Straits. The Andaman coast, at the western fringe of nominate *anaethetus* range, appears to be occupied only seasonally: none seen during a cruise over the continental shelf-break off Phuket in February but a similar cruise in early June produced 115, with 335 between Phiphi and Maa islands, Krabi, on 25 July (Kiørboe 1991, C. Robson). These are more than can be accounted for at the few known breeding-stations in the area (including only about 15 nests in the Phiphi group: BBCB-4).

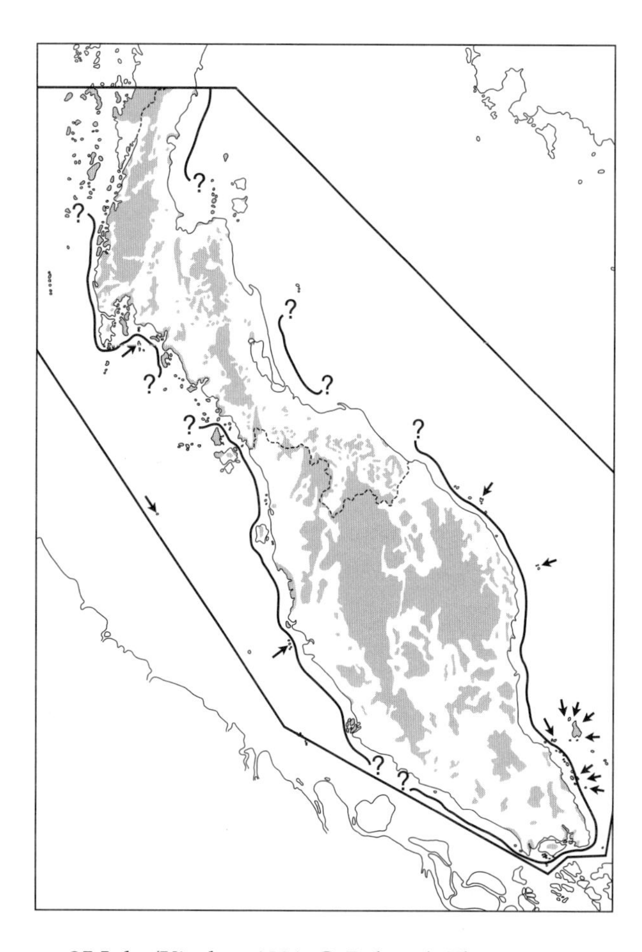

Within the Melaka Straits, a maximum 20 pairs has been found on Perak island, less than 20 in the Sembilan group (Perak estuary) and, in the early 1950s, 1000-plus in the Aruas (Indonesia) (Allen and Berwick 1950, Langham *et al.* 1974, Madoc 1956).

Off the E coast, at sea between the Terengganu oil-field (latitude 5°30′N) and Singapore, D.M. Simpson counted many more during July–October than January–April. Seasonal status further north has not been checked but some occur during breeding months around Tao island (Chumphon) (BBCB-9). All proven breeding off this side of the Peninsula, by a population estimated in the late 1940s at around 3000 pairs, has been in Malaysian waters. This included about 60 pairs on Barat (Redang group) and 100 on Tokong Burung (Tenggol) (Terengganu); and in the Pahang–Johor archipelago, ten in the Sri Buat group, 1000 on the Tokong Burung (Tioman) stacks and 50–250 each on Chibeh, Sepoi, Labas and Jahat stacks, 270 in the Lima group and 150–250 each on Belali, Gantong and Chondong stacks, and Yu island (Gibson-Hill 1949c, 1950c, Webber 1954).

Eight winter-dated specimens from Malaysian/Singapore waters are all juveniles, and a larger sample might show age-related differences in migration behaviour.

HABITATS AND ECOLOGY. More of a blue-water forager than other local tern species, apart from noddies, Sooty and possibly Roseate. Except around breeding stations and locally on migration routes, usually not found close to coasts, or within the ten-fathom depth contour. At sea, occurs patchily, and loafs (and probably roosts) in groups on floating driftwood, etc.

FORAGING AND FOOD. No information.

SOCIAL ORGANIZATION. Strongly gregarious while breeding.

MOVEMENTS. Breeding-stations are not attended during August/September–April and, as stated, seasonal changes of abundance at sea suggest organized movements into and out of the area. Small flocks passing south through Kelang outer harbour (Selangor), remote from usual habitat, in late September are likely to have been on passage (BR 1972–73), and above 90 percent of terns moving E to SE through the Singapore Straits during late June–late October are Bridled. Daily totals past Singapore island remain above 300 through September, with close to 1300 counted in less than two hours on 8 September and up to 80 per hour past Sultan shoal on 18–20 September (BR 1964, Ollington and Loh 1992, 1993). The fit with desertion of local breeding-sites is fair but not exact and, possibly, some of this movement is to opposite-season breeding destinations in the S hemisphere (Slater 1971). A juvenile at Malang Tiga buoy, Johor Straits, on 30 June (Ollington and Loh 1992) must have come from an egg laid well before the earliest recorded local date, hence might not have been of local origin.

SURVIVAL. No information.

SOCIAL INTERACTIONS. No information.

VOICE. A harsh *kok* is the common call, and a similar deep and musical note can be rapidly repeated, *kro-kro-kro-kro-kro* (Allen and Berwick 1950, G.C. Madoc).

BREEDING

Nest. Nests from just beyond the splash-zone to 100 m or more above water, typically but not exclusively on steep-sided stacks (see also Black-naped Tern). All parts of the slope are used although most birds select the domed summit, and use cover where available: grass (through which they burrow), exposed roots, rock crannies up to 0.5 m deep, the shelter of boulders, and recessed or overhung ledges. In the Arua islands, Madoc (1956) found eggs on ledges completely curtained by ferns and club-mosses. Some nests on bare rock incorporate rudimentary building materials: wisps of dry grass or fragments of dead pandan leaf, together with a few pebbles.

Eggs and brood. Eggs vary from white to stone-grey, light cream or pink-buff, flecked pale grey, lilac-grey, and light and dark purple- to chestnut-brown, exceptionally with some black; sometimes mainly white with only a light speckling of grey and black. Shape elliptical. Size (mm): 49.0–43.0 × 34.5–31.0 (mean 45.9 × 32.9, n=38). Full clutch one egg; *contra* BMP5, there are no records of two-egg clutches in this area.

Cycle. No information.

Seasonality. Extreme egg-dates are 8 June in Perak (occupied nest-sites in the Phiphi group on 24 May could have had eggs but were not reached for checking), and 12 August in E Johor, although this could have been a replacement after a raid. Most laying appears to be in June (Allen and Berwick 1950, Gibson-Hill 1949c, 1950c, Madoc 1936, Webber 1954).

MOULT. Four of eight October and November-dated first-winterers showed regular-descendant, single-locus moult of primaries, out to P6; the others (up to 21 November) had not started. June and July-dated adults from breeding stations off both coasts showed no moult (apart from one renewing the wing-tip, P9–10).

CONSERVATION. Systematic raiding of Bridled Tern colonies for eggs is a long tradition off Malaysian coasts, once regulated by custom on a seasonal or year-by-year set-aside basis (Gibson-Hill 1949c). Restraints of this kind have long since lapsed and the current breeding population is unlikely to be as large as it was in Gibson-Hill's day – although this is still a common bird in the Pahang–Johor archipelago and elsewhere. One tactic of the eggers has been the firing of breeding islands to make nest-finding easier. This would certainly destroy chicks but may have benefited terns in the longer run by promoting grass (a nesting habitat) on stack-tops at the expense of uninhabitable woodland. A new investigation is needed.

Sooty Tern; Nok Nangnual Gleb Dam (Thai); Burung Camar Angin (Malay)

Sterna fuscata Linnaeus 1766, *Systema Naturae* 12(1): 228. TL San Domingo, Dominican Republic.
Plate 41

GROUP RELATIONS. Free-standing.

GLOBAL RANGE. Tropical and subtropical oceans around the world, north in Asia to the Red Sea, Persian Gulf, Bay of Bengal islands and the Nansei islands; and south to Australia. This oceanic tern hardly occurs in continental-shelf waters and breeding-stations nearest the Peninsula are probably those on N Keeling island (1000 km southwest of Sumatra) and atolls at the SW edge of the Sin Cowe reefs between Sabah and Vietnam. The latter include Spratly island, on which about 500 pairs were breeding in August 1963 (Haile 1964), and Layang-layang Reef where in February 1990 several hundred had colonized coral rubble dredged up for a military runway (M. Akhir Othman, Wells 1991).

IDENTIFICATION/DESCRIPTION. A medium-large, pied tern with long tail-points, similar to Bridled but the entire upperparts are concolorous black, and the white of the forehead is a broad wedge, not extending back into eyebrows. Perched next to Bridled, Sooty is longer-winged and stands higher (BMP5). Young Sooty Terns are black-brown all over, white-flecked dorsally, rather like young Brown Noddies.

Bare-part colours. Iris deep brown; bill black; legs and feet black.

Size (mm). (Skin: 1 juvenile, not sexed): wing 294 (BMP5).

Weight. No data.

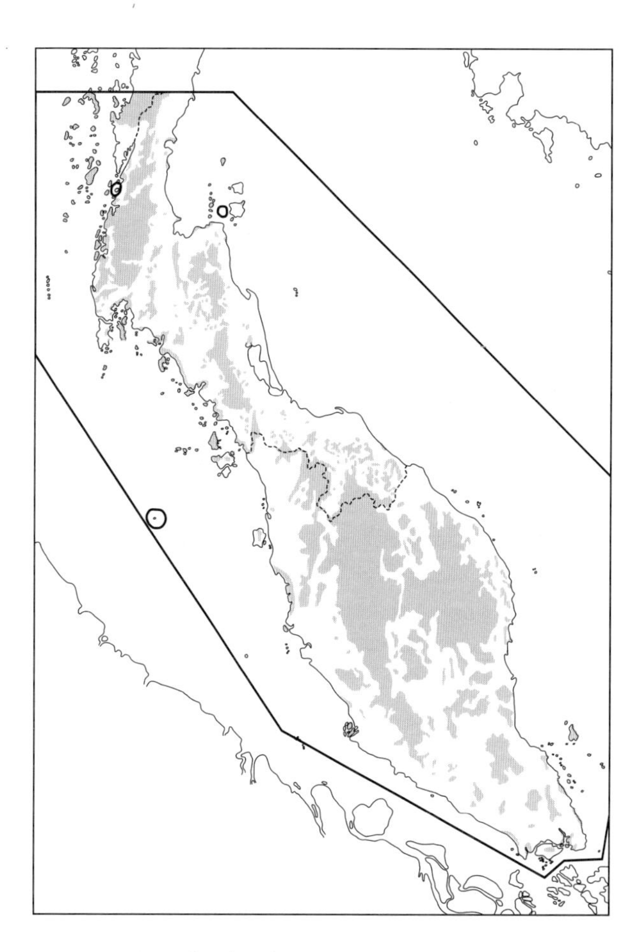

DISTRIBUTION. The few records are all from north of latitude 5°N. Historical summary: *Ran, Sur, Ked*, including Perak island, N Melaka Straits.

GEOGRAPHICAL VARIATION. In the range of Indo-Pacific *nubilosa* Sparrman 1788 (TL 'India orientalis').

STATUS AND POPULATION. Hardly more than vagrant. Known from a juvenile collected on the Ranong (Andaman Sea) coast in June 1957 (BLC) and summer sightings in the mid-northern Melaka Straits, within a few kilometres of Perak island: loafing with Bridled Terns on driftwood and, during 20–22 July 1973, a minimum three individuals on the island itself, including two engaged in repeated, noisy chase-flights (BR 1963, 1966, Langham *et al.* 1974). Off the E coast, one near Samui island in June 1983 (P.D. Coe). Extreme dates 12 June and 9 August.

HABITATS AND ECOLOGY. Blue-water sea. The Ranong bird is likely to have been a storm-drifted stray, and occurrence as far into continental shelf waters as Perak island is unexpected; still more so off the E coast.

FORAGING AND FOOD. No information.

SOCIAL ORGANIZATION. No local information, but highly gregarious at neighbouring breeding-stations.

MOVEMENTS. No information.

SURVIVAL. No information.

SOCIAL INTERACTIONS. No information.

VOICE. In July, Perak island birds gave the characteristic, loud *ker-waki-wak* call.

BREEDING. No population.

MOULT. No data.

CONSERVATION. No relevant issues.

Whiskered Tern; Nok Nangnual Gleb Khrao Khao (Thai); Burung Camar Tasik (Malay)

Chlidonias hybridus (Pallas) 1811, *Zoographia Rosso-Asiatica* 2: 338. TL S Volga and Sarpa Lake, SW Russia.

Plate 40

GROUP RELATIONS. Free-standing.

GLOBAL RANGE. Breeds in southern Africa, patchily across warm-temperate Eurasia from the Atlantic to Tadjikistan; in Ussuriland and NE China, not certainly south of the Yellow Sea; the northern Indian subcontinent from Kashmir to Bangladesh; and southern Australia (Mees 1977). Winters to the inner tropics in both hemispheres, as far as the Indian subcontinent and Sri Lanka; S Japan and Taiwan; SE Asia to the Greater Sunda islands, Bali and the Philippines; and Sulawesi and New Guinea. Vagrant in W Micronesia.

IDENTIFICATION/DESCRIPTION. A distinctive white facial stripe between black cap and charcoal-grey under-body (which is darker than rest of upper-parts) in summer. In winter plumage, most show a black band level from the rear margin of the eye to the nape, without the black 'ear-phones' of winter White-winged Black Tern, but some virtually lack black on the head. In flight, more reminiscent of a short-tailed Common Tern but upperparts are more uniformly pale grey (immatures of both show a dark inner leading-edge to the wing). Feeds quite differently, by dipping to the water-surface as in other marsh terns.

Bare-part colours. (Adults) iris dark brown; bill dark red in summer, blackish in winter; legs and feet red in summer, brownish red in winter.

Size. No data.

Weight. No data.

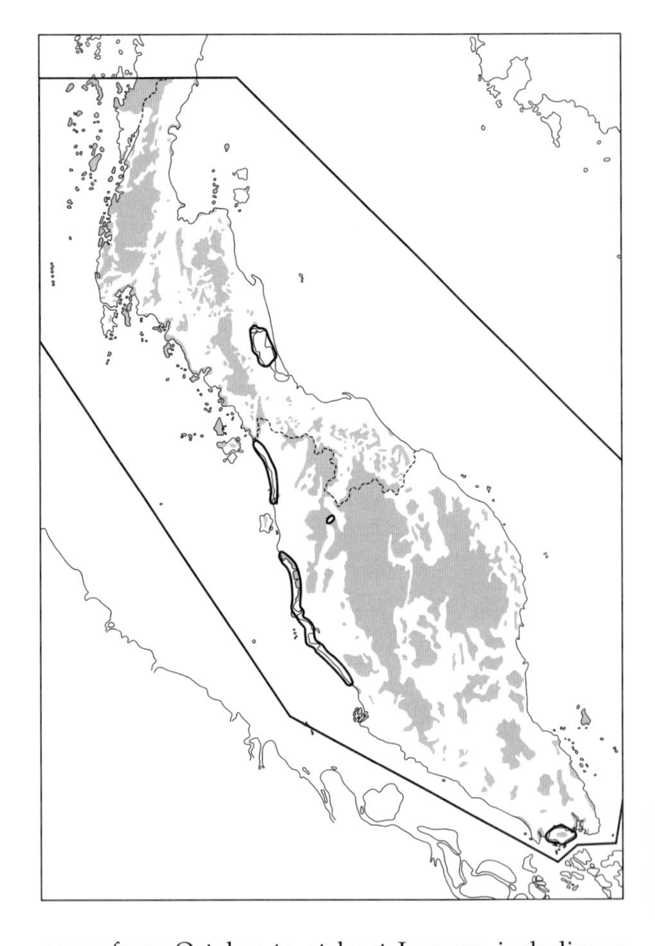

DISTRIBUTION. No reports from the Malaysian E coast. Historical summary: *Pht, Son, Pes, Ked, Pek, Sel, Sin*, with additional island records from Ketam (*Sel*) and Ubin (*Sin*).

GEOGRAPHICAL VARIATION. The only two individuals handled were northern, nominate *hybridus* (BR 1976–77). Plumage-cycles give no hint of southern subspecies occurring.

STATUS AND POPULATION. Passage migrant, non-breeding visitor and possible over-summerer; local and sparse to common. Occasional mid-season appearances on the SW Malaysian coast and paddy-lands, and on Singapore, suggest some winter mobility, but only two significant overwintering areas are known. These are: the Thalae Noi–Songkhla lake system (south at least to Kukut reserve), where hundreds occur from October to at least January, including a count of 752 on 20 January 1991 (Holmes and Wells 1975, Parish 1985, U. Treesucon); and the Matang–Larut coast of Perak, with gatherings of over 200 at Kalumpang and the adjacent Sangga estuary in January and March. By 1989, a wintering nucleus had also appeared on the irrigation system of a large new rice scheme at Seberang Perak, lower Perak, but aborted in the early 1990s after large-scale introduction of pesticides. A small group at Temengor reservoir, upper Perak river, on 16 September 1993 (R. Gregory-Smith) was far from usual passage routes, and this deep lake is an unlikely wintering site.

The only summer record to date is of 15, including two in bright plumage, at Thalae Noi on 25 June (BCSTB-13); presumed second-year birds not returning to the breeding-range.

HABITATS AND ECOLOGY. Wintering habitats include open, freshwater lakes and marsh, wet paddyland and its flooded canal systems, and mangrove coasts with broad intertidal mudflats. Passage movements are largely coastal, by-passing suitable-looking freshwater sites as little as 2–3 km inland (MBR 1986–87).

FORAGING AND FOOD. Forages in typical marsh-tern style, by quartering rather low and slowly over water and dipping to pick from the surface (see also White-winged Black Tern). Swennen and Marteijn (1985) have estimated 65 percent of feeding is in freshwater habitats versus 35 percent at river-mouths and on low-tide flats, but evidently with much local variation. Apparently less adapted to agriculture than White-winged Black Tern; does not share the latter's habit of following ploughs, etc.

SOCIAL ORGANIZATION. While foraging, stays mainly in monospecific parties of a few to several hundred birds; sometimes with White-winged Black Terns.

MOVEMENTS. Extreme early dates in autumn are 3 August on the Songkhla wetland and 15 September in Singapore, with signs of passage migration along the Melaka Straits coast until at least mid October. Spring return begins in the first week of March and the latest date (in Selangor) is 31 May, but it is not known when most adults leave (BR 1964, Meeswat and Prentice 1984, SINGAV-4).

SURVIVAL. No information.

SOCIAL INTERACTIONS. No information.

VOICE. When disturbed into flight, gives a thin *seerk*.

BREEDING. No population.

MOULT. Not studied, but autumn migrants retain traces of summer body-plumage to at least mid September, and renewal is more or less complete as of the second week of February. May-dated birds in a winter-type plumage are likely to have been second-summerers (BR 1964, ENGGANG-3).

CONSERVATION. Nominal protection may not defend the Thalae Noi–Songkhla wetland against being engineered, to the detriment of wildlife. The likely impact of an altered water-level regime on its marshland ecosystem needs careful study.

White-winged Black Tern; Nok Nangnual Gleb Dam Peek Khao (Thai); Burung Camar Bahu Putih (Malay)

Chlidonias leucopterus (Temminck) 1815, *Manuel d'Ornithologie*: 483. TL coasts of the Mediterranean.

Plate 40

GROUP RELATIONS. Free-standing.

GLOBAL RANGE. Breeds in mid-temperate Eurasia from central Europe to NW Mongolia, with outliers south to Iraq; then from Baikal east to Amurland and Sakhalin, and south to E Mongolia and NE China. Winters in sub-Saharan Africa, Madagascar, New Guinea and (mainly northern) Australia, sporadically north through tropical Asia to Sri Lanka, the E Indian subcontinent and SE China. Occasional as far as Micronesia and New Zealand.

IDENTIFICATION/DESCRIPTION. Feeding behaviour identifies it as a marsh tern (see Whiskered Tern). Smaller than Whiskered but closer to it than Little Tern, and broader-winged than the latter, with slower, light and floating flight. Summer plumage is distinctive, with a sexual difference in tail-colour: all white in males, tip variably pale grey in most, perhaps all, females. From other small, mainly white terns in winter by crown from above eye to nape extensively mottled black, with solidly black 'ear-phones' bordered posteriorly by a vertical finger of white. Grey of anterior upperparts (flight-feathers, wing leading-edge and upper mantle of juvenile dusky) always darker than rump and upper tail-coverts (not so in Whiskered Tern), but latter pure white only in summer adults. Like winter Whiskered, shows a small black spot at front of the eye.

Bare-part colours. (Adult) iris dark brown; bill black in winter, dark red in summer; legs and feet dusky red in winter, coral-red in summer.

Size (mm). (Skins: 10 males, 3 females; adult): wing 207–224 and 218–222; tail 69–76 and 77–80; bill 23.7–25.8 and 24.6–26.8; tarsus 18.4–20.6 and 19.0–20.1 (BMNH, ZRCNUS).

Weight (g). One November adult, 77.

DISTRIBUTION. Mainly the north and west. Historical summary: *Kra, Pht, Tra, Son, Pat, Pes, Ked, Pra, Pek, Sel, Mel, Joh, Sin*, including records from Libong, Penang and Tengah islands off the W coast; and Ubin, Singapore.

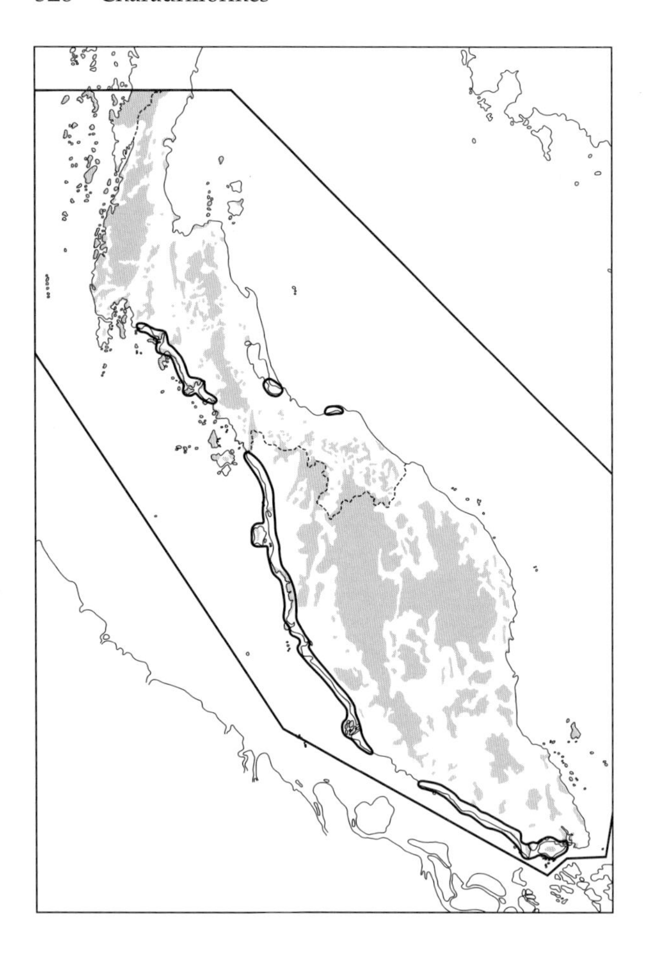

GEOGRAPHICAL VARIATION. None recognized.

STATUS AND POPULATION. Passage migrant and localized non-breeding visitor, with a small, sporadic presence of winter-plumaged, probable one-year-olds through summer, including flocks of up to 70 (usually much fewer) at Songkhla lake and in the Johor Straits and Singapore. Along passage routes at appropriate seasons, regular and common. Autumn migrants use the Thalae Songkhla wetland and Pattani bay. Otherwise, hardly known along the E seaboard and little recorded also in the NW, whereas in the Melaka Straits and around Singapore, during passage seasons, it is the commonest tern. Fewer over-winter but January roost- and foraging-flock counts of up to 600 have been made in Singapore and Selangor, and present then also on the Johor, Perak and Perlis coasts, with a few at Songkhla lake (AWB, Parish 1985, P.D. Round, SINGAV-3, Swennen *et al.* 1986, U. Treesucon).

HABITATS AND ECOLOGY. Primarily, and presumably originally, a bird of in-shore waters along muddy, mangrove-lined coasts and estuaries. On such coasts, they loaf on low-tide mudflats, and in April in Selangor up to 2200 have been counted at the seaside ash-ponds of Kapar power-station (Sebastian *et al.* 1993). Occurs in the brackish sector of Thalae Songkhla but not regularly in the upper, freshwater part of this lake–marsh system (only five among over 700 Whiskered Terns counted at Thalae Noi in late January 1991: U. Treesucon). On the other hand, much attracted to open, freshly turned and flooded, sub-coastal paddyland – which is not a major habitat of Whiskered Tern. Here, often-large parties regularly rest for long periods on high-mounted powerlines over open ground, closely spaced along the uppermost available cable (again, not a recorded habit of Whiskered or any other local tern species).

FORAGING AND FOOD. Like other marsh terns, feeds by dipping to the surface for small floating or surface prey; never by plunge-diving. On wet paddyland, dense flocks forage behind the plough. Swennen and Marteijn (1985) record proportionately little use made of intertidal mudflats for foraging, but coastal and estuarine waters have to be important. On falling tides at Kapar power-station (Selangor), large numbers gather over the cooling-water outfall, presumably after organisms killed in the circulation.

SOCIAL ORGANIZATION. Gregarious at all times.

MOVEMENTS. The earliest autumn date for adults (showing summer plumage) is 22 August, in Singapore (SINGAV-6). Build-up of migrants there and in the Melaka Straits is comparatively slow, with no 3-figure counts anywhere until early/mid October. Maximum numbers are reached during November, but with no defined end-point to autumn movements. Waves of spring migrants pass through Singapore and along the W coast mostly as of early March (a few high scores from Selangor in February: Silvius *et al.* 1987), build up to 4-figure counts in late March in Singapore and during late March–mid April in Selangor, then fall away by May (a last large roost-count, of 545, at Kapar power-station on 2 May). The latest date for adults anywhere in the Melaka Straits is 31 May (AWB, BR 1964).

There are spring and autumn records from Libong island, but main routes north of the Malaysian border have still to be mapped.

SURVIVAL. No information.

SOCIAL INTERACTIONS. No information.

VOICE. The flight-call is a light, sharp *kwik*.

BREEDING. No population.

MOULT. First-winterers show no wing-moult up to at least December, but 15 immatures dated April–May (most with some summer body-feathers) were in active or recent moult of the wing-tip, nearly all also in a second, complete wing-moult, out to between P5–P8, and a few a third, out to P3 (but none active at more than two loci overall). Eight non-juveniles dated September–November were in regular-descendant, single-locus moult between P5 and P8. One definite, late-May adult in almost full summer body-plumage had completed.

Last remnants of summer body-plumage are lost in early autumn and first traces of the next plumage appear in late February. Most adults are in body-moult in March, with full colours common by April. Immatures typically retain or renew winter-type plumage in spring, but some develop partial summer colours (BMNH, AWB, ZDUM, ZRCNUS).

CONSERVATION. See Brown-headed Gull for long-term issues in the Melaka Straits.

Brown Noddy; Nok Nodee (Thai); Burung Camar Anggok (Malay)

Anous stolidus (Linnaeus) 1758, *Systema Naturae* 10(1): 137. TL West Indies.

Plate 8

GROUP RELATIONS. Free-standing.

GLOBAL RANGE. Breeds on small, rocky islands in mostly blue waters of the tropical and low-temperate Indian Ocean south to Australia, and from Australia north in the W Pacific to the S Nansei islands, including Sunda shelf, Wallacean and Sulu Seas. Migrates/disperses within this gross range (cf. de Silva 1991).

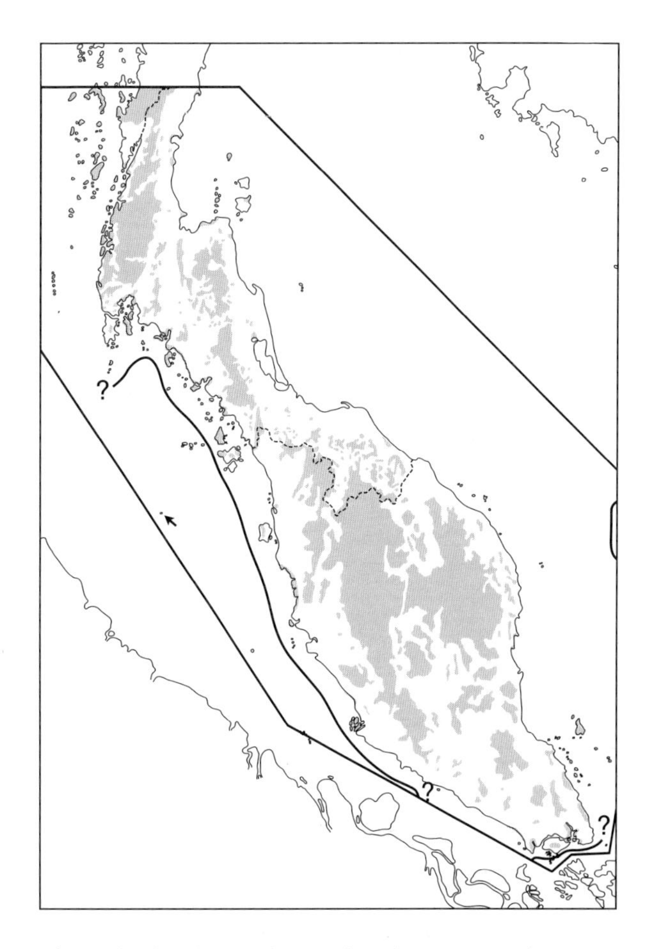

IDENTIFICATION/DESCRIPTION. At sea, flight is leisurely, typically fairly close to the water. Juvenile Sooty Terns are similarly almost all dark brown. However, by shape and behaviour in distant flight, Brown Noddy is more likely to be mistaken for some medium-sized petrel. The terminal notch of the rather heavy-looking, tapering tail is rarely conspicuous, and against a bright sea, surprisingly, the pale cap is not a very obvious field character. Juveniles are pale only on the forehead.

Bare-part colours. Iris deep brown; bill black, mouth-lining vermilion-red; legs and feet black.

Size (mm). (Skins: 1 male, 1 female; adult): wing 273 and 260; tail 160 and 142; bill 37.8 and 38.5; tarsus 25.0 and 26.0 (UMBRP, ZRCNUS).

Weight (g). One non-breeding adult female, 137.

DISTRIBUTION. Off mainly the W and S coasts. Historical summary: *Kra, Sat, Tru, Ked, Pek, Neg, Sin,* and off Penang island.

GEOGRAPHICAL VARIATION. Indo-Pacific *pileatus* Scopoli 1786 (TL Philippines).

STATUS AND POPULATION. Either resident or a breeding visitor; local and sparse to common. Most occur in the Melaka Straits where, to at least the late 1970s, a colony of 400–500 pairs bred in summer on Perak island, latitude 5°43'N (Madoc 1955, Madoc and Allen 1956, Langham 1976). In early March 1973, unknown numbers were roosting there overnight but it is not known whether some non-breeders stay year-round. Surveys at sea found none in the area in late January or March but a bird has been collected south of Perak island in early April and many seen between there and Penang in July. Southward, one recorded off Port Dickson (Negeri Sembilan) on 4 August and many near Jarak island, mid Straits, in mid November (Riley 1938, Robinson and Kloss 1921–24). During autumn, small numbers pass east through the Singapore Straits (BR 1964), perhaps out of the Melaka Straits.

In the NW, survey-cruises over the continental shelf-break off Phuket in November, February, April and June found none (Kiørboe 1991). The only records in this sector are of a bird in Tarutao national park waters (Satul) on 8 September and odd individuals near Maa island (Krabi) in November and December

(BBCB-9, C. Prentice). Apparently, no significant dispersal occurs in this direction.

Off the E coast, the only records are of small groups in the area of the Terengganu oil-field in late October. Their nearest likely breeding-station would be Damar rock (Indonesia), about 160 km off S Pahang (D.M. Simpson).

HABITATS AND ECOLOGY. The open sea; approaching mainland coasts only incidentally while on passage. On Perak island, non-breeders arrived to roost at and after dusk, and left again before dawn.

FORAGING AND FOOD. A bird at Perak island flew low and rather slowly, picking from the surface in the splash-zone.

SOCIAL ORGANIZATION. Roosts and breeds gregariously.

MOVEMENTS. See above.

SURVIVAL. No information.

SOCIAL INTERACTIONS. Nests are spaced out and nesters are aggressive towards neighbours. At Perak island, instances have been seen of prolonged grappling in the water below the breeding cliff (Madoc 1955).

VOICE. In flight, a sharp *chiri chok* (Madoc 1954).

BREEDING

Nest. On Perak island, sub-colonies were on ledges and niches of the steepest (lower) part of the eastern cliff, down to about 3 m above the splash-zone, with a few birds as high as 70 m, but clear of Brown Boobies using the gentler upper slopes of the island. Nests comprise gravel, driftwood scraps, other detritus (crab-parts, etc.), and feathers.

Eggs and brood. Eggs are matt white or pale sand, variably flecked brown and blotched and smeared lavender. Size (mm): 53.8–48.7 × 38.2–34.6 (mean 51.0 × 36.4, n=11). Full clutch one.

Cycle. No information.

Seasonality. Breeding confirmed on three visits to Perak island: 6 June 1954 (mostly well-incubated eggs); 24 June 1956 (mostly eggs, and a small number of chicks); and 20–22 July 1973 (a few chicks, but the intensity of aerial chasing then suggested most birds were still at an early stage of breeding). The following year, at least half the colony was still in attendance during daytime in early August, but nests could not be reached for checking (Langham 1976, Langham *et al.* 1974, Madoc 1954, 1955, 1956).

MOULT. Replacement of at least the inner primaries is regular-descendant. An adult male from Jarak was growing P5/6 on 16 November and a female at Perak island P7 on 3 March; wing-tip older in both cases (ZDUM, ZRCNUS).

CONSERVATION. When last checked in the late 1970s, Brown Noddies nesting on Perak island had maintained numbers. It is not known if the egg- and chick-raiding then directed at boobies has since been switched to terns.

Black Noddy; (no Thai name); Burung Camar Haji (Malay)

Anous minutus Boie 1844, Oken's *Isis* 37: 188. TL Raine island, Queensland.
Not illustrated in this volume

GROUP RELATIONS. Forms a superspecies with largely allopatric Indian Ocean *A. tenuirostris* (Lesser Noddy). They meet on Ashmore reef off NW Australia (HANZAB).

GLOBAL RANGE. A tree- and rock-crevice nester on small islands, in mainly blue waters of the tropical Atlantic and Pacific, west to SE Asia and northern Australia. In SE Asia, colonies have been reported from the Flores, Sulu and NW Java Seas, though with no breeding confirmed in W Indonesia for more than half a century. Vagrant in the S China Sea and west to the Bay of Bengal and Laccadives.

IDENTIFICATION/DESCRIPTION. Smaller and darker than Brown Noddy; adults have a brighter white cap and are proportionately longer-billed, with tail fan- rather than wedge-shaped. Wings appear broader and wing-beats are faster and more fluttery (King 1967, Slater 1971). The *minutus* group has lores black, sharp against white forecrown.

Bare-part colours. Iris brown; bill black; legs and feet dark reddish brown (BWP, HBI).

Size (mm). (Skin: 1 female; adult): wing 215; tail 116; bill 38; tarsus 31.7 (BMNH).

Weight. No data.

DISTRIBUTION. Historical summary: *?Mel.*

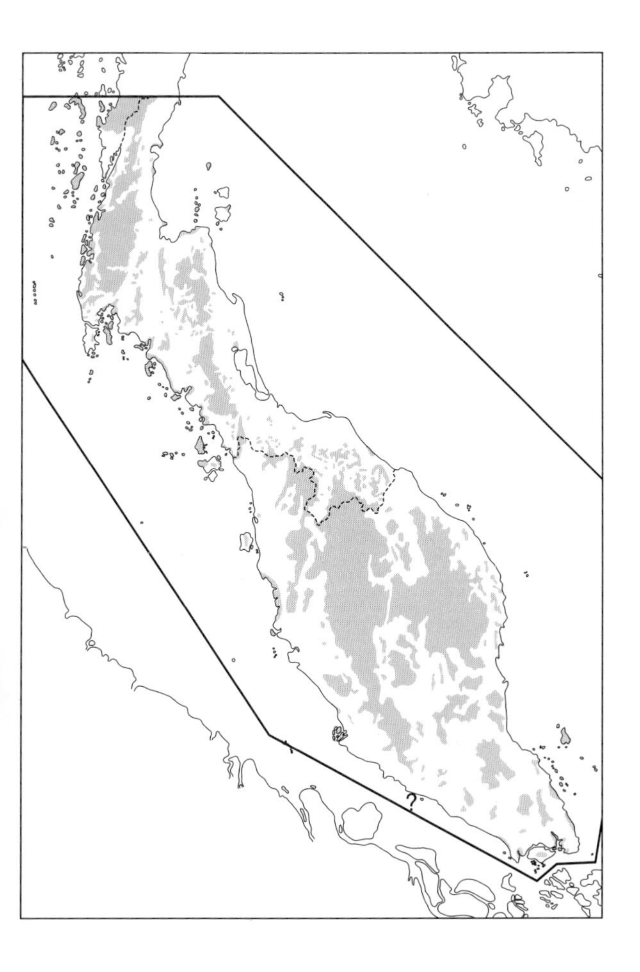

GEOGRAPHICAL VARIATION. The one specimen is SE Asian *worcesteri* McGregor 1911 (TL Cavilli island, Sulu Sea).

STATUS AND POPULATION. Included on the strength of a female labelled 'Malacca August 1865' in the A.C. Maingay collection (BMNH). The made-up skin is not the shape of a typical 19th century Melaka market item (and trading seems only to have been in land-birds). However, it is likely to have come off a ship and may not have been captured actually within the Straits.

HABITATS AND ECOLOGY. Open seas as a non-breeder.

FORAGING AND FOOD. No information.

SOCIAL ORGANIZATION. No information.

MOVEMENTS. No information.

SURVIVAL. No information.

SOCIAL INTERACTIONS. No information.

VOICE. No information.

BREEDING. No population.

MOULT. Undated, but P1 in moult, the rest of the wing slightly worn (BMNH).

CONSERVATION. No relevant issues.

Order COLUMBIFORMES

Family COLUMBIDAE

Pigeons and doves: 21 species

Rock Pigeon/Town Pigeon; Nok Phiraab Paa (Thai); Pergam Batu (Malay)

Columba livia Gmelin 1789, *Systema Naturae* 13(2): 769. TL S Europe.
Plate 42

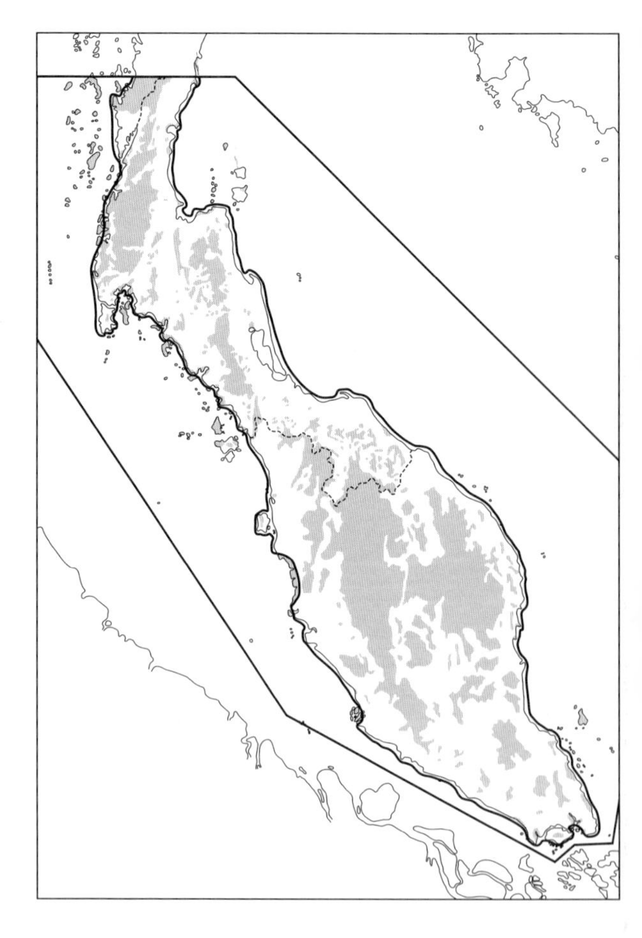

GROUP RELATIONS. Apparently free-standing; close to E Palaearctic *Columba rupestris* (Hill Pigeon) but they overlap in central Asia without interbreeding (Snow 1978).

GLOBAL RANGE. Wild on N Atlantic islands and across temperate Eurasia to NW China, south through the Sahara and the Indian subcontinent to Sri Lanka; possibly also into northern Burma. Populations of mostly domestic origin occupy the tropics and temperate zones virtually worldwide.

IDENTIFICATION/DESCRIPTION. Some flight-postures of lone dark- or grey-phase individuals, especially long-winged racing birds, momentarily suggest a falcon, but any resemblance is dispelled by small head-size, etc. Proportions of the colour-phases of feral birds have not been measured but most are grey or dark-chequered. The former have a wild-type, black wing- and tail-bar pattern, and some a white rump (wild Rock Pigeons of Asia are mostly grey-rumped: Vaurie 1965). Many show at least some other white feathering, often asymmetrical, but all-white individuals are in the minority, as are rufous and fully melanistic birds. Rufous variants are smaller than and never show the pale cap and dark dorsum of Pale-capped Pigeon, and Pale-capped is a tree bird.

Bare-part colours. (Adult) iris orange, periorbital skin grey-white; cere dull white, bill blackish; feet dull purple-red, part-feathered in some variants.

Size. No data.

Weight. No data.

DISTRIBUTION. Historical summary: all divisions and on Penang island.

GEOGRAPHICAL VARIATION. Deignan (1963) identified Thai populations as subspecies *intermedia* Strickland 1844 (TL India), but the regional link between domestic and wild stocks needs further study.

STATUS AND POPULATION. Resident, regular and common, but nowhere at the population-levels of some temperate-zone cities. Largest recent spot-counts at favoured sites in and around Singapore city have not exceeded 400 (SINGAV-3), and the breeding population at Batu Caves, a well-known site in Selangor, is not more than about 100 birds.

HABITATS AND ECOLOGY. At plains level and in settled uplands (Cameron Highlands) to at least 1500 m (SINGAV-1). Probably all Town Pigeons in the Peninsula depend absolutely on humans for food, and most are tied to cotes or buildings for nest-sites. Some breed in wild-type situations on cliffs and in cave entrances, but only where these abut habitation or religious sites (such as the Batu Caves temple complex) that are sources of food. There are no records of any use being made of trees, and a scarcity of colonizable ledges in modern architecture may keep them out of the newer town centres.

FORAGING AND FOOD. Exclusively seeds and domestic waste, taken from the ground. Uncovered waste is generally plentiful but Town Pigeons more commonly depend on hand-outs at regular feeding-stations. They take grass-seed from lawns, mown fields, etc., but have no other natural foraging opportunities.

SOCIAL ORGANIZATION. Strongly and permanently gregarious.

MOVEMENTS. None known among local birds but several recoveries of large, Taiwan-ringed pigeons imply international racers pass through the Peninsula, possibly after being released from ships at sea.

SURVIVAL. No information.

SOCIAL INTERACTIONS. There has been no proper study of Town Pigeon social behaviour in this area but displays (including the inflated-neck bow of courting males to females) appear generally as described worldwide.

VOICE. Not adequately described in this area.

BREEDING

Nest. A sparse layer of dead twigs in a cliff niche or on a sheltered ledge of a building. In urban Malaysia and Singapore, the keeping of free-flying pigeons is no longer regarded as neighbourly, and formerly common pigeon-cotes are now an unusual sight.

Eggs and brood. No local details, but full clutch two.

Cycle. No local data.

Seasonality. No exact information but breeding appears to continue year-round.

MOULT. No data.

CONSERVATION. No relevant issues.

Pale-capped Pigeon; Nok Lumphuu Daeng (Thai); Pergam Haji (Malay)

Columba punicea Blyth 1842, *Journal of the Asiatic Society of Bengal* 11: 461. TL Chaibasa, Bihar, NE India.

Plate 43

GROUP RELATIONS. Free-standing; apparently nearest to Bay of Bengal and SE Asian small-island *C. palumboides* (Andaman Wood Pigeon) and *C. argentina* (Silvery Wood Pigeon, Plate 43), all three with long, shallowly sloping foreheads and poorly developed neck-markings, superficially like imperial pigeons (Goodwin 1967). Silvery Wood Pigeon has been collected on Indonesian islands within sight of the S end of the Peninsula, and may have been seen on Jarak island, Melaka Straits (Gibson-Hill 1952a, Madoc 1957, Robinson 1907).

GLOBAL RANGE. Extreme S Tibet (Chumbi valley) and the NE Indian subcontinent; Hainan; and SE Asia from Burma, S Laos and central Vietnam (AMNH) to the Peninsula. Recorded nesting at about latitude 17°N in Burma but believed only to be a non-breeding migrant/dispersant in the SW of its range.

IDENTIFICATION/DESCRIPTION. Bulkier than Town Pigeon. Adults show a whitish cap from forehead to nape, sharp against vinous-brown face and underparts and deep purple-brown upperparts, the latter glossed green on the mantle and (in male) wing-coverts. Black feather-bases show as arrow-marks on the hind-neck. Rump to tail dark slate-grey, among the few specimens examined, upper tail-coverts and tail glossed green in males, purple in females. Has proportionately long toes.

Bare-part colours. (Adult) iris yellow shading outwards to orange, eyelid-rim plum-red; cere and base of bill plum-red, tip horn-white; feet dull purple-red (Robinson 1917).

Size (mm). (Skins: 5 males, 1 female; adult): wing 220–227 and 221; tail 131–151 and 141; bill 18.0–19.8 and 17.1; tarsus 24.6–28.5 and 25.6; mid-toe plus claw 41.2 (a male) (BMNH, ZRCNUS).

Weight. No data.

DISTRIBUTION. With one exception, all records are from the NW coast and islands, south (possibly) to the Langkawi group. Historical summary: *Ran, Phu, Pht, Tra, Sat, ?Ked.*

GEOGRAPHICAL VARIATION. None recognized.

STATUS AND POPULATION. A non-breeding visitor or long-distance dispersant, local and, perhaps, no longer more than occasional. The only recent

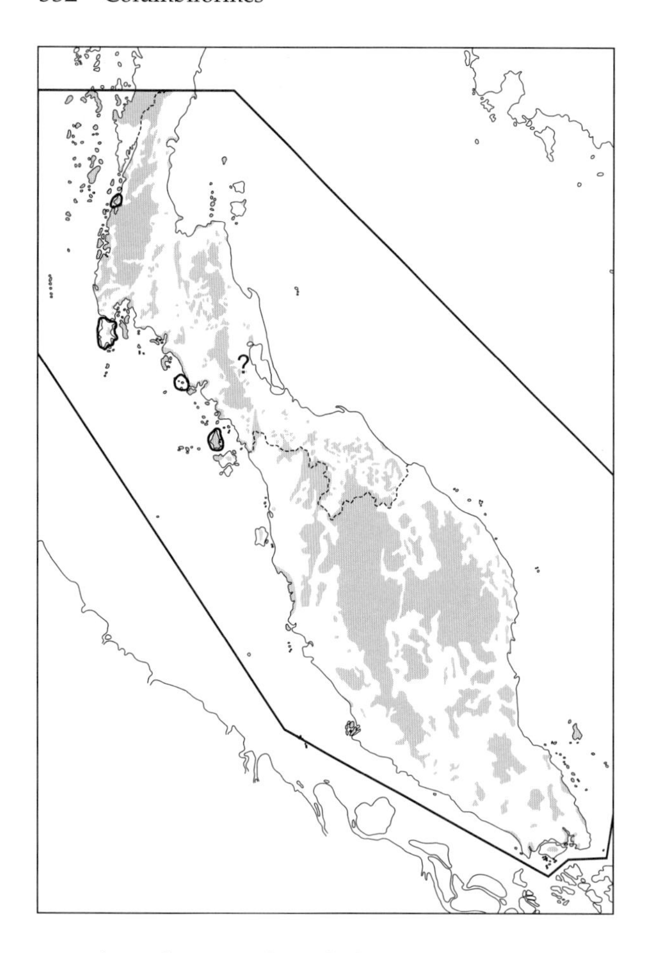

record is of one in degraded mangroves in Ranong (P.D. Round). Otherwise confirmed from Phuket, Muk island, where in the first week of January 1917 it was 'very common', and Tarutao (BMNH, Robinson 1917, Robinson and Kloss 1910–11). About six large, brown pigeons seen feeding together in a fruiting *Memecylon* sp. on Langgun island, NW Langkawi group, in February 1975 (van Balgooy *et al.* 1977) would have been this species or Mountain Imperial Pigeon, neither known there otherwise.

HABITATS AND ECOLOGY. Recorded in forest, including mangroves and mangrove scrub. One from Tarutao island was collected on the ground by a rocky stream (Robinson and Chasen 1936). On Muk (Trang), appeared daily at dusk to roost in tall mangroves, commuting to feed elsewhere (Robinson 1917).

FORAGING AND FOOD. Searches both on the ground and in fruiting trees (HBI, OBCB-14, -15). The *Memecylon* record is the only locally identified food-source, still to be confirmed.

SOCIAL ORGANIZATION. Non-breeders forage gregariously, and on Muk island roosted in groups of 30–40 (Robinson 1917).

MOVEMENTS. A June date for a specimen said to have been collected in Phatthalung needs to be confirmed. Other records fall during 4 January–13 March (BMP5).

SURVIVAL. No information.

SOCIAL INTERACTIONS. No information.

VOICE. No local record; described elsewhere as a moaning coo.

BREEDING. No population.

MOULT. Birds dated January–March showed none and were in fresh plumage (BMNH, ZRCNUS).

CONSERVATION. Both Pale-capped and Silvery Wood Pigeons are classed as globally vulnerable (BTW2). Communal roosting at fixed sites increases risk from hunting, and around the Peninsula Silvery is perhaps already extinct.

Spotted Dove; Nok Khao Yai (Thai); Tekukur Biasa (Malay)

Streptopelia chinensis (Scopoli) 1786, *Deliciae Florae et Fauna Insubricae* 2: 94. TL Guangzhou, China.

Plate 42

GROUP RELATIONS. Free-standing; perhaps nearest to Afro-Asian *S. senegalensis* (Laughing Dove) (Goodwin 1967).

GLOBAL RANGE. The Indian subcontinent and Sri Lanka, except in arid zones; China south from latitude about 40°N including Taiwan and Hainan; SE Asia to the Greater Sunda islands, Bali and the Philippines (still being colonized from the west); and the Lesser Sunda islands. Believed introduced in Sulawesi and the Moluccas, as also in Australia, Oceania and SW USA.

IDENTIFICATION/DESCRIPTION. Slender and proportionately long-tailed. When flushed, pale blue-grey primary coverts and long white wedge up the side of the tail are conspicuous (cf. Red Collared Dove). Zebra Dove has similar graduated tail-shape but is much smaller, with distinctive bounding flight-action. The broad, spotted hind-collar is diagnostic of adults. Collarless immatures have lesser wing-coverts blackish brown with a rufous-clay tip and inconspicuous shaft-stripe. These are mid brown with pale tip and bold black shaft-stripe in adults.

Bare-part colours. (Adult) iris grey-yellow to pale orange; bill black; feet dull purple-red.

Size (mm). (Skins: 7 males, 10 females; adult): wing 138–149 and 137–148; tail 126–143 and 119–135; bill 14.9–16.7 and 13.8–16.9; tarsus 22.3–27.1 and 23.7–25.5 (BMNH, UMZC).

Weight (g). Unsexed adults, 106–132 (n=6) (UMBRP).

DISTRIBUTION. Historical summary: all divisions except *Chu*, with additional island records from Phiphi, Lanta, Muk, Libong, Tarutao, Langkawi, Penang and Pangkor off the W coast; Phangan and Sibu (*Joh*) off the E coast; and Tekong, Ubin, Seletar, Berani, Retan Laut, Hantu, Pawai and Senang around Singapore. Some island occurrences may be introductions via the cage-bird trade.

GEOGRAPHICAL VARIATION. Subspecies *tigrina* Temminck 1810 (TL Java), of the far-NE Indian subcontinent and extreme S China to SE Asia and Wallacea.

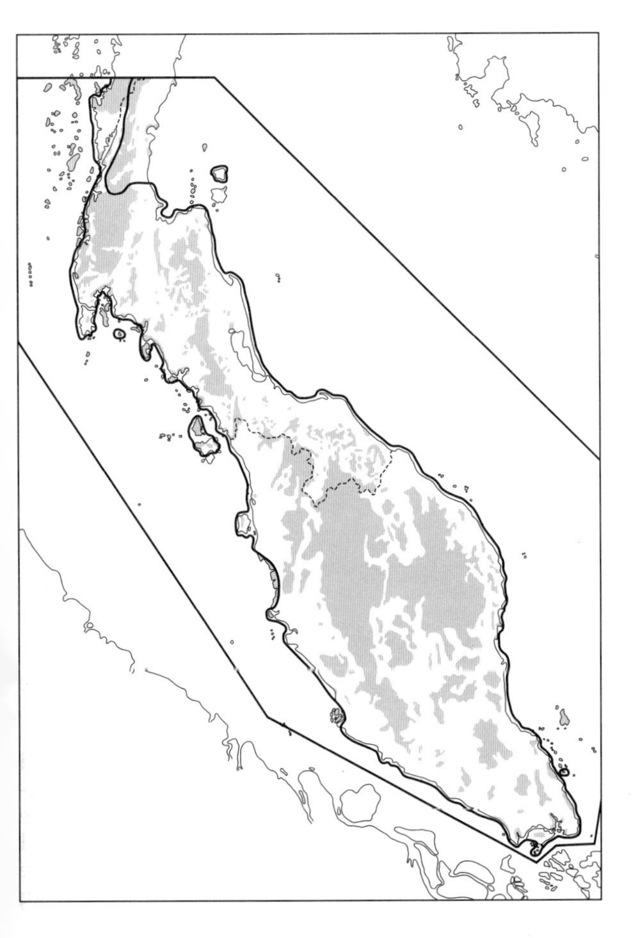

STATUS AND POPULATION. Resident, regular and common. An active dispersant, rapidly colonizing land newly deforested for settlement and agriculture.

HABITATS AND ECOLOGY. The grass/scrub mix of young beach dunes, and in all kinds of man-disturbed habitats elsewhere: from degraded back-mangroves to old mine-tailings, grazing-land, parks and gardens, and the edges of open-country waterways and roads; also agriculture, especially paddy-stubble and oil-palm and coconut plantings. Mostly at plains level but by natural dispersal or escape of captives, has found its way into upland crops and other cleared spaces of the Cameron Highlands, Main Range (BMP5). Exposed perches, especially high service-wires, are favoured daytime resting sites, but for retreat and roosting Spotted Doves depend on trees and palms.

FORAGING AND FOOD. Seeks small seeds on open ground.

SOCIAL ORGANIZATION. Often alone, and the commonest social unit is a pair, males advertising exclusive nest-territories. Many birds may gather at a rich seed-source, feeding and loafing in close proximity without aggression, but appear never to form cohesive flocks.

MOVEMENTS. Capacity to disperse is inferred from the speed at which new clearances are occupied, but has only once been demonstrated directly: a bird ringed at Kemaman, Terengganu, on 20 August and recaptured 22 days later 97 km further up the coast (BR 1969).

SURVIVAL. No information.

SOCIAL INTERACTIONS. Males (only?) perform a high, arching glide with tail part-fanned, thought to advertise presence in a nesting-territory.

VOICE. The male's loud advertisement-call is a clear, abruptly ending trisyllable *kuk-krrruu kur*, stressed on the mid and last notes or just the middle note, or without obvious stress. The Malay name, Tekukur, is onomatopoeic.

BREEDING

Nest. A flat platform of twigs augmented with finer material, about 15 cm across × 2–3 cm deep, for a pigeon, relatively dense. Most nests are built in a fork among the foliage of a smallish tree or shrub-top adjacent to open ground, less often in bamboo or a palm-crown, 1–14 but typically not above 3 m up. Unusual sites include a ledge beneath the roof of a field-shelter and on top of a small pile of sticks in open paddyland.

Eggs and brood. Eggs are glossy white. Shape elliptical. Size (mm): 26.4 × 21.1 and 27.2 × 22.5 (n=2). Full clutch two.

Cycle. No information.

Seasonality. Eggs found in January–May, July–September and November, with nestlings/young fledglings recorded from 11 February to 7 October (F.G.H. Allen, E.C.S. Baker, Edgar 1933, Madoc 1956a, NRCS, Ryves 1938, SINGAV-1, -2). More winter data may show it breeds year-round.

MOULT. Replacement of primaries is regular-descendant. Among 41 adults from throughout the Peninsula and covering all months, 13 showed active wing-moult during early March (P2/3)–early October (P8). Advanced birds are likely to have completed by May or June but the only ones handled actually showing fully fresh wings were dated October–December. This overall seasonality is broken by a Trang adult moulting P3/4 on 1 December, and common occurrence of suspensions during winter shows that not all moult-bouts run to completion (BMNH, UMZC, ZRC-NUS).

CONSERVATION. Not at risk overall, but directly affected by herbicides in agriculture, and regular trapping for the pet trade depresses population densities, particularly in suburban areas.

Red Collared Dove; Nok Khao Fai (Thai); Tekukur Merah (Malay)

Streptopelia tranquebarica (Hermann) 1804, F.L. Hammer's *Observationes Zoologicae*: 200. TL Tranquebar, SE India.

Plate 42

GROUP RELATIONS. Free-standing.

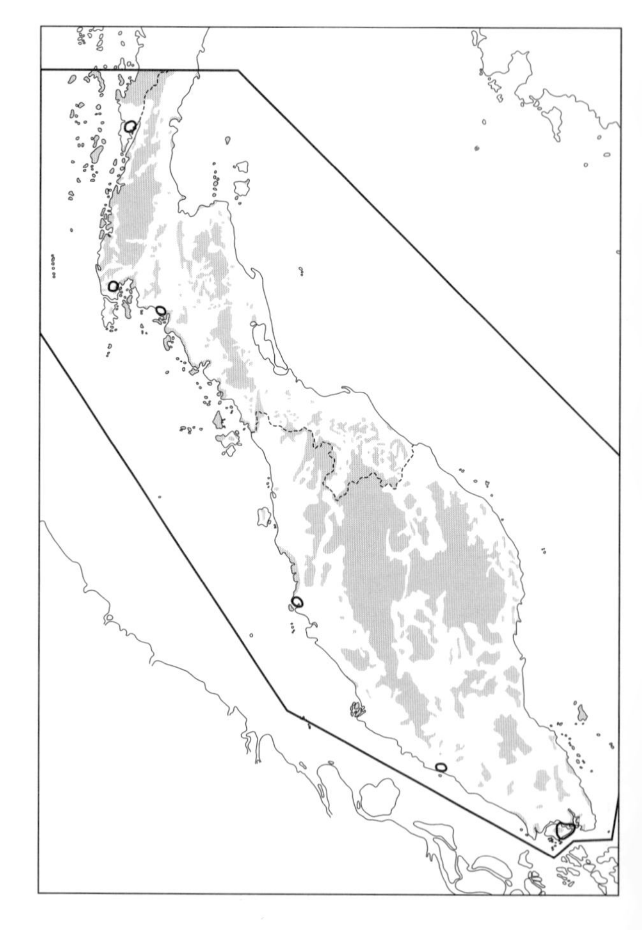

GLOBAL RANGE. The Indian subcontinent and the Andamans; China south from Hebei and Qinghai including Taiwan and Hainan; and SE Asia to the Peninsula and central Philippines. Some northern populations migrate or make long-distance dispersal movements. Vagrant Sri Lanka, and introduced in Sulawesi.

IDENTIFICATION/DESCRIPTION. Proportionately shorter-tailed than Spotted Dove, plain-backed, and the narrow, black half-collar is diagnostic of adults. From Spotted Dove on take-off also by broad, pale grey, apical tail-bar (interrupted only at the centre) rather than white corner-slashes, although the outer web of the outer tail-feather is white. Sexually dimorphic: adult male vinous-red back from the collar, adult female dull grey-brown, with less purely grey head. Juveniles resemble the female but lack a collar and show rufous tipping to primary coverts and flight-feathers.

Bare-part colours. (Adult) iris dark brown, eyelid-rim greenish yellow, periorbital skin blue-grey; bill slaty black; feet pink-brown anteriorly, dull grey behind.

Size (mm). (Skins: 2 males, 1 female; adult): wing 142, 143 and 137; tail 85 (one only) and 81; bill 14.1, 15.5 and 13.1; tarsus 19.6, 20.3 and 17.6 (BMNH, ZRC-NUS).

Weight. No data.

DISTRIBUTION. Established feral on the eastern half of Singapore island, where first reported in 1940. Elsewhere, singles, pairs and flocks of up to 20 have occurred erratically along the W coast south to Melaka. Historical summary: *Pak, Pha, Kra, Pek, Mel, Sin*, and on Ubin island, Singapore.

GEOGRAPHICAL VARIATION. Richly coloured *humilis* Temminck 1824 (TL Luzon), of the global range east from the Andamans and far-NE Indian subcontinent.

STATUS AND POPULATION. Singapore (including Ubin island) birds are resident, regular and common. Probably established from released captives, this population has grown as grassland foraging habitat expanded, initially on landfill for the new Changi airport and with continued reclamation of the island's coasts since. In late 1987, about 600 inhabited the NE, between Changi and Seletar, with some commuting to nearby Ubin (MBR 1986–87). Westward colonization has since carried them up to the city along the south coast and to the Senoko–Yishun area in the north (Singav-2, -4).

On the mainland of the Peninsula, status uncertain but unaided dispersal from the continental breeding-range is likely. Sightings cover at least the months January, March, July and October (Anonymous 1955, BBCB-7, BMNH, Edgar 1947), with an instance of nesting reported from Perak (Chasen 1934).

HABITATS AND ECOLOGY. Favours open grassland and paddy-stubble with scattered trees. Like Spotted Dove, loafs on exposed perches, including fence-lines.

FORAGING AND FOOD. Takes small seeds on the ground, but no local details available.

SOCIAL ORGANIZATION. Numbers forage and loaf in close proximity without aggression, but degree of flock-cohesion needs investigating. Lack of advertising-displays and loud calls suggests breeding-dispersion may differ from that of Spotted Dove, but this also needs investigating.

MOVEMENTS. The only direct evidence of long-distance movement comes from a bird 'grounded' with other migrants on an oil-rig 200 km off Terengganu, on 13 October 1982 (D.M. Simpson, MBR 1982–83).

SURVIVAL. No information.

SOCIAL INTERACTIONS. No advertising-displays are known and there are no reports of loud vocalizations. Copulation while perched on the frond of a coconut palm.

VOICE. A male in close-range bowing display to its mate gave a low, grumbling *ke<u>kurra</u>wu*, hurried and rapidly repeated.

BREEDING

Nest. A sparse platform, in one instance built of hard grass-stems. Sites recorded in Singapore: a hedge, a roadside tree, crowns of coconut palms and, once, on a garden greenhouse; 2–3 m above ground.

Eggs and brood. Eggs plain white; not otherwise described in this area. Full clutch two. Incubation period 14 days.

Cycle. Observed in captivity, a breeding male collected materials on the ground and carried them to his mate sitting in the developing nest, but did not assist in actual building. Both sexes incubate.

Seasonality. The Perak nesting attempt (outcome unrecorded) was in March. In Singapore, copulation seen on 24 March and eggs found in late March, April and mid July (Edgar 1947, SINGAV-1, -2, -3, -4).

MOULT. A Pakchan male and female dated 24 and 26 December were in active wing-moult, growing P10 and P5–6 respectively. An early December male from Singapore had finished (BMNH, ZRCNUS).

CONSERVATION. No key issues.

Barred Cuckoo Dove; Nok Khao Lai Yai (Thai); Te<u>ku</u>kur <u>Gu</u>nung (Malay)

Macropygia unchall (Wagler) 1827, *Systema Avium, pars 1, Genus Columba* 38. TL Java.

Plate 42

GROUP RELATIONS. Probably free-standing. Broadly overlaps *M. emiliani* (Ruddy Cuckoo Dove) in western Indonesia, hence is unlikely to be a member of its *phasianella* superspecies, ranging from the Andamans to Australia (CLBW, Goodwin 1967).

GLOBAL RANGE. Forested foothills of the Himalayas east from Kashmir; China south from Sichuan and Fujian, including Hainan; hill-tracts of continental SE Asia, Sumatra, Java, Bali, Lombok and Flores (AMNH).

IDENTIFICATION/DESCRIPTION. Seen in flight, the long-tailed shape of cuckoo doves is distinctive. In the field, paler, less rufous on head and underparts, and substantially larger than Little Cuckoo Dove. The sexes differ mainly in the extent of dark, ventral barring: over whole breast and sides of belly on a pale buff ground in the female, restricted to breast on a more vinous ground in the male. Sparse down-plumage of squab golden-buff (Robinson and Chasen 1936).

Bare-part colours. (Adult) iris white with outer ring amethyst, eyelid-rim red, periorbital skin purple-slate; bill black; feet dull purple-red (BMNH, Robinson and Chasen 1936).

Size (mm). (Skins: 4 males, 3 females; adult): wing 177–181 and 167–170; tail 159–181 and 146–162; bill 15.0–16.5 and 14.9–16.2; tarsus 22.8–24.9 (sexes combined) (BMNH).

Weight (g). Unsexed adults, 153–180 (n=4) (McClure 1964, UMBRP).

DISTRIBUTION. The Larut Range and Main Range, where recorded from Genting Highlands north to Cameron Highlands. Historical summary: *Pek, Phg, Sel.*

GEOGRAPHICAL VARIATION. Nominate *unchall* of the Sunda region, slightly smaller, paler, less pink on the head and breast than northern forms.

STATUS AND POPULATION. Resident, local and uncommon to more or less common, within a rather narrow habitat-zone.

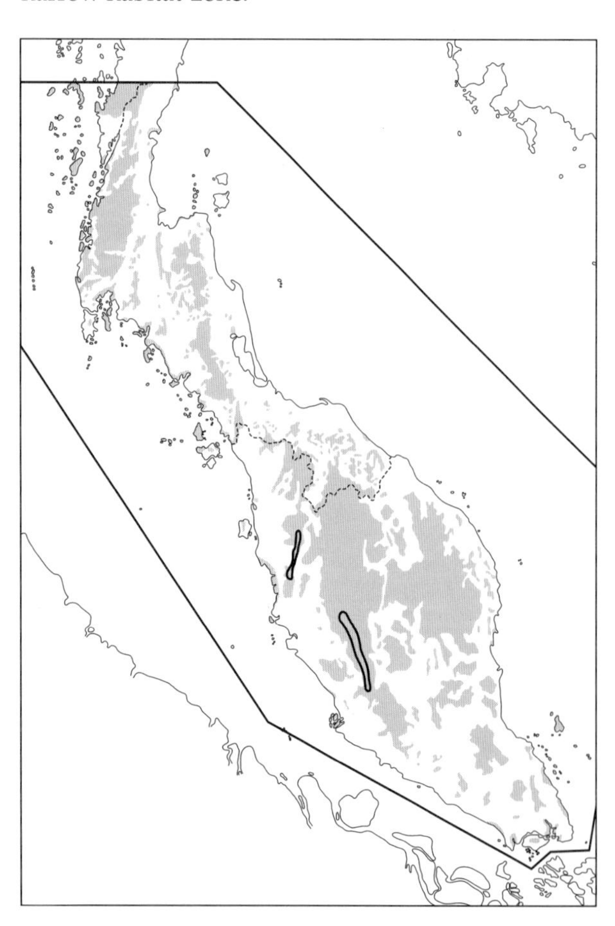

HABITATS AND ECOLOGY. Uses high crowns but often also found in disturbed edge-growth, strictly of Montane forest above about 1200 m, and this bird's core habitat lies above 1500 m in Upper Montane forest. Unlike Little Cuckoo Dove, does not disperse to the lowlands, and occurrence even in Lower Montane forest seems only to be sporadic.

FORAGING AND FOOD. Mainly arboreal, but finds some food on the ground. Occasionally met with foraging on quiet, open tracks through high-altitude forest.

SOCIAL ORGANIZATION. Associates in pairs and small, cohesive flocks.

MOVEMENTS. Parties move about, including vertically between forest-types, but dispersal distances are unknown.

SURVIVAL. No information.

SOCIAL INTERACTIONS. No information.

VOICE. A deep, muffled but powerful disyllable, hun-chu, falling and with the second note more carrying. The scientific name is onomatopoeic.

BREEDING

Nest. A loosely constructed twig platform about 15 cm across, sited in a horizontal branch-fork of a small tree, or on a rattan frond or pandan crown, 2–4 m up in low-stature forest, including secondary-growth, above 1200 m altitude – mostly higher.

Eggs and brood. Egg plain pearly white, slightly glossy. Shape elliptical. Size (mm): 32.8 × 24.9 (average). Full clutch one.

Cycle. No data.

Seasonality. Robinson and Chasen (1936) state that on the Selangor/Pahang boundary Barred Cuckoo Doves breed during December–March, but the only precisely dated nests are three from Cameron Highlands on 2, 3 and 5 September, one with a fledgling ready to fly. This would have hatched from an egg laid not later than late July, and apparent courtship behaviour by a pair at Fraser's Hill has been seen on 5 July. It is likely these dates describe the early and later parts of a single, long season (G.C. Madoc, Madoc 1956a, Robinson and Chasen 1936).

MOULT. Adults moulting flight-feathers have been collected on 11 February (P1, P8), 27 March (P2–3), 2 October (P9) and 31 October (P6) (BMNH, UMBRP), suggesting no obvious seasonality, and much overlap with the total breeding-season.

CONSERVATION. At the moment, no critical issues, but Montane forests are destined for more extensive disruption.

Little Cuckoo Dove; Nok Khao Lai Lek (Thai); Tekukur Api (Malay)

Macropygia ruficeps (Temminck) 1835, *Nouveau Recueil de Planches Coloriées d'Oiseaux* 95: plate 561. TL Java.

Plate 42

GROUP RELATIONS. Forms a superspecies with similarly small *M. mackinlayi* and *M. nigrirostris* (MacKinlay's and Black-billed Cuckoo Doves) of New Guinea east to the New Hebrides (Goodwin 1967).

GLOBAL RANGE. Hill-tracts of S Yunnan, N Vietnam and N Laos to S Burma, the Peninsula and Greater and Lesser Sunda islands east to Timor.

IDENTIFICATION/DESCRIPTION. The slender shape and proportionately long tail of the genus coupled with small size and rich chestnut colouring is diagnostic. Flight is fast, with quick flapping interspersed by brief, rocketing glides on part-closed wings. The sexes are separable in the field by prominent black spotting on the breast of the female versus buff-white fringing with only a few spots in the male. Immatures show black-and-buff barring on the mantle and broad, light rufous edging to the wing-coverts.

Bare-part colours. (Adult) iris pale grey; bill pinkish brown; feet grey-brown.

Size (mm). (Skins: 14 males, 13 females; adult): wing 138–147 and 134–144; tail 139–157 and 132–144; bill 12.5–14.0 and 12.3–14.1; tarsus 17.8–21.2 and 17.6–20.4 (BMNH, ZRCNUS).

Weight (g). Adults, 74–97 (n=3, the heaviest a male).

DISTRIBUTION. On and around the Larut Range, the Main Range from Telapa Buruk peak (*Neg*) north to the E–W highway (5°35'N), and on eastern outliers Benom and Tahan (BR 1972–73, R. Gregory-Smith, Hartert 1902, Medway 1972). Given its ability to use lowland habitats, likely to have reached other isolated mountains, and three birds at Sekayu (inland *Tru*) on 7 April 1988 suggest a probable presence on the E-coast Range. An unlikely absentee from northern mountains but, as with Barred Cuckoo Dove, continental populations terminate in SW Thailand (Boonsong and Round 1991). Historical summary: *Kel, Tru, Pra, Pek, Phg, Sel, Neg*.

GEOGRAPHICAL VARIATION. Endemic *malayana* Chasen and Kloss 1931 (TL the Gap, Selangor/Pahang divide); from *sumatrana* only by larger white tips on the male breast.

STATUS AND POPULATION. Resident, regular and common in the mountains; sparse to uncommon at plains level.

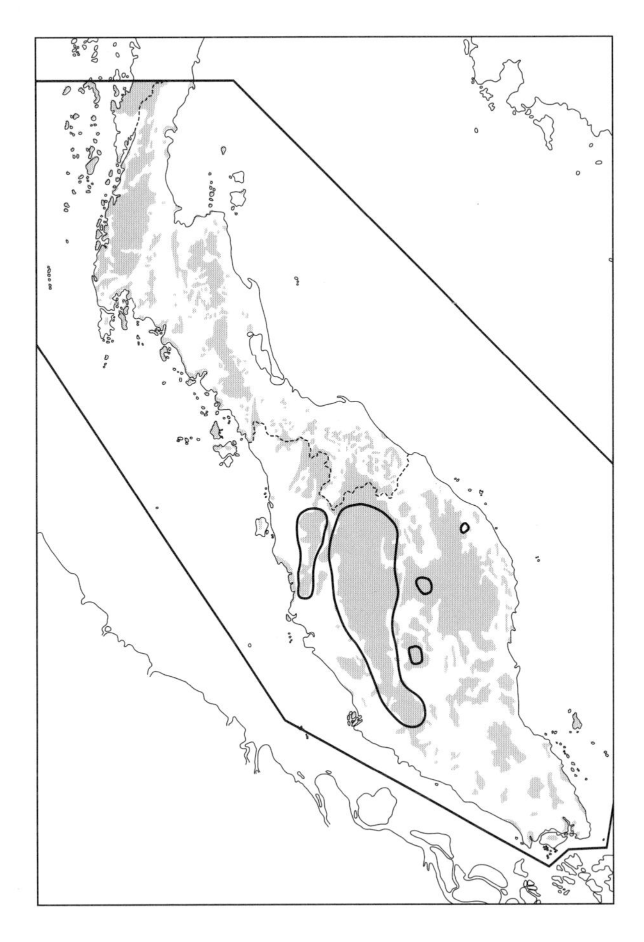

HABITATS AND ECOLOGY. Little Cuckoo Doves are permanently present, and have been found breeding, only above about 1000 m; commonest in Lower Montane forest but recorded to above 1800 m (Medway 1972). During 1966–1990, only two were mist-netted at night at the Fraser's Hill floodlights, whereas they regularly disperse by day. Year-round, pairs to small parties commute up and down mountain-slopes and have been found foraging in forest-edge and scrub 8–10 km into the lowland plain. One collected in mainland Penang (Stoliczka 1870) would have been still further out.

FORAGING AND FOOD. Said to visit swidden gardens, taking fruit such as chillies (Robinson and Chasen 1936), but all recent reports have been of harvesting seeds and small fruits (including figs) from tree-crowns, both in and out of forest. Unlike Barred Cuckoo Dove, not reported foraging on the ground, but well known as a visitor at mineral seeps, including hot springs along the base of the Main Range (BMNH, Butler 1899). Madoc (1956a) describes a flock of about 30 sipping scalding water while fluttering in clouds of steam over a spring at Ulu Yam, Selangor; also birds drinking (or possibly taking scraps) from the outflow of a hill-bungalow kitchen drain.

SOCIAL ORGANIZATION. Loners, pairs and small flocks; in the lowlands, almost invariably in small, cohesive flocks.

MOVEMENTS. No roosting reported in the lowlands, and dispersants are presumed to return to Montane habitat daily (but see Mountain Imperial Pigeon).

SURVIVAL. No information.

SOCIAL INTERACTIONS. No information.

VOICE. Males advertise inside forest, typically from a mid-stratum perch, repeating a high-pitched, frog-like disyllable, *urr-wok* (with purring first note), at a rate of about 11 calls per five seconds. A repeated, sharply-clipped *woo* is reported given by courting pairs (BMP5, G.C. Madoc).

BREEDING

Nest. A small platform built variously of twigs, moss, fern-frond parts and leaf skeletons, about 10 cm across, 1.5–5 m up in forest among the dead fronds or trapped litter of epiphytic ferns, on the frond of a tree-fern or under-stratum palm, or top of a stump; one on an old passerine nest in a sapling fork. Common also in dense tangles of resam ferns *Gleichenia* that overhang the steep bank of a road or sunlit track through forest.

Eggs and brood. Egg plain whitish. Shape elliptical but not described in detail. Full clutch one or two, in the ratio 7 : 5 (large sample), with no obvious date-bias.

Cycle. No data.

Seasonality. A reference to January eggs from Perak needs confirmation. Eggs otherwise reported in February–June and August–October, with a bird incubating or brooding on 30 October (F.G.H. Allen, Allin and Edgar 1948, BMP5, Bromley 1948b, G.C. Madoc, Madoc and Allen 1952, NRCS, Robinson and Chasen 1936).

MOULT. Replacement of primaries is mostly regular-descendant, with only one record of moult at two loci (P2 and 9). Among handlings covering all months except June, August, November and December, adults in active wing-moult are dated March–May and October, but with no seasonal progression obvious, and instances of suspension in February and September. Post-juvenile moult (P5–6) noted on 7 April (BMNH, ZRCNUS).

CONSERVATION. No immediate issues, but see Barred Cuckoo Dove.

Emerald Dove; Nok Khao Khieo (Thai); Punai Tanah (Malay)

Chalcophaps indica (Linnaeus) 1758, *Systema Naturae* 10(1): 164. TL Calcutta, NE India.
Plate 42

GROUP RELATIONS. Probably free-standing; widely sympatric with Wallacean–Australian *C. stephani* (Stephan's Dove), although they are said to be isolated by habitat.

GLOBAL RANGE. The Indian subcontinent from the Himalayan foothills, Sri Lanka and Bay of Bengal islands; the Nansei islands, Taiwan, Hainan and mainland S China from Guangdong to S Yunnan; SE Asia and Wallacea; and E New Guinea and N and E Australia. A regular dispersant, probably nomadic, in the Sunda region east at least to the Sulu islands; perhaps also elsewhere in the Philippines (McClure 1974).

IDENTIFICATION/DESCRIPTION. The common view is of a compact, dark pigeon flying fast and direct through the shady forest under-stratum. No other small, green-backed pigeon walks about on the ground, and Jambu Fruit Dove, the only other orange-billed species to be seen in forest, has green or pink-and-white underparts. From cheeks and throat to breast and flanks, the male is vinous, the female uniform rufous-brown, and females lack the pale blue-grey cap. Pale grey rump-bands show when birds flush from cover. Juveniles resemble the adult female but are duller and have rufous-tipped flight-feathers.

Bare-part colours. (Adult) iris dark brown; bill orange-red (pale-tipped in some), with base and cere purple-maroon and mouth-lining purplish; feet dull purple-red.

Size (mm). (Live; 3-figure samples of males and females; adult): wing 135–155 and 134–148 (respective juveniles down to 130 and 128); tail 71–98 and 75–96; bill 15.7–18.9 and 15.2–17.7; tarsus 25.0–30.0 (sexes combined) (UMBRP).

Weight (g). Large samples of adults: males, 103–171; females, 94–171. Heavy individuals of both sexes carry much subcutaneous fat.

DISTRIBUTION. Historical summary: all divisions except *Pat*, and on many additional islands: the Surin and Similan groups, Tarutao, Langkawi, Penang, Pangkor, Rembia and Pisang off the W coast; Phangan and Samui, Perhentian Besar, Redang, Tioman and Tulai off the E coast; and Ubin and Tekong, Singapore.

GEOGRAPHICAL VARIATION. Nominate *indica*, of most of the Asian range.

STATUS AND POPULATION. Regular and more or less common year-round, but nomadic. At population level near-continuously on the move, numbers per site varying with local supplies of fallen fruit.

HABITATS AND ECOLOGY. Emerald Doves inhabit the floor and lower- to mid-strata of evergreen and semi-evergreen Lowland and Lower Montane forests, mature and regenerating after disturbance; also old secondary forest, overgrown plantations and occasionally mangroves (BMP5). Birds disturbed from feeding commonly retreat to a tree perch, and probably also loaf and roost off the ground.

At long-term ringing-stations in forest in Selangor and Negeri Sembilan only 18 percent of the many birds marked were retrapped (UMBRP, M. Wong), and birds often appear in habitats where no breeding occurs; both suggestive of through-movement. Not infrequent collisions with darkened windows in or near woodland implies some dispersal through cover is by day, but large-scale (and locally concentrated) above-canopy movements at all altitudes are mainly or completely nocturnal (BMP5).

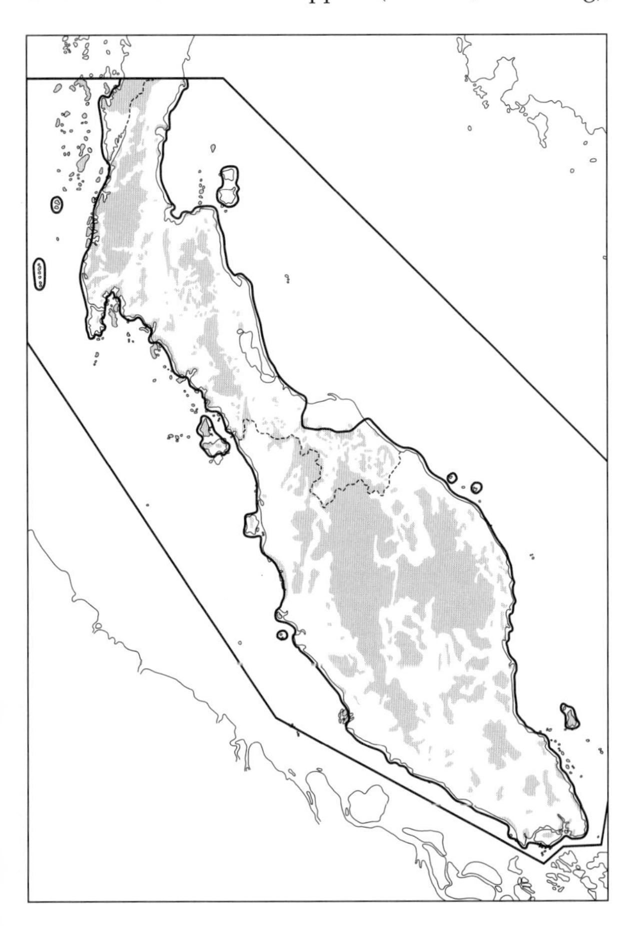

Daytime abundance varies with local fruiting but a feature of nocturnal dispersants is that some carry food in their crop and some of both sexes are obviously fat – the range of body-weights overall matching that measured in forest by day. Evidently, not all movements are sparked by deprivation, and models of nomadism in other environments (Newton 1972) suggest possibly the opposite could be true. As well as searching for fresh food-sources, some movement appears actually to be away from still-productive patches, evidently as an outcome of other factors. These, it is guessed, might include interference-stress due to localized population build-up (see below). Ultimately, the whole behaviour seems likely to be driven by the patchiness and instability in time of some of the main foods – and by the rate at which new patches fill. Among 169 adults taken at Fraser's Hill during 1966–1970, the sex ratio was 2.25 : 1 in favour of males, and among 216 taken there since it was 2.66 : 1. Daytime captures in forest, on the other hand, show a sex ratio at parity, implying males are more than twice as likely to participate in big movements than females (BMP5, UMBRP).

FORAGING AND FOOD. Foragers walk rapidly about, mainly under tree cover but for short distances also out onto paths and roads and into crops and gardens. Fallen fruit and seeds (including figs and bamboo), and occasional animal prey (alate termites), are harvested apparently strictly on the ground. Like *Treron* pigeons, Emerald Doves are seed predators. Experimental feeding with figs showed most seeds were crushed and destroyed by the muscular gizzard, and that only a few passed through to be dispersed intact (Lambert 1988). With cuckoo doves, this species also visits mineral seeps in forest.

SOCIAL ORGANIZATION. Mostly solitary. Foragers drawn to a rich fruit-drop show no overt aggression but react to nearby conspecifics.

MOVEMENTS. At floodlights on Fraser's Hill (Selangor/Pahang boundary), night-time interceptions peaked during October–December (mainly October and November) but with some in all months mist-nets were set there, i.e., excepting only June and July (BMP5, PERHILITAN, UMBRP).

Three long-distance recoveries from among these captures, in Cameron Highlands, W Sumatra and S Sumatra, over minimum ranges of 85, 500 and 800 km (BR 1972–73, 1974–75, MBR 1984–85), show an orientation that reflects only the general N–S lie of the land. None could be related to a breeding-site and all were made after intervals of several years. The most that can be said of individual movements is that some take in at least the width of the Melaka Straits.

SURVIVAL. The three longest recovery intervals of ringed birds have been between 40 and 45 months (UMBRP).

SOCIAL INTERACTIONS. Two or more birds may forage at a given fruit-fall, but independently. If they happen to meet, they circle and spar briefly, with wings stretched vertically over the back, exposing the rufous undersurface.

VOICE. The advertising-call is a short, dull but carrying coo with a brief, less carrying grace-note, *t'k oo*. This is repeated monotonously at a rate of about ten calls per 15 seconds, in bouts of varying length but typically of 4–12 calls.

BREEDING

Nest. A slight platform, built often of no more than the litter that collects on an under-stratum palm-frond, stabilized with thin, dead twigs. The midrib of a gently dipping *Salacca* palm or similar frond is the commonest site; others on record are a large leaf lying on top of a tangle of creepers, and a lateral branch-fork of a small tree, 1–5 m up; always in forest or at least semi-natural closed-canopy woodland.

Eggs and brood. Eggs are glossy, ivory to creamy white. Shape and size not adequately recorded. The full clutch is two but often only one egg survives to hatching, and the regular brood is one.

Cycle. A clutch observed over two weeks in July was incubated by a female. The parental role of males is not recorded.

Seasonality. Eggs or squabs found on 10 February (new fledgling) and during April–September, with sufficient records to suggest a genuinely limited season (F.G.H. Allen, BCSTB-13, BR 1978–79, G.C. Madoc, NRCS, Ryves 1938).

MOULT. Replacement of primaries is mostly regular-descendant, and common instances of moult at two loci appear to be due to re-starts after suspension. Overall, including among nocturnal dispersants, bilateral moult of primaries has been recorded in all months except March and June, without obvious seasonal progression. However, all records of early-stage activity (P1 or P2) were during mid August–early February (BMNH, UMBRP).

CONSERVATION. Tolerant of habitat disturbance, and males advertise in overgrown plantations, etc., but no breeding confirmed outside true forest. Cannot survive in the absence of substantial patches of at least semi-natural, mixed woodland.

Zebra Dove; Nok Khao Chawaa (Thai); Merbok Balam (Malay)

Geopelia striata (Linnaeus) 1766, *Systema Naturae* 12(1): 282. TL Java.
Plate 42

GROUP RELATIONS. Forms a superspecies, or perhaps still conspecific with, allopatric *G. maugeus* (Barred Dove) of S Wallacea and *G. placida* (Peaceful Dove) of Australia and S New Guinea (cf. CLBW, Harrison 1969).

GLOBAL RANGE. As a traditionally traded cage-bird in SE Asia, its range has been affected by artificial introductions. Likely to be indigenous through the Philippines south to N Sulawesi and from S Tenasserim to the Greater Sunda islands, Bali and Lombok, beyond which it is replaced by *G. maugeus*. Established feral from introductions in central and parts of NW Thailand, and on tropical islands elsewhere in the world (St Helena, Malagasy region, Hawaii, etc.).

IDENTIFICATION/DESCRIPTION. Grey face, diminutive size and hurried, rodent-like movements on the ground. Often flushes only at the last moment, and has characteristically bounding flight in which the bird shoots forward on nearly closed wings after a few rapid flaps. At take-off, white outer tips to tail look not unlike Spotted Dove, but body-size and flight-mode are quite different. Juveniles are densely barred dark rufous-brown above, with all flight-feathers tipped rufous-buff, and lack the vinous wash on the centre of the adult breast.

Adults of both sexes have the outer primary narrowed by emargination of both webs.

Bare-part colours. (Adult) iris opal-white, peri-orbital skin pale blue-green; bill pale blue; feet purple-pink, paler at the rear of the tarsus (BMNH).

Size (mm). (Skins: 39 males, 23 females; adult): wing 95–102 and 93–101; tail 90–102 and 83–100; bill 11.3–13.5 and 11.5–12.9; tarsus 19.3–22.2 and 18.4–20.2 (BMNH).

Weight (g). Unsexed adults, 50–72 (n=3) (UMBRP).

DISTRIBUTION. South from a natural limit in Pakchan and Chumphon. Historical summary: all divisions except *Sat*, and with additional island records from Lanta, Langkawi and Pangkor off the W coast; Phangan and Samui off the E coast; and Ubin, Tekong, Sentosa and Ayer Merbau around Singapore.

GEOGRAPHICAL VARIATION. If the superspecies arrangement is accepted, *G. striata* is monotypic.

STATUS AND POPULATION. Resident, regular and more or less common but in many settled areas kept well below potential population density by trapping for the pet trade.

HABITATS AND ECOLOGY. Breeds only in the plains, frequenting old coastal dunes, abandoned mine-tailings, fields and grazing-land, parks, suburban gardens, roadsides, etc. Like many open country birds, quick to exploit new agricultural clearings, but there is no sign yet of Zebra Doves moving into upland cultivation. Foragers avoid cover but more regularly rest in tree-crowns than on the exposed perches favoured by Spotted Dove in the same habitats.

FORAGING AND FOOD. Small seeds are taken exclusively on the ground and in the open, with a preference for bare soil or short grass.

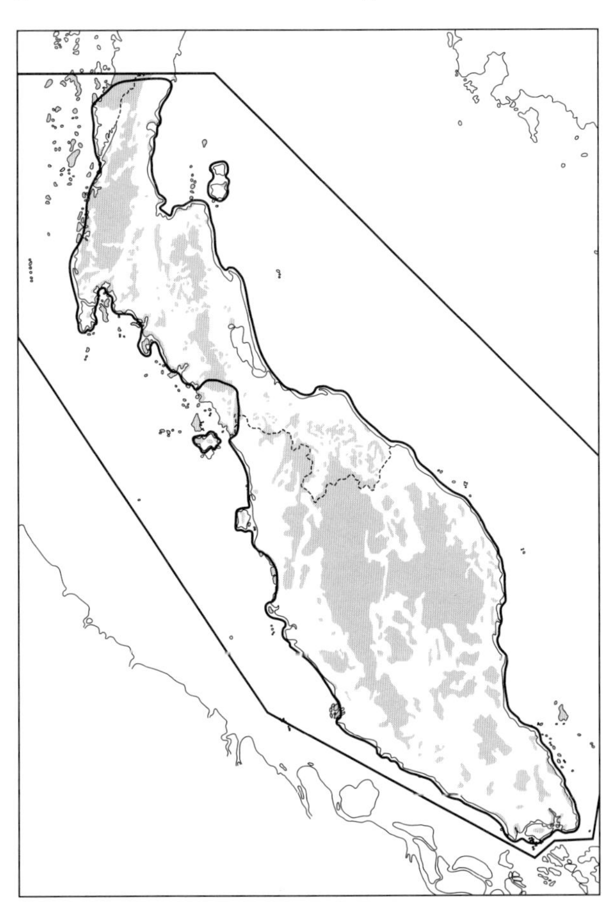

SOCIAL ORGANIZATION. Loud advertising-calls imply nesting pairs space themselves. Singles and pairs are the commonest foraging unit; less often small parties.

MOVEMENTS. Evidence for long-distance dispersal is compromised by the extent of trade in captives. A ringed bird recovered in December had moved 35 km on the coastal plain of Selangor, and another in May 480 km between Singapore and Berinchang summit (2030 m), Cameron Highlands, where mist-netted near floodlights at night (BMP5, McClure 1974). A bird by a road through Main Range forest at the Gap, Selangor/Pahang boundary, on 3 May (ENGGANG-1) was at least 15 km from regular habitat.

SURVIVAL. The longest ring-recovery interval is 72 months (BR 1980–81).

SOCIAL INTERACTIONS. Courtship display by the male involves a brisk bobbing with head down and tail up, accompanied by loud vocalizing (a series of single notes) while facing the female on a high perch. He also sings as they sit side by side.

VOICE. Loud advertising-calls include a light, rattling trill, *k-k-krrrror bo bo bo bo bo bo, k-k-krrror bo bo, k-k-krrror bo bo,* with variation in the number of *bo* notes added; also less far-carrying, shorter, whining rattles, *korr-r-r-rk* or a more accented *kwaurr-r-r-rk.*

BREEDING

Nest. A sparse little platform of twigs and fibre built 1–12 (mostly above 2) m up, commonly in a horizontal branch-fork of a small tree or the frond-base of a palm; occasionally in a bush.

Eggs and brood. Eggs are matt white. Shape elliptical. Size (mm): 22.6 × 16.6 (mean); 23.0–19.3 × 18.0–14.0 (n=5 from Perak).

Cycle. No information.

Seasonality. Eggs or squabs recorded during September–June (F.G.H. Allen, E.C.S. Baker, Baker 1922–30, Berwick 1952b, Edgar 1933, Madoc 1956a, McClure and Husain 1968, NRCS, Spittle 1949).

MOULT. Among many adults collected over the full length of the Peninsula, active, bilateral wing-moult occurred in all months September–June, i.e., showed a parallel with nesting. However, main months of early-stage activity (P1 or P2) were February and March and of near-completion (P9 or 10) May. Instances of suspended moult occur more or less year-round (BMNH, UMBRP, ZRCNUS).

CONSERVATION. Except perhaps in Singapore, populations have shown themselves able to withstand trapping for the pet trade. There are no other obvious conservation issues.

Nicobar Pigeon; Nok Chaapeenai (Thai); Punai Mas (Malay)

Caloenas nicobarica (Linnaeus) 1758, *Systema Naturae* 10(1): 164. TL Nicobar islands.
Plate 43

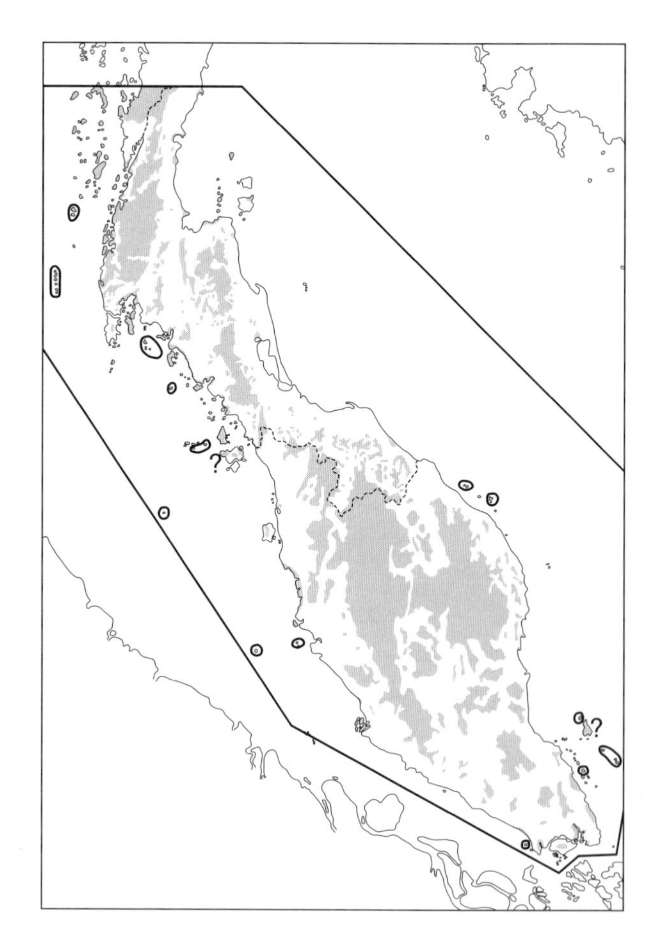

GROUP RELATIONS. Free-standing; perhaps closest to the *Gallicolumba* ground doves of the Philippines and Sulawesi to Polynesia (Goodwin 1967).

GLOBAL RANGE. A true small-island specialist, recorded from the Andamans, Nicobars and Mergui archipelago, and islands off S Vietnam and Cambodia, through maritime SE Asia, Wallacea, W Micronesia (Palau), and New Guinea to the Solomons.

IDENTIFICATION/DESCRIPTION. Black, stocky and galliform-shaped, with a long, fowl-like cape of iridescent, gold-shot green neck-hackles and distinctly short tail, contrastingly white in adults. Commonly walks or runs on the ground (where the rustling of litter may give away its presence in cover). Sexes alike, except that the knob on the cere is smaller in females (Robinson and Chasen 1936). Juveniles are black-tailed.

Bare-part colours. Iris light hazel-brown (immature), pearl-grey (adult), but the difference needs confirming; bill including cere black; feet plum-red, soles and claws yellow (BMNH, ZRCNUS).

Size (mm). (Skins: 2 males, 8 females; adult): wing 258, 264 and 251–262 (respective juveniles down to 247 and 236); tail 85, 98 and 79–89; bill 22.3, 26.1 and 22.2–25.3; tarsus 43.7, 49.5 and 41.0–45.9 (BMNH, UMZC, ZRCNUS).

Weight. No data.

DISTRIBUTION. Historical summary: ?*Chu, Ran, Pha, Kra, Tra, Sat, Tru, Pek, Phg, Joh,* exclusively on small islands, including: the Surin and Similan groups, Phiphi and Maa (*Kra*), Rok Nok (*Tra*), small islands of the Tarutao national park (Ta Nga, Nipis), Perak, Rembia, Jarak, and Pisang and Sauh (*Joh*) off the W coast; Serenggeh, the Perhentians, Redang and the Pahang–Johor archipelago (Tulai, Tinggi, Pemanggil and Aur) off the E coast. There has been no confirmation of claims from the Langkawi group or Tioman, and unknown in Singapore territory.

GEOGRAPHICAL VARIATION. Widespread nominate *nicobarica*.

STATUS AND POPULATION. Resident overall but local and now scarce; hunted for food and parts, and long exploited for the pet trade.

HABITATS AND ECOLOGY. Small-island specialist ('super-tramp') status is well established, with no records from any large landmass in this area. Haunts tree-cover, from scrubby strand woodland to tall, closed-canopy forest, and forages strictly on the ground. Often described as escaping by running but on Redang island I have flushed one directly into the forest canopy. Loafs and roosts in trees.

Said not to be continuously present on all of the islands from which it has been recorded, and assumed to make inter-island sea-crossings. A round-up of W-coast reports shows occurrence in late August and all months October–April, in general support of opinion that it quits the Melaka Straits during the mid northern summer (Robinson and Kloss 1922a, Robinson and Chasen 1936). Off the E coast, on the other hand, reported only in April, May, July and September, but these happen to be months of usually calm weather, favoured for sea-trips. Status through the rest of the year needs checking.

FORAGING AND FOOD. Forages apparently only on the ground, and possession of gizzard-stones implies an ability to reduce hard fruit-parts and seeds. On the Similan islands, seen consuming large seeds from part-eaten fruits (?*Manilkara* sp.) dropped by squirrels (P.D. Round).

SOCIAL ORGANIZATION. Elsewhere in its range, breeds in large, dense rookeries, but none recorded nearer to this area than the N Nicobars (Oates 1890). The only local sign of social breeding is a record of association with Pied Imperial Pigeons. Otherwise little known, but encountered on the forest floor alone, in pairs and, occasionally, small groups (including both adults and immatures).

MOVEMENTS. No over-water dispersal actually reported, and this could occur mostly at night.

SURVIVAL. No information.

SOCIAL INTERACTIONS. No information.

VOICE. No information.

BREEDING

Nest. Two on Serenggeh island, Terengganu, described as deep platforms of twigs, about 30 cm across × 23 cm deep, built about 4 m up in forks of trees (*Eugenia* sp.).

Eggs and brood. Egg inadequately described. Size (mm): 43.0 × 33.0 and 48.0 × 34.5 (n=2). Full clutch one.

Cycle. No information.

Seasonality. An egg from Jarak island on 5 April and one dated September supposedly from Tioman (but more likely from one of its satellites). Empty nests on Serenggeh island on 31 May (Berwick 1952a, b).

MOULT. Most replacement of primaries is regular-descendant, but one bird examined had dropped feathers at two loci. Among adults, active wing-moult recorded in January, June and July; post-juvenile moult in April and July, but with signs of suspension or arrest (between P2 and P8) common in both age-classes through much of the year (BMNH, ZRCNUS).

CONSERVATION. Globally near-threatened (BTW2). Relentless trapping for food, the pet trade and, perhaps, still for 'bezoar' gizzard-stones, prized for their decorative and supposed medicinal properties (Wolfe 1951), has long held populations down. Disturbance from the recent explosion of beach tourism on islands could undermine the value of some still-inhabited sites.

Cinnamon-headed Green Pigeon; Nok Plao Daeng (Thai); Punai Bakau (Malay)

Treron fulvicollis (Wagler) 1827, *Systema Avium, pars 1, Genus Columba* 8. TL Sumatra.
Plate 45

GROUP RELATIONS. Free-standing; its nearest relative is believed to be to *T. olax* (Little Green Pigeon) (Goodwin 1967).

GLOBAL RANGE. Borneo, Sumatra and intervening S China Sea islands, the Peninsula and Tenasserim north to about latitude 12°N (Mergui); apparently formerly also extreme-S Vietnam (AMNH, Delacour 1970).

IDENTIFICATION/DESCRIPTION. Adult male hardly confusable with any other pigeon. Adult female with care from female Thick-billed Green Pigeon by a combination of dark-streaked, bright canary-yellow tibial trousers, grey rather than green flanks and more extensive red on base of bill. Juveniles like adult female except, possibly, for bill colour, which has not been described.

Bare-part colours. (Adult) iris light orange or outer ring pink, inner blue (a colour-shift perhaps related to level of excitement), eyelid-rim orange, periorbital skin light grey-green; basal half of bill rich red, sharply demarcated from greenish white tip; feet dull purplish red (BMNH, Riley 1938).

Size (mm). (Skins: 15 males, 10 females; adult): wing 139–153 and 140–147; tail 75–89 and 71–80; bill 14.5–17.1 and 13.3–16.8; tarsus 19.3–24.6 and 21.3–25.5 (BMNH).

Weight (g). A male, about 170; a female, about 163 (BMNH).

DISTRIBUTION. Historical summary: *Pak, Sur, Pha, Phu, Tra, Nar, Pek, Phg, Sel, Mel, Joh, Sin,* with additional island records from Penang, Tioman and Ubin (Singapore), but only a fraction of this range is still occupied.

GEOGRAPHICAL VARIATION. Nominate *fulvicollis,* of the mainland and Sumatra.

STATUS AND POPULATION. Resident but even in remaining core habitat local and uncommon. Its status in Pakchan is unknown, but not recently recorded anywhere in Thailand (Boonsong and

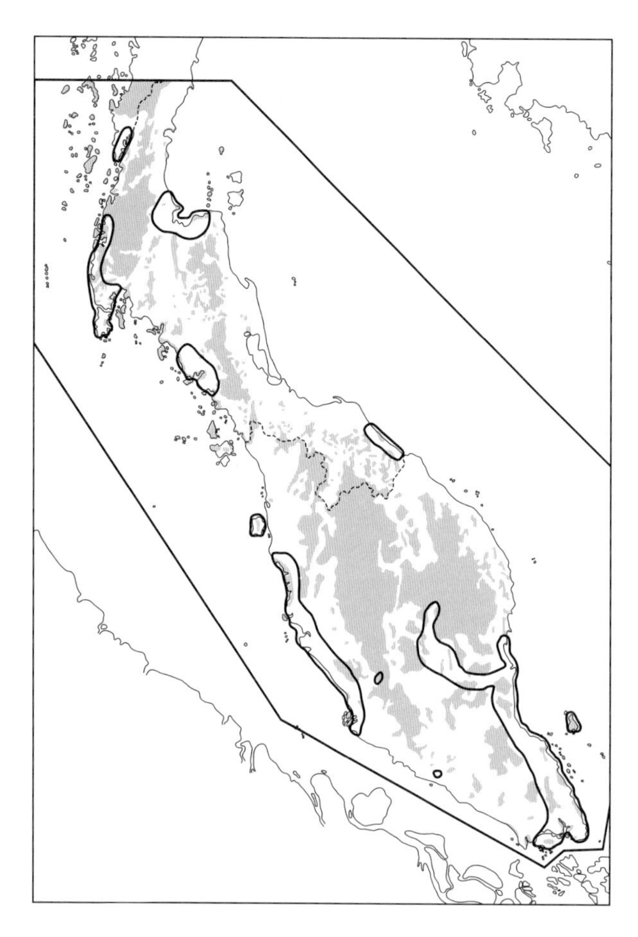

Round 1991) or, apart from rare wanderers, along the Malaysian W coast. Now found mostly in the far SE, south from Kuantan. Records on the middle Tembeling river in August–September 1971, and a more recent loner at Kuala Lompat, Kerau wildlife reserve (BR 1970–71, F.R. Lambert), may only have been of transients, but a linked population might also persist in the Pahang drainage. Most formerly regular inland range in S Johor has been deforested but small numbers may be expected along the Endau and Rompin rivers, Pahang/Johor border, and birds still occur sporadically in Singapore.

HABITATS AND ECOLOGY. Core habitat is mixed swamp-forest, including peatswamp, now heavily fragmented but formerly extensive behind both coasts and in the lower valleys of large rivers. Some use is also made of nearby strand woodland, mangroves and even wooded gardens (Butler 1899, G.C. Madoc). Higher-elevation, dry-land forests are visited perhaps only occasionally, by non-breeders.

Not among the dispersing frugivorous pigeons mist-netted at night at Fraser's Hill (UMBRP), but reported a few times elsewhere far from remaining regular range, including in the west near Melaka, at around 1200 m on the Selangor/Pahang divide, and on Penang island. Evidently, at least some wandering comparable to that of other forest-living fruit pigeons occurs. The southern islands of Tioman, Ubin and Singapore (Batchelor 1958, BMP5, BR 1968, MBR 1986–87, SINGAV-2, -6) may yet prove to be part of regular range.

FORAGING AND FOOD. Takes figs, like other medium-sized *Treron* pigeons, but perhaps not a fig specialist. At Kuala Lompat, recorded eating the small, pink-purple, canopy fruit of *Ficus binnendykii* (Lambert 1989). On the Pakchan river, W.R. Davison (Hume and Davison 1878) saw it feeding on small, red fruit of forest-edge bushes (not identified).

SOCIAL ORGANIZATION. No information.

MOVEMENTS. No direct information. Apparent dispersants away from core habitat have been recorded in January, February, April, June and July.

SURVIVAL. No information.

SOCIAL INTERACTIONS. No information.

VOICE. No information.

BREEDING

Nest. A sparse platform of twigs built 2–4 m up in a branch fork of a small tree. Sites include streamside saplings in subcoastal forest, scrub on a river islet, tembusu trees *Fagraea fragrans* in a garden adjacent to riverside mangroves, and mangrove forest itself.

Eggs and brood. Eggs are glossy white. Shape elliptical. Size (mm): 30.0–25.6 × 23.4–20.0 (n=14). Full clutch two. One clutch hatched 14 days after the start of incubation.

Cycle. Both pair-members incubate.

Seasonality. Eggs reported in January, February and April–June (E.C.S. Baker, Baker 1922–30, Butler 1899, G.C. Madoc).

MOULT. Replacement of primaries is regular-descendant. Among 28 adults from throughout the Peninsula, nine showed active wing-moult in March, May, August, September and December, with early-stage moult (P1 to P2) only in March and May, stage P5 or beyond from May onwards. One instance of suspension at P7 in mid December (BMNH).

CONSERVATION. Classed as near-threatened globally (BTW2) but in the Peninsula one of the most threatened birds. What remains of its extreme lowland, core forest habitat is under heavy pressure of conversion to other land-uses.

Little Green Pigeon; Nok Plao Lek Hua Thao (Thai); Punai Daun (Malay)

Treron olax (Temminck) 1823, *Nouveau Recueil de Planches Coloriées d'Oiseaux* 41: plate 241. TL Padang, W Sumatra.

Plate 45

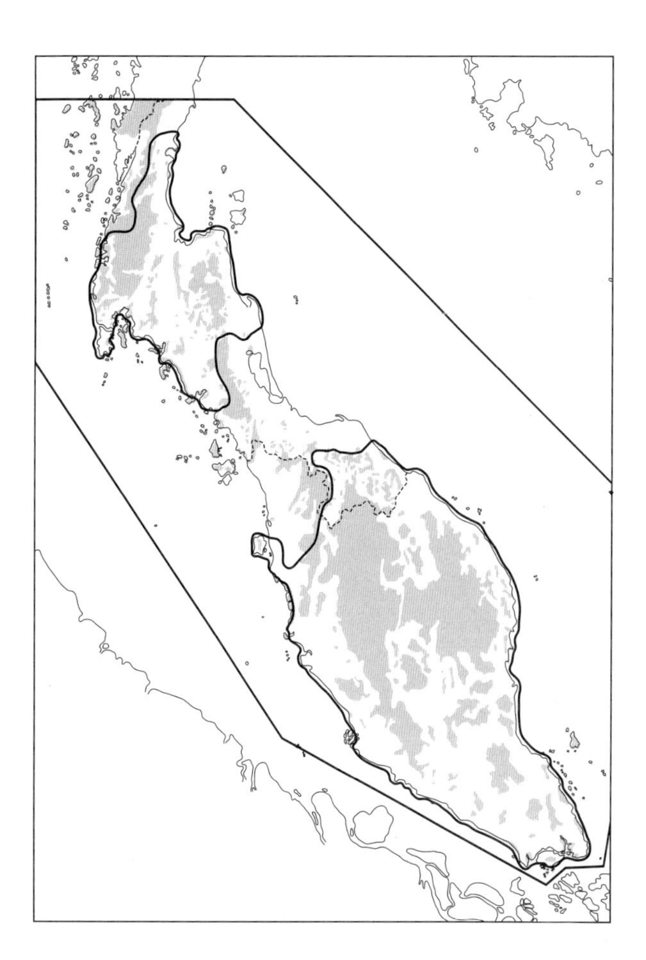

GROUP RELATIONS. Free-standing (see Cinnamon-headed Green Pigeon).

GLOBAL RANGE. Borneo, Sumatra, Banka and other intervening islands, and the Peninsula.

IDENTIFICATION/DESCRIPTION. Even in isolation, smallness is fairly obvious, and the adult male combination of grey head, orange breast and maroon back is diagnostic. The female is separable from female Pink-necked and Orange-breasted Green Pigeons (in shared edge habitat) by size, duller grey-green tone and whitish eye, and from Pink-necked also by clear grey rather than green cap.

Bare-part colours. (Adult) inner ring of iris white, outer ring buff or pink; eyelid-rim yellow and periorbital skin pale grey-blue; bill whitish, cere pale blue-green; feet dull purple-red (BMNH).

Size (mm). (Skins: 42 males, 27 females; adult): wing 117–130 and 118–128; tail 59–72 and 59–70; bill 12.4–15.4 and 11.6–13.6; tarsus 19.0–21.7 and 16.7–21.3 (BMNH, UMZC).

Weight (g). One adult male dispersant, 77.3 (UMBRP).

DISTRIBUTION. Historical summary: all divisions except *Pak, Ran, Pht, Son, Pat, Sat, Pes, Ked*, with additional island records from Penang, and Ubin and Tekong (Singapore) (Chasen 1924, MBR 1986–87).

GEOGRAPHICAL VARIATION. None recognized.

STATUS AND POPULATION. Resident, regular and more or less common in the south, apparently naturally rarer in more seasonal areas. In Thailand, also much hunted and now sparse there – with recent records only from the Tha Sae drainage, 10°50'N (Chumphon) and pairs at two localities in Krabi, including Khao Phanom Bencha national park (BCSTB-12, P.D. Round).

HABITATS AND ECOLOGY. Plains-level inland forests, especially disturbed, edge and second-growth situations, but avoids obviously seasonal (more deciduous) areas, including far-NW Malaysia. By day, found only below the hill-foot boundary, but wanders. In Cameron Highlands and on Fraser's Hill some have been taken at floodlights evidently while dispersing across the Main Range, although in negligible numbers compared, e.g., with night-moving Thick-billed Green Pigeon and Jambu Fruit Dove (BMP5, UMBRP).

FORAGING AND FOOD. Opportunistic, and may 'trap-line' around more dependable fruit-sources over a possibly large area. Like other forest pigeons, a canopy fig-eater, recorded at *Ficus caulicarpa, obscura, heteropleura, binnendykii* and *pisocarpa*, and banyan species, with fruit-sizes in the small-diameter range 5.4–11.6 mm, but mostly below 8 mm (Lambert 1989, BR 1972–73). Also favours tiny non-fig fruit, and numbers gather at mass fruitings of small, pioneer trees (Euphorbiaceae, etc.) along the margins of lowland logging roads and other openings.

SOCIAL ORGANIZATION. Pairs breed alone but, like most fruit pigeons, *olax* is gregarious at fruit-sources, and non-breeders move around in small, apparently cohesive parties.

MOVEMENTS. None monitored but some individual dispersal movements are assumed to carry birds across at least the width of the Main Range. Recorded at hill-top lights in April, May, August, September and November.

SURVIVAL. No information.

SOCIAL INTERACTIONS. No information.

VOICE. No information.

BREEDING

Nest. Only one confirmed: a flimsy platform of small twigs 4 m up, towards the outer end of a horizontal branch of a plantation rubber tree, 200 m from forest.

Eggs and brood. Eggs not adequately described. Full clutch two.

Cycle. No information.

Seasonality. Copulation in early April, eggs on 14 June (BCSTB-12, Ryves 1938).

MOULT. Replacement of primaries is regular-descendant, with exceptional instances of double-locus moult probably due to re-starts after suspension. Among 74 adults from throughout the Peninsula, active wing-moult occurred in all months March–November. Barring a few instances of suspended moult, all early-stage records (P1 to P2) fell in the first four months and all late-stage records (P9 or 10) in the last four, indicating a broad seasonality (BMNH, ZRCNUS).

CONSERVATION. Ability to harvest pioneer second-growth fruit makes this pigeon less vulnerable to the effects of logging than its more narrowly canopy fig-dependent congeners, but significant patches of natural mixed regrowth are a minimum survival requirement.

Pink-necked Green Pigeon; Nok Plao Khaw See Muang (Thai); Punai Kericau (Malay)

Treron vernans (Linnaeus) 1771, *Mantissa Plantarum Altera Generum*, appendix *Regni Animalis*: 526. TL Philippines.

Plate 45

GROUP RELATIONS. Free-standing; apparently nearest to *T. bicincta* (Orange-breasted Green Pigeon) (Goodwin 1967).

GLOBAL RANGE. SE Thailand to S Vietnam, and S Tenasserim and W Thailand to the Greater Sunda islands, Bali and the Philippines; Sulawesi, Halmahera, Lombok and Sumbawa (Bishop 1992).

IDENTIFICATION/DESCRIPTION. The expected green pigeon away from forest. Adult male from Little Green Pigeon most immediately by larger size and green back; other age/sex-classes by their size, clearer green (less grey-toned) body, green rather than grey cap, and dark eye. A dark subterminal band across the whole tail (including central feathers) and lack of grey on the nape separate all classes from Orange-breasted Green Pigeon (which see). Both Pink-necked and Orange-breasted show a coppery wash on the upper tail-coverts, often obvious while birds clamber among branches as they feed. In the usual, excited group-feeding situation, the iris of both sexes of Pink-necked flushes red and appears dark.

Bare-part colours. (Adult) outer ring of iris lavender to pink, inner ring bright blue, but the whole eye commonly flushes dark red; bill pale grey-blue to dull white with bluish tip; cere as bill-base (contrastingly pale yellowish in juveniles); feet dull purple-red (BMNH).

Size (mm). (Skins: 40 males, 26 females; adult): wing 140–151 and 131–148; tail 77–90 and 72–87; bill 14.1–16.5 and 14.0–15.8; tarsus 21.6–24.7 and 20.6–24.2 (BMNH).

Weight. No data.

DISTRIBUTION. Historical summary: all divisions except *Kel*, and on many additional islands, including Yao Yai, Lanta group (Bubu), Libong, Tarutao, Langkawi, Penang and Pisang off the W coast; Phangan and Samui, Redang and the Pahang–Johor archipelago (Tulai, Tioman, Dayang, Rawa, Tinggi and Sibu) off the E coast; and Tekong, Ubin, Seletar, St John's, Berani, Sentosa, Semakau, Hantu, Pawai and Ayer Merbau around Singapore.

GEOGRAPHICAL VARIATION. Subspecies *griseicapilla* Schlegel 1863 (TL SE Sumatra), of the mainland, Sumatra and Borneo.

STATUS AND POPULATION. Resident, regular and common; by a large margin the commonest *Treron* of the settled and cultivated lowlands although, along with other green pigeons, in Thailand has been reduced by hunting (Round 1988).

HABITATS AND ECOLOGY. A statement that in Tenasserim, including Pakchan, Pink-necked only

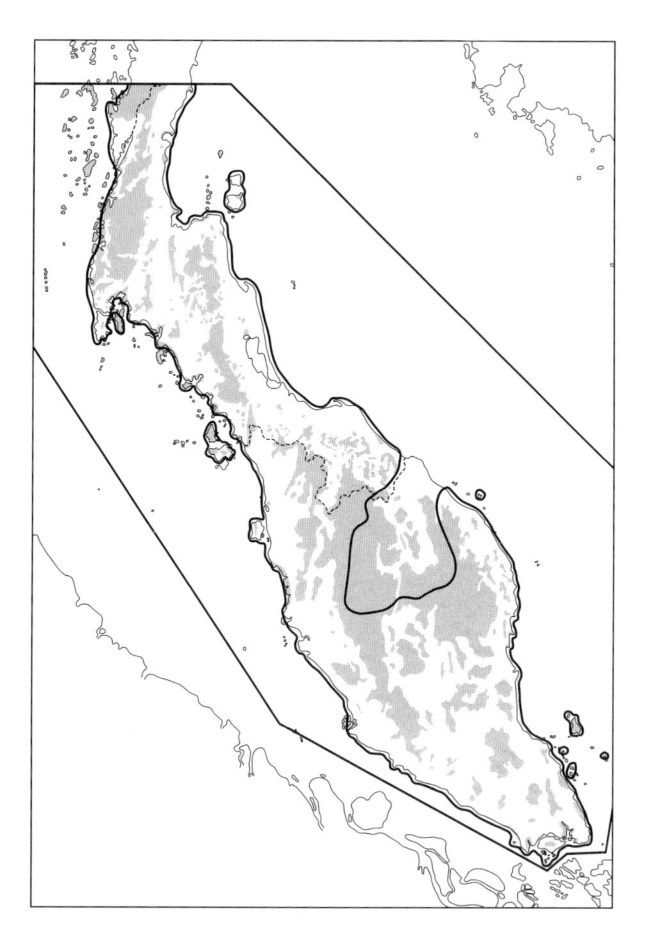

rarely occurs outside forest (Hume and Davison 1878) is curiously at odds with its decidedly non-forest behaviour elsewhere in the Peninsula. Uses forest on small islands and follows some large rivers into their forested upper reaches; otherwise inhabits disturbed and man-made habitats, strictly at plains level (there are no records from upland agriculture). Needs only sufficient scrub and tree cover to provide a rotation of arboreal fruit crops. Apparently not a nocturnal wanderer, with none identified among over 3000 pigeons mist-netted at floodlights at Fraser's Hill during three decades, nor at any of the lighthouses from which there are bird-strike records (BMP5, UMBRP). Differs from its forest relatives also in mass-roosting at traditional, fixed sites that draw hundreds of birds from an evidently wide foraging area, and may aid the spread of information about food whereabouts. Swamps, including mangroves, are favoured roosting habitat; also tree-covered in-shore islets.

FORAGING AND FOOD. Foragers 'trap-line' around regular fruit-sources, even entering gardens and town parks to appear promptly at banyans *Ficus benjamina*, etc., as they come into crop. Small banyan figs are taken avidly but figs may be less of a keystone item of diet than the mass fruitings of common second-growth Euphorbiaceae, etc. (e.g., *Glochidion, Breynia, Vitex, Macaranga, Muntingia* species), which these birds are able to reach acrobatically on the thinnest of branches. This suggested difference from forest *Treron* species could influence the extent to which Pink-necked must disperse.

Like other green pigeons, hardly ever descends to the ground. A record from Sentosa island of some drinking from a drain (SINGAV-4) is exceptional.

SOCIAL ORGANIZATION. Pairs nest alone but non-breeders forage in apparently cohesive parties, several to many of which may converge at mass roosts and major fruit-sources. It is not known how constant individual membership of a group is but the same-sized groups visit isolated fruit-trees from day to day.

MOVEMENTS. No evidence of more than daily ranging behaviour, the extent of which has not been measured. Communal roost-sites are occupied long-term.

SURVIVAL. No information.

SOCIAL INTERACTIONS. Though they travel in a group, once at a source of fruit males in particular become aggressive, vocalizing, chasing and vigorously tail-bobbing in temporary defence of foraging-patches within the canopy.

VOICE. As with all *Treron* species, the whistling, rasping male 'song' is hard to describe. Detail varies but three-part structure is usual: a shallowly rising sequence of three resonant whines, a crescendo of three rapid, gurgling tremolos, and falling tail of three short growls, *kaun kaun kaun, kiruirio kiruirio kiruirio kau kau kau*. Variants include the running of initial notes into one sustained whine.

BREEDING

Nest. A minimal platform of thin twigs, sparse enough for eggs to be seen from below, built on a horizontal support 1–10 m up. Sites range from a low bush isolated in a reedbed, a tall hedge and garden ornamentals to bamboos, palm-crowns, saplings and trees, commonly next to open space. Closed-canopy woodland is avoided, although the edge of mangrove forest is used.

Eggs and brood. Eggs are plain white, virtually glossless. Shape elliptical. Size (mm): 28.9–26.8 × 21.8–20.3 (n=5), but two averages, 24.8 × 20.0 and 25.6 × 19.2, suggest this range is not representative. Full clutch two.

Cycle. The male collects and passes twigs to the female as she sits in the developing nest, but appears not to build. Both sexes incubate.

Seasonality. Eggs in all months November–August, with no records outside this period (E.C.S. Baker, BMP5, Madoc 1956a, McClure and Husain 1968, NRCS, Robinson and Chasen 1936, Ryves 1938, SINGAV-1, -2, -4).

MOULT. Replacement of primaries is regular-descendant. A series of 92 adults from the length of the Peninsula and covering all months showed wing-moult almost exclusively during March–November. All early-stage records (P1 or P2) fell during March–July, with mid or later stages (P5 outwards) only as of June (BMNH, ZRCNUS). Individuals at P10 in late January and mid March may have re-started after suspension. Post-juvenile moult may continue later, with records of stages P5 and P7 in late November.

CONSERVATION. Communal roosting at traditional sites exposes this species to heavy shooting pressure, which may be a threat in Thailand.

Orange-breasted Green Pigeon; Nok Plao Ok See Muang Namtaan (Thai); Punai Siam (Malay)

Treron bicincta (Jerdon) 1840, *Madras Journal of Literature and Science* 12(28): 13. TL coast south of Tellicherry, Kerala, SW India.

Plate 45

GROUP RELATIONS. Free-standing (see Pink-necked Green Pigeon).

GLOBAL RANGE. Apart from the arid NW, the Indian subcontinent from the Himalayan foothills, and Sri Lanka; Hainan; SE Asia from Burma, S Laos and S Vietnam to the Peninsula, and Java and Bali (van Balen 1991a). Vagrant Taiwan.

IDENTIFICATION/DESCRIPTION. From Pink-necked Green Pigeon by larger size, lack of pink on the neck and by grey nape and hind-crown of an otherwise green head. A dark tail-bar is interrupted centrally and the broad, pale grey terminal band is conspicuous enough to show in flight. Belly and tibial trousers are rather bright lime-yellow, and the wing-bar clear yellow (versus cream in Pink-necked).

Bare-part colours. (Adult) outer ring of iris pink, amethyst or yellow, inner ring blue, and periorbital skin sage-green; bill pale greenish horn to greenish grey, cere brighter; feet dull purple-red.

Size (mm). (Skins: 12 males, 11 females; adult): wing 151–165 and 153–164; tail 80–99 and 75–96; bill 14.2–17.8 and 15.7–16.8; tarsus 22.3–26.4 and 22.1–24.5 (BMNH, TISTR, ZRCNUS).

Weight. No data.

DISTRIBUTION. South of Phatthalung, known only from the W coast, recently as far as Port Dickson (Negeri Sembilan) (2°30′N). Historical summary: *Pak, Chu, Ran, Pha, Nak, Phu, Kra, Pht, Tra, Ked, Pra, Pek, Sel, Neg, ?Mel*, with additional NW island records from Phayam, the Surins and Yao Yai.

GEOGRAPHICAL VARIATION. Nominate *bicincta*.

STATUS AND POPULATION. Resident; local and sparse in the south but, where hunting permits, evidently fairly common in the north.

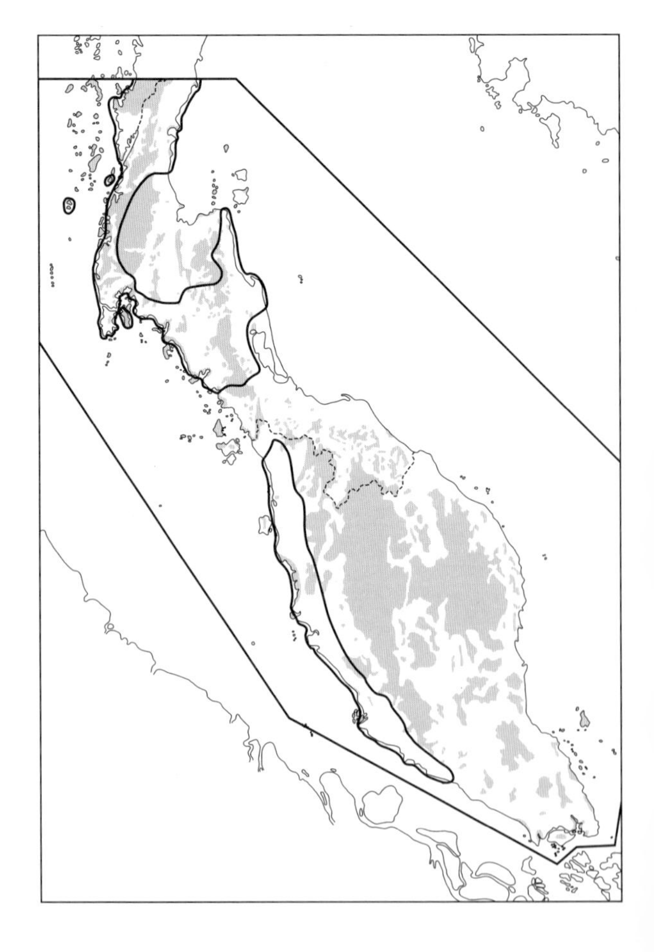

HABITATS AND ECOLOGY. Exclusively at plains level and, in the south, mainly coastal. Favours some of the same scrub habitats as Pink-necked, and joins it at traditional communal roosts, e.g., a few with some 200 of the latter on a small mangrove islet off the beach at Si Rusa, Port Dickson, Negeri Sembilan, in August and September (MBR 1986–87).

None identified among night-time dispersants netted at Fraser's Hill, etc., or from lighthouses.

FORAGING AND FOOD. Small fruit of second-growth bushes and trees in coastal scrub (BR 1970–71); none identified, and no other information.

SOCIAL ORGANIZATION. No information on breeding dispersion but non-breeders form small, apparently cohesive foraging parties and, as stated, roost communally in much larger gatherings.

MOVEMENTS. No information but seems to behave like Pink-necked Green Pigeon.

SURVIVAL. No information.

SOCIAL INTERACTIONS. No information.

VOICE. No information.

BREEDING. No information.

MOULT. Twenty adults from Chumphon and Pakchan south to Selangor collected during September–February and June showed no wing-moult, suggesting a Pink-necked type of seasonality (BMNH, ZRCNUS).

CONSERVATION. No issues identified, apart from hunting at roosts.

Thick-billed Green Pigeon; Nok Khao Plao Thammadaa (Thai); Punai Lengguak (Malay)

Treron curvirostra (Gmelin) 1789, *Systema Naturae* 13(2): 777. TL Rawang, Selangor.
Plate 44

GROUP RELATIONS. Closely related to *T. griseicauda* (Grey-cheeked Green Pigeon), apparently also to *T. teysmannii*, *T. floris* and *T. psittacea* (Sumba, Flores and Timor Green Pigeons), allopatric from Java to Sulawesi and through the Lesser Sunda islands (Goodwin 1967). Viewing island by island replacement against the known mobility of *curvirostra*, it seems likely these forms actually exclude one another, hence a superspecies arrangement is preferred.

GLOBAL RANGE. Himalayan foothills east from central Nepal, and hill-tracts of the extreme NE Indian subcontinent; S Yunnan and Hainan; SE Asia south to Sumatra, Borneo and intervening islands, and W-central Philippines.

IDENTIFICATION/DESCRIPTION. Medium-small and compact. Purely green front separates it from other maroon-backed male *Treron*, and a combination of red cere and conspicuously broad, sage-green periorbital ring identifies both sexes. Female from female Cinnamon-headed Green Pigeon also by green rather than grey flanks and creamy white rather than bright yellow on trousers.

Bare-part colours. (Adult) outer ring of iris cream, pink, orange-red, bronze or brown and inner ring blue, colour changing according to excitement level; broad, periorbital ring bright sage-green; bill pale greenish with base of lower mandible and side of cere (completely feathered dorsally) rich red; feet dull purple-red (BMNH, Robinson 1917, Robinson and Chasen 1936, Robinson and Kloss 1921–24, UMBRP).

Size (mm). (Live and skins: 3-figure samples of males and females; adult): wing 125–145 and 123–144 (except for 1 Penang captive, possibly imported, none of either sex above 139 south of Thailand); tail 67–86 and 60–84; bill from rear edge nostril 12.9–15.5 and 13.5–15.7; tarsus 21.7–24.7 and 21.9–24.4 (BMNH, UMBRP).

Weight (g). Dispersing adults at Fraser's Hill: males, 112–161 (mean 138); females, 117–171 (mean 131). Respective juveniles down to 96 and 87 (UMBRP).

DISTRIBUTION. Historical summary: all divisions except *Son*, *Pat*, *Yal*, *Kel*, *Tru*, *Pra*, with additional island records from Phayam, the Surin group, Phiphi, Libong, Tarutao, Langkawi, Penang, Pangkor, Rembia, Angsa and Pisang off the W coast; Samui off the E coast; and Ubin and St John's, Singapore.

GEOGRAPHICAL VARIATION. Nominate *curvirostra* grades into slightly paler, larger *nipalensis* Hodgson 1836 (TL Nepal) in the Thai provinces, but individual variation suggests their distributions may be affected by dispersal movements. Some Pakchan specimens are no larger than from Johor (BMNH); on the other hand, size-range at Fraser's Hill (latitude 3°43'N) implies no *nipalensis* occur that far south.

STATUS AND POPULATION. Resident, regular and, overall, more or less common year-round. The most frequently met-with green pigeon in Lowland forest, but nomadic.

HABITATS AND ECOLOGY. Occupies mainly the upper canopy of evergreen and semi-evergreen

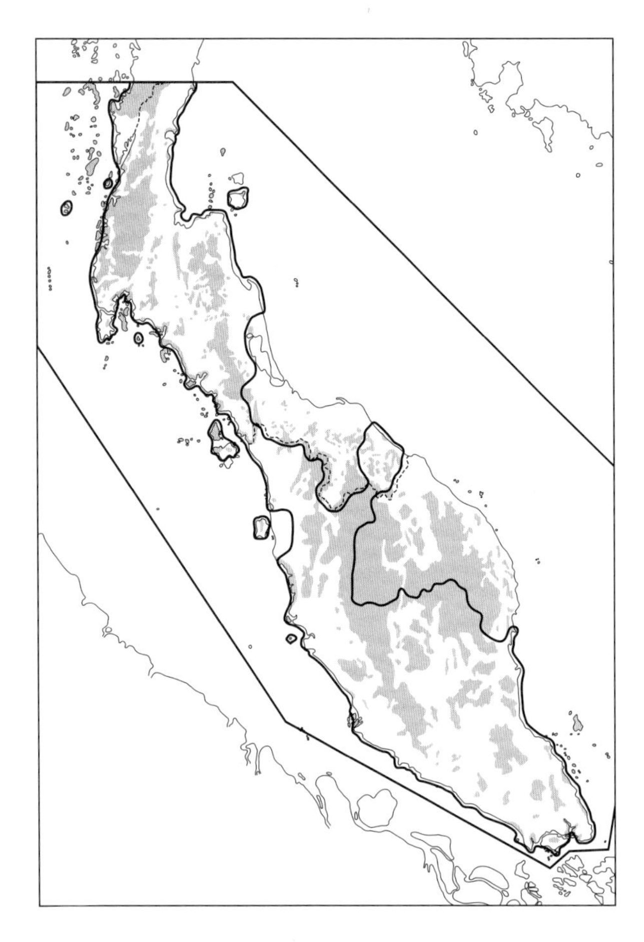

Lowland forest, mature, disturbed and regenerating, in the plains and on mountains (by day) to about 1000 m altitude (at or a short way past the Montane ecotone). Long-distance dispersal takes place at night. Three hundred and sixty Thick-bills have been mist-netted at floodlights on Fraser's Hill since migration studies began there in 1965, distributed through all months in which nets have been set, i.e., excluding only June and July, but peaking in October–November (BMP5, BR 1972–73, UMBRP). An invasion of Singapore and its southern islands during July–August 1986 (MBR 1986–87) implies these movements also occur at mid summer. All age/sex-classes participate, including some young still in completely juvenile plumage. Data from 1970 onwards confirm a finding from earlier samples that the adult sex ratio among night-fliers is at parity (*contra* Emerald Dove and Jambu Fruit Dove).

FORAGING AND FOOD. Like several other *Treron* pigeons of forest, appears to depend on figs as a keystone item of diet, and is one of the more consistent visitors to large-crowned, canopy-fruiting strangling and other tall forms of Lowland forest. In Taman Negara and at Kuala Lompat, Kerau wildlife reserve (Pahang), Lambert (1989) recorded it at 20 of 25 bird-attracting *Ficus* species under regular observation, with figs in the small-diameter size-range 5.4–34.4, mostly below 12 mm. Large fruits are softened by rotation in the bill before being swallowed.

Occasionally visits fruit-crops outside forest but rarely seen at any thing other than figs. One curious exception involved three birds in my Selangor garden that joined domestic Guineafowl and Town Pigeons being given grain and pellet food on the ground, though it could not be proved that they actually fed (MBR 1984–85).

In common with other *Treron* pigeons, Thick-billed is a seed predator, with muscular gizzard that sometimes contains grit. Proportionately few seeds pass through the gut to be dispersed intact (Lambert 1988).

SOCIAL ORGANIZATION. As with other *Treron* pigeons, pairs nest alone but non-breeders move around by day in small, cohesive parties, joining with others at large fruit-sources. No mass roosting has been reported.

MOVEMENTS. No ring-recoveries. The scale of nocturnal journeys can be guessed only from evidence of strikes on Melaka Straits lighthouses, including at Angsa and One-Fathom Bank, 42 km off Selangor, and corpses floating in the tide in Kemang bay (Negeri Sembilan), showing that some birds attempt sea-crossings (BMP5, BR 1969, Robinson and Kloss 1922). As with Emerald Dove, nocturnal dispersants show a wide range of body-weights and heavy birds carry substantial fat.

SURVIVAL. No information.

SOCIAL INTERACTIONS. No information.

VOICE. No good description.

BREEDING

Nest. A sparse platform of thin twigs, built 6–16 m up, typically in a thin branch-fork (exceptional sites: the top of an old stump and over a deserted munia nest), in forest but often close to openings; also in rubber plantation bordering forest.

Eggs and brood. Eggs are white and slightly glossy. Shape elliptical. Full clutch two.

Cycle. The male collects and every half minute or so passes twigs to the female as she sits and forms the nest.

Seasonality. A male with large testes on 22 December; eggs during January–August; a brood of half-grown squabs on 17 September (F.G.H. Allen, BMNH, BMP5, G.C. Madoc, NRCS, Robinson and Chasen 1936, Ryves 1938).

MOULT. Replacement of primaries is mostly regular-descendant. A few instances of activity at two loci account for the only inner-hand moult seen late in the season. Among 106 adults from throughout the Peninsula and covering all months, wing-moult occurred mainly during May–October, with a few early-stage records (P1 or P2) as of mid April. Forty-two percent of the large October sample had already completed and, except for a suspension, the few November birds handled were all close to it (at P8, P10, P10). A single instance between December and March (P10 on 11 February) could have resulted from a suspension.

Post-juvenile moult follows an overlapping but slightly later schedule than adults, with heavy activity from September to at least November, though the only December juvenile handled had suspended after P7. Juveniles also show more intensive moult than adults, with up to six adjacent primaries in overlapping growth.

CONSERVATION. An already apparent problem, likely to become critical for this and other forest fig specialists, is the decline of canopy-fruiting, epiphytic figs as intensified logging reaches the outer (upper) limit of remaining Lowland forest, eliminating big, old trees (mostly Dipterocarpaceae) that host fig germination.

Large Green Pigeon; Nok Plao Yai (Thai); Punai Bakuk (Malay)

Treron capellei (Temminck) 1822, *Nouveau Recueil de Planches Coloriées d'Oiseaux* 24: plate 143. TL W Java.

Plate 44

GROUP RELATIONS. Free-standing.

GLOBAL RANGE. Borneo, W Java, Sumatra, the Peninsula and Tenasserim to latitude 12°30′N in the Mergui archipelago (Anderson 1887).

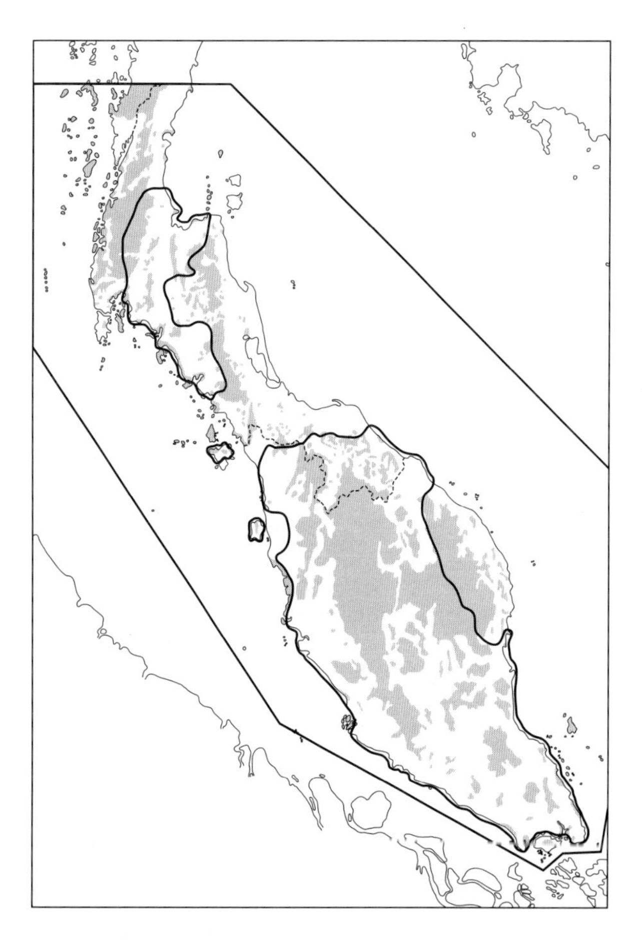

IDENTIFICATION/DESCRIPTION. Large size and relatively slow wing-beat are noticeable in flight. Perched, all pale green apart from orange (male) or yellowish (female) central breast-patch. Habitat, size, large bill and dark eye all clearly separate it from Orange-breasted Green Pigeon.

Bare-part colours. (Adult) iris deep reddish brown, eyelid-rim yellow; cere and bill pale green, shading to horn-white at the bill-tip; feet yellow (BMNH).

Size (mm). (Skins: 29 males, 8 females; adult): wing 191–207 and 190–211; tail 102–129 and 101–122; bill 26.6–27.6 and 25.1–28.2; tarsus 28.3–32.8 and 28.9–31.1 (BMNH, ZDUM, ZRCNUS).

Weight (g). A male, about 455; two females, about 340, 369 (BMNH).

DISTRIBUTION. Historical summary: *Sur, Kra, Tra, Yal, Nar, Ked, Kel, Pek, Phg, Sel, Neg, Mel, Joh;* also on Langkawi and (formerly) Penang islands.

GEOGRAPHICAL VARIATION. Subspecies *magnirostris* Strickland 1844 (TL Melaka), of the global range except Java.

STATUS AND POPULATION. Resident and, in typical habitat, present year-round, but also an at least occasional long-distance dispersant. Regular and more or less common where large tracts of tall, closed-canopy forest remain at plains level, but so much of this habitat has been lost that it has disappeared from most former range. Believed close to extinction in Thailand, and Chalerm Prakiat wildlife sanctuary, Narathiwat, where one was seen on 3 June 1992 (BBCB-9), may be its last Thai locality (no records elsewhere since the early 1970s: TISTR).

HABITATS AND ECOLOGY. Evergreen and semi-evergreen Lowland forest, including swamp-forest, mature or well regenerated and with tall timber left after disturbance. One of a cohort of forest birds that rarely ranges much past the foot of significant slopes. The Langkawi island population is regular up to about 200 m elevation. On the mainland, exceptional upland sightings include a party at a fruiting fig tree high on the Main Range in Kelantan, and a bird in Lower Montane forest at Fraser's Hill (BR 1968, R.P. Jaensch). A casualty at floodlights at Fraser's on 20 September (BR 1970–71) shows some dispersal out of usual habitat is nocturnal.

It has been suggested Large Green avoids Green Imperial Pigeon, or that they occupy different forest types (Wells 1990b), but both have been collected at the foot of Pulai ridge, S Johor (BMNH), and numbers seen feeding together by Kenering lake, N Perak (Sutari Supari).

FORAGING AND FOOD. A fig specialist, using its powerful bill to take fruit larger than tackled by smaller congeners. At Kuala Lompat, Kerau wildlife reserve (Pahang), recorded at 12 of 25 bird-attracting *Ficus* species regularly monitored (Lambert 1989), with a preponderance of records from four: *cucurbitina*, *dubia*, *stupenda* and *subcordata*, all stranglers with large, high-canopy crowns and figs in the small-diameter size-range 20.3–34.8 mm.

SOCIAL ORGANIZATION. Nesting dispersion unknown but non-breeders move around the forest in cohesive parties.

MOVEMENTS. The Fraser's Hill floodlight casualty supplies the only evidence this pigeon makes nocturnal dispersal movements.

SURVIVAL. No information.

SOCIAL INTERACTIONS. Copulations occur on high, exposed boughs, with much preliminary head-bobbing by the female (ENGGANG-3).

VOICE. Deep, rich growling notes of Black Hornbill *Anthracoceros malayanus* voice-quality, but not described in detail.

BREEDING

Nest. Undescribed.

Eggs and brood. Undescribed.

Cycle. No information.

Seasonality. Copulations on 30 January and 2 July (BMP5, ENGGANG-3).

MOULT. Replacement of primaries is regular-descendant. Among 49 adults from Trang to Johor covering January–April and July–November, wing-moult began in March, with 75–100 percent incidence as of April. Early-stage records (P1 to P2) occurred only in March–April, most birds were at P6 or beyond by August, and at P10 as of mid September. A female at P4 on 20 September might have continued on, but no October–February birds showed moult (two late-stage records in March, including P9 on 2 March, could have been re-starts after suspension). Provisionally, it appears Large is timed like Thick-billed Green Pigeon (BMNH, UMZC, ZDUM, ZRCNUS).

CONSERVATION. Globally near-threatened (BTW2), and at definite risk from plains-level deforestation. It will shortly depend absolutely on a small clutch of wildlife refuges and reservoir catchments with valley-bottom forest below the hill-foot boundary. Retention of enough large strangling figs of the right species to provide a dependable, year-round supply of fruit is critical.

Yellow-vented Green Pigeon; Nok Plao Haang Khem Hua Peek Daeng (Thai); Punai Ekor Panjang (Malay)

Treron seimundi (Robinson) 1910, *Bulletin of the British Ornithologists' Club* 25: 98. TL Semangko Pass (the Gap), Selangor/Pahang boundary.

Plate 44

GROUP RELATIONS. Forms a superspecies with W Indonesian *T. oxyura* (Sumatran Green Pigeon).

GLOBAL RANGE. The Annamite Range in central and S Vietnam, hill-tracts of SE and western Thailand, and the Malayan Main Range; also to neighbouring lowlands, and recorded once in central Thailand (Aagaard 1932, ZRCNUS).

IDENTIFICATION/DESCRIPTION. Tail-shape of flying birds is of some help. Perched, only adult males show yellow lower tail-coverts, and the most obvious feature of both sexes is their face-pattern: bright blue skin extending back from the bill along bare lores to encircle the eye. Adult females lack maroon on the wing-coverts but show a black patch on the carpal bend.

Bare-part colours. (Adult) outer ring of iris fawn to pink, inner ring blue; orbital skin and lores intense cobalt-blue; bill and cere the same blue, greying towards the tip; feet dull purple-red (Chasen 1934, BMNH).

Size (mm). (Live and skins: 4 males, 5 females; adult): wing 155–159 and 142–152; tail 138–160 and 118–131; bill 20.8–21.7 and 18.5 (1 only) (depth at gonys in two males 6.9 and 8.8); tarsus 23.1–24.9 and 22.0 (1 only) (BMNH, UMBRP, ZDUM, ZRCNUS).

Weight (g). Four females, 150–166 (BMNH, UMBRP, ZDUM).

DISTRIBUTION. Recorded patchily along the Main Range from the latitude of the E–W highway (5°35′N) to the Gap, Selangor/Pahang boundary (R. Gregory-Smith), with a probable seen in the Larut Range at Maxwell's Hill (Bromley 1952); also at points on the W coast, including back-mangroves at the Sala river-mouth (Kedah), in coastal forest at Batu bay and Katak point, Dindings district of Perak, and on nearby Rembia island. Historical summary: *Ked, Pek, Phg, Sel.*

GEOGRAPHICAL VARIATION. Nominate *seimundi*, showing variable development of a peach-pink flush on the breast and side of the neck of the adult male.

STATUS AND POPULATION. Resident overall but mobile; sparse to more or less common. Seen almost as often as Thick-billed Green Pigeon in the area of the Gap, and probably as frequent at this altitude elsewhere on the Main Range, but lowland occurrences are genuinely sparse.

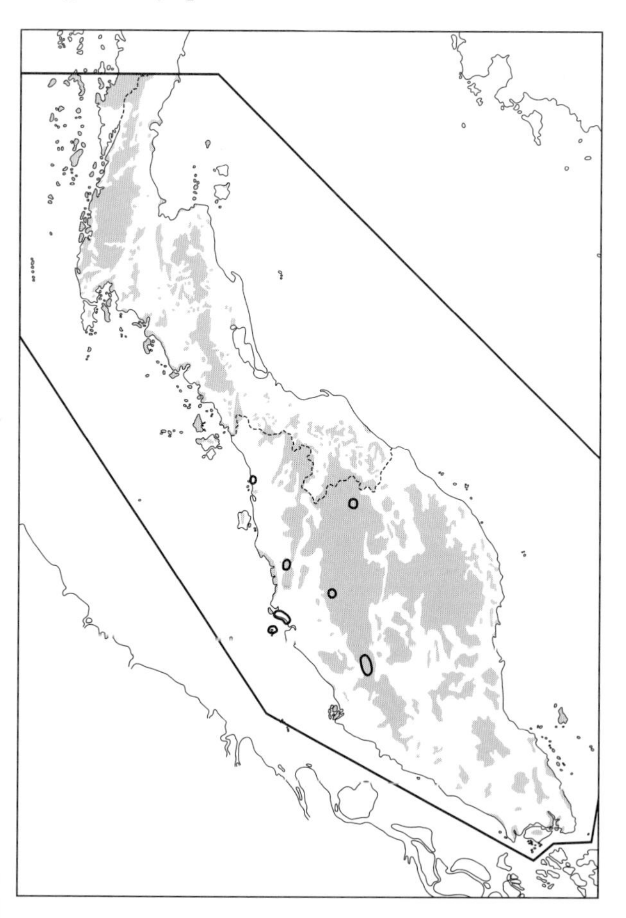

HABITATS AND ECOLOGY. Lowland and mountain records alike have been from forest, or at least the fringe of woodland. On Korbu peak (Perak/Pahang boundary), birds are said to have been collected at or above 1400 m, 'from high trees on which they were feeding' (Robinson and Chasen 1936), but most records are from a rather narrow altitudinal band covering the Lowland/Lower Montane forest ecotone.

Yellow-vented is now also known to be among those frugivorous pigeons dispersing at night, with small numbers mist-netted at floodlights on the crest of the Main Range at Fraser's Hill in April and September–November (BR 1978–79, PERHILITAN). This discovery makes better sense of coastal and island occurrences (in April, June and August).

FORAGING AND FOOD. There is no record of food taken on the coast but in mountain forest this pigeon is a fig specialist. Around the Gap, birds have been recorded only at large-crowned, medium- to large-fruited, canopy-height *Ficus* of three types (no species identified), two of which this heavy-billed bird shares with Thick-billed Green Pigeon. Only Yellow-vented has been seen at the third, which bears round, red figs about 30 mm in diameter out of which parts are bitten and swallowed piecemeal.

SOCIAL ORGANIZATION. Breeding dispersion is not known but foragers move around in apparently cohesive parties of up to about 20 birds.

MOVEMENTS. Lowland dispersants recorded 30–40 km out from mountain habitat.

SURVIVAL. No information.

SOCIAL INTERACTIONS. No information.

VOICE. No local details (in continental Thailand, P.D. Round describes a distinctive, high-pitched, metallic *clank* preceding the bubbling/wailing part of the call).

BREEDING

Nest. Not described.

Eggs and brood. Not described.

Cycle. No information.

Seasonality. A bird believed to have been a young juvenile seen in the company of an adult on the Perak coast in June (Robinson and Chasen 1936).

MOULT. Replacement of primaries appears to be regular-descendant. No wing-moult in four March and April adults but other individuals dated late April and mid August showed mid- and late-stage suspension. A dispersing female intercepted on 23 October was growing P3–4 (BMNH, UMBRP, ZRCNUS), offering no clearer picture of a population schedule.

CONSERVATION. Globally near-threatened (BTW2). Logging will extend through most of the mid-mountain foraging zone in the near future and maintenance of appropriate *Ficus* populations must become an issue.

Wedge-tailed Green Pigeon; Nok Plao Haang Phlua (Thai); Punai Bukit (Malay)

Treron sphenura (Vigors) 1831, *Proceedings of the Committee of Science and Correspondence of the Zoological Society of London* 1: 173. TL Simla-Almora area, Himachal Pradesh, NW India.
Plate 44

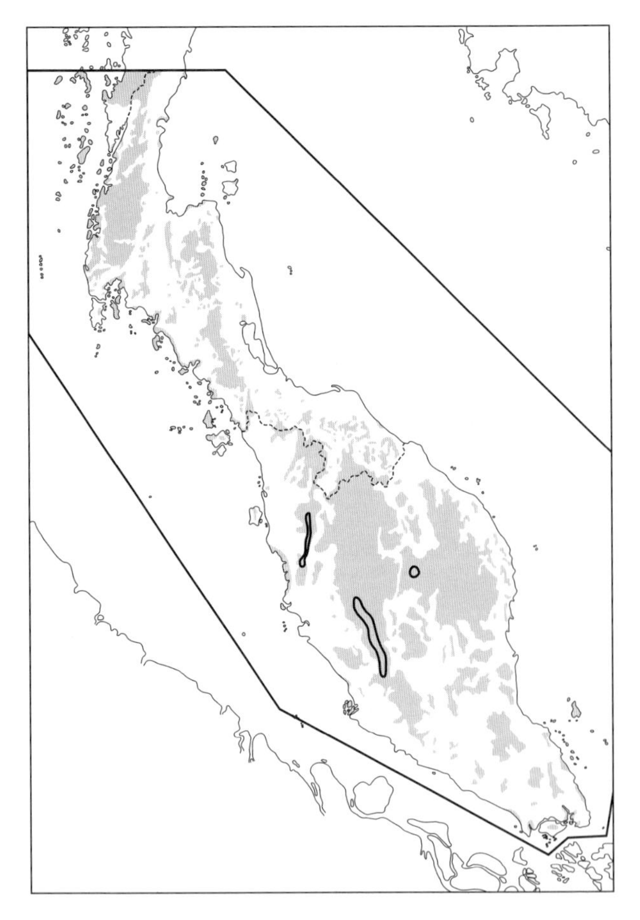

GROUP RELATIONS. Uncertain; apparently close to northern subtropical *T. seiboldii* and *T. formosae* (White-bellied and Whistling Green Pigeons) (Goodwin 1967).

GLOBAL RANGE. The forested Himalayas east from Kashmir, and hill-tracts of the extreme NE Indian subcontinent; SE Tibet, Sichuan, Yunnan and Hainan; hill-tracts of SE Asia to Sumatra and Java; and Lombok.

IDENTIFICATION/DESCRIPTION. Blue-billed like Yellow-vented Green Pigeon, and males of both have maroon lesser wing-coverts, but paler green overall and has lores fully feathered.

Bare-part colours. (Adult) outer ring of iris pink, inner ring blue (in a live bird at a distance, eye appeared entirely clear, light blue), eyelid-rim blue; cere and base of bill blue, shading to greyish apically; feet dull purple-red.

Size (mm). (Skins: 3 males, 4 females; adult): wing 162–172 and 164–167; tail 118–128 and 105–112; bill from rear edge nostril 12.6–13.4 and 12.9–13.2; tarsus 24.3–24.4 and 21.7–25.1 (BMNH, ZRCNUS).

Weight (g). One unsexed adult, 205 (McClure 1964).

DISTRIBUTION. Above 1200 m on the Larut Range; the Main Range between Cameron Highlands and Genting Highlands; and on Tahan, Taman Negara. Historical summary: *Kel, Pek, Phg, Sel.*

GEOGRAPHICAL VARIATION. An endemic subspecies, *robinsoni* Ogilvie-Grant 1906 (TL Tahan mountain), in which males lack orange on crown and breast, and maroon is confined to wing-coverts, not extending across the mantle. From Sumatran *etorques* by creamy rather than cinnamon lower tail-coverts (Violani 1980).

STATUS AND POPULATION. Resident but local and uncommon to sparse, including at known sites of easy accessibility.

HABITATS AND ECOLOGY. Strictly Montane forest from about 1200 m altitude to at least 1800 m in the Upper Montane zone, and rather hard to find. *Contra* BMP5, not known to make nocturnal dispersal movements, and its whole ecology may differ from neighbouring Yellow-vented and Thick-billed Green Pigeons. Gathers at fruiting trees but by no means exclusive to high crowns; parties have been seen resting close to the ground in dense, forest-edge thickets.

FORAGING AND FOOD. No records. Large-crowned, mass-fruiting *Ficus* become less of a feature of forest with distance above the Lowland/Montane ecotone and this bird's bill, thin and delicate compared with the deep, robustly hooked bills of fig-dependent Yellow-vented and Thick-billed Green Pigeons, implies the taking of relatively small fruit (perhaps not predominantly figs).

SOCIAL ORGANIZATION. Like other *Treron* species, pairs nest alone but non-breeders consort in small parties (up to eight birds recorded: MBR 1982–83).

MOVEMENTS. None known.

SURVIVAL. No information.

SOCIAL INTERACTIONS. No information.

VOICE. No information.

BREEDING

Nest. Only one reported, sited 12 m up and well out on a lateral branch of an exotic pine, in a garden at Fraser's Hill.

Eggs and brood. Not described.

Cycle. Over a three-hour period at mid-day, only the male incubated.

Seasonality. The one nest, contents unchecked but parent incubating, is dated 3 June (A. Jeyarajasingam).

MOULT. Replacement of primaries is regular-descendant. A January adult showed no moult, one dated 9 February had dropped P1, two in early June were growing P1 and P5–6, two in late July P7 and P7–8, and one in mid September P6, i.e., on an only loosely seasonal schedule (BMNH, ZRCNUS).

CONSERVATION. No immediate threat to this species, which is able to use regenerating as well as mature forest.

Jambu Fruit Dove; Nok Plao Naa Daeng (Thai); Punai Jambu (Malay)

Ptilinopus jambu (Gmelin) 1789, *Systema Naturae* 13(2): 784. TL Sumatra.
Plate 45

GROUP RELATIONS. Free-standing.

GLOBAL RANGE. Far-W Java (sporadic), Borneo, Belitung, Banka, Sumatra and the Peninsula to latitude approximately 8°N (BBCB-8).

IDENTIFICATION/DESCRIPTION. A combination of intensely grass-green upperparts, green or pale (never brown) underparts, clear orange bill and whitish periorbital ring is diagnostic. Sexually dimorphic: the female has a mauve- rather than rose-pink face, green rather than white breast, and lacks the male's bright pink chest-spot. The pale underbody, particularly of the adult male, is conspicuous in flight. Young juvenile from female by duller green tone, mainly green face and lack of the maroon-brown chin-patch found in both adults.

The tip of the outer primary is deeply emarginated (attenuated) in adults, but not in juveniles.

Bare-part colours. Outer ring of iris red-brown, narrow inner ring brown to orange-brown (juvenile), iris all orange (adult); periorbital skin palest blue-green; bill and cere clear orange; feet dull purple-red (BMNH, UMBRP).

Size (mm). (Live and skins: 3-figure samples of males and females; adult): wing 135–148 and 128–140 (juveniles down to 122); tail 81–97 and 77–87; bill 15.4–18.2 and 14.7–17.0; tarsus 19.0–20.0 and 18.7–20.0 (UMBRP, UMZC, ZRCNUS).

Weight (g). Large samples of nocturnal dispersants: adult males, 118–175 (mean 142); adult females, 116–162 (mean 132). Juveniles mostly below 110 (down to 72), gaining towards the end of post-juvenile wing-moult. This large age-difference may have a bearing on the development of the adult wing-tip slot.

DISTRIBUTION. North to Krabi. Historical summary: *Kra, Pht, Sat, Yal, Nar, Pes, Ked, Kel, Tru, Pra, Pek, Phg, Sel, Neg, Mel, Joh, Sin,* with additional island records from Penang, Rembia, Angsa, Undan (*Mel*)

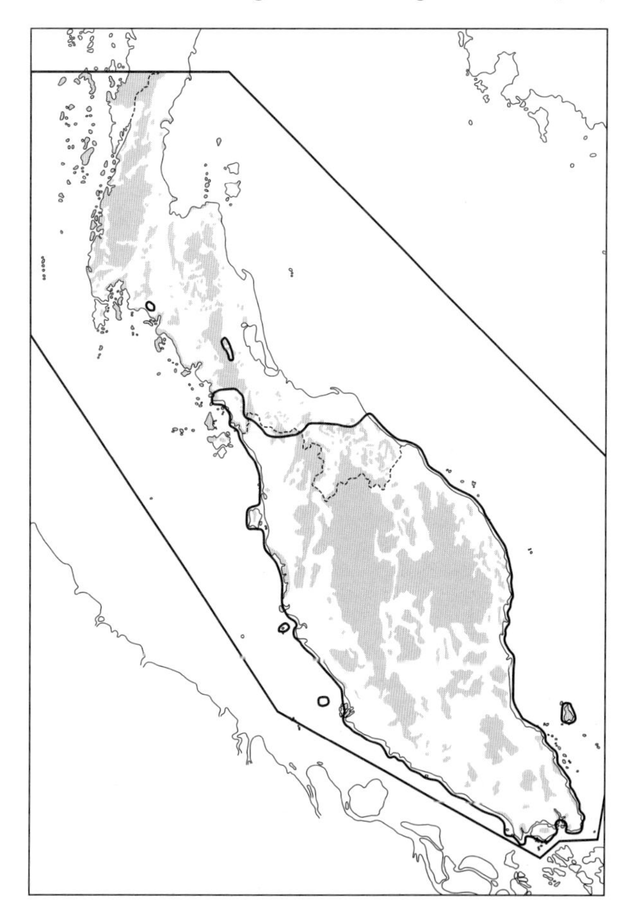

and Pisang off the W coast; and Tioman off the E coast, all within the likely range of dispersants.

GEOGRAPHICAL VARIATION. None recognized.

STATUS AND POPULATION. Resident in that it breeds in the Peninsula and is found year-round overall, but nomadic, with no obvious seasonality to its comings and goings. Local and uncommon to sparse. A record of 60–80 along a short stretch of the Tembeling river, Pahang, including up to 20 feeding in a single fruiting crown (*Eugenia* sp.) over several days in late June 1994 (K.D. Bishop), is entirely exceptional. At its northernmost localities in Krabi, recorded in different years in December, April, May and July (BBCB-8, BBCB-9, BCSTB-12, -13). Deeper into the mainland range, Lambert (1987) saw it in only six of 21 consecutive months of regular fieldwork at Kuala Lompat, Pahang.

HABITATS AND ECOLOGY. The almost exclusive habitat is closed-canopy, well regenerated to mature, evergreen to semi-evergreen Lowland forest, at plains level and to an uncertain distance up the submontane slope (Holmes 1973). Exceptional daytime appearances in other habitats have been noted in Singapore (MBR 1986–87, SINGAV-4) and Selangor, where over three weeks in early 1977 up to four regularly visited fruiting *Breynia* (Euphorbiaceae) shrubs in my suburban garden.

In terms of numbers captured, this is the greatest of the pigeon nomads dispersing at night. Since migration studies began there in 1965, over 2400 have been mist-netted at floodlights on Fraser's Hill, with strikes at lights elsewhere on the Main Range (Cameron Highlands, the Gap), on the Larut Range, and in the W-coast lowlands south to Singapore; also at all Melaka Straits lighthouses from which bird-strike records are available (Kuala Selangor, One-Fathom Bank, Angsa, Undan). Numbers at Fraser's Hill surge during September–November (BMP5, PERHILITAN, UMBRP) but, like Emerald Dove and Thick-billed Green Pigeon, some have been taken in all months nets have been set there, i.e., excluding only June and July.

To a lesser extent than in Emerald Dove the sex ratio of adult dispersants favours males, at 1.3 : 1 in a sample of 399 since 1970 against 1.5 : 1 among many more from the 1960s (BMP5). Some of the great difference in numbers between these periods is due to the proportion of juveniles taken: from 53 down to 20 percent overall. Perhaps the on-going fragmentation of Lowland forest is now reducing breeding success.

FORAGING AND FOOD. Unlike *Treron* pigeons, does not do the regular round of mass-fruiting *Ficus*. At Kuala Lompat, was seen to take figs only occasionally, from six species: *delosyce, pellucido-punctata, trichocarpa, crassiramea, dubia* and *stupenda* (mean small diameter of fruit in the range 10.1–27.4 mm) (Lambert 1989). Though all of these crop in the main canopy, most encounters with feeding Jambus have been in lower layers of the forest. Here, it has been speculated that loners seek scarcer, individually nutritious fruits (Wells 1988), but the evidence is still equivocal. Attraction to mass-fruiting *Breynia* and *Eugenia* has been noted, and one of the few breeding attempts reported coincided with a locally synchronized, mid-stratum fruiting of *Diplospora malaccensis* (Rubiaceae), which also drew many generalist frugivores (Lambert 1987).

An observation from Borneo of the taking of fallen fruit on the ground (Smythies 1981) has not been repeated locally and must be exceptional behaviour (see also Thick-billed Green Pigeon).

SOCIAL ORGANIZATION. Pairs nest alone and most encounters in forest have been with loners. Apart from the concentration on the Tembeling river, a party of eight is the largest number seen together during daytime (MBR 1986–87).

MOVEMENTS. A bird ringed as a dispersant at Fraser's Hill was shot 260 km NNW, at Bukit Selambau, Kedah (BMP5), but after an interval of more than one year, giving no idea of the scope of individual journeys. Off-shore lighthouse-strikes imply some span the Melaka Straits, and this has been confirmed by a second Fraser's Hill ring-recovery, at Duri, near Pekanbaru, central Sumatra (BR 1972–73).

SURVIVAL. No information.

SOCIAL INTERACTIONS. No information.

VOICE. The only call recorded is a low *coo*, rather like that of Emerald Dove but without the introductory click (Boonsong and Round 1991, SINGAV-1).

BREEDING

Nest. A small, sparse, twig platform through which contents can be seen from below, built 3–5 m up on a thin lateral branch-fork of a small, lower- to mid-stratum tree in closed-canopy forest.

Eggs and brood. Egg plain white; no other details available. Full clutch one.

Cycle. Both sexes incubate and tend the nestling.

Seasonality. Only five nests reported, with eggs during early May–July and a well-feathered squab in August (BR 1970–71, 1976–77, MBR 1984- 85, 1986–87, NRCS).

MOULT. Double-locus moult of primaries, as far apart as P1 and P9, is common, perhaps as a result of re-starting after a suspension (noted anywhere between P5 and P9). The many adults examined covered all months except January and June but revealed no regular progression of wing-moult. Including many instances of unilateral moult, incidence among dispersants peaked at 47 percent in September, but at all stages from P2 to P10 (BMP5, UMBRP). Only during breeding months were adults free of moult.

Juveniles show more intensive wing-moult than adults, with up to six adjacent primaries in overlapping growth and, at population level, incidence over 60 percent among birds handled in both September and October. Again, some had not started by November or even December, the latest a female at only P6 on 9 February (BMP5).

CONSERVATION. The decline in numbers of juveniles intercepted at Fraser's Hill, and in total numbers of birds seen there in recent years, suggests populations are under stress, it is guessed, from outright loss of forest habitat or its changing character as a result of logging.

Green Imperial Pigeon; Nok Lumphuu Khieo (Thai); Pergam Besar (Malay)

Ducula aenea (Linnaeus) 1766, *Systema Naturae* 12(1): 283. TL Manila, Philippines.
Plate 43

GROUP RELATIONS. The most widespread member of a superspecies ranging from India to the Society islands, central Pacific; also including *D. perspicillata* and *D. concinna* (White-spectacled and Blue-tailed Imperial Pigeons) that replace *aenea*, and each other, in E Wallacea (CLBW, Goodwin 1967).

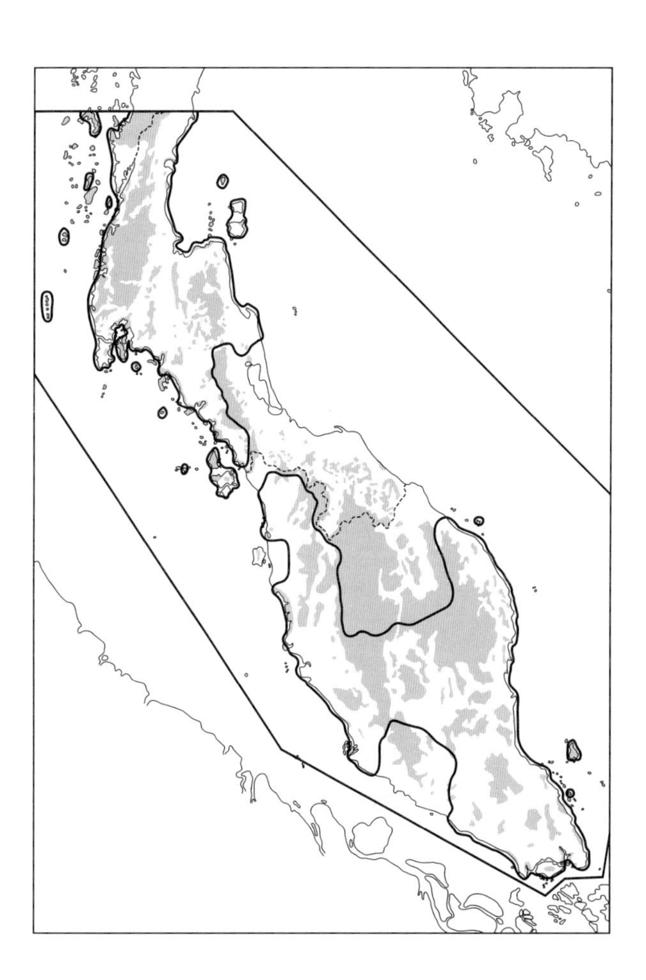

GLOBAL RANGE. The S and E Indian subcontinent, Sri Lanka and Bay of Bengal islands; S Guangdong, S Yunnan and Hainan; SE Asia to the Greater Sunda is lands and Philippines; Wallacea to the Talaud and Sula islands, and the Lesser Sundas as far as Alor (possibly Timor).

IDENTIFICATION/DESCRIPTION. Large size and relatively slow wing-beat identify both Green and Mountain Imperial Pigeons. In overhead flight, with care, from Mountain by lower tail-coverts contrastingly darker than belly, and tail without pale terminal bar. At close range, juveniles show colder grey underparts than adults, and lack their vinous wash (Riley 1938). As in other imperial pigeons, the proximal half of the tarsus is feathered.

Bare-part colours. (Adult) iris dark brown, to red with outer ring lilac; narrow eyelid-rim plum-red; bill lead-blue, cere more purplish; feet dull purple-red (BMNH, Riley 1938, Robinson and Chasen 1936, ZRCNUS).

Size (mm). (Skins: 22 males, 8 females; adult): wing 219–245 and 219–246; tail 128–151 and 128–145; bill 20.4–25.9 and 23.1–25.1; tarsus 32.2–35.7 and 31.0–32.9 (BMNH, ZRCNUS).

Weight (g). From the Thai provinces: a male, about 600; a female about 430 (BMNH, TISTR).

DISTRIBUTION. Formerly throughout, but hunting and habitat-loss have forced a large contraction of range on the mainland. Historical summary: *Pak, Chu, Ran, Sur, Pha, Nak, Phu, Kra, Tra, Sat, Ked, Tru, Pek, Phg, Sel, Joh, Sin*. Also on many additional islands, including Lanbyi, St Luke's, Chang, the Surins (where abundant in 1975/76), the Similan group (abundant), Yao Noi and Yao Yai (Phangnga bay), Phiphi, Muk, Rok Nok and Rok Nai (*Tra*), Tarutao and Ladang, the Langkawi group (where in March–April 1970 the only record was of a small group crossing between Tuba and Dayang Bunting islands, the latter since burned) and Bidan (Kedah) off the W coast (i.e., not any further into the Melaka Straits); Tao, Phangan and Samui, Redang (where it may not have survived recent tourist developments) and the Pahang–Johor archipelago (Tioman and Tinggi) off the E coast; and Ubin, Singapore.

GEOGRAPHICAL VARIATION. Continental *sylvatica* Tickell 1833 (TL Bihar, N India) identified in the north, *polia* Oberholser 1917 (TL Siantan, Anamba islands), said to be slightly larger and less bronzy backed, in the south. Thirty wing-lengths suggest size-variation is more individual than geographical, although none from north of Trang is above 234 mm. The real latitudinal difference is in development of a dark vinous hind-collar: bold in the north, slight to absent south from Trang.

STATUS AND POPULATION. Resident, local, and sparse to common. Extirpated from large areas of former mainland range, it is believed due to loss of plains-level (particularly subcoastal) forests, assisted in places by heavy hunting (cf. Madoc 1956a). Still occurs on some larger forested islands off both coasts, and on the mainland in the lowlands of N Perak, S Pahang and Johor, including around the Tasek Bera swamp system (R.P. Jaensch) and valley-bottom forests of the Endau-Rompin conservation area (MBR 1984–85, 1986–87, Wells 1990b). Sightings at fruiting *Ficus* by Kenering lake, Perak valley, in 1992 and 1993 (SINGAV-6) are virtually the only recent Malaysian records west of the Main Range, and a small group in the upper Sok valley, Surat Thani, in June 1985 is the only record from the mainland of the Thai provinces in 30 years (BLC).

HABITATS AND ECOLOGY. Inhabits tall evergreen and semi-evergreen Lowland forest, mature and well regenerated after selective logging. Crosses onto hill-slopes on islands but, except while dispersing, strictly in the extreme lowlands of the mainland. By day, forages and lounges in pairs or small groups, and at certain seasons (as formerly in the Langat valley, Selangor: Madoc 1956a) said to flight to large, communal roosts. These have been described as in or at the edge of mangrove forest, which is also said to be nesting habitat (Robinson and Chasen 1936).

FORAGING AND FOOD. Apart from presence among other large pigeons attending fig-crops in lakeside forest at Kenering, Perak (Sutari Supari), and figs found cramming the crops of shot birds (Madoc 1956a), nothing is known about diet or food-finding.

SOCIAL ORGANIZATION. Moves around the forest mostly in pairs or small parties and, as stated, said to form mass roosts, but none of these reported in recent years.

MOVEMENTS. A few have struck lights on the crest of the Larut Range, Perak (T. Gunasegaran), the only evidence this species resembles other Lowland forest fruit pigeons in at least occasionally dispersing at night.

SURVIVAL. No information.

SOCIAL INTERACTIONS. No information.

VOICE. Various groaning coos, rich, deep and resonant: *koo oooo; koo krrrroo-u; krrroo-krrroo-krrru* (with shortening vowel); and two on a falling pitch: *kroo-kroo-kroo-kroo* and *krrroo ooo-ooo*.

BREEDING

Nest. Not described. On Tioman island, said to have been found 3–18 m up in mangrove forest.

Eggs and brood. Egg white and slightly glossy; no other details. Full clutch one.

Cycle. No information.

Seasonality. Active nests in mid September and January–March (Robinson and Chasen 1936).

MOULT. Replacement of at least the inner hand is regular-descendant, but one of 13 active moulters examined showed renewal at the wing-tip out from P8, simultaneous with P3. Among 30 adults covering all months except March and November, active wing-moult occurred during February–October, with late-stage replacement as of August and one recent completion on 29 October, but with suspension or arrest (between P2 and P10) common through most of the year (BMNH, ZRCNUS).

CONSERVATION. Not recorded in Taman Negara, and only one wildlife reserve on the mainland is known to hold significant numbers. Much depends on the security of larger forested islands, a growing number of which is now exposed to settlement and tourism developments.

Mountain Imperial Pigeon; Nok Muum (Thai); Pergam Gunung (Malay)

Ducula badia (Raffles) 1822, *Transactions of the Linnean Society* 13(2): 317. TL Benkulen, SW Sumatra.
Plate 43

GROUP RELATIONS. Forms a superspecies with *D. lacernulata* (Dark-backed Imperial Pigeon) and possibly also *D. cineracea* (Timor Imperial Pigeon) collectively of Java, Bali and the Lesser Sunda islands east to Timor and Wetar (CLBW, Goodwin 1967).

GLOBAL RANGE. The forested Himalayas and foothills east from Nepal, and hill-tracts of both the extreme NE and SW Indian subcontinent; W and S Yunnan and Hainan; and hill-tracts and adjacent lowlands of SE Asia to Borneo and Sumatra (W Java reached perhaps by occasional dispersants from Sumatra).

IDENTIFICATION/DESCRIPTION. The only big pigeon of Montane forest, with steady flight on deliberately and deeply flapped wings. From Green Imperial in a good flight view by pale terminal band on tail, and lower tail-coverts lighter rather than darker than tail.

Bare-part colours. (Adult) iris pearl-white, eyelid-rim plum-red; bill pink with whitish tip; feet dull purple-red.

Size (mm). (Skins: 7 males, 3 females; adult): wing 223–240 and 231–233; tail 153–165 and 158–168; bill 20.8–23.6 and 20.5–22.1; tarsus 30.5 and 29.5–31.9 (BMNH, ZDUM, ZRCNUS).

Weight (g). One unsexed adult, 316.

DISTRIBUTION. Historical summary: *Nar, Kel, Pra, Pek, Phg, Sel, Neg, Mel.* Geographically unlikely reports from Tarutao island need confirming, against the possibility of confusion with Pale-capped Pigeon (which see). The northern Peninsula is an unexplained range-gap, continental populations terminating on the Tenasserim/SW Thailand divide.

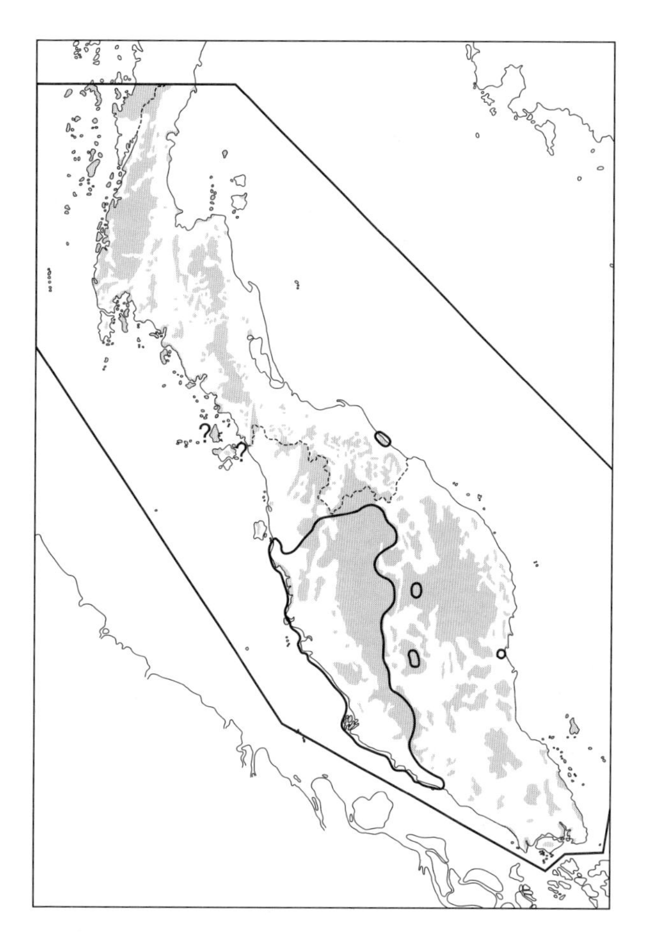

GEOGRAPHICAL VARIATION. Nominate *badia*, of the Sunda region.

STATUS AND POPULATION. Resident, regular and common on the Larut and Main Ranges. A record from Chalerm Prakiat wildlife sanctuary, Narathiwat, implies a presence on the adjacent north tip of the Main Range, but actually confirmed to occur only between Telapa Buruk peak (Negeri Sembilan) and latitude 5°35'N (the E–W highway) (BR 1965, R. Gregory-Smith). Also on the Benom and Tahan massifs (Medway 1972, Robinson and Chasen 1936) but, so far, not from any of the latter's outliers, or the E-coast Range.

Dispersants to the western lowlands are confirmed 'from the neighbour hood of Penang' (not the island) south to the Melaka/Johor border. Eastwards, a bird from near Kuantan (Pahang) was 90 km from the nearest known pocket of breeding population (Batchelor 1958, BMNH, Robinson and Chasen 1936).

HABITATS AND ECOLOGY. Mountain Imperials frequent the canopy of mature and disturbed forest, come to the edge and, where unmolested, often loaf quite low by small roads through forest – even on service-wires. From evidence of advertising behaviour, they breed only in Montane forest, to at least 1500 m altitude, but move about with the fruit supply. At the same time, present year-round in surrounding lowlands, on the W-coast plain as far afield as the mangrove zone.

One trapped at floodlights on the Main Range at Fraser's Hill (BMP5) is likely to have been disturbed from roost in nearby forest; there is no other evidence of night-time dispersal. Movement to and from the lowlands is diurnal and loners and twos and threes are commonly to be seen making long, high flights over the mountain slope. In the plain, habitats include both dry-land and swamp-forests, and birds regularly occur over the coast. Communal roosts have been encountered in peatswamp and mangrove forests.

FORAGING AND FOOD. On the Main Range, numbers drop locally when figs are scarce, but suspiciously few records exist of feeding in Montane forest at any time. In the lowlands, some have been seen with Green Imperials and Large Green Pigeons at fig-crops by Kenering lake, Perak river (Sutari Supari). At Kuala Lompat, in the lowlands east of Benom peak (Pahang), ones and twos visited *Ficus crassiramea* trees (mean small diameter of fruit 18.8 mm) and, once, a larger-fruited *F. cucurbitina* (diameter 22.6 mm) (Lambert 1987). Lowland fruit resources are evidently an attraction, but more of the significance of altitudinal commuting would be resolved if it could be learned what Mountain Imperial Pigeons do in mangroves. Robinson and Chasen (1936) claim leaves and buds of certain mangrove trees are eaten, but do not quote sources and there has been no confirmation of such behaviour.

SOCIAL ORGANIZATION. Pairs nest alone, and loners and pairs are typical in the mountains; groups (not above 4–5 individuals) only occasional. These are also the regular commuting units, but once in the lowlands parties commonly coalesce into larger flocks. The latter are likely to be roost groups, met with mainly at dusk and dawn but occasionally also during the day at actual feeding sites. The wide scatter of sought-after fruit-trees in the lowlands may favour a local centre of information-exchange, and a previous impression that individuals always commute back to the mountains to roost no longer holds.

MOVEMENTS. Journeys of 30–40 km between the mountains and coastal roosts appear to be routine, but nothing is known about how frequently individuals make them.

SURVIVAL. No information.

SOCIAL INTERACTIONS. Display-flight over the forest canopy is deeply undulating, with a steep, flapping up-swoop to a vertical stall and volplaning dive into the next U-loop.

VOICE. The advertising-call of males is a deep, powerful but muffled *korroomp roomp*, repeated at intervals from an exposed perch in the top of the forest, and answered by neighbours. The stressed note is given as the puffed neck lunges deeply forward, the second note as it tucks back up upright again. Pair-members make short-range contact with a grunt (G.C. Madoc).

BREEDING

Nest. A typically sparse, twig platform, diameter 20–25 cm, built 3–4 m up on a flattish support in a low, densely foliaged tree, in one instance overhanging a much-used mountain road; also on pandan and tree-fern crowns.

Eggs and brood. The egg is more or less glossless white. Shape elliptical. Size (mm): 40.8 × 30.0 (n=1). Full clutch one.

Cycle. No information.

Seasonality. Egg and chick dates indicate laying during late December–April, June, July and September (two October squabs) (F.G.H. Allen, Allen 1953, Bromley 1948b, G.C. Madoc, Madoc 1956a, Madoc and Allen 1952, NRCS, Robinson and Chasen 1936, ZRCNUS), based on data pooled over many years.

MOULT. Replacement of primaries is regular-descendant. Among 20 adults, the few in active wing-moult (P3 to P5) were dated March–May and October. Four showed suspension or arrest (at between P2 and P5) in January–February, and other non-moulters were all dated September–March, implying seasonality (BMNH, ZDUM, ZRCNUS).

CONSERVATION. More needs to be learned about the relative importance of foraging in lowland versus mountain habitats, and especially about the role of mangroves.

Pied Imperial Pigeon; Nok Lumphuu Khao (Thai); Pergam Rawa (Malay)

Ducula bicolor (Scopoli) 1786, *Deliciae Florae et Faunae Insubricae* 2: 94. TL New Guinea.
Plate 43

GROUP RELATIONS. Said to form a superspecies with grey-headed NW Australian *D. constans* and Sulawesian *D. luctuosa* (Silver-tipped Imperial Pigeon), but more research on breeding limits is needed. Variation in the area of the Moluccas suggests some secondary contact with other populations that have not diverged to species level.

GLOBAL RANGE. At its most inclusive, the Andamans and Nicobars, and islands and mainland coasts from W Burma (Arakan) and the Gulf of Bangkok to the Greater Sunda islands, Bali and W and S Philippines; Lombok (Nash and Nash 1987), N Sulawesi and the Moluccas; and New Guinea to the Bismarck archipelago and northern Australia.

IDENTIFICATION/DESCRIPTION. A distinctive large, pied pigeon, usually in a party, typically remote from the regular habitats of (pied) Town Pigeon. Proportionately longer, sharper-winged (tip = P8 or 9) and shorter-tailed than the other imperial pigeons. A minority of apparent adults from Malaysian coasts north to Kedah and Terengganu shows variably black-tipped lower tail-coverts, as found in the far east of the range. The white parts of fresh-plumaged adults are flushed ivory-cream, perhaps by preening from lipid-producing feathers described for this species by Berthold (1967). Juveniles are duller, with pale orange-buff spots on the upper wing-coverts.

Bare-part colours. (Adult) iris brown to red-brown; cere and bill lead-blue, darker greyish at tip; feet pale purple-blue (Oates 1883, Robinson and Chasen 1936).

Size (mm). (Skins: 11 males, 7 females; adult): wing 224–239 and 218–233; tail 112–130 and 114–125; bill 20.7–24.2 (sexes combined); tarsus 29.3–35.1 and 27.9–34.0 (BMNH, ZDUM, ZRCNUS).

Weight. No data.

DISTRIBUTION. Both coasts, but with gaps in the NE. Historical summary: all divisions except *Pak, Nak, Pht, Son, Pat, Yal, Nar, Pes, Kel, Pra*. Additional islands occupied include the Surin and Similan groups, Phiphi, Maa, Chuak (*Tra*), Tarutao and Ta Nga (*Sat*), Dayang Bunting and outliers of the Langkawi group (but no recent records), Paya, Penang, Rembia, Jarak, islands of the Kelang estuary and Pisang off the W coast; the Ang Thong national park group, Kra (*Nak*), Serenggeh, the Perhentians, the Redang group, Bidung Laut (now mostly devegetated), Kapas and Tenggol (*Tru*), and throughout the Pahang–Johor archipelago off the E coast. Only occasional around Singapore, with records from Merambong (Johor Straits), the main island, Sentosa, St John's, Semakau and Pawai.

GEOGRAPHICAL VARIATION. Nominate *bicolor*.

STATUS AND POPULATION. Resident, regular and uncommon to common, present year-round through most of the range indicated, except the Singapore archipelago which mostly lacks mature forest and is visited only intermittently.

HABITATS AND ECOLOGY. An island specialist, breeding and roosting, usually gregariously, only on well isolated, wooded islets but commuting daily to feed in the forests of larger islands; less regularly also to patches of mainland coastal forest, such as on isolated promontories; also to tracts of well-grown mainland mangroves.

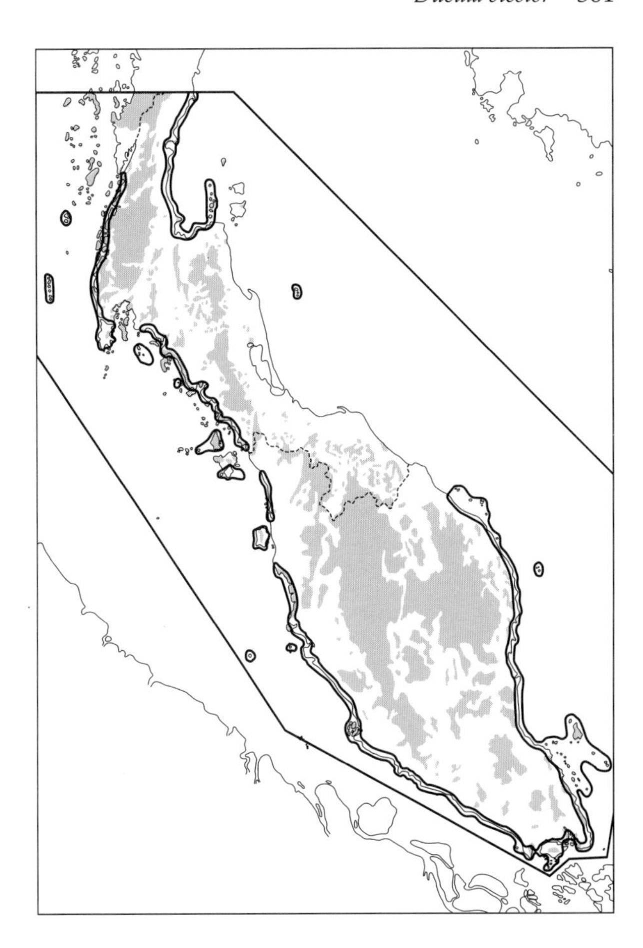

FORAGING AND FOOD. A fig-eater like its congeners, but also takes other foods, as indicated by the many seeds voided by brooding adults and young below nests (a potent source of diet information not yet studied). In Singapore, one seen taking fruit of an exotic, garden palm *Ptychosperma macarthurii* (SINGAV-4). It has been suggested this pigeon's seed-dispersal capabilities have been important in determining small-island vegetation around the Peninsula. Over 90 percent of the plant species of Jarak island, Melaka Straits, for example, are typically bird-dispersed (Wyatt-Smith 1951a).

SOCIAL ORGANIZATION. Unlike other fruit pigeons, including other imperial pigeons, often nests (as well as forages and roosts) gregariously. Commutes to and from feeding-grounds in coherent parties, typically of 10–30 birds.

MOVEMENTS. Local diurnal feeding movements are all that have been observed, and the most distant regularly occupied islands would be reachable from nearest staging points in probably less than one hour of flying.

SURVIVAL No information.

SOCIAL INTERACTIONS. No information.

VOICE. Coming from tree-crowns containing many active birds, a deep, sighing coo of two deliberate notes, the first falling in pitch, the second even: *ooo krrrooo*.

BREEDING

Nest. A sparse, shallow, twig platform, diameter 25–30 cm, built 1.5–7 m up in scrubby trees or on small palms or pandan tops, often in loose colonies (including an estimated 50 pairs on Serenggeh island, Terengganu).

Eggs and brood. Egg glossy white. Shape typically a rather long ellipse. Size (mm): 46.0–42.8 × 32.0–30.3 (n=6). Full clutch one.

Cycle. No information.

Seasonality. On Malaysian E-coast islands, eggs or squabs at dates that imply laying during April–July (a last fledgling newly out of the nest in late August) (F.G.H. Allen, Berwick 1952b, BR 1980–81, G.C. Madoc, ZRCNUS).

MOULT. Replacement at least of the inner hand is regular-descendant, with a few instances of simultaneous inner hand and wing-tip moult, possibly after a previous suspension. Among 27 adults covering all months, active wing-moult occurred in April, June, August–October and December (late-stages as of late August), with instances of suspension or arrest (at P1 to P9) especially during November–March (BMNH, ZDUM, ZRCNUS).

CONSERVATION. Ordinarily, Pied Imperial Pigeons live in remote places, far from contact with settlement. Impacts of the spread of beach tourism to small islands need to be monitored.

Order PSITTACIFORMES

Family PSITTACIDAE

Parrots, hanging parrots and parakeets: five species

This is one of the great families of birds traded through SE Asia. Many exotics have from time to time escaped or been released in the Peninsula. Most have not survived there but three species now breed wild and, locally, show evidence of maintaining themselves. These are the globally near-threatened Tanimbar Cockatoo *Cacatua goffini* on Singapore island and satellites (St John's, Sentosa) (SINGAV-1, -2, -4); Indo-Burmese Rose-ringed Parakeet *Psittacula krameri* in Singapore and Penang (Choy Wai Mun, ENGGANG -1, -3, SINGAV-2); and, also in Singapore, Red-breasted Parakeet *P. alexandri* (native in the far north of the Peninsula) (BR 1978–79, SINGAV-1).

Blue-rumped Parrot; Nok Hok Yai (Thai); Bayan Puting (Malay)

Psittinus cyanurus (Forster) 1795, *Faunula Indica*: 6. TL Melaka.
Plate 46

GROUP RELATIONS. Free-standing, with no obviously close relatives.

GLOBAL RANGE. Borneo, Sumatra and the Peninsula, and SW Thailand and Tenasserim respectively to 13° and about 14°N (BBCB-8, BMNH). One of the Sundaic birds believed to have occurred in the past in far-S Vietnam (Delacour 1970).

IDENTIFICATION/DESCRIPTION. A medium-small parrot with short tail and broad, blunt head giving compact, stocky appearance, particularly in overhead flight. Perched, both adults show a maroon patch on the inner leading-edge of the wing, with lower lesser wing-coverts and axillaries scarlet, forming a conspicuous patch against slaty black flight-feathers when the wing is raised. The adult female has head brown, with rich coppery tone to the cap that is either an age or plumage-cycle factor, chin yellow and a small, blue patch on the back. The male has a lavender-blue head, yellow pectoral tuft, indigo-black mantle and primary-coverts, and back to upper tail-coverts bright blue, but takes more than one moult to develop full colours. With age, yellow-tinged underparts become blue-grey and the rest of the plumage brighter overall. There is some evidence also of an intermediate, presumed subadult plumage in males, with brown head showing no more than blue feather-tips at the side (a bird from Pakchan with red upper mandible and male measurements had female plumage and fully brown head).

Juveniles of both sexes have uniformly grass-green head and body, with yellow fringing on the wing-coverts; males soon distinguished by the reddening of the upper mandible (BMNH, UMZC).

Bare-part colours. (Adult) iris creamy white, eyelids dusky green; cere dusky green, bill dark horn (female), with upper mandible orange-red (male); feet dirty sage-green.

Size (mm). (Skins: 30 males, 16 females; adult): wing 120–131 and 120–123 (immatures of both range 1–2 mm shorter); tail 41–49 and 40–50; bill from cere 18.8–20.8 and 18.3–19.9; tarsus 13.0–15.4 and 13.5–14.5 (BMNH, UMZC, ZRCNUS).

Weight. No data.

DISTRIBUTION. Historical summary: all divisions except *Ran, Pha, Nak, Phu, Pht, Son, Pat, Pra,* with no other island records.

GEOGRAPHICAL VARIATION. Nominate *cyanurus,* of the global range except the W Sumatran islands.

STATUS AND POPULATION. Resident, regular and more or less common in the south; local and now sparse north of Malaysia (past status in the Thai provinces not recorded, but many century-old specimens exist from Pakchan).

HABITATS AND ECOLOGY. Primarily, dry-land evergreen and semi-evergreen Lowland forest, mature and selectively logged; more or less strictly at plains level. A party of four crossing a 1300 m ridge of the Main Range between the Selangor and Sempam valleys at Fraser's Hill on 30 November 1970 (BR 1970–71) is still the only record above the hill-foot boundary. Visits edge vegetation and the gap-phase growth of forest clearings; exceptionally also

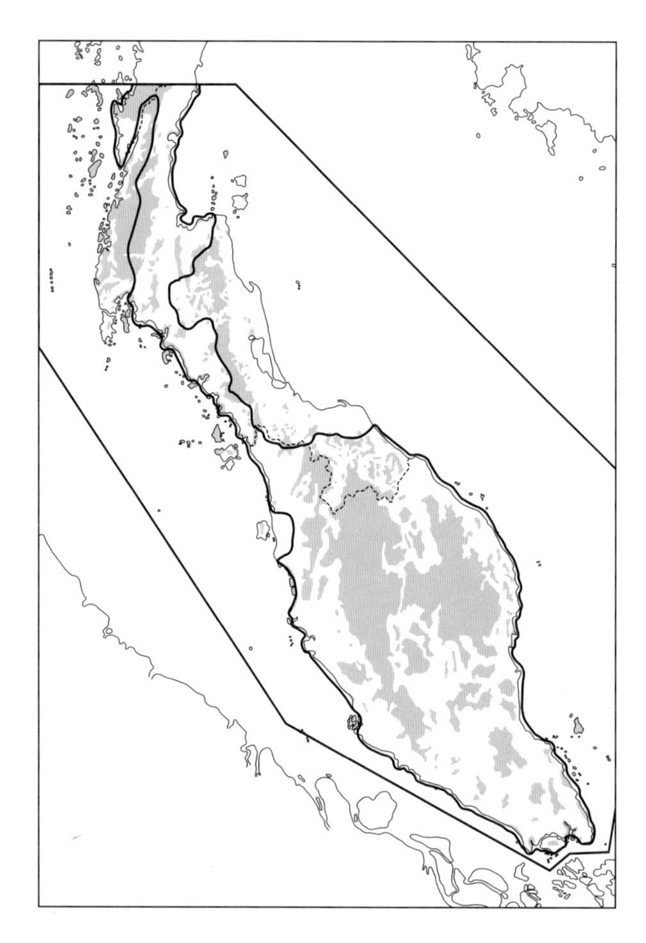

mangroves where dispersants may occasionally roost (Nisbet 1968, Robinson 1927), but not yet recorded from subcoastal peatswamp forest. Out of forest, dispersants enter coconut plantations (Wells 1958) and, in the 1960s, discovered lipid-rich (but protein-poor) oil-palm fruit, although this parrot has not fulfilled predictions of becoming an agricultural pest (BMP5, Ward and Wood 1967).

FORAGING AND FOOD. Like some other forest-dwelling seed-eaters, either patrols a very large home-range or follows seed-flushes nomadically. A seed-predator, recorded opening the pods of the tree legume *Parkia speciosa* (G.C. Madoc), but otherwise little observed. Eats the mesocarp off oil-palm fruits extracted individually from the bunch (Ward and Wood 1967).

SOCIAL ORGANIZATION. Breeding pairs are typically solitary. Otherwise, mostly gregarious, dispersing and foraging in parties of up to 20 (more usually ten or less).

MOVEMENTS. Long-distance, possibly nomadic dispersal is suspected. Some individual journeys are guessed to cover the width-equivalent of the Main Range.

SURVIVAL. No information.

SOCIAL INTERACTIONS. No information.

VOICE. Silent while feeding and loafing but when flying in groups communicates continuously with tinkling, two- and three-note whistles: *tee-link*, *whee-chi-chi*, audible even when the flock is too high overhead to be easily spotted.

BREEDING

Nest. A small, natural hole at least 30 m up a live, forest tree, including *Shorea* species.

Eggs and brood. Eggs are plain white. Size (mm): 26.5–23.1 × 21.3–20.3 (n=7). Full clutch said to be three, but confirmation required.

Cycle. No information.

Seasonality. A female and a pair inspecting (knot) holes in large forest dipterocarps in Singapore and Negeri Sembilan, in late November and mid February; three clutches with sitting adults in small holes high in forest trees in Perak, all dated 20 May (E.C.S. Baker, BMP5, SINGAV-2).

MOULT. Moult of primaries is commonly at two loci up to five feathers apart, but a few birds examined showed a single-locus, regular-descendant pattern. Suspensions or arrests are frequent. Among 63 birds collected in all months except February, wing-moult showed no obvious seasonal progression and occurred more or less year-round (BMNH, UMZC, ZRCNUS).

CONSERVATION. The breeding habitat is now heavily fragmented, and in Thailand has been virtually wiped out. Individual mobility should be a plus-factor but its solitary breeding has rendered this parrot more sensitive to forest-loss than co-occurring, colonial, Long-tailed Parakeet. Globally near-threatened (BTW2).

Vernal Hanging Parrot; Nok Hok Lek Paak Daeng (Thai); Burung Serindit Rambai (Malay)

Loriculus vernalis (Sparrman) 1787, *Museum Carlsonianum, in quo novas et selectas Aves* 2: 29. TL Cachar district, NE India.

Plate 46

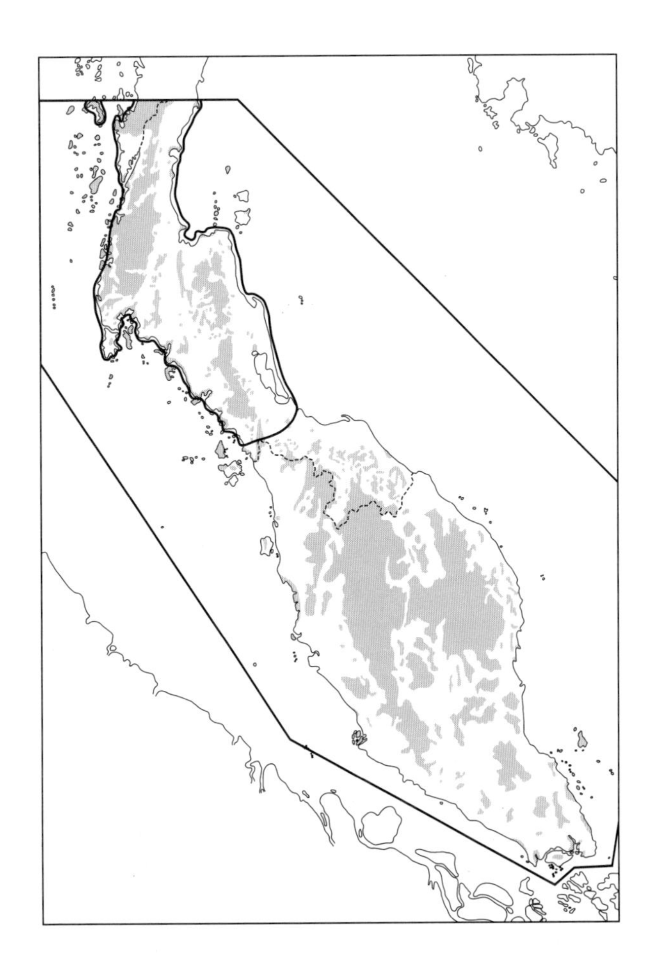

GROUP RELATIONS. On morphological grounds, including female colours, likely to form a superspecies with *L. beryllinus*, *galgulus* and *philippensis* (Ceylon and Blue-crowned Hanging Parrots, and Colasisi). A narrow overlap of range between *vernalis* and *galgulus* in the Peninsula could be due to non-breeding dispersal.

GLOBAL RANGE. Himalayan foothills east from Nepal and the far-NE and E coast of the Indian subcontinent, hill-tracts of S India, and the Bay of Bengal islands; Yunnan east possibly to Guangdong; and continental SE Asia to the Peninsula.

IDENTIFICATION/DESCRIPTION. A tiny, stubby, bullet-headed parrot; all age/sex-classes grass-green with turquoise-blue underwing and lower tail-surface; rump and upper tail-coverts red, in juveniles duller and green-mixed. Adult male brighter overall than female, with a bluer-washed throat. Flight fast and bouncing, alternating rapid flapping with rocketing on closed wings.

Bare-part colours. (Adult) iris white; bill orange-red; feet yellow to orange-yellow (BMNH).

Size (mm). (Skins: 9 males, 9 females; adult): wing 83–89 and 85–90; tail 34–39 and 36–39; bill 10.4–11.7 and 10.0–11.7; tarsus 9.3–12.2 and 9.4–11.4 (BMNH, ZRCNUS).

Weight. No data.

DISTRIBUTION. South to Songkhla and Satul (Thaleban national park). Historical summary: *Pak, Chu, Ran, Sur, Pha, Nak, Phu, Kra, Pht, Tra, Son, Sat,* with additional island records from Lanbyi (*Pak*).

GEOGRAPHICAL VARIATION. Endemic *phileticus* Deignan 1956 (TL Ban Phra Muang, Trang).

STATUS AND POPULATION. Resident, regular and common; the only reasonably numerous parrot in the Thai provinces, but it is not known how far south into the Peninsula breeding actually occurs. Dispersants wander well outside presumed forest breeding-habitat.

HABITATS AND ECOLOGY. Evergreen and semi-evergreen, dry-land Lowland forest, mature and logged, at plains level and to an unmapped distance up mountain slopes; also in forest-edge, orchard and tall-scrub habitats, and beach-strand woodland, particularly with mature casuarinas (Holmes and Wells 1975).

FORAGING AND FOOD. Silent when feeding and difficult to detect among foliage. No specific information on diet.

SOCIAL ORGANIZATION. Typically in pairs or small parties.

MOVEMENTS. No information.

SURVIVAL. No information.

SOCIAL INTERACTIONS. No information from the wild. Like other *Loriculus* species, sleeps exclusively (and day-roosts mainly) hanging upside down, usually by both feet (Buckley 1968).

VOICE. The main flight-call is a shrill, squeaking *pe-zeez-eet*, the first note often difficult to distinguish (Boonsong and Round 1991).

BREEDING. No records.

MOULT. Pattern undescribed. Among 18 adults dated December–March and May, July, only one male (from Phangnga) showed wing-moult, growing P6–7 on 31 May. December individuals were in fresh plumage (BMNH, ZRCNUS).

CONSERVATION. In Thailand, populations have resisted the effects of trapping for the wildlife trade more successfully than Blue-rumped Parrot.

Blue-crowned Hanging Parrot; Nok Hok Lek Paak Dam (Thai); Burung Serindit Biasa (Malay)

Loriculus galgulus (Linnaeus) 1758, *Systema Naturae* 10(1): 103. TL Melaka.
Plate 46

GROUP RELATIONS. See Vernal Hanging Parrot. Except for a neighbouring Sulu-island race of *L. philippensis*, this is the only black-billed member of the superspecies.

GLOBAL RANGE. Borneo, Sumatra and intervening islands, and the Peninsula.

IDENTIFICATION/DESCRIPTION. Slightly smaller than Vernal Hanging Parrot; similarly grass-green with turquoise-blue underwing and lower tail-surface, and red rump and upper tail-coverts. From Vernal by bill and foot colour, coppery yellow mantle and a dark blue spot on the crown; all parts brighter and clearer in adult males, which also have bright yellow lower back and a large red breast-shield. Juveniles from adult female by shorter upper tail-coverts and no blue on crown; young male underparts slightly more yellowish green than in female. In flight, Blue-crowned not separable from Vernal, except possibly by voice.

Bare-part colours. (Adult) iris dark brown; bill yellow-horn (juvenile), black (adult); feet grey-green.

Size (mm). (Skins: 37 males, 29 females; adult): wing 84–89 and 81–91; tail 30–36 and 30–35; bill 10.2–12.1 and 9.4–11.4; tarsus 10.8–11.5 and 11.1–11.7 (BMNH).

Weight (g). An adult, 28 (Lambert 1987).

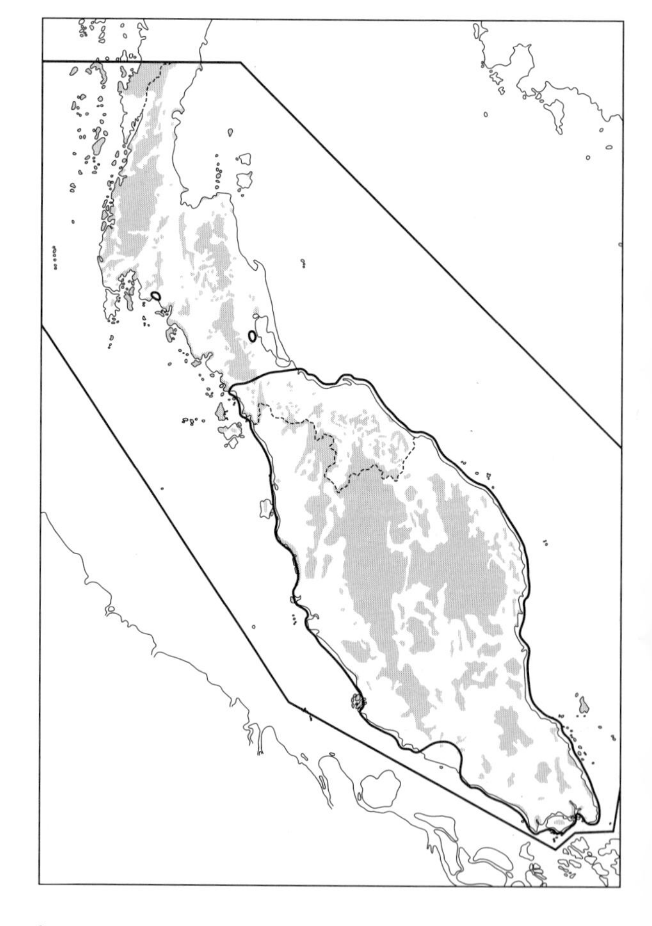

DISTRIBUTION. The only hanging parrot recorded south from Perlis, Yala and Pattani. Historical summary: *Kra, Pht, Son, Pat, Sat, Yal, Nar, Pes, Ked, Kel, Tru, Pra, Pek, Phg, Sel, Neg, Joh, Sin.* Island records from Ubin and St John's, Singapore, are believed to be of released captives.

GEOGRAPHICAL VARIATION. None recognized.

STATUS AND POPULATION. Only a few remain in Singapore, mostly in NE parts of the main island. On the mainland, resident, regular and common to latitude about 7°N, i.e., at about the boundary between Malaysian and Thai-Burmese Lowland forest types. Sparse, perhaps only as a non-breeding dispersant, northward to Phatthalung (a male collected in April) and the Krabi coast (a sighting on 4 March) (BBCB-9, Bonhote 1901).

HABITATS AND ECOLOGY. The landward edge of mangroves, strand woodland (including casuarinas), tall scrub and secondary woodland, orchards, wooded gardens and parkland, the forest-edge and canopy of mature and logged dry-land evergreen and semi-evergreen Lowland forest at all elevations. Often visits Lower Montane and occasionally Upper Montane forest, with records to over 2000 m (a sighting at the summit of Tahan, Taman Negara: Robinson 1927). Like other Sundaic parrots, either 'trap-lines' around the food-sources of a large, communal home-range or is truly nomadic.

FORAGING AND FOOD. Raids orchards and takes the mesocarp of oil-palm fruits (Buckley 1968, Wood 1968), but only a few wild foods have been identified. At Kuala Lompat, Kerau wildlife reserve (Pahang), Lambert (1987) recorded occasional feeding visits to *Ficus caulocarpa, virens, delosyce, pisocarpa* and *kerkenhovenii,* most with dull-coloured figs, mean small diameter 12 mm or less. *F. crassiramea* and *F. stupenda* are two larger-fruited species attended. They also visit flowers, regularly attracted, e.g., to coral trees *Erythrina* spp., apparently for nectar but this has not been proven in the field.

SOCIAL ORGANIZATION. Breeds in lone pairs and disperses in ones and twos, sometimes in small parties, to a recorded maximum group-size of 30 (Batchelor 1958).

MOVEMENTS. Two night-time mist-net captures at floodlights on the crest of the Main Range at Fraser's Hill, on 11 April and 1 December 1969 (BMP5), could have been of birds disturbed from nearby roosts, but also suggest genuine nocturnal dispersal (as among frugivorous forest pigeons).

SURVIVAL. No information.

SOCIAL INTERACTIONS. Buckley (1968) has described the behaviour of captives trapped in Selangor. Aggressive actions spacing individuals at food-sources include lunging at opponent's feet, gaping and various wing movements: holding the carpus of the folded wing out from the body to reveal lining colours or, more rarely, stretching the whole wing out or up. Males courtship-feed females with a regurgitated food-bolus. The most distinctive male courtship display is a run with body stiffly erect and red plumage-parts ruffled.

As Vernal, sleeps and rests hanging upside down, usually by both feet. To defecate in this position, transfers to one foot and flexes the body 45°, raising the tail. Other maintenance behaviour includes 'indirect' scratching of head and bill by bringing the foot over the lowered wing (Buckley 1968).

VOICE. Threat actions are accompanied by a throaty, grating sound, and male courtship by a *jeet* call. Gives a shrill *trrirt* while feeding, and a disyllabic *tirrit* or *squeak-it* (the Malay name *serin-dit* is onomatopoeic) may have warning or alarm function. Flight-calls are a shrill, squeaky *tsee* or *dzi*, and (in a group) a rapid *ti-ti-ti-tit* and ringing *ti ti ti ti ti ...*

BREEDING

Nest. In disturbed forest, holes up to 12 m above ground in a dead palm *Oncosperma* sp. and live and dead trees, including one drowned in a newly-filled reservoir. Entrance 7.5 cm wide; a small nest-cavity was floored with wood-chips, a much larger one filled to within 15 cm of the entrance with leaf and fern-frond pieces. Hanging Parrots, among the few parrots known to build rather than merely excavate, cut nest-material and are said to carry it tucked into the plumage.

Eggs and brood. Eggs are glossless white. Shape near-spherical. Size (mm): 18.3–16.8 × 15.2–14.7 (n=3). Full clutch apparently four.

Cycle. No information.

Seasonality. Nest-hole excavation on 13 March in Johor, and active nests in Perak and Selangor in February, March, May and early August (Chasen 1939, C.M. Francis, NRCS, SINGAV-2).

MOULT. The replacement sequence has not been worked out, but primaries commonly moult at two loci, up to ten feathers apart. Among 81 birds covering all months except June and November, wing-moult was concentrated into the period May–late October (78 percent incidence in August) (BMNH, UMZC, ZRCNUS).

CONSERVATION. Like Vernal Hanging Parrot, has withstood traditional trapping for the pet trade, but is reduced to a low level in Singapore (even though much protected nesting-habitat still occurs there). In the agricultural lowlands of the mainland, dependant on retention of a diversified landscape that includes, at minimum, substantial patches of tall, semi-natural woodland cover.

Red-breasted Parakeet; Nok Khaek Tao (Thai); Bayan Api (Malay)

Psittacula alexandri (Linnaeus) 1758, *Systema Naturae* 10(1): 97. TL Java.
Plate 46

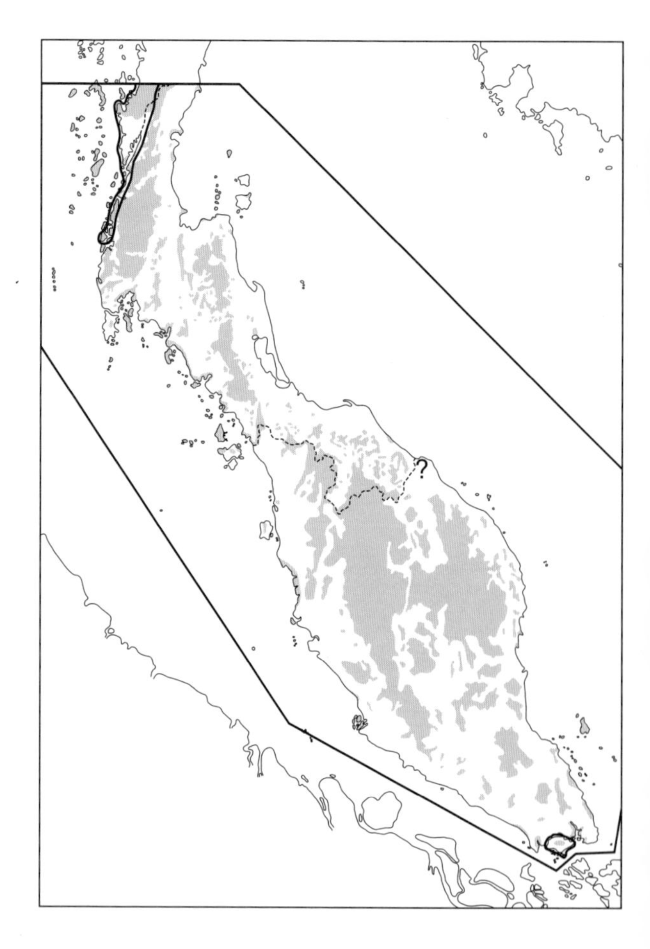

GROUP RELATIONS. Uncertain. Despite size-differences, probably closest to allopatric Sino-Himalayan *P. derbiana* and the small-island endemic *P. caniceps* (Derbyan and Nicobar Parakeets).

GLOBAL RANGE. E Himalayan foothills, hill-tracts of the far-NE Indian subcontinent, and the Andaman islands; extreme SE Tibet; from Yunnan possibly to Guangdong, including Hainan; SE Asia to the Peninsula, then W Sumatran islands, far-S Borneo, Java and Bali.

IDENTIFICATION/DESCRIPTION. Adults from Long-tailed Parakeet mainly by violet-grey head with narrow, black frontal band back to eye-level, and vinous-pink breast and upper belly. Sexed by upper mandible colour, and males are longer-tailed, generally brighter, with a blue tinge to pink underparts. Juveniles are all-green-bodied and have a green crown; in the field, probably difficult to separate from same-stage Long-tailed.

Bare-part colours. (Adult) iris lemon-yellow (male), whitish (female); bill black (female), with upper mandible clear red (male); feet pale olive-green.

Size (mm). (Skin: 1 NW male; adult): wing 155; tail 155; bill from cere 23.8; tarsus 15.8 (BMNH).

Weight. No data.

DISTRIBUTION. In the past, apparently, south to about the Malaysian border; introduced in Singapore (BMP5). Historical summary: *Pak, Ran, Pha, Kel, Sin*, with other island records from Lao (*Ran*), Phra Thong (*Pha*) off the W coast, and St John's (recent releases?), Singapore.

GEOGRAPHICAL VARIATION. The indigenous northern population is continental Asian *fasciata* P.L.S. Müller 1776 (TL Arakan, W Burma). Singapore birds have never been determined.

STATUS AND POPULATION. A presumed resident in the NW lowlands, recorded south to Phra Thong island in the Li river estuary (Phangnga), but the only modern reports are from coastal Ranong: some collected there in May–June 1955 and a flock of 20-plus in mangroves at Bang Ben in mid February 1995 (BLC, H. Jacobs). The recent situation in Pakchan is unknown but probably heavily trapped for the pet trade everywhere. In August 1889, W.R. Davison reported a flock by the Kelantan river near Kota Baru, which must be counted within possible former dispersal limits (BMP5, Davison 1889).

First recorded feral on Singapore island in 1943; other releases have probably occurred since and wild eggs were collected there in January 1951 (F.G.H. Allen, Gibson-Hill 1952). Later thought to have failed (BMP5) but small numbers were back by 1979, including a flock of about 15 at Tuas in January that year. Peak roost and flock counts are now in the 25–30 range, and juveniles imply breeding has been regular since at least the mid 1980s (BIRDLINE 1993, MBR 1986–87, SINGAV-1, -3, -4, -6).

HABITATS AND ECOLOGY. Singapore birds occur in a variety of woodland and semi-open situations. The only confirmed habitat in the NW is mangroves, but this cannot be the whole picture.

FORAGING AND FOOD. No information.

SOCIAL ORGANIZATION. Nesting by lone pairs is recorded in Singapore, but normally gregarious at all times. Moves, forages and roosts in cohesive parties, and elsewhere in its range breeds colonially.

MOVEMENTS. No information.

SURVIVAL. No information.

SOCIAL INTERACTIONS. No information.

VOICE. No information.

BREEDING

Nest. Tree-holes at Loyang, Singapore.

Eggs and brood. Not described.

Cycle. Both pair-members tend nestlings.

Seasonality. In Singapore, eggs collected in January, behaviour suggestive of young in the nest in early April, and flying juveniles reported in February and May; in Phangnga, a juvenile collected on 17 February (F.G.H. Allen, BIRDLINE 1993, BMNH, SINGAV-1, -6).

MOULT. An adult male from Maliwun district, Pakchan, growing P7 on 12 May (BMNH).

CONSERVATION. Too little is known about habitat requirements in the NW range but effective checks on trapping, and planning for reintroduction where suitable conditions can be established, are significant issues.

Long-tailed Parakeet; (no Thai name); Bayan Nuri (Malay)

Psittacula longicauda (Boddaert) 1783, *Table des Planches Enluminéez d'Histoire Naturelle*: 53.
TL Melaka.
Plate 46

GROUP RELATIONS. Apparently free-standing.

GLOBAL RANGE. The Andaman and Nicobar islands; Sumatra, Borneo and intervening islands, and southern part of the Peninsula.

IDENTIFICATION/DESCRIPTION. Size as Red-breasted and Rose-ringed Parakeets, with the same swift, direct flight. From them overhead by bright lime-yellow underparts, including lower wing-coverts, sharp against olive-black flight-feathers. Adult males are much longer-tailed than other age/sex-classes, with conspicuous rose-pink head that is only capped green. Pink of females and immatures is duller and restricted to the side of the face (the green of the cap continuous with remaining upperparts), and their malar-stripe is dark green rather than black. The head of young juveniles is all-green, unpatterned.

Bare-part colours. (Adult) iris pale yellow; bill dark horn (female), with upper mandible clear red (male); feet slaty.

Size (mm). (Skins: 22 males, 10 females; adult): wing 142–153 and 132–153; tail 201–269 and 79–115; bill from cere 21.2–24.2 and 18.8–23.4; tarsus 21.3–23.0 and 20.3–23.4 (BMNH, ZRCNUS).

Weight. No data.

DISTRIBUTION. North at plains level to N Kedah (Sintok district) in the west, N Terengganu in the east. Historical summary: *Ked, Tru, Pek, Phg, Sel, Neg, Mel, Joh, Sin*, with additional island records from Tekong, Ubin and Sentosa, Singapore.

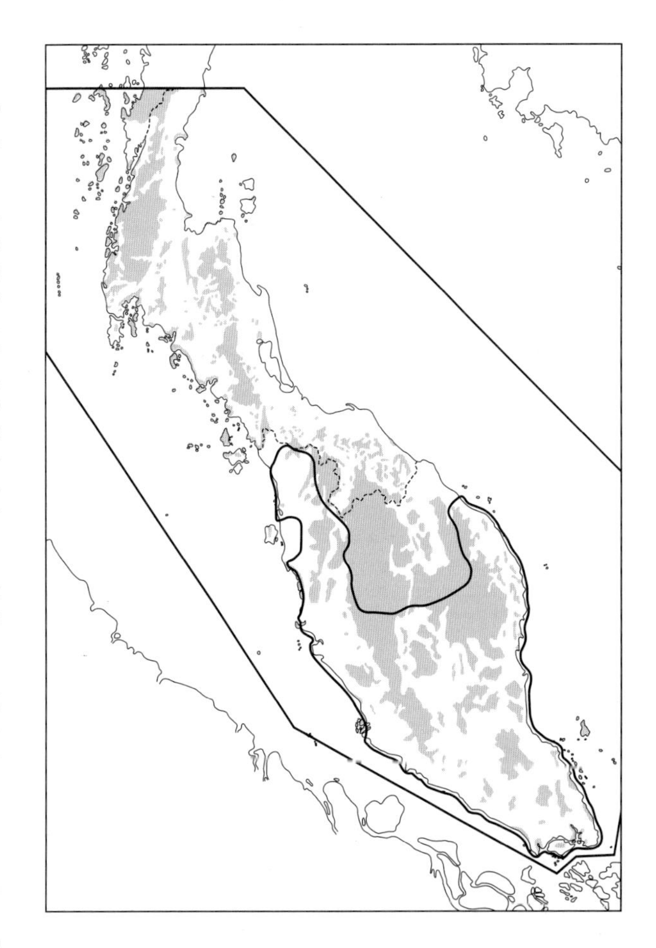

GEOGRAPHICAL VARIATION. Nominate *longicauda*, of the global range except Indian Ocean islands.

STATUS AND POPULATION. Resident, regular and uncommon to common. Large losses must have occurred with deforestation of river-valleys and coastal plains but, overall, Long-tailed Parakeets are still plentiful. Capacity to forage outside forest and nest colonially (near-unique among Sunda rain forest birds, and *contra* Blue-rumped Parrot) may have combined to allow significant breeding to continue in small forest fragments, where oil-palm has replaced much former natural habitat but provides a large new source of food. Relic forest now tends to be removed from the plantation landscape, but settlement of Singapore by breeders in the 1980s suggests that, at least for a time, neighbouring populations may actually have expanded.

HABITATS AND ECOLOGY. Exclusive to plains-level habitats; not found at all above the steepland boundary. Within this zone, forest, especially extreme lowland swamp- (including peatswamp) forest, with a good supply of dead emergents, is core habitat, and the species is forest-dependent for most nesting. Not so for food, and comings and goings in a variety of non-forest habitats range from more or less daily presence to visits of a few consecutive days at intervals of up to several years. If Long-tails 'trap-line' around food-sources they must do so over huge, communal home-ranges, and the long interval between some local appearances rather suggests true nomadism. Pest-level invasion of southern oil-palm estates in the 1960s (Ward and Wood 1967, Wood 1968) is consistent with both behaviours. On the other hand, no nocturnal movements are known (compare other obligate frugivores of Lowland forest), breeding stations are used long-term and some forests, especially swamp-forests, hold parakeets year-round. Large, communal roosts, typical of wide-ranging, opportunistic frugivores and granivores, have been reported in N Sumatra (CLBS) but not from the Peninsula.

FORAGING AND FOOD. Recorded eating blossoms of a red-flowered forest *Bombax* (Robinson 1927) but, apparently, mainly a seed-predator. The few wild sources identified include *Macaranga* and *Ixonanthes* spp., *Vitex pubescens* and *Lagerstroemia* sp. (Bucknill and Chasen 1927, Spittle 1952). In Pasoh research forest, Negeri Sembilan, a party stripped fruits from the high crown of a keruing, *Dipterocarpus crinitus*, wrenching them free of their wings then biting through the pericarp wall to extract the seed. Under the tree, 23.3 percent of discarded fruit had been de-seeded (G.W.H. Davison, MBR 1982–83). Three birds eating fruits of *Sonneratia alba* on Ubin island (SINGAV-6) supply the only direct local record of a bird feeding on a mangrove species. In oil-palm plantations, ripe palm-nuts are extracted individually and held in the foot while mesocarp is scooped off with the lower mandible, typically on a perch away from the fruit-bunch (Wood 1968).

SOCIAL ORGANIZATION. Characteristically gregarious at all times, breeding colonially and moving and feeding in cohesive flocks of a few to 50-plus birds.

MOVEMENTS. No definite information but Singapore birds commute across the Johor Straits to and from the mainland (Hails and Jarvis 1987).

SURVIVAL. No information.

SOCIAL INTERACTIONS. On a high branch of a dead tree in early morning, three consecutive matings by a pair were initiated by the female. She approached the male and bill-touched several times; he mounted and touched alternate sides of her head or neck for about one minute before copulation. This lasted 55 seconds before separation and preening. At second and third approaches, the male responded with much head-bobbing and bill-touching before copulation. The entire sequence occupied 11 minutes (SINGAV-2).

VOICE. The flight-call, given alone or in parties, is a loud, discordant *kiak*.

BREEDING

Nest. Site, a dead tree or upright, emergent spur in or on the edge of forest, often where trees have drowned following a stream blockage. Holes, 6–20 m above ground, may pre-exist but where wood is sufficiently rot-softened are usually excavated by the parakeets themselves. One examined was about 50 cm deep, floored with finely shredded bark. Colony-size varies, with up to 16 pairs counted using a single snag. Lone nesting pairs are unusual.

Eggs and brood. Eggs are highly glossed, plain white. Shape near-spherical. Size (mm): 29.4 × 26.6 (mean, n=4). Full clutch two.

Cycle. No information.

Seasonality. Copulation recorded in October and January; eggs in December and February; active nests, stage unchecked, in February–May; nestlings and new fledglings in May–July and October (Chasen 1939, Madoc 1956a, MBR 1984–85, 1986–87, NRCS, SINGAV-1, -3, -4, -6). Regular monitoring of colonies is needed to define a seasonality.

MOULT. The sequence of primary replacement has not been worked out, but only single-locus moult seen. Among 34 adults, 11 showed active wing-moult in April, May, August (P4 to P9) and December (P2 to P10), with instances of suspension or arrest in June, July, November and December (BMNH, UMZC, ZRCNUS). Again, no seasonality is obvious.

CONSERVATION. The prediction that Long-tailed Parakeet would develop into a significant pest of oil-palm (BMP5, Wood 1968) has not materialized, probably partly because of the retreat of breeding-habitat. Clearance of forest relics from the plantation landscape is a damaging development for this species.

Order CUCULIFORMES

Family CUCULIDAE

Cuckoos and malkohas: 22 species

Pied Cuckoo; Nok Kha-khuu Ngawn Khao Dam (Thai); Burung Sewah Jakubin (Malay)

Clamator jacobinus (Boddaert) 1783, *Table des Planches Enluminéez d'Histoire Naturelle*: 53. TL Coromandel coast, SE India.

GROUP RELATIONS. Free-standing.

GLOBAL RANGE. Sub-Saharan Africa, the Indian subcontinent and Sri Lanka, SE Tibet, and central Burma. A transequatorial migrant in Africa. Scarce to absent in Asia during the northern winter; it is guessed most Asian breeders also winter in Africa (identified in southern Africa and on likely passage dates in S Arabia and on W Indian Ocean islands).

IDENTIFICATION/DESCRIPTION. Line drawing, below. Slightly smaller than Chestnut-winged Cuckoo and crest not as tall, but comportment similar. Entire upperparts including sides of face black (adult) or sooty brown with whitish fringing on lesser and median wing-coverts (juvenile), sharply demarcated from white (adult) or faintly buff-washed (juvenile) underparts, from chin. All age/sex-classes show a short, white bar over the upper base of the primaries and white tips to all except central tail-feathers.

Pied Cuckoo

Bare-part colours. (Burmese adult) iris red-brown; bill black, mouth-lining flesh-pink; feet lead-grey (Oates 1883).

Size. No data.

Weight. No data.

DISTRIBUTION. Historical summary: *Phu*.

GEOGRAPHICAL VARIATION. Unknown; the nearest (central Burmese) breeding population is nominate *jacobinus*.

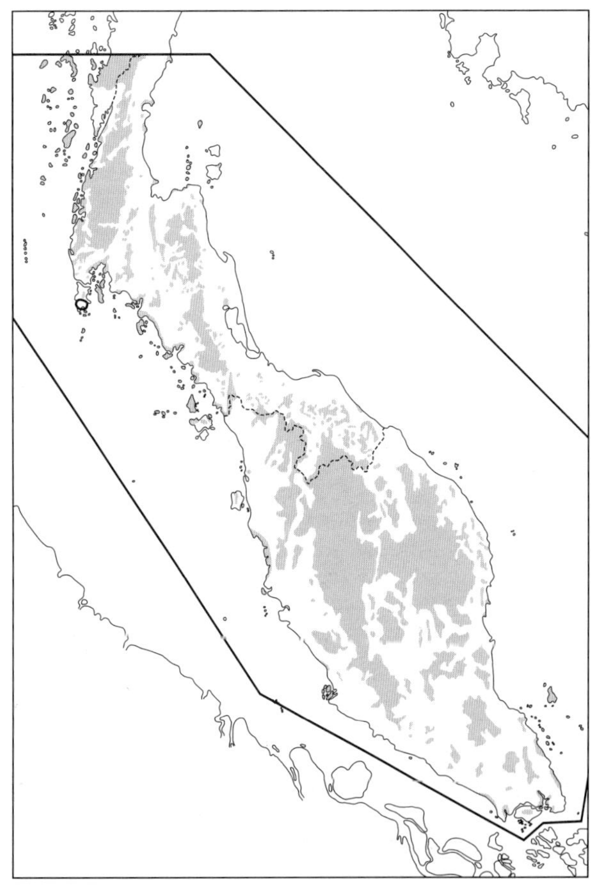

STATUS AND POPULATION. Vagrant; one near Wat Chalong, Phuket, on 5 January 1995 (H. Jacobs), studied at close quarters as it fed among branches and foliage of a roadside sapling in open mining land. The expected autumn migration bearing from breeding areas in S Asia is SW. This unlikely occurrence could have arisen from freak 'mirror-image' reversal to SE. The date implies migration had ended.

HABITATS AND ECOLOGY. Seen in an area of low trees among dredge-mine and aquaculture lagoons. Semi-arid scrubland and open, wooded savanna are usual habitat in the regular range.

FORAGING AND FOOD. Foliage-gleaning; no other information.

SOCIAL ORGANIZATION. No information.

MOVEMENTS. No information.

SURVIVAL. No information.

SOCIAL INTERACTIONS. No information.

VOICE. No information.

BREEDING. No population.

MOULT. No data, but tail appeared worn, indicating an adult at that date.

CONSERVATION. No issues.

Chestnut-winged Cuckoo; Nok Kha-khuu Ngawn (Thai); Burung Sewah Kepak Merah (Malay)

Clamator coromandus (Linnaeus) 1766, *Systema Naturae* 12(1): 171. TL Coromandel coast, SE India.
Plate 47

GROUP RELATIONS. Free-standing.

GLOBAL RANGE. Breeds in the Himalayan foothills east from Garhwal, and the far-NE Indian subcontinent; China south of a line Sichuan–Gansu–Jiangsu, including Hainan; and continental SE Asia to S Vietnam, Cambodia, SW Thailand and Tenasserim. Most populations migrate, wintering in S India and Sri Lanka; the Peninsula to the Greater Sunda islands and Philippines; and Sulawesi. Vagrant W Micronesia.

IDENTIFICATION/DESCRIPTION. A slender, long-tailed cuckoo with distinctively tall, flexible crest held part- to fully erect. Glossy black head and face, upper body, scapulars and tail contrast sharply with white hind-collar, light orange-rufous chin to breast, rufous-chestnut wings (flight-feathers broadly tipped dull brown), and white tail-corners. Juveniles are duller orange below, have crown-feathers, wing-coverts and secondaries buff-tipped, dorsal body-feathering rufous-edged, and tail dark brown tipped dirty white (but are typically part-moulted by the time they arrive).

Bare-part colours. Iris hazel- to rich brown; bill all-black or with lower mandible brown-tinged, mouth-line pink-orange in autumn juveniles; feet blue-grey.

Size (mm). (Live and skins: 53 adults, most not sexed): wing 156–168 (males span this range); tail 209–252 (no definite male below 233); bill 26.3–31.1; tarsus 23.7–27.9 (BMNH, UMBRP, ZRCNUS).

Weight (g). Adults, 66.4–83.8 (n=44) (UMBRP).

DISTRIBUTION. Historical summary: *Sur, Nak, Phu, Kra, Tra, Sat, Ked, Kel, Pek, Phg, Sel, Neg, Mel, Joh, Sin,* with additional island records from Lanta, Libong, Tarutao, Langkawi, Penang and (on passage) Rembia and Pisang off the W coast; and Ubin, Singapore.

GEOGRAPHICAL VARIATION. None recognized.

STATUS AND POPULATION. A non-breeding visitor and passage-migrant, regular but uncommon; recorded in all months September–May. Not especially secretive but erratic contacts suggest winterers wander rather than establish stable home-ranges. A late January capture at floodlights on Fraser's Hill, well above recorded daytime habitat (BR 1980–81), implies mid winter dispersal, but a bird ringed at Klebang, Melaka, in mid January was retrapped a month later less than 1 km away (B.D. Bond).

HABITATS AND ECOLOGY. The landward fringe of mangrove forest; orchards and other plantations, riverbank thickets, patches of secondary-growth and tall scrub bordering cultivation; occasionally beds of tall reeds (BR 1965, 1968). Winters away from habitation but, on passage, recorded a few times from wooded gardens; throughout, at plains level and on lower hill-slopes, with daytime records not above 400 m.

FORAGING AND FOOD. No information.

SOCIAL ORGANIZATION. Solitary.

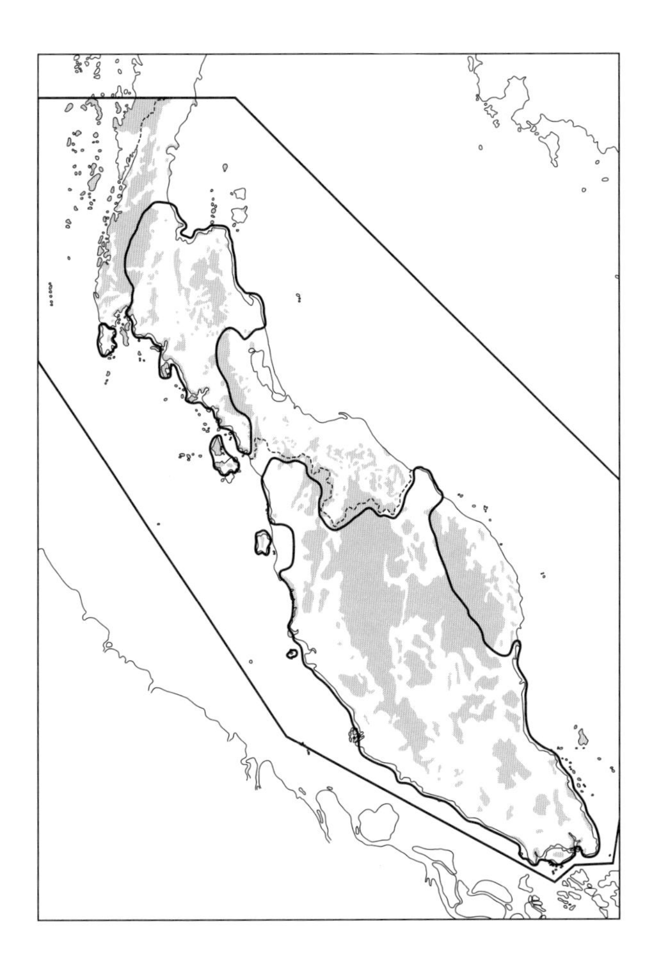

MOVEMENTS. Extreme passage-dates are 21 September (at floodlights on Fraser's Hill), and 13 and 15 May in Selangor and Krabi (BR 1964, 1968, BBCB-9). In autumn at Fraser's, night-time captures have continued to 26 November, with heaviest passage during late October–early November (and a strike on One-Fathom Bank lighthouse during that period). Spring migration is hardly known; one night-time interception on 16 April.

SURVIVAL. No information.

SOCIAL INTERACTIONS. No information.

VOICE. Not recorded; apparently silent in winter.

BREEDING. No population.

MOULT. Primaries moult at up to three loci. Adults arrive in more or less fresh plumage, suggestive of moult completed before autumn migration. First-winterers arrive part-way through post-juvenile moult, active or suspended, the most retarded individual seen having renewed only P1–3 and T1 by 18 December. Probably, this is the age-cohort also in wing- and tail-moult through January–February (BMNH, UMBRP).

CONSERVATION. No critical issues.

Large Hawk Cuckoo; Nok Kha-khuu Yieo Yai (Thai); Burung Sewah Tekukur Besar (Malay)

Cuculus sparverioides Vigors 1831, *Proceedings of the Committee of Science and Correspondence of the Zoological Society of London* 1(14): 173. TL Simla–Almora area, Himachal Pradesh, NW India.

Plate 48

GROUP RELATIONS. Free-standing; probably closest to S Asian *C. varius* (Common Hawk Cuckoo).

GLOBAL RANGE. Breeds in the Himalayas east from Pakistan, and in hill-tracts of the far-NE Indian subcontinent; SE Tibet; China south from Sichuan, Gansu and the lower Changjiang valley, probably including Hainan; and hill-tracts of SE Asia to Sumatra and Borneo. Northern populations migrate, wintering south through the Indian subcontinent and SE Asia to the Greater Sunda islands and N and central Philippines. Vagrant in Sulawesi.

IDENTIFICATION/DESCRIPTION. Migrant and resident subspecies differ substantially in size, the former by far the largest *Cuculus* in the area. Apart from some white on the lores, adults of both have head down to malar level grey-brown, and upper body and wings plain bronze-brown. Below, chin dark grey, breast-band orange-rufous (broader and richer in residents), throat and remaining underparts white; black-streaked back to breast (just on breast in residents), black barred (bars with buff posterior border) on flanks, trousers and belly, leaving lower tail-coverts plain white. Lower wing-coverts narrowly barred, underside of flight-feathers broadly barred (and tipped) dark grey. Both surfaces of the tail show 3–4 ash-grey bars (penultimate narrowest), each shading distally to black then narrowly fringed dull orange-buff, the tail narrowly tipped rufous-and-white.

Resident juvenile undescribed, but both subspecies have an intermediate, subadult plumage: cap grey-bronze, upperparts and wings dull, dark brown barred rufous (richer in residents, duller and paler in migrants), flight-feathers rufous-notched on their outer webs and with extreme tips white (the juvenile set?). Below, chin grey, rest of underparts white to buff-white (without breast-band), boldly streaked blackish, streaks disintegrating into spots on belly and broadening into chevron bars on rear flanks. Lower wing-surface as adult but coverts plain white. Non-moulting residents in this plumage, but with adult-patterned underparts (including a narrow breast-band), suggest either that final plumage is acquired over more than one moult or that some subadult features are retained by the adult female.

Bare-part colours. (Adult) iris tawny-yellow to hazel-brown, eyelid-rim bright yellow; upper mandible and bill-tip black, rest of lower mandible greenish or yellow; feet orange-yellow.

Size (mm). (Live and skins: 3 residents, 7 migrants; subadult to adult, none sexed): wing 183–191 and 233–246; tail 164–175 and 198–222; bill 24.0–24.5 and 25.0–29.9; tarsus 23.0–24.0 and 25.0–29.3 (BMNH, UMBRP, ZRCNUS).

Weight (g). Autumn migrant adults, 130.0, 130.9 (TISTR, UMBRP).

DISTRIBUTION. Resident on the Larut Range and Main Range, where known from Genting Highlands north to Cameron Highlands (ENGGANG-2); also on eastern outliers Tahan and Benom. Historical summary: (residents) *Kel, Pek, Phg, Sel*; (migrants) *Sur, Pha, Phu, Kra, Tra, Phg, Sel, Sin*, with additional island records from Yao Yai, Lanta (wintering?) and the Langkawi group (Dayang Bunting) (*Ked*) off the W coast; and St John's, Singapore.

GEOGRAPHICAL VARIATION. Residents are small, richer-coloured *bocki* Wardlaw Ramsay 1886 (TL Mt Sagu, W Sumatra) of Sumatra, the Peninsula and Borneo; migrants nominate *sparverioides*, of the remaining global range.

STATUS AND POPULATION. Resident, non-breeding visitor and a probable passage migrant. Residents are regular and more or less common, migrants local and sparse, but recorded in all winter months.

HABITATS AND ECOLOGY. Resident at 1100–1800 m, occupying the edge and interior canopy of Lower and tall Upper Montane forest, where males sing from shaded perches high in the larger trees and are hard to pin-point. Reports of calling in forest below the Montane zone, down to 200 m altitude in the Gombak valley (Selangor), on Jelebu Pass (Negeri Sembilan), and below 100 m in the lowlands east of Benom (Pahang), are liable to refer to a confusing call of Moustached Hawk Cuckoo.

Migrants are reported from mangroves, patches of tall secondary-growth, scrub on otherwise open ground, and orchards; not in closed-canopy inland

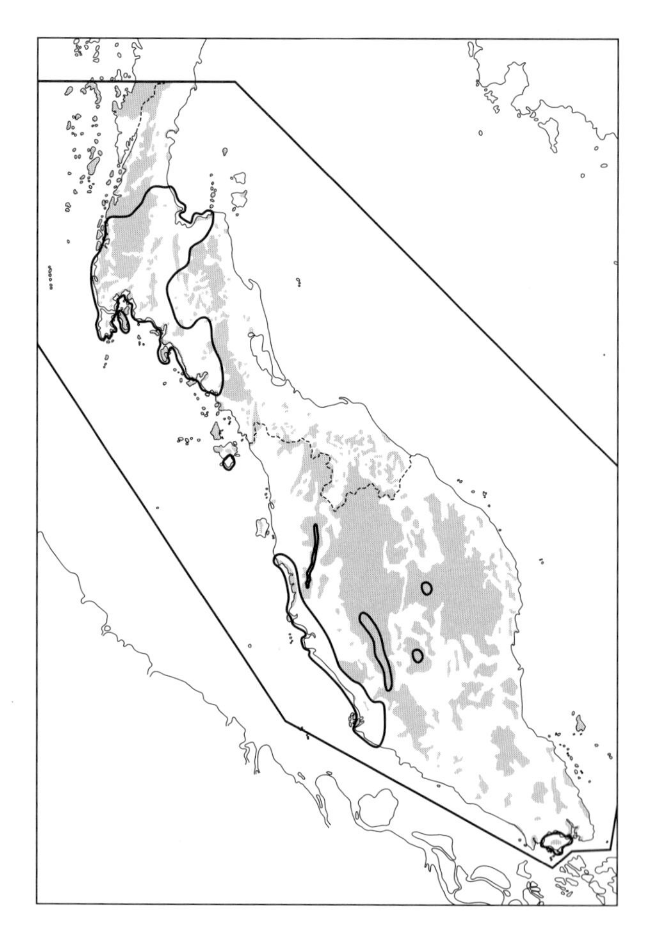

forest and only at plains level, hence there is no overlap of habitat with the resident population.

FORAGING AND FOOD. Brief sorties to the ground, apparently for arthropods, by a migrant in a Singapore orchard (MBR 1984–85); no other information.

SOCIAL ORGANIZATION. Resident males maintain individual territories, calling from one or a few neighbouring crowns for at least several days at a stretch, occasionally close to a neighbour, and bouts of counter-singing occur. Migrants are solitary.

MOVEMENTS. Extreme passage-dates are 24 October (N Selangor coast) and 22 March (Singapore: SINGAV-1). Incidence of records is too low to be sure of the duration of passage-seasons but a small flurry of sightings in Singapore (SINGAV-2) implies autumn movement continues to at least mid November. One mist-netted at floodlights on Fraser's Hill on 8 November (BMP5).

SURVIVAL. No information.

SOCIAL INTERACTIONS. No information.

VOICE. Migrants are silent. Resident male *bocki* has two loud calls: (1), with white throat puffed and mouth widely opened, typically 6–8 deliberately spaced, powerful and increasingly emphatic disyllables (a single record from Fraser's Hill of the trisyllable regular in other parts of the range), rising steadily to a screaming climax, *pee-ha pee-ha pee-ha . . . pee-ha pee-hee pee-hee*; (2) a faster sequence of more hurried couplets, *pi-hi*, rising in semi-tones to a shrill climax, with brief tail-off of usually two simple notes. Female vocalizations have not been identified.

On the Main Range, vocal during mid September–late May.

BREEDING. Not recorded; local brood-hosts unknown, but a watch should be kept on laughing thrushes *Garrulax* spp.

MOULT. A late March subadult resident showed slightly worn wing-tips but no moult. First-winter migrants arrive in what appears to be full subadult plumage, and the relatively fresh plumage of adults suggests a moult completed before migration. They show no more activity to at least mid January (BMNH, ZDUM, ZRCNUS).

CONSERVATION. No issues with migrants. Residents are under no immediate threat but, as for other Montane forest-dependent birds, highland development policies, especially on the Main Range, could alter the situation.

Moustached Hawk Cuckoo; Nok Kha-khuu Yieo Lek (Thai); Burung Sewah Tekukur Kecil (Malay)

Cuculus vagans S. Müller 1845, *Verhandelingen over der Natuurlijke Geschiedenis de Nederlandsche Overzeesche Bezittingen . . . Land- en Volkenkunde* 8: 233. TL Java.

Plate 48

GROUP RELATIONS. Free-standing.

GLOBAL RANGE. The Greater Sunda islands, the Peninsula and SW Thailand and Tenasserim respectively to 13° and 14°N, and far-SE Thailand and S Laos.

IDENTIFICATION/DESCRIPTION. Smaller, proportionately longer-tailed than other hawk cuckoos. From them also by white cheek, leaving a dark, down-slanting moustache-mark, and white of throat curving narrowly up behind dark ear-coverts. Adult head and face, including moustache, grey-black, sharp against white parts; upper body and wings dark bronze-brown, with some orange-bay edging at side of neck that spills onto breast; and outer webs of flight-feathers obscurely toothed pale stone-grey. Below, entirely creamy white streaked black-brown from lower throat to flanks and trousers, leaving lower tail-coverts plain. Tail stone-grey with four black-brown bars exposed beyond coverts, both dark and light sets widening distally and with terminal dark bar narrowly fringed white. All ages show lower wing-coverts plain creamy white and underside of flight-feathers barred and broadly tipped dark grey. Wing-tip P7.

No young handled, but a fledgling being fed by its fosterer showed a moustached face-pattern and adult-type, black-and-white-tipped tail (P.D. Round). An apparent subadult plumage resembles adult, but with obscure, grey-rufous barring over the upperparts, stone-grey edging on rump and upper tail-coverts, and pale-tipped flight-feathers (the retained juvenile set?).

Bare-part colours. (Adult) iris dark brown, eyelid-rim bright yellow; upper mandible and whole bill-tip black, rest of bill greenish yellow; feet orange-yellow (UMBRP).

Size (mm). (Live and skins: 6 males, 4 females): wing 142–150 and 144 (1 only); tail 135–150 and 130–134; bill 21.8 (1 male); tarsus 19.8–20.3 and 20.9 (1 only) (BMNH, UMBRP, ZDUM, ZRCNUS). The dimorphism of tail-length needs testing in a larger sample.

Weight (g). Adult males, 58.2 and 54.5–63.4 (including repeat weights of a ringed bird).

DISTRIBUTION. Historical summary: all divisions except *Pha, Pht, Tra, Pat, Yal, Nar, Kel, Tru, Pra, Pek, Mel, Sin*, with no additional island records.

GEOGRAPHICAL VARIATION. None recognized.

STATUS AND POPULATION. Resident; regular and uncommon to more or less common in the north; local and uncommon to sparse south of Kedah, with southernmost records at latitude 2°35′N, along the Pahang/Johor border (Segamat district and the Endau-Rompin conservation area) (BR 1972–73, Wells 1990b).

HABITATS AND ECOLOGY. The under-stratum to lower canopy of mature to lightly logged and regenerating semi-evergreen and evergreen, dry-land Lowland forest, at plains level and on slopes to about 900 m altitude (close to the Montane ecotone). In Krabi, where it parasitizes the forest-edge babbler *Trichastoma abbotti*, typical of secondary and regenerating forest (P.D. Round).

FORAGING AND FOOD. No information.

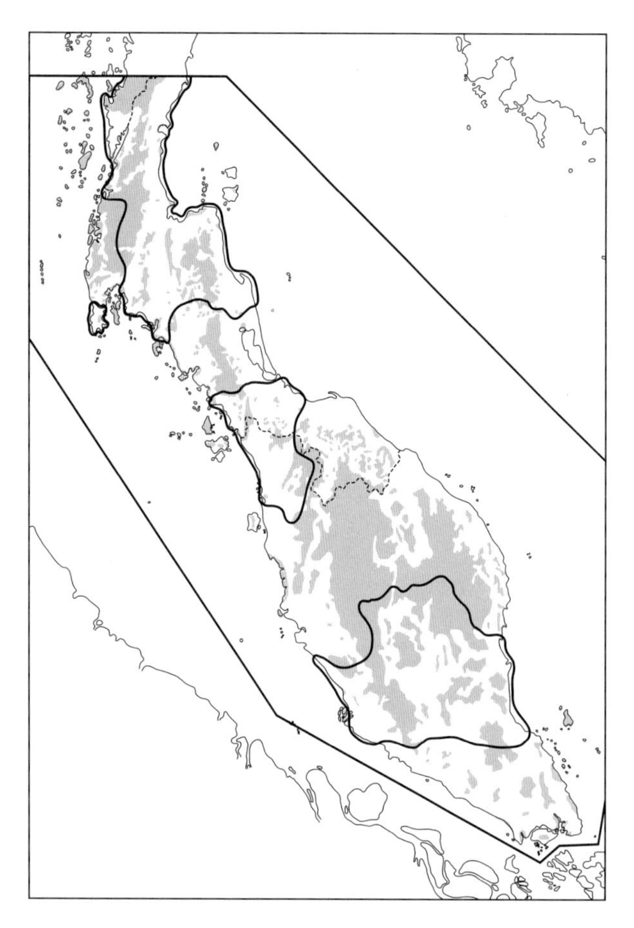

SOCIAL ORGANIZATION. Males maintain regular singing-stations and are presumed to be territorial. At a ringing-site in the upper Gombak valley, Selangor, an evidently sedentary bird was handled three times during 13 months.

MOVEMENTS. None reported.

SURVIVAL. No information.

SOCIAL INTERACTIONS. No information.

VOICE. Males have two loud calls: (1) an even-pitched disyllable, *kan ko*, melancholy but carrying, repeated monotonously from a canopy perch at a rate of about one call every two seconds; (2) a rarer, rising sequence of a few simple, spaced notes, giving way to hurried couplets and accelerating to a screaming climax, *hee hee hee hee, . . . hi-hi hi-hi hi-hi hi-hi*, abruptly terminated, without the falling tail-notes of Large Hawk Cuckoo. Female vocalizations unknown.

In Malaysia, vocal during late October–May.

BREEDING. At Khao Pra-Bang Khram, Krabi, on 24 August a juvenile attended by an Abbott's Babbler (BBCB-8). An adult there chased by an Asian Paradise-flycatcher *Terpsiphone paradisi* does not necessarily demonstrate a breeding connection.

MOULT. Primaries moult at up to four loci. Five adults dated late April–June and early September showed active wing-moult; others in October, December, January and March–early May, none (BMNH, UMBRP, ZDUM).

CONSERVATION. Use of the submontane slope implies no immediate threat, but commonest in plains-level forests and these could be core habitat.

Hodgson's Hawk Cuckoo; Nok Kha-khuu Yieo Ok Daeng (Thai); Burung Sewah Hantu (Malay)

Cuculus fugax Horsfield 1821, *Transactions of the Linnean Society* 13(1): 178. TL Java.
Plate 48

GROUP RELATIONS. Free-standing, although reports of unusual vocalizations in the Philippines (J. Scharringa) suggest a complex of possibly more than one species. Research is needed.

GLOBAL RANGE. Breeds in the Himalayan foothills east from Nepal, and the far-NE Indian subcontinent; Pacific Russia south from Amurland, Japan, China south and east of a line Heilongjiang–Sichuan, including Hainan; and SE Asia to the Greater Sunda islands and Philippines. Northern populations migrate, wintering in the eastern tropics to the Sunda region. Vagrant in N Wallacea and W Micronesia.

IDENTIFICATION/DESCRIPTION. Stockier, proportionately shorter-tailed than Moustached Hawk Cuckoo, and from it at all ages by fully dark face down to malar level, leaving no moustache-mark. Not much smaller than more similarly patterned resident Large Hawk Cuckoo, but only migrants share the latter's habitat. These are distinctively pale grey, never show dark belly-barring, and occupy only the lower part of the forest vegetation column.

Adult resident Hodgson's has head dark grey-brown relieved only by a little white on the lores and variable white spot on the side of the nape (in some, expanded to a white hind-collar that breaks only mid-dorsally); upperparts dark dun-brown with dull rufous bars on outer webs of flight-feathers; tail ash-grey with three or four black bars exposed beyond coverts, the apical bar wider and tail-tip pink-rufous, whitening laterally. Below, point of chin charcoal-grey, rest of underparts creamy white boldly black-streaked from lower throat to lower breast, trousers and flanks (on which streaks often split into long arrow-marks). Streak-width varies individually, but tends to broaden posteriorly, and streaks are variably edged orange-rust, particularly on the breast. Lower wing-coverts are pink-tinged white, plain or dark-barred, and the underside of flight-feathers is broadly barred and tipped dark grey. Wing-tip P7/8 subequal, versus P8 in migrants (Chasen and Kloss 1927).

Adult migrants are quite different: plain steel-grey above, darker on the head, paler on rump and upper tail-coverts, and with no rufous barring on flight-feathers. They show little white on the nape, but most have one inner tertial strikingly whiter than the rest, plain, or with dark notches or bars. Tail as in residents except penultimate dark bar obviously narrower than others, and often incomplete. Below, dark grey streaks vary in width, commonly with white invading out along the feather-shaft, splitting them into long arrow-marks (broader chevrons on rear flanks). In fine-streaked individuals, edging expands to form a more or less solidly pink-rufous breast and upper belly.

In juvenile plumage, head to throat and upperparts are sooty black, with narrow white feather-fringing and a white patch on the side of the nape; remaining underparts whitish with long, blackish droplet-marks that break into dots on the belly. Subadults retain juvenile-type, pale-tipped flight-feathers but show entirely rufous-barred upperparts, including wings. The few first-autumn migrants seen in this plumage are also brown-backed rather than grey, but brighter-barred than residents, and most show the pale tertial.

Bare-part colours. Iris dull grey-brown (immature), hazel-brown to orange (resident adult), cream-brown to pale orange-brown (migrant adult), eyelid-rim bright yellow; bill including nostril area green, with culmen and whole tip black; feet bright yellow.

Size (mm). Residents (live and skins: 3 males, 9 females; adult): wing 174–177 and 173–177; tail 132–147 and 137–149; bill 25.0–26.6, bill from front edge nostril 17.3–18.9 (sexes combined); tarsus 21.8–23.0 (sexes combined). Migrants (live and skins: 37 adults, most not sexed): wing 167–193; tail 123–153; bill 21.8–25.8, bill from front edge nostril 14.7–17.1; tarsus 18.5–24.0 (BMNH, UMBRP, ZDUM, ZRCNUS). Young juveniles are liable to be small-billed.

Weight (g). Adult residents, 74.8, 76.5; autumn migrants, 69.1–93.0, mostly less than 80.0 (n=12).

DISTRIBUTION. Historical summary: (residents) *Chu, Sur, Pha, Nak, Kra, Pht, Tra, Sat, Pes, Ked, Pra, Pek, Phg, Sel, Neg, Mel, Joh, Sin*, with additional island records from Lanta, Tarutao, Langkawi and Penang off the W coast, and Tioman off the E coast; (migrants) *Tra, Phg, Sel, Neg, Sin*, with additional island records

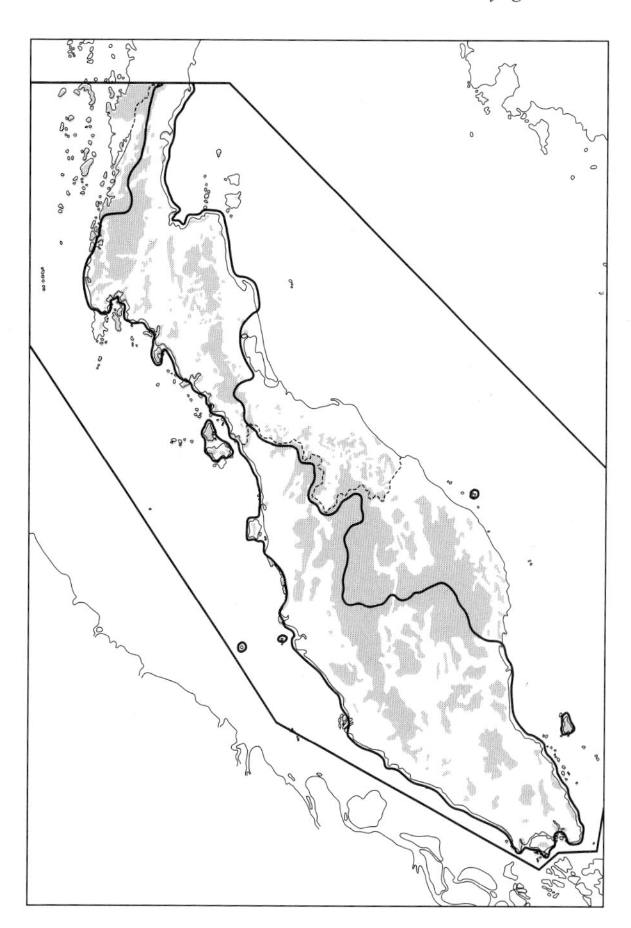

from Tarutao, Rembia and Jarak off the W coast, Redang off the E coast, and St John's, Singapore.

GEOGRAPHICAL VARIATION. Residents are nominate *fugax*. A claim that *fugax* is also a migrant (BMP5) has not been supported by more recent fieldwork. While two first-winterers (from Redang island and Kuala Tembeling, Pahang) show a mix of characters suggestive of intergrades (BMNH, ZRCNUS), over two decades, all the birds intercepted at lights and well-enough described have been northern *nisicolor* Blyth 1843 (TL Nepal).

STATUS AND POPULATION. Resident, a non-breeding visitor and, on evidence of a strike on One-Fathom Bank lighthouse, Melaka Straits, passage migrant; both subspecies regular, and uncommon to more or less common. Migrant *nisicolor* has been recorded during late August–late January and in March–May. The February gap needs investigating.

HABITATS AND ECOLOGY. Residents frequent the mid and lower strata of evergreen and semi-evergreen, dry-land Lowland forest, mature and regenerating after disturbance, mainly at plains level but also on slopes, to about 250 m. Overwintering habitats of migrants are less known but include patches of secondary-growth and dense forest-edge, from plains level to 1200 m. The few recorded from the interior of forest have been on likely passage dates.

FORAGING AND FOOD. No information.

SOCIAL ORGANIZATION. Presumed resident males call from regular spots in forest and are guessed to be territorial.

MOVEMENTS. Intergrades (above) were collected on 19 August and 2 September, paralleling the early arrival of some other tropical cuckoos (see Drongo, Violet, etc.). Extreme dates of full *nisicolor* are 24 and 27 September, at lights on Fraser's Hill and in mountain forest of S Negeri Sembilan (BMNH, BMP5), and 12 and 19 May, in Negeri Sembilan and Trang (RTFD). On evidence of night-time interceptions, autumn passage continues to mid December (latest date 18 December: MBR 1986–87). The span of spring passage is unknown.

SURVIVAL. No information.

SOCIAL INTERACTIONS. No information.

VOICE. Resident male calls: (1) a rather shrill disyllable, *jee kwik*, repeated on a more or less even pitch at about eight calls per ten seconds; (2) a fast, excited mixture of shrill couplets and triplets, *pi-fi* or *pi-fi-fi*, accelerating up-scale to a quick succession of twittering climaxes (commonly three), then tailing off in a brief rattle of monosyllables. (2) is given mostly after a bout of *jee kwik* calling. Female vocalizations have not been identified.

In Malaysia, territorial males call during February–August, virtually round the clock over moonlit periods of April.

BREEDING. On 6 July 1990 at Khao Pra-Bang Khram, Krabi, two neighbouring fledglings called incessantly, one with a harsh yelp the other with a burring tone, easily separated. The burring call was heard again on 10 July of the following year (P.D. Round). No fosterers were seen on these occasions, but Hodgson's is the only *Cuculus* recorded resident on Penang island and a fledgling cuckoo being fed by a White-rumped Shama *Copsychus malabaricus* at the forested edge of Ayer Hitam reservoir on 26 August (K. Kumar) could have been this species. Reports of fostering by Black-and-yellow Broadbill *Eurylaimus ochromalus* refer to Indian Cuckoo *C. micropterus* (BR 1978–79).

MOULT. Among residents, both subadults and adults moult primaries at up to four loci. Birds covering November–January, March, July and August showed active wing-moult only in July and August (not all individuals). The August-dated intergrade was in heavy general (including wing-) moult, but nearly all full *nisicolor* complete before arrival, appearing in autumn in fresh plumage, with no sign of renewed moult during winter (BMNH, ZDUM, ZRCNUS).

CONSERVATION. Plains-level forest may be core habitat for residents.

Indian Cuckoo; Nok Kha-khuu Phan India (Thai); Burung Sewah India (Malay)

Cuculus micropterus Gould 1837, *Proceedings of the Zoological Society of London* 5: 137. TL Himalayas.

Plate 48

GROUP RELATIONS. A possible allospecies of the island endemic *C. crassirostris* (Sulawesi 'Hawk' Cuckoo). They differ in extent of barring on anterior underparts, pattern of lower wing-coverts, tone of brown parts and proportions of the wing (shorter and rounder in *crassirostris*), but all plumages are otherwise generally similar, as are the loud vocalizations of males (which bear no resemblance to those of Asian hawk cuckoos).

GLOBAL RANGE. Except for its dry NW, the Indian subcontinent from the Himalayan foothills, Sri Lanka and Bay of Bengal islands; Pacific Russia south from Amurland; China south and east of a line NE provinces–Sichuan, including Hainan; and SE Asia to the Greater Sunda islands. Northern populations migrate, wintering through the southern breeding-range east in SE Asia to the Philippines. Vagrant to E Wallacea (Ternate).

IDENTIFICATION/DESCRIPTION. Indian and Oriental Cuckoos show no masked head-pattern or streaking on the breast. Adult Indian has cap to nape iron-grey, shading over the face to plain pale grey on chin, throat and whole upper breast (adult male), or with upper breast rufous-buff and black-brown barred (adult female); upper body and wings plain bronze-brown. Remaining underparts are creamy white, boldly barred black down to trousers and flanks, leaving centre belly to lower tail-coverts plain white. Upper surface of tail as back but notched rufous, and small rufous-and-white shaft-marks of the central feather-pair expand as bars on more lateral feathers; the whole tail with a broad, black apical band, and white tip. Tropical residents are smaller, generally darker-toned than migrants.

Fledglings have head to breast and entire upperparts deep chocolate-brown, feathers tipped (scapulars barred and tipped) creamy white, broadly enough over the head and breast (apart from around bill and eye) to make these appear entirely white; rest of underparts white with variable black barring on the rear flanks. Lower wing-coverts are plain creamy white (subsequently black-barred) and the underside of the flight-feathers broadly barred and tipped grey, as they are at all stages. Subadults retain pale-tipped flight-feathers but otherwise resemble adults, except for being blacker on the crown, with remaining upperparts dark chocolate rather than bronze-brown, the mantle and short scapulars sparsely, elsewhere (including secondaries and inner primaries) more densely, barred, notched or tipped dull rufous. Some rufous notches and shaft-marks of the tail expand into partial bars across all feathers rather than just laterally. Below, dark barring shows through a pink-grey wash virtually up to the chin.

Bare-part colours. (Non-juveniles) iris hazel-brown to dark brown, eyelid-rim bright yellow; upper mandible and bill-tip black, rest of lower mandible yellow-horn to greenish (in a resident female, grey); feet yellow to orange-yellow.

Size (mm). Residents (skins: 2 males, 3 females; adult): wing 177, 179 and 165–169 (juveniles down to 155); tail 140–144 (females only); bill from front edge nostril 17.0 (1 female); tarsus 19.7 (1 female) (Colebrook-Robjent 1978, Riley 1938). Migrants (live and skins: 22 adults, most not sexed): wing 181–221; tail 135–174; bill 24.2–30.5, bill from front edge nostril 20.4 (1 only); tarsus 20.7–23.0 (BMNH, UMBRP, ZRC-NUS). Juveniles are liable to have small bills.

Weight (g). *C.m. concretus* intercepted at Fraser's Hill in autumn, 63.0 and 69.3; autumn nominate *micropterus*, 77.5–121.8 (n=17) (UMBRP).

DISTRIBUTION. Historical summary: (residents) *Chu, Pha, Kra, Pht, Tra, Son, Sat, Yal, Nar, Pes, Ked, Kel, Tru, Pek, Phg, Sel, Neg, Mel, Joh,* with no definite island records although I have seen a bar-bellied *Cuculus* resembling this species in forest on Pangkor (*Pek*) in mid August; (migrants) *Phu, Tra, Ked, Pek, Phg, Sel, Joh, Sin,* with island records from the Langkawi group (Langkawi, Dayang Bunting), Rembia, Jarak and Pisang off the W coast; and Ubin and Sentosa, Singapore.

GEOGRAPHICAL VARIATION. Residents are small, dark *concretus* S. Müller 1845 (TL Java), also of the Greater Sunda islands. Nominate *micropterus* of the rest of the range is the dominant migrant, including two size-classes, unrelated to sex: a common one in the wing-length range 181–208 mm and scarcer, large birds 220 mm-plus, representing probably more than one geographical population.

STATUS AND POPULATION. Resident, non-breeding visitor and passage migrant; regular and

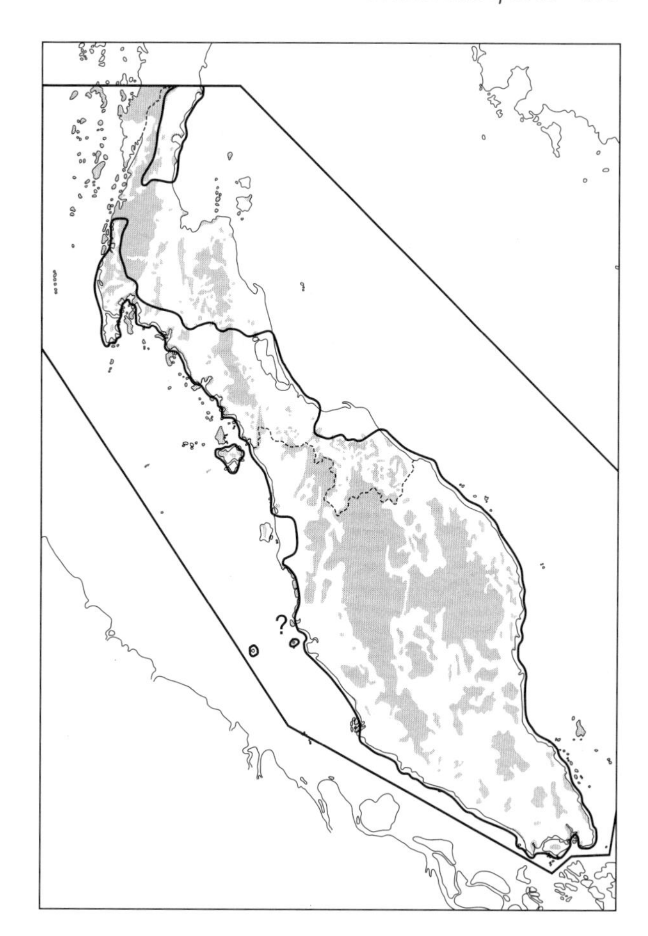

uncommon to common. Subspecies *concretus* has been confirmed north to Phatthalung (BLC). Where (or whether) it intergrades with breeding nominate *micropterus* is unknown, but two *concretus* intercepted among other late October migrants at Fraser's Hill suggest a possibly more extensive northern range.

Records of Indian Cuckoos away from the habitat of residents span all months of the northern winter but show a sharp dip through December–January, suggesting many migrants move on, perhaps into Indonesia. Early winter occurrence on small islands of the Melaka Straits and a strike on One-Fathom Bank lighthouse, 42 km off Selangor (Robinson and Kloss 1922), give direct evidence of through-passage.

HABITATS AND ECOLOGY. Residents frequent the canopy of tall evergreen and semi-evergreen, dry-land Lowland forest, mature and well-regenerated after logging, at plains level and on slopes to about 800 m. Dates suggest silent Indian Cuckoos found sporadically in overgrown plantations and other secondary woodland, sometimes even low scrub, and occasionally parkland and wooded gardens, are migrants. Occurrence of migrants in the tall-forest habitat of residents (BMP5) has not been verified.

FORAGING AND FOOD. The stomach of a breeding female *concretus* collected in Johor was crammed with green and other caterpillars (Colebrook-Robjent

1978). Apparent migrants harvest defoliating caterpillars, and emerge from cover to take flying termites.

SOCIAL ORGANIZATION. Calling resident males are spaced in forest and counter-sing, which suggests they are territorial.

MOVEMENTS. Extreme dates on Singapore island, outside the known range of residents, are 14 September and 7 May (SINGAV-3, -6). Singapore records pooled over a decade peak through October–November, matching night-time captures during 10 October–27 November at the Fraser's Hill floodlights, then drop sharply by December. The latest autumn date on small islands of the Melaka Straits is 9 December (ZRCNUS). A resurgence in Singapore suggests spring passage runs over three months from early February, although migrants have been intercepted at Fraser's only in early April (BMP5).

SURVIVAL. No information.

SOCIAL INTERACTIONS. No additional information.

VOICE. The advertising-call of resident males is a powerful, far-carrying *wa ha ha hu* or alternating *wa hu ha hu*, repeated once or twice per minute for long periods, typically from a concealed perch in the canopy but occasionally given in flight. Rarely, they add a fifth note, *wa hu ha hu ho* or *wa ha ha hu ho*, and this variant has been reported once outside forest, given apparently by a spring migrant. Timbre- and pitch-differences often detectable between neighbouring singers could be an outcome of acoustics in forest. A loud, hurried bubbling, up-inflected at the end or in crescendo form, is believed to be a female call.

Calling by residents is rarely heard outside the period January–August, and in Malaysia is most general and intense during March–June. Northward, the season ends as early as June. Occasional, brief vocalizing by presumed migrants occurs from early February.

BREEDING

Brood-host. Four young fledglings in Selangor were all being tended by Black-and-yellow Broadbills *Eurylaimus ochromalus*. There are no other host records.

Eggs and brood. The egg is known from a single oviduct specimen, shot-damaged. Ground-colour pale pinkish grey with small spots of grey concentrated around the equator, overlain by evenly distributed, larger (1 mm) spots of dark liver-brown, i.e., of the 'drongo' type described for the species in the Indian subcontinent (Becking 1981). It also quite closely matches the Black-and-yellow Broadbill egg.

Cycle. No information.

Seasonality. An egg collected in Johor on 29 April, and fledglings and full juveniles in Narathiwat, Kelantan, Perak and Selangor are dated June–early September (BMNH, BMP5, BR 1978–79, Cranbrook and Wells 1981, MBR 1984–85, UMZC, ZRCNUS).

MOULT. A breeding female in irregular-pattern tail-moult on 29 April; there is no other information on residents. First-winter migrants arrive in subadult plumage (some showing a scatter of white-fringed juvenile body-feathers), with flight-feathers either unmoulted or at early-stage suspension (1–3 inner primaries adult), and wing-moult is still suspended in January. Adults arrive relatively fresh, apparently after a moult, and winter handlings (up to mid March) have shown no new activity.

CONSERVATION. Widespread occurrence on slopes, and use of partly logged forest by both cuckoo and brood-host, suggest no immediate threat either to residents or migrants.

Oriental Cuckoo; Nok Kha-khuu Phan Himalai (Thai); Burung Sewah Himalaya (Malay)

Cuculus saturatus Blyth 1843, *Journal of the Asiatic Society of Bengal* 12: 942. TL Nepal.
Plate 48

GROUP RELATIONS. Free-standing.

GLOBAL RANGE. Breeds across temperate and low-arctic Eurasia from longitude about 30°E (possibly the Baltic) to Anadyrland, Kamchatka and Japan, south to the Altai, N Mongolia, Korea, China south and east of a line NE provinces–Sichuan, including Taiwan; in the Himalayas and hill-tracts of the far-NE Indian subcontinent; and mountains of N Burma, N Vietnam and the Sunda region and Lesser Sunda islands to Timor. Most continental populations migrate, wintering from Bay of Bengal islands through the Sunda region, mainly south of the equator; and in Wallacea, W Micronesia, New Guinea, the Solomons and Australia, straggling to New Zealand.

IDENTIFICATION/DESCRIPTION. Entire upperparts and chin to upper breast of adult male clear grey, sharp against remaining white underparts, which are boldly black-barred back to flanks, trousers and upper belly; tail black, with white dots spaced along feather-shafts and a narrow white tip. Lower wing-coverts white, narrowly barred dark grey. In the grey-phase adult female, plain grey of chin and throat gives way to a rufous-grey (occasionally quite rich rufous) upper breast which is dark-barred, merging into pattern of remaining underparts. Residents are a shade darker than migrants overall with richer buff on the lower tail-coverts (latter plain to barred in all subspecies).

An erythristic (hepatic) morph, confirmed in the Peninsula only among female migrants but in Sumatra and Java also known among residents (NNML), has entire upperparts, from cap and sides of face, clear rufous, some birds richer toned from back to upper tail-coverts, some with white frosting on forehead and supercilium. Below white, chin to upper breast variably washed rufous, and both surfaces, from bill-base and chin, boldly black-barred (individual feathers typically showing three bars); dorsal barring generally narrower from back to upper tail-coverts. Flight-feathers mostly blackish, with rufous confined to a pattern of deep notches along the margins of both webs. Tail-feathers fully black-barred in a chevron pattern, the apical bar broader than the rest; tail-tip narrowly white, and white dots are spaced along rufous parts of the feather-shafts.

Local juveniles are iron-grey above, feathers sharply and broadly fringed white; underparts white, barred black from chin to lower tail-coverts; and flight-feathers and tail are sooty black, white-tipped and with dull rufous notching on outer webs. White shaft-marks of the tail are larger than in adult, and on lateral feathers link with notches to form partial bars. Among first-autumn migrants still in mostly juvenile plumage, extent of rufous varies individually, from almost none to more than in residents, including on wing- and upper tail-coverts. No subadult plumage has been identified, although post-juvenile body-moult begins before wings.

Bare-part colours. Iris dark brown (fledgling), brown or dark reddish (resident adult), tawny to pale yellow (migrant adult), eyelid-rim bright yellow; upper mandible and bill-tip blackish, rest of lower mandible greenish to yellow-horn, chick mouth-lining bright red; feet bright yellow.

Size (mm). Residents (skins: 1 male, 1 female; adult): wing 150 and 142; tail 133 and 131; bill 22.4 (a female); tarsus 16.6 (a male). Migrants (live and skins; 5 adults, none sexed): wing 169–190; tail 140–147; bill 24.6–27.9; tarsus 19.5–20.8 (UMBRP, ZRCNUS).

Weight (g). Autumn passage migrants, 74.3–79.0 (n=3) (UMBRP).

DISTRIBUTION. Resident on the Main Range, with records from latitude about 5°20′N south to Genting Highlands. Historical summary: (residents) *Kel, Pek, Phg, Sel*; (migrants) *Chu, Pha, Phu, Phg, Sel, Joh, Sin*, with passage-dated island records from Angsa (*Sel*) and the Arua group (Indonesian waters), Melaka Straits.

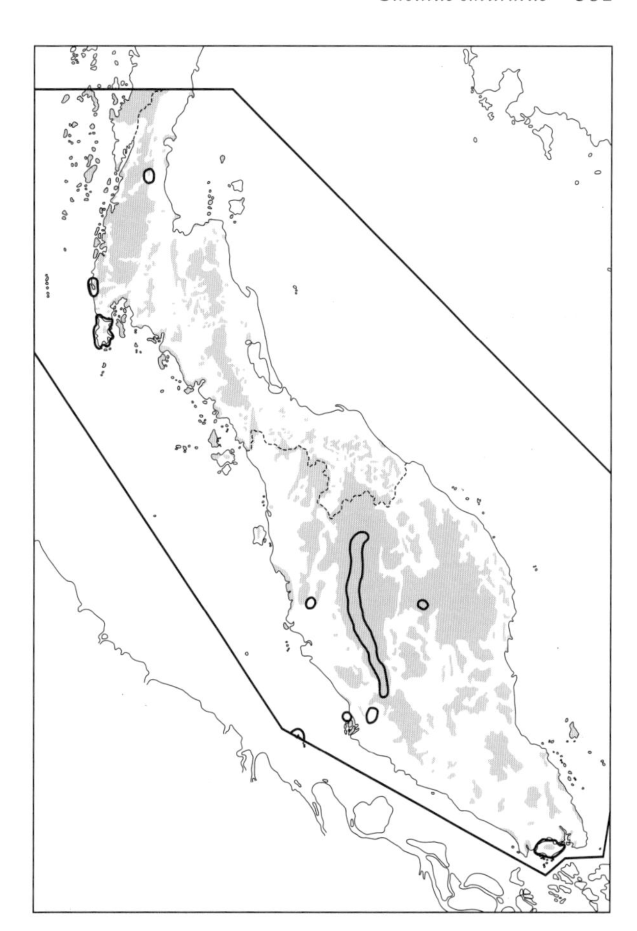

GEOGRAPHICAL VARIATION. Residents are dwarf *lepidus* S. Müller 1845 (TL Timor), of the Sunda and Lesser Sunda island range except Borneo (although tropical subspecies-limits need reviewing). Migrants have been assigned to nominate *saturatus* and larger *horsfieldi* Moore 1857 (TL Java) (BMP5), although individual size-variation in the northern continental breeding-range (Wells 1972) suggests it may not be useful to uphold the second name.

STATUS AND POPULATION. Resident, passage migrant and possible non-breeding visitor. Breeders are regular and more or less common but within surprisingly restricted limits given (a) the local range of the regular brood-host, (b) the fact that, at least occasionally, individuals disperse through the lowlands (a record at Teku river-mouth, foot of the Tahan massif, and one from the extreme lowlands of the Perak river-valley: BMP5). Migrants are local and, given the number of records from Java, sparse, suggesting the Peninsula is bypassed or mostly overflown, although there have been several recent sightings on Phuket island (BCSTB-12). Among *Cuculus* migrants intercepted at floodlights on Fraser's Hill, Oriental was ten times rarer than Indian Cuckoo.

HABITATS AND ECOLOGY. Residents frequent the mid and canopy strata of tall Montane forest between about 950–1700 m. Habitats of the lowland dispersants were not specified but are likely to have been at the edge of, if not in, forest (Kuala Teku is still in mature forest). Northern migrants have occurred in coastal casuarina woodland, at the edge of inland forest, and in tall timber of suburban parkland; the few daytime records all at plains level (Holmes and Wells 1975, SINGAV-4).

FORAGING AND FOOD. No information beyond a diet of caterpillars, small grasshoppers and spider egg-masses fed to a nestling by fosterers (Madoc 1956c).

SOCIAL ORGANIZATION. Resident males call from limited areas in forest and are presumed to be territorial.

MOVEMENTS. The few records of northern migrants fall during 7 October–13 November and 14 February–23 March, which are passage dates elsewhere in SE Asia (Wells and Becking 1975). Lowland *lepidus* specimens (a post-juvenile and adult) are dated 31 July and 8 September, and a possible *lepidus* (wing 150 mm) has been trapped at floodlights on Fraser's Hill on 28 September (BMP5).

SURVIVAL. No information.

SOCIAL INTERACTIONS. No information.

VOICE. Males advertise from perches mostly at canopy level, sometimes concealed among foliage but often with little attempt made to hide. The predominant call is a sequence of three dull, mellow but carrying notes on a monotone, with a brief introduction: *up who who who*, lasting one second and given at a rate of about three calls every ten seconds. Occasional variants, resembling dominant calls from other parts of the world range – but all within the repertoire of single individuals – subtract or add a *who* and/or omit the grace-note.

The main season is January–July but vigorous calling has also been heard in late October.

BREEDING

Brood-host. The only confirmed host is Chestnut-crowned Warbler *Seicercus castaniceps*, although highest-altitude cuckoo territories are out of the regular range of *castaniceps* into that of congener *S. montis*. What was believed to have been a Drongo Cuckoo chick taken from a nest of *S. castaniceps* near the Gap (Robinson 1928) has been reidentified as Oriental Cuckoo (BMNH).

Eggs and brood. Single eggs in nests of *S. castaniceps*, unlikely to belong to any other species: almost glossless, creamy white, finely and sparsely speckled dull brown, with a much denser peppering of the same colour concentrated into a ring round the broad end. Size (mm): 19.0 × 11.8, 18.2 × 11.3 (n=2). The colour-match with plain white host eggs is imperfect, but *C. castaniceps* nests are domed and built in low-light situations.

Cycle. Both foster-parents feed the chick, in some instances delivering food while hovering.

Seasonality. Eggs have been found in late February, March, early May and June; young fledglings in late February, March and late July (Allen 1953, BMNH, Madoc 1956b, 1956c).

MOULT. Late July and early September residents showed active wing-moult, a February adult none. Five migrant adults dated October–November also showed none.

CONSERVATION. Migrants raise no issues and, for the moment, residents are not threatened, but see Large Hawk Cuckoo.

Banded Bay Cuckoo; Nok Kha-khuu Lai (Thai); Burung Sewah Takuwih (Malay)

Cacomantis sonneratii (Latham) 1790, *Index Ornithologicus* 1: 215. TL India.
Plate 49

GROUP RELATIONS. Free-standing. Stresemann and Stresemann (1961) found order of primary replacement differed from other *Cacomantis* species, but their proposed generic split has not been widely followed.

GLOBAL RANGE. Sri Lanka and, except for the arid NW, the Indian subcontinent; S Sichuan and Yunnan; and SE Asia to the Greater Sunda islands and Palawan.

IDENTIFICATION/DESCRIPTION. A small cuckoo; size of other *Cacomantis* species but rather longer-billed. Adults are tawny-rufous above, white-streaked from forehead variably to forecrown, then narrowly and densely barred black back to upper tail-coverts; flight-feathers and tail black-brown, finely notched rufous along the outer webs of inner secondaries and central tail-feathers. Other tail-feathers have inner web pale rufous and incompletely brown-barred, the whole tail with a broad, sub-apical dark bar and white tip (widening laterally). White below, up to chin and anterior face as far as lores, with fine white supercilium arching back to cut off rufous ear-covert patch, the whole face and underparts transversely pencilled black, much finer and rather more densely than in other *Cacomantis* species. Lower wing-coverts as underparts, underside of flight-feathers plain black-brown with a pale, rufous-pink slash angled obliquely across the secondaries and inner primaries.

Full juvenile plumage not described from the Peninsula, but flight-feathers are rufous-tipped and odd dorsal body-feathers retained by post-juveniles are dull brown with a white fringe. Small-billed juveniles from Java (subspecies *musicus*), on the other hand, have cap and upperparts light, clear rufous, rest of head and neck buff-white, and underparts white. Barring on both surfaces is coarser and more spaced than in adults, the black subterminal rim of individual ventral feathers giving a scalloped rather than strictly transverse pattern; tail as in adult but with sub-apical black bar of underside narrower and incomplete (NNML). Like other local *Cacomantis* species, moults directly into adult colours, head and body ahead of pale-tipped flight-feathers.

Bare-part colours. (Adult) iris light brown, brown or red; upper mandible and bill-tip black, rest of lower mandible greenish grey; feet dull, pale green to yellowish green.

Size (mm). (Skins: 7 males, 7 females; adult): wing 106–112 and 110–122; tail 90–103 and 91–106; bill 22.0–23.4 (sexes combined); bill from front edge nostril 14.7–17.1 and 14.6–16.7; tarsus 16.4–16.8 (sexes combined) (BMNH, NNML, ZRCNUS).

Weight (g). No data.

DISTRIBUTION. Historical summary: all divisions except *Pak, Chu, Pat, Kel*, with additional island records from Penang and Ubin, Singapore.

GEOGRAPHICAL VARIATION. Small-sized, near-endemic *malayanus* Chasen and Kloss 1931 (TL Kuala Lumpur), said to range into Tenasserim. Average wing-length declines north to south, but unevenly: six adults north from Trang 112–120, eight from Johor and Singapore 106–116 mm. Two from Ubin island and the Perak coast have been identified as darker *schlegeli* (TL Sumatra), but re-compared with topotypes the Ubin bird is not as rufous and may merely be an unusual *malayanus* variant (BMNH, Gibson-Hill 1949, Riley 1938, ZRCNUS).

STATUS AND POPULATION. Resident, regular and more or less common.

HABITATS AND ECOLOGY. The upper levels of evergreen and semi-evergreen, dry-land Lowland forest, mature and disturbed; forest-edge and tall secondary-growth; old rubber plantations (particularly where overgrown) and other part-wooded habitats, occasionally entering wooded gardens; at plains level

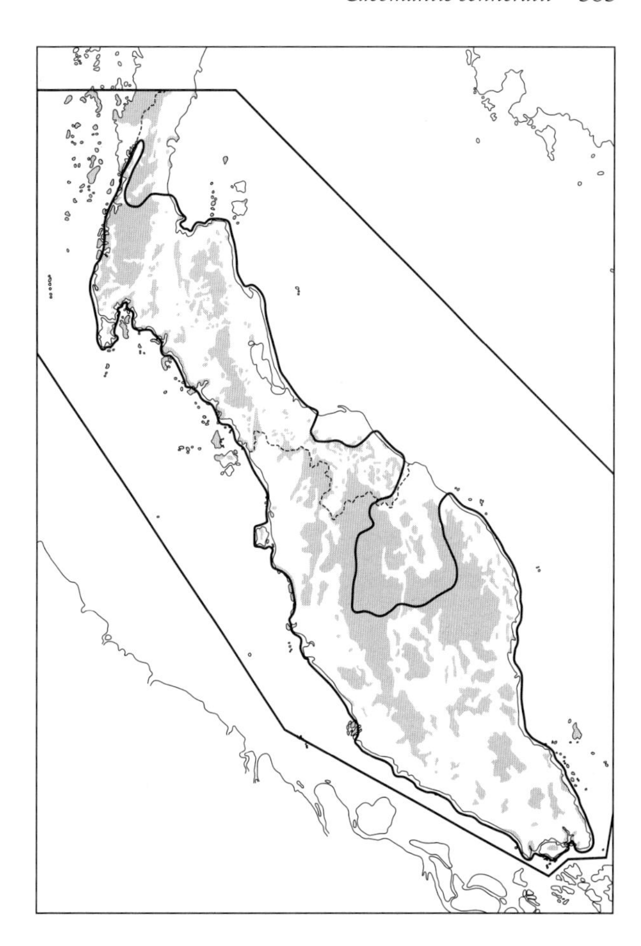

and on slopes to about 900 m. A dark-banded, rufous *Cacomantis* has been seen, and one mist-netted at floodlights, at 1300 m on Fraser's Hill, but neither safely identified to species (BR 1969).

FORAGING AND FOOD. Foliage-searches down to 2–3 m from the ground, usually higher. Diet not recorded, but sallies after swarming alate termites (Bromley 1948).

SOCIAL ORGANIZATION. Mainly solitary. Males call territorially from regular patches of habitat, but may interact at close range: four counter-calling in a single tree-crown at Nee Soon, Singapore central catchment area, on 27 May (SINGAV-3).

MOVEMENTS. None confirmed.

SURVIVAL. No information.

SOCIAL INTERACTIONS. No other information.

VOICE. The commonest loud call is a plaintive, hurried, shallowly and uniformly descending, four-note whistle, *few-few-few-few* (compare the more powerful, strident call of Indian Cuckoo). A second, less frequent call is louder, more complex: a sequence of 3–4 simple, spaced notes giving way to 2–3 rapid stutters, *fee, fee, fee, fee, fihihi-hi-hi fihihi-hi-hi fihihi-hi-hi*, on an overall rising scale, abruptly terminated.

In the south, calling occurs in all months but only irregularly outside the period late December–August, and at peak intensity (including sometimes at night) during February–June (Chasen 1939, Holttum 1950).

BREEDING

Brood-hosts. The only confirmed host-species in non-forest, forest-edge and semi-evergreen forest habitats is Common Iora *Aegithina tiphia*. In closed-canopy evergreen forest, presumably, other hosts operate, e.g., at Khao Chong (Trang) a juvenile being fed by a White-bellied Yuhina *Yuhina zantholeuca*.

Eggs and brood. Eggs have not been described. Fosterers attend solitary young.

Cycle. No information.

Seasonality. Fledglings recorded late May–late July (Batchelor 1958, BBCB-9, BCSTB-11, -13, BMP5, Bromley 1948a, P.D. Round).

MOULT. Primaries are replaced at up to three loci. In a small sample of adults, active wing-moult occurred in July, August and late October; other birds dated January–March and September–October showed none (BMNH, UMBRP, ZRCNUS).

CONSERVATION. Forest may be core habitat but abundance and presence of brood-hosts elsewhere imply there is no serious threat to this species.

Plaintive Cuckoo; Nok Ee-waab Takaten (Thai); Burung Sewah Mati Anak (Malay)

Cacomantis merulinus (Scopoli) 1786, *Deliciae Florae et Fauna Insubricae* 2: 89. TL Panay, Philippines.

Plate 49

GROUP RELATIONS. Probably free-standing. Evidence for biological differences and breeding-sympatry between *merulinus* and ventrally-grey S Asian *passerinus* seems insufficient to warrant recognition of separate species. Another extensively grey population occurs in Sulawesi.

GLOBAL RANGE. At its most inclusive, the Indian subcontinent from the Himalayan foothills; SE Tibet; China south from Sichuan, Guizhou and Fujian, including Hainan; SE Asia to the Greater Sunda islands, Bali and the Philippines; and Sulawesi. Himalayan birds migrate, wintering to Sri Lanka; the eastern situation is unknown.

IDENTIFICATION/DESCRIPTION. Grey-phase adults have head to breast light grey, paler below; upper body and wings bronzy, rump and upper tail-coverts clear slate-grey; tail black, all except the central feather-pair tipped white and with inner webs barred white across virtually their whole width. Remaining underparts and lower wing-coverts buff-rufous, the tone varying geographically; underside of flight-feathers with a whitish slash angled obliquely across the lower base of the secondaries and inner primaries, and a white patch on the lower base of the inner web of the outermost primary (cf. Rusty-breasted Cuckoo *C. sepulchralis*).

That all grey-phase birds examined in museum collections have been sexed male could be an outcome of the difficulty of finding cuckoos that are not singing. It also implies grey is standard for males. A record of a rufous bird with grey lores and greyish, un-barred wing-coverts, i.e., probably half-moulted, being courted by a grey male (Lim 1987, MBR 1986–87) suggests some females are also grey, but wholly rufous adults (aged by their plain-tipped flight-feathers) occur as well. These are bright rufous above, the cap streaked, barred or occasionally spotted black, and upperparts fully black-barred back to upper tail-coverts. Some individuals show a short, white streak above and below the eye, the rest of the face and underparts from chin buff-white to pale rufous, narrowly barred black. Tail barred black-and-rufous on both webs, the rufous bars closely approaching or meeting across the shaft, and dominant over black (but tail-feathers are never edged rufous, *contra* Rusty-breasted Cuckoo). Underwing is as in grey-phase birds.

Juveniles are clay-yellow to pale rufous, whiter below and completely barred sooty black, densely (giving a smudged effect) back to mantle and breast; flight-feathers margined and tipped clay-buff; tail-feathers dark, with dull rufous barring on both webs that extends only about half-way towards the shaft (cf. Rusty-breasted Cuckoo). Lower wing-coverts are whitish rather than rufous, plain or finely dark-barred. Moult from this plumage is direct into one or other adult colour-phase, i.e., no separate subadult body-plumage has been identified.

Bare-part colours. (Adults) iris brown to dark red, eyelid-rim greyish and non-contrasting (cf. Rusty-breasted Cuckoo); upper mandible black, lower pinkish, or bill all-black; mouth-lining bright red; feet yellow (MBR 1986–87).

Size (mm). (Skins: 28 males, 5 females; adult): wing 101–110 and 100–106; tail 92–111 and 89–108; bill

19.7–21.8 (sexes combined); tarsus 15.3–18.3 (sexes combined) (BMNH, ZDUM, ZRCNUS).

Weight (g). Adults, 21.3–26.6 (n=4) (UMBRP, ZDUM).

DISTRIBUTION. Historical summary: in all divisions except *Pra*, with additional island records from Yao Yai, Lanta, Tarutao, the Langkawi group (Langkawi, Langgun) and Penang off the W coast; Samui off the E coast (the *Cacomantis* on Tioman has still to be identified to species); and Tekong and Ubin, Singapore.

GEOGRAPHICAL VARIATION. Richer-toned northern *querulus* Heine 1863 (TL Bengal to China), averaging slightly larger, intergrades with paler *threnodes* Cabanis and Heine 1862 (TL Melaka) – wing not above 106 mm, head clearer grey, more differentiated from colour of upper body – between latitudes about 5° and 6°N.

STATUS AND POPULATION. Resident, regular and more or less common. Deignan (1963) guessed non-breeding migrants might reach northern areas but this has not been confirmed (a *Cacomantis* taken at flood-lights on Fraser's Hill was not identified to species).

HABITATS AND ECOLOGY. Occasionally mangroves and heavily disturbed inland forest, typically along river-courses; more commonly in unkempt tree plantations (rubber, teak), patches and belts of tall scrub and other secondary-growth, wooded parks and gardens, shade-trees over crops, etc.; mostly at plains level, but residents have found their way into agriculture in Cameron Highlands (Main Range) where small numbers occur around tea plantations to at least 1500 m.

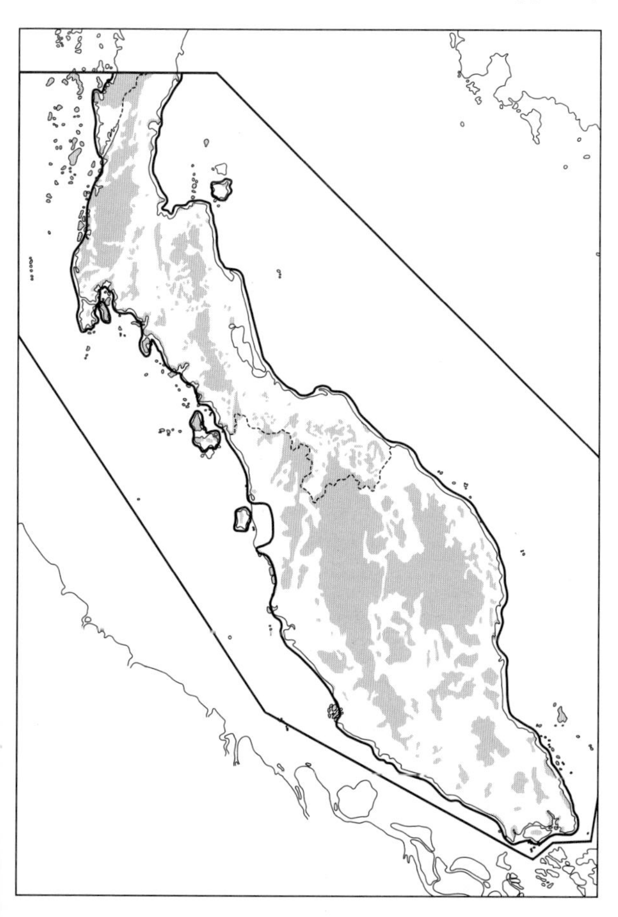

FOOD AND FORAGING. No information.

SOCIAL ORGANIZATION. Typically solitary; males call from regular sites, often over several consecutive days, and are presumed to be territorial.

MOVEMENTS. No information.

SURVIVAL. No information.

SOCIAL INTERACTIONS. One record of a courting male feeding a female a caterpillar (Lim 1987).

VOICE. (1) A shallowly descending, spaced sequence of 3–6 short whistles ending in a brief, abruptly descending trill (sometimes with a hint of a tail); (2) 3–4 spaced trisyllables, *ti-ter-weet*, stepping shallowly up-scale (cf. Rusty-bellied Cuckoo); (3) a fast, squealing, *treetreetreetree* or *preepreepreepree*, shallowly falling in pitch (cf. Little Bronze Cuckoo). All are within the repertoire of individual males. Female vocalizations have not been described.

Males advertise from a perch near the top of a tree, usually hidden in foliage, only exceptionally exposed (cf. Banded Bay Cuckoo), mostly by day but sometimes continuing far into the night. The season in the south is late October–late July.

BREEDING

Brood hosts. Few positive records: in Krabi and Selangor, young juveniles attended by Dark-necked Tailorbird *Orthotomus atrogularis* and Yellow-bellied Prinia *Prinia flaviventris*. Both these host species have reached Cameron Highlands tea plantations.

Eggs and brood. No eggs positively identified.

Cycle. No information.

Seasonality. Fledglings during early June–late August (R.R. Kersley, R.V. Lansdown, Robinson 1927, P.D. Round).

MOULT. As in other parasitic cuckoos, post-juvenile body-moult precedes wing- and tail-moult. Primaries are replaced at up to three loci. Among 56 adults from throughout the Peninsula and covering all months except June, active wing-moult occurred only during July–September (incidence 65 percent over this period), although advanced individuals (near-complete by late July) are likely to have started in June or earlier. Post-juvenile wing-moult occurs later, during October–February, with suspensions or arrests common (BMNH, UMZC, ZDUM, ZRCNUS).

CONSERVATION. No critical issues.

Rusty-breasted Cuckoo; Nok Kha-khuu Haang Phaen (Thai); Burung Sewah Gila (Malay)

Cacomantis sepulchralis (S. Müller) 1843, *Verhandelingen over de Natuurlijke Geschiedenis der Nederlandsche Overzeesche Bezittingen . . . Land- en Volkenkunde* 6: 177 (TL Java and Sumatra).
Plate 49

GROUP RELATIONS. Likely to be part of a superspecies. Allopatric *C. heinrichi* (Moluccan Cuckoo) is close morphologically but otherwise little known, and *sepulchralis* vocalizations support a link with E Wallacean/Australasian *C. variolosus* (Brush Cuckoo). More research is needed.

GLOBAL RANGE. Tenasserim and the Peninsula south from latitude about 12°N (BMNH), the Greater Sunda islands, Bali and the Philippines; and Wallacea east to Flores and Seram.

IDENTIFICATION/DESCRIPTION. Shape of Plaintive Cuckoo; slightly larger size and proportionately slightly longer tail are not useful as field-characters. Most adults are uniform bronze-grey above, including wings, shading to clear slate-grey on rump and upper tail-coverts. Underparts, including lower wing-coverts, are plain pink-rufous, washed greyish over chin and throat but with no sharp colour-demarcation (*contra* grey-phase Plaintive Cuckoo). Tail black with narrow white tip (widening laterally) and all except central feather-pair toothed white along the margin of the inner web (versus inner web more or less completely barred in Plaintive Cuckoo). An oblique, whitish slash across the underside of the secondaries and inner primaries is as in Plaintive Cuckoo, but white on the outer primary forms a complete, angled bar across the underside of the inner web, rather than just a basal spot.

Juveniles resemble same-stage Plaintive Cuckoo: clay-yellow to buff above, white below, washed pale buff over throat and breast, and entirely barred sooty black, densest over head and anterior body, sparser over belly and lower tail-coverts. Flight- and tail-feathers are dark brown, the former tipped and latter toothed dull rufous, but tooth-marks extend not more than about one-third across the width of the web.

Grey, adult-type plumage is acquired direct at post-juvenile moult, head and body before flight-feathers and tail, as in other *Cacomantis* species, and grey birds can be either sex. Fully black-barred, richly rufous individuals, adult on the evidence of plain-tipped flight-feathers, have been collected in Sumatra and Java, and among few local juveniles examined some showed evidence of moulting directly into a similar plumage. All such birds also show a distinctive tail-pattern, in which marginal notching is replaced by a continuous rufous edge to webs, the rest of the feather black-brown (BMNH, NNML, ZDUM, ZRCNUS). No such birds have been sexed but the probability is that some adult female Rusty-breasted Cuckoos are erythristic.

Bare-part colours. Iris grey-brown (juvenile), hazel-brown (adult), eyelid-rim greenish yellow (juvenile), contrastingly clear yellow (adult); upper mandible black, lower pink-yellow, or bill all-black; feet yellow-horn (juvenile), yellow (adult).

Size (mm). (Skins: 9 males, 5 females; adult): wing 111–118 and 110–116; tail 108–119 and 104–117; bill 18.3–21.1 (sexes combined); tarsus 16.7–18.0 (sexes combined) (BMNH, ZDUM, ZRCNUS).

Weight (g). Adults, 28.1–38.0 (n=10) (UMBRP).

DISTRIBUTION. Historical summary: *Ran, Nak, Kra, Tra, Sat, Yal, Nar, Pes, Ked, Tru, Pek, Phg, Sel, Neg, Joh, Sin*, with additional island records from Muk (*Tra*) off the W coast; and Tekong, Ubin and Sentosa, Singapore.

GEOGRAPHICAL VARIATION. Nominate *sepulchralis*, of the mainland and Greater and Lesser Sunda islands.

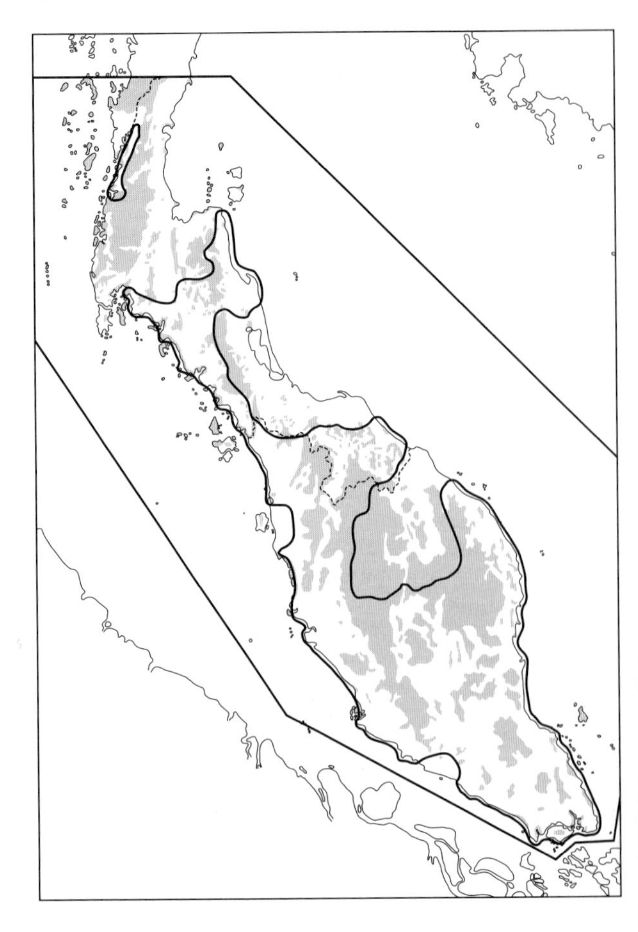

STATUS AND POPULATION. Resident, regular and more or less common.

HABITATS AND ECOLOGY. Mangrove forest; dry-land semi-evergreen and evergreen Lowland forest, mature and disturbed; and forest-edge and overgrown plantations, at plains level and on slopes to around 600 m (BMP5).

FORAGING AND FOOD. No direct information, although mist-net captures imply some foraging down to the under-stratum of forest.

SOCIAL ORGANIZATION. As in related species, males call from regular patches of habitat and are presumed to be territorial.

MOVEMENTS. None recorded.

SURVIVAL. No information.

SOCIAL INTERACTIONS. No information.

VOICE. Only two calls are confirmed: (1) a paced, gradually descending sequence of 10–15 melancholy whistles, *few, few, few* . . . at an even rate of about three notes per two seconds; (2) a sequence of 3–4 three- or four-note phrases, *ti-ter-wee* or *ti-teter-wee*, stepping shallowly up-scale, confusable with similar call of Plantive Cuckoo, although a four-note version has still to be confirmed in Plaintive.

Males call from mid to upper levels of woodland vegetation, like Plaintive, from a well-concealed perch. The overall season in the south is late December–August.

BREEDING. No information; local brood-hosts not identified.

MOULT. At least in adults, primaries moult at up to three loci. Among 25 adults covering all months except October and November, active wing-moult occurred only during late April–September. Instances of post-juvenile wing-moult are dated September and January (BMNH, BMP5, UMBRP, ZRCNUS).

CONSERVATION. Widespread occurrence in secondary woodland suggests no immediate threat, but this is mainly a forest species, absent from well-kept plantation habitat.

Drongo Cuckoo; Nok Kha-khuu Saeng-saew (Thai); Burung Sewah Sawai (Malay)

Surniculus lugubris (Horsfield) 1821, *Transactions of the Linnean Society* 13(1): 179. TL Java.
Plate 49

GROUP RELATIONS. Free-standing. Commonly placed near the koels, especially Papuan *Caliechthrus* (White-crowned Koel) which is black with similar markings, but larger, lacks the underwing pattern and has a quite different voice. Resemblance to *Cacomantis* (vocalizations, size, wing-pattern, one subspecies with a rufous juvenile) is generally stronger.

GLOBAL RANGE. Breeds through the Indian subcontinent from the Himalayan foothills, and Sri Lanka; China south from a line Fujian–Sichuan; SE Asia to the Greater Sunda islands, Bali and the Philippines; and Sulawesi to the Moluccas. Northern populations migrate, wintering south to Sumatra.

IDENTIFICATION/DESCRIPTION. Adults are black, glossed bottle-green, usually with a few white feathers on the nape, some white on the tibial trousers, and fine but variable white barring on the lower tail-coverts. Extreme tail-tip white and the outermost pair of tail-feathers narrowly but fully white-barred. Always shows an oblique white slash across the lower base of the secondaries and inner primaries, and the white across the lower inner web of the outermost primary is as in Rusty-breasted Cuckoo.

Juvenile dull black, with the same distribution of white as in adult, plus a round dot of white subterminally on all head, body and upper wing-covert feathers, a short row of white-barred feathers on the margin of the carpus and broader white tail-tip. Adult plumage is acquired direct but not always at a single moult, and the relative timing of post-juvenile wing-moult is uncertain.

Bare-part colours. (Adult) iris hazel- to dark brown; bill black, mouth-lining pink; feet lead-grey.

Size (mm). (Live and skins: 66 adults, most not sexed): wing 118–150; tail 104–143; bill 20.3–24.5; tarsus 14.6–17.1 (BMNH, UMBRP, ZDUM, ZRCNUS).

Weight (g). Subspecies *brachyurus*, 26.0–35.8 (n=6, including migrants); longer-winged autumn migrants, 32.5–43.3 (n=41) (M. Wong, UMBRP).

DISTRIBUTION. Historical summary: all divisions except *Ran, Mel*, with additional island records from the Similans, Yao Yai, Lanta, Libong, Tarutao, Langkawi, Perak, Penang, the Sembilan group (Rembia), Jarak and Pisang off the W coast; Samui off the E coast; and Ubin and St John's, Singapore.

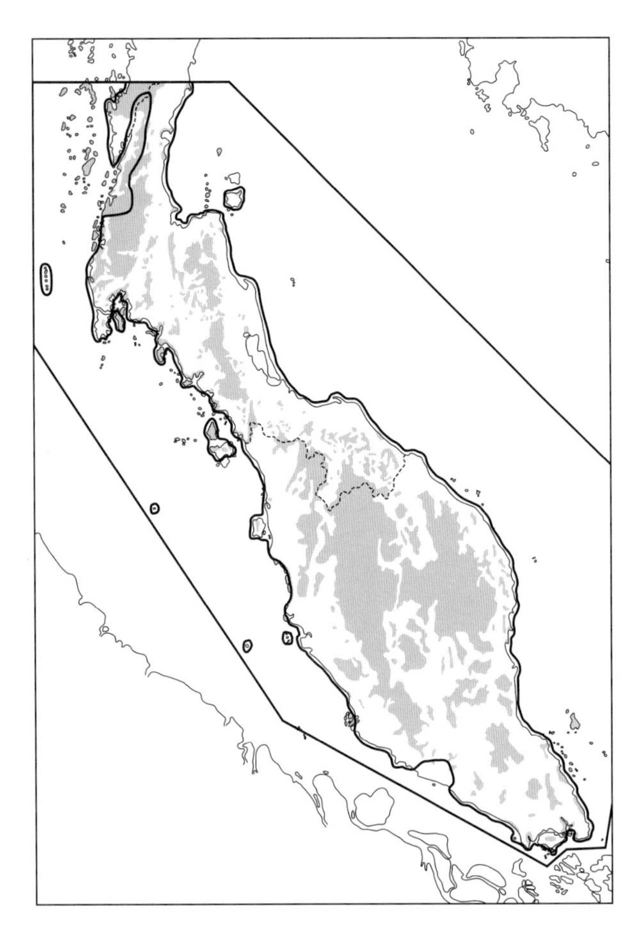

GEOGRAPHICAL VARIATION. From Singapore north at least to Phuket, Nakhon Si Thammarat and Samui island (BMNH, TISTR, USNM), residents are small *brachyurus* Stresemann 1913 (TL Bentong, Pahang) (wing 118–129, tail 104–117 mm), also of Sumatra, Borneo and intervening islands, and possibly Palawan. No certain non-migrants have been handled from anywhere further north. Larger migrants (adult wing 130–150 mm) have been lumped as northern *dicruroides* Hodgson 1839 (TL Nepal) but bimodal variation in tail-length (main and minor peaks at 130 and 139, not sex-linked) that correlates loosely with normally varying wing-length suggests the possibility of more than one population occurring.

STATUS AND POPULATION. Resident, a non-breeding visitor and passage migrant; regular and, in forest, more or less common. During autumn passage, by far the commonest cuckoo species intercepted at floodlights while crossing the Main Range at Fraser's Hill.

HABITATS AND ECOLOGY. Dry-land semi-evergreen and evergreen Lowland forest, mature and disturbed, at all altitudes, and occasional in Lower Montane forest, to about 1200 m. In the lowlands, makes lesser use also of tall secondary-growth, well-grown tree (including pine) plantations and nearby wooded gardens. The wintering habitats of non-breeding visitors have not been separately identified but, on passage, migrants occur out to the landward edge of mangroves.

FORAGING AND FOOD. Little known, but aerial-sallies after swarming termites.

SOCIAL ORGANIZATION. Males vocalize from limited patches of habitat, counter-call energetically when they happen to make contact, and are assumed to be territorial.

MOVEMENTS. Night-flying autumn migrants have been intercepted at Fraser's Hill during 5 August–6 December, which period also covers the few coastal and Melaka Straits lighthouse-strike reports (BMNH, ZDUM). Records at Fraser's since 1970 show nearly all August–September birds to have been subspecies *brachyurus* (latest date 5 October), indicating an early passage of birds originating somewhere close to, or even within, the Peninsula. A few *brachyurus*-sized birds are also on the move at night during mid winter (BR 1974–75).

The earliest definite long-winged migrant in autumn is dated 25 September. Spring passage has not been charted.

SURVIVAL. No information.

SOCIAL INTERACTIONS. Nothing beyond vocal interactions. Males regularly call from fully exposed perches at canopy level, maximizing the audibility of their song. This behaviour supplies a possible reason for drongo-like appearance – but mimicking a pugnacious model does not block attention from real drongos. Greater Racket-tailed Drongo *Dicrurus paradiseus* displaces and chases off singing Drongo Cuckoos.

VOICE. The male advertising-call is an even-paced sequence of 5–7 short, brisk whistles rising steadily up the scale, *pwi, pwi, pwi, pwi, pwi, pwi, pwi*. An excited male-interaction call is the same rising sequence but of an equivalent number of short trills, sometimes with a brief, hurried tail on a falling scale. Female vocalizations unknown.

The overall calling-season is January–August, starting occasionally as early as November.

BREEDING

Brood-hosts. Single instances of lone fledglings fed by pairs of Sooty-capped, Chestnut-winged and Striped Tit Babblers, *Malacopteron affine*, *Stachyris erythroptera* and *Macronous gularis*, with a provisionally identified egg in a nest of Horsfield's Babbler *Trichastoma sepiarium* (a proven fosterer in Java).

Eggs and brood. The egg was scrawled and blotched black and dark brown on a pale pink ground and, apart from slightly larger size and more pitted surface texture, closely matched eggs of the babbler host. Shape broad elliptical. Size (mm): 22.5 × 17.0.

Cycle. No information.

Seasonality. Fledglings during early May–early July, and an egg on 14 July (Allen 1958, BBCB-9, BMP5, ENGGANG-1).

MOULT. At least in adults, primaries are replaced at up to three loci. Virtually the only active wing-moult seen has been in subspecies *brachyurus* during July–September, including among nocturnal migrants taken at Fraser's Hill. Long-winged migrants covering all months October–March showed none, apart from a moulting immature intercepted on 11 October and a few birds dated December–February suspended with up to five inner primaries renewed, perhaps before arrival (BMP5).

CONSERVATION. Capacity to exploit disturbed forests on slopes, and use of forest-edge brood-hosts, suggest no serious threat to this species.

Little Bronze Cuckoo; Nok Kha-khuu See Thong Daeng (Thai); Burung Sewah Daun (Malay)

Chrysococcyx minutillus Gould 1859, *Proceedings of the Zoological Society of London* 27: 128. TL Port Essington, far-N Australia.

Plate 50

GROUP RELATIONS. Hybridizes with *C. russatus* (Gould's Bronze Cuckoo) in far-northern Australia but they are extensively sympatric, with no evidence of interbreeding, in Borneo (Parker 1981). Widely known as *C. malayanus*, but as E.W. Oates long ago pointed out, T.S. Raffles's description of the type of '*malayanus*' fits a female Violet Cuckoo rather than the present species.

GLOBAL RANGE. Presumed or shown to breed in N and NE Australia; and Borneo, W Java, Sumatra and the Peninsula north to latitude about 9°N. A record from S Vietnam has been discredited and one from Cambodia cannot be substantiated (Parker 1981). Far-southern populations migrate, wintering north to New Guinea, possibly also to parts of Wallacea.

IDENTIFICATION/DESCRIPTION. Smallest cuckoo of the area, hardly more than sparrow-sized. Adult male dull purplish bronze-shot green above with contrasting bottle-green cap, freckled white on lores and forehead back to eye-level. Sides of face to above eye, underparts and lower wing-coverts grey-white, face and throat freckled, elsewhere barred sooty black, bars broadening and progressively more spaced on flanks and belly. Adult female from male by greener, less bronze-shot dorsum, non-contrasting cap and less conspicuous frosting on the forehead. In both, all tail-feathers except plain bronze-green central pair have a black subterminal band and white spot at the tip of the inner web, spot increasing in size laterally. The outermost feather is banded black-and-white; intermediate pairs have greenish outer and rufous inner webs. Patterning on the underwing is more or less as in *Cacomantis* species.

Fledglings are duller than adults, without frosting on the head, and with underparts plain, unmarked grey-white. Adult-type plumage seems to be acquired direct, but possibly not all at one moult, ventral bars appearing first on the lower wing-coverts, then along the upper margin of the flanks.

Bare-part colours. (Adult) iris and eyelid-rim both bright red (male), dark brown with rim pale lime-green (female); bill black; feet black (UMBRP).

Size (mm). (Skins: 6 males, 4 females; adult): wing 91–97 and 83–94; tail 59–66 and 61–63; bill 16.8–19.5, bill-width across nostrils 5.6–6.5 (sexes combined); tarsus 16.4 (a female) (BMNH, Parker 1981, ZRC-NUS).

Weight (g). A laying female, 17.7.

DISTRIBUTION. Unrecorded in the far north. Historical summary: *Sur, Kra, Tra, Son, Pat, Yal, Nar, Pes, Ked, Pra, Pek, Phg, Sel, Neg, Mel, Joh, Sin*, with additional island records from Penang off the W coast; and Ubin, Sentosa and Sudong, Singapore.

GEOGRAPHICAL VARIATION. Apparently endemic *peninsularis* Parker 1981 (TL vicinity of Narathiwat town). S.A. Parker tentatively identified a bird collected during daylight of 17 December 1969 in scrub at 1300 m on Fraser's Hill (Main Range) as a female *C. russatus* (Gould's Bronze Cuckoo), closest to the Bornean–Philippine subspecies *aheneus*, but with more white than usual on the forecrown, and less rufous in the tail than usual in either this species or *minutillus*. Typical of *russatus*, the bill is relatively narrow at its base (as viewed from above), but other measurements, and general colour and pattern of this specimen, are hardly distinguishable from *minutillus*.

STATUS AND POPULATION. Resident, regular and, in the south, more or less common.

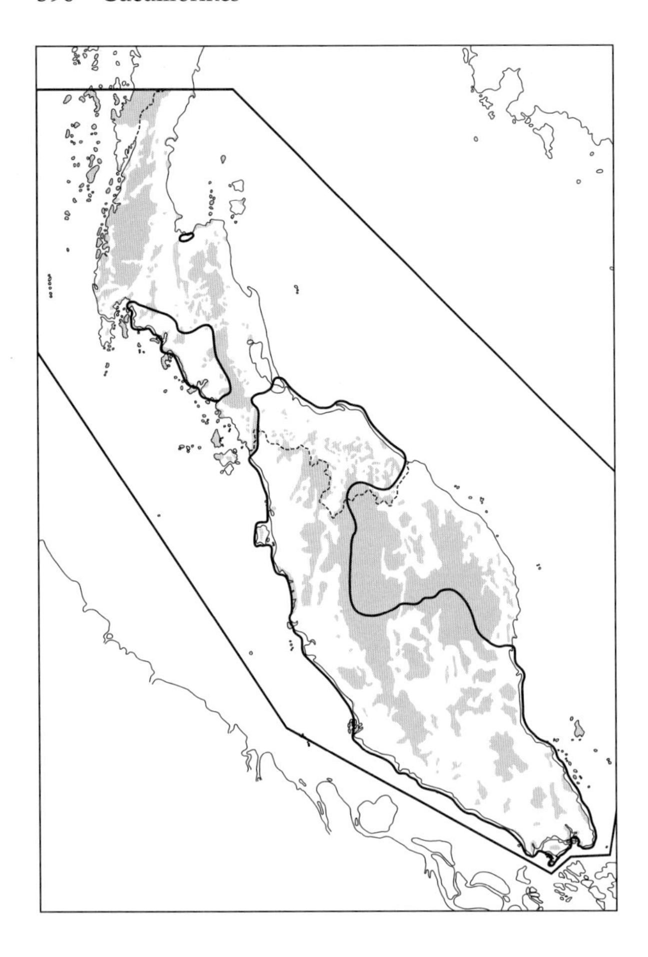

HABITATS AND ECOLOGY. Mangrove forest, scrub with scattered trees and other secondary-growth, tree plantations (especially where over-grown), and wooded gardens. Not generally considered to enter closed-canopy inland forest (BMP5) but in the upper Gombak valley, Selangor, song indistinguishable from that of *minutillus* has been heard in forest to an altitude of about 250 m, and sightings exist from isolated clearings and forested riverbanks in Pahang. On evidence of calling, however, much sparser there than in its other habitats.

FORAGING AND FOOD. Searches foliage for caterpillars (SINGAV-1).

SOCIAL ORGANIZATION. Like most other parasitic cuckoos, males are vocal in a particular habitat patch for a few days then appear to move on, perhaps within a larger territory. Mainly solitary, but males interact vocally where they meet.

MOVEMENTS. None known.

SURVIVAL. No information.

SOCIAL INTERACTIONS. Vocalizing males regularly respond to one another, and parties of up to five birds, evidently including more than one male, mutual-chase with much excited counter-calling (SINGAV-3, -6) – as recorded also for Banded Bay, Drongo and Violet Cuckoos.

VOICE. Males have two regular advertising-calls: (1) 3–5 (mostly four) light, reedy notes on a shallowly falling scale, *rhew rhew rhew rhew* or *eug eug eug eug*; and (2) a less-often-heard, thin, high-pitched, drawn-out trill reeling down the scale. In addition, bouts of *eug* calling are sometimes interrupted by a short, rising screech, *wireeg-reeg-reeg*. A common response to a calling neighbour begins *eug eug* then runs into 2–3 repeats of a hurried *euga-wireeg-reeg-reeg* sequence (G.C. Madoc).

Calling occurs in all months but only sparsely during October–November. Female vocalizations have not been identified.

BREEDING

Brood hosts. The exclusive proven host is Golden-bellied Gerygone *G. sulphurea*. A Brown-throated Sunbird *Anthreptes malacensis*, with similar nest-structure, has been seen to attack a singing male but this may be a generic response to any small, bar-bellied cuckoo (see Violet Cuckoo).

Eggs and brood. The egg is dark olive-green, colour densest at the poles, i.e., very different from the pink-white, brown-speckled egg of *Gerygone*, and larger (though no exact measurements available). Low-light surroundings in a closed-over, purse-shaped nest may reduce the importance of egg-matching.

Cycle. The nestling ejects host eggs. A bird recently hatched on 25 March was tended by fosterers until at least 26 May (Bromley 1941).

Seasonality. Eggs on 19 and 28 March and in August, and fledglings tended by fosterers in all months April–October (BIRDLINE 1992, BMP5, Ollington and Loh 1992).

MOULT. Primaries moult at up to three loci. Active wing-moult of adults recorded in June (a male still with large testes), July, September and January (BMNH).

CONSERVATION. No critical issues.

Horsfield's Bronze Cuckoo; (no Thai name); **Burung Sewah Australia** (Malay)

Chrysococcyx basalis (Horsfield) 1821, *Transactions of the Linnean Society* 13(1): 179. TL Java.
Plate 50

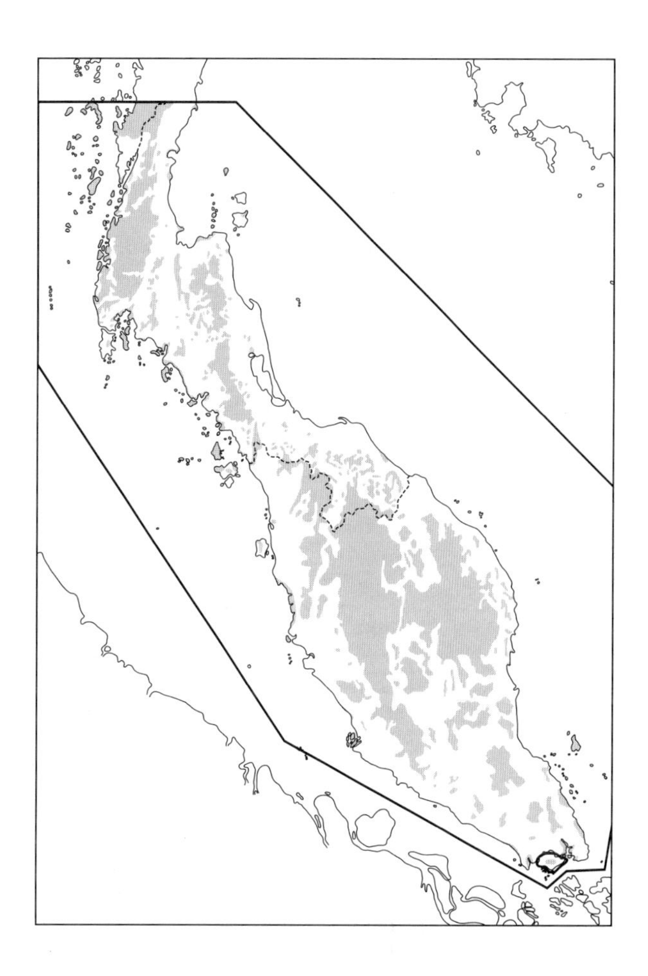

GROUP RELATIONS. Free-standing.

GLOBAL RANGE. Breeds through Tasmania and Australia, migrating within Australia and north to the Aru and Lesser Sunda islands, Sulawesi, Borneo, Bali, Java, S Sumatra and the southern tip of the Peninsula. Vagrant on Christmas island, Indian Ocean.

IDENTIFICATION/DESCRIPTION. Slightly larger than Little Bronze Cuckoo; upperparts dull bronze-green commonly with fine but obvious white or pale buff edging to mantle and scapular feathers (a possible juvenile character). Cap to hind-neck light to dark brown, with a conspicuous black-brown band from the eye curving back over the ear-coverts; long eyebrow and rest of face and underparts white, narrowly streaked bronze-brown on the throat and dark-barred over the upper breast, lower wing-coverts and sides (only) of the body, back to tail-level. Central tail-feathers as upper body, the outer pair black-and-white-banded, intermediates with basal half bright rufous, outer half bronze-green, darkening apically and with a white tip.

Bare-part colours. (Adult) iris red-brown; bill black; feet grey.

Size (mm). (Skin: 1 adult female): wing 100; tail (moulting); bill 14.8; tarsus 19.0 (BMNH).

Weight. No data.

DISTRIBUTION. Historical summary: *Sin* and island satellite Sentosa.

GEOGRAPHICAL VARIATION. None recognized.

STATUS AND POPULATION. A non-breeding visitor, apparently less than annual and in tiny numbers, at the very edge of winter range; including a specimen dated 1879 and acceptable field identifications of a total five individuals over the years 1986, 1990, 1991 and 1993 (BIRDLINE 1993, BMNH, Ollington and Loh 1992, SINGAV-4).

HABITATS AND ECOLOGY. One sighting in secondary *Acacia* woodland, all others on the virtually open, sandy ground of the reclaimed Changi coast, where a preference has been noted for areas of sprawling *Ipomoea pes-caprae*. Foragers perch directly on the ground or on fence-lines and low bushes, never above about 1.5 m, and have been described as very confiding, allowing close approach (BIRDLINE 1993).

FORAGING AND FOOD. No additional information.

SOCIAL ORGANIZATION. Apparently solitary; two is the largest number proven to have been present at Changi at any one time.

MOVEMENTS. A few unsubstantiated records are June- and September-dated; those accepted fall in the period 7 July–28 August.

SURVIVAL. No information.

SOCIAL INTERACTIONS. No information.

VOICE. Not recorded; apparently silent in the non-breeding area.

BREEDING. No population.

MOULT. An adult female collected on 19 July showed active moult of primaries at three loci (P4, 6/7 and 9/10), and of central tail-feathers.

CONSERVATION. No critical issues.

Asian Emerald Cuckoo; Nok Kha-khuu Moradok (Thai); Burung Sewah Zamrud (Malay)

Chrysococcyx maculatus (Gmelin) 1788, *Systema Naturae* 13(1): 404. TL Sri Lanka.
Plate 50

GROUP RELATIONS. Free-standing.

GLOBAL RANGE. The Himalayan foothills east from Garhwal and hill-tracts of the far-NE Indian subcontinent; SE Tibet; China from Sichuan and Hubei south to Guizhou, Yunnan and Hainan; and SE Asia to S Burma, NW Thailand and central Vietnam. Some populations migrate, wintering in the eastern Indian subcontinent, Sri Lanka and the Bay of Bengal islands, and mainland SE Asia. Vagrant in Sumatra.

IDENTIFICATION/DESCRIPTION. The adult male is gold-shot, emerald-green; underparts from lower breast clean-cut white with broad, well-spaced bars of bronze-green to, on the lower tail-coverts, emerald-green. The outer two primaries have white shafts and, as in Violet Cuckoo *C. xanthorhynchus*, the outer tail-feather is black-and-white-banded, and outer two pairs white-tipped. Adult females have cap to hindneck rufous, remaining upperparts bronze-green; entire underparts white, tinged rufous on throat and flanks, and barred bronze-green, bars narrow anteriorly, broadening and more spaced on body. Central tail-feathers are as upper body but with darker tip, the next pair with rufous outer web, then feathers progressively more rufous, leaving only a sub-apical dark bar. As in male, the outermost feather is black-and-white-barred, and outer two pairs are white-tipped.

Youngest individuals seen show juvenile (or possibly subadult), black-and-white-barred feathers scattered through the green of the male throat and breast, some scapulars with buff tips, and some forehead feathers clay-yellow with narrow black bars, on dates up to early January. The number of pre-adult plumages is not known.

Bare-part colours. (Adult) iris and eyelid-rim both blood-red (male), female undescribed in this area; bill bi-coloured, rich yellow with black tip; feet dark olive-brown.

Size (mm). (Skins: 1 male, 3 females; first-winterers): wing 110 and 110–113; tail 66 and 67–70; bill 16.8, 16.9 (females only); tarsus 13.4–13.6 (females only) (BMNH, ZRCNUS).

Weight. No data.

DISTRIBUTION. Historical summary: *Pha, Kra, Pht, Tra, Sat, Phg, ?Sel, ?Mel,* with no island records.

GEOGRAPHICAL VARIATION. None recognized.

STATUS AND POPULATION. A non-breeding visitor in small numbers to northern areas. Not more than vagrant in Malaysia, where recently reported from the Tembeling valley, Taman Negara; older records from Selangor and Melaka are no longer confirmable.

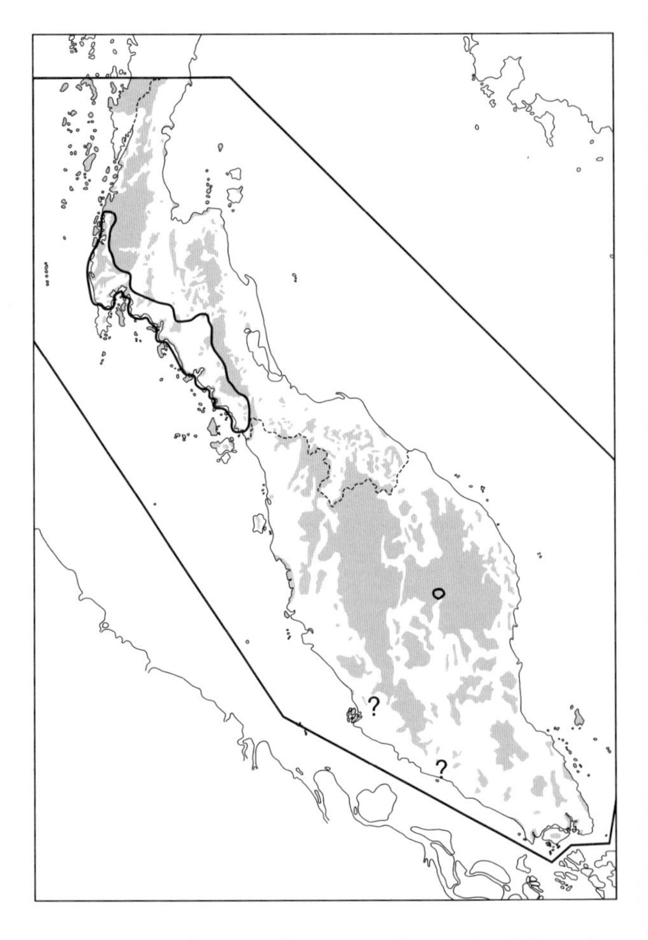

HABITATS AND ECOLOGY. The canopy of semi-evergreen and evergreen Lowland forest, and forest-edge, at plains level and on (lower?) slopes. Two specimens are from the E-central (Trang border) Range but lack information on altitude or situation. In central Thailand, reported from parkland and wooded gardens.

FORAGING AND FOOD. An adult male photographed in Taman Negara hunted over outer branches and foliage of a riverbank rain tree *Samanea saman* (A. Jeyarajasingam).

SOCIAL ORGANIZATION. Solitary.

MOVEMENTS. Reliable dates are in the range 15 December–5 March.

SURVIVAL. No information.

SOCIAL INTERACTIONS. No information.

VOICE. Not reported; probably silent in winter.

BREEDING. No population.

MOULT. Three first-winterers dated December–early January showed all-fresh flight-feathers; another had suspended after renewing P1–5, 7–8 (BMNH, ZRCNUS).

CONSERVATION. No issues established.

Violet Cuckoo; Nok Kha-khuu See Muang (Thai); Burung Sewah Puteri (Malay)

Chrysococcyx xanthorhynchus (Horsfield) 1821, *Transactions of the Linnean Society* 13(1): 179. TL Java.

Plate 50

GROUP RELATIONS. Free-standing.

GLOBAL RANGE. The far-NE Indian subcontinent and Bay of Bengal islands; Yunnan; and (except N Laos and northern Vietnam?) SE Asia to the Greater Sunda islands and Philippines. Some populations migrate, wintering within the SE Asian breeding-range evidently as far as Sumatra. Vagrant in S India.

IDENTIFICATION/DESCRIPTION. The disyllabic flight-call and dipping flight make advertising adult males easy to identify from a distance. In most field views, their intensely iridescent purple-violet colour appears black or dull, dark chocolate; but uniformly dark chin to breast, sharp against dark-barred white underparts, separates from all other small cuckoos except Asian Emerald. The outermost tail-feather is black-and-white-barred and the outer two pairs are white-tipped. Adult female from Asian Emerald Cuckoo by entirely bronze-green upperparts, including head, and from other local green cuckoos by fineness and density of ventral dark-barring, especially on the face where it extends to lores, ear-coverts and over the eye. Central tail-feather pair as back but with deep bottle-green tip, the outermost broadly barred black-and-white. Intermediate feathers, out from the centre, are rufous, with green on the inner web disintegrating progressively into blobs. The three outer feathers are white-tipped. All age/sex-classes have lower wing-coverts white, narrowly dark-barred, with an oblique, *Cacomantis*-like slash of white and cinnamon across the lower base of the flight-feathers, including inner webs of all primaries.

The young juvenile is rufous above, with black-streaked cap and hind-neck, rest of upperparts including wing-coverts broadly barred brown; underparts and face grey-white, dark-barred as in other age-classes; flight- and tail-feathers dark brown, the former edged and tipped rufous, the latter edged rufous and with rufous-and-green bars. Both sexes appear to pass through a subadult stage in which upperparts are bronze-green, heavily edged and barred rufous-chestnut, with juvenile-type flight-feathers and tail; replaced by adult plumage in stages.

Bare-part colours. (Adult) iris and eyelid-rim blood-red (male), female inadequately decribed; bill orange with vermilion-red base (male), dark horn with yellow base (female and juvenile); feet olive-brown to olive-grey (BMNH, WWFM).

Size (mm). (Live and skins: 18 males, 9 females; adult): wing 98–113 and 96–107; tail 65–74 and 67–74; bill 16.1–17.0 and 15.9–18.0; tarsus 13.1–13.7 and 13.4 (1 only) (BMNH, CHULA, RTFD, UMBRP, ZDUM, ZRCNUS).

Weight (g). Autumn migrants: adult males, 19.9–24.0 (n=10); adult females, 20.5–25.6 (n=7); immatures down to 17.7 (UMBRP).

DISTRIBUTION. Historical summary: all divisions except *Pha, Phu, Ked, Pra,* with additional island records only from Pisang off the W coast; and Ubin and Sentosa, Singapore.

GEOGRAPHICAL VARIATION. None recognized. Wing-lengths of summer-dated, presumed resident, adult nominate *xanthorhynchus*, from Singapore north to Ranong, are in the range 96–104 mm (sexes combined). Only four of 36 migrants intercepted at flood-lights on Fraser's Hill (Main Range) were larger, up to 113 mm (BMP5).

STATUS AND POPULATION. Resident, a presumed non-breeding visitor and probable passage migrant, more or less regular and uncommon to fairly common.

HABITATS AND ECOLOGY. Vocalizing, presumed residents occupy the canopy of dry-land semi-evergreen and evergreen Lowland forest, mature and disturbed, at plains level and on slopes to around 500 m altitude; also forest-edge and, less regularly, secondary-growth, overgrown tree plantations and

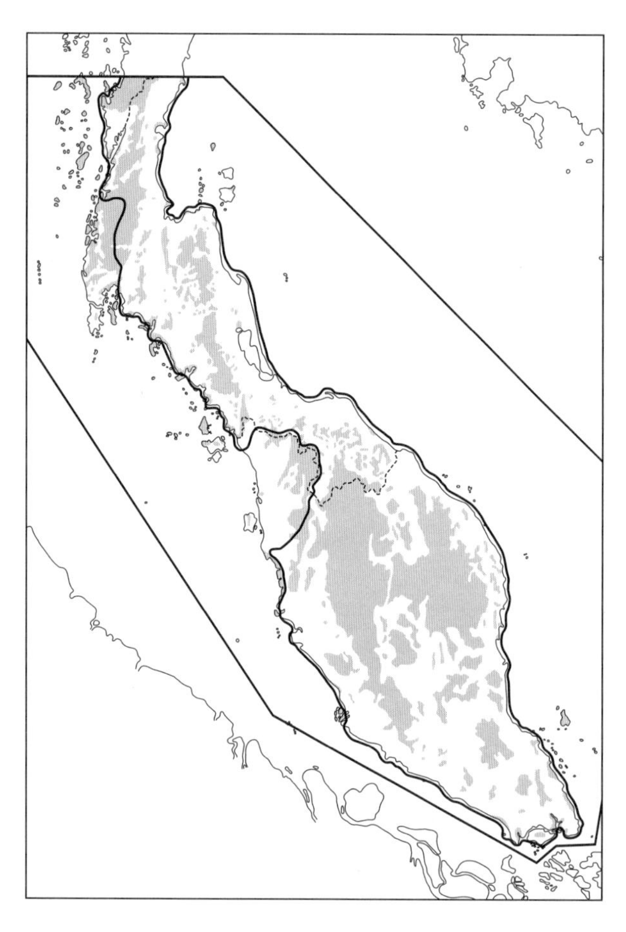

nearby wooded gardens and parkland. The habitats of migrants have not been separately identified.

FORAGING AND FOOD. An adult male visiting my garden took large, leaf-eating beetle larvae from a hog-plum *Spondias*, in one sortie by running sideways along a horizontal branch and snatching upwards at overhead foliage.

SOCIAL ORGANIZATION. Lone, territorial males advertise with long, circuitous song-flights over the forest canopy and, less often, sing from high, exposed perches. Where neighbours make contact they counter-call vigorously.

MOVEMENTS. Migrants, one third of them first-winterers, have been intercepted at floodlights on Fraser's Hill only in autumn, during 7 August–31 December (BMP5), and have been recorded on Pisang island (Melaka Staits) within this period. Nothing is known about return movements.

SURVIVAL. No information.

SOCIAL INTERACTIONS. Two adult males confronting at an apparent territorial boundary perched on high, exposed branches a few metres apart and sang vigorously over several minutes, regular *kie-vik* call-sequences running directly into crescendo trills.

VOICE. The principal advertising-call, given mostly in flight but also from high perches, is a sharp *kie-vik*, repeated once per second or faster, and audible over several hundred metres. Other less commonly heard calls given by males are (1) a long, twittering trill, swelling and accelerating, (2) a shrill shriek, *kree-cha* (G.C. Madoc). Female vocalizations have not been identified.

BREEDING

Brood-hosts. A lone juvenile being fed by a pair of Brown-throated Sunbirds *Anthreptes malacensis* in secondary woodland on Singapore island during late May–early June 1989 (SINGAV-3) is the only record. Other hosts must serve in inland forest.

Eggs and brood. Eggs not described.

Cycle. No information.

Seasonality. No other information.

MOULT. Primaries are replaced at up to three loci. Adults (including a few migrants) in active wing-moult are dated late April and July–October (most August–September), with earliest completions in July (BMNH). Migrating first-winterers intercepted at Fraser's Hill as of late August have all been in part-adult plumage, most with moult suspended but some active, including in wings and tail (UMBRP). Such birds are mostly October-dated. Elsewhere, post-juvenile moult noted in March and May.

CONSERVATION. Only natural forest is permanently occupied. Within this core habitat, ability to use slopes and disturbed, including logged, sites, plus at least occasional breeding in secondary-growth, suggest this cuckoo is not at serious risk.

Koel; Nok Ga-wow (Thai); Burung Sewah Tahu (Malay)

Eudynamys scolopacea (Linnaeus) 1758, *Systema Naturae* 10(1): 111. TL Kerala, SW India.
Plate 47

GROUP RELATIONS. Species-limits among *Eudynamys* koels are not resolved. Brood-host differences have been cited in support of splitting Asian *scolopacea* (corvids) from Sulawesian *melanorhyncha* (starlings) and Australasian *cyanocephala* (friarbirds and orioles), but equivalent variation is found at single species level in some other cuckoo genera, e.g., *Cuculus*.

GLOBAL RANGE. At its most inclusive, the Indian subcontinent, Sri Lanka and Bay of Bengal islands; China south of a line Sichuan–Gansu–Shaanxi–lower Changjiang valley, including Hainan; SE Asia; Wallacea; and New Guinea to the Solomons and Australia. Breeds through most of this range but not in inner tropical Sundaland (only recently in the southern Peninsula). Outer-latitude populations of both hemispheres migrate, northern birds through S and SE Asia as far as Sumatra and Borneo.

IDENTIFICATION/DESCRIPTION. About House Crow *Corvus splendens* size but proportionately longer-tailed. For its size, adroit at hiding in scanty cover, but over at least eight months of the year made obvious by noisy behaviour. Adult males are uniform glossy blue-black (occasionally green-shot black). Females are deep brown to glossy bronze-black, boldly and broadly pale-streaked over the head and throat, streaks changing to droplets on the neck, large spots over the upper body and wing-coverts, and narrow bars on the flight-feathers, upper tail-coverts and both surfaces of the tail. Their colour ranges from white (on bronze) to bright cinnamon-rufous (on brown), and rufous-marked birds also show a rufous malar-stripe. Underparts otherwise buff to white with narrow, blackish chevron-bars, heaviest on flanks and trousers.

Fledglings of both sexes are bronze-black (crow-like?), with only fine white apical spotting on the head, upperparts including flight-feathers, and breast; rest of underparts black-and-white-barred (the dominant bar-colour varying individually). At least the lateral tail-feathers are also barred. Pale tips may wear but what could be a separate subadult plumage is more or less plain dark above, including centre of tail, and barred below, with pale-tipped flight-feathers that may be the retained juvenile set. Moult into adult body-plumage starts ahead of flight-feathers fully separated in some autumn migrants.

Bare-part colours. Iris blood-red (adult male), light brown to orange-red (adult female); bill black (juvenile), all pale jade-green (adult male), or jade with a slaty base (at least some adult females); feet olive-slate.

Size (mm). (Skins: 43 males, 26 females; adult): wing 188–222 and 191–225; tail 178–206 and 176–208; bill 28.4–37.1 and 29.0–38.0; tarsus 31.7–38.2 and 30.6–37.7 (BMNH, UMZC, ZDUM, ZRCNUS).

Weight (g). Small-sized migrant males, 202 and 242.

DISTRIBUTION. Historical summary: all divisions except *Pak, Nak,* with additional island records, mostly of migrants, from the Similan group, Nakha Yai and Rang (*Phu*), Phiphi, Lanta and Kradan (*Kra*), Rok (*Tra*), the Langkawi group, Paya, Bidan, Perak (*Ked*), Penang (including residents), the Sembilan group (Lalang, Rembia), Jarak and Pisang off the W coast; Tao, Ang Thong, Phangan and Samui (including residents), the Perhentians, Redang, Bidung Laut and Tulai off the E coast; and Ubin, St John's and Sentosa (including residents) around Singapore.

GEOGRAPHICAL VARIATION. Females of the breeding population appear all to be of the deep brown, richly rufous-marked type, wing not below 209 mm. Males collected outside extreme migration dates are similarly big, wing not below 207 mm. They also have the largest bills, not below 34.0 mm, and fit

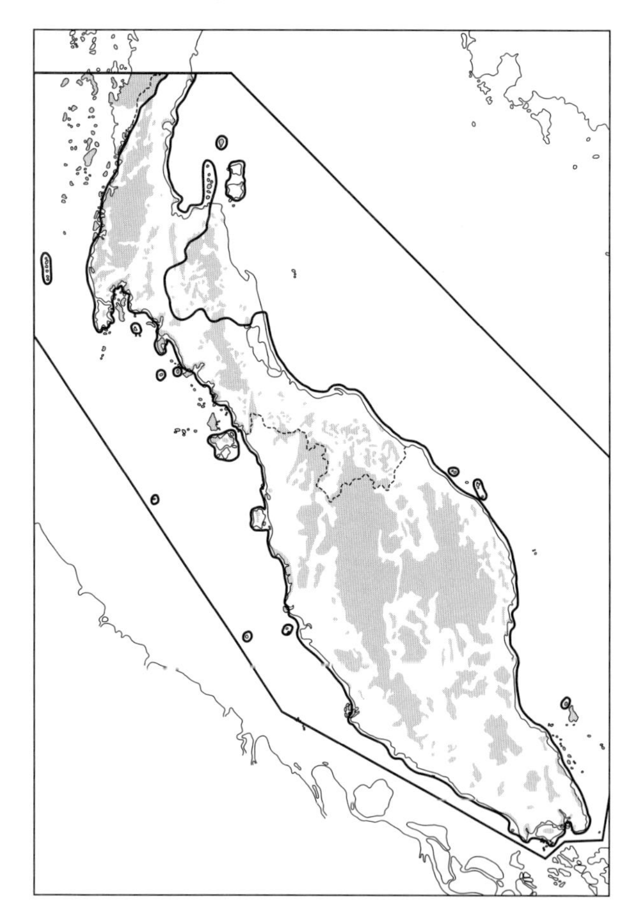

subspecies *malayana* Cabanis and Heine 1862 (TL Sumatra) of the far-NE Indian subcontinent and western and southern SE Asia to the Lesser Sunda islands. In the migrant swarm on small islands, away from breeding-habitat and brood-hosts, *malayana*-type females are outnumbered by bronze-black, white-marked birds. With these also occur intergrades, and males over the whole extent of wing and bill-size variation, but tending to cluster with either rufous- or white-marked females. Bronze-and-white females have been identified as nominate *scolopacea* of the Indian subcontinent to the Bay of Bengal islands (Gibson-Hill 1950e), but range too large: wing up to 210 versus not above 195 mm in India, and are a better fit for more or less identical-plumaged *chinensis* Cabanis and Heine 1863 (TL Guangzhou) of China and eastern continental SE Asia, wing-range 186–213 mm (BMNH). With wide overlap in size and similar amounts of plumage variation (intergrades with rufous-striped cap occur in both areas), however, the need for a separate name *chinensis* should be re-examined.

STATUS AND POPULATION. Resident and a non-breeding visitor and evident passage-migrant, regular and common. Breeding Koels have long been widespread in the cultivated coastal plains south to about 6°N (including Kelantan) and along the immediate W coast as far as Penang. In the Georgetown–Butterworth area, brood-parasitism expanded into a localized feral population of House Crows. This crow has since spread over much of the rest of western Malaysia, and breeding Koels have followed. By 1985, good numbers of summer residents had established in NW Selangor, with first records that year along the Kelang valley inland to greater Kuala Lumpur (where breeding is now common). Two years later, suspected non-migrants were in the S archipelago of Singapore (MBR 1986–87), and definite residents have since also spread over the main island. On the Malaysian E-coast, which House Crows have not reached, the situation appears unchanged.

Apart from a few interceptions on passage, migrants have not been detected inland, but are plentiful along coasts, crowding onto small, forested islands often far off shore (and where late-January records suggest some must overwinter).

HABITATS AND ECOLOGY. Residents occupy mangrove forest, dense secondary woodland and scrub, orchards, plantations, parkland and wooded gardens, ranging far into suburbs. Migrants make use of at least some of these habitats plus, on small islands, the canopy of mature, dry-land forest (which residents avoid). Occasional passage birds also occur in *Phragmites* reedbeds (BMP5).

FORAGING AND FOOD. Little information, except that fruit seems to be important. Mainly arboreal but occasionally searches on the ground.

SOCIAL ORGANIZATION. In breeding areas, males maintain more or less exclusive space, switching between a few regular calling-sites that in areas of dense occupation can be as little as 200 m from a neighbour. Such small territories typically do not include or even lie close to crow nests, and appear only to be visited by females ranging out over bigger spaces (implying their mating system might be promiscuous).

By contrast, migrants of both sexes appear to crowd the available space on small islands, typically far off shore and without corvids. No-one seems to have looked into why Koels find these attractive or why, even at mid winter, they are so vocal there. One tempting, as yet entirely untested idea is that noisy little islands are leks, inducing females to mate before or while they travel north (comparable to reeves *Philomachus pugnax* visiting leks in the N temperate-zone *en route* to the arctic), and supplying one possible (if far-fetched) explanation of why individuals with part-*malayana* characteristics occur so often, out of geographical context, in the breeding-ranges of the northern subspecies.

MOVEMENTS. Extreme dates away from breeding-habitat are 21 July (three on treeless Perak island during a caterpillar plague, sheltering from the sun in rock-crevices) and, before the southward spread of breeders, 11, 12 and 16 April in Singapore, Melaka and the Pahang–Johor archipelago (BR 1964, 1980–81). In the NW, Phiphi still held plenty on 12 April, but nearby Rok island was deserted by early May (BCSTB-12). Duration of passage movements is not well known, but autumn migrants have been mist-netted at floodlights on Fraser's Hill up to 31 October and birds seen at unlikely locations (including on Perak island) up to 23 December (Langham 1976). In spring, predator-kill remains on Perak island in early March are likely to have been of returnees (BMP5, BR 1972–73, ZRCNUS).

SURVIVAL. No information.

SOCIAL INTERACTIONS. Apparent courtship-feeding: a male offering a female dark red, very ripe fan palm (*Livistona*) fruits (SINGAV-6). A female searching among stones on the ground was closely attended by two obviously excited House Crows, which it entirely ignored.

VOICE. With some year-to-year variation, male advertisement-calling is seasonal, in the south starting during late November–early January and finishing during early July–mid September. The male repertoire includes at least seven loud calls: (1) a sequence of spaced disyllables, *koel*, that starts with a few subdued notes, gains in power, often with increasing emphasis on the second syllable, and stops abruptly; (2) a strident *kroik kroik kroik* . . . Both these calls are answered by neighbouring males. (3) A fast-tempo bubbling of about ten notes, *koelkoelkoelkoel* . . . or *koikoikoikoi* . . ., in a shallow crescendo; (4) a powerful, explosive *kaek*, repeated several times with nape feathers ruffled as a female arrives in the male's calling-tree, and in subsequent pursuit-flights (this is the only loud call made out of cover); (5) *ku-ik*, a less excited version of (4); (6) a rolling, up-scale *keroik-eroik-eroik-eroik* . . .; and (7) a more subdued, even-toned *woikwoikwoikwoik . . .*, the last two calls given mainly at dusk, from roost-perches. As stated, overwintering migrants are also very noisy, at least on islands (and in sharp contrast to other wintering cuckoo species).

The female has a strident bubbling call. A handled *malayana* female gave deafening shrieks that almost immediately summoned a large mob of House Crows. Nestlings are said to mimic crow calls, but this has not been confirmed locally.

BREEDING

Brood-hosts. House Crow and Large-billed Crow *Corvus macrorhynchos* are the only proven fosterers. House Crow is now the dominant host in the south; indeed, Koels in Singapore have been noted as gathering at House Crow population enclaves in preference to areas holding only Large-bills.

Eggs and brood. Eggs not reliably described from this area. A Large-billed Crow nest in Kelantan is said to have contained the host clutch of four plus two Koel eggs and a chick.

Cycle. No information.

Seasonality. Eggs in late February and late April, and nestlings on 30 April (MBR 1986–87, Ollington and Loh 1992, Robinson 1927, UMZC), but adult behaviour implies a longer season.

MOULT. Adult primaries are replaced at up to three loci, and suspensions or arrests are common, including among passage birds (a male intercepted on 12 October migrating on an equal mixture of old and newish flight-feathers). Seasonality varies with population. Twenty-one adult *malayana* (both sexes) dated 29 November–6 May showed no wing-moult, whereas a male on the last date had started at P9, and two dated 8 July and 9 October were both active. Among small-sized migrants, a first-winter male from Fraser's Hill on 31 October was in 50 percent adult body-plumage, but had replaced no flight- or tail-feathers. Similar birds are in active wing- and tail-moult during January–early April (BMNH, UMZC, ZDUM, ZRCNUS).

CONSERVATION. Resident populations are in an expansion phase, with prospects of more breeding-range in-fill as the House Crow host spreads further.

Black-bellied Malkoha; Nok Bangrawk Lek Thong Thao (Thai); **Burung Cenuk Perut Hitam** (Malay)

Phaenicophaeus diardi (Lesson) 1830, *Traité d'Ornithologie* 2: 132. TL Sumatra.
Plate 51

GROUP RELATIONS. Free-standing.

GLOBAL RANGE. Borneo, Sumatra and the Peninsula, and in SW Thailand and Tenasserim to latitudes about 13° and 14°N.

IDENTIFICATION/DESCRIPTION. Most similar to Chestnut-bellied Malkoha. Much smaller and shorter-tailed (wing/tail ratio 0.60–0.63) but, in isolation, also confusable with Green-billed Malkoha, and their habitats overlap. The grey of the head and front of Black-bellied is darker than in Green-billed (contrasting less with wings), grades to slaty black on the belly and lower tail-coverts, and butts directly against the bill, with no lightening or interposed white. Also, no more than a trace of white occurs around the face-patch (but white similarly slight in some juvenile Green-billed). In both species, feather-shafts of the head and anterior body are produced into long, fine, black bristles, but Black-bellied lacks the additional black shaft-streaks conspicuous in Green-billed. It also has different eye-colours.

Bare-part colours. (Adult) iris pale blue or dark brown (not identified to sex), periorbital patch (velvety skin, as in other species) blood-red; bill light pea-green; feet lead-grey.

Size (mm). (Skins: 15 males, 9 females; adult): wing 121–135 and 126–133; tail 195–220 and 203–221; bill 28.3–33.5 and 30.0–33.4; tarsus 28.3–33.8 and 31.2–33.5 (UMZC, ZDUM, ZRCNUS).

Weight. No data.

DISTRIBUTION. Historical summary: all divisions except *Phu*, *Pat*, but extinct *Sin* for at least 30 years; no other island records.

GEOGRAPHICAL VARIATION. Nominate *diardi*, of the global range except Borneo.

STATUS AND POPULATION. Resident and regular; more or less common in original forest, uncommon in other habitats.

HABITATS AND ECOLOGY. The interior canopy and mid-stratum of semi-evergreen and evergreen Lowland forest, including peatswamp forest, mature

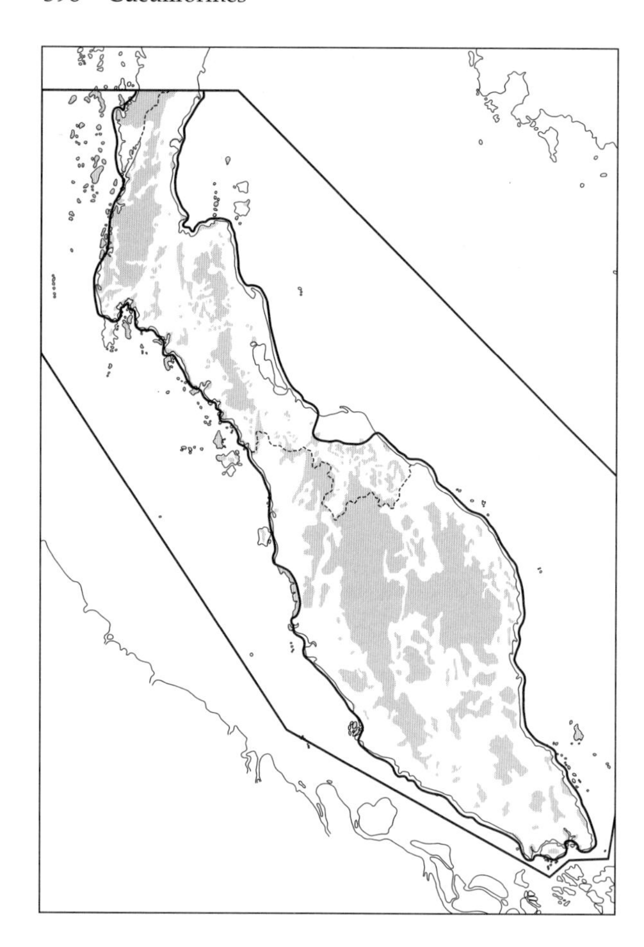

to quite heavily logged; at plains level and on hill-slopes typically to about 200 m, but in Malaysia occasionally higher (a bird found two days running in a Lower Montane forest mixed-species foraging-flock at 1200 m on Rabong peak, S Kelantan: BMP5). At low density also in secondary-growth and patches of old, densely overgrown rubber plantation.

FORAGING AND FOOD. Like other malkohas, hunts while sneaking about among leafy creepers and outer branchlets of dense crowns, but no information on food.

SOCIAL ORGANIZATION. Loners or in pairs.

MOVEMENTS. None recorded.

SURVIVAL. No information.

SOCIAL INTERACTIONS. No information.

VOICE. A gruff, froglike *gwaup* and hurried disyllable, *gwagaup* ; also a louder, more carrying *pauk* that is hard to separate from the advertising-call of Banded Pitta *Pitta guajana*.

BREEDING

Nest. Only one confirmed: 5 m up in a forest-edge thicket, a pigeon-like saucer built of dead twigs, but with a slight lining of green leaves. Similar, 15–20 cm diameter nests collected by W.A.T. Kellow in Perak are undoubtedly of malkohas, but cannot be confirmed as this species.

Eggs and brood. Eggs glossless, plain, chalky white, but no other details available. Full clutch two.

Cycle. Both pair-members gather nest-materials.

Seasonality. Eggs in Kedah on 26 March, nest-building in Pahang in early April (E.C.S. Baker, Chasen 1939, NRCS).

MOULT. Primaries are replaced at up to three loci. Among 27 adults covering all months except December, January and April, wing-moult occurred during early May–early November (most November birds none); advanced individuals completed as early as mid July (UMZC, ZDUM, ZRCNUS).

CONSERVATION. Has no definitely self-sustaining population outside natural forest, but widespread on slopes and able to use regrowth, hence not at immediate risk.

Chestnut-bellied Malkoha; Nok Bangrawk Lek Thong Daeng (Thai); Burung Cenuk Kecil (Malay)

Phaenicophaeus sumatranus (Raffles) 1822, *Transactions of the Linnean Society* 13(2): 287. TL Sumatra.

Plate 51

GROUP RELATIONS. Free-standing.

GLOBAL RANGE. Borneo, Sumatra and intervening islands, the Peninsula, and Tenasserim to latitude at least 12°N.

IDENTIFICATION/DESCRIPTION. Slightly larger but proportions and general coloration (including dark, white-tipped tail) as Black-bellied Malkoha. In the field, wings appear darker, more obviously glossed green, and the face-patch is orange- rather than blood-red. Both species have black-feathered lores, and the upper margin of the face-patch of Chestnut-bellied is finely bordered black. Dark chestnut belly to lower tail-coverts can appear black in poor light.

Bare-part colours. (Adult) iris whitish, pale blue, brown, dark red with blue outer ring, or entirely red-orange (colours not identified to sex, and may vary with excitement level); periorbital patch orange-red; bill light pea-green; feet slate-blue to greyish.

Size (mm). (Skins: 8 males, 8 females; adult): wing 138–148 and 138–150; tail 212–232 and 200–232; bill 32.7–37.9 and 32.8–37.1; tarsus 31.8–37.7 and 33.6–38.1 (ZRCNUS).

Weight. No data.

DISTRIBUTION. Historical summary: all divisions except *Chu, Nak, Phu, Pat, Yal,* with no additional island records.

GEOGRAPHICAL VARIATION. Nominate *sumatranus,* of the global range except W Sumatran islands and Borneo.

STATUS AND POPULATION. Resident, regular and uncommon to locally common; in most habitats (except on Singapore), the least frequently met malkoha species.

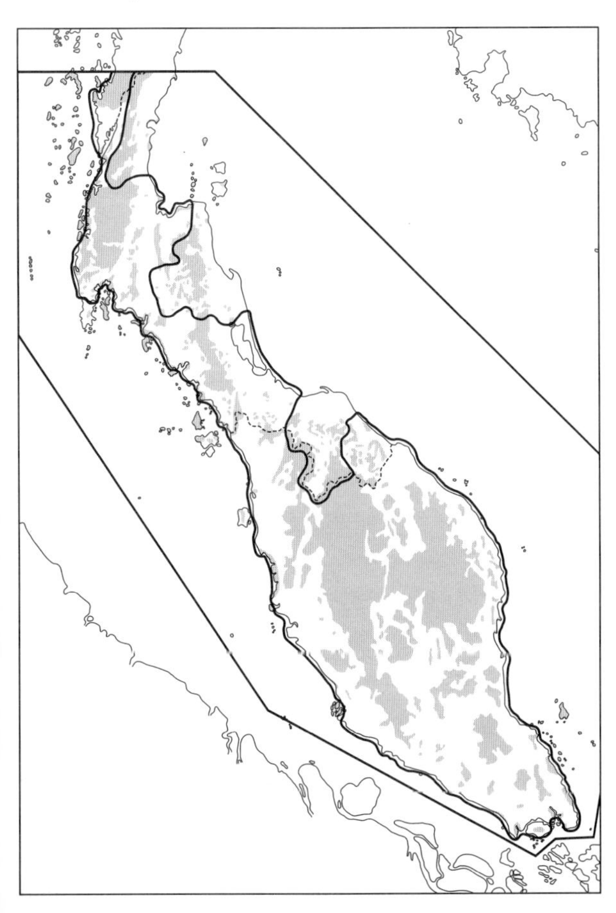

HABITATS AND ECOLOGY. Apart from Green-billed in the north, the only malkoha entering mainland mangrove forests (also in Singapore). Inland, its range of habitats and foraging-strata are as for Black-bellied Malkoha, but Chestnut-bellied is more strictly a plains-level species. Recorded far over the steepland boundary only on the sandstone mountains of Taman Negara where, on Tahan, it reaches close to the Montane ecotone (Ogilvie-Grant 1908, ZRCNUS).

FORAGING AND FOOD. Hunting habits are not obviously different from other malkohas, and how co-occurrent species partition resources is unknown. Like Black-bellied, sometimes joins mixed-species foraging-flocks. Food identified: small fruits and seeds (recovered unspecified from stomachs), an agamid lizard *Calotes cristatellus*, cicadas, large orthopterans and a 20 cm stick caterpillar (Hails and Jarvis 1987, J. Nabhitabhata, Robinson 1928).

SOCIAL ORGANIZATION. Loners, pairs and, occasionally, small parties (noted in Ayer Keroh forest, Melaka, where it is unusually common).

MOVEMENTS. None recorded.

SURVIVAL. No information.

SOCIAL INTERACTIONS. No information.

VOICE. A sharp *chak*, like a squirrel alarm-note, has been linked to this species, but needs confirming.

BREEDING

Nest. 1.5–6 m up, in regrowth at the edge of a forest path and in a vertical, 4-pronged branch-fork of a rubber tree on a Kedah plantation; saucer-shaped, built of short, dead twigs and pieces of vine stem, and neatly lined with green leaves.

Eggs and brood. Eggs are glossless, plain, chalky white. Shape broad elliptical. Size (mm): 30.3 × 23.4, 28.2 × 23.0 (n=2). Full clutch two.

Cycle. No information.

Seasonality. Nest-building in mid January, June and mid July, copulation on 20 February, well-incubated eggs on 16 and 23 March (Kelham 1881–83, G.C. Madoc, MBR 1986–87, Ollington and Loh 1992, SINGAV-3).

MOULT. Replacement of primaries recorded at one and two loci. Among 19 adults covering all months except April and September, ten showed active wing-moult during late May–late August only.

CONSERVATION. Absence from hill-slopes over most of the Peninsula implies Chestnut-bellied is at greater risk from forest-loss than other malkoha species. Including in Singapore (Hails and Jarvis 1987), rarely found far from natural forest, and is much less widespread in plantation and secondary-growth than Black-bellied Malkoha.

Green-billed Malkoha; Nok Bangrawk Yai (Thai); Burung Cenuk Kera (Malay)

Phaenicophaeus tristis (Lesson) 1830, *Traité d'Ornithologie* 2: 132. TL Bengal.
Plate 51

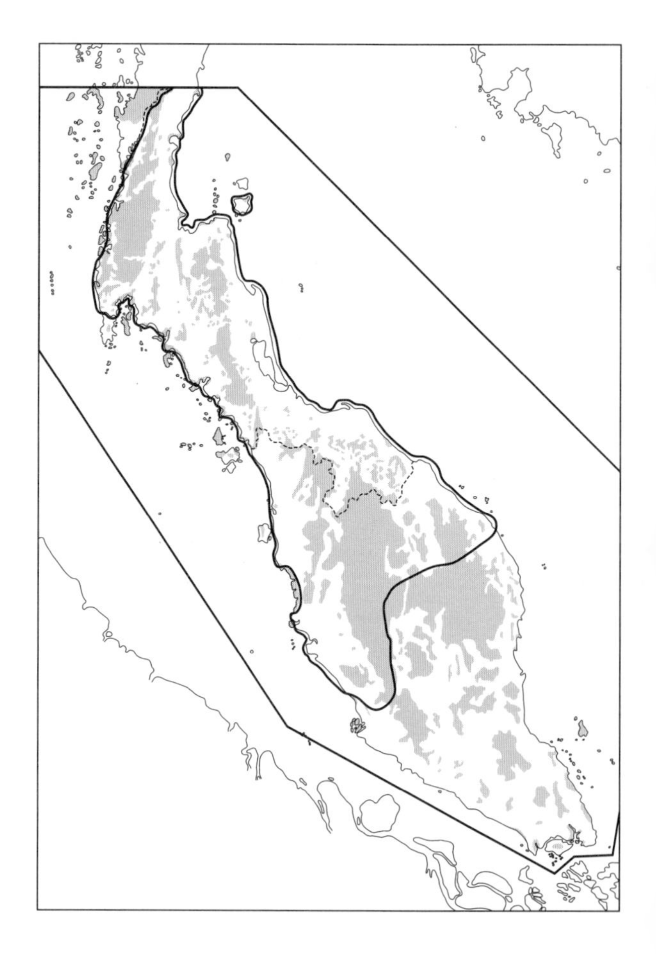

GROUP RELATIONS. Free-standing.

GLOBAL RANGE. The Himalayan foothills east from Gharwal and the NE Indian subcontinent; Guangdong to Yunnan, including Hainan; and SE Asia to Sumatra and the Kangean islands (E Java Sea).

IDENTIFICATION/DESCRIPTION. Large, with an impressively long, conspicuously white-tipped tail (other grey-bodied species have white tips less than half as deep). From Black-bellied and Chestnut-bellied Malkohas in the field by proportions (wing/tail ratio 0.43–0.47); head and underparts paler grey, showing black shaft-streaks; a whitish forehead; and white extending narrowly back round the margin of the dull crimson face-patch. Juveniles lack iridescence on the upperparts.

Bare-part colours. (Adult) iris hazel to dark brown or crimson (not identified to sex), periorbital patch dull, rather dark crimson; bill light pea-green, dark red round the nostril; feet grey-green.

Size (mm). (Skins: 21 males, 10 females; adult): wing 149–163 and 153–161; tail 291–370 and 312–348; bill 32.0–40.2 and 31.3–37.2; tarsus 33.8–41.8 and 33.7–38.6 (BMNH, UMZC, ZRCNUS).

Weight. No data.

DISTRIBUTION. South to latitude about 3°N. Historical summary: all divisions except *Pak, Phu, Neg, Mel, Joh, Sin,* and occurs on Samui island.

GEOGRAPHICAL VARIATION. Continental SE Asian *longicaudatus* Blyth 1842 (TL Moulmein, Tenasserim).

STATUS AND POPULATION. Resident, regular and uncommon to common, according to habitat-zone; recorded south to the Terengganu valley in the eastern lowlands and Genting Highlands (ENGGANG-3) and Kuala Lumpur district in the west.

HABITATS AND ECOLOGY. Coastal strand and the landward fringe of mangrove forest; thickets, bamboo brakes and dense edge-growth in and around lowland agriculture and grazing-grounds; orchards, overgrown plantations, paperbark *Melaleuca* stands; and the edge and mid-stratum of inland mixed forest, evergreen to semi-deciduous, especially in dense regrowth, at plains level and on hills to 1500 m (along ridge-crests to the lower limits of the Upper Montane zone). The complete chain of habitats is occupied in the north, but south from Perlis–Songkhla (an important floristic boundary in Lowland forest) Green-bills have not been found in inland mixed forest below about 850 m (on the Main and Larut Ranges: Bromley 1952), i.e., are mostly in Montane forest, where they are rather uncommon. On present evidence, therefore, two Malaysian populations are isolated by altitude as well as habitat.

FORAGING AND FOOD. As other malkoha species, by sneaking about among the outer branches of dense crowns, thickets, etc. No local information on prey.

SOCIAL ORGANIZATION. Loners and pairs.

MOVEMENTS. None recorded.

SURVIVAL. No information.

SOCIAL INTERACTIONS. No information.

VOICE. Single rather hoarse notes, *kaup* and a sharper *krup*, or hurried *kluk-rup-rup*. A bird approaching a nest gave a single, hollow *kok* (G.C Madoc). Occasionally, in diving flight off a high perch, similar notes are run into a rattle, *kwo-kwo-kwo-kwo-kwo . . .*

BREEDING

Nest. Built 2.5–6 m up in a tree-crown or shrub (non-forest records in *Bougainvillea*, *Morinda*, *Garcinia*); a thin, shallow saucer of twigs with a green-leaf lining, about 18 cm across.

Eggs and brood. Eggs are glossless, plain, chalky white. Shape elliptical; no other reliable description. Full clutch two eggs, apparently sometimes three, but a brood of three from Kelantan included a runt.

Cycle. No information.

Seasonality. In the Kelantan and Selangor lowlands, and Perak highlands, both eggs and nestlings in January and March, on dates that imply laying begins in December (F.G.H. Allen, Berwick 1952, G.C. Madoc, WFVZ).

MOULT. Primaries are replaced at up to three loci. Among 38 adults covering all months except April, nine showed active wing-moult, and three others intermediate suspensions, during early May–late October; with plumage fresh up to January (BMNH, UMZC, ZRCNUS).

CONSERVATION. Probably no critical issues.

Raffles's Malkoha; Nok Bangrawk Daeng (Thai); Burung Cenuk Kerak (Malay)

Phaenicophaeus chlorophaeus Raffles 1822, *Transactions of the Linnean Society* 13(2): 288. TL Sumatra.

Plate 51

GROUP RELATIONS. Free-standing.

GLOBAL RANGE. Borneo, Banka, Sumatra, the Peninsula, and Tenasserim and SW Thailand to about 15°20′N.

IDENTIFICATION/DESCRIPTION. Smallest local malkoha, and the only one in which the sexes differ strongly. Males are mainly bright chestnut above and below, darkest on the mantle; back to upper tail-coverts and tail blackish, the tail darkening distally and with a broad white tip; belly dark grey shading to black on lower tail-coverts. All dorsal black parts and both surfaces of the tail are finely barred dull bronze (bars detectable only at close range). Females have head, neck and underparts pale grey, shading to buff on belly, with chestnut flanks and black lower tail-coverts; upperparts dark chestnut, and tail-feathers chestnut with black subterminal band and white tip.

Bare-part colours. (Adult) iris dark brown, peri-orbital patch pale verditer-green; bill light green; feet slate-blue.

Size (mm). (Skins: 17 males, 20 females; adult): wing 110–119 and 111–121; tail 152–174 and 162–184; bill 26.4–30.3 and 26.7–30.0; tarsus 23.6–28.9 and 21.6–28.9 (UMZC, ZDUM, ZRCNUS).

Weight (g). An adult male, 49.0.

DISTRIBUTION. Historical summary: all divisions except *Phu*, *Pat*, and found on Penang island.

GEOGRAPHICAL VARIATION. Nominate *chlorophaeus*, of the global range except the W Sumatran islands and Borneo.

STATUS AND POPULATION. Resident, regular and common.

HABITATS AND ECOLOGY. The edge and mid-stratum of evergreen to semi-deciduous Lowland forest, including peatswamp forest, at plains level and on slopes across the Montane ecotone to about 1000 m (Bromley 1952). Commonest in dense regrowth following disturbance, including storm-damage, logging, etc.; also in extensive secondary-growth and old, overgrown rubber plantations adjacent to forest. Occasional itinerants find quite isolated patches of such habitats.

FORAGING AND FOOD. Foraging behaviour generally as in other malkohas. Prey includes phasmids (Hume and Davison 1878, Robinson 1927).

SOCIAL ORGANIZATION. Loners or in pairs, occasionally small (family?) parties.

MOVEMENTS. None recorded.

SURVIVAL. No information.

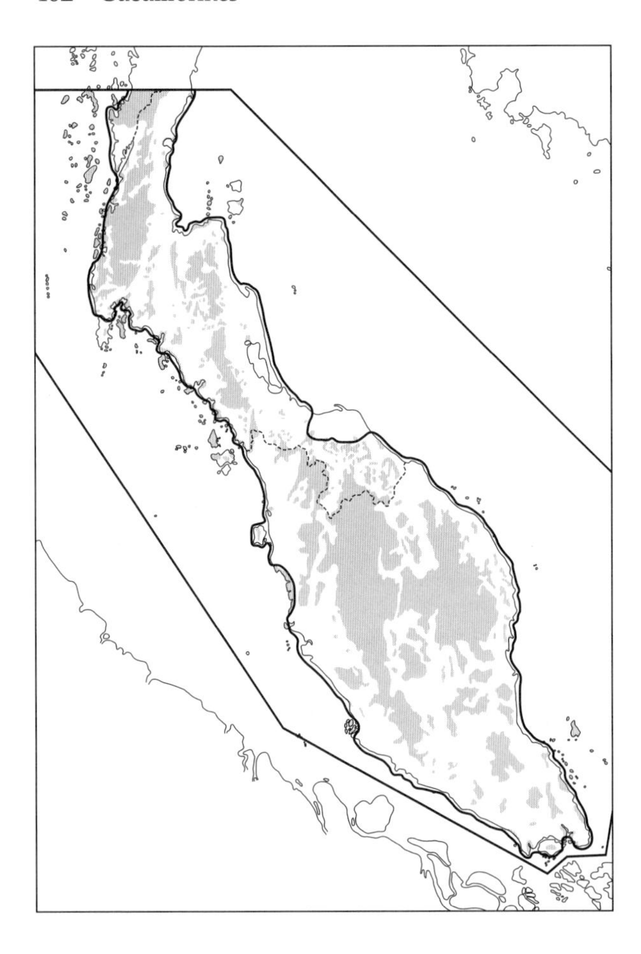

SOCIAL INTERACTIONS. No information.

VOICE. Three or four querulous, cat-like mews, well-spaced and on a steeply falling scale, *kiaow kiaow kiaow kiaow*; callers not identified to sex. Vocally remote from other Asian malkohas, although see Chestnut-breasted.

BREEDING

Nest. Only one described, 3 m up in a forest thicket; as with other malkohas, a shallow saucer of twigs lined with green leaves.

Eggs and brood. No reliable description of eggs; measurements from Larut district, Perak, given by E.C.S. Baker seem too large relative to some other malkohas and may not belong to this species. Full clutch two.

Cycle. A nest built exclusively by the male.

Seasonality. Nest-building in March, eggs in late April and May (F.G.H. Allen, Chasen 1939, G.C. Madoc).

MOULT. Primaries are replaced at up to three loci. Among 46 adults covering all months except May, June and December, 28 showed active wing-moult during early July–late November (including 87 percent of August birds). Exceptionally, one on 3 March had dropped P1, 10 (UMZC, ZRCNUS).

CONSERVATION. Success in regrowth and on hill-slopes suggests no immediate threat to this species.

Red-billed Malkoha; Nok Bangrawk Paak Daeng (Thai); Burung Cenuk Api (Malay)

Phaenicophaeus javanicus Horsfield 1821, *Transactions of the Linnean Society* 13(1): 178. TL Java.
Plate 51

GROUP RELATIONS. Free-standing.

GLOBAL RANGE. The Greater Sunda islands and the Peninsula, and SW Thailand and Tenasserim respectively to about 13° and 14°N.

IDENTIFICATION/DESCRIPTION. The relatively small face-patch (a broad periorbital ring) is bluish, more or less as in Raffles's Malkoha, but this considerably larger bird has a diagnostically all-red rather than green bill. Entire upperparts, except for white tail-feather tips, grey, palest on the head, darker, green-shot on wings and tail (the latter finely 'self-barred', as in male Raffles's Malkoha). Below, lower face and throat to breast orange-rust, flanks and belly pale grey and lower tail-coverts chestnut. The youngest bird handled resembled an adult but primary coverts were rufous-washed, with pale fringing. As in most malkoha species, full juveniles are poorly known.

Bare-part colours. (Adult) iris whitish, light to deep brown or claret-red (not identified to sex), periorbital ring light blue; bill coral-red with some black at base of culmen (in juveniles also at tip); feet greenish or bluish slate.

Size (mm). (Skins: 20 males, 8 females; adult): wing 137–150 and 144–151; tail 236–272 and 234–270; bill 28.7–33.5 and 32.1–33.1; tarsus 32.5–37.2 and 33.8–38.2 (BMNH, UMZC, ZDUM, ZRCNUS).

Weight. No data.

DISTRIBUTION. Historical summary: all divisions except *Pra*, *Sin*, but with no other island records.

GEOGRAPHICAL VARIATION. Subspecies *pallidus* Robinson and Kloss 1921 (TL Jerai peak), of the global range except Java and the Natuna islands.

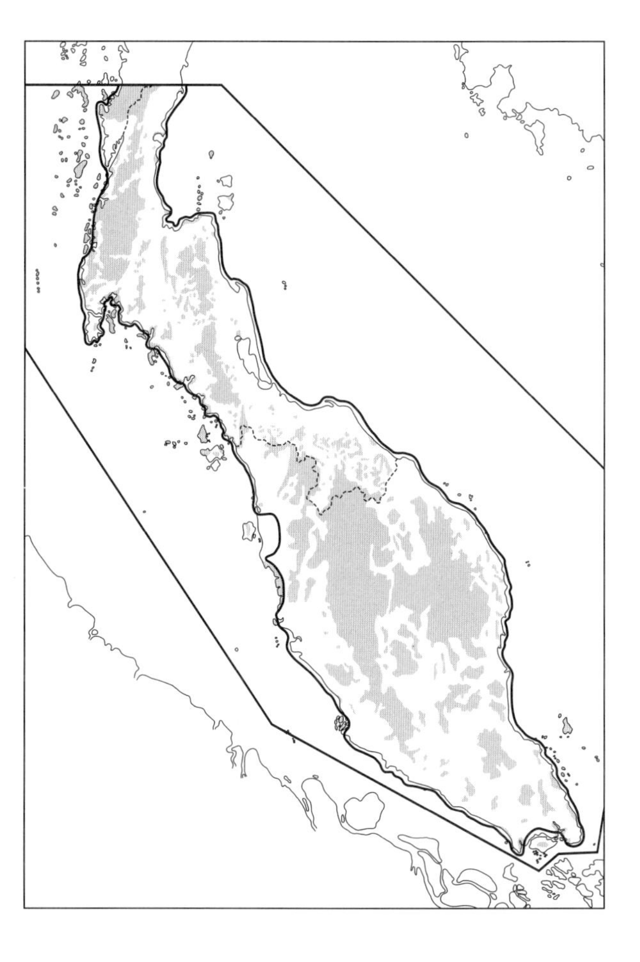

STATUS AND POPULATION. Resident, regular and uncommon to more or less common.

HABITATS AND ECOLOGY. The edge and mid-stratum of evergreen and semi-evergreen Lowland and Lower Montane forests, mature and regenerating after disturbance, from plains level to at least 1200 m. Enters dense, elfin forest along high, steep ridges, and on the plateau of Jerai peak, Kedah (before clearance for the tourist resort) was common in *Baeckia frutescens* scrub.

FORAGING AND FOOD. Foraging behaviour as other malkoha species. Caterpillars and phasmids identified among prey (ENGGANG-2, Robinson 1928).

SOCIAL ORGANIZATION. Typically solitary.

MOVEMENTS. None recorded.

SURVIVAL. No information.

SOCIAL INTERACTIONS. No information.

VOICE. A soft *taup* (at close range, *k'taup*); a hoarse *turk-urk* or doubled *turk turk urk-urk*; and *kuk*, repeated many times like a scolding squirrel (G.C. Madoc).

BREEDING. The one egg-date is 1 June (ZRCNUS); no other information available.

MOULT. Primaries are replaced at one or two loci. Among 28 adults covering all months except October, seven showed active wing-moult during early May–September and in November, with an instance of suspension at P4 in late August (BMNH, UMZC, ZDUM, ZRCNUS).

CONSERVATION. Use of forest regrowth and hill-slopes suggests habitat-loss is not yet threatening.

Chestnut-breasted Malkoha; Nok Bangrawk Khieo Ok Daeng (Thai); Burung Cenuk Birah (Malay)

Phaenicophaeus curvirostris (Shaw and Nodder) 1810, *Vivarium Naturae, or The Naturalist's Miscellany* 21: plate 905. TL W Java.

Plate 51

GROUP RELATIONS. Forms a superspecies with Sulawesian endemic *P. calyorhynchus* (Yellow-billed Malkoha) (CLBW).

GLOBAL RANGE. The Palawan group, Bali, the Greater Sunda islands and Peninsula, and SW Thailand and Tenasserim respectively to 14°58'N (Bung Kroeng Kavia) and 15°20'N.

IDENTIFICATION/DESCRIPTION. Barring tail-length, the largest malkoha, and the only species without white tail-tips. Cap to nape, sides of face and chin mid grey; crescentic red face-patch finely bordered white dorsally and confluent with red of the bill; rest of upperparts to basal two thirds of tail deep, glossy green. Apical third of tail and all underparts except blackish belly, rich mahogany-chestnut, the overlap of graduated feathers in the closed tail giving the impression of an entirely chestnut undersurface. The sexes differ only in eye colour. Young juveniles have a dark bill, head grey-and-white streaked, tail-feathers relatively narrow and inner pairs entirely green, or with rufous confined to subterminal blotches.

Bare-part colours. Iris grey to brown (juvenile), light blue (adult male), golden yellow (adult female), periorbital patch blood-red; bill slaty blue (young juvenile), light pea-green, basal half of lower mandible and matching edge of upper red (adults); feet dark slaty blue (Madoc 1956b).

Size (mm). (Skins: 24 males, 27 females; adult): wing 171–180 and 168–176; tail 238–271 and 230–263; bill 42.1–44.7 and 39.9–44.4; tarsus 36.0–43.5 and 39.5–42.7 (UMZC, ZDUM, ZRCNUS).

Weight (g). Two adults, 188, 190.

DISTRIBUTION. Historical summary: all divisions except *Sin*, with additional island records from Langkawi, Penang and Tioman.

GEOGRAPHICAL VARIATION. Subspecies *singularis* Parrot 1907 (TL Sumatra), of the mainland and Sumatra.

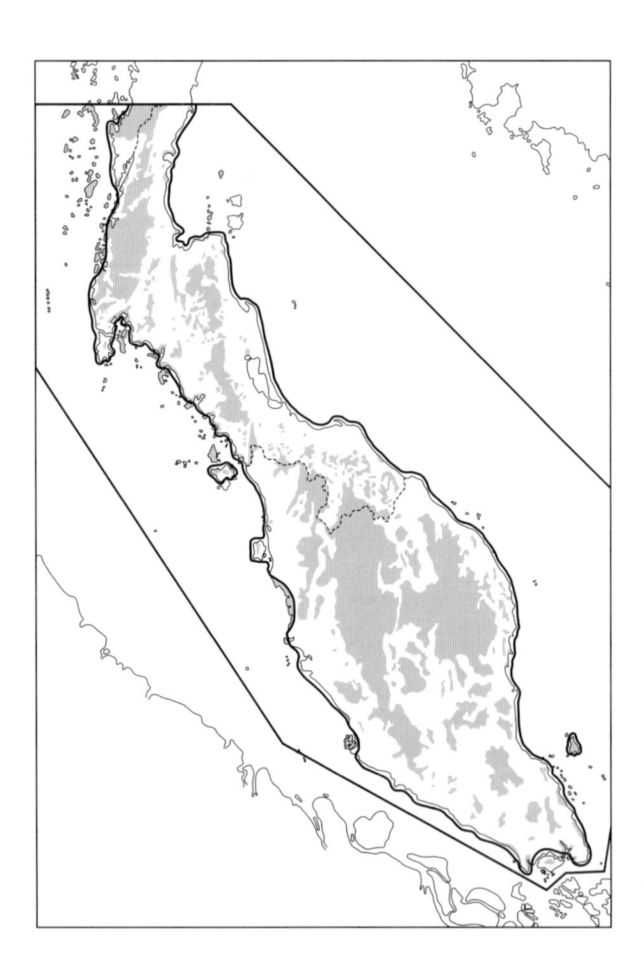

STATUS AND POPULATION. Resident, regular and common.

HABITATS AND ECOLOGY. The edge and interior mid-stratum of Lowland forest, from evergreen to semi-deciduous, also peatswamp forest, at plains level and on slopes to about 1000 m, just across the Montane ecotone. As with other malkohas, often in areas of dense foliage, including regrowth in windthrow gaps, or after selective logging. Also in strand woodland, and enters old, overgrown rubber plantation adjacent to forest (Batchelor 1958). On Langkawi island, where it is the only malkoha species, ranges into mangrove forest (BMP5).

FORAGING AND FOOD. As other malkoha species, while sneaking quietly about among vines and dense foliage of outer branches; and occasionally joins mixed-species foraging-flocks. Orthopterans, cicadas and hairy caterpillars have been identified among prey of adults (Chasen 1939, ENGGANG-3, Kelham 1881–83). Items brought to nestlings were mostly large to very large orthopterans, also a 15 cm phasmid, a butterfly, caterpillars, and a skink and a small snake, both about 10 cm long (Madoc 1956c).

SOCIAL ORGANIZATION. Usually solitary.

MOVEMENTS. None recorded.

SURVIVAL. No information.

SOCIAL INTERACTIONS. No information.

VOICE. No loud calls described. Madoc (1956b) heard a single, gentle *konk* from breeders approaching the nest, and two foragers communicating with a harsh cat-like *miaou*. Nestlings anticipating food give a bubbling hiss.

BREEDING

Nest. Built 2.5–10 m up, in a leafy crown of coastal strand scrub, a forest-edge fig, and in the multiple crown-fork of a young dipterocarp *Shorea collina* in a forest arboretum: a thick, loose platform of twigs with dried leaves still attached, finer twigs lining a small, shallow egg-chamber. A male added twigs and leaves to its nest up to the stage of incubation.

Eggs and brood. Eggs are plain, glossless white; no other reliable description. Full clutch 2–3 eggs, and broods of both sizes reported. Pre-fledged hatchlings are grey-black.

Cycle. Both pair-members incubate, tend nestlings and carry discarded prey parts off the nest.

Seasonality. Eggs reported in January–March, June and July, nestlings in June and July, and a recent fledgling following and begging intensely from a parent on 26 September (E.C.S. Baker, BR 1976–77, Edgar 1933, G.C. Madoc, Madoc 1956b, MBR 1984–85, K.S. Ong).

MOULT. Primaries are replaced at up to three, usually not above two, loci. Among 53 adults covering all months and the full length of the Peninsula, 20 showed active wing-moult during late April–early November (incidence above 80 percent in July and August), only four (in two cases unilateral) outside this period, with a few instances of suspension or arrest in both seasons (UMZC, ZDUM, ZRCNUS).

CONSERVATION. See Red-billed Malkoha, although Chestnut-breasted does not occur so deeply into the generally safer Montane zone.

Family CENTROPODIDAE

Coucals: three species

Short-toed Coucal; (no Thai name); Burung But-but Hutan (Malay)

Centropus rectunguis Strickland 1846, *Proceedings of the Zoological Society of London* 14: 104. TL Melaka.

Plate 47

GROUP RELATIONS. Probably free-standing.

GLOBAL RANGE. Borneo, Sumatra and the Peninsula north to latitude 5°20′N.

IDENTIFICATION/DESCRIPTION. Size intermediate between Lesser and Greater Coucals. In the field, colours and pattern as Greater but more violet-shot on breast, nape and tail, and tail proportionately slightly shorter (wing/tail ratio 0.85–0.88). In the hand (within their common geographical range), wing not above 173 versus not below 202 mm, and chord of first (hind) claw approximately 12, versus 27 mm. Juvenile rich rufous from forehead to mantle and, below, dirty white back to belly and legs; head, body and wing-coverts all heavily barred black-brown, at 2–3 bars per feather. Secondaries barred only apically and, unlike Greater Coucal, the primaries lack a dark tip (BMNH, UMZC, ZRCNUS).

Bare-part colours. (Adult) iris red; bill black; feet black.

Size (mm). (Live and skins: 11 adults, most not sexed): wing 153–173; tail 171–215; bill 35.2–40.4; tarsus 47.5–51.4 (BMNH, M. Wong, ZRCNUS). The sexes probably differ in size.

Weight (g). One large (female?) adult, 237.5 (M. Wong).

DISTRIBUTION. Historical summary: *Kel, Tru, Pra, Pek, Phg, Sel, Neg, ?Mel, Joh,* with no island records.

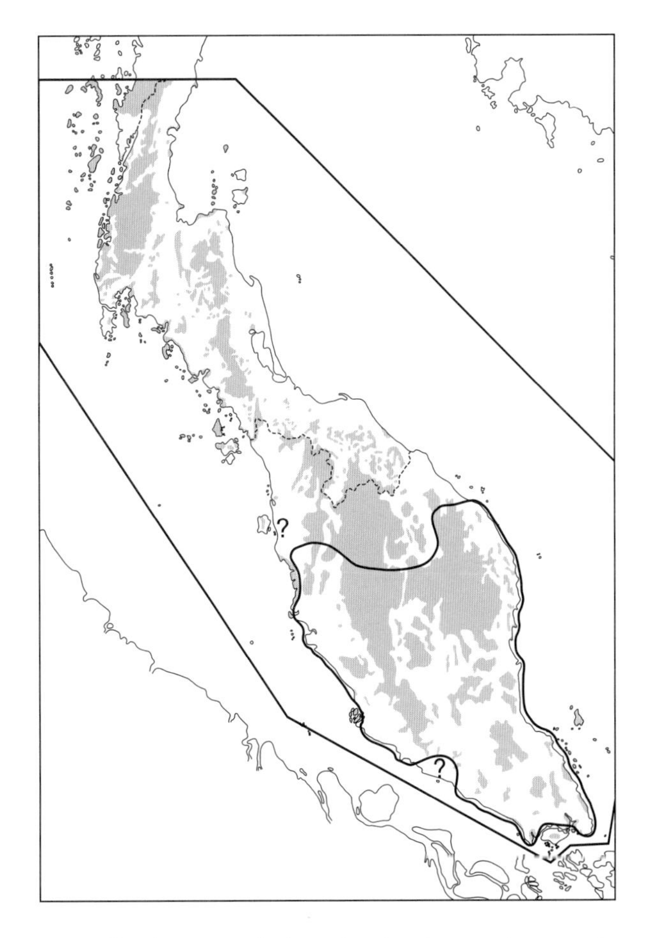

GEOGRAPHICAL VARIATION. None recognized.

STATUS AND POPULATION. Resident, more or less regular and uncommon to more or less common. On evidence of vocalizations, lives widely spaced at a naturally low population density, but perhaps only territory-holders vocalize.

HABITATS AND ECOLOGY. The ground and under-stratum of evergreen, closed-canopy Lowland forest, also peatswamp forest, mature and well regenerated; mainly at plains level, occasionally on hill-slopes up to about 600 m altitude. Emerges into scrub and rank grass in small clearings, but mostly stays inside forest, and tends not to be found close to Greater Coucal in the latter's forest-edge habitats.

FORAGING AND FOOD. Forages mainly on the ground. No natural food identified but, like Greater Coucal, evidently an opportunistic predator; one visiting mist-nets in Pasoh research forest, Negeri Sembilan, killed (by biting the skull) all trapped birds it could reach.

SOCIAL ORGANIZATION. Solitary.

MOVEMENTS. None recorded.

SURVIVAL. No information.

SOCIAL INTERACTION. No information.

VOICE. The loud advertising-call is a ponderous sequence typically of five deep, solomn *buup* notes, on a declining scale. A faster series on a rising scale has been heard from an bird active in a clearing at dusk. Two other, possible alarm- or threat-calls are tentatively ascribed to this species: a snorting, squirrel-like *hut, hut, hut* ... and an explosive, sneezing scold, *jeezaw*, similar to Greater Coucal.

Noisiest during November–March, but calling also recorded in May and August.

BREEDING

Nest. Recorded once: an untidy globe of leaves, some still attached to bitten-off twigs, lined with teased palm-frond pith, lodged 2 m up in the fronds of a stemless *Salacca* palm in mature forest.

Eggs and brood. Not described.

Cycle. No information.

Seasonality. The nest, with adults in attendance, is dated 12 September. Single, dependent fledglings accompanied by an adult recorded on 17 and 21 May (BMNH, BR 1978–79, NRCS).

MOULT. Primaries are replaced at up to four loci. Two August adults were in active wing-moult; others dated March, May and November showed none (BMNH, ZRCNUS).

CONSERVATION. Incidence of calling suggests core habitat lies below the steepland boundary, and there are no records from recently logged forest. Both factors place this coucal in the front rank of species threatened by habitat-loss. Classed as near-threatened globally (BTW2).

Greater Coucal; Nok Gra-puut Yai (Thai); Burung But-but Cari Anak (Malay)

Centropus sinensis (J.F. Stephens) 1815, Shaw's *General Zoology or Systematic Natural History (Aves)* 9(1): 51. TL Ningbo, Zhejiang, China.

Plate 47

GROUP RELATIONS. The non-black *kangeanensis* of Java Sea islands and small-billed *andamanensis* (Andaman Brown Coucal) have been treated as subspecies of *sinensis*. Allopatric Wallacean *C. celebensis* and Philippine *C. unirufus* (Bay and Rufous Coucals) are also its close relatives, probably at superspecies level (CLBW).

GLOBAL RANGE. Apart from the far NW, the Indian subcontinent and Sri Lanka; China south from Zhejiang, Guizhou and Yunnan, including Hainan; and SE Asia to the Greater Sunda islands, Bali and the W Philippines (Palawan and the Sulu archipelago).

IDENTIFICATION/DESCRIPTION. The big coucal of forest-edge and disturbed habitats. From Lesser in the field by much larger size, no pale shaft-streaks on the upperparts, and bright rufous-chestnut of back and wings sharply abutting black of head and body. From Short-toed (which see), by larger size and proportionately slightly longer tail (wing/tail ratio 0.72–0.77), neither character easily judged in the field. The habitat-range of Greater overlaps that of both other local coucals, but all species are readily identified by their advertising-calls. Juveniles have wing-coverts, inner secondaries and the apical quarter of other flight-feathers barred and tipped blackish (tips solidly dull brown in adult); head and rest of body back to upper tail-coverts dull black narrowly barred dirty white, with 2–3 narrow, whitish bars across apical quarter of otherwise black tail. Head-barring can be retained through a minimum two generations of adult-type (unbarred) flight-feathers.

Bare-part colours. (Adult) iris red; bill black; feet black.

Size (mm). (Skins: 12 males, 12 females; adult): wing 185–224 and 205–236; tail 236–312 and 262–322; bill 33.7–42.3 and 40.0–47.6; tarsus 53.1–60.1 and 54.9–62.5

(UMZC, ZDUM, ZRCNUS). Females average ten percent larger than males.

Weight (g). A southern female, 416.6.

DISTRIBUTION. Historical summary: all divisions, with additional island records from Kam Yai, the Surins, Yao Yai, Phiphi, Muk, Lanta, Libong, Tarutao, the Langkawi group (Langkawi, Langgun) and ?Rembia off the W coast; Tao, Ang Thong, Phangan and Samui off the E coast; and Tekong, Ubin, Sentosa, Senang and Retan Laut around Singapore.

GEOGRAPHICAL VARIATION. Smaller, marginally richer rufous *intermedius* Hume 1873 (TL Theyetmyo, Burma) of the continental range east from NE India intergrades with larger, more massive-billed, Sundaic *bubutus* Horsfield 1821 (TL Java) between latitudes about 6° and 5°N. North and south of this zone, respectively, wing-length ranges are: males 185–210 and 202–224, females 205–216 and 226–236 mm.

STATUS AND POPULATION. Resident, regular and common.

HABITATS AND ECOLOGY. Mostly under cover at the interface of dense, closed, woody vegetation and open ground; probably originally along the banks of rivers large enough to break the forest canopy. Now widely also in logged-out forest, overgrown plantation and in and around patches of secondary-growth bordering cultivation, grazing-land, reservoirs, quiet roads, etc. Mainly at plains level, from the landward edge of mangroves, but small numbers follow appropriate habitat into hills, with records to about 700 m. Where undisturbed, emerges from cover into clearings, rural gardens, on verges, etc., and in the morning and after rain loners or pairs select exposed perches to sun-bathe.

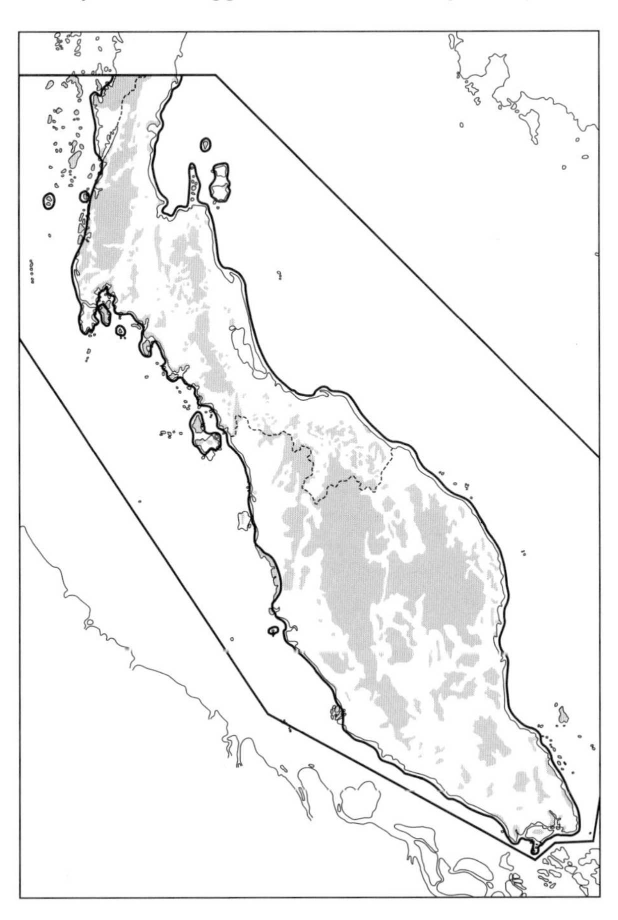

FORAGING AND FOOD. An opportunistic predator hunting on the ground and scrambling among thickets, 2–4 m up. In rural gardens, commonly searches under dense herbage for large *Achatina* snails, which are smashed before being extracted.

SOCIAL ORGANIZATION. Solitary or in pairs.

MOVEMENTS. None reported.

SURVIVAL. No information.

SOCIAL INTERACTIONS. See below.

VOICE. The full, loud advertising-call comprises 20-plus *bup* notes, low and mellow (but less deeply mournful than in Short-toed Coucal), delivered at first briskly in a sharply descending series which then inverts and labours slowly back, with notes progressively more spaced and emphatic, to end at about the original pitch. Both sexes make this call and pairs commonly duet, so accurately to begin with that only a slight tremolo of overlap is detectable, but getting progressively out of step. Other, shorter calls are: (1) a deep, deliberate three- or four-note *bup bup bup . . .* on a declining scale; (2) a swearing sneeze, *tchayorr*; and (3) a rather rapid, high, knocking rattle, *lotoklotoklotoklotok . . .*; the latter two calls often linked.

BREEDING

Nest. A large globe with a lateral entrance, built of grass or palm leaflets, one externally disguised with fronds of ferns that were growing around it. Sites include fern tangles and pandan crowns, up to 2.5 m above ground.

Eggs and brood. Eggs are plain white; no other local details available. Full clutch two.

Cycle. No information.

Seasonality. Eggs recorded in January, May and July; nestlings in February and on 5 August (F.G.H. Allen, BMP5, Chasen 1939, G.C. Madoc, Madoc 1956a, Robinson 1927).

MOULT. Primaries are replaced at up to four loci, often asymmetrical. Adults in active wing-moult recorded in September and December–February; others dated February–late August showed none (UMZC, ZDUM, ZRCNUS).

CONSERVATION. No critical issues.

Lesser Coucal; Nok Gra-puut Lek (Thai); Burung But-but Kecil (Malay)

Centropus bengalensis (Gmelin) 1788, *Systema Naturae* 13(1): 412. TL Bengal.
Plate 47

GROUP RELATIONS. Perhaps not conspecific (cf. BMP5), but on evidence of habitat requirements and morphology likely to be the geographical representative of Afrotropical *C. grilli* (Black Coucal), forming a superspecies.

GLOBAL RANGE. SW India, foothills east from the central Himalayas and the NE Indian subcontinent; S China from the lower Changjiang valley including Taiwan and Hainan; SE Asia to the Greater Sunda islands, Bali and the Philippines; and Wallacea.

IDENTIFICATION/DESCRIPTION. About one quarter the mass of Greater Coucal, and only the wings are bright rufous. Mantle to back, scapulars and inner secondaries are dull brown with white shaft-streaks. Adult otherwise black, feather-shafts of the head and anterior body stout and conspicuously glossy. Below, whole underwing pale chestnut, versus only the flight-feathers of Greater and Short-toed Coucals. Young juveniles are grey-buff above, streaked blackish from cap to mantle, with shining white feather-shafts conspicuous on mantle, scapulars and sides of breast; wings and hind-body barred black and pale chestnut; remaining underparts dirty white, with variable black barring on flanks and thighs; tail buff-rufous, narrowly and densely barred black. Adult plumage is acquired over two-plus moults, via a stage at which head and upper body are dun-brown, finely streaked white.

Bare-part colours. Iris brown (juvenile), red (adult); bill horn with dark culmen (juvenile), black with pale lower base (adult); feet slate-black.

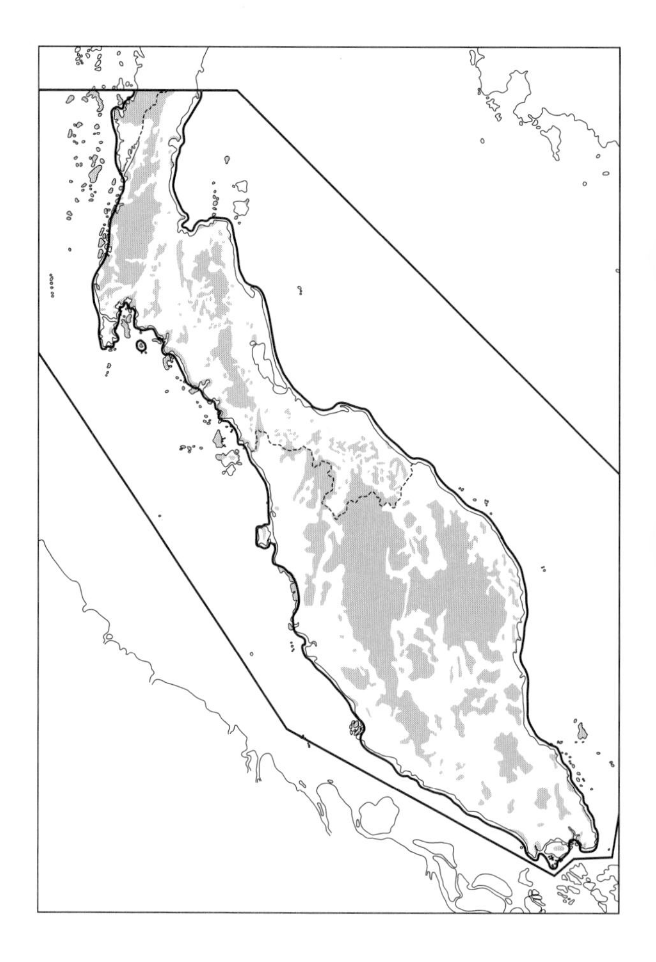

Size (mm). (Live and skins: 7 males, 12 females; adult): wing 137–142 and 149–160; tail 152–176 and 173–194; bill 23.0–25.6 and 25.4–28.3; tarsus 35.7–39.1 and 40.1–43.8; first (hind) claw about 29, i.e., actually longer than in Greater Coucal (UMBRP, UMZC, ZRC-NUS). On wing-length, females average nine percent larger than males.

Weight (g). Adult males, 79.3–92.0 (n=3) (UMBRP).

DISTRIBUTION. Historical summary: all divisions, with additional island records from Phiphi and Penang off the W coast; Sudong and Ayer Merbau, Singapore.

GEOGRAPHICAL VARIATION. Subspecies *javanensis* Dumont 1818 (TL Java), also of the rest of island SE Asia, with black plumage shot glossy green.

STATUS AND POPULATION. Resident, regular and common.

HABITATS AND ECOLOGY. Meets Greater Coucal at the edge of thickets but the core habitat is open *Imperata* grassland, both dry and marshy, especially where studded with low bushes (*Melastoma*, etc.), used as sunning-perches, look-outs and song-posts. Also in standing rice and reedbeds. The main population occupies the settled, agricultural plains but odd birds have been recorded in remote clearings, e.g., the Kuala Tahan meadow, Taman Negara (ENGGANG-3), reached either via the banks and shoals of large rivers through forest or, perhaps, by occasional more direct dispersal – as also suggested by occurrence in more or less isolated hill-station agriculture (to around 1500 m in Cameron Highlands: BR 1965).

FORAGING AND FOOD. Items recorded being carried back to nests include a large orthopteran, a mantid and an agamid lizard *Calotes versicolor* (SINGAV-1, -6).

SOCIAL ORGANIZATION. Mainly solitary, less often pairs.

MOVEMENTS. Two birds on a grassy plot at the Gap, Selangor/Pahang boundary (ENGGANG-2), a short distance below the Fraser's Hill settlement, imply some upland clearings could be found via roads. The only record actually at Fraser's, on the other hand, is of a bird mist-netted at floodlights after dark (BR 1970–71). If not disturbed from a nearby roost, this might have been over-flying forest.

SURVIVAL. Two retrap-intervals of 15 months each (UMBRP).

SOCIAL INTERACTIONS. Offerings of a leaf and a grasshopper during courtship, although the sexes were not distinguished (SINGAV-6).

VOICE. Loud advertising-calls are (1) a long sequence of popping notes that starts at a deliberate pace and accelerates as it rolls down scale, *haup, haup, haup, haup . . . hau hau hau . . . ho-ho-ho-ho*; (2) 3–4 hiccups following by knocking, staccato rattles, *hup hup hup, t-t-tok, t-t-tok, t-t-tok.*

BREEDING

Nest. Typically in open grassland, 0.2–1.5 m off the ground, supported by and incorporating tall grass-stems (less often in low bushes, once in a legume cover-crop); a oval (rarely flattened) globe about 25 cm high × 18 cm across with large entrance at the side (occasionally at the top), loosely built of green and dead *Imperata* grass-blades, occasionally with a sparse, green-leaf lining to the egg-chamber.

Eggs and brood. Eggs slightly glossy to chalky, plain white. Shape normal to longish elliptical. Size (mm): 31.8–28.7 × 26.7–22.8 (n=6). Full clutch two, occasionally three. Young nestlings are black-skinned with long, grey-white, bristly down on the head and upperparts.

Cycle. A male has been collected off incubated eggs, but the mating system is unknown (related African *grilli* in similar habitats is polyandrous). As recorded in some African coucals, including *grilli*, downy young disturbed in the nest eject large quantities of foul-smelling, liquid excrement.

Seasonality. Egg- and chick-dates indicate laying in all months December–July, and occasionally later (recent fledglings recorded to early October) (F.G.H. Allen, Edgar 1933, Fry *et al.* 1988, Madoc 1956a, NRCS, Riley 1938, Spittle 1949).

MOULT. Primaries are replaced at up to three loci. Adults showing active wing-moult recorded in August, October, November and February (BMP5, UMBRP, ZRCNUS).

CONSERVATION. No critical issues.

Order STRIGIFORMES

Family STRIGIDAE

Scops, eagle, fish and wood owls, owlets, boobooks and marsh owls: 16 species

White-fronted Scops Owl; Nok Khao Naa Paak Khao (Thai); Burung Hantu Kening Putih (Malay)

Otus sagittatus (Cassin) 1848, *Proceedings of the Academy of Natural Sciences of Philadelphia* 4: 121. TL Melaka.

Plate 52

GROUP RELATIONS. Free-standing.

GLOBAL RANGE. Tenasserim and SW Thailand, respectively from latitudes about 16° and 12°50′N, to the Peninsula. Possibly also northern Sumatra: a single BMNH specimen labelled 'Acheen' (Aceh province) from the nineteenth-century H. Whitely collection, which on independent evidence is suspected of having included mislabellings (see Collared Scops Owl).

IDENTIFICATION AND DESCRIPTION. Largest of the local scops owls, with a proportionately long, fairly boldly barred tail, 58–64 percent of wing-length (Marshall 1978, UMBRP). Facial-disc pearl-white with fine, transverse pencilling (also on the upper breast) and a smoky brown periocular smudge that gives a spectacled appearance – both characters lacking in smaller Reddish Scops Owl *O. rufescens*. The forehead and forecrown of some Reddish Scops are whitish, but in White-fronted white extends as a band above the eye to the inner (medial) border of the ear-tufts. In the hand, dark-pointed buff spots from cap to upper tail-coverts are similar to those of Reddish Scops, but diamond-shaped dark spots on the underparts are more elongate. Sexes alike; the juvenile has not been described.

Bare-part colours. (Adult) iris dark brown, eyelid-rim pink; bill flesh-white, cere tinged pale greenish; toes and naked extremity of tarsus pale flesh-pink.

Size (mm). (Live and skins: 10 adults, most not sexed): wing 175–192; tail 105–122; bill from skull 21.8–24.4; tarsus 29.5–37.0 (BMNH, UMBRP).

Weight (g). Adults, 109.1–138.5 (n=9) (UMBRP).

DISTRIBUTION. Historical summary: *Pak, Sur, Nak, Tra, ?Nar, Phg, Neg, Mel*, with no island records.

GEOGRAPHICAL VARIATION. None recognized.

STATUS AND POPULATION. Resident, apparently local and sparse but status obscured by its generally silent behaviour. At Pasoh research forest, Negeri Sembilan, long-term mist-netting at night showed it not less rare and, in mature forest, actually commoner than other scops owls (BMP5, UMBRP). A 15 ha block of mature-forest understorey held one repeating resident and three others captured once each over 26 months, hence is likely to have overlapped the regular activity-space of not less than one pair. Four birds over 25 months in 17 ha of regenerating logged forest nearby also included one repeater, on one occasion taken with a second individual.

HABITATS AND ECOLOGY. Dry-land evergreen and semi-evergreen Lowland forest, mature and regenerating, at plains level and on slopes to at least

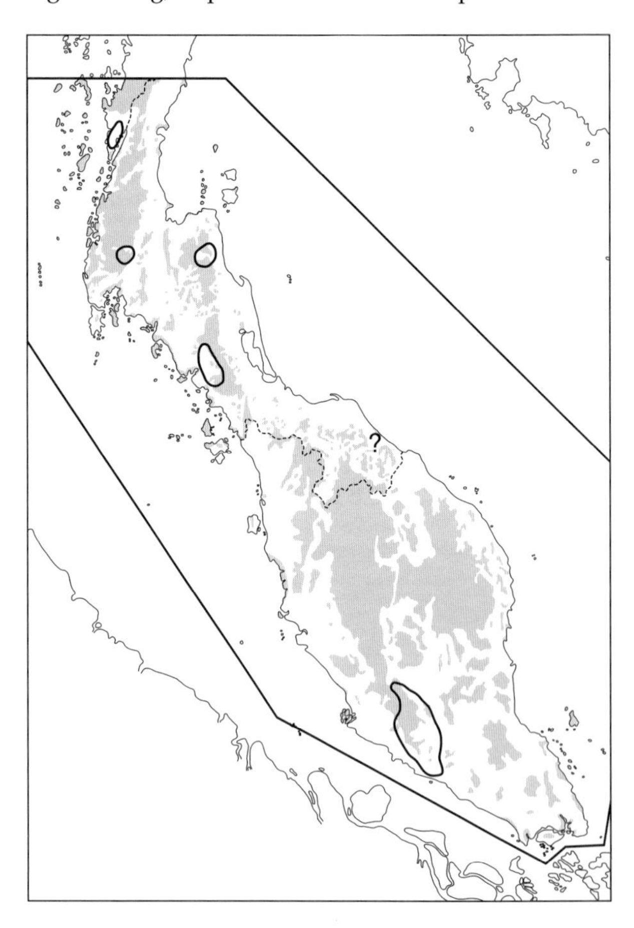

600 m (BMP5). The vegetation column-space used most is unknown but all captures have been in mist-nets set on the ground. Some capture sites have shown a gappy canopy, but with relatively dense under-storey vegetation everywhere.

FORAGING AND FOOD. A stomach contained mostly moths (Hume and Davison 1878); no other information.

SOCIAL ORGANIZATION. At Pasoh, two mist-netted 100 m apart on the same night may have been pair-members, but its silence compared with other resident *Otus* species suggests unusual spacing behaviour.

MOVEMENTS. None known.

SURVIVAL. No significant information.

SOCIAL INTERACTIONS. No information.

VOICE. A soft, low moan from a bird held for ringing. A rarely-heard call tentatively ascribed to this owl is a high, soft, even-toned *hu-u-u-u-u*, like Reddish Scops Owl but without the terminal fade (B. King).

BREEDING. Not reliably recorded. Eggs (several clutches) sent from Perak to E.C.S. Baker are a close size-match for Collared Scops Owl and may have been wrongly identified.

MOULT. Only single-locus replacement of primaries recorded, but pattern not confirmed to be regular-descendant. At Pasoh, active wing-moult noted during 5 July (P6–7)–29 September (P7–9), the last individual growing the same feathers on 14 August of the following year. Two at mid-stage wing-moult were also growing the whole tail. Other handlings in late September, December, January and March showed no moult (UMBRP).

CONSERVATION. Able to exist in regenerating forest but not yet found on recently logged sites, and only a few records are from slopes. Plains-level forest may be core habitat, placing this species at risk from habitat-loss. Globally vulnerable (BTW2).

Reddish Scops Owl; Nok Khao Daeng (Thai); Burung Hantu Merah (Malay)

Otus rufescens (Horsfield) 1821, *Transactions of the Linnean Society* 13(1): 140. TL Java.
Plate 52

GROUP RELATIONS. Apparently free-standing.

GLOBAL RANGE. W Java, Borneo, Banka, Sumatra and the southern Peninsula. A record from the Sulu islands has been rejected as probably based on a mislabelled specimen from neighbouring Borneo (CLBP).

IDENTIFICATION AND DESCRIPTION. Identified in the field mainly by call, and unlikely to be seen unless a caller is tracked to its perch. A tiny, stubby owl, dark-eyed and rufescent. Facial-disc mostly rufous-brown, not 'spectacled' as in White-fronted Scops Owl, with a narrow, dark lateral margin and surmounted by a broad, triangular forehead-patch of whitish to rich buff, paler than the face. Upperparts rufous-brown, spotted as in White-fronted. Underparts plain, rich rufous-buff with dark, diamond-shaped dots that increase in size down to belly and flanks, lacking chevron- or bar-extensions. From similar-sized Mountain Scops Owl by eye-colour, no fan of wispy feathers around the face and obscure rather than sharply defined white stripe along the scapulars (outer webs plain cinnamon-buff with a small, dark sub-apical spot). Sexes apparently alike; juvenile not described.

Bare-part colours. (Adult) iris dark brown (I have handled one bird with dull amber eyes), eyelid-rim pink; bill white; toes and bare outer third of tarsus pale flesh-pink, more or less as in White-fronted Scops Owl.

Size (mm). (Live and skins: 13 adults, most not sexed): wing 121–130; tail 61–68; bill from cere 13.6–13.8; tarsus 24.0–24.4 (BMNH, UMBRP, ZRCNUS).

Weight (g). Adults, 70.5–83.1 (n=11) (UMBRP, M. Wong).

DISTRIBUTION. South from latitude about 8°N, but only two localities known in Thailand. Historical summary: *Nak, Nar, Tru, Pek, Phg, Sel, Neg, Mel, Joh,* with no island records.

GEOGRAPHICAL VARIATION. Endemic *malayensis* Hachisuka 1934 (TL Melaka), slightly paler and redder, less heavily marked on the upperparts than nominate *rufescens* of the rest of the Sunda region.

STATUS AND POPULATION. Resident, in the south regular and uncommon to more or less common. In Thailand, missing from some well-explored,

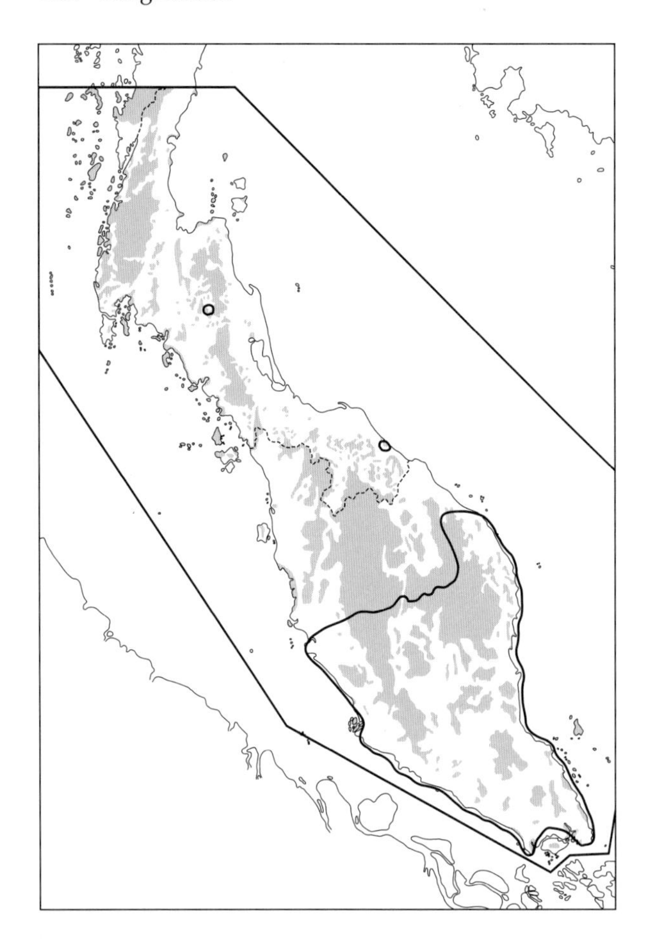

superficially suitable-looking forest fragments. Known there only from a recently discovered population in Chalerm Prakiat wildlife sanctuary swamp-forest, lowland Narathiwat and a bird live-trapped apparently in the Thung Song area of Nakhon Si Thammarat (BBCB-4, Marshall 1978). Mist-netting over 26 and 25 months, respectively, in 15 and 17 ha blocks of mature and regenerating forest at Pasoh, Negeri Sembilan, took one (repeating) and two individuals, the latter on a single night.

HABITATS AND ECOLOGY. Song-perches are typically within 1–2 m of the forest floor, and pooled observations suggest this owl lives entirely in the under-stratum, in mature and more or less closed-canopy regenerating Lowland forest, both dry-land and peatswamp. Also persists in lightly logged forest. The few good records above the steepland boundary are from mature forest to only about 200 m altitude. Identification of three netted in Lower Montane forest at 1200–1500 m on Benom (Pahang) and the nearby Main Range at Fraser's Hill (BR 1966, 1967) has been questioned; this zone needs more study. Apparently not in semi-evergreen to deciduous forests, which may account for its limited distribution northwards.

FORAGING AND FOOD. No information.

SOCIAL ORGANIZATION. Apparently solitary; sustained vocalizing from fixed song-posts suggests individuals defend space against conspecifics. The few records of two being mist-netted more or less together may have been of pair-members, but in no case has sex been checked independently.

MOVEMENTS. None known.

SURVIVAL. No information.

SOCIAL INTERACTIONS. No information.

VOICE. A high, soft *hu-u-u-u-uuu*, lasting about 0.5 seconds, with a slight downward fade at the end, repeated at length every 7–11 seconds. Sonagrams show individual calls are actually shallow crescendos, in a narrow frequency range at close to 1 kHz (Marshall 1978).

BREEDING. Not recorded.

MOULT. Replacement of the primaries appears to be regular-descendent, but with instances of asymmetry between wings. Records of active wing-moult fall during 9 July (P1–2)–7 October (P9), but with one at P10 as early as 14 August. Birds handled in December and February–May showed no moult (BMNH, UMBRP, ZRCNUS).

CONSERVATION. Regardless of the identity of mountain birds, the characteristic call of Reddish Scops has been recorded only in plains-level forest, which must be core habitat for this owl. As such, it is threatened by clearance and, in Thailand, is likely to be close to extinction.

Mountain Scops Owl; Nok Khao Phukhao (Thai); Burung Hantu Gunung (Malay)

Otus spilocephalus (Blyth) 1846, *Journal of the Asiatic Society of Bengal* 15: 8. TL Darjeeling, NE India.

Plate 52

GROUP RELATIONS. Uncertain, pending more information on the Montane forest scops owls of Sumatra.

GLOBAL RANGE. The Himalayas east from Pakistan and hill-tracts of the far-NE Indian subcontinent; China south from Yunnan and Fujian including Taiwan and Hainan; and SE Asia to Sumatra and Borneo (Javan *angelinae* does not represent this species, even though it occupies equivalent habitat: Marshall 1978).

IDENTIFICATION AND DESCRIPTION. A tiny, stubby, dark cinnamon-brown owl, size of Reddish Scops but with extensive blackish freckling on the upperparts, a bold line of dark-edged, white feathers along the outer margin of the scapulars, vermiculated rather than spotted underparts, long, bristly feathering around the upper mandible (framing the face in a wispy fan), and clear yellow eyes. Sexes apparently alike. Juvenile upperparts are paler, more gingery brown that in adult, clearly marked only on the cap, which has black dots ranged in narrow, transverse rows (BMNH).

Bare-part colours. (Adult) iris lemon-yellow; bill flesh-white; toes and naked apical quarter of tarsus flesh-white.

Size (mm). (Live and skins, from Malaysia only: 13 adults, most not sexed): wing 127–139 (the largest a male); tail 62–72; bill from cere 10.2–12.0; tarsus 22.2–25.0 (BMNH, UMBRP, ZDUM, ZRCNUS).

Weight (g). Unsexed *vulpes*, 59.5–77.0 (n=19); two males 68.0, 69.0 (McClure 1964, UMBRP).

DISTRIBUTION. Historical summary: *Sur*, *Nak*, *Kel*, *Tru*, *Pek*, *Phg*, *Sel*, including the high, northern end of the E-central Range, the Larut Range, the Main Range south to Genting Highlands, and outliers Lawit off the north end of the E-coast Range, Benom (*Phg*), and Tahan and Rabong (Taman Negara).

GEOGRAPHICAL VARIATION. Continental SE Asian *siamensis* Robinson and Kloss 1922 (TL Khao Nong, Surat Thani) on the E-central Range; endemic *vulpes* Ogilvie-Grant 1906 (TL Gunung Tahan) in Malaysia, the latter browner (less rufous), with black and pale markings bolder throughout.

STATUS AND POPULATION. Resident, regular and common.

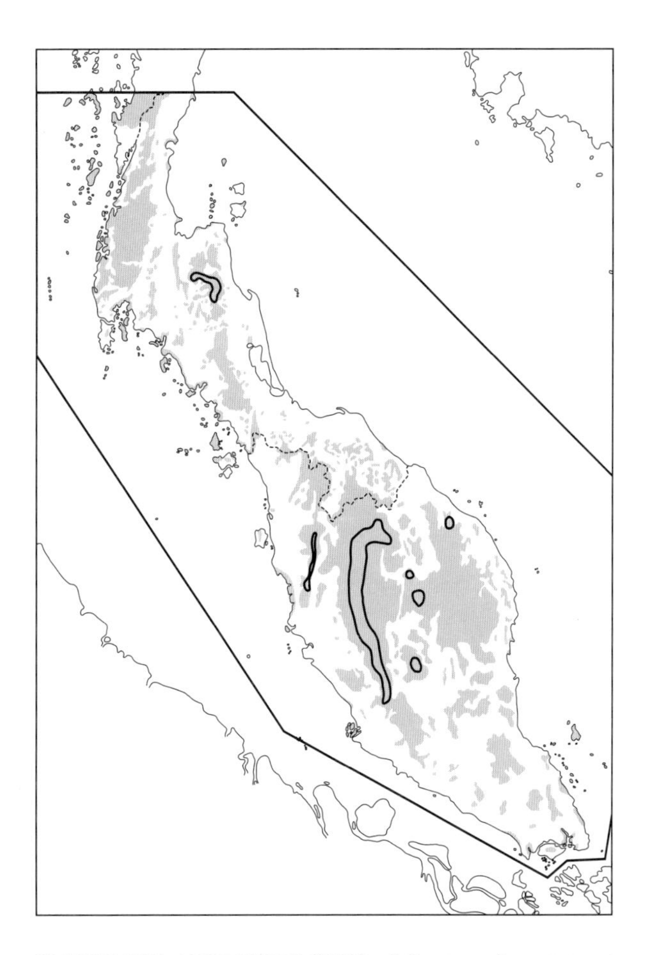

HABITATS AND ECOLOGY. Montane forest to at least 1900 m. On high mountains, a few also occupy the uppermost zone of Lowland forest, with records in the Main Range down to about 800 m (e.g., below the Gap, Selangor/Pahang boundary). This fringe is not occupied in the absence of a core, Montane population and is likely to depend on regular downward dispersal. Everywhere, song-perches are typically low, in dense under-stratum vegetation, and night-time mist-net captures suggest this owl lives mostly at that level.

FORAGING AND FOOD. No information.

SOCIAL ORGANIZATION. Apparently solitary. Calling from regular spots in forest and forest-edge vegetation continues year-round, implying foraging-space is defended against conspecifics.

MOVEMENTS. None known.

SURVIVAL. The longest retrap-interval, at site of ringing, is 37 months (McClure 1964).

SOCIAL INTERACTIONS. No information.

VOICE. Two brief, silvery notes, *plew plew* (pure-toned, at close to 2 KHz), about 0.5 seconds apart in the range of *siamensis*, one second apart in the range of *vulpes*; respectively, at one call every five and 13 seconds (Marshall 1978), in long bouts, mostly during dark hours but occasionally for up to 90 minutes after dawn.

BREEDING

Nest. Not described.

Eggs and brood. An oviducal egg, plain, matt white. Shape near-spherical. Size (mm): 31.4 × 27.7 (n=1). Full clutch unrecorded, but from Fraser's Hill a report of a fledged brood of two.

Cycle. No information.

Seasonality. At Fraser's Hill, an egg on 31 March and two young attended by an adult on 17 June; from Benom (Pahang), a juvenile dated 5 August (BMNH, BMP5, SINGAV-2).

MOULT. An adult in early-stage wing-moult (P1–2) on 9 June; others handled in December, February and March showed none.

CONSERVATION. Probably no critical issues; makes use of dense re-growth at the disturbed edge of forest.

Oriental Scops Owl; Nok Khao Huu Yao Lek (Thai); Burung Hantu Kuang Kuik (Malay)

Otus sunia (Hodgson) 1836, *Asiatick Researches* 19: 175. TL Nepal.
Plate 52

GROUP RELATIONS. Nowhere do the breeding-ranges of *sunia* and similar W Palaearctic *scops* and Afrotropical–S Arabian *senegalensis* actually meet, but advertising-calls are sufficiently different to suggest they are good species (Roberts and King 1986); related probably at superspecies level.

GLOBAL RANGE. Breeds in the Indian subcontinent from the Himalayan foothills, Sri Lanka and Bay of Bengal islands; Pacific Russia south from Amurland, Japan, Korea, China east of a line Heilongjiang–N Yunnan, including Taiwan and Hainan; and continental SE Asia excluding the Peninsula. Northern populations migrate, wintering in the Indian subcontinent, S China and SE Asia to the Peninsula and N Sumatra (BMP5, Marshall 1978, NNML).

IDENTIFICATION AND DESCRIPTION. A tiny, slender, yellow-eyed owl with conspicuously white-notched primaries, barred tail and a bold, black-and-white stripe along the scapulars (see also Mountain Scops Owl). Head, upperparts and breast vary from cold grey to bright rufous (most individuals sortable into one or other category, but with some intermediates), finely and densely peppered and vermiculated blackish, with a scatter of boldly white-marked feathers on upper mantle and wing-coverts, and white bar from side of bill over anterior part of eye. The facial-disc of reddest individuals is pale rufous; grey in others, contrasting where head-plumage is otherwise reddish. Below, reddest individuals are more or less plain rufous from chin to breast; most others a mixture of rufous, grey and white (in varying proportions), and dark-streaked. Behind the breast, predominantly white, with black-brown shaft-lines expanding into fine, multiple cross-bars that outline bands and notches of the other colours. Similar shaft-marks show on the cap. Sexes apparently alike.

When surprised at roost, often stretches and sleeks itself to extraordinary thinness, with eyes near-shut, flushing only at the last moment.

Bare-part colours. (Adult) iris bright yellow; bill lead-grey; feet including naked extremity of tarsus pinkish grey.

Size (mm). (Live and skins: 12 adults, most not sexed): wing 130–149; tail 56–65; bill from cere 11.4–12.2; tarsus 20.0–22.5 (BMNH, UMBRP, ZDUM, ZRCNUS).

Weight (g). Arriving autumn migrants, age/sex-classes not separated, 54.4–71.2 (n=11); three overwinterers 53.3, 55.2 and 69.1 (UMBRP).

DISTRIBUTION. Historical summary: *Chu, Ran, Nak, Phu, Kra, Pht, Tra, Ked, Phg, Sel, Neg, Mel, Joh, Sin*, with additional W-coast island records from Libong, Langkawi (overwintering) and, on autumn migration dates, Rembia (Perak estuary), Jarak and the Indonesian Arua group (implying migrants penetrate further down Sumatra than actual records there suggest); and off the E coast a January (wintering?) record from Tao (*Chu*).

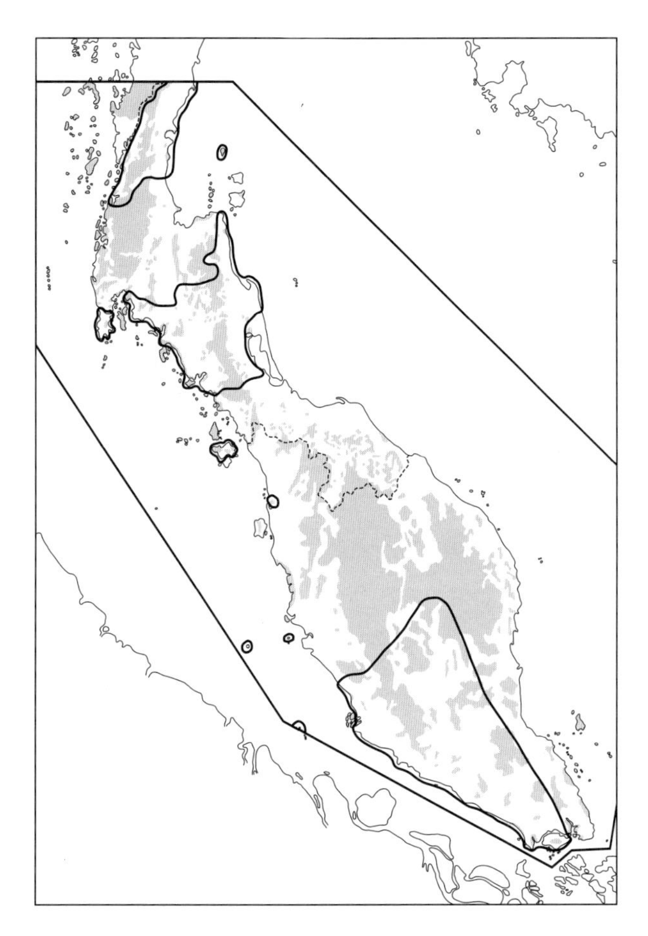

GEOGRAPHICAL VARIATION. NE Asian *stictonotus* Sharpe 1875 (TL China) has been identified among migrants south to Trang (BMNH, Deignan 1963). It averages longer-winged (not below 138 mm: Dementiev and Gladkov 1951–54) than S China-breeding *malayanus* Hays 1845 (TL Melaka), with tarsus feathered to the base of the toes versus apical quarter bare. Malaysian wing-lengths range into an area of overlap but all specimens checked have shown only the *malayanus* tarsus (BMNH, ZRCNUS).

STATUS AND POPULATION. Non-breeding visitor and, in small numbers, evidently also a passage-migrant (a strike on One-Fathom Bank lighthouse); local and sparse to uncommon, but silence makes it harder to find than most resident owls and no realistic estimate of winter abundance exists. There have been no recent records from well-monitored Singapore island.

HABITATS AND ECOLOGY. At mid winter, in mangroves, tall scrub, secondary-growth, wooded gardens, palm and rubber plantations, and other semi-open habitats (no record from original, closed-canopy forest inland), from plains level to 900 m (G.W.H. Davison, Robinson and Kloss 1916). In Selangor and Negeri Sembilan, fidelity to wintering-site demonstrated by several between-season retraps of ringed birds (BMP5, UMBRP).

FORAGING AND FOOD. No information.

SOCIAL ORGANIZATION. Nothing is recorded about night-time dispersion, but day-roosts alone or in parties, including six-plus birds in a tall, dense hedge on a Selangor oil-palm plantation that evidently overwintered as a group (J.E. Duckett).

MOVEMENTS. Extreme dates are 28 October and 27 March. Interceptions at lights on Fraser's Hill, in the Malaysian W-coast plain, and at Melaka Straits lighthouses, show autumn passage continues to at least 19 December (BMP5). An overwinterer ringed on 21 January 1966 on the Jelebu Pass, Negeri Sembilan, was trapped again 45 km NW at Kuala Lumpur on the following 13 December, presumably during its next southward passage (BR 1966). Spring passage uncharted.

SURVIVAL. The longest retrap-interval, on site of ringing at the interface of mangrove forest and coconut plantation in Selangor, is 71 months, suggesting a mimimum seven successful southward migrations by this individual.

SOCIAL INTERACTIONS. No information.

VOICE. No record; evidently silent during the wintering period.

BREEDING. No population.

MOULT. None recorded. Migrants appear to complete both post-juvenile and post-breeding moults before they reach the wintering area.

CONSERVATION. No critical issues.

Small-island Scops Owl; (no Thai name); Burung Hantu Kembara (Malay)
Otus sp.
Plate 52

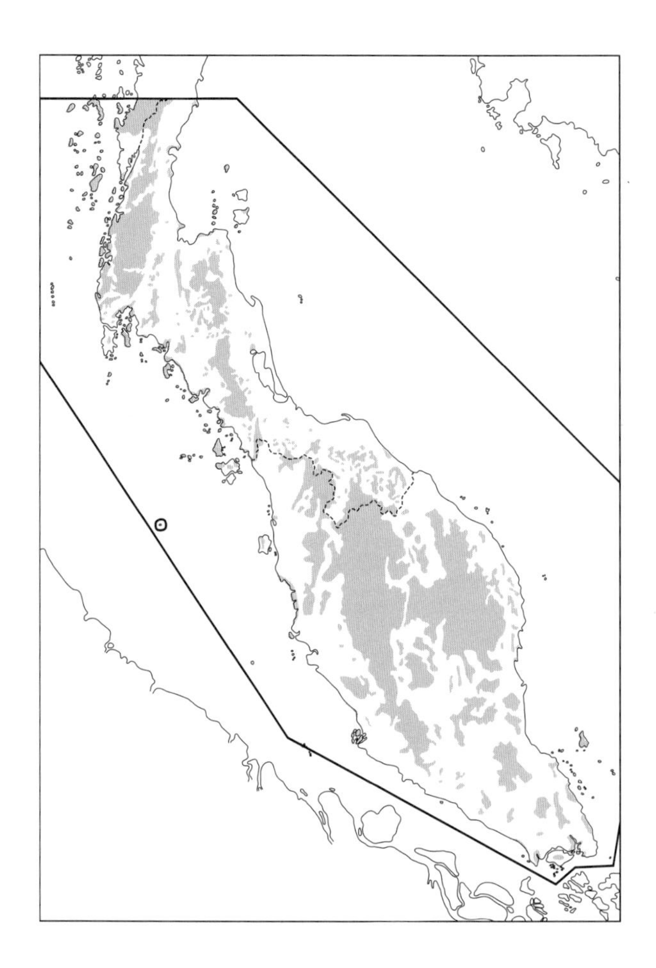

GROUP RELATIONS. A minimum six species, allopatric on small and oceanic islands, form the *manadensis* group. Apparently without continental representatives (Marshall 1978), their interrelationships have not yet been resolved to the point of defining superspecies.

GLOBAL RANGE. Collectively, the Nansei islands and Lanyu (Taiwan); Biak island (NW New Guinea) and Wallacea; Sunda shelf and W Sumatran islands and the Nicobars; the Seychelles, Pemba, Comoros and Madagascar; and Sao Tomé (Gulf of Guinea) (Marshall 1978).

IDENTIFICATION/DESCRIPTION. From colour photographs, superficially similar to intermediate colour-phase Oriental Scops Owl but with longer ear-tufts and proportionately larger, more powerful-looking feet, characteristic of the *manadensis* group. Sexes apparently alike.

Bare-part colours. (Adult) iris bright yellow; no other data.

Size (mm). None handled.

DISTRIBUTION. Reported only from Perak island, N-central Melaka Straits. Historical summary: *Ked.*

GEOGRAPHICAL VARIATION. Vocalizations define species-limits but have not been heard in Malaysia, hence the Perak island birds are still without a name. The nearest neighbouring (Nicobar) population is also unidentified to species.

STATUS AND POPULATION. A breeding vagrant recorded during three consecutive visits to Perak island: on 22–23 December 1975 a lone adult, on 28 February–1 March a pair with four recent fledglings (raised either on the ground or in a rock recess), and on 29–30 March another loner; none thereafter (BR 1976–77, Langham 1976). Not seen on visits in 1973–74, hence perhaps only a single pair of island-seeking dispersants occurred together at this unlikely, treeless site, remaining long enough to breed. The propagule then either died out or moved on.

Four is an unexpectedly large brood for a strigid owl in the Peninsula, but capacity to establish a population nucleus quickly is a recognized feature of small-island specialists (Diamond 1975).

HABITATS AND ECOLOGY. It seems unlikely Perak island is typical habitat. Only recently vegetated (see Brown Booby), at the time of the observations some of its lower and mid slopes had been colonized by a dense, waist-high growth of ferns and grass, but absolutely no trees. All observations were around the entrance to a small, rocky recess about 80 m up from the tideline, which may have served as both nest- and family-party roost-site.

FORAGING AND FOOD. No information. At the time, Perak island supported abundant rats *Rattus diardii* and some insect life.

SOCIAL ORGANIZATION. No additional information.

MOVEMENTS. Over-water dispersal is a presumed key feature of the biology of Small-island Scops Owls, but possible sources of colonization around the Peninsula have hardly been investigated.

SURVIVAL. No information.

SOCIAL INTERACTIONS. No information.

VOICE. No information.

BREEDING. No additional information.

MOULT. No data.

CONSERVATION. No issues identified. Island habitats of the type used by related owls elsewhere in SE Asia are plentiful in Peninsular waters.

Collared Scops Owl; Nok Huuk (Khao Guu) (Thai); Burung Hantu Reban (Malay)

Otus bakkamoena Pennant 1769, *Indian Zoology*: 3 and plate 3. TL Sri Lanka.
Plate 52

GROUP RELATIONS. Roberts and King (1986) propose splitting E Himalayan–E Asian populations from *bakkamoena* of the Indian subcontinent and Sri Lanka on grounds of different, non-intergrading territorial calls, said to be uniform within respective ranges. Both call-types seem to occur in the Peninsula, together with level-toned calls identified as intermediate (Marshall 1978). The repertoires of individual pairs in Pahang and Selangor (including around my own garden) contain all variants (level and up- and down-inflected). This suggests a need for more cross-checks before the new taxonomy is confirmed.

GLOBAL RANGE. The Indian subcontinent from the Himalayan foothills, and Sri Lanka; Ussuriland, Sakhalin, Japan, Korea, China east of a line Heilongjiang–Sichuan, including Taiwan and Hainan; and SE Asia to the Greater Sunda islands and Bali. Northern populations are likely to migrate.

IDENTIFICATION AND DESCRIPTION. A small, stocky owl, second in size to White-fronted among local *Otus* species. Upperparts finely and densely peppered and vermiculated dark brown, with rows of diamond- to chevron-shaped dark spots, densest on the cap; hind-collar, stripe along scapulars, facial-disc and broad band from bill along brow to inner webs of the ear-tuft feathers pale clay to warm buff, a smudge round the upper part of the eye dark brown, and outer side of ear-tuft contrasting blackish. Below, pale clay to warm buff with fine, dark shaft-lines that expand into rhomboids mid-way and near the feather-tip, from which fine pencilling extends out across webs. Tarsal feathering covers the basal joint of the toes but leaves the second joint exposed. Sexes alike; juveniles need further study.

Bare-part colours. (Adult) iris dark brown, eyelid-rim reddish brown; bill whitish horn to pale grey-green, tip and cere darker; exposed toes pinkish grey.

Size (mm). (Live and skins: 49 adults, most not sexed): wing 143–170; tail 71–90; bill from cere 13.7–15.7; tarsus 30.6–32.8 (BMNH, UMBRP, ZDUM, ZRCNUS).

Weight (g). Malaysian mainland adults, 94.1–119.4 (n=27); two from Langkawi 112.9, 140.8.

DISTRIBUTION. Historical summary: all divisions except *Yal* and *Pra*, with additional island records from Lanta, Tarutao, the Langkawi group (Langkawi, Dayang Bunting) and Penang off the W coast; Tioman off the E coast; and Ubin, Berani and Sentosa, Singapore.

GEOGRAPHICAL VARIATION. Birds with Peninsular-type foot-feathering, body patterning and

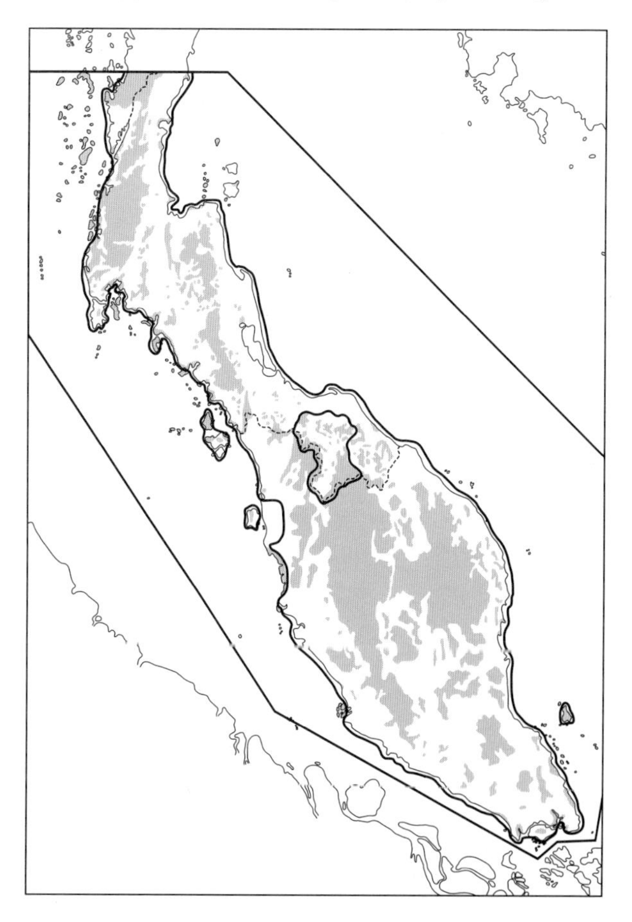

range of pale-part tones (variation individual and continuous in both sexes) occur from Java and Sumatra north through Tenasserim to central Burma, and also in S Vietnam; size smallest in the far south (Java), largest in the north. Except on the Langkawi islands, wing-length in the Peninsula is in the range 143–157 mm, not obviously clinal but Singapore birds average slightly smaller than elsewhere. Deignan (1950) identified these as subspecies *hypnodes* (TL Siak estuary area, E Sumatra), but Mees (1986) has lumped Sumatran *hypnodes* with Javan *lempiji* Horsfield 1821, hence the latter's range undoubtedly also extends to the continent.

Langkawi and Dayang Bunting island birds are absolutely larger: five in the wing-range 161–170 mm (BMNH, UMBRP). Since all collections are winter-dated, they have been suspected of being extralimital migrants, but no such birds have occurred elsewhere in the Peninsula and in all other respects they resemble residents from the opposite mainland. They also occur in habitat that holds vocalizing territory-holders and, probably, these will be shown to be one and the same. (Two supposed migrants in the nineteenth-century H. Whiteley collection labelled Sumatra, wing 170 and 174 mm, foot-feathering over the second toe-joint, prove not to be separable from non-migratory E Palaearctic *O.b. semitorques*, and are likely to have been mislocated in a trade shipment: BMNH, Gurney 1879.) As Langkawi birds are not larger than *lempiji* at the northern edge of its range, no reason has yet been found to name them separately.

STATUS AND POPULATION. Evidently resident everywhere, regular and, in settled and forest-edge habitats, common. On vocal evidence, uncommon in the interior of mature, closed-canopy forest, and mist-net captures at Pasoh (Negeri Sembilan) and other plains-level forest sites suggest densities not above, and perhaps below, those of Reddish and White-fronted Scops Owls. Twenty-six months of netting in 15 ha of mature understorey produced only one (repeating) individual, versus four (non-repeating) over 25 months in 17 ha of nearby regenerating forest.

HABITATS AND ECOLOGY. A mainly woodland-edge owl, in open secondary-growth and logged forest, plantations, orchards, parkland and large, well-planted gardens (far into suburbia), up to the landward margin of mangroves. On evidence of vocalizations, the interior of mature forest may be only marginal habitat, occupied at proportionately low density. Almost exclusively at plains level, with only a few records above the steepland boundary: one in mature forest at 200 m on Benom (Medway 1972), another of a singing bird by the road at the Gap, 850 m, Selangor/Pahang boundary (BR 1982–83), not found subsequently and perhaps moving through. Normally depends entirely on trees, roosting in foliage, but cases of regular use of open beams inside buildings have been reported on two Malaysian plantations (Duckett 1978, MBR 1984–85). In Singapore, a pair actually nested in a house porch (SINGAV-2, -3). Predators may include other, larger owls; Duckett (1978) reports a flee-and-hide reaction to imitations of the calls of Spotted Wood Owl *Strix seloputo*, and use of buildings may be a related response. Typically entirely nocturnal, but daytime dust- and water-bathing is reported (Maccoll 1962).

FORAGING AND FOOD. For so common an owl, comparatively little known. Duckett (1978) found pellets contained mostly insect parts (roaches and orthopterans identified), and in two instances bones of a lizard and a jaw and humerus of a small rodent. Singapore fledglings were fed a roach, cricket and caterpillar, with an adult seen carrying a small snake in its feet (SINGAV-4).

SOCIAL ORGANIZATION. Calling in all months (least during the general season of moult), including at times by both pair-members, suggests defence of foraging-space against conspecifics.

MOVEMENTS. None known.

SURVIVAL. In central Malaysia, retrap-intervals range up to 65 months, all at site of ringing (UMBRP).

SOCIAL INTERACTIONS. No information.

VOICE. A soft, unresonant *pu-up*, even-toned or, more usually, inflected down on the second note; less often a slightly up-inflected *pu-ep*, all typically at 11–15 (but sometimes up to 40-) second intervals, and all within the repertoire of individual pairs. A higher-pitched, more accented *ki-op*, obviously down-turned, is repeated at the same interval. Another, more occasional call is a short *hu-u* or *wha-a*, softer than the regular disyllable and repeated at around 5–6 second intervals. Pair-members are often differently toned, but sex of callers has not been identified.

Song in the Langkawi islands sounds the same as on the mainland.

BREEDING

Nest. The regular natural site is a tree-hole or hollow stump-top, 3–9 m up; one nest recorded in the frond-base of a coconut palm (Madoc 1956a). Sometimes breeds close to buildings, and a Singapore pair nested in successive years behind a pipe under the corner of a porch roof (SINGAV-2, -3).

Eggs and brood. Eggs are plain, matt white. Shape near-spherical. Size (mm): 32.0 × 27.0 (n=1). Clutch typically two but with a few records of three and four eggs, and one brood of four but three is the largest number of chicks recorded off the nest (SINGAV-3).

Cycle. Size-difference between siblings suggests incubation starts with egg one.

Seasonality. Egg and chick records imply laying in all months January–June, with earliest nestlings on 4 February and latest fledglings newly out of the nest on 9 August (Ollington and Loh 1992, SINGAV-2, ZRCNUS).

MOULT. Replacement of primaries is single-locus, but not definitely regular-descendant. In a large sample of adults covering all months and most of the length of the Peninsula, active wing-moult occurred during late May (P2)–August. An exceptional (minimum third year) adult at P1–2 on 23 August and P9 on 20 December, was back on a typical mid-year schedule in the following season. Several ringed individuals have demonstrated annual cyclicity of wing-moult, over as much as four consecutive years.

CONSERVATION. Probably no critical issues, but few occur in extensive, cleanly kept plantations.

Barred Eagle Owl; Nok Khao Yai Phan Sumaatraa (Thai); Burung Hantu Bubu (Malay)

Bubo sumatranus (Raffles) 1822, *Transactions of the Linnean Society* 13(2): 279. TL Sumatra.
Plate 53

GROUP RELATIONS. Free-standing, but with vocal and some morphological resemblances to allopatric, continental *B. nipalensis* (Spot-bellied Eagle Owl).

GLOBAL RANGE. From about latitude 13°N in SW Thailand to the Greater Sunda islands and Bali.

IDENTIFICATION/DESCRIPTION. A large, chunky owl with big, dark eyes in a silvery grey facial-disc margined black over the bill and along upper and outer edges. Outer (lower) border of ear-tufts also black, remainder narrowly barred black-and-white. Rest of upperparts, from forehead, deep, dull brown narrowly barred light rufous, bars paling to stone-buff on the wing-coverts. Outer webs of short scapulars white, forming a conspicuous stripe finely spotted or barred black. Below, black-barred white, bars narrow and dense down to breast level (and on feet), then broader and progressively more spaced. The outer three primaries are plain sooty black, other flight-feathers broadly barred with ash-grey mottling. Five narrow bars across the sooty black tail are similar. Sexes alike. Chick-down white; juveniles like adults but with pale tips to flight-feathers. At all ages, foot-feathering covers the third but not the terminal toe-joint.

From similar-sized Wood Owls by large ear-tufts, held drooped and erecting at 45 degrees rather than upright, as in Fish Owls. From the latter by dark eyes, clearly barred underparts and feathered feet.

Bare-part colours. (Adult) iris dark brown, eyelid-rim yellow; bill pale horn-yellow; exposed toe-tips yellow.

Size (mm). (Skins: 7 males, 7 females; adult): wing 335–346 and 351–380; tail 164–185 and 175–199; bill from cere 26.6–30.3 and 29.1–33.8; tarsus not measured (BMNH, UMZC, ZRCNUS).

Weight. No data.

DISTRIBUTION. Historical summary: *Pak, Sur, Nak, Kra, Tra, Sat, Nar, Kel, Pek, Phg, Sel, Neg, Mel, Joh*; extinct *Sin* since the mid 1920s (Gibson-Hill 1950a), with no other island records.

GEOGRAPHICAL VARIATION. Nominate *sumatranus* of the mainland, Sumatra and Banka.

STATUS AND POPULATION. Resident, regular except in the far north, and uncommon to more or less common.

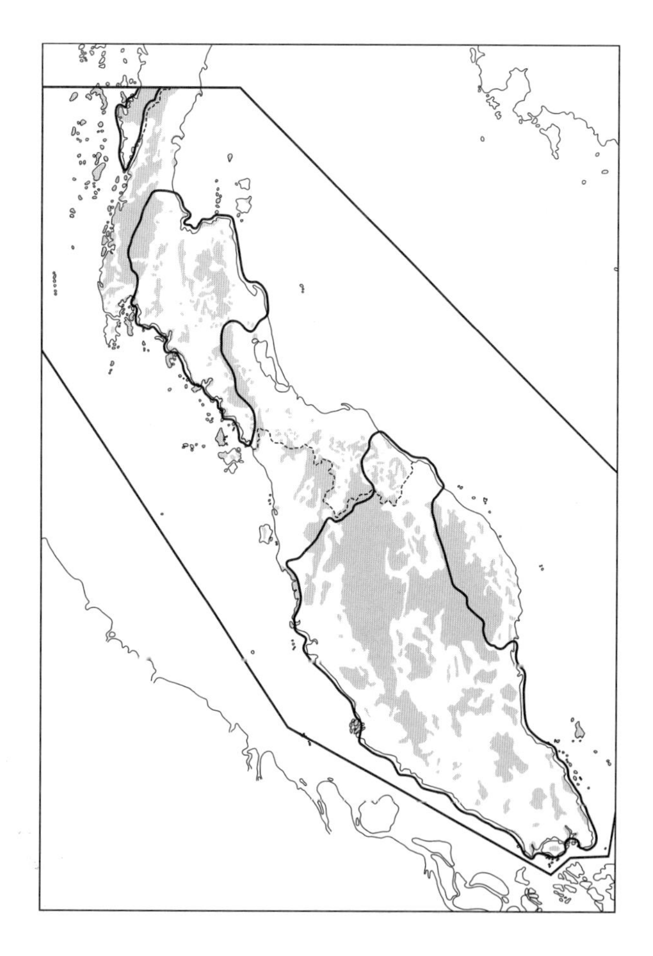

HABITATS AND ECOLOGY. The edge and interior of evergreen and semi-evergreen Lowland forest, mature and well-regenerated, at plains level and on slopeland to around 600 m; exceptionally higher, with a few records from Montane forest and edge to 1400 m (BMNH, BR 1976–77, R.P. Jaensch). Also, mature rubber plantation and abandoned orchard and plantation habitat reverting to secondary-growth, plus nearby wooded gardens (in Malaysia at least, relatively unafraid of people). Evidently less dependent on tall timber than equivalent-sized Wood Owls.

FORAGING AND FOOD. Little observed, but still-hunts from perches at mid and canopy levels, and in the open outside forest, e.g., birds visiting my garden from adjacent woodland hunted from the tops of dead trees on a lawn. Their prey-locating movements were U-shaped head-swings. A launch into a leafy top must have been aimed at some small item, but this same pair also took Town Pigeon, evidently from a roost on a nearby house. A bird at the foot of Si Suk ridge (Surat Thani) observed carrying a red flying squirrel *Petaurista* sp. (BBCB-4).

SOCIAL ORGANIZATION. Territorial males call year-round, and territories are occupied long-term; a patch of abandoned plantation and fringing gardens on the outskirts of Kuala Lumpur held one or a pair of birds for a minimum 14 years.

MOVEMENTS. None recorded.

SURVIVAL. No direct information.

SOCIAL INTERACTIONS. No information.

VOICE. Versatile. The commonest loud advertising-call (only ever given by one pair-member, presumably the male) is a pair of powerful, rather deep, dull, distinctly spaced notes, *huh huh*; repeated in slow succession for long periods. Occasional short bouts are single-noted, or the sequence lapses to a four-note *huh huh hu-hu*. Another uncommon variant is a three-note *huh h-hu* repeated every 7–10 seconds, extending gradually, with progressive emphasis on the first note and eventual dropping of the last, to give a two-note *huh huh* at a more regular 20-second interval. Three other, rather different call-types are (1) an explosive *goh-gohgohgohgohgohgoh-gau-gau-gau*, like the greatly amplified call of a house gecko, rarely repeated, and given not more than 2–3 times per night; (2) a low, grumbling *wuk, wuhuh-wurahu wuhu-wurahu wuhu-wurahu*; and (3) single soft, reedy whistles, *kwayor, tiyaw*, or a more compressed *tyaw*.

Male and female repertoires have not been separated.

BREEDING

Nest. One record: a hole 10 m up the dead trunk of a large *Alstonia augustifolia* in old secondary-growth. From Sumatra, there are reports of the use of frond-cups of the epiphytic bird's-nest fern *Asplenium nidus*, with no material added.

Eggs and brood. Eggs not reliably described. Four said to have come from Larut district, Perak (Dodsworth 1913), are evident owl eggs but at 57.7–53.8 × 44.9–42.8 mm are too large for safe acceptance. Full clutch-size not confirmed but only single downy young have been seen off the nest.

Cycle. A juvenile that fledged in April was still with parents, and returning to the nest, in August. It had left by the start of their next breeding attempt in November. A second chick appeared in January.

Seasonality. Single, downy young accompanied by a parent in January, late February and April–mid June (ENGGANG-1, -2, -3, MBR 1984–85, NRCS, Robinson and Kloss 1924).

MOULT. All records of primary moult have been single-locus. Of 15 adults covering all months except September and December, four showed active wing-moult in mid and late March (P4, P5; inners new), July and mid October (P8), with an instance of post-juvenile moult (P8) in mid November (BMNH, UMZC, ZDUM, ZRCNUS).

CONSERVATION. Plains-level Lowland forest is core habitat, but capacity to breed in disturbed and secondary-growth habitats suggest no major threat overall.

Dusky Eagle Owl; Nok Khao Yai See Khlam (Thai); Burung Hantu Bertanduk (Malay)

Bubo coromandus (Latham) 1790, *Index Ornithologicus* 1: 53. TL Coromandel coast, SE India.
Plate 53

GROUP RELATIONS. Free-standing.

GLOBAL RANGE. The Indian subcontinent except the far NW; SE China (Jiangxi, Zhejiang, Fujian); and western and central Burma to Tenasserim; vagrant in SW Thailand and the Peninsula.

IDENTIFICATION/DESCRIPTION. A large, pale-eyed, horned owl, erecting tall ear-tufts upright when alert (HBI). Facial-disc grey with fine shaft-lines, brow and outer margin blackish. Upperparts from forehead dull sooty brown, variably darker on the cap; head, neck and median wing-coverts with dark feather-centres and outer webs peppered ash grey and black. Lacks a pale stripe along the scapulars. Below, grey-white shading to clay-buff on legs and lower tail-coverts, with bold, sooty shaft-streaks and dark peppering aligned in bars, densely but too fine to be seen at a distance. Flight-feathers sooty, secondaries and base of primaries broadly barred with mottled ash. Narrower bars on tail do not fully cross the central feather-pair. Bristly feathering covers the top of the toes out to their terminal joint. Sexes alike.

From equivalent-sized Brown Fish Owl by feathered feet and erect ear-tuft stance (BMNH).

Bare-part colours. (Adult) iris pale yellow; bill greenish horn to blue-grey, with blackish base; exposed parts of toes lead-grey (BMNH, Robinson 1911).

Size (mm). (Skins: 3 males; adult): wing 370–400; tail 191–198; bill from cere 28.6–30.7; tarsus not measured (BMNH).

Weight. No data.

DISTRIBUTION. Historical summary: *Chu, Pek, Mel.*

GEOGRAPHICAL VARIATION. Dark-toned *klossii* Robinson 1911 (TL Semanggol ridge, Perak), from Assam to SE Asia (AMNH).

STATUS AND POPULATION. Vagrant, known from not more than four specimens: a mid-nineteenth century bird in A.C. Maingay's Melaka collection; one claimed from Dindings district, SW Perak; the type of *klossii* from the Semanggol ridge, mid Perak, in May 1910; and one dated December 1915 from near Ban Salui, Chumphon (BMNH, Chasen 1939, Robinson 1911). The 80-year gap in records suggests these apparent non-breeding migrants or dispersants genuinely no longer occur and that their population of origin might now be extinct.

HABITATS AND ECOLOGY. The type locality in Perak is a forested ridge. Elsewhere in its range, *klossii* inhabits open agricultural land with scattered tall trees and palm groves (Smythies 1953).

FORAGING AND FOOD. No information.

SOCIAL ORGANIZATION. No information.

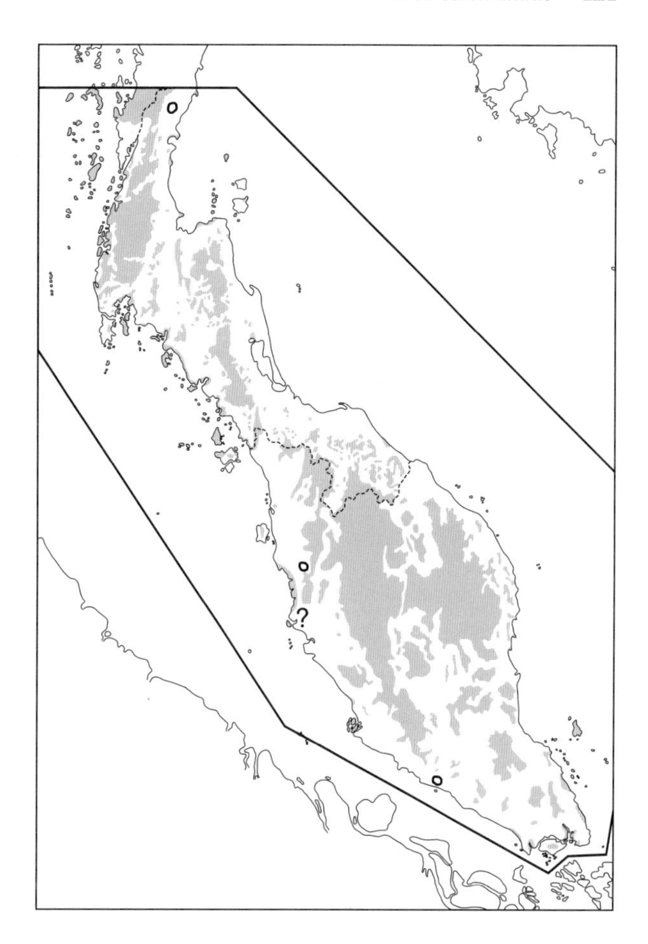

MOVEMENTS. None recorded although calling could hardly have gone unnoticed had residents occurred in typical habitat.

SURVIVAL. No information.

SOCIAL INTERACTIONS. No information.

VOICE. Not recorded in the Peninsula.

BREEDING. Apparently no population.

MOULT. One dated 22 May growing P5. December and January birds showed none (BMNH).

CONSERVATION. No issues.

Brown Fish Owl; Nok Theut Theeu Phan Neua (Thai); **Burung Hantu Ikan** (Malay)

Ketupa zeylonensis (Gmelin) 1788, *Systema Naturae* 13(1): 287. TL Sri Lanka.
Plate 53

GROUP RELATIONS. Free-standing.

GLOBAL RANGE. SW Asia from S Turkey and the E Mediterranean to Iran; the Indian subcontinent and Sri Lanka; far-S China from Guangdong to Yunnan, including Hainan; and continental SE Asia as far as the Peninsula.

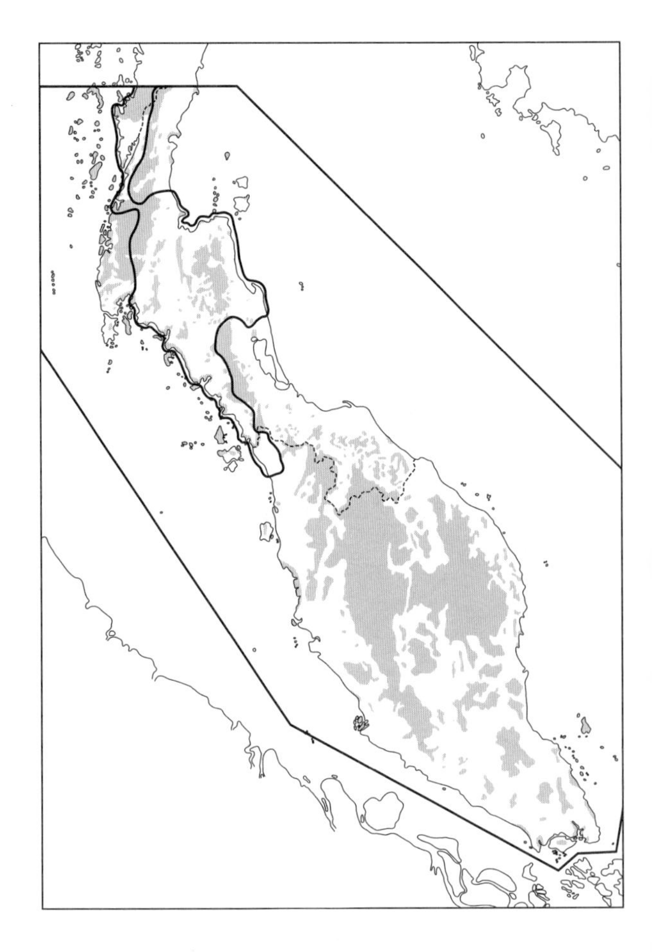

IDENTIFICATION/DESCRIPTION. Large, yellow-eyed, with long, bare tarsi, shaggy, laterally inclined ear-tufts, and white chin and throat. Like commoner Buffy Fish Owl but ash-brown rather than tawny-yellow, without white on the forehead and brows, and bigger (only in the far north are largest Buffy about the size of smallest Brown). Cap and hind-neck show blackish shaft-streaks, the hind-neck also finely and densely barred cinnamon. Rest of the upperparts, including wing-coverts, coarsely mottled black, per feather the black cutting off a large, pale notch on each web, enclosing a brown spot. Below, pale ashy with narrow black shaft-streaks and fine, dense cinnamon barring detectable only in a close view. Sexes alike. Juveniles lack mottling on the upperparts, with black confined to shaft-streaks throughout.

Bare-part colours. (Adult) iris bright yellow; bill greenish grey with black tip; feet including tarsi dirty grey to grey-green (BMNH, ZRCNUS).

Size (mm). (Skins: 5 adults, none reliably sexed): wing 352–408; tail 178–197; bill from cere 30.0–32.2; tarsus 67.8–76.3 (BMNH, ZRCNUS).

Weight. No data.

DISTRIBUTION. South to slightly above latitude 6°N but no records from the eastern plain below Nakhon Si Thammarat. Historical summary: *Pak, Ran, Sur, Nak, Kra, Tra, Sat, Pes, Ked,* and no island records.

GEOGRAPHICAL VARIATION. Subspecies *leschenault* Temminck 1820 (TL Chandarnagar, Bengal), of the NE Indian subcontinent and western SE Asia.

STATUS AND POPULATION. Local and uncommon to sparse, but evidently resident. Specimen- and other field-dates cover January, March, May–July, September, November and December (Meyer de Schauensee 1934, 1946, MBR 1984–85, 1986–87, Robinson and Kloss 1910–11, 1921–24, Robinson 1914a), with breeding confirmed at the (former?) southern limit of range in N Kedah (G.C. Madoc).

HABITATS AND ECOLOGY. The most often-cited habitat is plains-level woodland abutting paddyland. This may still apply in the north, and describes the 1940 Kedah nesting-site, but in the south this mixed landscape has become scarce. The only recent reports in Malaysia (both in Perlis), have been from semi-deciduous forest, including a loner day-roosting in a relic strip sheltering a watercourse through a sugar-cane plantation and another at night in mid-stratum cover by a track through more continuous, old logged forest, not close to water; both sites low-lying (MBR 1984–85, 1986–87).

FORAGING AND FOOD. No information.

SOCIAL ORGANIZATION. No information.

MOVEMENTS. None known.

SURVIVAL. No information.

SOCIAL INTERACTIONS. No information.

VOICE. At night in Perlis, loud, complaining squawks and deep-toned grumbling notes, *gwoop, gwok,* etc. (MBR 1986–87). Boonsong and Round (1991) describe a succession of deep mutterings rising to a maniacal laugh, a hoarse, mournful scream, and a soft, deep *hup-hup-hu* delivered fast with the last note audible only at close range (the 'drum' call).

BREEDING

Nest. Recorded only from N Kedah, in a relic stand of paperbark *Melaleuca cajuputi* trees in paddyland carved out of swamp-forest on the coastal plain: one 21 m up in the abandoned stick nest of a diurnal raptor, to which fresh green leaves are thought to have been added (unlikely owl behaviour); the other only 4 m up, with an egg laid directly on wood fragments in a hollowed branch-stub.

Eggs and brood. Eggs plain white, chalky textured with a slightly rugose surface; more or less glossless. Shape short elliptical. Size (mm): 59.2–55.4 × 48.5–46.2 (n=3). One presumed full, incubated clutch of two eggs.

Cycle. No information.

Seasonality. The clutch and a single fresh egg are dated 6 and 11 December (G.C. Madoc).

MOULT. Adults dated December, January, March and June showed none, with fresh plumage in December (BMNH, ZRCNUS).

CONSERVATION. No significant stands of paperbark forest survive in NW Malaysia and both the recent Perlis sites have since been deforested. Habitat they represented now hardly occurs south of the border and is scarce throughout the Peninsula. The shortage of modern records of this owl is becoming conspicuous.

Buffy Fish Owl; Nok Theut Theuu Malayu (Thai); Burung Hantu Kuning (Malay)

Ketupa ketupu (Horsfield) 1821, *Transactions of the Linnean Society* 13(1): 141. TL Java.
Plate 53

GROUP RELATIONS. Free-standing.

GLOBAL RANGE. Assam, and patchily from W Burma, S Laos and central Vietnam to the Greater Sunda islands and Bali; one record from the Cocos-Keeling group.

IDENTIFICATION/DESCRIPTION. Has the same appearance, including stance of ragged ear-tufts, as Brown Fish Owl but slightly to substantially smaller, and forehead to brow as well as chin to upper throat are prominently white. Other plumage tawny-yellow rather than ash-brown, against which dark streaking shows more strikingly; entirely without transverse barring, and less intricately mottled, the pale notches of adult dorsal feathers lacking an enclosed spot. Sexes similar, and dorsal pattern of the juvenile as in Brown Fish Owl.

Bare-part colours. (Adult) iris bright yellow, eyelid blackish; bill slaty grey, cere slightly paler; feet including bare tarsi pale flesh-grey.

Size (mm). (Skins: 14 males, 15 females; adult): wing 322–346 and 317–356; tail 159–175 and 153–177; bill from cere 26.6–31.1 and 27.8–32.5; tarsus 62.0–74.7 and 64.5–72.4 (UMZC, ZRCNUS).

Weight. No data.

DISTRIBUTION. Historical summary: all divisions except *Pra*, with additional island records from Rang (*Phu*), Yao Yai, Lanta and Penang off the W coast; and Ubin (Singapore).

GEOGRAPHICAL VARIATION. Collected over the same era and stored together, 33 adults from the length of the Peninsula (Chumphon to Singapore) show no directional trends of colour, pattern or size, although the outright largest individual came from the far north. Upperparts are standard. Underparts vary slightly in strength of streaking and warmness of ground colour, but strictly individually, with palest Chumphon and Ranong birds exactly matchable among others from Singapore (including Ubin island). At the rich-toned extreme, five from between Johor and Phuket match a small series of W-Javan nominate *ketupu*. Five topotypes of northern continental *aagaardi* Neumann 1935 (TL vicinity of Narathiwat town – well south of Phuket) are actually average-toned, which suggests either that this name be applied throughout the Peninsula or that the Peninsula as a whole is in a zone of intergradation and that an alternative name must be sought for continental populations. Comparable average-toned birds also occur on Sumatra (NNML).

STATUS AND POPULATION. Resident, regular and uncommon to more or less common, and over a range of habitats, excluding the interior of inland forest, the most often-encountered large owl. Since the mid 1980s, status on Singapore island has recovered

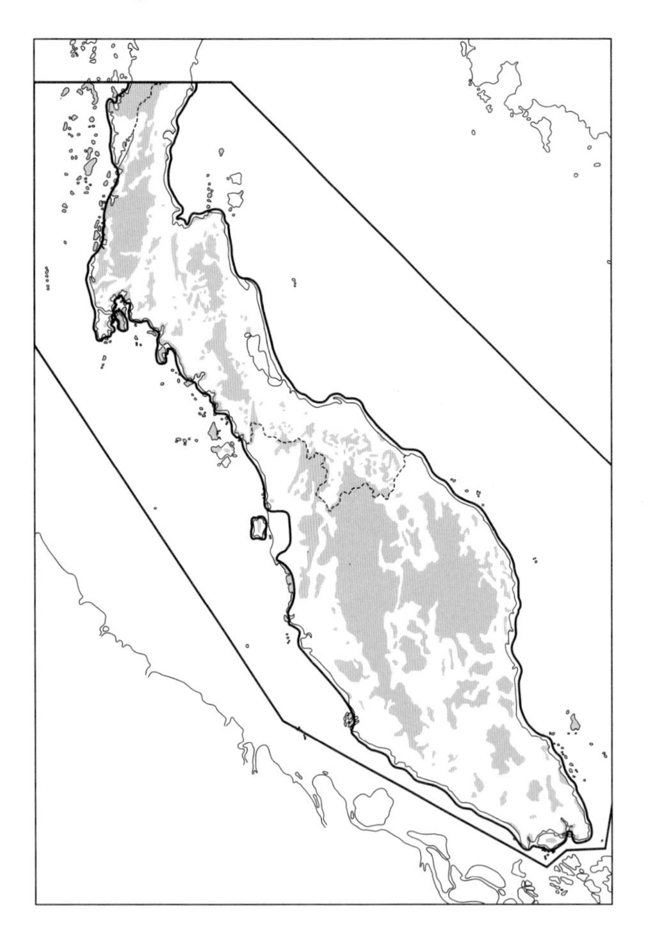

from vagrant to small-scale resident (MBR 1986–87), perhaps via immigrants from Ubin in the Johor Straits.

HABITATS AND ECOLOGY. Exclusively at plains level, in forest-edge, secondary-growth, bamboo stands, orchards, palm and rubber plantations, and parkland and large, rural gardens close to wetlands of many kinds: mangrove creeks, swampy pools, fish-ponds and reservoirs, streams and rivers, including waterways through inland forest large enough to break the canopy. Also recorded from large, open and vegetated sink-holes in limestone karst. Where unmolested, like Barred Eagle Owl, relatively unafraid of people and except when nesting will roost on a shaded but often otherwise exposed perch, over open water where available, and with family members close by.

FORAGING AND FOOD. Still-hunts mostly in wetlands, dropping from an overhead perch or waiting low, at the edge of water. Prey includes fish (a tame bird regularly killed catfish by biting through the gill-chamber), anurans, small snakes, rats, crustaceans, large aquatic insects and, in one instance, a tortoise (Annandale and Robinson 1903, H.L. Bell).

SOCIAL ORGANIZATION. Forages alone, but established pairs remain in the nesting-area year-round.

MOVEMENTS. None recorded.

SURVIVAL. No information.

SOCIAL INTERACTIONS. No information.

VOICE. From pairs, a soft hiss, soft mews and (reacting to observers) rather high-pitched, screeching yelps, *yiark, yark, yark, yeek*, etc. From a hunting bird, a low, rather hoarse 1.5–2 second whistle or harsher wheeze, every 1–3 minutes (H.L. Bell), these long calls audible for 100–200 m down a forested river. Other calls linked tentatively with this species are: (1) a plaintive, wailing *ur-lee*, given in flight as the bird leaves its day-roost; (2), by a probable pair, a powerful, explosive wail, *guaai-uh*, delivered about ten times at intervals of a few seconds then followed a short distance off by deep, muffled drumming sound, *huh hoohoohoohoohoo*, the first note discrete, five others run together on a shallowly declining pitch. Each drum then answered by a similar *hoop huhuhuhuh hoo*, middle notes rumbled but on an even rather than declining pitch. Maintaining this difference, two birds kept up a mumbled conversation over 20 minutes, while moving slowly away.

BREEDING

Nest. Without adding material of its own, makes use of abandoned nests of diurnal raptors (including Brahminy Kite), tree-holes, the frond-cup of bird's-nest fern, large clumps of epiphytic orchids, etc., 3–18 m up; recorded in mangrove forest, durian and coconut groves, and a garden ornamental only 10 m from a bungalow verandah.

Eggs and brood. Egg plain white. Shape short elliptical. Size (mm): 47.3 × 42.5, 49.0 × 43.3 (n=2). Full clutch one, exceptionally two, but the maximum recorded brood is one.

Cycle. Some pairs appear to be active at a less-than-annual interval: at a Negeri Sembilan nest, eggs laid evidently in December (hatched in January) and again in July, presumably by the same female. Others bring off only one brood per year, seasonally: pairs at Rantau Panjang, coastal Selangor, fledged young successively in November, November and late October, and at nearby Kuala Selangor nature park in October and late December.

Seasonality. Egg- and chick-dates from Malaysia suggest a total pattern of laying approaching that of Barn Owl *Tyto alba*, locally with more than one surge between early July and April (latest egg 29 April) (Berwick 1952b, Chasen 1939, J.E. Duckett, ENGGANG-2, G.C. Madoc, McClure and Husain 1968, C.J. Mead, NRCS).

MOULT. Moult of primaries recorded at one or two loci. Among 47 adults covering all months and the full length of the Peninsula, 24 showed active wing-moult during March and May–January, with fresh plumage in early July–early February and instances of tail-moult (T1) in May and January, implying no clear seasonality overall (BMNH, UMZC, ZRCNUS).

CONSERVATION. Given the range of habitats used, apparently no critical issues.

Spotted Wood Owl; Nok Khao Paa Lang Juut (Thai); **Burung Hantu Carik Kafan** (Malay)

Strix seloputo Horsfield 1821, *Transactions of the Linnean Society* 13(1): 140. TL Java.
Plate 53

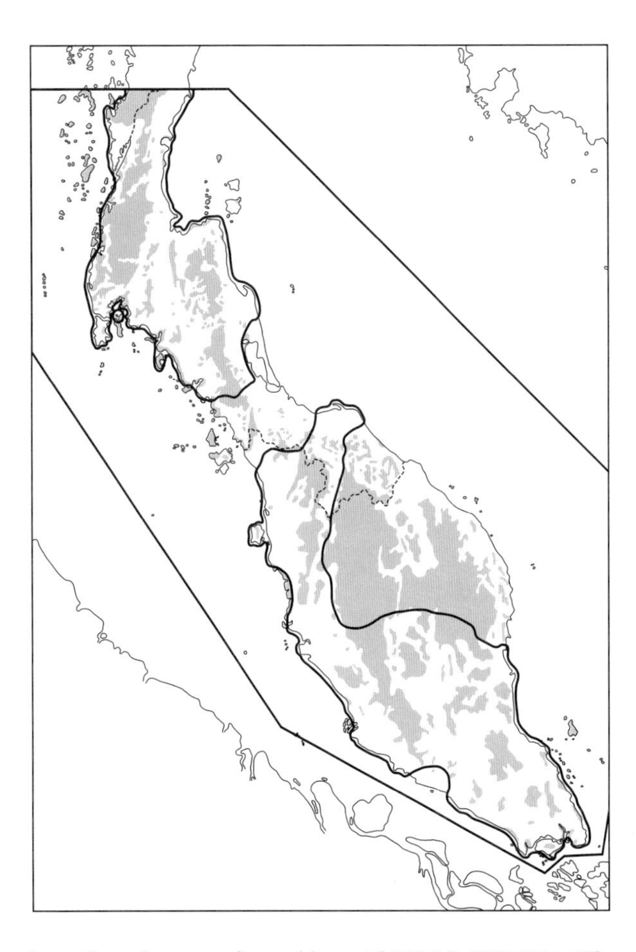

GROUP RELATIONS. Free-standing.

GLOBAL RANGE. NE and central Thailand, Cambodia and far-S Vietnam, and S Burma to Sumatra and Java, including the Bawean island group (Java Sea); also Palawan and the Calamian group, W Philippines. Its northern continental limit is uncertain, but a voice-description from Mandalay (Smythies 1953) is surely not of this species.

IDENTIFICATION/DESCRIPTION. Size of, and in some of the same habitats as, Fish Owls and Barred Eagle Owl, but only this species lacks ear-tufts. Facial-disc plain rufous-buff, in strong contrast to dark eyes and rest of head. Entire upperparts from disc-margin rich, dark chocolate-brown with bold, irregularly shaped flecks of white in roughly transverse rows, each fleck encircled blackish. Underparts white with long, wispy, ginger-buff basal barbs showing through and three-plus deep chocolate-brown bars per feather, wider than interposed white on breast, progressively narrower than white towards feet and lower tail-coverts. From Brown Wood Owl in their narrow zone of habitat overlap by lack of white on forehead, brow and scapulars, wider spacing of ventral dark bars and, apart from white tip, unbarred tail (white dots at incipient bar-positions show clearly only on inner webs of lateral feathers, typically hidden in the field).

Bare-part colours. (Adult) iris deep brown; bill blackish; unfeathered apical quarter of toes dark horn.

Size (mm). (Skins: 9 males, 7 females; adults): wing 339–351 and 354–370; tail 174–198 and 173–197; bill from cere 24.1–26.6 and 25.4–28.2; tarsus not measured (BMNH, UMZC, ZDUM, ZRCNUS).

Weight (g). An adult male, 1011 (ZDUM).

DISTRIBUTION. Historical summary: all divisions except *Chu, Son, Sat, Nar, Pes, Kel, Tru, Mel*, with additional island records from Boi Yai, Libong, Lanta and Penang off the W coast; and Ubin, St John's and Sentosa, Singapore.

GEOGRAPHICAL VARIATION. Nominate *seloputo*, apparently of the global range except the Philippines and Bawean.

STATUS AND POPULATION. Resident, regular and more or less common. Twenty years ago, it reached a southern limit of range in Pahang and Negeri Sembilan (BMP5). Like Buffy Fish Owl, has since spread, with a first report from E Johor in March 1979 and territorial calling on Singapore island as of late 1985; breeding there confirmed by mid 1986 (MBR 1986–87). Singapore residents have recently occupied a minimum seven sites (including the mid-city botanical gardens) on the main island, and reached three satellites.

On the southern mainland of the Peninsula, highest hunting densities appear to be in palm plantations, even though these habitats are short of possible nest-sites. The large rise in acreage of oil-palm (with attendant rat populations) may be a factor in renewed spread.

HABITATS AND ECOLOGY. Strictly at plains level; recorded in mangroves, strand casuarina woodland (BBCB-7, Eve and Guigue 1982), at the edge of logged forest with relic tall trees, orchards, mature rubber and especially coconut and oil-palm plantations, and wooded parkland. Not in closed-canopy inland forest, although typical territories feature clumps of large, shady trees in the high, interior canopy of which birds roost, emerging onto more exposed perches at dusk before starting to hunt.

On a Negeri Sembilan oil-palm estate, active Spotted Wood and Barn Owl nests have been found only 12 m apart (S. Karuppiah).

FORAGING AND FOOD. Beetle remains identified from stomach contents (Hume and Davison 1878). In oil-palm plantation, still-hunts in exactly the situations used by Barn Owls, waiting alone on a lower frond 2–3 m above a trackway or other open space. No captures recorded in this situation, but the circumstances suggest that rats are a target.

SOCIAL ORGANIZATION. Territorial pairs advertise vocally more or less year-round. Unlike non-territorial Barn Owl in some of the same habitats, no larger social groups reported.

MOVEMENTS. None recorded.

SURVIVAL. No information.

SOCIAL INTERACTIONS. No information other than under Voice.

VOICE. A single deep, powerful *who*, scaringly loud at close range, by both pair-members, one answering the other, and responded to by more distant neighbours; given at all times of night but mainly in the late evening and shortly before dawn. A second, more muffled but still loud call has a hurried tail on a lower and falling pitch, *who hu-hu-hu*. A pair with a fledgling recently off the nest met observers with short, deep, throbbing alarm-rattles, similar to the tail of the second call.

BREEDING

Nest. Sited 2–18 m up: in the frond-cup of a large bird's-nest fern on a high side-branch of a large tree isolated in paddyland, but close to woodland; in a hollow petai tree *Parkia* in a village garden; and in a hollow-topped tree-stump among oil-palms. Eggs are laid directly on accumulated litter, with no material added.

Eggs and brood. Egg plain, creamy white, rough-surfaced but with a slight gloss. Shape short elliptical. Size (mm): 50.3 × 42.8 (mean, n=2). Incubated clutches of two eggs recorded twice, but clutch evidently occasionally at least three. Most breeding attempts fledge not more than a single young, but one record of three by a pair in a Kuala Lumpur park (BR 1964).

Cycle. No information.

Seasonality. Nestling-dates imply laying from December (confirmed January) until mid year; recent fledglings in early March, April, June and August (BBCB-7, BR 1964, ENGGANG-1, S. Karuppiah, G.C. Madoc, SINGAV-3).

MOULT. Primaries are replaced at one or two loci, pattern not resolved. Among 18 adults covering all months except June, active wing-moult occurred in March–May, July, August and late November (P3); with completion as of August, and other non-moulters dated December–February (BMNH, ZDUM, UMZC, ZRCNUS).

CONSERVATION. Near habitation, too often shot for superstitious reasons associated with the loud call, but well-enough entrenched in other man-made habitats. The Thai wildlife trade could be an issue in the north.

Brown Wood Owl; Nok Khao Paa See Namtaan (Thai); Burung Hantu Punggur (Malay)

Strix leptogrammica Temminck 1831, *Nouveau Recueil de Planches Coloriées d'Oiseaux* 88: plate 525. TL Borneo.

Plate 53

GROUP RELATIONS. Free-standing.

GLOBAL RANGE. Except in the far NW, the Indian subcontinent from the Himalayan foothills, and Sri Lanka; China south of a line Zhejiang–Yunnan including Taiwan and Hainan; and SE Asia to the Greater Sunda islands.

IDENTIFICATION/DESCRIPTION. Size roughly that of Barred Eagle and Spotted Wood Owls. 'Earless', and from Spotted Wood Owl by narrow buff-white band across the forehead and brow to behind eye-level, and white chin and throat, framing the face. Facial-disc cinnamon-buff, ventrally whitish, contrasting with dark eye and dark, periocular smudge that joins blackish feathering around the bill. Head otherwise plain deep brown. Rest of upperparts darkish brown except for paler, faintly barred collar, a stripe along the short scapulars formed by their narrowly dark-barred, whitish outer webs, and finely buff-barred rump to upper tail-coverts (concealed in the perched bird). Underparts below throat, dirty buff, barred dark brown from breast to feet and lower tail-coverts, more finely and densely than in Spotted

Wood Owl, and tail with about ten narrow buff-white bars exposed across its full width.

Bare-part colours. (Adult) iris deep brown; bill pale bluish- or greenish horn, tip yellower; unfeathered apical quarter of toes dull blue-grey (BMNH, Riley 1938).

Size (mm). (Skins: 14 adults, most not sexed): wing 333–371; tail 173–207; bill from cere 22.4–28.9; tarsus not measured (BMNH, ZDUM, ZRCNUS).

DISTRIBUTION. The southernmost record, a road-kill at Desaru, SE Johor (SINGAV-3). Historical summary: *Chu, Sur, Nak, Kra, Pht, Tra, Sat, Kel, Pek, Phg, Sel, Neg, Mel, Joh,* with an island record from Lanta (*Kra*).

GEOGRAPHICAL VARIATION. Endemic or near-endemic *maingayi* Hume and Davison 1878 (TL Melaka).

STATUS AND POPULATION. Resident, local and uncommon, apparently naturally at low population density, e.g., only one pair known in the 1200 ha of closed-canopy Lowland forest at the Pasoh research site, Negeri Sembilan, but calls much less than Spotted Wood Owl and probably overlooked.

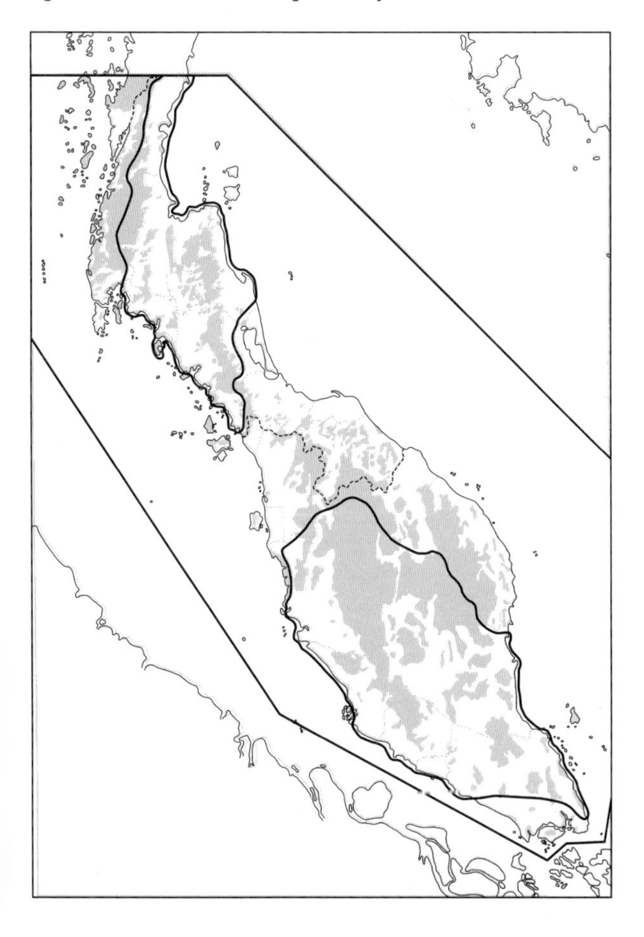

HABITATS AND ECOLOGY. Emerges to hunt over tracks and small roads through and at the edge of forest; otherwise the interior of tall, closed-canopy, evergreen and semi-evergreen forests at plains level and on slopes to 1700 m, i.e., marginally into the Upper Montane zone (BMP5). Repeat observations at regular sites suggest it is sedentary over the whole of this altitudinal range.

In lowland Taman Negara, feathers have been recovered from a limestone cave, implying possible use of a non-tree site for roosting or nesting (G.W.H. Davison).

FORAGING AND FOOD. Still-hunts from a branch perch with a view of the ground, but no information on prey.

SOCIAL ORGANIZATION. The largest social unit is the territorial pair, or parents with a dependent offspring.

MOVEMENTS. None recorded.

SURVIVAL. No information.

SOCIAL ORGANIZATION. No information.

VOICE. A rich, tremulous *huhuhuhoo*, usually not repeated; given at night and occasionally before dark.

BREEDING

Nest. Not described.

Eggs and brood. Egg not described and clutch unknown, but only single fledglings have been recorded attended by adults.

Cycle. Both parents tend young, and at Khao Pra-Bang Khram, Krabi, a young newly off the nest on 30 March was still roosting with parents on 11 May.

Seasonality. Between Krabi and Negeri Sembilan: recent fledglings in late March and early April; others an estimated six weeks off the nest in mid May, and mid August (BBCB-7, C.M. Francis, MBR 1982–83, ZRCNUS).

MOULT. The few records of primary moult are all single-locus, but do not resolve replacement pattern. Among adults, active wing-moult recorded in mid December (P1–2, P2) and late April (P3), with non-moulters in August, September and January (BMNH, ZRCNUS).

CONSERVATION. Occurrence high on slopes suggests no immediate threat from habitat-loss, but the few actual breeding records have all been in plains-level forest. It is not known how this owl responds to logging disturbance.

Collared Owlet; Nok Khao Khre (Thai); Burung Hantu Kerdil (Malay)

Glaucidium brodiei (Burton) 1836, *Proceedings of the Zoological Society of London* 3: 152. TL Simla, W Himalayas.

Plate 52

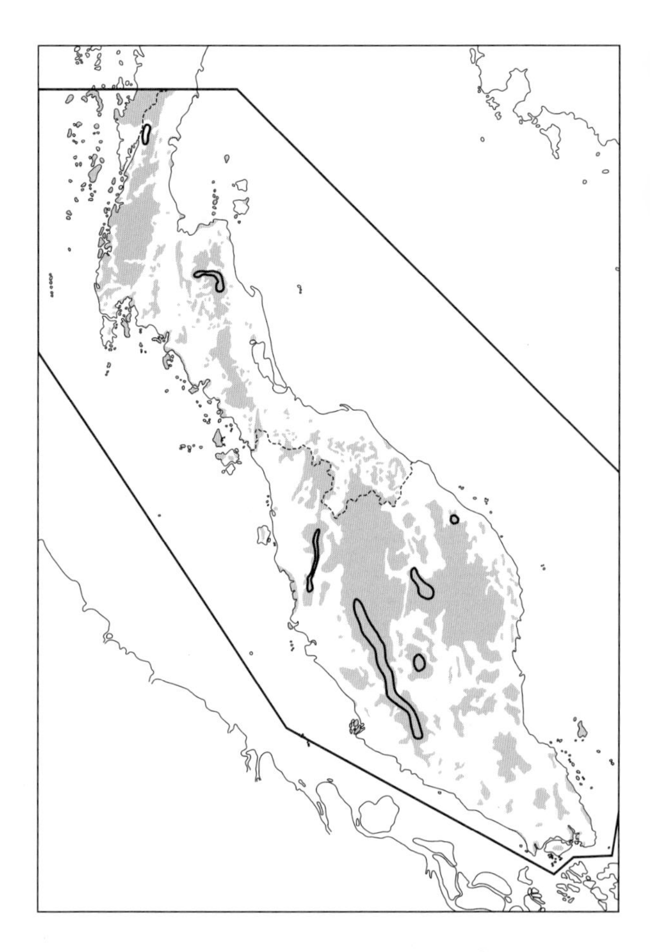

GROUP RELATIONS. Free-standing, although a N Sarawak population known to have different calls needs more research.

GLOBAL RANGE. The Himalayas and hill-tracts of the far-NE Indian subcontinent; China south from Gansu, Shaanxi and the lower Changjiang, including Taiwan and Hainan; and SE Asia to Sumatra and Borneo.

IDENTIFICATION/DESCRIPTION. Tiny and 'earless', *contra* Mountain Scops Owl in the same habitat. Pale yellow eyes are ringed dark and set off by a short, white brow-streak margined above with black. Head otherwise ash-grey and finely white-spotted, spots in concentric rows on the face, which lacks an obvious disc. The lower nape shows a face-simulating pair of dark 'eyes' set in an orange-buff patch topped by a whitish 'brow-line'. Body overall dun brown (an orange-rufous phase in the Himalayan range seems not to occur in SE Asia), narrowly barred buff to buff-white on both surfaces, with tail fully brown-and-white barred above and below. Sexes alike. The local juvenile has not been described but, elsewhere, cap to mantle are unmarked brown except for white shaft-lines on forecrown. In all age-groups, tarsus fully feathered, and the nostrils in this species are remarkable, lateral-pointing tubes.

Build, weight and size-dimorphism quite closely parallel Black-thighed Falconet.

Bare-part colours. (Adult) iris clear, pale yellow; bill grey-green to yellow-green, paling at the tip; toes grey-green to dirty yellow-green.

Size (mm). (Live and skins: 4 males, 5 females; adult): wing 86–89 and 92–101; tail 46–49 and 50–64; bill from cere 11.0–11.3 and 11.4–11.8; tarsus 18.5–19.5 and 17.3–20.3 (UMBRP, ZRCNUS). On wing-length, females average nine percent larger than males.

Weight (g). Unsexed adults, 44.9–58.1 (n=6) (McClure 1964, Medway 1972, UMBRP).

DISTRIBUTION. The NW, E-central and Larut Ranges, the Main Range between 4°30′ and 2°40′N but certainly more widespread, and on eastern outliers: Lawit off the N end of the East-coast Range, Benom and, in Taman Negara, Tahan, Tulang Rabong and Rabong. Historical summary: *Ran, Sur, Nak, Kel, Tru, Pek, Phg, Sel, Neg.*

GEOGRAPHICAL VARIATION. Nominate *brodiei*, of the global range excluding Taiwan and the Greater Sunda islands.

STATUS AND POPULATION. Resident, regular and more or less common; familiar vocally, but hard to see.

HABITATS AND ECOLOGY. Only exceptionally on mountains without a significant spread of Montane forest. Typically at mid-column levels (mist-netting suggests less often the under-stratum) of the interior and edge of Montane forest, recorded to 1800 m (Medway 1972). At low density, also on the Lowland forest slope, down to 700 m in Malaysia, lower in Thailand including at 400 m on Khao Luang peak, north end of the E-central range, and virtually to plains level on the upper Pakchan estuary, N Ranong (BMP5, King 1966, Robinson and Kloss 1921–24).

Calls mostly by day and all mist-net captures have been during daytime, implying this owlet is mainly diurnal.

FORAGING AND FOOD. No information, but a play-back or good imitation of an owlet advertising-call, at any time of day, causes instant commotion among neighbouring passerines, up to bulbul size. Size-dimorphism is symptomatic of a bird predator and, in the hand, Collared Owlet is as nervous, quick and aggressive as a falconet or sparrowhawk.

SOCIAL ORGANIZATION. Unknown, but calling from predictable sites in the forest implies defence of a territory.

MOVEMENTS. None recorded.

SURVIVAL. The only recovery reported involved the mummified corpse of a bird trapped behind the netted-off eaves of a bungalow at Fraser's Hill, 73 months after ringing in nearby forest.

SOCIAL INTERACTIONS. No information.

VOICE. A flat monotone, *poh po-poh poh*, given in short bouts with about two seconds between calls; far-carrying but highly ventriloquial and very hard to locate. No other sounds identified.

BREEDING. No records, but elsewhere uses the abandoned holes of small woodpeckers, barbets, etc. (another falconet parallel).

MOULT. Primaries are replaced at one or two loci. In a small sample, active wing-moult occurred in late June, September and late November (with fresh plumage up to early March); non-moulters in February, March, May and June (UMBRP, ZRCNUS).

CONSERVATION. Occupies disturbed as well as pristine forest, and no threats envisaged beyond the highland development issues that could ultimately affect all mountain birds.

Asian Barred Owlet; Nok Khao Mong (Thai); Burung Hantu Bersiul (Malay)

Glaucidium castanopterum (Horsfield) 1821, *Transactions of the Linnean Society* 13(1): 140. TL Java.

GROUP RELATIONS. Similarity of vocalizations suggests Indonesian and continental Asian populations are treatable as one species, size and colour differences notwithstanding. Indonesian birds are as red above as some S Asian Jungle Owlets (*G. radiatum*), but by convergence only.

GLOBAL RANGE. Foothills of the Himalayas and hill-tracts of the far-NE Indian subcontinent; SE Tibet; China south from Gansu, Shaanxi and the lower Changjiang, including Hainan; continental SE Asia to S Vietnam and the Peninsula, and Java and Bali.

IDENTIFICATION/DESCRIPTION. Line drawing, page 430. A small, stocky owl, size of Collared Scops. Like the smaller Collared Owlet, has a prominent tail, yellow eyes and broad, rounded head lacking ear-tufts or obvious facial-disc. Lores and wide malar-stripe are white; rest of face and all upperparts sooty brown, narrowly and densely barred cream-buff, each bar highlighted by blackish margins. White on outer webs of short scapulars and median wing-coverts forms a pair of bands, with other wing-coverts barred rufous. Flight-feathers and tail sooty, the former notched cream-rust to white on outer webs and banded across inner webs, the latter showing five complete white bars and a white fringe. Below, a large, white patch on lower throat; chin and breast as upperparts; flanks boldly striped rufous-brown; belly to lower tail-coverts plain white. Fully feathered tarsi are pale brown. Sexes apparently similar; the local juvenile is undescribed.

Bare-part colours. (Adult) iris bright yellow; bill greenish to olive-yellow, bluish at base, paler yellowish at tip; toes greenish yellow through sparse white bristles that cover their whole length (BMNH, Robinson and Kloss 1921–24).

Size (mm). (Skin: 1 female; adult): wing 147; tail 78; bill from cere 14.8; tarsus not measured (BMNH).

Weight. No data.

DISTRIBUTION. Historical summary: *Chu*. An H.M. Smith specimen listed by Riley (1938) from Khao Luang, Nakhon Si Thammarat, is probably from SW Thailand as the collector appears to have been in Prachuap Khiri Khan province over the period in question.

GEOGRAPHICAL VARIATION. Subspecies *bruegeli* Parrot 1907 (TL Ban Sam Kok, central Thailand), of Tenasserim east to Laos and Cambodia.

STATUS AND POPULATION. A presumed local resident. Known from five birds collected at Ban Map Ammarit, latitude 10°52′N, during October–January 1915/16 and a recent sighting in Tha Sae district, both lowland Chumphon (Baker 1919–20, BMNH, P.D. Round). One of a suite of non-forest species believed likely to spread further into the Peninsula.

HABITATS AND ECOLOGY. In forests opened by logging and among scattered trees and bamboos of

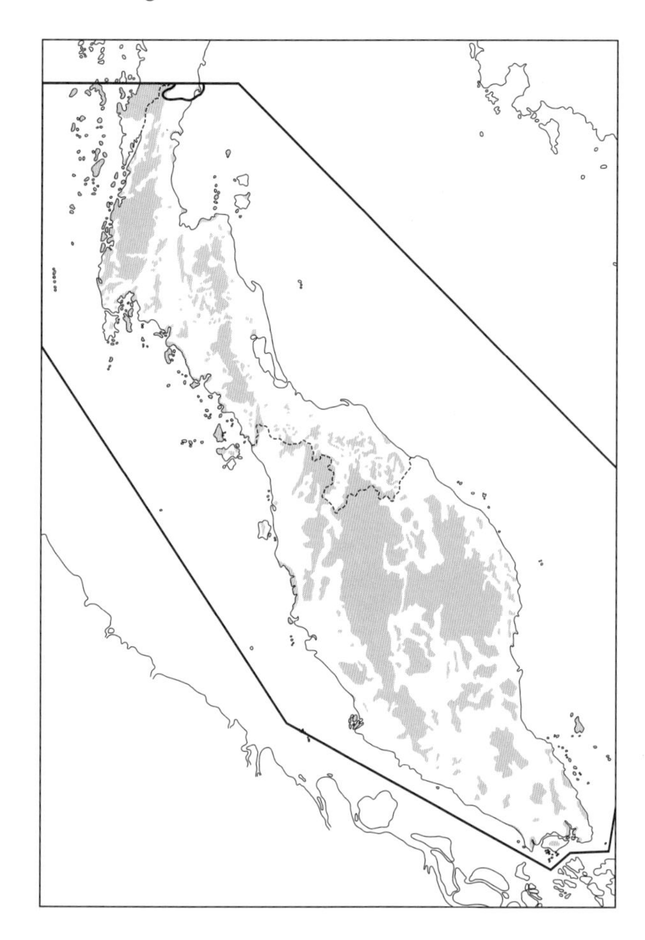

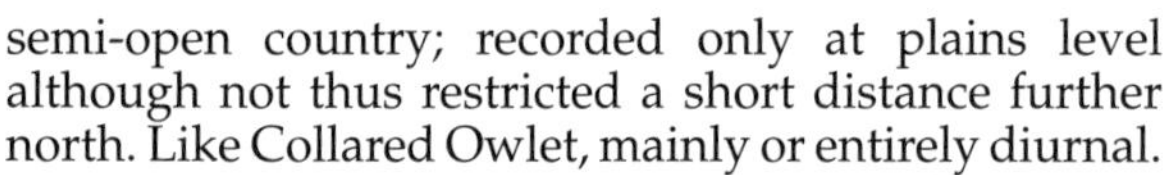
semi-open country; recorded only at plains level although not thus restricted a short distance further north. Like Collared Owlet, mainly or entirely diurnal.

FORAGING AND FOOD. No information.

SOCIAL ORGANIZATION. No information.

MOVEMENTS. None recorded.

SURVIVAL. No information.

SOCIAL INTERACTIONS. No information.

Asian Barred Owlet

VOICE. Loud calls: (1) a long trill that declines in pitch while increasing in volume; (2) mellow, widely spaced *poop* notes giving way to a long series of two-note squawks rising in pitch and volume, and abruptly terminated (Boonsong and Round 1991). The potentially confusable rising call of Moustached Hawk Cuckoo is whistled, not a squawk.

BREEDING. Not recorded.

MOULT. A January adult showed none (BMNH).

CONSERVATION. No issues identified.

Brown Boobook; Nok Khao Yieo (Thai); Burung Hantu Betemak (Malay)

Ninox scutulata (Raffles) 1822, *Transactions of the Linnean Society* 13(2): 280. TL Sumatra.
Plate 54

GROUP RELATIONS. Apparently free-standing.

GLOBAL RANGE. Other than Pakistan (Roberts 1991), the Indian subcontinent, Sri Lanka and Bay of Bengal islands; extreme SE Pacific Russia from S Amurland, Japan, Korea, China east of a line Heilongjiang–Yunnan including Taiwan and Hainan; and SE Asia to the Greater Sunda islands, Bali and the Philippines. Northern populations migrate, wintering through the eastern tropical breeding-range and beyond, to the Moluccas and Lesser Sunda islands as far as Wetar. Vagrant in NW Australia.

IDENTIFICATION/DESCRIPTION. About twice the bulk of Collared Scops Owl. Head without ear-tufts or well-defined facial-disc. Proportionately large, brilliant yellow eyes contrast with generally dark brown head, including face, set off by white immediately above the bill. Crown slightly darker than upper body in some residents, slightly greyer in some migrants (Robinson 1917), but differences are subtle, apply only in series, and are not detectable in the field. Remaining upperparts dark brown, with large white spots on the scapulars and inner secondaries, and prominent tail evenly dark-barred on both surfaces (four bars exposed dorsally). Below, chin and lower tail-coverts white, rest of underparts only slightly paler brown than the back, feathers margined white to buff-white, more widely in migrants, forming clear streaks throughout; less so in residents whose breast shows more solidly brown. Legs mottled dark brown and orange-buff. Wings relatively long: tip P7 or 7–8 in residents, mostly P8 in migrants, but with some population overlap. The sexes are similar; local juvenile undescribed.

Bare-part colours. (Adult) iris bright yellow; cere and bill greenish horn, blacker towards tip; toes and exposed extremity of tarsus yellow, rest of foot feathered.

Size (mm). Residents (live and skins: 19 adults, most not sexed): wing 176–202; tail 103–122; bill from cere 12.8–14.7; tarsus 22.6–26.2. Migrants (live and skins: 15 adults, most not sexed): wing 214–225; tail 111–127; bill from cere 12.8–15.2; tarsus 23.2–30.5 (UMBRP, ZDUM, ZRCNUS).

Weight (g). Residents, 145.5–172.4 (n=5); an arriving autumn migrant, 187.1 (UMBRP).

DISTRIBUTION. Historical summary: (residents) all divisions except *Pak, Chu, Nak, Pht, Son, Sat, Pra,* with additional island records from Lanta, the Langkawi group (Langkawi, Langgun) and Penang off the W coast; and Ubin, Singapore; (migrants) *Ran, Kra, Tra, Ked, Pek, Phg, Sel, Sin,* including on the Surin islands, Phiphi, Lanta (wintering), Libong, the Langkawi group (Dayang Bunting) and Jarak off the W coast; and Seletar and Sentosa, Singapore.

GEOGRAPHICAL VARIATION. Residents are nominate *scutulata,* of SW Thailand to Sumatra (Dickinson 1975); migrants have not definitely been identified. Birds of N tropical as well as Palaearctic origin are claimed, but this is unconfirmed (Chasen 1939, Gibson-Hill 1949b).

STATUS AND POPULATION. Resident and a non-breeding visitor and passage migrant; regular and more or less common overall, but little is known about winterers.

HABITATS AND ECOLOGY. Residents occupy the edge and interior mid-stratum to canopy of inland

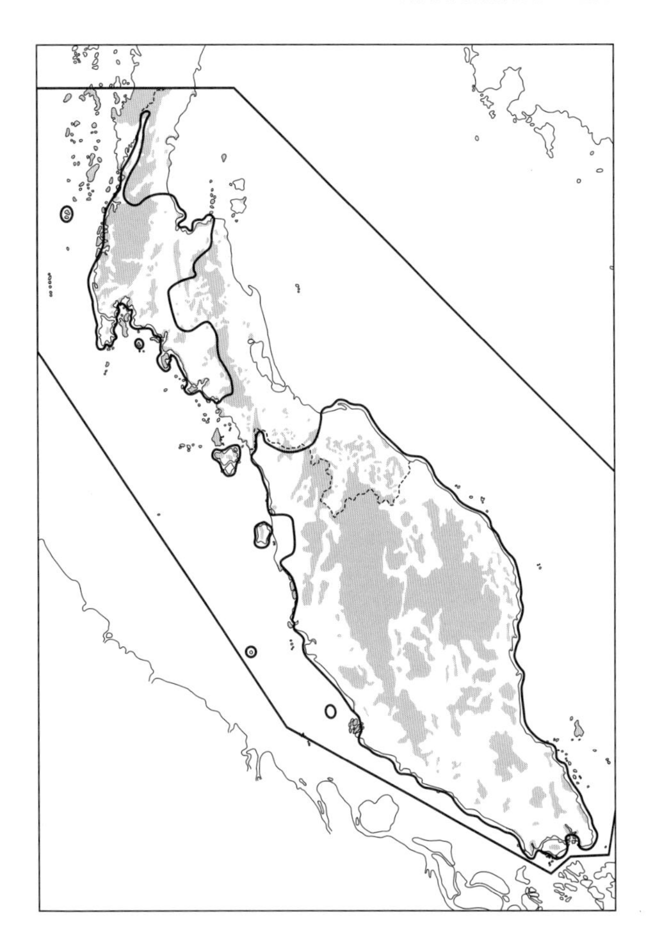

forest, including peatswamp forest, mature and regenerating after disturbance, also the landward edge of mangroves; less often, tall secondary-growth, and occasionally parkland and wooded gardens – on evidence of regular vocalizing, more or less strictly at plains level. Except for a bird at the Gap on 11 August, the very few records of song from above the steepland boundary (on the Main Range in Kelantan and Pahang) have been at likely passage dates (mid September, early April), and daytime records of birds in slope forest (up to 1500 m) are winter-dated (late October–March) (ENGGANG-1, -2, -3, MBR 1984–85). All are assumed to have been of migrants, at inhabited localities such as Genting Highlands perhaps attracted to lights that draw in large numbers of forest insects. Migrants also winter in the lowlands, including in secondary-growth, down to sea-level.

FORAGING AND FOOD. Moths and beetles identified in stomach contents (Hume and Davison 1878). A bird in the Kuala Lompat clearing, Krau wildlife reserve, hunted insects attracted to an illuminated white wall by waiting on a nearby service-wire between fast, agile sallies that took prey both in flight and off surfaces. At Khao Yai national park, E-central Thailand, Brown Boobooks chased fast-flying molossid bats as they emerged from a roost (BBCB-7)

SOCIAL ORGANIZATION. Calling through most of the year (June–July are the only silent months) implies residents defend a permanent territory. Callers are drawn quickly to play-back of tape-recorded song, reacting in the daytime as well as after dark.

MOVEMENTS. From night-time interceptions off-shore (at Melaka Straits lighthouses One-Fathom Bank and Undan, and on rigs or ships in the Terengganu oil-field), plus occurrence in unlikely habitat on small islands, extreme autumn migration dates are 2 October and 19 December. In spring, the only date on record is 5 March, from Jarak island. Autumn sightings off Terengganu imply direct crossings of the Gulf of Thailand (BMP5, MBR 1982–83, 1986–87, SINGAV-1, -6, ZRCNUS).

SURVIVAL. No information.

SOCIAL INTERACTIONS. No information.

VOICE. The only call identified is a light, melodious but unvarying disyllable, *whu-ep*, with the second note higher; repeated in lengthy bouts at a rate of about seven calls per ten seconds (BMP5).

BREEDING

Nest. Only two described: in holes (one commandeered from nesting Dollarbirds, who themselves would have taken it from a woodpecker or barbet), 10 m up tall mangrove trees, *Sonneratia* sp. One nest-chamber was 30 cm below the lip of the entrance, unlined, with eggs laid directly onto rotted wood-fragments.

Eggs and brood. Egg plain white, slightly glossed. Size (mm): 37.2 × 31.3 (n=1). One full (incubated) clutch of two eggs, but broods of 1–3 fledglings on record.

Cycle. No information.

Seasonality. In Malaysia and Singapore: laying in late March, a chick in early May and fledglings on 24 June (Edgar 1933, MBR 1986–87).

MOULT. Only single-locus moult of primaries recorded, but pattern of replacement uncertain. Among 26 residents from Phuket to Singapore, covering all months except May and June, five showed active wing-moult in late March (P1–2) and July–mid September (P8–9), with last pre-starters and earliest completions overlapping in July. Migrants arrive either completely fresh or with P1–4 or 5 a shade less worn that the outer hand, signifying suspended moult or an unusual wear-pattern. No new activity reported through the rest of the winter (BMNH, UMBRP, ZRCNUS).

CONSERVATION. The range of habitats occupied does not include clean agriculture, and abundance of residents is so obviously skewed to original, plains-level forest that this population must be considered under significant threat from habitat-loss.

Short-eared Owl; Nok Khao Meow Huu San (Thai); Burung Hantu Tuli (Malay)

Asio flammeus (Pontoppidan) 1763, *Den danske Atlas eller Konge-riget Dannemark* 1: 617. TL Sweden.
Plate 54

GROUP RELATIONS. Free-standing.

GLOBAL RANGE. Breeds at temperate to low-arctic latitudes in N and S America, Iceland, and across Eurasia to Ussuriland and Sakhalin, south to the N Mediterranean and Caspian, N Kazakhstan, N Mongolia and far-N China (Nei Mongol); with tropical outliers in the W Indies, N Andes, and Pacific (Pohnpei, Hawaii, Galapagos). Northern populations migrate or are eruptive, reaching Mexico; N and NE Africa; SW and S Asia as far as Sri Lanka; Japan and S China; and SE Asia as far as the Peninsula, NW Borneo (Kidd 1978) and the Philippines. Vagrant in the Java Sea (Kangean islands) and W-central Pacific.

IDENTIFICATION/DESCRIPTION. Short, upright ear-tufts are inconspicuous in the field. Slightly larger than a Barn Owl. The only medium-sized owl active diurnally, and in open, treeless habitats, loafing and roosting on the ground. Full facial-disc greyish buff with fine, dark marginal ruff, dark periocular smudge around pale eye, and brow white back from sides of bill. The rest of the body tawny-yellow, rufescent above, whiter below; head and underparts to belly prominently streaked black, remaining upperparts including wing-coverts streaked and mottled black. Central tail-feathers (T1–2) black, tipped and laterally toothed pale tawny-yellow, each pale mark enclosing a dark spot; others pale tawny-yellow with black bars. In flight, long wings show buff-white below, rufous-tawny above, with black tip and carpal-patch visible on both surfaces.

Bare-part colours. (Adult) iris clear yellow, eyelids black; bill slaty black; exposed toe-tip dark yellow-grey, rest of foot feathered (ZRCNUS).

Size (mm). (Skins: 4 adults, none reliably sexed): wing 306, 307, 318, 322; tail 136–149; bill from cere 16.7–17.1; tarsus not measured (BMNH, ZRCNUS).

Weight. No data.

DISTRIBUTION. Historical summary: *Sel*, *Sin*, and on Langkawi island (*Ked*).

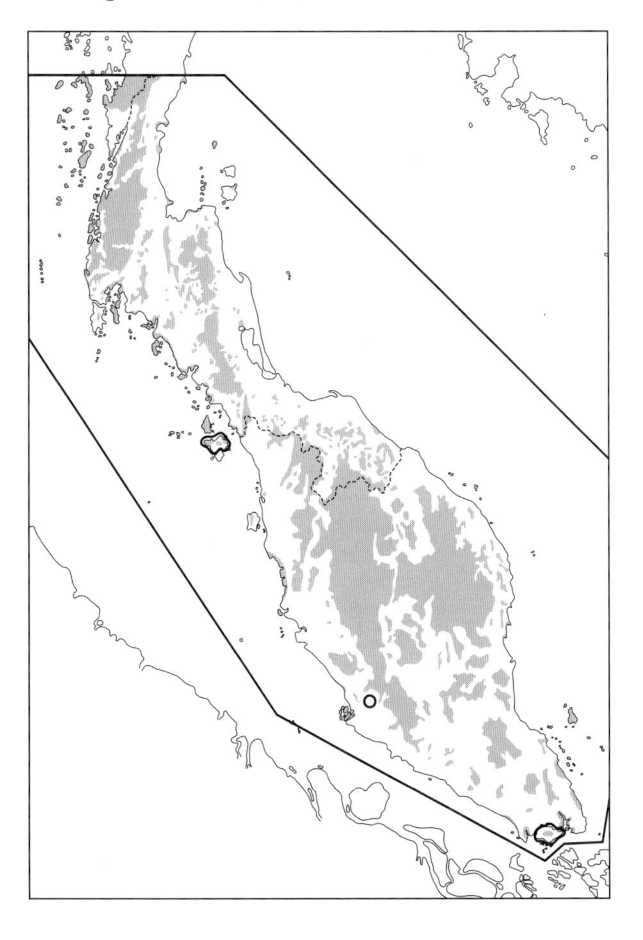

GEOGRAPHICAL VARIATION. Nominate *flammeus*, of the Holarctic range.

STATUS AND POPULATION. A non-breeding visitor, local and rare (only just beyond vagrant status): recorded in the winters 1900/01, 1929/30, 1940/41, 1967/68, 1968/69, 1987/88 and 1992/93, mostly on well-monitored Singapore island.

HABITATS AND ECOLOGY. Circumstances of early records are lost. Since 1967, sites have included an earth road through newly planted rubber, reedbeds on open dredge-mine land, and sparsely vegetated to bare sandfill on the Changi and Tuas coasts of Singapore (BIRDLINE-8, BMP5, SINGAV-2). One of two on an evening flight across reedbeds at Sungai Way, Selangor, passed low over a Cattle Egret roost, immediately arousing a pack of about 40 egrets that forced it up some 50 m before it escaped (BR 1969).

FORAGING AND FOOD. No information.

SOCIAL ORGANIZATION. Mostly loners; on the one occasion, two together.

MOVEMENTS. Recorded in all months between 30 November–13 March, with most reports in January (BIRDLINE-8, Chasen and Kloss 1931, ZRCNUS).

SURVIVAL. No information.

SOCIAL INTERACTIONS. No information.

VOICE. Not recorded; vocal apparently only in breeding areas.

BREEDING. No population.

MOULT. November and January-dated adults showed none (ZRCNUS).

CONSERVATION. No issues.

Family TYTONIDAE

Barn and bay owls: two species

Barn Owl; Nok Sehk Khao (Thai); Burung Pungguk Jelapang (Malay)

Tyto alba (Scopoli) 1769, *Annus 1, Historico-Naturalis*: 21. TL Friuli, N Italy.
Plate 54

GROUP RELATIONS. Feather-pattern details, especially of the upperparts, indicate Wallacean endemic *T. rosenbergii* (Sulawesi Owl) is an *alba* relative. Despite the size-difference, they may form a superspecies.

GLOBAL RANGE. From S- to mid-temperate N America and Atlantic islands; Africa and the Malagasy region; temperate-zone Europe to SW Asia; the Indian subcontinent, Sri Lanka and the Andaman islands; Yunnan (vagrant) (Cheng 1987); SE Asia to

Sumatra, Java and Bali; the Lesser Sunda islands, Australia and S New Guinea; and the tropical Pacific east to central Polynesia. Introduced in Hawaii and, recently, parts of NW Borneo.

IDENTIFICATION/DESCRIPTION. A medium-sized owl with thin-looking (short-feathered) legs and ventrally complete ruff round a more or less circular facial-disc. Disc white, contrasting with blackish eye and smoky brown pre- or periocular smudge. Upperparts honey-buff, heavily mottled pale grey; entire underparts including underwing white, most females with a yellow-buff wash across the breast. Both sexes are lightly but distinctly black-dotted below, dots largest on breast, and black-and-white spotted above. Juveniles resemble adults.

Bare-part colours. (Adult) iris black-brown; bill flesh-white; feet dull horn-pink, white tarsal feathering short and bristly, exposing skin colour.

Size (mm). (Live and skins: 14 males, 27 females; adult, sexed by breast colour): wing 285–315 (mean 299) and 280–325 (mean 300); tail 119–134 (sexes combined); bill from cere 20.5–23.3 (sexes combined); tarsus 66.8–71.8 (sexes combined); mid-toe plus claw 59.0–68.1 (sexes combined) (UMBRP, ZDUM, ZRC-NUS).

Weight (g). Adult males, (480) 510–650 (mean 555, n=13); adult females, (500) 530–690 (mean 612, n=26) (A.C. Sebastian). Chicks hatch at mean 18.5 and reach an asymptote slightly above mean adult weight before fledging (Lenton 1984).

DISTRIBUTION. Only a few reports from north of Malaysia. Historical summary: *Sur, Pht, Sat, Pes, Ked, Kel, Tru, Pra, Pek, Phg, Sel, Neg, Mel, Joh, Sin,* with additional island records from Penang and Ketam (Kelang estuary) off the W coast; and Sentosa, Singapore.

GEOGRAPHICAL VARIATION. Size and density of dots on the breast and size of the dark spot at the tip of primary six align the Malaysian breeding population with heavily marked S-hemisphere *javanica* Gmelin 1788 (TL Java) rather than continental populations (Lenton 1985).

STATUS AND POPULATION. Formerly vagrant, now resident, regular and common north to at least the Malaysian/Thai border. Presumed wanderers dated 1881 (Perak) and 1889, 1925 and 1931 (Singapore island) (BMNH, Kelham 1881–83, Lenton 1985) formed the whole record until the late 1960s when one or more groups colonized the SW lowlands, probably from southern Sumatra where large agricultural settlement schemes were later found to hold Barn Owls (Holmes 1977).

Discovered on a Johor oil-palm estate in October 1968, one of two pairs occupying the loft-spaces of adjacent bungalows fledged the first known brood of two young in April or May 1969 (BR 1969). In February 1970 a military aircraft struck a Barn Owl

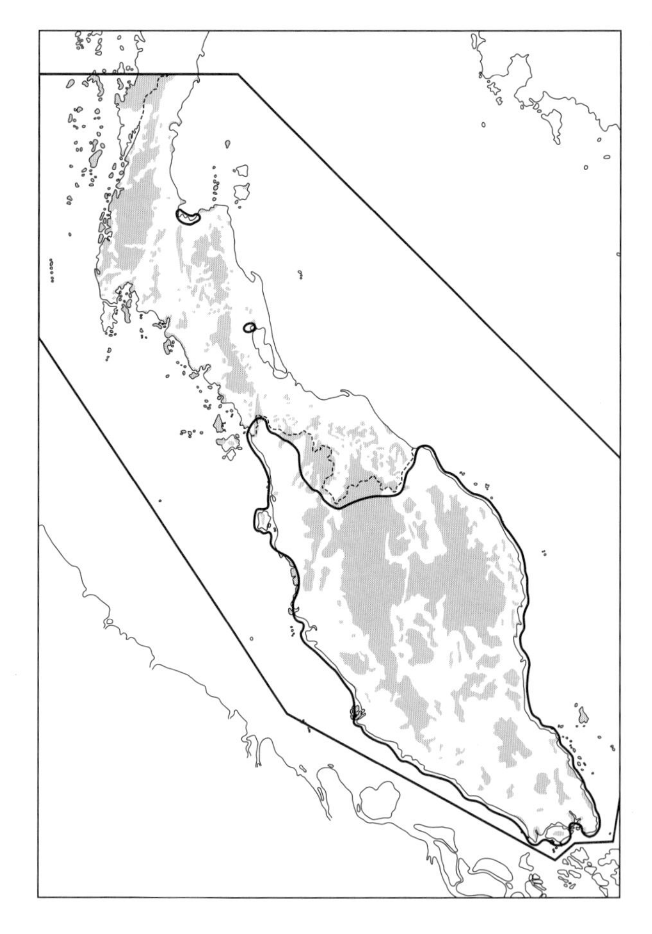

over Changi airbase, Singapore, and in June that year a brood of six young was taken from a rice-barn at Tanjung Karang, NW Selangor. Twelve months on, a bird was ringed and released on Penang island and in December 1973 five were seen in Satul paddy-fields at close to 7°N (B.D. Bond, Holmes and Wells 1975). The western bias of many more nests and roost-sites reported during 1976–77, densest between Johor and Selangor, makes it likely all of these early occurrences were part of a single colonizing sweep north along the coastal plain. Over the same period, a few birds also appeared in S Kelantan and Terengganu. Partly through management of nest-sites, they have since spread more or less throughout the settled lowlands of Malaysia, as of the 1980s with good numbers also in Singapore. North of the border, however, the only additional records have been of a bird at Thalae Noi in December 1978 and two in the Bandon bay mangrove-zone in October 1986 (Anonymous 1981, MBR 1982–83, 1986–87, Swennen *et al.* 1986).

HABITATS AND ECOLOGY. Barn Owls live predominantly in non-natural habitats, mostly paddy-land and oil-palm plantations. Early spread involved both but is best connected with the rise of oil-palm *Elaeis guineensis* as a plantation crop in the south, supplying a settlement-habitat where immigrants from Indonesia would not have found one before the 1960s. Also used are the degraded to cleared landward edge of mangrove forest, rough grassland (further bird-strikes over Changi airfield: MBR 1984–85), coconut plantings (favoured roost habitat for birds without access to a nest-cavity) and villages and towns (including Singapore city).

Among over two thousand nests examined, less than 20 have been in a natural tree- or rock-cavity (BR 1976–77, Duckett 1991, K. Kumar). Most of the initial spread appears to have been supported by breeding in roof-spaces, at typically only one pair per structure. Suitable buildings with ceilings are at a premium in most rural landscapes, and from the size of regular outside gatherings (up to 37 birds counted at one on the Carey island estates, Selangor), by the late 1970s some W-coast populations had already outstripped their local supply (Lenton 1980). To lift this constraint on rate of increase and attainable density in palm crops, pole-mounted nest-boxes were introduced. Over three trial years from 1976–77, only those boxes set next to already-occupied buildings were accepted. Subsequently, others far out in croplands became just as attractive, it was guessed, to colonists themselves raised as nestlings in the early favoured boxes. Fresh trials in the late 1980s (Duckett 1991), and one begun in 1989 on NW Selangor paddyland, showed no such delay, with first boxes occupied in less than one month, regardless of position relative to buildings. On paddyland, it was possible to show that some of the pioneers were indeed birds that had fledged from established box-schemes elsewhere in the area; also that in making their move they had switched crops, from oil-palm to rice.

As of the 1990s, the box-nesting habit has spread through most of Malaysia, with occupation delays still evident only in the far NW (Kedah and Perlis). In mid 1994, the total number of boxes up in agricultural crops in Malaysia was estimated at around 9000, including 1300 in paddyland (J.E. Duckett, Ministry of Agriculture). At a rough average 40 percent occupancy during main breeding months (commonly up to 80 percent in oil-palm), probably most of the Malaysian Barn Owl population is now box bred.

Non-breeding birds, and breeding males, day-roost in palm-crowns, buildings and spare boxes, and in a few instances (in Pahang, Kelantan and Perlis) have been found in natural caves (BR 1976–77, MBR 1982–83).

FORAGING AND FOOD. A party of 15–20 birds quartering at dusk over a palm-estate burn-off showed unusual behaviour. Hunting in the Peninsula is normally from a perch. Favoured perches are typically 3–5 m up, on a pole-top or lower frond beneath an often-continuous oil-palm canopy, wherever there is open access to the ground below. In young palm plantings, before this under canopy space develops, birds often wait near or actually on the ground for prey crossing trackways (Lenton 1984a). Radio-tagged adults were on the wing between hunting perches for not more than three percent of the night.

Links with oil-palm and irrigated paddy are via the dense populations of rats these crops support, year-round. Ninety-eight and 99.4 percent of some 3500 and 22,500 prey items recovered from oral pellets collected at nest- and roost-sites in oil-palm habitat were from rodents, including seven *Rattus* species taken more or less in order of availability, hence heavily dominated by Malaysian Wood Rat *R. tiomanicus*. The latter is displaced by Ricefield Rat *R. argentiventer* in paddyland pellets. Body weights, estimated from bone measurements, were in the same range and frequency as obtained by separate live-trapping of rats in owl habitat, implying prey are taken opportunistically rather than selected by size (but to an upper limit of around 220 g). Males servicing a mate and brood commonly eat the head of a rat and deliver only the decapitated body, which is then more easily accessed by chicks learning to feed independently. Over 60 percent of pellets collected from nests lacked skull remains (Lenton 1984a, Medway and Yong 1970, Smal 1989).

The small balance of non-rodent items in pellet samples included mainly shrews, a few large insects, anurans and birds, and one bat *Scotophilus kuhlii* probably taken in a roof-space (Lenton 1984a). On the other hand, Barn Owls have twice been mist-netted at a back-mangrove shorebird roost, one of them virtually on top of an already-netted Mongolian Plover, which suggests some individuals could have other specializations. Size and powerful feet in this subspecies may be adaptations for the taking of relatively large prey.

SOCIAL ORGANIZATION. Pairs have nested successfully in boxes only 50–60 m apart, and the few chase-flights witnessed imply only a small space around the nest itself is actually defended (although even a large roof-space, where continuous, never seems to hold more than one breeding pair).

Interactions among foragers are less known but casual observations show still-hunters tolerate other individuals close by, and there are records of communal loafing at night. On a Selangor oil-palm plantation, radio-tagged adults foraged individually over 20–239 ha (Lenton 1984a). Only a fraction of total space was used per night but with no evidence even of this being exclusive. Actual numbers foraging per unit area of habitat have never been measured but, even with early emigration, the production of some box-schemes (in 1000 ha of E Negeri Sembilan oil-palm, over 3000 young fledged by up to 139 pairs during only 27 months, with some breeding in every month of that period: Duckett 1991) suggests these could be high.

A female found dead on a nest in a bungalow chimney on a Selangor plantation had been ringed as a breeder on the same nest five years previously, showing fidelity to a successful site. Among 51 adults (including 44 females) ringed at nest-boxes on paddyland in NW Selangor and retrapped while day-roosting 9–24 months later, 45 percent of females were in the same box and 55 percent had changed, but over distances of not more than 1 km. Two of those faithful to boxes and retrapped twice or more were with their original mates, but most of the small sample of males caught shifted, in one case at only one day's interval from a female with five chicks to another box with another female 700 m away, then ten months later back with the first female in the original box. The second female may not have bred, but another paddyland male trapped with separate females ran a brood of six and clutch of eight concurrently in nest-boxes also 700 m apart. Another unlikely pair, breeding then retrapped together ten months later, were siblings still in the box of their birth (A.C. Sebastian).

MOVEMENTS. Forty-nine distant recoveries of ringed birds included 28 (57 percent) at 2–15 km, 13 (26 percent) at 16–30 km, four (8 percent) at 31–100 km and four over 100 km from site of ringing; maximum 223 km and including one sea-crossing from Negeri Sembilan to Riau, E Sumatra. All were ringed as chicks aged 3–5 weeks, but age correlates only weakly with distance; indeed, the two longest journeys were made by individuals only three and five months old. Given that pioneer colonizers of new nest-box schemes appear mainly to be young birds, perhaps most dispersal occurs in the first few months of life. No breeding-age bird in possession of a nest-box has been retrapped more than 2 km distant.

SURVIVAL. The longest recovery-interval is 96 months, a bird ringed as a nestling on a N Selangor oil-palm estate (A. Jeyarajasingam). Recovery of ringed birds of known age suggests mortality risk is age-related. Twenty-five percent of those 12-plus months old (n=16) were dead, the rest well and in possession of nest-boxes. At 7–11 months old (n=8), 50 percent were dead or rescued from traps (mostly waterfowl nets set in paddyland) that would certainly have killed. At 1–6 months old (n=17), all were dead or rescued from traps. One such released youngster reappeared eight months later, as a breeder 16 km away. In order of incidence, causes of death were: electrocution on uninsulated power-wires, nets, drowning, disablement (several with no visible injury but unable to move), and road-kill and other collisions.

SOCIAL INTERACTIONS. The only defensive actions recorded around the nest-site are brief chase-flights, and vocalizing by the incumbent male. Pairs copulating at the nest are mostly silent, but very noisy if on an outside perch. When mounted, the male grips the female's rump in his feet and crown feathers in his bill, drawing her head back (Lenton 1984).

VOICE. Before mating, pair-members exchange a short, soft *squeark*, repeated about six times in bouts of 10–15 seconds. During copulation, this changes to a fast chattering by the male and long, hoarse screeches by the female. Similar screeches are given by males chasing off intruders, but away from the area of the nest Barn Owls are silent. Nestlings give the defensive rasping hiss from week two but do not bill-snap until near fully grown, in week seven (S. Karuppiah).

BREEDING

Nest. Predominantly in roof-spaces accessed via open eaves; occasionally on secluded external ledges (typically where access to an enclosed space has been blocked off) and, now, widely in pole-mounted wooden nest-boxes. Choice of a natural tree-hole is rare and the few cave-sites identified have only been shown to be roosts. No nest is built and eggs are laid on, at most, a carpet of pellets, bones and feathers.

Eggs and brood. Eggs are plain, glossless white. Shape near-spherical. Size (mm): 45.5–39.0 × 34.5–31.4 (mean 41.9 × 33.1, n=146); mean fresh weight 26.1 g. Discounting dead eggs accumulated from past layings, clutch varies in the range 3–9 (mean 6.6, n=36). Eggs are laid at 2–3 day intervals and incubated from egg one, with correspondingly staggered hatching (mean development period 32.6 days). Among clutches producing at least one chick, hatching success varied from 30 to 100 percent, yielding broods of 1–9 chicks (mean 4.6 in oil-palm, 3.5 in paddyland), in oil-palm an average four (maximum seven) fledging (Lenton 1984, UMBRP). Chicks leave the nest at 59–65 days old but are fed by parents for up to three more weeks, and day-roost at or near the nest during this period.

In both oil-palm and paddyland habitats, two successive broods are regular and a third not unusual.

Cycle. Copulations continue through incubation into the nestling phase, at 7–8 per night during egg-laying and, later, whenever the male delivers food. Incubation is by the female and she leaves the nest only briefly until chicks are near half-grown. During that period all food is brought to the nest by the male. Thereafter, from about the point when the brood reaches its peak phase of demand, both parents hunt.

At the beginning-stages of nest-box usage in Selangor paddyland, most new colonists hatched and reared consistently smaller broods than pairs established in nearby roof-spaces. In identical hunting and nest-climate conditions, many of their embryos died just before hatching. Boxes suffered more frequent disturbance than roof-spaces, but tended towards increased success in later years, which hints at the importance of parental age and experience.

An unknown proportion of females starts laying at less than one year old, including three ringed birds trapped in paddyland nest-boxes with eggs or chicks that fixed a start at eight, eight and eleven months.

Seasonality. Egg-laying in all months, but with surges during July–September and December–February, and less common third clutches as of March. In NW Selangor paddyland, peaks of egg-laying shift with the harvest season (staggered by latitude), when rats are likely to be easier to reach. Successive clutches are often laid hard on the departure of young from the nest, with a few records of brief overlap (Lenton 1984, 1984a, UMBRP).

MOULT. Post-juvenile wing- and tail-moult has been studied in captives. As of age 41–44 weeks, primaries are replaced in regular, uninterrupted ascendant and descendant order from P6; secondaries irregularly from S2 and S12; tail irregularly, mostly from T1. Two females completed in 294 days (one moving directly into a second wing-moult); two males in 166 and 330-plus days. Adult patterns are unknown but a 22-month collection of flight-feathers shed at nests and roost-sites showed some moult in all months except November, with most during March–July, i.e., in general inverse relation to breeding activity (Lenton 1984a).

CONSERVATION. An impressive enough reduction in crop damage and saving on chemical pesticides has followed nest-box trials in both oil-palm and paddy that the future of what started as a natural invasion ought to be assured. It will still depend on land managers dedicated to maintaining and replacing nest-boxes, particularly during palm re-planting operations. A serious though probably now receding risk to settled breeders is from 'second-generation' anticoagulant rodenticides acting as secondary poisons (Duckett 1984, Mohd Basri Wahid and Abdul Halim Hassan 1985). These have been linked to incidents of local population collapse.

Oriental Bay Owl; Nok Sehk Daeng (Thai); Burung Pungguk Api (Malay)

Phodilus badius (Horsfield) 1821, *Transactions of the Linnean Society* 13(1): 139. TL Java.

Plate 54

GROUP RELATIONS. Free-standing. Prigogine (1973) concludes *badius* and *P. prigoginei* (Congo Bay Owl) are too different to be congeneric.

GEOGRAPHICAL RANGE. The Himalayan foothills east from Nepal, NE and SW extremes of the Indian subcontinent, and Sri Lanka; S Yunnan, Guangxi and Hainan; and SE Asia to the Greater Sunda islands, Bali and (one record) Samar (Philippines).

IDENTIFICATION/DESCRIPTION. About half the mass of Barn Owl, but chunky. Burnished coppery pink upperparts, so impressive in the hand, cannot be appreciated by flashlight but pink-buff underparts and proportionately huge black eyes set in a milk-white face resemble no other forest owl. The facial-disc, outlined by a ventrally complete, brown ruff, is more convincingly mammal-like than in Barn Owl, with enlarged ventral ruff-feathers erectable to form a 'jaw' below the bill; top corners rounded out as viverrid or mustelid carnivore 'ears'; and a broad wedge of pinkish feathering from forecrown to bill, counter-shaded brown laterally, simulating a muzzle. The back of the nape carries a small, central patch of whitish feathers each with a black dot, in some instances crudely resembling a pair of close-set eyes (see below).

Sexes are alike and, from the evidence of a single colour photograph of captives, juveniles resemble adults.

Bare-part colours. (Adult) iris deep blackish brown, eyelids white; bill ivory-white; feet pale pink-grey, fully buff-white feathered to the base of the toes.

Size (mm). (Live and skins: 13 adults, most not sexed): wing 188–211 (no definite female below 199); tail 78–90; bill from cere 20.5–23.3; tarsus 42.6–49.9; longest (second) toe plus claw 49.5–52.1 (BMNH, UMBRP, ZDUM, ZRCNUS).

Weight (g). Adults, 255–308 (n=5, the heaviest a male) (UMBRP).

DISTRIBUTION. Historical summary: *Chu, Pha, Nak, Phu, Kra, Pht, Tra, Sat, Ked, Tru, Pra, Pek, Phg, Sel, Neg, Mel, Joh*; extinct *Sin* since the late 1920s, but with

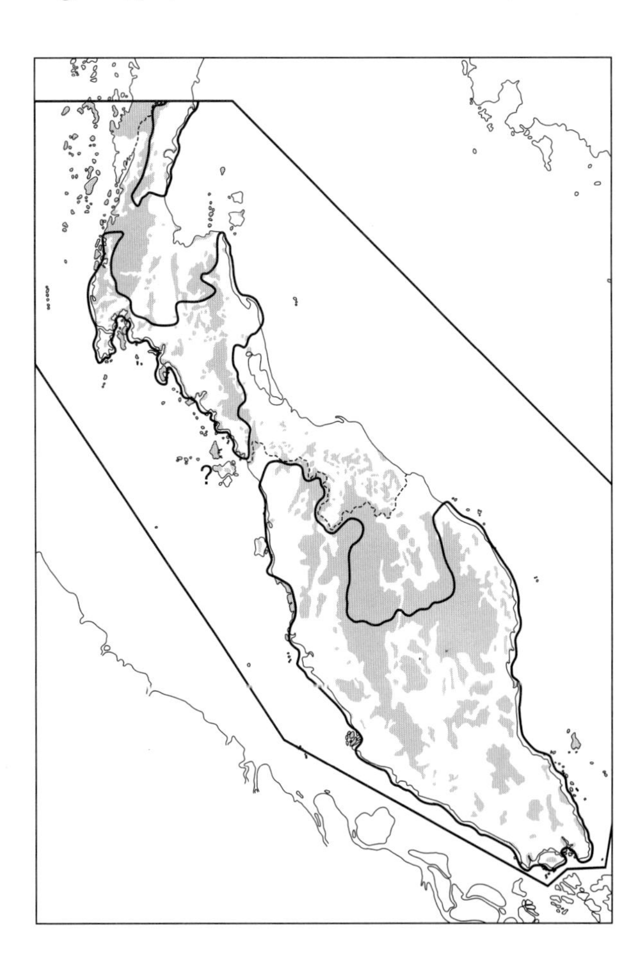

other recent island records from Lanta and (unconfirmed) Langkawi.

GEOGRAPHICAL VARIATION. Nominate *badius*, of the SE Asian range.

STATUS AND POPULATION. Resident, regular and more or less common in the south; uncommon to sparse north of Malaysia, with no reports from extensively deciduous forest habitats.

HABITATS AND ECOLOGY. Mid and lower strata of evergreen and semi-evergreen Lowland forest, including peatswamp; less often Lower Montane forest, from plains level to at least 1200 m (BMP5). Occasionally also at the edge of mangroves, in mature orchard, secondary-growth, overgrown rubber plantation, etc., sometimes far from true forest. In Negeri Sembilan, a pair laid in a pole-mounted nest-box in mature oil-palm plantation (J.E. Duckett).

FORAGING AND FOOD. Little known, but loners still-hunt in the forest under-stratum, often while clinging to a pendant vine, sapling stem or the bark of a tree-bole, on which large, strong feet allow them to sit upright with ease (Marshall 1966). Side-to-side rocking of the head may assist in location of prey. None identified, although a bird in the Endau-Rompin conservation area, Johor, took a lively interest in bats flapping in a mist-net.

SOCIAL ORGANIZATION. Solitary, but individuals call for long spells from fixed points in forest that are maintained from night to night, suggestive of advertising a territory.

MOVEMENTS. None known.

SURVIVAL. No information.

SOCIAL INTERACTIONS. Defensive *cum* threat display of an adult cornered in a nest-box included: arching the wings and rocking them forward, with carpal joint fully extended to show maximum area head-on; bending the body forward and head-lunging with bill-snapping and sudden closure of the eyes to expose startling white eyelids. Eyes were reopened as the head was withdrawn (J.E. Duckett). A more extreme behaviour (also recorded in Barn Owl), by a bird just released after ringing, included the same arched-wing stance but with rocking from side to side on stretched legs and a sudden deep bow and shaking of the head while facing more or less back between the feet. After 1–2 seconds with the nape-spot 'eyes' presented, the head was flung up and forward exposing the full disc, enormous black real eyes and open bill (Wells 1986). Unlike Barn Owl, threatened Bay Owls do not seem to hiss.

VOICE. A common call, given year-round, is a low, soft, frogmouth-like *hu-li*. The full vocalization is a much louder, strikingly musical sequence of three notes, stressed on the second, and up to four individually rising, tremulous phrases starting successively lower down the scale: *oo <u>hlii</u> hoo, hu-i-li, hu-i-li, hu-i-li, hu-i-li*. Often, only a part of this sequence is given. A bird netted for ringing gave a brief, piercing wail while in a holding-bag (BMP5).

BREEDING. One occupation of a nest-box and a report of two juveniles raised as nestlings, said to have been taken from a hollow trunk before it was bulldozed on to a fire in a Terengganu land-clearance scheme (MBR 1982-83), imply nesting in tree-holes. Nothing else recorded.

MOULT. Wing-moult pattern unknown. Adults active (P8, P3) in late July and mid September; 11 others dated August, September, November–February, April and May showed no moult (BMNH, UMBRP, ZDUM, ZRCNUS).

CONSERVATION. On evidence of advertising-calls, commonest by far in Lowland forest at plains level, and at risk if (as seems likely) this is core habitat.

Order CAPRIMULGIFORMES

Family PODARGIDAE

Frogmouths: three species

Large Frogmouth; Nok Paak Gob Yak (Thai); Burung Segan Besar (Malay)

Batrachostomus auritus (J.E. Gray) 1829, Griffith's *Animal Kingdom arranged by Baron Cuvier* 7: 114. TL Sumatra.

Plate 54

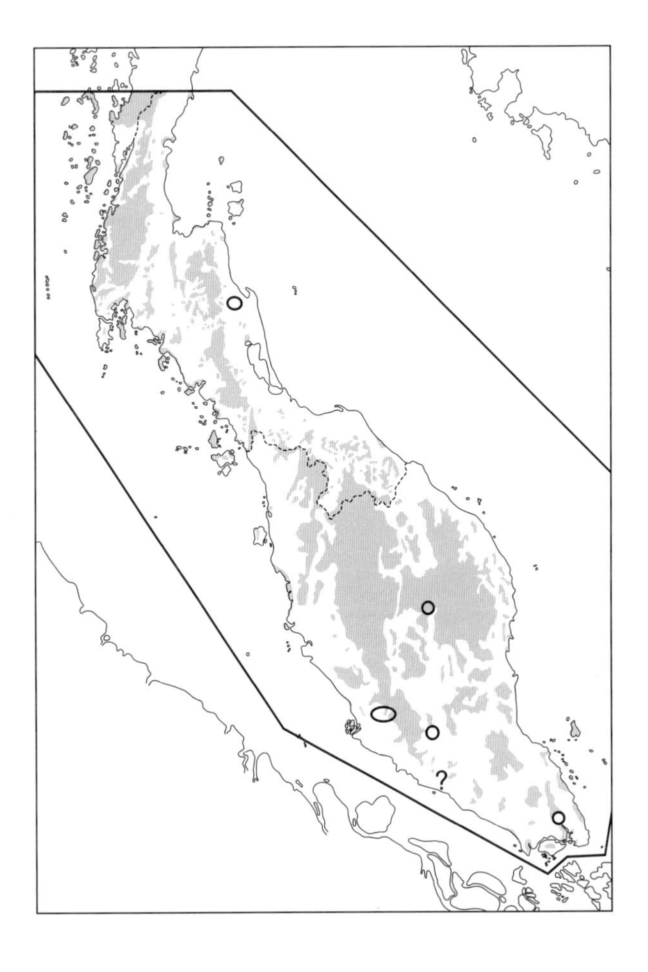

GROUP RELATIONS. Free-standing.

GLOBAL RANGE. The Peninsula, Sumatra, Borneo and Bunguran island, N Natuna group.

IDENTIFICATION/DESCRIPTION. Size of a Bay Owl; enormous in comparison with other local frogmouths. Its other prominent features are the long, narrowly barred tail, fanned when the bird becomes excited, long white wisps projecting back along the head from the angle of the mouth and side of the crown, white hind-collar, and rows of white triangular marks set in black on the wing-coverts. No morphs have been defined but individuals vary in the rufous versus vinous tone of their plumage, development of white flecking on the crown and throat, and of black apical dots on scapular feathers, and degree of contrast between light and dark tail-bars (outlined in black in all cases). Which, if any, of these differences is sexual is not known. Juvenile unknown.

Bare-part colours. (Adult) iris dull brown, apparently with a contrasting eyelid-rim; no other details available.

Size (mm). (Skins: 17 adults, none sexed): wing 247–277; tail 182–213; bill 33.0–38.1; tarsus 21.4–25.0 (BMNH).

Weight. No data.

DISTRIBUTION. Until recently, overlooked through lack of information on vocalizations. Historical summary: *Nak, Phg, Sel, Neg, ?Mel, Joh,* including no islands. The Nakhon Si Thammarat record is nineteenth-century; there are no others from Thailand.

GEOGRAPHICAL VARIATION. None recognized.

STATUS AND POPULATION. Resident, local, and sparse or uncommon. Vocalizes less often than its smaller congeners hence harder to detect, but responds to tape-recordings. Searched for with tapes extensively enough to confirm population density is naturally low, e.g., only two pairs have been found in the 1200 ha of Pasoh research forest, Negeri Sembilan, centre of the Peninsular range as presently understood.

HABITATS AND ECOLOGY. The interior canopy and mid-stratum of closed-canopy evergreen Lowland forest, from mature to regenerating after disturbance, and appearing to prefer regenerating, even second-growth areas (still in such habitat on the immediate outskirts of Kuala Lumpur). All records have been at plains level, with no known occurrence above the steepland boundary.

FORAGING AND FOOD. No information.

SOCIAL ORGANIZATION. Hardly known but repeated occurrence of a calling bird in given patches of forest, sometimes lurable to a tape-recorder, suggests territoriality. On two occasions, two adults have been found day-roosting together, including sleeping side by side in deep shade, 5 m up on a looped rattan stem (BR 1972-73, ENGGANG-1).

MOVEMENTS. None known.

SURVIVAL. No information.

SOCIAL INTERACTIONS. No additional information.

VOICE. A powerful, throbbing rattle, even-toned or with first note lower, or rising slightly over the last few notes (A.B. van den Berg). All variants are within the repertoire of a single individual.

BREEDING. No details available, but a bird reported flushed off a nest in regenerating forest near Kota Tinggi, Johor, on 27 June 1983 (MBR 1982-83).

MOULT. No data.

CONSERVATION. As a plains-level specialist, its habitat is already highly fragmented and under threat. Known from three conservation areas, the capacity of this large species to survive in isolated blocks of regenerating and old secondary forest needs study (BTW2).

Gould's Frogmouth; Nok Paak Gob Paktai (Thai); Burung Segan Bintik Mas (Malay)

Batrachostomus stellatus (Gould) 1837, *Proceedings of the Zoological Society of London* 5: 43. TL Melaka.

Plate 54

GROUP RELATIONS. Free-standing.

GLOBAL RANGE. The Peninsula, Sumatra, Borneo and intervening islands (Bangka, Bunguran).

IDENTIFICATION/DESCRIPTION. Size of a small scops owl (Reddish in the same habitat), but slenderer and longer-tailed. Black-margined white blobs along the scapulars are as in Javan Frogmouth but Gould's has an extra row across the wing-coverts. Its underparts are uniformly scallop-patterned (feathers buff-white with dark margins), without contrasting white blobs across the breast. Gould's also lacks the exaggerated wispy feathering about the head of Javan. Most individuals are either rufous-chestnut or dark mahogany (cf. Marshall 1978), but two of 12 mist-netted at Pasoh research forest, Negeri Sembilan (one retrapped repeatedly over several years), had an overall brownish grey cast to the plumage. They seem to represent an uncommon alternative morph — not identified to sex. There is no confirmed difference between the sexes, although a colour-tone difference might have been expected. The young juvenile is plain, vinous-tinted rufous below, upperparts including wing-coverts and tail rufous, feathering narrowly barred sooty black; flight-feathers dark brown with broad rufous edging along outer webs (BMNH).

Bare-part colours. (Adult) iris bronze to light yellow, eyelid-rim yellow; upper mandible light horn-brown, lower horn-yellow; feet dull, wax-yellow.

Size (mm). (Live and skins: 19 adults, most not sexed): wing 119–132; tail 113–130; bill 20.0–27.9; tarsus 13.5–15.6 (BMNH, UMBRP, ZRCNUS).

Weight (g). Adults, 43.5–60.6 (n=14) (UMBRP).

DISTRIBUTION. The mainland south from latitude approximately 9°N. Historical summary: *Sur, Kra, Pht, Sat, Tru, Pek, Phg, Sel, Neg, Joh.*

GEOGRAPHICAL VARIATION. None recognized.

STATUS AND POPULATION. Resident, regular and, at least in the south, more or less common. Twenty-six months of mist-netting in the understorey of 15 ha of the mature core of Pasoh research forest, Negeri Sembilan, caught five individuals, two retrapped up to six times each over several years, each in spaces not more than 150 m across, and others at positions suggesting probably two resident pairs.

HABITATS AND ECOLOGY. Mid to understratum levels of closed-canopy, evergreen Lowland forest, mature and well-regenerated. The highest altitude record (in Selangor) is from less than 200 m above the steepland boundary, and core habitat is strictly at plains level. Nests have been found in regenerating forest (including old secondary-growth), but the importance of mature habitat is suggested by comparative capture rates at Pasoh, where an almost equivalent period of mist-netting on 17 ha

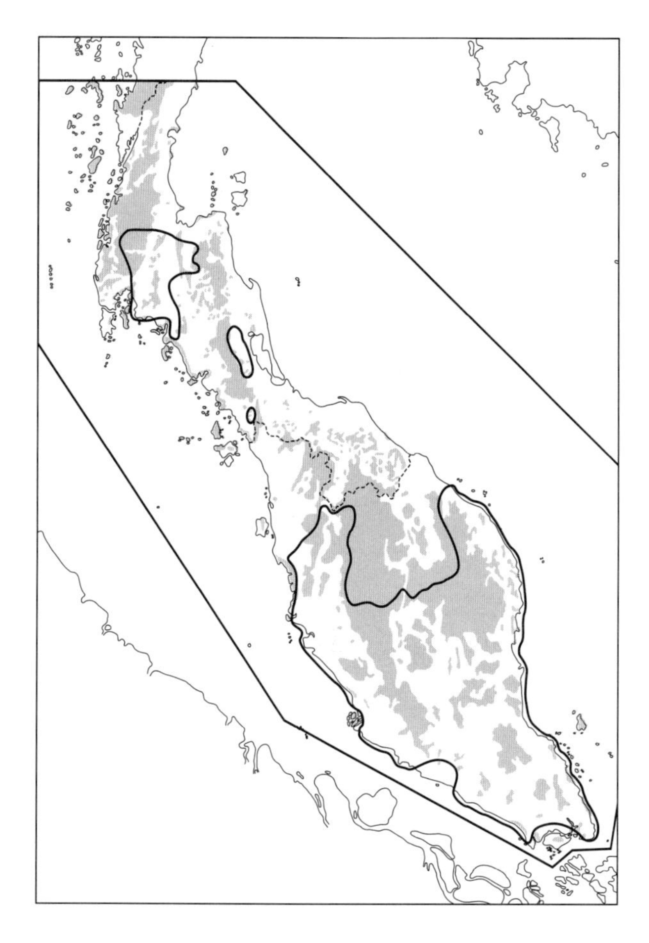

of the 20-year regenerated forest took only one bird, once.

Day-roosts perched longways on a branch.

FORAGING AND FOOD. A bird caught at night for ringing regurgitated a large orthopteran and a cicada. Food brought to a nestling included large insects (G.C. Madoc).

SOCIAL ORGANIZATION. No direct information, but capture and retrap positions of ringed birds at Pasoh suggest fairly rigid spacing between pairs.

MOVEMENTS. None known.

SURVIVAL. The longest retrap-interval is 31 months (UMBRP).

SOCIAL INTERACTIONS. No information.

VOICE. A kitten-like mew by a bird freshly released after ringing (BR 1962). In the wild, soft, trembling whistles: *twai-i-i luk* (the last syllable stepped down), *ooo-li-o*, and *teuoo-oo-li* (the last syllable stepped up), believed to be male territorial advertising-calls. Female vocalizations not identified. The hunger call of a nestling, a feeble *wiu-yiu* (G.C. Madoc, Marshall 1978, A.B. van den Berg).

BREEDING

Nest. On slender saplings in the understorey of mature, regenerating and, in one instance, secondary forest. About 40 mm across, a soft, shallow cup built exclusively of white fibre resembling silk, but which has not yet been analysed and may include plant pappus or down, bound on and round a 1–2 cm thick, horizontal lower branch, 1.5–3 m from the ground. (See plate 29 of Smythies 1960 for a Malayan example.)

Eggs and brood. Egg plain white. Size (mm): 28.2 × 19.2 (n=1). Clutch one, incubated by the parent sitting crossways on the branch, tenting nest plus egg under the lower breast feathers like a treeswift. Incubation period unknown; one fledging period 20 days (G.C Madoc).

Cycle. The chick outgrows the small nest and transfers to the branch support. One has also been found perched on a parent's back, on the ground beneath a nest-site.

Seasonality. Eggs in November and March, adults with brood-patches in November, December, January and February, and nestlings in late November (hatched 24 November), February, March, June and early August (BR 1969, G.C. Madoc, NRCS, OBCB-6, U. Treesucon).

MOULT. Sequence of primary moult not known. Birds handled in all months except April, May and October showed wing-moult only in late June (P3, P5) and early August (P4 and 10 unilateral), and suspended at P2/3 on 20 August (BMNH, UMBRP, ZRCNUS).

CONSERVATION. Another Lowland forest species not occurring outside closed-canopy cover nor much above the steepland boundary, with range already fragmented and much reduced by habitat-loss.

Javan Frogmouth; Nok Paak Gob Phan Chawaa (Thai); Burung Segan Jawa (Malay)

Batrachostomus javensis (Horsfield) 1821, *Transactions of the Linnean Society* 13(1): 141. TL Java.
Plate 54

GROUP RELATIONS. A recently discovered nest is unexpectedly different from one of nominate *javensis*, leaving open the possibility that inclusive treatment of this difficult group (BMP5, Marshall 1978) might still be up for review.

GLOBAL RANGE. Based on vocalizations and morphology, N, W and SE Thailand, and S Burma to the Greater Sunda islands; also Palawan and Culion, W Philippines (Marshall 1978).

IDENTIFICATION/DESCRIPTION. Slightly smaller than Gould's Frogmouth in the south, overlaps in the north; with a similar pale hind-collar and row of black-margined white marks on the scapulars, but no second row on the wing-coverts. Males are ash-brown, wings and breast slightly more rufous, flecked and vermiculated in a 'bark-and-lichen' pattern of black, white and buff, coarsely and with obvious black spotting on the upperparts in the south, finely in the north; belly to lower tail-coverts creamy white. The female is rufous-chestnut, with buff lower tail-coverts and more and narrower tail-bars. Both sexes show long, wispy plumage above the bill and around the eyes, framing the head, and a distinctive scatter of white, part- to fully black-margined feathers over the breast, forming almost a band across the lower breast of males.

Bare-part colours. (Adult) iris lemon yellow; bill yellowish to pinkish horn; feet flesh-white.

Size (mm). (Live and skins: 20 adults; sex of many not reported): wing 111–123 (males over almost the full range); tail 108–119; bill 17.2–20.2; tarsus 13.5–15.1 (BMNH, BMP5, UMBRP).

Weight (g). Adult *affinis*, 40.8–54.8 (n=4) (UMBRP).

DISTRIBUTION. Historical summary: all divisions except *Pak, Pha, Phu, Tra, Pat, Sat, Yal, Kel, Tru, Pra, Mel, Sin*, with no island records.

GEOGRAPHICAL VARIATION. Northern *continentalis* Stresemann 1937 (TL Thaungyin valley, N Tenasserim), with brown parts of male finely patterned, has been identified south to Khao Luang peak, Nakhon Si Thammarat (TISTR); southern *affinis* Blyth 1847 (TL Melaka), with male coarsely patterned and black-spotted on the mantle, and female darker, richer rufous, north to Narathiwat (CHULA). They intergrade in SE Thailand (Marshall 1978) but the situation in the Peninsula remains unknown.

STATUS AND POPULATION. Resident, regular and more or less common. Sound contacts suggest that in central Malaysia it is at least as common, or commoner, than Gould's Frogmouth in the same forests. However, 26 months of netting in 15 ha of mature forest at Pasoh took only three individuals, none re-caught, which implies they may not have been so regularly active at under-stratum level (or that they show some other behaviour reducing the risk of capture).

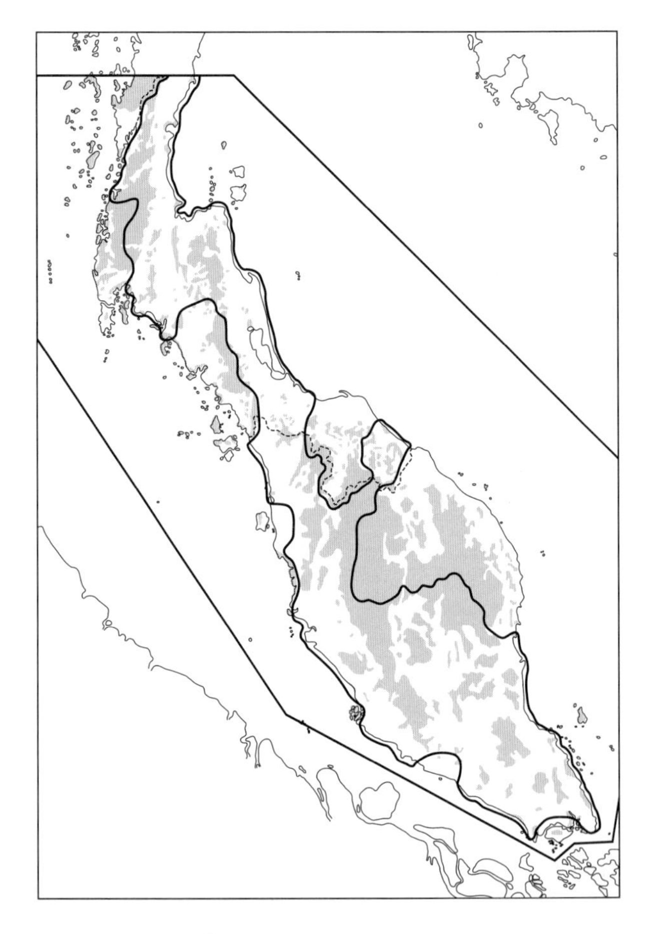

HABITATS AND ECOLOGY. Mid and lower strata of closed-canopy evergreen and semi-evergreen Lowland forest, mature and regenerating, at plains level and on slopes to 750 m; also in overgrown rubber plantation where this butts onto forest. Day-roosts in creeper tangles, among dead leaves, etc., 1.5–12 m up.

FORAGING AND FOOD. No information.

SOCIAL ORGANIZATION. No direct information but frequency of calling, response to tape-recordings and a small amount of ringing data suggest spaced pairs defend a territory.

MOVEMENTS. None known.

SURVIVAL. No information.

SOCIAL INTERACTIONS. No information.

VOICE. Calls of male *continentalis* include wailing mews, *gwaiau* and a shorter *gwao*, a soft, trembling *tyau-ui*, and a trill of *kwit* notes. Male *affinis* calls are mostly the same, plus a series of querulous, rippling whistles, *gwair-rrr*, well-spaced and giving way to a slow, rasping sequence, *gwarr, gwark, gwark, gwa-orr, gwa-orr*. A call heard in Perlis and Pahang, *gweer, gweer, gweer, gwair, gwair, gwai-or* seems to be a version of this. The territorial song of both females is a sharp quacking, *gwaa gwaa gwaa gwaa*, falling in pitch (BMP5, Marshall 1978).

BREEDING

Nest. The few published descriptions of small frogmouth nests (E.C.S. Baker, Butler 1899) are suggestive of Gould's, although one clutch of two eggs may have been of this species. One nest in Kedah, identified from a brooding adult, was built on a 10 cm thick, lower lateral branch of a rubber tree, 7 m above a well-used plantation road and about 20 m from tall forest. Saucer-shaped, it was wide enough to accommodate an adult and two chicks side by side, and built at least externally of blackish vegetable material, i.e., from a distance was reminiscent of nests of Hodgson's and Ceylon Frogmouths rather than the tiny nest described from Java, although the latter did also include vegetable material.

Eggs and brood. Egg not reliably described. The Kedah brood was of two chicks in blackish down plumage, sitting either side of an adult male perched upright on the nest.

Cycle. Day-brooding in such an open site supplies a possible function for the cryptic colour and patterning of male plumage.

Seasonality. Nestlings on 26 February (S. Gunasegaran).

MOULT. Replacement of primaries single-locus but often asymmetrical; sequence unknown. Active wing-moult recorded in July (P10), September (P4/5) and October (a female at P4/9 with mid secondaries and T1 also moulting). Non-moulters handled in November and January—March (BMNH, TISTR, UMBRP).

CONSERVATION. Despite records almost to the Montane forest ecotone, Javan Frogmouth is not nearly as common on slopes as in plains-level forest below the steepland boundary. This threatened habitat may be crucial.

Family CAPRIMULGIDAE

Nightjars: five species

Malaysian Eared Nightjar; Nok Tob Yung Phan Malayu (Thai); Burung Tukang Taptibau (Malay)

Eurostopodus temminckii (Gould) 1838, *Icones Avium* 2: plate 16. TL Borneo.
Plate 55

GROUP RELATIONS. Free-standing.

GLOBAL RANGE. Borneo, Belitung, Banka, Sumatra and the Peninsula north to slightly above latitude 6°N.

IDENTIFICATION/DESCRIPTION. A medium-sized, dark-plumaged nightjar. Cap finely peppered vinous to chestnut (individually variable), paler than the rest of the head and with a flange of lateral hind-crown feathers forming the back-directed 'ears'; lores and face to just above eye-level rich chestnut finely barred black; narrow hind-collar cream-buff; remaining upperparts including wing-coverts black, densely freckled rich rufous and cream-buff; inner webs of short scapulars wholly cream-buff, outer webs black, forming a high-contrast stripe. Flight-feathers black with narrow rufous marks on both webs, reduced to freckles on the secondaries; tail as upperparts but with obscure black bands, offset across feather-shafts. Neither wings nor tail show a pale flash. Below, chin and upper throat as face; a broad band across lower throat, connecting with hind-collar, white; rest of the underparts black, upper breast finely barred chestnut, remainder with broad, rufous-cream feather-tips narrowly fringed black. Sexes similar. The chick hatches in rufous-chestnut down with forehead to crown rich buffy yellow, browning as down wears (G.C. Madoc). Juvenile has mantle plain black, rest of upperparts more faintly marked than in adults, short scapulars barred rufous and dark brown, with black tips.

Calls at dusk and dawn, in high, fast, swooping, crook-winged flight near and over forest.

Bare-part colours. (Adult) iris deep brown with blue cast; bill pale brown to flesh-pink with black-brown tip; feet dark brown.

Size (mm). (Live and skins: 12 males, 13 females; adult): wing 195–211 and 199–210; tail 123–139 and 119–132; bill 7.5–10.3 and 8.1–11.2; tarsus 15.0–15.6 (sexes combined) (BMNH, UMBRP).

Weight (g). Breeding adults, 99.6–116.6 (n=4) (UMBRP).

DISTRIBUTION. North more or less to the Malayan/Thai-Burmese Lowland forest floristic boundary. Historical summary: *Yal, Nar, Ked, Tru, Pek, Phg, Sel, Neg, Mel, Joh, Sin*, and on Penang island.

GEOGRAPHICAL VARIATION. None recognized.

STATUS AND POPULATION. Resident, regular and common. During March 1973, adults were captured off two nests in 15 ha of mature plains-level Lowland forest at Pasoh, Negeri Sembilan.

HABITATS AND ECOLOGY. Evergreen Lowland forest, mature and well regenerated, from plains level to slightly above the Montane ecotone, recorded to around 1000 m on the Main Range (MBR 1982–83); also in lowland peatswamp and tall secondary forest. Day-roosts against a dead-leaf background on the forest floor, but at night, between feeding-bouts, rests crosswise on thin branches 2–5 m above ground (BMP5). By age 19 days, flying young are also able to land on branches (G.C. Madoc).

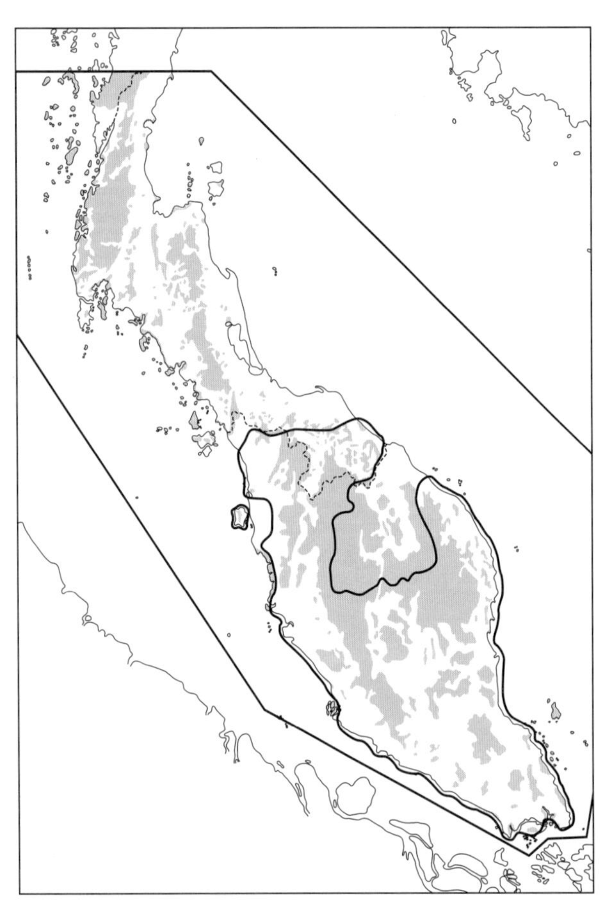

FORAGING AND FOOD. As darkness falls, comes low to hunt silently, a few metres above ground in forest clearings; probably also over the surface of the canopy, but direct observations are lacking. Food has not been studied.

SOCIAL ORGANIZATION. The short, intensive bout of calling 15–20 minutes before dark and again at dawn is a social event, typically with several individuals in the air together. Apart from a short period centred on May (a breeding month), recorded year-round, but its function is unknown.

MOVEMENTS. None known.

SURVIVAL. No information.

SOCIAL INTERACTIONS. Roosts alone, occasionally two birds (pair-members?) in close proximity during the day. An adult flushed off a newly hatched chick flew 10 m then flopped onto leaves, writhing about in a distraction display while uttering a penetrating, squealing hiss (G.C. Madoc).

VOICE. The loud advertising-call, given only in flight, is a high, ringing *tap ti-bau*, sometimes repeated with more emphasis on the first note, *tap ti-bau*, and answered by other birds nearby. A parent calling a chick while sitting on the ground gave a persistent, grunting *uk uk uk uk*.

BREEDING

Nest. Unmodified leaf litter, exposed or sheltered (in one instance under the fronds of a stemless bertam palm *Eugeissona tristis*).

Eggs and brood. Egg creamy white with smears of light red-brown and grey-purple evenly distributed to more heavily marked at the broad end; variably glossless to slightly glossy. Shape short elliptical. Size (mm): 34.9 × 26.3, 36.1 × 25.6 (n=2). There is only one local record of a two-egg clutch; all others, including at hatching, have been of singles. Young move off the nest from day one but return to the laying spot. They are growing flight-feathers by day ten and can fly by day 19, well ahead of body-moult.

Cycle. No other information.

Seasonality. Eggs found in all months January–July and on 28 September, but with most records in March (BMP5, ENGGANG-2, Madoc 1936, NRCS, UMBRP).

MOULT. Replacement of primaries is single-locus and regular-descendant, but often asymmetrical between wings. Among 45 adults covering all months except May and December, eight were in active wing-moult in March, April, June, July, November and January, but with no seasonal progression obvious. Year-round, most show none, including breeders handled in March and September (BMNH, UMBRP).

CONSERVATION. Currently only at three sites on Singapore island, all in the central catchment forest. On the mainland, wide altitudinal occurrence in a variety of forests suggests no immediate threat, but it needs substantial patches of natural cover and does not survive in clean plantation agriculture.

Great Eared Nightjar; Nok Tob Yung Yak (Thai); Burung Tukang Besar (Malay)

Eurostopodus macrotis (Vigors) 1831, *Proceedings of the Committee of Science and Correspondence of the Zoological Society of London* 1: 97. TL Manila.

Plate 55

GROUP RELATIONS. Free-standing. If it can still be found, there would be value in checking the vocalizations of the Simeulue island isolate, *jacobsoni*, which is *macrotis*-sized but has some of the plumage-characters of *E. temminckii*.

GLOBAL RANGE. The W Ghats and far-NE Indian subcontinent; W Yunnan (vagrant); SE Asia except the far NE, to the Peninsula, Simeulue island (W Sumatra) and the Philippines; also Sulawesi, including Peleng and Sangihe islands.

IDENTIFICATION/DESCRIPTION. A minimum 50 percent larger than any other local nightjar, with prominently banded tail, long wings (tip P9) and stately flight. Cap (with rear 'ear' flanges) finely peppered vinous buff, in sharp contrast to lores, side of face to just above eye-level, chin and upper throat which are narrowly barred black and dark chestnut. Hind-collar buff, linked to a broad white band across the lower throat; remaining upperparts including wing-coverts rufous and cream, vermiculated black and with outer webs of short scapulars mainly black (not as conspicuous as in Malaysian Eared Nightjar). Rest of underparts more or less as in the smaller species, but with a second white band across the lower breast and, in some individuals, the area between the bands plain black. Cream is the dominant ground-colour of the inner secondaries; other flight-feathers are sooty black, all extensively freckled rufous, freckling organized into bars on the primaries. Tail multi-banded black, clay-yellow and grey-white, the pale bars freckled with black. Sexes similar. Juveniles are little known, but have flight-feathers narrower than in adult, with rufous tips.

Bare-part colours. (Adult) iris deep brown with a blue cast; bill purple-flesh with a black tip; feet dark fleshy brown (BMNH, Riley 1938).

Size (mm). (Skins: 7 males, 4 females; adult): wing 285–309 and 301–318; tail 204–221 and 202–226; bill 9.2–11.2 (sexes combined); tarsus 18.7–20.7 (sexes combined) (BMNH).

Weight. No data.

DISTRIBUTION. On the W-coast plain, south to the Juru river and Kulim district, opposite Penang island. One record from N Kelantan but the limit of regular range on the eastern plain seems to be further north. Historical summary: *Pak, Chu, Ran, Sur, Pha, Phu, Kra, Tra, Sat, Pes, Ked, Kel, Pra*, with an additional island record from Lanta.

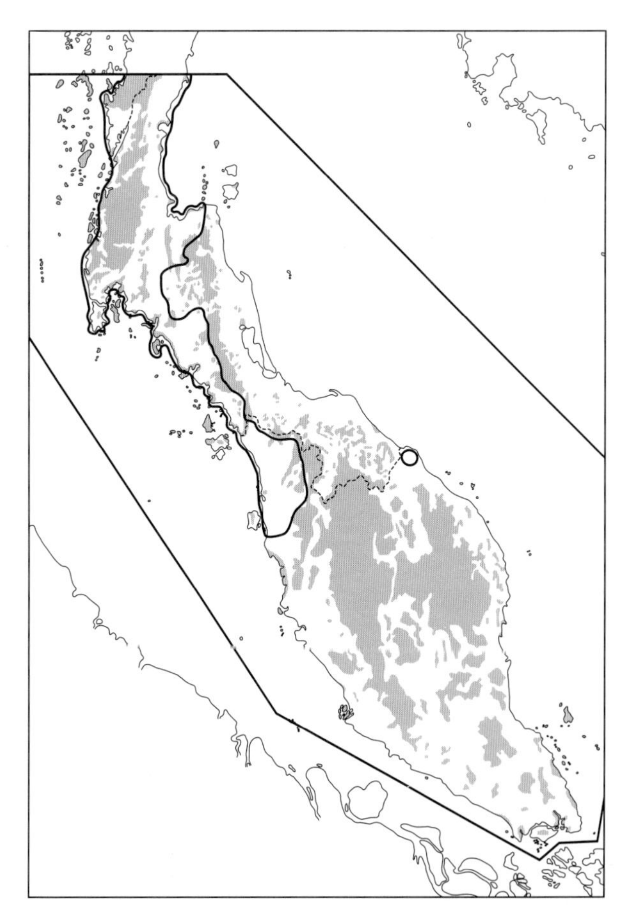

GEOGRAPHICAL VARIATION. Large, dull-toned *cerviniceps* Gould 1838 (TL Trang), of the eastern continental range.

STATUS AND POPULATION. Resident, regular and more or less common.

HABITATS AND ECOLOGY. Evergreen to near-deciduous Lowland forest, mature and disturbed, and including nearby teak and rubber plantations, ranging out over scrub and fallow paddylands, locally as far as the landward edge of mangroves. Strictly at plains level.

FORAGING AND FOOD. Soon after dusk, noted quartering slowly over dry paddyland, a few metres above ground. Food not identified.

SOCIAL ORGANIZATION. Like Malaysian Eared Nightjar, indulges in dusk and dawn song-flights, often with two or more individuals in view at once. Flights are not as high or swift, but evening calling continues longer, until well after dark. Silent during a summer wet-season period centred on May–June. In continental Thailand, day-roosts on the forest floor in loose groups of 6–10 (P.D. Round), but this social behaviour has not yet been reported from the Peninsula.

MOVEMENTS. None reported.

SURVIVAL. No information.

SOCIAL INTERACTIONS. No information.

VOICE. A piping *pink, piu-eeu*, lighter, less emphatic than in Malaysian Eared Nightjar. The first note is sharp but not always given. When it is, it is noticeably spaced from notes two and three. Calling is mostly in flight but a long bout recorded from an apparently fixed point at the edge of forest in Perlis suggested it came from a perch.

BREEDING

Nest. None; egg laid directly on the ground.

Eggs and brood. No local description. An egg collected in Narathiwat (BMP5) has been re-identified as belonging to Malaysian Eared Nightjar and constitutes the only breeding record of that species from Thailand.

Cycle. No information.

Seasonality. An adult brooding a chick in scrubby mangroves at Merbok estuary, Kedah, on 4 March (R. Gregory-Smith).

MOULT. Replacement of at least the inner primaries is regular-descendant. Fifteen birds covering the period September—March showed no active wing-moult, but some early to mid-stage suspensions (four of post-juvenile moult) during December–February (BMNH).

CONSERVATION. Deciduous forest is a favoured habitat now severely restricted in the Peninsula. More information is needed on the use made of tree plantations, but small numbers appear able to maintain themselves out of true forest.

Grey Nightjar; Nok Tob Yung Phu Khao (Thai); Burung Tukang Kelabu (Malay)

Caprimulgus indicus Latham 1790, *Index Ornithologicus* 2: 588. TL India.
Plate 55

GROUP RELATIONS. Apparently free-standing.

GLOBAL RANGE. Breeds in the Himalayas, the Indian subcontinent and Sri Lanka; SE Tibet; NE Mongolia, Transbaikalia to Amurland, Japan, Korea, China south and east of a line Heilongjiang–Sichuan; and from N Burma to NW and W Thailand, with an outlier on Palau, W Micronesia. Northern populations migrate, wintering from the breeding range through SE Asia to the Greater Sunda islands and, in small numbers, the Philippines and W Micronesia; vagrant N Wallacea and Irian Jaya.

IDENTIFICATION/DESCRIPTION. About the size of Large-tailed Nightjar. From it when perched in good light by colder grey upperparts, less obviously pale cap, more extensive rufous barring on the primaries (especially in females) and wing-tip folding close to the tip of the tail. Upperparts silvery white, finely peppered grey-black, the effect darkest on mantle and lesser wing-coverts, more iron-grey elsewhere. A row of short, cinnamon to white flashes forms a narrow hind-collar; the outer webs of a row of short scapulars are white to buff set off by black inner webs and, either side, by rows of feathers barred cinnamon and black; and primary and outer median wing-coverts are freckled and broadly tipped cinnamon-rufous. All remaining upperparts, from cap to upper tail-coverts, are streaked black, boldly back to mantle. Flight-feathers are sooty with light rufous bars on the basal half, tips barred and freckled ash grey, and a median band across P7–9 and the inner web of P10 is white in males, cinnamon-rufous in females. T1 is barred black and ash-grey, the pale bars broader and freckled black; grey replaced by cinnamon on remaining feathers, and all are broadly dark-tipped. A subterminal band of white across T2–T5 of males (only), seen from below, has only half the depth (25 mm) of the equivalent apical tail-flash of Large-tailed Nightjar. Below, chin to upper throat finely vermiculated grey and white, with a laterally expanded white band across lower throat, and breast peppered grey with fine blackish shaft-lines; rest of underparts creamy white with narrow bars of dark grey. From Large-tailed Nightjar in flight, by less conspicuous or no white tail-flashes.

Bare-part colours. (Adult) iris deep brown with a violet cast; bill dark vinous-brown, lining of enormous mouth pink; feet dark grey-brown.

Size (mm). (Live and skins: 10 males, 4 females; adult): wing 202–217 and 197–212; tail 120–134 and 114–128; bill 9.7–11.1 (sexes combined); tarsus 15.4–17.5 (sexes combined) (BMNH, UMBRP).

Weight (g). Migrants intercepted at Fraser's Hill, 78.7–91.8 (n=5) (UMBRP).

DISTRIBUTION. Under-recorded in the north. Historical summary: *Pak, Kra, Tra, Son, Sat, Nar, Pes, Ked, Tru, Pek, Phg, Sel, Mel, Sin,* with additional island records, mostly on passage dates, from Libong and Rok (*Tra*), Tarutao, Langkawi (wintering), Perak, Rembia, Jarak and Pisang off the W coast; Tioman off the E coast; and Sentosa, Singapore.

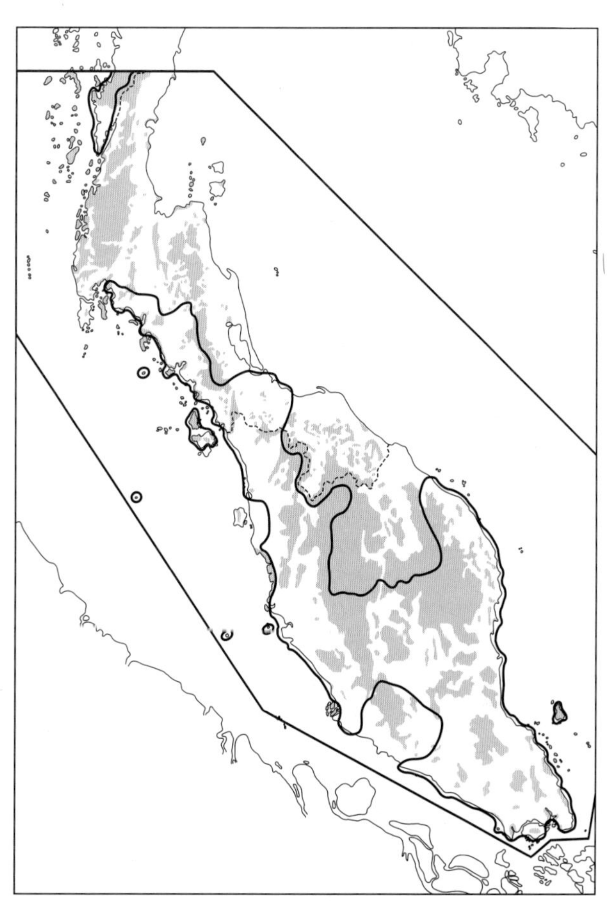

GEOGRAPHICAL VARIATION. Most are E Palaearctic-breeding *jotaka* Temminck and Schlegel 1847 (TL Japan), but subtropical *hazarae* Whistler and Kinnear 1935 (TL Abbottabad, N Pakistan), browner above with heavier black streaking, blacker on the breast and with broader, browner barring on the lower tail-coverts, wing-range 187–208 mm (BMNH, HBI, Vaurie 1965) has been identified from Tarutao island (Deignan 1963). A short-winged bird ringed and released after capture at floodlights on Fraser's Hill may have been this subspecies (BMP5).

STATUS AND POPULATION. A non-breeding visitor and passage migrant, local and uncommon to more or less common. On a few recent occasions, solitary nightjars have been noted foraging in typical Grey situations along quiet roads through Lower Montane forest at Fraser's Hill during the northern summer (June, August). Occasional Grey Nightjars may oversummer, or this or another as yet unidentified species could be a rare resident. A search is needed.

HABITATS AND ECOLOGY. Winters at the edge of and over mangroves, inland forest, secondary-growth and overgrown plantations, from plains level to at least 1500 m (McClure 1964). South of latitude about 6°N mostly Montane, but there are mid-winter lowland records from Melaka and Singapore (AMNH, SINGAV-2). On passage, turns up more widely, including in strand scrub on coasts. This is the only local *Caprimulgus* regularly day-roosting in trees, perched longwise on horizontal boughs from only a metre or so up in scrub to main canopy level in mature forest.

FORAGING AND FOOD. Hunts around the canopy of forest and down to low levels in clearings. Waits on service-wires and other high perches along forest roads but also feeds during prolonged periods of hawking. Diet not analysed but on several consecutive dawns in February one came for moths attracted to a light on a forest bungalow at Maxwell's Hill, Larut Range (R.P. Jaensch).

SOCIAL ORGANIZATION. Winterers are mainly solitary but birds halting during the southward passage season sometimes forage in a loose group.

MOVEMENTS. Interceptions at Fraser's Hill, strikes on Melaka Straits lighthouses (One-Fathom Bank) and sightings on remote islands and drilling-rigs and ships in the Terengganu off-shore oil-field (BMNH, BMP5, Langham 1976, MBR 1982–83) show autumn passage runs from early October (earliest date 7 October) to at least early December, with a spring return during April–early May (extreme dates 4 April and 3 May). Records 200 km off Terengganu at both seasons suggest direct crossings of the Gulf of Thailand.

SURVIVAL. No information.

SOCIAL INTERACTIONS. No information.

VOICE. Calls only occasionally in wintering habitat: bouts of a rather slow, low-pitched, monotone rattle, *tuk-tuk-tuk-tuk-tuk-tuk . . .*, given mostly from a perch, but on one occasion heard briefly from a spring migrant passing overhead in the dark.

BREEDING. No population.

MOULT. In a small sample, replacement of primaries apparently regular-descendant. Among 15 *jotaka*, active wing-moult recorded in early December (P2), mid January (P1–2), late February (P5–6) and mid April (P6 and heavy body-moult), but four other December birds showed wings all, or all except the wing-tip (P8–10), fresh. Age-classes have not been separated and comparative schedules need more study (BMNH, BMP5).

CONSERVATION. No critical issues.

Large-tailed Nightjar; Nok Tob Yung Haang Yao (Thai); Burung Tukang Kubur (Malay)

Caprimulgus macrurus Horsfield 1821, *Transactions of the Linnean Society* 13(1): 142. TL Java.
Plate 55

GROUP RELATIONS. Allopatric *macrurus*, Philippine *manillensis* and Sulawesian *celebensis* form a superspecies which, despite some marginal overlap in India, could also be taken to include S Asian *atripennis* (Jerdon's Nightjar) (cf. Mees 1985a, Rozendaal 1990). Advertising-calls have diverged in all cases.

GLOBAL RANGE. The Himalayan foothills east from Himachal Pradesh, the Ganges valley, NE coast of the Indian subcontinent, and the Andamans; S Yunnan and Hainan; SE Asia to the Greater Sunda islands, Bali and Palawan; Wallacea excluding Sulawesi; and New Guinea to New Britain and northern Australia.

IDENTIFICATION/DESCRIPTION. A medium-sized nightjar, as Grey but with blunter wings, folding well short of the longer tail-tip, and both sexes show a large, pale tail-flash. Cap to nape peppered vinous-grey with bold central slashes of black; hind-collar tawny; mantle peppered tawny and black; back to upper tail-coverts greyer, with narrow streaks and some cross-bars of black. Scapulars pale vinous-grey with a bar of black set off by bold cream outer-web edging and rows of black, cinnamon-edged feathers above and below. Wing-coverts peppered dark tawny, medians paler, these and greater coverts with black centres and bold cream tips. Flight-feathers sooty black with tips freckled ash-grey, secondaries, inner primaries and outer web of outermost primary barred rufous. P7–9 have rufous only at their base and show a bold, median band extending to inner web of P10, all-white in males, smaller and with outer webs cinnamon in females. Tail ash-grey, variably peppered and narrowly barred black, with some cinnamon barring on lateral feathers and the apical part of the outer two pairs (T4–5) broadly white (up to 55 mm deep in males, 30 in females), without a dark tip. Below, face and chin to sides of throat tawny-rufous finely barred black, with a large white patch central on the lower throat, its posterior edge boldly barred cinnamon and black. Breast black, feathers fringed with a peppering of cinnamon to grey; belly to lower tail-coverts buff with narrow, sooty brown bars.

Chick-down mealy brown. Juveniles have a smaller throat-spot and, as in other nightjars, flight-feathers are narrower than in adult.

Bare-part colours. (Adult) iris deep brown; bill horn-brown with blackish tip; feet pink-brown.

Size (mm). (Live and skins: 29 males, 16 females; adult): wing 188–202 and 183–199 (juveniles down to 178); tail 135–157 and 127–143; bill 9.2–10.9 (sexes combined); tarsus 14.0–17.8 (sexes combined) (BMNH, UMBRP).

Weight (g). Adult males, 65.0–82.3 (n=6); adult females, 64.5–71.0 (n=3).

DISTRIBUTION. Historical summary: all divisions, with additional island records from Ra (*Pha*), Rang (*Phu*), Lanta and Mai Ngam (*Kra*), Libong, Langkawi, Penang, Pangkor and Besar (*Mel*) off the W coast; Phangan and Sibu (*Joh*) off the E coast; and Tekong, Ubin, Retan Laut, St John's, Berani, Sudong, Senang and Ayer Merbau around Singapore.

GEOGRAPHICAL VARIATION. Subspecies *bimaculatus* Peale 1848 (TL Singapore), of the eastern continent and Sumatra. Range-wide, shows a N–S cline of decreasing size (Mees 1977a, Riley 1938), but this is not obvious in the Peninsula.

STATUS AND POPULATION. Resident, regular and common, reaching peak population density in parkland and large suburban gardens of the southern half of the Peninsula.

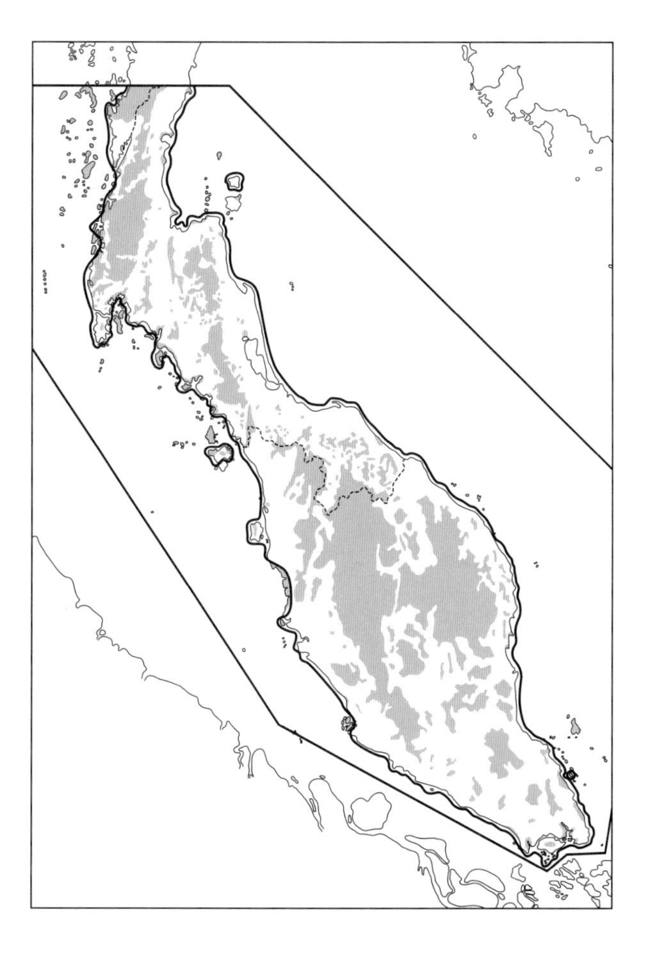

HABITATS AND ECOLOGY. Open ground in a wide variety of plains-level situations, from degraded back-mangroves and dune scrub to the margins and islands of large rivers, tracks and spaces in plantations and other cultivation, grazing-grounds, old mine-tailings and other grassland, and parks and large gardens (well into suburbia), wherever scattered trees, posts, service-wires, etc., supply overhead song- and scanning perches. Day-roosts on the ground against disruptive soil and leaf-litter backgrounds, typically in shadow at the edge of clear space; also on the floor of closed-canopy secondary-growth, overgrown rubber plantings, etc., but not past the edge of natural mixed forest. Like other *Caprimulgus* nightjars, commonly sits on warm metalled and earth roads after dark.

FORAGING AND FOOD. Quarters and aerial-sallies, mostly from perches above ground. Along roadsides, etc., loners and pairs take up regular stations on wiring in shadow immediately above street lamps, capturing most food on sallies within a radius of only a few metres. Attracted to dusk termite swarms. Drinks from open water by hovering briefly then dipping to scoop, swallow-like, from the surface.

SOCIAL ORGANIZATION. Faithfulness to song- and scanning perches suggests pairs hold exclusive territory for at least the duration of the calling-season.

MOVEMENTS. None recorded.

SURVIVAL. The longest of very few retrap-intervals, 40 months (UMBRP).

SOCIAL INTERACTIONS. No information.

VOICE. The loud advertising-call, given from a perch, is an explosive, resonating *tchonk* or *tch'nk*, commonly in bursts of 2–4 notes, or sustained for up to several minutes (a record 4.7 minutes: Evans 1950), at 1–4 notes per second, often with only a brief pause between bouts. Long bouts are a feature of the breeding-season but song occurs through much of the year (in Selangor, a variable, roughly three-month silence is centred on July–August). Calls at any time of night (very occasionally also during daytime: Saunders 1923) but is most intense at dusk and for a brief period at dawn, with neighbours answering often at a slight but consistently different pitch.

The close-range contact-call of both sexes, given when perched (including on the ground) and in short flights, is a low, grunting *ork-ork-ork-ork* . . . Females grunt in the vicinity of chicks, and hiss during distraction display, but their full repertoire is uncertain.

BREEDING

Nest. None; eggs are laid directly on short grass, bare soil (occasionally gravel) or leaf litter, in open sites, typically but not always in shadow. Recorded at least once nesting in litter collected on the flat roof of a building.

Eggs and brood. Eggs are pink-buff, irregularly spotted and blotched pink- to chestnut-brown and pale purple-brown, with purple-grey blotches generally concentrated at one end. Against most backgrounds they are camouflaged, but are easy to spot on grass. Shape elliptical. Size (mm): 35.1–28.7 × 24.0–22.1 (n=6). Clutch two, laid up to four days apart and sometimes of markedly different size. Chicks move off the laying-site at day one, and move again nightly, siblings often separating. They fly at day 15, while still in body down.

Cycle. Apparently only females incubate and brood during daytime. Flushed off young chicks, the parent flies a few metres then crash-lands, giving injured-wing distraction display and gaping widely, with or without a hiss, repeating the process progressively further away from the nest.

Seasonality. Egg- and chick-dates extrapolate to laying in all months January–July, and September–mid October, with a strong peak in March–April (Edgar 1933, NRCS, SINGAV-1, ZRCNUS).

MOULT. Replacement of primaries is regular-descendant, with up to three inner feathers in overlapping growth but no overlap past P7–8. Among 38 adults covering all months, 15 showed active wing-moult during late April–late August (with no August moult at less than stage P9). Most post-juvenile moult occurs on the same schedule, but with a few instances (including late starts) recorded up to December (BMNH, BMP5, R.R. Kersley, UMBRP, UMZC).

CONSERVATION. No critical issues. Use of insecticide fogging machines has been observed to drive territory-holders out of favoured garden habitat as insect populations fall, but this is strictly a local issue.

Savanna Nightjar; Nok Tob Yung Paa Khok (Thai); Burung Tukang Padang (Malay)

Caprimulgus affinis Horsfield 1821, *Transactions of the Linnean Society* 13(1): 142. TL Java.
Plate 55

GROUP RELATIONS. Free-standing. Despite some morphological divergence, populations in continental and island SE Asia still have identical vocalizations.

GLOBAL RANGE. The Indian subcontinent from the Himalayan foothills; far-S China from Fujian to Yunnan including Taiwan; SE Asia to Sumatra, Java, Bali, S and W Borneo and the Philippines; and Sulawesi and the Lesser Sunda islands. Vagrant on Christmas island, Indian Ocean.

IDENTIFICATION/DESCRIPTION. Smaller and, in the north, paler than other local nightjars; crown black-streaked in southern birds, without conspicuous dark dorsal markings in northern ones. Both have a prominent hind-collar of orange-buff streaks, and cinnamon stripe along the scapulars. Flight-feathers sooty, barred rufous and tipped mottled ash, a median band across P7–9 plus inner web of P10 white in males, white with outer webs cinnamon in females. Tail sooty with freckled ash-brown bars that in northern birds shade proximally to cinnamon, the outer two feathers (T4–5) wholly white in males, same as rest of tail in females. Below, lower throat-patch white and divided mid-ventrally, breast marked with orange-buff arrowheads, and belly buff, narrowly barred dark brown. Juveniles are paler, sandier than adults, with flight-feathers broadly tipped rufous and chin and throat entirely vermiculated grey, lacking white patches.

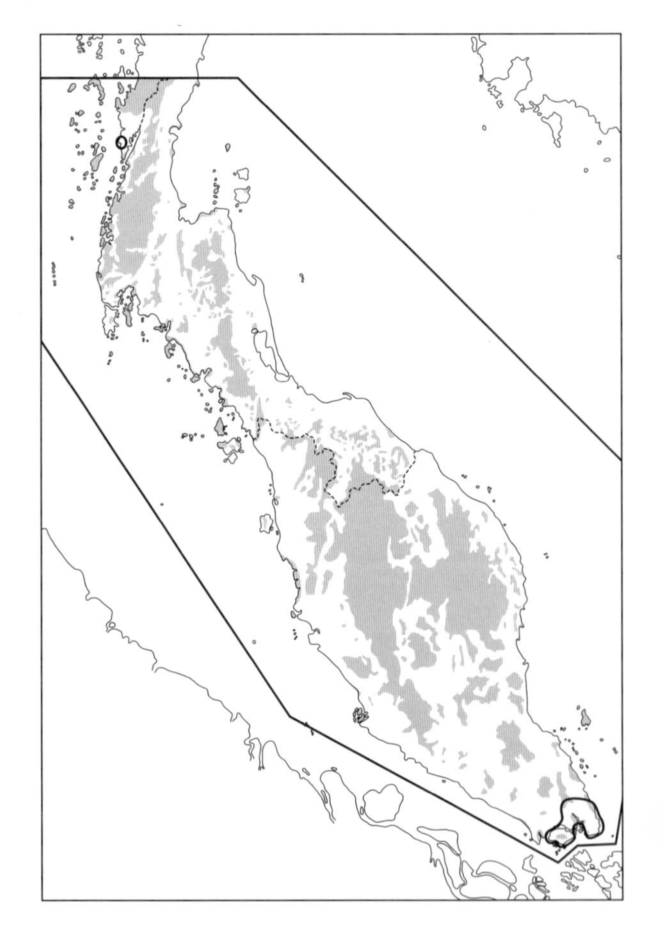

Bare-part colours. (Adult) iris deep brown; bill black; feet brownish (BMNH).

Size (mm). (Skins: 1 northern female, 1 Sumatran male; adults): wing 187 and 161; other measurements of the Sumatran bird only: tail 92; bill 8.5; tarsus 20.5 (BMNH, Riley 1938). Both populations of this open-ground species have a proportionately long tarsus.

Weight. No data.

DISTRIBUTION. In the far north and far south. Historical summary: *Pak, Joh, Sin*, including on Seletar and Sentosa islands, Singapore.

GEOGRAPHICAL VARIATION. At the northern border of the Peninsula, large, relatively pale, continental *monticolus* Franklin 1831 (TL Ganges between Benares and Calcutta). Southern birds have not been handled but are assumed to be small, more heavily marked nominate *affinis*, as on neighbouring islands of Indonesia (CLBS).

STATUS AND POPULATION. Known in the north from a single adult female collected at Champang, Pakchan, on 20 December 1903 (Riley 1938); perhaps vagrant there but outlying pockets of resident population are a strong possibility.

In the south, has recently colonized Singapore, where coastal land-claiming through the 1980s created new ecological conditions favouring settlement. Discovered in mid 1988: 16 birds, including a nesting pair, counted on an area of bare landfill at Tuas, west end of the island, on 21 May. Within a few months, present at comparable bare to grassy sites round more or less all of the rest of the coastline. By early 1989, also in SE Johor: calling heard at Tanjung Sepang, on open grassland at Jason's Bay and inland at Muntahak, i.e., to about 1°50′N (SINGAV-2, -3). Further northward spread is expected.

HABITATS AND ECOLOGY. In the south, demands more completely treeless ground than Large-tailed Nightjar. Found so far on bare landfill (used until it floods: BIRDLINE 1993); open grassland, rough and mown (including golf-courses); open shores of reservoirs; and, as in Java and Sumatra, towns (SINGAV-4, -6).

FORAGING AND FOOD. No direct information.

SOCIAL ORGANIZATION. No direct information, but breeds under relatively crowded conditions that suggest territories, if they exist, are likely to be small. The function of loud calling (recorded in all months except June–August) is not known.

MOVEMENTS. None reported, but an obviously active dispersant.

SURVIVAL. No information.

SOCIAL INTERACTIONS. A bird flushed off eggs gave an on-the-ground distraction display.

VOICE. The only vocalization reported is a single, sharp, sneezing *cherweesh*, uttered in flight and while perched.

BREEDING

Nest. None; eggs are laid directly on bare ground.

Eggs and brood. Eggs light brown, mottled darker brown. No information on shape or size. Clutch two; incubation and fledging periods unknown.

Cycle. No information.

Seasonality. Full clutches on 16–21 May and 27 June (BIRDLINE 1993, Ollington and Loh 1993, SINGAV-2).

MOULT. No data.

CONSERVATION. No critical issues.

Order APODIFORMES

Family APODIDAE

Swifts: 12 species

Glossy Swiftlet; Nok En Thong Khao (Thai); Burung Layang-layang Licin (Malay)

Collocalia esculenta (Linnaeus) 1758, *Systema Naturae* 10(1): 191. TL Ambon, Moluccas.
Plate 56

GROUP RELATIONS. Local field and laboratory studies have advanced understanding of the relationship between green- and blue-glossed forms, commonly believed to replace each other in the Sunda Region. Somadikarta (1986) showed them sympatric in the highlands of Sumatra and Borneo and on the basis of a supposed mixed colony in SE Sumatra raised green *linchi* Horsfield and Moore 1854 (TL Java) to species rank. He speculated *linchi* had died out in mainland Asia, but Lim (1994) found both green and blue birds, and a high proportion of colour-mixes, in breeding-colonies of the Selangor plain and adjacent Main Range. Electrophoresis of tissue enzyme extracts showed good samples of all these forms to be genetically uniform. Javan topotypes have not been tested but, evidently, no taxonomic split is justified by geographical arguments put forward to date. As shown for other swift groups by Delacour and Mayr (1945a), gloss-tone may vary with the extent of wear of individual feathers.

GLOBAL RANGE. The Andamans, Nicobars and Mergui archipelago to the Greater Sunda islands and Bali; Christmas Island (Indian Ocean); Wallacea and New Guinea to the Bismarcks, Solomons, New Caledonia and New Hebrides.

IDENTIFICATION/DESCRIPTION. Tiny; smallest swift species of the area, more or less square-tailed and with light, fluttering flight. Entire upperparts, including adult flight-feathers and tail, uniform blackish in the field but in the hand glossed electric-blue or deep bottle-green (or in feather-by-feather combination). Chin to breast, flanks and sides of belly dull grey, narrowly fringed white on the breast in a scaly pattern; centre belly white; underwing and lower tail-coverts as upperparts but tail-coverts with white fringing. The hind-toe of most birds has a small feather-tuft on its upper surface.

Bare-part colours. All blackish.

Size (mm). (Live: 3-figure samples of males and females; adult): wing 98–112 and 98–110; tail 37–46 and 37–45; bill 4.3–4.8 (sexes combined); tarsus 6.8–7.7 (sexes combined) (BMNH, C.J. Hails, UMBRP).

Weight (g). A 3-figure sample of Selangor adults, 7.1–11.4; and a separate mean, 8.3 (n=114) (C.J. Hails, Hails and Amirrudin 1981).

DISTRIBUTION. Patchy north of Malaysia. Historical summary: *Ran, Pha, Nak, Yal, Nar, Pes, Ked, Kel, Tru, Pek, Phg, Sel, Neg, Mel, Joh, Sin*, with sightings over Langgun island lake, Langkawi group (van Balgooy *et al.* 1977); there are no other island records.

GEOGRAPHICAL VARIATION. Thai populations have not been determined. South of the border, subspecies *cyanoptila* Oberholser 1906 (TL Bunguran, N

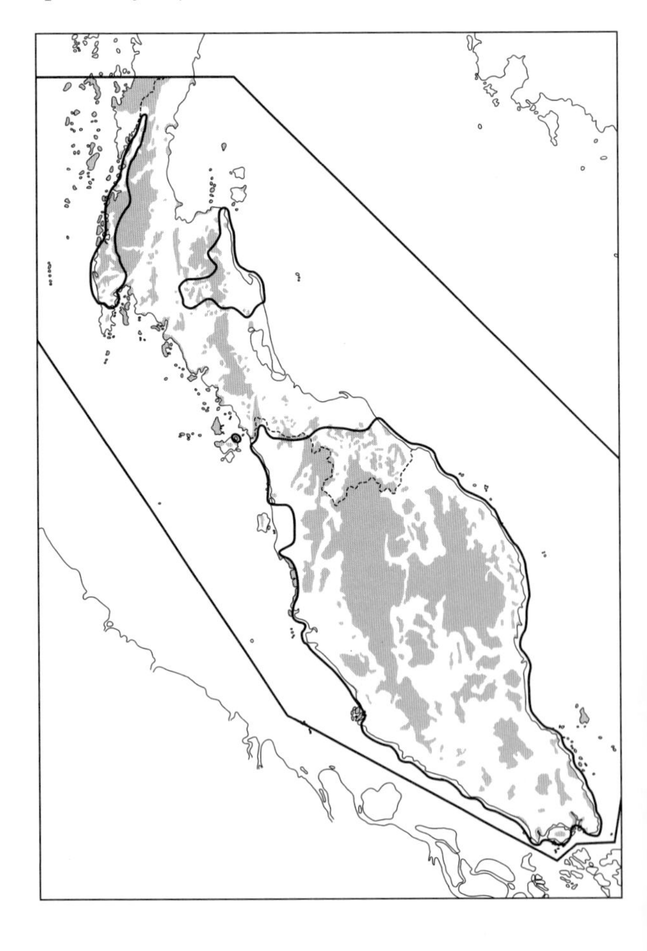

Natuna islands) is characterized as being blue, but the taxonomic importance of gloss-tone needs re-assessing and could lead to a new review.

STATUS AND POPULATION. Resident; regular and common to abundant in Malaysia, local and sparse elsewhere (including on Singapore main island where incidence has begun to increase but is still at less than ten records per year, apparently all in the period November–February, i.e., the Malaysian non-breeding season).

HABITATS AND ECOLOGY. Breeds wherever suitable sites occur close to expanses of open green cover, from the edge of suburbia in the settled plains to Upper Montane forest on the Main Range (an extreme record at 1900 m in Cameron Highlands (Allen 1948), but unlike some *Aerodramus* swiftlet species, not actually in towns.

FORAGING AND FOOD. Forages over all kinds of open, settled, planted and forested environments, from shorelines to the highest summits, but with a preference for tree cover. More large flocks occur over forest than over open ground (Waugh and Hails 1983). Concentrates in the lowest airspace occupied by feeding swifts. Studies in Selangor found diurnal shifts (upward in the afternoon) but, on average, with 30 percent of individuals in the first 10 m of space, and mean height lower over forest than open ground. Slow speed plus high manoeuvrability – three times that of House Swift *Apus nipalensis* on a ratio tail-length (mm)/weight (g) – allows foraging close to the 'skin' of forest, following its contours and even venturing inside the canopy (Hails and Amirrudin 1981, Waugh and Hails 1983).

From analyses of food-boluses carried in the throat for delivery to nestlings, hymenopterans (mainly flying ants and chalcidoid wasps) form nearly half of the prey (48.3 percent), with dipterans 26.7, homopteran bugs 12.4 and beetles 9.5 percent of separable items. The occasional caterpillar may be snatched from a silk suspension-thread. Adult diet, from stomach rather than throat contents, includes a high proportion of beetles. Range of food collected and of sites hunted (the food and foraging niches) are both greater over forest than open ground (a 26 percent difference), but tend to even out in wet weather when swarming ants and termites increase in availability everywhere (Hails and Amirrudin 1981, Waugh and Hails 1983).

SOCIAL ORGANIZATION. Colonies vary from several thousand to below ten pairs but breeding appears always to be social. Also forages in company, and rich sites attract large flocks. There is no evidence from ringing of any exchange of adults between nest-colonies, even though these may overlap in their total foraging-space.

MOVEMENTS. None monitored.

SURVIVAL. No information.

SOCIAL INTERACTIONS. No information.

VOICE. Shrill chirrups and burbling notes. Makes no echolocation rattle-call.

BREEDING

Nest. Selects a rock or cement surface in a cave, culvert or disused building, typically in twilight but always within sight of an entrance. Much less often, selects some deeply and permanently shaded nook outside. Nests are built mainly of filamentous lichen, with whole rhizomes and roots of small epiphytic plants and a minor amount of moss, stranded through and fixed by hardening salivary cement to a vertical or overhung surface, often in close enough contact with other nests to form clumps (additions part-founded on their neighbours). The cup is elongate, inside-rim measurements 69–54 × 52–36 mm (n=5).

Eggs and brood. Eggs are plain white. Shape blunt, subelliptical. Size (mm): 18.7–17.3 × 12.2–11.9 (n=14), fresh weight (g) 1.0–1.5. At two Selangor colonies, full clutch normally two, one in less than five percent of nests (mean 1.96, n=240). In the Ampang colony, Selangor: mean laying interval 3.35 days; mean development interval 23.5 days; mean hatch interval between siblings 2.3 days; and mean nestling period 35.3 days.

At Ampang, total egg success (fledglings from eggs laid) averaged 24.5 percent over several seasons, and 71.1 percent of successful nests fledged two young. This proved to be the most productive brood-size (experimentally enlarged broods included).

Cycle. Both sexes incubate and tend nestlings, and most pairs make more than one breeding attempt, females re-laying a mean 12.7 days after fledging of the previous brood. A substantial increase in both fat and non-fat weights over winter levels occurs in both sexes in March, with overall drop in April as egg-laying reaches its peak. Hails and Turner (1985) also find evidence that fat rather than protein reserves limit egg-production, and that laying continues only as long as the female recoups enough fat in excess of daily maintenance needs through efficient feeding. This is influenced by weather and aerial plankton supply. Bryant and Hails (1983) suggest spaced hatching of siblings increases productivity by separating their peaks of energy demand, reducing stress on the parents.

Seasonality. In Selangor and on the adjacent Main Range, eggs in all months early February–November, with final broods off at the beginning of January, but peak incidence of laying of the first clutch is in April and production for the year may stop as early as August. Within colonies, the breeding-cycle is asynchronous overall but can be synchronized in patches of nests. Localized cropping by a visiting nest predator is one among several possible explanations, none yet tested (BMP5, Hails and Turner 1985, NRCS).

MOULT. Replacement of primaries is regular-descendant with usually only one feather in growth at a time. In Selangor, it begins in April (45 percent growing P1 or P2 on 30 April), reaches 90 percent incidence in mid–late summer, with earliest finishers dated August and a population finish in early winter (60 percent of birds complete and most others at P9 or P10 on 1 October; only one of 14 still at P10 on 22 November). Exceptionally late completions, up to February (C.J. Hails), may be of post-juvenile moult. Advanced birds show that full individual wing-moult occupies about five months.

CONSERVATION. No critical issues. Probably most breeders now use man-made sites; and culverts under new roads continue to expand the range available.

Waterfall Swift; (no Thai name); Burung Layang-layang Hantu (Malay)

Hydrochous gigas (Hartert and Butler) 1901, *Bulletin of the British Ornithologists' Club* 11: 65. TL the Gap, Selangor/Pahang boundary.

Plate 56

GROUP RELATIONS. Free-standing. Generic separation from other grey swiftlets is supported by a combination of morphology (mainly size), nesting behaviour and lack of ability to echolocate in darkness (Brooke 1972).

GLOBAL RANGE. Java, Borneo (sight records only), Sumatra and the S Peninsula.

IDENTIFICATION/DESCRIPTION. Mass slightly greater but, in the field, shape and flight-action most closely resemble House Swift. At a W Javan site, powered flight was direct with rapid but deep and smooth strokes, and gliding on wings held only just below the horizontal; the tail-fork showed only during turns in free airspace above the forest canopy (King 1987).

In the hand, lateral upper tail-coverts have a pale margin to the outer web. Otherwise, uniformly dark upperparts are lightly glossed greenish. Underparts are all brownish black with shaft-streaks slightly bolder on belly and flanks, conspicuously so on lower tail-coverts. Lessers darker and glossier than other lower wing-coverts. As in *Aerodramus* species, the eye is proportionately large.

Bare-part colours. (Adult) all blackish.

Size (mm). (Live: 5, age/sex-classes not separated): wing 156–168; tail 56–67, tail-fork 3 (1 only, in a 65 mm tail); bill 6.5 (1 only); tarsus not measured (BMP5, UMBRP).

Weight (g). Full-grown birds, age-class not checked, 36.5–45.9 (mean 39.4, n=6) (UMBRP).

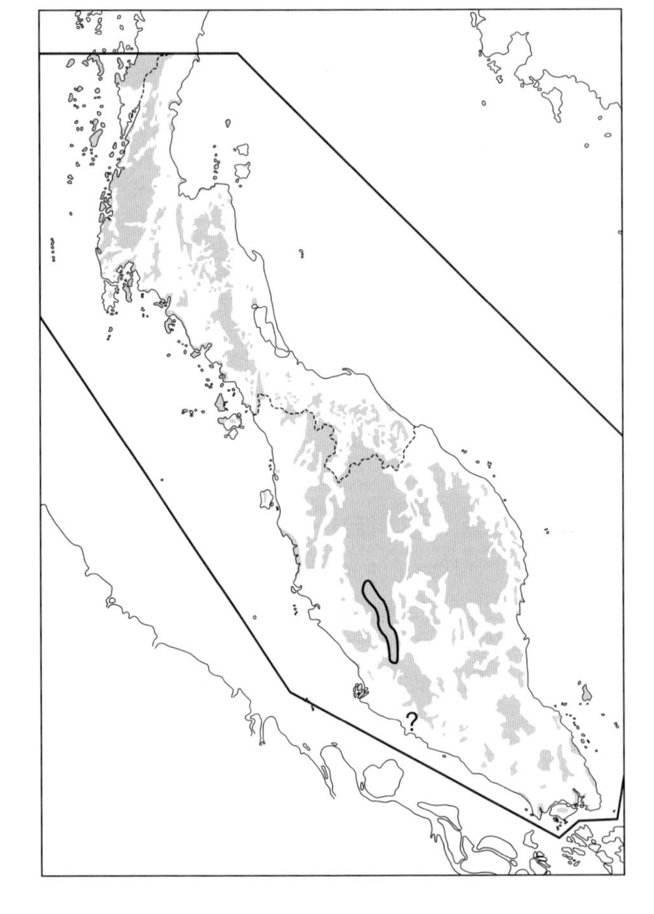

DISTRIBUTION. Confirmed only on the southern Main Range, between Genting Simpah (Selangor/Pahang boundary) and Cameron Highlands, with a provisional sight-record from the SW lowlands. Historical summary: *Phg, Sel, ?Neg.*

GEOGRAPHICAL VARIATION. None recognized.

STATUS AND POPULATION. Evidently local and sparse; known from the type, six mist-net captures and a sight record. Dates of captures (over several years and all on the Main Range) imply passage status, but a nest identified by site and construction as belonging to this species has been found in Cameron Highlands (Allen 1960a, Becking 1971).

HABITATS AND ECOLOGY. Confirmed identifications are all from Montane forest, between approximately 800–1500 m, including at waterfalls (the nesting habitat) and in nets set for nocturnal migrants at floodlights. The type specimen, from the Gap, is presumed to have been shot by day and Waterfall Swifts are known to be active diurnally elsewhere in their range, but all local mist-net captures have been after dark.

A bird tested for navigation ability in darkness immediately slowed its flight when lights in the test room were switched off, circled with wing-tips brushing the ceiling and collided with walls or other obstacles, down which it mostly fluttered to the floor. It refused to take off in darkness and at no time produced an echolocation rattle (Medway and Wells 1969).

FORAGING AND FOOD. Among several swift species mist-netted at night around floodlights at Fraser's Hill, Waterfall Swift is the only one to have shown evidence of having recently fed. A bird taken as late as 0300 hours had a distended throat and by dawn had regurgitated several pellets of prey-remains, implying that it had fed well into the night. Eye-size suggests good low-light vision and it may have hunted insects drawn to the lights, although no swift was ever seen to do this.

SOCIAL ORGANIZATION. No information.

MOVEMENTS. Apart from the nest-record, contacts are dated 10 October–28 November and 15 March (BMP5, UMBRP), suggestive of some through-movement.

SURVIVAL. No information.

SOCIAL INTERACTIONS. No information.

VOICE. The only sound produced by a captive, in a holding-bag and while being handled and free-flown in a room, was a brief, *Apus*-like chittering.

BREEDING

Nest. Sited on a rock ledge within the permanent spray zone of a mountain waterfall, accessed by flying through a 6 m gap in the tree canopy, along the stream-bed and, during heavy flow, apparently through the water-curtain (behaviour confirmed in Java). Shape, a truncated cone 9 cm high × 9 cm maximum width with nest-chamber 37 mm across × 12 mm deep, built mainly of two types of liverwort (*Mastigophora* and *Herberta* spp.) with some green moss and fern material and a few body feathers, fixed to the ledge and to a lesser extent reinforced elsewhere with salivary cement kept soft by the wetness of the site. The sitting adult was continuously sprinkled but orientated so that its head was sheltered.

Eggs and brood. Egg plain, glossless white. Shape subelliptical. Size (mm): 28.9 × 19.0 (n=1). Full clutch one.

Cycle. No information.

Seasonality. A fresh egg dated 22 April (Allen 1960, 1961, 1961b, Becking 1971, WFVZ).

MOULT. The five October–November birds showed none (UMBRP); no other information.

CONSERVATION. No certain issues identified, but considered near-threatened globally (BTW2).

Himalayan Swiftlet; Nok En Phan Himalai (Thai); **Burung Layang-layang Himalaya** (Malay)

Aerodramus brevirostris (McClelland) 1840, *Proceedings of the Zoological Society of London* 7: 155. TL Assam, NE India.

Not illustrated in this volume

GROUP RELATIONS. Uncertain. Outstanding issues include the placing of short-winged continental populations relative to species such as *A. unicolor* (Indian Swiftlet). *A. (b.) rogersi* Deignan 1955, the so-called Indochinese Swiftlet described from Kanchanaburi province, SW Thailand, and identified in the Peninsula but of unknown status (Deignan 1963), is one of these. Said to be pale-rumped like northwestern nominate *brevirostris*, but classical Himalayan Swiftlet features – feathered tarsus and white basal barbs on back-feathers – are not among its listed characters. Wing-length variation (116–128 mm) is enough to suggest it might even include more than one taxon (cf. Medway 1962, 1966a).

Evidence that ability to echolocate in darkness with a rattle-call might have evolved more than once among grey swiftlets (Medway and Pye 1977) has been used as an argument for down-grading its importance as a generic character and re-merging *Aerodramus* into *Collocalia* (Christidis and Boles 1994). Comparing tissue enzymes, Lim (1994) has shown one species (*fuciphagus*) to be no closer genetically to *Collocalia* than it is to House Swift *Apus nipalensis*, upholding the split.

GLOBAL RANGE. As currently understood, breeds in the Himalayas east from Himachal Pradesh and in hill-tracts of the far-NE Indian subcontinent; SE Tibet; Yunnan, Sichuan and the Changjiang basin east to Hubei; possibly parts of northern continental SE Asia (a bird with large testes collected mid March in

NW Thailand: Deignan 1945); with an outlying population in the mountains of Java, but not elsewhere in the inner tropics (cf. Dickinson 1989, Wells 1975). Some northern populations migrate, wintering to the Bay of Bengal islands and SE Asia as far as the Peninsula, probably also Sumatra (CLBS, and I have seen grey swiftlets at sea off the N tip of Sumatra).

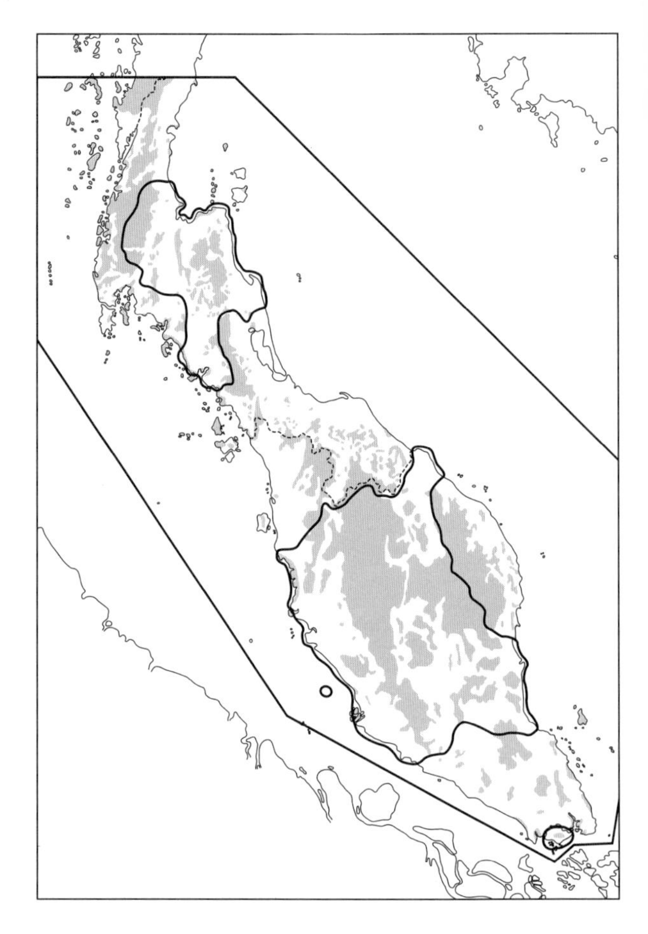

IDENTIFICATION/DESCRIPTION. Given that field identifications are rarely linkable with a confirmation in the hand, there is still no certainty Himalayan can be separated from other grey swiftlets in free flight. On date and other circumstantial evidence, medium-large swiftlets with pale rump, distinctly forked tail and rather stiff-winged, flicking flight, fast-gliding on wings held slightly below the horizontal, are believed to be this species. In the hand, nearest to Black-nest Swiftlet *A. maximus* on measurements, but not as massive and with tail-fork absolutely and proportionately deeper (16–20 percent of standard tail-length). Another useful separating detail is the light versus, in *maximus*, heavy feathering of the outside tarsus (AMNH, BMNH, BMP5, ZDUM).

Bare-part colours. (Adult) all blackish.

Size (mm). (Live and skins: 10 adults, most not sexed): wing 120–131 (the largest bird a female); tail 49–57, tail-fork 8.1–10.6; bill 3.7–5.2; tarsus 9.7–11.9 (AMNH, BMNH, ZDUM, UMBRP).

Weight (g). Two autumn passage-season adults, 10.0, 15.3 (UMBRP).

DISTRIBUTION. Historical summary: *Sur, Nak, Tra, Kel, Pek, Phg, Sel, Neg, Sin.*

GEOGRAPHICAL VARIATION. Wing-length over 128 mm indicates a Sino-Himalayan migrant (populations subtlely differentiated on rump-tone). Below this size-limit, *rogersi* enters the picture, and with it an identification problem that may not be resolved until more populations are described from their breeding-sites, in direct association with nests. Deignan (1963) reported what he determined to be *rogersi* in Surat Thani, and birds in the area of size-overlap (121–128 mm) occur at least as far as Selangor (BMNH).

STATUS AND POPULATION. A non-breeding visitor, local but more or less common; at least in the south, present in all months October–March. Autumn captures (including apparent *rogersi*) at One-Fathom Bank lighthouse (off Selangor), active passage south over Singapore and spring landfall on the N Selangor coast (AMNH, Ollington and Loh 1992, 1993, SINGAV-3, -4, ZRCNUS) imply some also continue on into Indonesia.

HABITATS AND ECOLOGY. Though most records are at likely migration dates, and field identification leaves a margin of uncertainty, many Himalayan Swiftlets appear to winter in the Peninsula, at all elevations and mainly over forest. They are most visible in hill country but a late January sighting of strikingly pale-rumped birds over Pasoh research forest, lowland Negeri Sembilan, must refer to this species. Hundreds over sub-coastal paddyland in NW Selangor on 8 December (R.P. Jaensch) could still have been on the move, but specimens have been collected in the same area in mid January (AMNH, BMNH). It is assumed that wintering flocks roost on the wing.

FORAGING AND FOOD. Grey swiftlets as a group use the middle airspace occupied by foraging swifts, at a mean 50–60 m above vegetation surfaces (Waugh and Hails 1983), but with much variation and no information specific to Himalayan Swiftlet.

SOCIAL ORGANIZATION. In flocks at all times; loners are the exception.

MOVEMENTS. In autumn, large southward movements of grey swiftlets, believed to include Himalayan, have occurred over the Selangor plain during 10 October–20 November. Over Singapore, SE to W-moving migrants as of 7 October, a large arrival on the W end of the island on 13 October, and activity noted to mid November, including thousands crossing the S archipelago on 14–15 November (BIRDLINE 1992, BR 1964, Ollington and Loh 1992, 1993, SINGAV-3). On the Main Range at Fraser's Hill, night-flying birds have been mist-netted around floodlights during 1–16 November, and collected at One-Fathom Bank lighthouse up to 27 November.

In spring, reported arriving on the N Selangor coast on 11 February, with large numbers over Selangor and the adjacent Main Range up to late March (including several thousand moving through the Gap, Selangor/Pahang divide, on 23–25 March) (BR 1964, SINGAV-3).

SURVIVAL. No information.

SOCIAL INTERACTIONS. No information.

VOICE. No information except that, like other *Aerodramus* species, makes echolocating clicks (the rattle-call) as it approaches surfaces, and sporadically also in free airspace.

BREEDING. No proven population.

MOULT. Adults dated 11–27 January showed none (BMNH, ZDUM).

CONSERVATION. No critical issues for migrants, except that reduction of forest cover must affect the supply and diversity of aerial plankton.

Black-nest Swiftlet; Nok En Hang See Liam (Thai); Burung Layang-layang Padi (Malay)

Aerodramus maximus (Hume) 1878, *Stray Feathers* 6: 49. TL S Tenasserim.
Plate 56

GROUP RELATIONS. Apparently free-standing. Not many swiftlet rattle-calls have been analysed but the distinctive single-pulse click of *maximus* is divergent. It may even indicate a separate evolution of echolocation ability among swiftlets (cf. Medway and Pye 1977).

GLOBAL RANGE. Breeds in the Himalayas east from Bhutan and in SE Tibet; Tenasserim to the Peninsula, Sumatra, Java, Borneo and possibly Palawan (collected there but no nesting reported: AMNH, Dickinson 1989). Evidently, some populations disperse or migrate, wintering in and around the southern breeding-range (BR 1963, 1964).

IDENTIFICATION/DESCRIPTION. Short of a direct size comparison, not known to be separable in the field from Edible-nest Swiftlet *A. fuciphagus*. Rump a subtle shade paler than back and upper tail-coverts, less obviously so than in most Himalayan Swiftlets reaching the Peninsula. As long-winged as many of the latter but more massive, with wing proportionately broader and tail less deeply notched (fork 7–11.5 percent of standard tail-length). In the hand, separated from Himalayan also by the outer side of the tarsus being heavily feathered.

Bare-part colours. All blackish.

Size (mm). (Skins: 10 adults, none sexed): wing 128–137; tail 47–58, tail-fork 2.3–6.1; bill 5.2–6.2; tarsus 10.8–13.2 (BMNH, ZDUM).

Weight (g). Breeding adults from Tioman island, 17.3–20.0 (n=3); a winterer from Benom peak, 13.6 (BMNH, ZDUM).

DISTRIBUTION. Historical summary: *Pak, Pha, Kra, Pht, Tra, Son, Sat, Kel, Tru, Phg, Sel, Neg, Joh, Sin,*

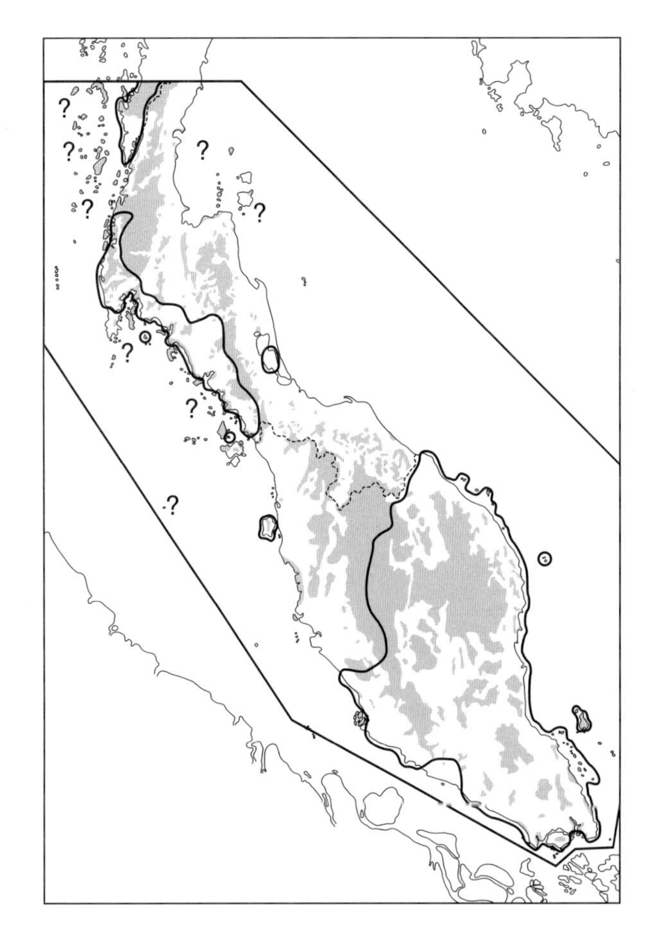

breeding on islands south to Penang (but known there from just a pair in a colony of Edible-nest Swiftlets, and unknown in the Langkawi group) along the W coast; at a minimum 24 colonies from Thalae

Sap-Songkhla to the Pahang–Johor archipelago (south to Yu island) along the E coast, with a possibility of others north to Chumphon (Brandt 1966, Giles 1936); and on Sentosa, Singapore, with one small group on the main island.

GEOGRAPHICAL VARIATION. Pale-rumped nominate *maximus* of the NW breeding-range, replaced by others in island SE Asia (although the situation in Sumatra needs a further review).

STATUS AND POPULATION. Resident and a non-breeding visitor, more or less regular (especially in winter) and common. All recently reported breeding-colonies have been on small islands, up to 26 km off the nearest alternative land, with other even more remote colonies probably yet to be located in the NW (cf. Brockelman and Nadee 1977). The only mainland site is still the ex-Town Hall, Kuala Lumpur, where up to the 1970s a few bred in a colony of Edible-nest Swiftlets (BMP5). A fire and renovations pushed this colony out to an adjacent site, where it thrives, but in 1993 included no black nests.

The only population estimates in the main breeding habitat are extrapolations from commercial nest-harvesting (Medway 1966). During the early 1960s, the average annual take by licensees on Tioman (Pahang) suggested this 114 km^2 island held not less than 11,000 breeding adults.

During winter months, flocks foraging over hill forests inland, at all elevations and far from likely colony-sites, have been presumed to include northern migrants.

HABITATS AND ECOLOGY. As a forager, not distinguished from Himalayan Swiftlet, and over mountain forest they have been collected from the same flocks.

FORAGING AND FOOD. No information separating it from other grey swiftlets.

SOCIAL ORGANIZATION. Gregarious throughout. Breeds in colonies of a few to over 400 pairs (Gibson-Hill 1948c), exclusively or with other *Aerodramus* species.

MOVEMENTS. Winterers have the potential of roosting on the wing, and birds using ridge-crest updraught could be the source of night-time interceptions at floodlights, e.g., at Fraser's Hill two mist-netted on 16/17 November. A lone square-tailed grey swiftlet, either this species or Edible-nest Swiftlet *A. fuciphagus*, has been seen on Perak island, mid-north Melaka Straits, in late July (Langham *et al.* 1974); unexpectedly early in summer for a long-distance migrant.

SURVIVAL. No information.

SOCIAL INTERACTIONS. No information.

VOICE. Shrill chirps, burbling and chittering notes, on the nest and in flight (BMP5). The echolocation rattle, given in darkness and as birds approach surfaces (including water), is a series of clicks, each a single burst of sound in the 1.5–7 kHz frequency range, given at rates varying from 3–11 clicks per second (interval down to 90 milliseconds). This is the one species tested that uses a single rather than double-pulse click (Medway and Pye 1977).

BREEDING

Nest. Selects the twilight zone to completely dark interior of fissures, caves, tunnels and, rarely, deserted buildings, from the shoreline to about 900 m (on Kajang peak, Tioman island). Builds on vertical and overhung rock, concrete and occasionally wooden-plank surfaces. The nest is of hardening salivary cement (by dry weight just over half protein), heavily laminated with swiftlet body- and flight-feathers, giving it the black appearance. Both sexes contribute, spreading a cement foundation then adding layers to the developing rim in short (4–60 second) bouts, interspersed with preening which, since birds also moult through the breeding-season, is the probable main source of feathers. Building activity is exclusively nocturnal, concentrated around midnight and again just before dawn, and from foundation to the laying of the egg takes 35–48 days.

Eggs and brood. Egg plain matt white. Shape blunt, subelliptical. Size (mm): 23.5–21.9 × 16.0–15.3 (n=5); mean 24.1 × 16.2 (n=10 from Lima island, E Johor). Full clutch one. The combined incubation and nestling period averages 71 days.

Cycle. At Sentosa island colonies, most breeders start with a nest of the previous year. If harvested, this nest can be replaced a maximum twice per season, but the incidence of re-laying declines with the third nest (down to 63 percent, from 97 percent among original pairs at the second nest).

Seasonality. Poorly recorded overall, and affected by nest-harvesting. Combining records from Krabi and Songkhla to Singapore: eggs in March, April, May and September, chicks in early April, June, July and September (Berwick 1952, BMNH, BMP5, Brandt 1966, Chasen 1939, Gibson-Hill 1948c, Kang *et al.* 1991, Langham 1980, Medway 1966, SINGAV-1).

MOULT. Replacement of primaries is regular-descendant, with three instances of stage P6 moult in late June. Birds dated December, January, March and April showed no moult (BMNH, UMBRP).

CONSERVATION. Unfettered nest-collecting is a threat. With the consumerism expected in mainland China, pressure on commercial species of swiftlets will increase everywhere (see Edible-nest Swiftlet).

Edible-nest Swiftlet; Nok En Gin Rang (Thai); **Burung Layang-layang Gua** (Malay)

Aerodramus fuciphagus (Thunberg) 1812, *Konglige Vetenskaps Academiens Handlingar* 33: 153.

TL Java.

Plate 56

GROUP RELATIONS. Perhaps free-standing, if it is accepted that all E Asian–Wallacean builders of 'white' nests with few or no feathers and no vegetable inclusions constitute one species, *fuciphagus* (cf. Medway 1966). Re-splitting into two or more species within clines of changing rump-colour (Salomonsen 1983) draws on no fresh understanding of behaviour where different-looking populations meet, and more research is needed.

GLOBAL RANGE. Bay of Bengal islands; Hainan; SE Asia from SW Burma and N Vietnam to the Greater Sunda islands, Bali and the W Philippines; and the Lesser Sunda islands east to Timor.

IDENTIFICATION/DESCRIPTION. Smallest of the local grey swiftlets, overlapping only smallest Himalayan Swiftlets on wing-length, but with proportions of tail-fork intermediate between this species and Black-nest Swiftlet: 9–15.5 percent of standard tail-length (n=12). Throughout the Peninsula, the rump is at least a shade lighter than back and upper tail-coverts, tone varying geographically.

Bare-part colours. (Adult) all blackish.

Size (mm). (Skins: 12 adults, most not sexed): wing 107–120; tail 44.4–51.2, tail-fork 4.2–7.5; bill 4.2–5.4; tarsus 9.1–11.3 (BMNH, UMBRP).

Weight. No data.

DISTRIBUTION. Undoubtedly more widespread in the north. Historical summary: all divisions except *Chu, Ran, Nak, Phu, Pat, Yal, Nar, Pes, Kel, Pra,* with most breeding-colonies on islands, including Tika (*Pak*), the Phiphi group, Lanta, the Tarutao group, Penang and the Sembilan group off the W coast; Phangan and Samui, outcrops in Thalae Sap-Songkhla, the Perhentian, Redang and Tenggol groups, and the Pahang–Johor archipelago (Tulai south to Yu) off the E coast; and on Sentosa, Singapore.

GEOGRAPHICAL VARIATION. Rump-colour darkens with decreasing latitude. Northern *germani* Oustalet 1876 (TL Saigon), rump pale grey with prominent black shaft-lines, has been recognized south definitely to Songkhla in the east, Penang in the west (BMP5); and at a breeding cave on the Sembilan islands (Perak estuary) Allen (1948) had an impression of pale rumps. More nearly uniform dark *amechana* Oberholser 1912 (TL Anamba Islands, S China Sea), rump sooty grey, virtually unstreaked, breeds from Singapore to Selangor and in the Pahang–Johor archipelago, beyond which more research is needed.

STATUS AND POPULATION. More or less regular, common, and resident – breeders returning to roost at the nesting-colony site year-round. Nearly all colonies are on islands or the immediate mainland coast. The most inland example appears still to be in central Kuala Lumpur city, now on the top floor of an abandoned building 150 m away from its old site in the former Town Hall (BMP5), but in July 1993 at the same strength (about 80 pairs) as when first reported in August 1946 (Gibson-Hill 1948c).

HABITATS AND ECOLOGY. Tolerates smaller, more illuminated breeding-sites than Black-nest Swiftlet, closer to the shoreline on smaller, less wooded islets (Gibson-Hill 1948c), but these are average differences and no absolute choice-distinctions are known between species. Many larger, twilight to

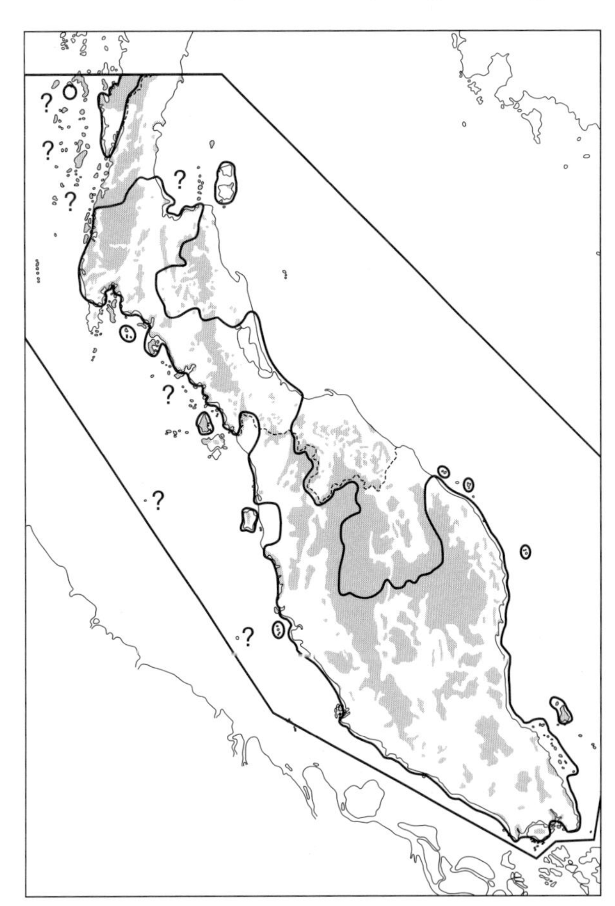

completely dark caves are shared, with evidence of some segregation only by height off the floor. In the Phiphi group (Krabi), Boswall and Kanwanich (1978) found Edible-nest Swiftlets tended to build higher, a behaviour perhaps selected for by centuries of nest-collectors favouring white against black nests. At regularly harvested sites, Edible-nest are also more sensitive to disturbance than Black-nest Swiftlets, leaving the nest and flying out more quickly, and more readily deserting (Berwick 1952, Kang Nee *et al.* 1991).

FORAGING AND FOOD. Non-breeders exit from the roost at dawn and return at dusk, at some island colonies (perhaps far from feeding grounds) with both movements made entirely in darkness (Boswall and Kanwanich 1978). They forage over all kinds of open and forested habitats, and at middle height for swifts, i.e., lower than *Apus* and *Hirundapus* species, but have not generally been distinguished from other grey swiftlets (Waugh and Hails 1983). Almost half the prey items in food-boluses brought to nestlings at a Penang island colony were hymenopterans, especially chalcidoid wasps (dependably including figwasps and their parasites), followed in numerical importance by mayflies, homopteran bugs and dipterans (Langham 1980).

SOCIAL ORGANIZATION. Gregarious at all times. Breeding groups range from a few pairs in small, near-surface grottos, to 500 at an artificial site in Penang (Langham 1980), and some larger colonies are probable.

MOVEMENTS. None confirmed, but solitary grey swiftlets that could have been this species or Black-nest Swiftlet, on Jarak and Perak islands in early January and July, were far from any known or likely breeding-site (a minimum 140 km sea-crossing to have reached Perak). One mist-netted at night at Fraser's Hill on 16 August (BR 1969) was evidently also far from a home colony, and likely to have been roosting on the wing in local ridge-crest updraught.

SURVIVAL. No information.

SOCIAL INTERACTIONS. Copulations occur by and on the nest (Langham 1980).

VOICE. Chirps and burbles in flight and at the nest in daylight. In darkness and at any time when approaching surfaces, gives echolocation clicks at a rate of 6–17 per second, each a pair of 2-millisecond pulses in the frequency range 2–9 kHz (Indonesian data from Medway and Pye 1977).

BREEDING

Nest. The largest colonies are deep inside secluded fissures, caves, tunnels and unoccupied buildings (some purposefully emptied to attract this species), in conditions ranging from deep shade to full, permanent darkness. Vertical to overhung rock, concrete and plank surfaces are accepted, and small breaks are sometimes used to help support nests (the whole of the Kuala Lumpur colony is on a 1 cm ledge close to the ceiling of a high corridor, with not a single nest on any lower, sheer part of the wall). As with Black-nest Swiftlets, the foundation is a patch of salivary cement out of which a cup rim is built up by progressive layering, over a minimum 40 days to the laying of the first egg. Nests are commonly pure cement but some have a few swiftlet body-feathers admixed, and this behaviour varies between colonies (most Kuala Lumpur nests have feathers). Built against a wall, the cup is near semi-circular, rim-diameters 69–65 × 38–30mm (n=4).

Eggs and brood. Eggs are plain matt white. Shape blunt, subelliptical. Size (mm): 20.6 × 13.4, 19.6 × 12.8 (n=2, from Kuala Lumpur), weight about 1.2 g (average). Full clutch occasionally only one, mostly two eggs, laid a mean 3.3 days apart (interval longer at replacement nests, which are also less successful), with hatching staggered by the same interval after an average 23-day incubation period. The total incubation–nestling period is 68 days. At a well-guarded Penang colony, fledging success over the full season averaged 40.4 percent, with a clutch-size of two the most productive.

Cycle. At harvested sites, pairs are able to replace their nest twice in a season. Where the initial nest survives, it can be used for up to three successive broods, and some nests have a still longer life-span.

Seasonality. A Penang colony is believed to have started laying in August, with peaks during October–December and in February, steep decline in March, and last hatchings due in April or May. Elsewhere, eggs in April (Songkhla), May (Perak), and May–August in Kuala Lumpur, i.e., nearly year-round overall, but few data from north of Malaysia (Allen 1948, Brandt 1966, Kang Nee *et al.* 1991, Langham 1980).

MOULT. Replacement of primaries is regular-descendant, but sometimes at two loci per wing as a result of re-starts after suspensions, with moult of secondaries starting later but generally overlapping primaries (Langham 1980). At his Penang colony, Langham found a high incidence of primary moult through September–March, but no evidence of an absolute break in activity. Moulting and breeding overlap widely at the level of the individual.

CONSERVATION. See Black-nest Swiftlet. White nests have a substantially higher market value than black nests. At the moment, only the few colonies well-guarded in private hands are harvested on anything approaching a sustainable schedule, and any future 'farming' industry will need to regulate itself in greater accordance with the facts of swiftlet biology (Kang Nee *et al.* 1991). Where this will leave species other than the desired *fuciphagus* is not yet clear, but some control of Black-nest numbers in favour of Edible-nest Swiftlets at mixed colonies has been practiced in the past (e.g., Giles 1936). Capacity of deforested landscapes to generate the aerial insect plankton needed to sustain large colonies tied to a fixed breeding-site is another, quite separate issue.

Silver-rumped Spinetail; Nok En Lek Hang Nam Taphok Khao (Thai); Burung Layang-layang Tongkeng Perak (Malay)

Rhaphidura leucopygialis (Blyth) 1849, *Journal of the Asiatic Society of Bengal* 18: 809. TL Penang island.

Plate 56

GROUP RELATIONS. Uncertain; perhaps closest to Afrotropical *R. sabini* (Sabine's Spinetail).

GLOBAL RANGE. The Greater Sunda islands and the Peninsula to far-S Tenasserim.

IDENTIFICATION/DESCRIPTION. Mass of a grey swiftlet but with larger wings. In particular, inner primaries are proportionately much longer, producing a characteristically broad, 'butter-knife' wing-tip. Entirely deep, glossy black except for lower back to upper tail-coverts sharply demarcated silvery grey to white with black rachial streaks, overlapping the tail to the base of its spines. Flight weaving, fluttery, bat-like and relatively slow.

Bare-part colours. (Adult) iris blackish brown; bill blackish; feet dark purple-flesh.

Size (mm). (Skins: 6 males, 5 females; adult): wing 117–124 and 117–122; inclusive tail 36.6–38.6 and 35.3–38.5, longest (central) spines approximately 9; bill 4.3–6.4 (sexes combined); tarsus 10.4–12.2 (sexes combined) (BMNH, ZDUM).

Weight. No data.

DISTRIBUTION. Historical summary: all divisions except *Phu, Son, Pat, Pra,* with additional W-coast island records from Lanta, ?Tarutao, Penang and Pangkor.

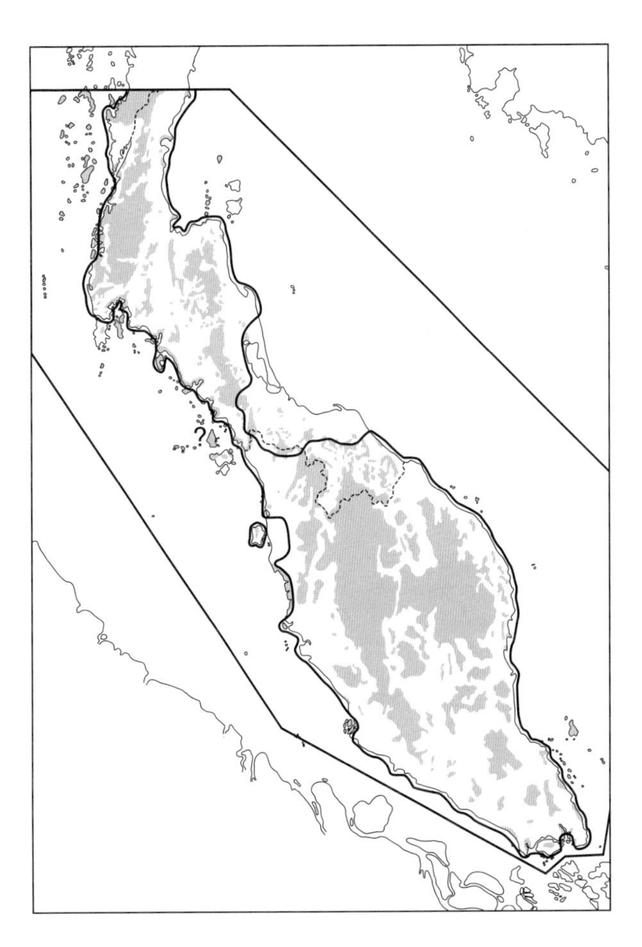

GEOGRAPHICAL VARIATION. None recognized.

STATUS AND POPULATION. Resident, regular and common, at plains level and in hills to around 1200 m but believed not to live permanently above the Montane ecotone.

HABITATS AND ECOLOGY. Not found away from the canopy and clearings of mature and well-grown evergreen and semi-evergreen Lowland forest, including peatswamp forest; less regularly Lower Montane forest (ENGGANG-1, -3). Particularly favours forest watercourses wide enough to break the tree canopy, hawking along the stream a few metres above its surface.

FORAGING AND FOOD. Foraging other than over water and clearings is close to the 'skin' of the forest canopy, including around emergent crowns. With Glossy Swiftlet and Whiskered Treeswift, this spinetail occupies the lowest level of all swift airspace, with 31 percent of foraging records 10 m or less from the vegetation surface (Waugh and Hails 1983). Drinks in flight by dipping down to scoop from stream.

SOCIAL ORGANIZATION. Forages mostly in small parties. Roosting and nesting dispersion is not known in the Peninsula but communal use of a hollow tree is reported from Borneo.

MOVEMENTS. None known.

SURVIVAL. No information.

SOCIAL INTERACTIONS. No information.

VOICE. No information.

BREEDING. Copulation in flight over forest on 15 February and a female with maturing eggs collected in Trang on 12 March (ENGGANG-1, Riley 1938). No other data.

MOULT. Replacement of primaries is regular-descendant, commonly with two adjacent inner-hand feathers in overlapping growth, out to stage P6. Among 25 apparent adults covering all months except February, June and December, 14 showed active wing-moult during late May–early November (P10), with latest starts in July, 100 percent activity (n=9) in August and earliest completion in late August. Others dated January and March–May showed none, indicating sharp seasonality (BMNH, ZDUM).

CONSERVATION. If, as seems likely, it depends on over-mature, hollow trees for roosting and nesting, logging and other forestry practices could have a negative impact; but it is not excluded from logged forest and some fieldwork is called for.

White-throated Needletail; Nok En Yai Khaw Khao (Thai); Burung Layang-layang Ekor Runcing Utara (Malay)

Hirundapus caudacutus (Latham) 1801, *Index Ornithologicus, Supplementum*: 57. TL New South Wales.

Plate 57

GROUP RELATIONS. Likely to form a superspecies with *H. cochinchinensis* (Silver-backed Needletail), believed to be isolated by altitude where their breeding-ranges meet in the eastern Himalayas (Inskipp and Inskipp 1985, Ripley 1982).

GLOBAL RANGE. Breeds in what may be two separated ranges: across southern Siberia east of the Urals to Sakhalin and the Kurile islands, south to Mongolia, NE China, Korea and central Japan; and in the Himalayas east from Pakistan, hill-tracts of the far-NE Indian subcontinent, and SE Tibet to Sichuan and N Yunnan. Northern and some southern populations migrate, wintering mainly in Australia (a few to New Zealand), north to S New Guinea and perhaps in Wallacea.

IDENTIFICATION/DESCRIPTION. Generic shape: for a swift, very large but streamlined, torpedo-shaped head and body; proportionately broad hand, noticeable in soaring flight; wings swept distinctly back during high-speed flapping and gliding. As in all giant needletails, the lower tail-coverts and band along the flank form a horseshoe of white, sharp against dark belly. In good light, light brown saddle, paling to fawn in the centre of the back, and tail more or less square-cut when opened due to short, inconspicuous spines, separate White-throated and Silver-backed from Brown-backed Needletail. Chin and throat of some Silver-backed Needletails are distinctly paler grey than breast, but no match for the clear, sharply demarcated white of this species. At close range, shows tertials margined white on the inner web. Lores and narrow forehead-band are either white or concolorous with the rest of the cap.

Bare-part colours. (Adult) iris deep brown; bill blackish; feet purple-slate (HBI).

Size (mm). Wing 191–212; tail including spines 48–60 (BMP5); no local data.

Weight. No information.

DISTRIBUTION. A concentration of records (none very recent) in W-central Malaysia must reflect observer effort. Historical summary: *Phg, Sel, Neg*.

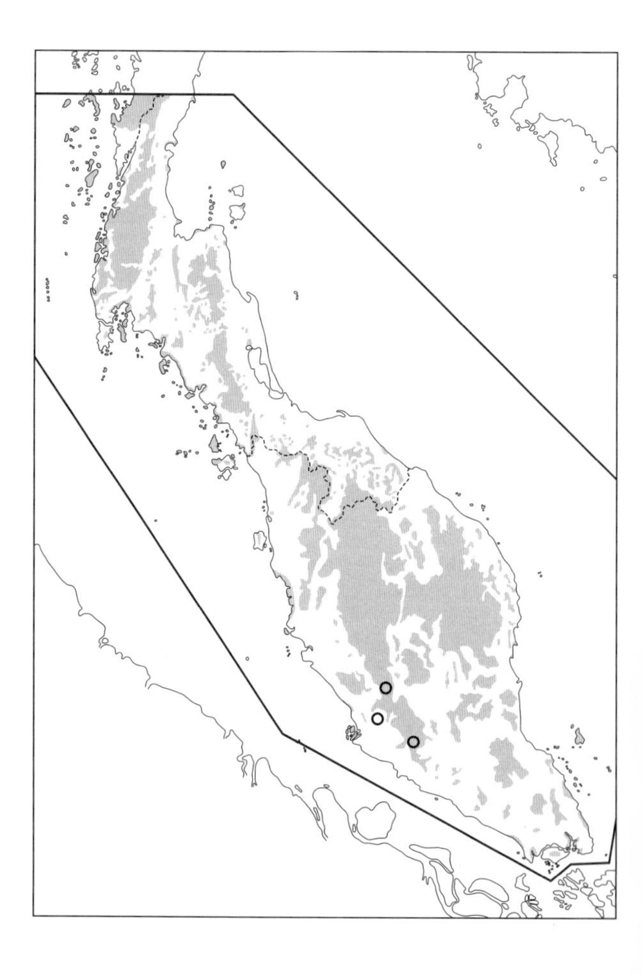

GEOGRAPHICAL VARIATION. None handled in the Peninsula and field sightings have not been good enough to identify subspecies. On geographical grounds, since it has been collected on a potential autumn passage date in W Java (Mees 1985), southern *nudipes* (with all-dark head-top) is more likely than northern nominate *caudacutus*.

STATUS AND POPULATION. Passage migrant at only a little above the status of vagrant, and several records in the local literature are no longer considered dependable. Except for a bird with other swifts moving north over the mid-Selangor plain ahead of a March storm (BR 1976–77), sightings have all been over the crest and passes of the Main Range, between Jelebu (Negeri Sembilan) and Fraser's Hill (BR 1963, 1964, 1965).

HABITATS AND ECOLOGY. No relevant information.

FORAGING AND FOOD. No information.

SOCIAL ORGANIZATION. Singles and groups of up to five.

MOVEMENTS. Still-acceptable limiting passage dates are 15 November, at Fraser's Hill, and 18 March–15 May. Remains of a small-spined *Hirundapus* picked up under the trig-beacon of Bunga Buah peak, Selangor, in late October (BR 1966) were not separated from commoner Silver-backed Needletail.

SURVIVAL. No information.

SOCIAL INTERACTIONS. No information.

VOICE. No information.

BREEDING. No population.

MOULT. No information.

CONSERVATION. No relevant issues.

Silver-backed Needletail; Nok En Yai Hua Taa Dam (Thai); Burung Layang-layang Ekor Runcing Indocina (Malay)

Hirundapus cochinchinensis (Oustalet) 1878, *Bulletin de la Société Philomathique de Paris* series 7(2): 52. TL Saigon.

Plate 57

GROUP RELATIONS. See White-throated Needletail.

GLOBAL RANGE. In summer, along the foot of the Himalayas east from Nepal and in the far-NE Indian subcontinent; Taiwan and possibly elsewhere in S China (on passage, once, Hong Kong: Chalmers 1986); and continental SE Asia apparently east of a line NW Burma–SE Thailand, including Cambodia and S Vietnam. Some populations migrate, wintering from an unknown northern limit to the Greater Sunda islands and Bali; possibly entering W Wallacea.

IDENTIFICATION/DESCRIPTION. As White-throated Needletail in all essential characters except the head shows no white and the underparts are blacker, as dark as in Brown-backed Needletail. Throat pale- to smoky grey, but tone distinguishable from breast only at close range, not in a typical field view. From Brown-backed Needletail *H. giganteus* by slightly smaller size if they are seen together; otherwise by sandy fawn saddle, and tail more or less square-cut in all postures, with white lower tail-coverts (which extend a common distance along the webbed part of the tail of all *Hirundapus*) appearing to reach almost to the tail-tip because projecting spines are too fine to be obvious.

Bare-part colours. (Adult) iris deep brown; bill blackish; feet purplish to pale lavender (Robinson 1928).

Size (mm). (Live and skins: 14 adults, most not sexed): wing 173–192 (known males not below 182, females up to 187); total tail 46–49, spines 2–7 (longest not above 13 percent of standard tail-length); bill 7.9–9.5; tarsus 15.2–16.8 (BMNH, UMBRP, ZDUM).

Weight (g). Autumn migrants, 83.8, 90.0 and 111.0 (the last carrying much fat).

DISTRIBUTION. Presumably overlooked in the north. Historical summary: *Pha, Ked, Pek, Phg, Sel, Neg, Joh, Sin*, with additional island records from Langkawi and, during spring passage, Tioman (BR 1970–71, 1980–81).

GEOGRAPHICAL VARIATION. Subspecies have been named on throat-tone but Mees (1973) shows this character to be a continuous, evidently individual, variable.

STATUS AND POPULATION. A non-breeding visitor recorded in all months September–April. In small numbers, probably also a passage migrant, and most Singapore records are at passage dates. Local

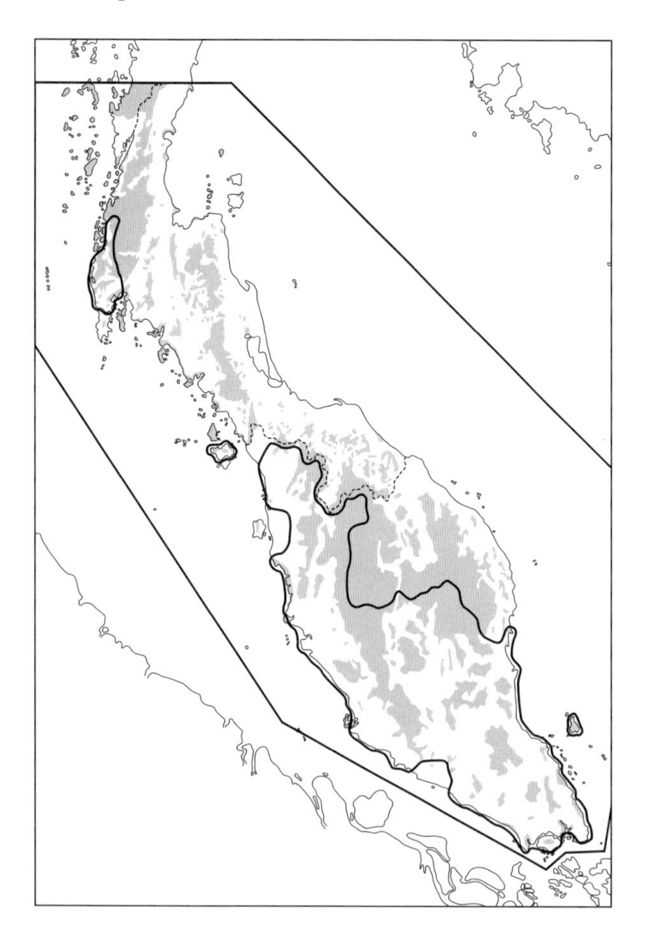

and uncommon to common; wintering parties have a patchy distribution (are perhaps nomadic).

HABITATS AND ECOLOGY. Daily foraging distances are likely to be great, but most records imply flocks stay close to, or over, forest or other mixed woodland terrain. Recorded to at least 1500 m across summits of the Main and Larut Ranges, and on isolated peaks such as Tapis (E Pahang) and Chabang Tiga (Johor) (BR 1970–71, SINGAV-3), but in largest wintering numbers at plains level. Biggest flocks, of 50–250, are reported over coastal forest and adjoining paddyland on Langkawi island, and forested and scrubby headlands of the Pahang coast (BR 1968, 1969, 1970–71).

FORAGING AND FOOD. Little information except that all giant needletails forage mostly at the top of swift airspace, cover large distances at high speed and flock in thermals and other updraughts, where they may specialize on swarming insects caught in the rising air (Waugh and Hails 1983). During hot, dry-season weather on Langkawi island, a flock of about 100 dipped to drink in a paddyland irrigation canal.

SOCIAL ORGANIZATION. On passage, typically in ones and twos (occasionally parties) but, as stated, overwinterers concentrate sometimes in considerable flocks, perhaps mutually attracted to temporary food-patches. The observation of mass drinking suggests flocks may be durable.

MOVEMENTS. The earliest autumn date is 8 September (three at McRitchie reservoir, Singapore), with ones and twos passing south over the summit of Tapis, E Pahang, during 28 September. Ten mist-netted at night around the Fraser's Hill floodlights, crest of the Main Range, during 28 October–3 December (one casualty carried heavy subcutaneous fat) are also likely to have been on the move, although roosting by winterers on ridge-crest updraught cannot be ruled out (BMP5, SINGAV-4, UMBRP). There are no definite records of spring movement, but latest dates are 16 and 23 April: ten or more over the coast of Tioman island and 25 over Panti summit, Johor (BR 1980–81, SINGAV-3).

SURVIVAL. No information.

SOCIAL INTERACTIONS. No information.

VOICE. No information.

BREEDING. No known population.

MOULT. Birds dated October–December and February showed no wing-moult, but body-moult noted in November (UMBRP).

CONSERVATION. No defined issues. As for other swifts, continued clearance of forest must affect the supply and distribution of prey.

Brown-backed Needletail; Nok En Yai Hua Taa Khao (Thai); Burung Layang-layang Ekor Runcing Biasa (Malay)

Hirundapus giganteus (Temminck) 1825, *Nouveau Recueil de Planches Coloriées d'Oiseaux* 61: plate 364. TL Banten, W Java.

Plate 57

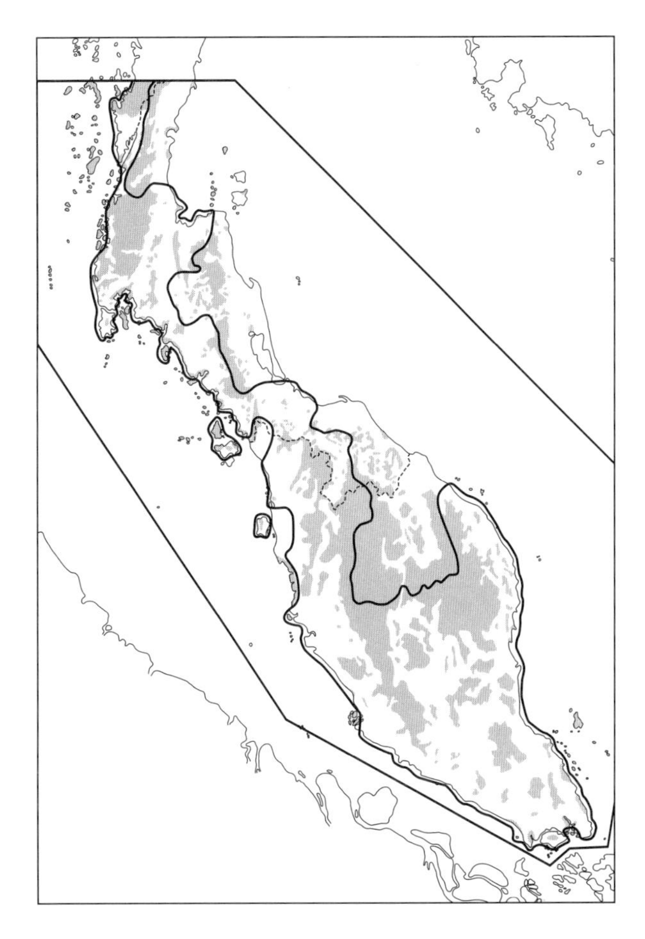

GROUP RELATIONS. Uncertain. Lumped by some with larger, allopatric *H. celebensis* (Purple Needletail) of the Philippines and Sulawesi. The latter has a white loral spot like northern *H.g. indicus* but is as glossy as members of the *H. caudacutus* group, and Wallacean birds have tail-spines weaker and shorter, much less graduated out from the tail-centre than in *giganteus*, giving the tail a shorter, squarer shape (Mees 1985, NNML). The one Philippine specimen examined (from Mindoro) had a much more *giganteus*-like tail (AMNH), suggesting a need for further study.

GLOBAL RANGE. Hill-tracts of the far-NE and SW Indian subcontinent, Sri Lanka and the Andamans; and SE Asia from Burma, Laos and S Vietnam to the Greater Sunda islands, Bali and Palawan (Mees 1985). Some northern populations are migratory, wintering from an unknown northern limit to the Peninsula and Melaka Straits islands; presumably also Sumatra but with no formal record.

IDENTIFICATION/DESCRIPTION. Heavier-bodied but not longer-winged than the other giant needletails. Dorsal saddle dull mid brown, head and body otherwise uniform black-brown, including throat; lightly glossed only on the wings and tail. In flight, similar to other species but much longer (around 25 percent of standard tail-length), stouter and more strongly graduated tail-spines can be seen at a distance, giving the fanned tail a rounded margin well clear of the white lower tail-coverts. Lores either dark, concolorous with the rest of the face, or sharply white; occasionally an intermediate tawny.

Bare-part colours. (Adult) iris deep brown; bill blackish; feet pink-grey to purplish slate.

Size (mm). (Live and skins: 39 adults, most not sexed): wing 185–209 (no difference among known males and females); total tail 57–76, longest (T1) spines about 17.0; bill 8.9–10.0; tarsus 19.3–21.0 (BMNH, BMP5, UMBRP, ZDUM).

Weight (g). A male *giganteus*, 142.0; an *indicus* dated May, 139.1 (UMBRP, ZDUM).

DISTRIBUTION. Historical summary: all divisions except *Chu, Nak, Pht, Pat, Nar, Pes, Kel, Pra*, with additional W-coast island records (status unknown) from Lanta, Tarutao, Langkawi, Penang, Pangkor and Pisang.

GEOGRAPHICAL VARIATION. Resident nominate *giganteus* is dark-lored, and such birds have not been found north of Pakchan. White-lored birds are northern migrant *indicus* Hume 1973 (TL Andamans and S India). The status of tawny-lored intermediates, collected in the far south, is unknown.

STATUS AND POPULATION. Resident and a non-breeding visitor, regular and more or less common at plains level and on mountains to at least 1500 m, with summer records to S Johor but, in recent years, a near-complete gap during April–August in Singapore. It is rather common there in other months, especially December–March (BIRDLINE 1993, SINGAV-2, -3), although the specimen-backed southern limit of migrant *indicus* is still only Pisang island, off W Johor (AMNH, Robinson 1927). Presumed resident *giganteus* has been collected in summer on some larger islands of the nearby Riau archipelago (Indonesia) but its Singapore population may now be at a low ebb.

A December-dated collection from Pisang (too small an island to be likely to support residents) includes both subspecies, implying local foragers link up temporarily with migrants, or that some Peninsular populations themselves include migrants (BMP5).

HABITATS AND ECOLOGY. Daily movements are likely to be long, and Brown-backed Needletails appear intermittently over all types of habitats, but are dependably linked to forest cover, up to the Upper Montane zone. Around Ban Bang Tieo (Krabi), a villager has reported large needletails, probably this species, roosting in tree-hollows, where they are caught for food (P.D. Round).

FORAGING AND FOOD. Like other giant needletails, forages mostly in the top sector of swift airspace, moving long distances at high speed and gathering where insects are liable to be caught in rising air, including in thermals and updraught over scarps, and even over large fires (many Brown-backs attended a forest fire on Cape Rachado, Negeri Sembilan, in mid August). It has been suggested this species and congeners seek scattered swarms of hymenopterans, termites, etc., rather than feed opportunistically (Morse and Liago 1968, Waugh and Hails 1983). Food of a mist-netted *indicus* held overnight for ringing included exclusively large, winged ants, of only four morpho-species among 32 head-capsules recovered from regurgitated pellets (BR 1974–75).

Brown-backed Needletails bathe and drink while skimming over open water, typically in the evening.

SOCIAL ORGANIZATION. Never seen in the flock-sizes sometimes attained by wintering Silver-backed Needletail, but parties of 10–20 riding up-currents over ridges, etc., are not uncommon year-round.

MOVEMENTS. Autumn influx into Singapore begins fairly regularly in the second week of September, and at Fraser's Hill 21 night-flying birds (only *indicus* confirmed) have been netted at floodlights during 3 September–17 November. In spring, most leave Singapore by late March, and flocks in S Perak known to have included *indicus* also declined in March. But at Fraser's Hill a night-flying *indicus* has been netted on 17 May (BIRDLINE 1993, BMP5, BR 1974–75, Edgar 1947).

SURVIVAL. No information.

SOCIAL INTERACTIONS. No record of actual copulation on the wing, but small, noisy courting parties fly not far above the forest canopy. Displaying in pairs, the individual flying above and slightly ahead glides briefly on sharply up-canted wings, with short bouts of slow, deep flapping.

VOICE. During sexual flights, a brittle squeak, *chirrwiek*, repeated 2–3 times; also a single thin *chiek* (Bromley 1948a).

BREEDING. Not described locally but assumed to nest in hollows of forest trees. Two birds exploring a knot-hole in a dead Seraya *Shorea curtisii* on Bukit Timah hill, Singapore, on 6 February (MBR 1982–83) supply the only direct supporting evidence.

MOULT. Replacement of primaries is regular-descendant, with up to three adjacent inner feathers in overlapping growth, and two out to stage P9. Among 19 presumed resident *giganteus* covering all months except December, January, May and October, seven showed active wing-moult during early April (P1–3)–July, with completions as of late June and all three July records at stage P10. August birds were all fresh, with other non-moulters dated September and December–early March (BMNH, ZRCNUS), indicating an unexpectedly short, concentrated season. Passage-dated *indicus* show no moult, but none has been handled at mid winter (UMBRP).

CONSERVATION. More information is needed on this swift's breeding and roosting biology relative to impacts of logging on the supply of large, hollow trees in forest.

Asian Palm Swift; Nok En Taan (Thai); Burung Layang-layang Lontar (Malay)

Cypsiurus balasiensis (J.E. Gray) 1829, Griffith's *Animal Kingdom arranged by Baron Cuvier* 7: 60. TL Calcutta.

Plate 56

GROUP RELATIONS. Forms a superspecies with *C. parvus* (African Palm Swift).

GLOBAL RANGE. Sri Lanka, the Indian subcontinent except the arid NW; S Yunnan and Hainan; and SE Asia to the Greater Sunda islands, Bali and the Philippines.

IDENTIFICATION/DESCRIPTION. A small, slender, all-sooty grey swift with same mass as Glossy Swiftlet but proportionately much longer, narrower, more tapering wings and long, narrow, deeply forked tail, the fork apparent only as birds bank in flight. Common in the vicinity of fan palms and infallibly identified by its 4-syllable flight-call (see Voice). The first plumage of the nestling is teleoptile, without the early down of *C. parvus* (Hails and Turner 1984) and, as in most swifts, the longest primaries and outermost tail-feathers of juveniles are broader, blunter-ended than those of adults.

Bare-part colours. (Adult) iris blackish; bill blackish; feet blackish with whitish tarsal callosity and sole.

Size (mm). (Live and skins: 32 adults, most not sexed): wing 109–121 (both sexes to the top of this range); tail 45–57, tail-fork 16.3–23.5; bill 5.2–6.4; tarsus 7.9–9.8.

Weight (g). Late July adults, 8.3–10.0 (n=17); juveniles, 8.3–9.9 (n=3).

DISTRIBUTION. Historical summary: all divisions, with additional island records from Lanta, Langkawi, Penang and Pangkor off the W coast; Phangan and Samui off the E coast; and Ubin, St John's and Sentosa, Singapore.

GEOGRAPHICAL VARIATION. Subspecies *infumatus* Sclater 1865 (TL Banjarmasin, S Kalimantan), of E Asia.

STATUS AND POPULATION. Resident, regular and common.

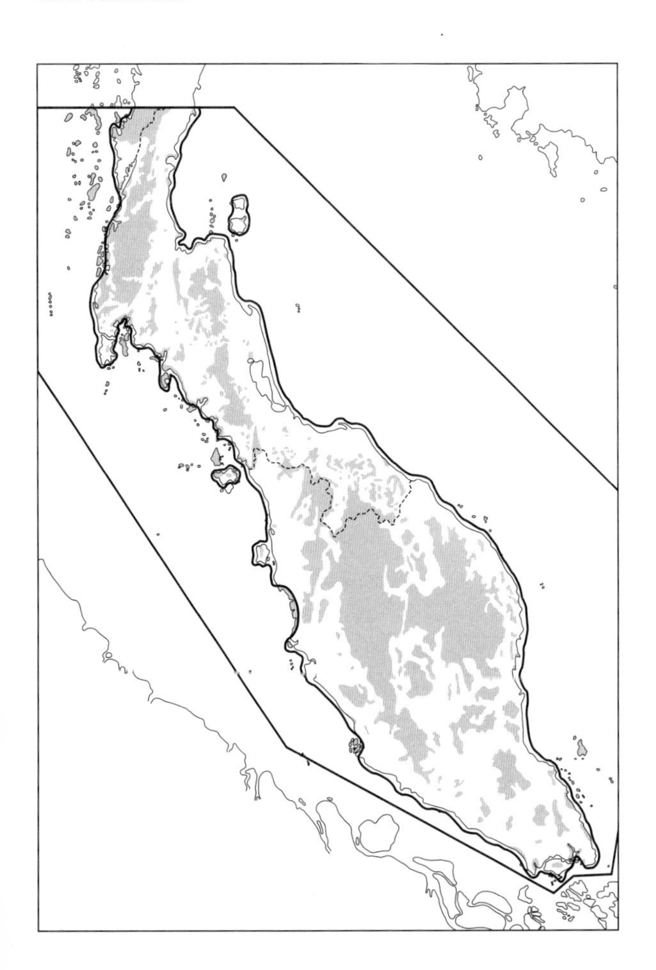

HABITATS AND ECOLOGY. Small colonies reside year-round in the neighbourhood of tree fan palms *Borassus* and *Livistona* spp., free-standing in parks, gardens and open agriculture (tall *B. flabellifer* is a feature of paddyland and grazing-ground landscapes south to latitude about 6°N), or with crowns emergent from the general level of the forest canopy, at plains level and on slopes, locally, as on Tahan massif, Taman Negara, to around 1200 m in the Lower Montane zone. Birds roost, and nest, in the midrib channel of the upper (outer) surface of a pendant frond, sheltered by the next overlapping frond.

FORAGING AND FOOD. Feeds in the lower part of airspace occupied by swifts, at a rough mean 13 m above open ground, but three times higher over the canopy of forest. Prey items identified in boluses delivered to nestlings, and in nestling faeces, at a suburban Kuala Lumpur colony included a combined 61 percent hymenopterans (mostly flying ants), 14 percent alate termites, ten percent dipterans, nine percent beetles, and smaller proportions mainly of homopteran bugs and mayflies (Hails and Turner 1984, Waugh and Hails 1983).

SOCIAL ORGANIZATION. Forages mainly alone, rarely more than 4–5 together, and breeding-colonies range from a few to not above 15–20 pairs.

MOVEMENTS. None recorded.

SURVIVAL. No information.

SOCIAL INTERACTIONS. Pre-breeders indulge in tightly whirling, noisy, communal courtship flights in the vicinity of the colony site.

VOICE. A high-pitched, hurried *tiketitee*, given on the wing around colony trees, while foraging, and particularly during courtship flights. Another flight-call is an insistent, repeated *feek*.

BREEDING

Nest. Rarely less than 3 m up; an open cup built of seed-pappus (reed *Phragmites* sp. and silk-cotton *Ceiba pentandra* identified) with a small (less than five percent) inclusion of feathers, agglutinated, strengthened at the rim and fixed with salivary cement into the midrib channel of the upper surface of a pendant palm-frond. Measurements (mm) (chord from the top of the attachment to the front of the rim × external width): 70 × 50, 50 × 40 (n=2).

Eggs and brood. Eggs plain, matt white. Size (mm): 17.8 × 11.5 (mean, n=6); fresh-laid weight (g) 1.2 (mean, n=6). Clutch two (only one of a sample of 15 nests had a clutch of one); eggs laid at an interval of two days and, unlike those of African *C. parvus*, not glued to the nest. Mean incubation and nestling periods are 18.3 and 28.5 days, the chick reaching an asymptote weight nearly 25 percent above adult weight before fledging. Mostly, only one chick fledges, and at one colony during one season, overall fledging-success from eggs laid was 38 percent.

Cycle. Both sexes incubate (sitting vertically, facing into the leaf), in sum for about 78 percent of pre-hatching time. Food-boluses are delivered to chicks at a mean rate of one per 45 minutes, with interval shortest (down to 10 minutes) in the early morning, longest (over three hours) during the mid-day period. Up to two broods are raised per season, with the second clutch started 8–26 days after the fledging of brood one.

Seasonality. Active nests are recorded in all months December–July, in some years with some young in the nest until August (BMP5, Hails and Turner 1984).

MOULT. Replacement of primaries is regular-descendant, with instances of overlapping growth between adjacent feathers over the whole tract. Seventeen birds at a Kuala Lumpur colony-site on 28 July, after breeding had ended, were all moulting wings: one at P1–3 (post-juvenile schedule), the rest between P7–8 and P9–10 (two suspended at P7). Eight of these were also moulting outer tail-feathers. Of 15 from a wider area and span of years, and covering all months except September, November and December, five showed active wing-moult in mid and late May (P3, P1–2), June and October (P8, P10), with completions as of about early July. Others dated January–April showed no moult, confirming the general seasonality; also that moult and breeding coincide.

CONSERVATION. No critical issues.

Pacific Swift; Nok En Taphok Khao Haang Chehk (Thai); Burung Layang-layang Timur (Malay)

Apus pacificus Latham 1801, *Index Ornithologicus, Supplementum*: 58. TL New South Wales.
Plate 57

GROUP RELATIONS. Lack (1956) included NE Indian *Apus acuticauda* (Dark-rumped Swift) in a species *pacificus*. Certain of its characters (glossy black upperparts, plain black lower tail-coverts sharp against white-fringed belly) are matched in some E Burmese *p. cooki* (BMNH), but not in geographically closer *p. leuconyx*, and Vaurie (1959) cites differences in tail-shape and preferred nest-site. More probably, *pacificus* and *acuticauda* are a superspecies.

GLOBAL RANGE. Breeds in temperate-zone Siberia from the Altai and upper Ob east to Kamchatka and Japan; the Himalayas and hill-tracts of the far-NE Indian subcontinent; the Nansei islands, China including Taiwan and islands towards Luzon; and SE Asia, in Burma and NW Thailand. Most populations migrate, wintering through the Indian subcontinent and continental SE Asia, and in New Guinea and Australia to New Zealand.

IDENTIFICATION/DESCRIPTION. A rather large, rakish swift with long, tapering, scimitar-shaped wings and long, proportionately narrow tail, markedly forked when opened. Flight direct, on powerful, measured wing-beats, lacking the whirring action of House Swift *A. nipalensis*. Intensity and glossiness of black, development of pale fringing on the upperparts, and width and conspicuousness of the white rump-band vary with breeding origin. Otherwise, chin and throat white, breast and belly (and in most also lower tail-coverts) sooty black with broad, grey-white fringes forming a scalloped pattern; lower tail-coverts of some plain black.

Bare-part colours. (Adult) iris black-brown; bill blackish; feet dark pink-grey (BMNH).

Size (mm). (Live and skins: 27 adults, most not sexed): wing 168–183; tail 65–83, tail-fork 21–35; bill 9.2 (1 only); tarsus 12.0, 13.1 (2 only) (BMNH, UMBRP, ZDUM).

Weight (g). Night-fliers intercepted at Fraser's Hill in October–December, 36.7–53.0 (n=20) (UMBRP).

DISTRIBUTION. Historical summary: all divisions except *Ran*, *Nak*, with additional island records (on likely passage dates) from Phiphi, Lanta, Tarutao, Langkawi, Penang and Pangkor off the W coast; Phangan, the Redang group and the Pahang–Johor archipelago (Tulai) off the E coast; and St John's, Sentosa, Semakau and Sudong, Singapore.

GEOGRAPHICAL VARIATION. Three subspecies identified, on uniformity and tone of upperparts, width of rump-band, and strength of dark shaft-streaking on rump and throat. N Palaearctic *pacificus* is virtually unglossed black-brown above, with narrow, pale grey edging, and head and nape obviously lighter than mantle; rump-band about 20 mm wide, with shaft-lines fine. SE Palaearctic *kanoi* Yamashina 1942 (TL Lanyu island) is glossy brownish black, pale edging slight to absent, and head and nape only slightly lighter than mantle; rump-band about 15 mm wide, again, with shaft-lines fine. SE Asian-breeding *cooki* Harington 1913 (TL Gokteik gorge, E Burma) is glossy black above, with fringing slight to absent, and head and nape scarcely lighter than mantle;

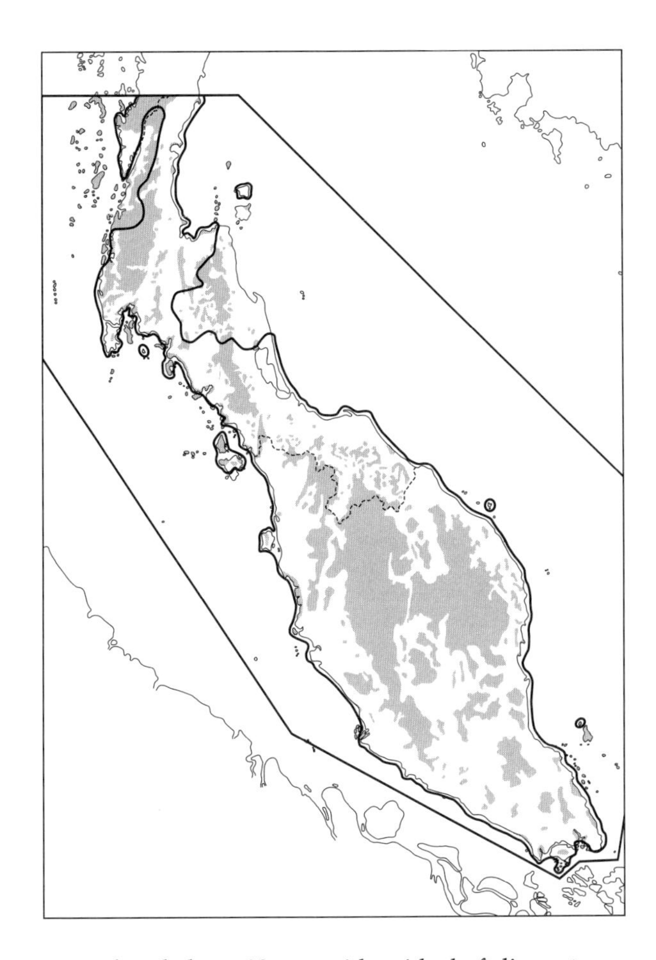

rump-band about 10 mm wide with shaft-lines strong and numerous (Deignan 1956). Apparent non-migrants seen in June in W Surat Thani, well south of the known breeding-range, showed no white on the rump. They have not yet been identified.

STATUS AND POPULATION. For an hour or more on two successive afternoons in late June 1985 a flock of about 40 soared over a low, forested ridge close to limestone cliffs (typical nesting habitat) at the edge of Khao Sok national park, Surat Thani. In Burma, young are still in the nest in early July (BMNH) hence either these had failed to migrate from winter quarters (occasional mid-summer stragglers have also been seen in Kelantan: Young 1941) or they were nesting locally. None showed any sign of a rump-band, hence they may not have been the expected, tropical-breeding *cooki*. Otherwise, a passage migrant and non-breeding winter visitor, more or less regular and common. The Peninsula is believed to be the southern terminus of wintering in SE Asia (Mees 1973) and overwinterers, widespread through the Thai provinces and forested areas of Kedah and N Perak, including the upper valley of the Perak river, thin out in the south. At mid winter, sometimes large parties make erratic appearances in Selangor, Pahang and Negeri Sembilan, but apart from a pair over Bukit Timah nature reserve on 7 January (Ollington and Loh 1993), disappear from Singapore for over two months, late November–mid February. By their narrow, inconspicuous rump-bands, Kedah and Perak winterers have been identified as *cooki* or *kanoi*. Both have been collected in January and February at Selangor/Pahang boundary passes (Deignan 1956, ZDUM, ZRCNUS), whereas nominate *pacificus* has been confirmed only in autumn and spring. Possibly all overwinterers are these southern races.

HABITATS AND ECOLOGY. Occurs over all kinds of terrain and habitats, but with a strong foraging preference for forest (Waugh and Hails 1983), from coastal plains to at least 1400 m on mountains. Overwinterers are commonest in the lowlands (parties descending to drink along rivers) but feeding-movements sometimes take numbers through quite high mountain passes, including of the Main Range.

FORAGING AND FOOD. Erratic occurrence suggests flocks move far in the course of a day's foraging, and out-and-return movements noted through Main Range passes, suggest some journeys take in both lowland plains. With Needletails and House Swift, Pacific feeds at the top of swift airspace, with mean foraging heights measured in Selangor of 134 m over open ground and 185 m over forest (Waugh and Hails 1983). Diet has not been studied in this area, but recorded at termite swarms (Bromley 1948), and swifts travelling long distances have the capacity to specialize on scattered resources.

SOCIAL ORGANIZATION. Always in parties and sometimes large flocks, which can number many thousands on migration.

MOVEMENTS. There are no records from north of Malaysia, but south of the border movements span the width of the Peninsula at both seasons. Earliest autumn dates are from the lower Kelantan valley and Terengganu, as of mid July and with numbers building up through August, but none after the third week of October (Young 1941), so that, apparently, this is not a wintering area. These early swifts may move clear of the Peninsula as in most years none appears in the west and south before mid (and usually late) September (an isolated record of a coasting party in Selangor on 3 August but none in W Johor–Singapore before 10 September: BR 1974–75, SINGAV-1, -3). In these sectors, heaviest southward movements are in October (including large numbers exiting over the Melaka Straits from Cape Rachado, Negeri Sembilan: BMP5), tailing off through late November. Migration is not always easy to distinguish from foraging movements but in the south and west return passage appears to run from mid February (large numbers arriving over the N Selangor coast on 11 February) to late May or later: extreme dates 20 and 28 May in Singapore and Selangor; early June in Kelantan. Throughout the W-coast plain (including over Cape Rachado and the Main Range) it peaks in the last third of March (BMP5, BR 1972–73, SINGAV-3) but not until April–May in Kelantan (Young 1941), which may be touched by a separate stream at both seasons.

From their dates, birds mist-netted at floodlights on Fraser's Hill in October–early November are assumed to have been migrating at night (BMP5). The status of 18 (in a flock?) caught on 23 December and one on 27 December is less certain. None identified to subspecies.

SURVIVAL. No information.

SOCIAL INTERACTIONS. No information.

VOICE. Ordinarily silent in winter, but I have heard screaming from northbound flocks over the W coast in mid April, and Young (1941) reported it during autumn passage through Kelantan.

BREEDING. None confirmed.

MOULT. Two dated 11 October, no check on age or subspecies, were renewing P1 and P3 respectively. Specimens of adult *cooki* and *kanoi* dated October, December–February and late May showed no moult (BMNH, UMBRP, ZDUM).

CONSERVATION. Not at issue except that, like most swift species, prefers to forage over forest. If this reflects density and richness of the aerial insect plankton generated, loss of forest cover may be affecting energy-supply.

House Swift; Nok En Baan (Thai); Burung Layang-layang Rumah (Malay)

Apus nipalensis (Hodgson) 1836, *Journal of the Asiatic Society of Bengal* 5: 780. TL central Nepal.
Plate 57

GROUP RELATIONS. Separated from Afro-Indian *A. affinis* on the basis that no intergradation has been reported between its dark, forked-tailed population found along the E Himalayan foothills and the closely approaching, pale, square-tailed Indian bird. This may be premature (cf. Brooke 1971), but accords with treatment of *A. pacificus* and *acuticauda* in the same area. Habitat selection and similarity of nesting behaviour, vocalizations, etc., imply *nipalensis* and *affinis* are not more than allospecies.

GLOBAL RANGE. The Himalayan foothills east from W Nepal and the far-NE Indian subcontinent; SE Japan; China south of a line Sichuan–Fujian including Taiwan and Hainan; SE Asia to the Greater Sunda islands, Bali and the N Philippines; and S Sulawesi and Sumba. Vagrant in N Australia.

IDENTIFICATION/DESCRIPTION. A medium-sized swift, all dark except for white chin, throat and rump-band, but a piebald individual with white underparts has been reported from Subang airport, Selangor (BR 1978–79). Head and body of juvenile narrowly grey-fringed and, as in most swifts, juvenile flight-feathers are finely edged white. Appears chunky bodied in flight, and smaller, less rakish than Pacific Swift, with only shallowly forked tail (no field posture shows the fork prominently) and proportionately shorter wings. In level flight, wing-action fast relative to the measured strokes of Pacific Swift.

Bare-part colours. (Adult) iris blackish; bill black; feet dark purple-flesh, blacker on the toes.

Size (mm). (Live and skins: 12 males, 14 females; adult): wing 134–144 and 131–142; tail 46–54 and 45–53, tail-fork 3.4–7.5 (sexes combined); bill 6.7–7.5 (sexes combined); tarsus 10.9, 11.0 (2 males only) (BMNH, UMBRP, ZDUM).

Weight (g). Adults, sexes not separated, 24.5–36.3 (n=34) (McClure 1964, UMBRP).

DISTRIBUTION. Patchy north of Malaysia. Historical summary: all divisions except *Ran, Nak, Pht, Pat, Nar,* with additional island records from Chuak and Muk (*Tra*), Tarutao, the Langkawi group, Perak, Penang, Pangkor, Ketam (Kelang estuary), Besar (*Mel*) and Pisang off the W coast; the Redang group (nesting on Lima), Kapas and the Pahang–Johor archipelago (Tioman, Sibu) off the E coast; and Tekong, Sahajat, Ubin, Seletar, Unum, St John's, Sentosa, Senang, Pawai and Sudong around Singapore.

GEOGRAPHICAL VARIATION. Dorsally fully black *subfurcatus* Blyth 1849 (TL Penang) is the probably exclusive resident form, but Brooke (1971) identified a brown-headed, sooty-backed bird from Trang as northern nominate *nipalensis*.

STATUS AND POPULATION. Resident, regular and common to abundant north to the Malaysian/Thai border; thereafter only in scattered colonies, mostly coastal. The *nipalensis* from Trang has not been re-examined but may show that occasional non-breeding migrants reach this area from the north. A loner on Perak island, mid N Melaka Straits, in mid November could have been such a migrant.

The density of population in the south, from coasts to at least 1500 m in mountain settlements (Berwick 1947), is believed due to the adoption of man-made sites for nesting. All kinds of structures are accepted, including bridges, jetties, wharfs, and buildings of all

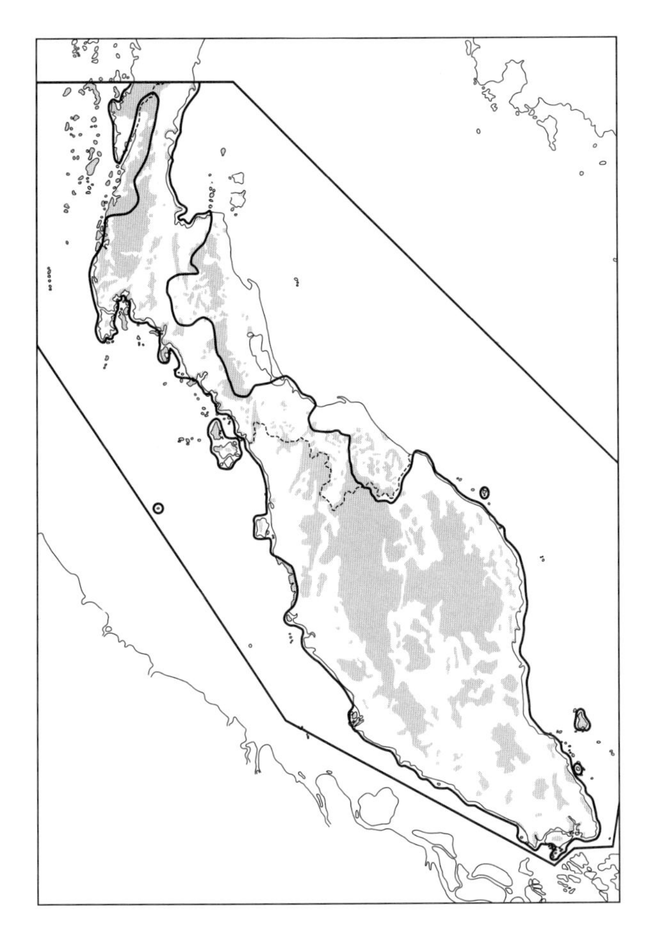

sizes, heights and situations, ranging from the completely isolated to busy urban centres. Stone and concrete are the most widely settled surfaces, replicating original limestone-cliff habitat. Cliffs themselves are used only locally, and most sizeable natural colonies are close enough to urban populations to make it difficult to decide which way colonizing influence has run. South of latitude 3°N (the southern limit of cliffs), breeders are exclusively commensal, and towns such as Melaka and Singapore have held big populations for well over a century (Kelham 1881–83).

Contrary to expectation, there has been no recent spread of commensal behaviour north of Malaysia. Known from Phuket town and at isolated concrete bridges in Yala and Phangnga provinces (Holmes and Wells 1975), the one more recent record of an artificial colony-site is a lighthouse on Lanta island (U. Treesucon). Despite the abundance of tower-karst limestone, cliff-nesting remains at least as sparse as in Malaysia, with only one recent discovery, at Ban Nai Chong (Krabi), adding to sites on Muk and Chuak islands (Trang) noted 80 years ago.

HABITATS AND ECOLOGY. Active by day at all altitudes (on the Main Range to at least 2000 m) but observations in Selangor show periodic, presumably food-related, swings of preference between forest and non-forest habitats (Waugh and Hails 1983). Overall, greater numbers forage above tree-cover. Rural nesting cliffs are occupied continuously but, except when actually building, town birds mostly move out over green habitats, returning only to provision nests and to roost in them.

FORAGING AND FOOD. Hunts communally in the upper sector of swift airspace and, like most other species, higher above forest than open ground (a mean 185 versus 115 m). A faecal sample analysed from a season's accumulation at a Kuala Lumpur breeding site showed 57 percent of identifiable items were flying ants and a further 20 percent hymenopterans of other kinds, with beetles next in importance (Waugh and Hails 1983). Regularly attends swarms of alate termites (5.5 percent of diet), including of the large *Macrotermes carbonarius* (Bromley 1948, Spittle 1952).

SOCIAL ORGANIZATION. Gregarious at all times. Breeders typically associate in a few to 20–30 closely contacting nests, but scattered, neighbouring groups can total hundreds of pairs. What constitutes the biological limits of a given colony in this situation has not been defined. It has been suggested that, outside the breeding period, nests are not necessarily occupied by the same birds from night to night (Batchelor 1958).

MOVEMENTS. Other than an occurrence on Perak island, no long-distance movement confirmed. Kelham (1881–83) matched a bird from Singapore with Indian *A. affinis* but may not have accounted for plumage-wear in local *subfurcatus*. True migrants are still no more than a possibility, and this is not on the list of swift species to have been intercepted at lights at night, i.e., to show evidence of movement or roosting on the wing at night.

SURVIVAL. No information.

SOCIAL INTERACTIONS. No additional information.

VOICE. Noisy around active nests; also after settling into roosts and again at dawn before emerging. Gives rattling trills, *wir-r-r-r-r*, *wi-hi-hi-r-r-r-r*, etc., in shallow cescendo form; and in free flight a stuttering *t't't'tir-r-r*, reeling down scale.

BREEDING

Nest. Builds well back in nooks and recesses, sheltered from the sun and weather, typically high but at only 3–4 m up in the covered ways of old-fashioned streetside buildings. Natural rock, building stone, concrete, steel and plank surfaces are accepted, with founder nests built into top angles, usually incorporating a corner and commonly with some small irregularity providing vertical suppport. Neighbouring nests then overlap to form continuous, irregular 'village' clusters, durable from year to year. Individual nests are founded on and strengthened throughout by hardening salivary cement, into which dry grass stems, casuarina needles, feathers, occasional scraps of paper, polythene, etc, are incorporated as the rim develops, untidily finished on the outside but smooth on the inside, and unlined. Final shape is constrained by the site, from shallow saucer fixed against an overhang to bulky, semi-globular, but always with a constricted side entrance. Occasionally, House Swifts take over the large, mud-built cup-nests of Pacific Swallow *Hirundo tahitica*.

Eggs and brood. Eggs are plain, glossless white. Shape blunt, subelliptical. Size (mm): 25.1–22.3 × 16.4–14.6 (mean 23.3 × 15.4, n=12). Clutch 2–3, but broods of three recorded only up to pin-feather age.

Cycle. Nests with two successive broods, assumed to be of the same parents, reported in Perak: first young flying in mid May, second clutch laid in June.

Seasonality. Diurnal nest-visiting begins by September, with active nests in all months mid December–mid August, but mostly as of March. On 14 August, a colony on Ubin island jetty (Singapore) contained young about to fly (Edgar 1933, SINGAV-2, Spittle 1949).

MOULT. Replacement of primaries is regular-descendent, with up to three adjacent feathers in overlapping growth, out to at least stage P5. Among 41 adults covering January, March–June and August, first active wing-moult occurred in April (five of eight dated 15–18 April at P1 or P1–2), with 89 percent incidence during May–June, but none beyond stage P5. Only a few had not started by June, and one dated 1 August had reached P8. At population-level, decidedly seasonal, and moult overlaps broadly with breeding. The individual cycle has not been studied (BMNH, P.T. Green, UMBRP, ZDUM).

CONSERVATION. No critical issues. Urban renewal in Malaysia and Singapore has reduced the availability of nest-sites on some classes of buildings but is unlikely to threaten populations.

Family HEMIPROCNIDAE

Treeswifts: two species

Grey-rumped Treeswift; Nok En-faa Taphok See Thao (Thai); Burung Layang-layang Berjambul Tongkeng Kelabu (Malay)

Hemiprocne longipennis (Rafinesque) 1802. *Bulletin de la Société Philomathique de Paris* 3: 153. TL Java.

Plate 57

GROUP RELATIONS. Forms a superspecies with *H. coronata* (Crested Treeswift) of S and northern SE Asia. For a time they were treated as conspecific but show consistent differences in face and upperpart colour-pattern, and tail morphology (Brooke 1969). Where ranges meet in SW Thailand, there have been no signs of interbreeding, body-size actually diverges, and the two birds appear mostly to occupy different forest types.

GLOBAL RANGE. From latitudes about 14°N in Tenasserim (Tavoy district) and 13° in SW Thailand, to the Peninsula, Greater Sunda islands, Bali and the western Sulu archipelago (as far as Tawitawi); also Lombok and Sulawesi to the Sula islands (W Moluccas).

IDENTIFICATION/DESCRIPTION. Tree-perching habits, with upright stance and wing-tips that scissor across deeply forked tail, extending level with or actually past its often tightly closed, spike-like tip, identify local members of this family in the field. Grey-rumped is much the larger, pale on belly and rump, lacks a white-striped face-pattern, and its 25 mm-tall flap-like forehead-crest is often raised. Adult cap to mantle, wing-coverts and upper tail-coverts, deep glossy bottle-green, bluish on the head and median coverts (but blueness varies with plumage wear); lower mantle to back green-grey, shading to green-tinged powder-grey on the rump. Innermost median wing-coverts and adjacent tertials are grey-white, remaining flight-feathers uniform blue-black. Below, mid grey from chin to breast and flanks; centre of belly to lower tail-coverts white. The sexes differ on ear-covert colour: black in females, with variable extent of dark rufous (but always bordered above by black) in males. On the wing, as large and rakish as a Pacific Swift, but pale parts are conspicuous, tail is longer and more deeply forked (obvious while wheeling and gliding), and flapping flight is typically stiff-winged. Noisy in company.

The young chick has pale smoky down, wearing off to reveal erupting juvenile plumage about two weeks before flight. Juvenile upperparts other than tertials sooty black, all feathers tipped white and with subapical band of rufous-brown on the head, variable elsewhere; tertials whitish with brown border; remaining flight-feathers black with white tip over narrow subapical zone of brown to rufous-brown.

Below, smoky-white, all feathers with narrow subapical band of dark chocolate and white tip. Full-grown, the juvenile tail-streamer (T5) is shorter, broader and blunter-tipped than in adult, as in other tree- and most typical swifts.

Bare-part colours. (Adult) iris deep brown; bill black; feet dark purplish grey.

Size (mm). (Skins: 17 males, 10 females; adult): wing 156–169 and 159–174; tail 83–104 and 83–102; bill 5.3–6.5 and 5.8–7.2; tarsus 8.2–8.8 (sexes combined) (BMNH).

Weight. No data.

DISTRIBUTION. Historical summary: all divisions, with additional island records from Penang and Pangkor off the W coast; Tinggi (*Joh*) off the E coast; and Tekong and Ayer Merbau, Singapore.

GEOGRAPHICAL VARIATION. Subspecies *harterti* Stresemann 1913 (TL Deli, NE Sumatra), of the mainland and Sumatra (except possibly the extreme south) to Borneo: a shade darker below than Javan, Bali and Wallacean populations, and tending to darken towards the throat.

STATUS AND POPULATION. Resident, regular and common, breeding over its full altitudinal range into the Montane zone (G.C. Madoc). Declining in some suburban areas, including on Singapore main island where the largest party of non-breeders recently recorded was of only five birds (Ollington and Loh 1992).

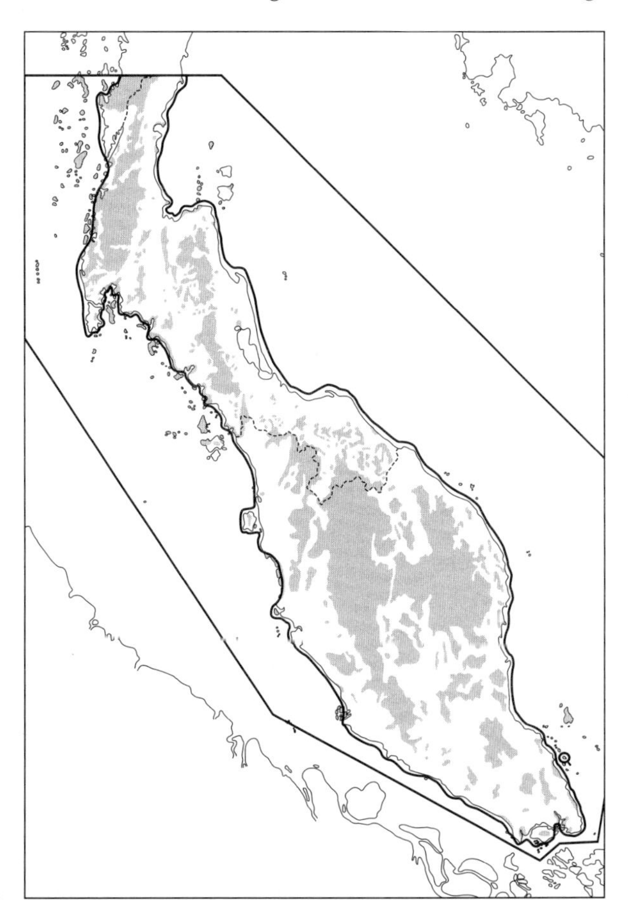

HABITATS AND ECOLOGY. Uses bare or dead-wood perches high on exposed crowns in mangroves, coastal strand woodland and all kinds of inland forest, including subcoastal peatswamp, at plains level and on slopes to at least 1200 m, i.e. into lower Montane forest. Commonest at the edge of forest, and where disturbance has opened out gaps in the canopy, with extensive use also of man-made habitats such as tall-timbered parks and gardens, mature rubber plantation, etc.

As with other treeswifts, juvenile plumage simulates lichen-mottled bark of the nest-support. This cryptic adaptation is enhanced while parents are not in attendance by the chick's habit of sitting rigidly upright, motionless, bill aligned with the body and contrastingly dark eyes closed – a convincing branch-stub.

FORAGING AND FOOD. Appears to search mainly on the wing rather than fly directly to prey already located from a scanning perch. Sorties of several minutes' duration are made within 300–400 m radius of the home crown, and generally in the lower part of communal swift airspace: a mean 47 m above forest cover and 35 m above open ground (Waugh and Hails 1983) although, unlike Whiskered Treeswift *H. comata*, Grey-rumped stays well clear of vegetation surfaces.

Commonly attends termite swarms, which is one reason why foraging activity tends to peak after rain and in the late evening. Otherwise, diet is not recorded in this area, although versatile flight, from the fast pace of a large typical swift to the manoeuvrability of a swallow should give access to a large range of prey types.

SOCIAL ORGANIZATION. Actual nests are dispersed but several breeding pairs may occupy a given neighbourhood (Madoc 1956a), and neighbours may be in view while foraging, which could assist the process of food-finding. Between sorties, family-members associate by returning to the same or a nearby perch in the home crown. Outside the breeding-season, during late October–late January, parties of five to over 50 converge to roost and forage from some favoured tree at the edge of (or sometimes far from) forest, where they interact constantly. Typically, the same crowns are reoccupied from year to year, implying at least some users should be adults. It is not known what social groupings are maintained in such gatherings but, as they fly in, returning foragers are always greeted by a chorus of neighbours. A large, noisy party (that must have formed immediately alongside a breeding territory) has also been seen to accompany the first flights of a late fledgling, and a group to mob a perched Black-thighed Falconet – likely predator of nestlings (Allen 1952a, Glenister 1951).

MOVEMENTS. No other information.

SURVIVAL. No information.

SOCIAL INTERACTIONS. No information.

VOICE. Noisy in most social contexts, including in flight, and birds are greeted by already-perched mates and others as they return. All loud calls are shrill hysterical-sounding shrieks (Bromley 1948): *kee*, single or as a string of notes; *whit-kep*, the first syllable both stressed and higher-sounding than the second; and longer *kip-kee-kep*, repeated a few times and the commonest greeting call given from a perch. Fledglings expecting to be fed cheep loudly and persistently.

BREEDING

Nest. A tiny rim of salivary cement with bryophyte scraps, slivers of bark and small feathers incorporated before it hardens, built out as a lip from a thin (often pencil-thin), typically exposed branch at canopy level, 8–30 m up (commonly in the upper half of this range). One nest measured 36 × 24, maximum outside depth 12 mm.

Eggs and brood. The egg is plain, more or less glossless white. Size (mm): 25.6 × 17.4 (average). Clutch one egg, filling and standing proud of the nest-cup. There is no separate record of incubation and fledging periods, but combined development time exceeds 50 days (an egg on 7 June had hatched by 3 July, with young newly on the wing on 1 August).

Cycle. Both pair-members nest-build and both incubate and brood, by perching on the support-twig, facing and straddling the nest, completely tenting it under fluffed out lower breast- and belly-feathers. In this position, nesting and merely resting adults cannot be told apart. The young chick is fed a regurgitated bolus of food and, as it develops, appears to take some of this directly from inside the parent's mouth. Feeding intervals are shortest in the evening. Well before reaching full size, the chick outgrows the nest and, about the time mottled juvenile plumage erupts, transfers to the support-branch.

Seasonality. Egg-dates imply most laying during early February–early June, occasional to September (mid- and late October fledglings in Penang and Singapore) (Allen 1952a, E.C.S. Baker, BMP5, Gibson-Hill 1950g, Madoc 1956a, NRCS, ZRCNUS).

MOULT. Replacement of primaries is regular-descendant, with instances of overlapping growth of two adjacent feathers out to stage P8. Among 42 adults covering all months except October, and the full length of the Peninsula, 24 showed active wing-moult during mid March (P1) – early September (P9, P9), with no starts later than June and incidence 100 percent during June–August (n=19 birds). Sixteen dated November–February showed no moult (BMNH), confirming a fairly sharp seasonality, and probable overlap with breeding.

Post-juvenile moult replaces head and body plumage (ear-covert colours at an early stage), whereas juvenile tail, flight-feathers and some coverts are retained to the next complete moult of the following year (although pale edging is lost early due to wear).

CONSERVATION. No critical issues. Local suburban declines have occurred where habitat remains ideal and may have more to do with food abundance, linked to the indiscriminate use of aerial insecticides.

Whiskered Treeswift; Nok En-faa Khrao Khao (Thai); Layang-layang Berjambul Kecil (Malay)

Hemiprocne comata (Temminck) 1824, *Nouveau Recueil de Planches Coloriées d'Oiseaux* 45: plate 268. TL Sumatra.

Plate 57

GROUP RELATIONS. Free-standing.

GLOBAL RANGE. S Tenasserim from latitude about 12°N (Mergui district) and the Peninsula to Sumatra, Borneo and the Philippines.

IDENTIFICATION/DESCRIPTION. Shape and stance as Grey-rumped Treeswift but about half the mass, and with only a short crest. Shows the same stiff-winged flapping-flight action but with much faster, almost fluttering beat, and hardly any gliding or soaring. Adults are darker overall: head to nape and sides of throat glossy blue-black (green-shot when fresh), with long, lanceolate feathers forming two parallel white stripes, over the bill and from lores over eye to hind-nape, and from chin along jawline back to side of neck; lower tail-coverts, long scapulars and adjacent inner webs of tertials white; remaining scapulars, wing-coverts, rest of flight-feathers and tail as head; body bronze-olive. The sexes differ as in Grey-rumped Treeswift: ear-coverts glossy blackish in females, partly dark rufous in males.

As with Grey-rumped, the unattended chick sits motionless, upright and stub-like, bill aligned with body and dark eye closed, but in this area has been described only from the field, not in the hand. Down sparse and grey; juvenile plumage mottled brown and cream dorsally, tan-brown and grey ventrally, flight-feathers shiny brown with cream-tan tips. White facial stripes are shorter than in adult and evidently not formed of hackle points (McClure 1979).

Bare-part colours. (Adult) iris deep brown; bill black; feet dark lead-grey (BMNH).

Size (mm). (Skins: 10 males, 12 females; adult): wing 118–130 and 120–130; tail 67–79 and 71–78; bill 4.5–5.3 (sexes combined); tarsus 6.5–6.7 (sexes combined) (BMNH).

Weight. No data.

DISTRIBUTION. Historical summary: all divisions except *Phu, Pat, Pra, Mel,* with additional island records from Tarutao and Ladang (Satul) off the W coast; and Ubin, Singapore.

GEOGRAPHICAL VARIATION. Nominate *comata*, of the global range west of the Philippines.

STATUS AND POPULATION. Resident, regular and more or less common, but few recent records from Singapore.

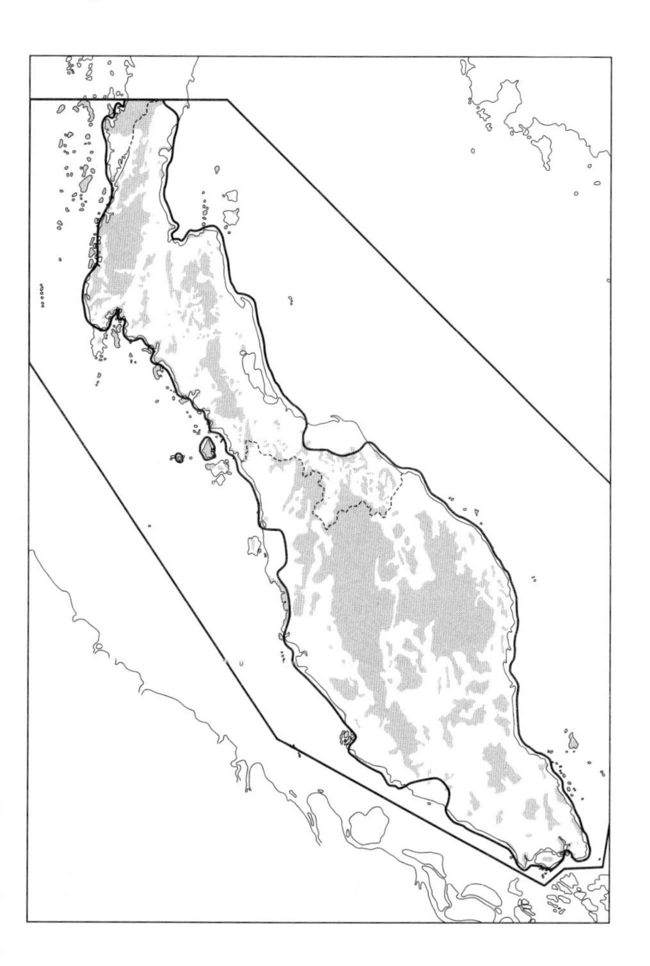

HABITATS AND ECOLOGY. The canopy and edge of mainly evergreen Lowland forest, mature and disturbed, at plains level and on slopes to 1100 m, reaching the lowest part of the Lower Montane zone (NRCS); much less often in mature orchards (of durian, etc.). Regular foraging perches, mostly on bare, terminal twigs, are typically well down the profile of the canopy, at mid-column height on the edge of a gap, and in particularly open, airy situations occasionally even inside the canopy; always below the average perch-height of Grey-rumped Treeswift.

FORAGING AND FOOD. Makes short sorties, typically of less than one minute, around just a few crowns, returning reliably to the same perch. Slowness and exceptional manoeuvrability, with momentary hovers, allow it to hunt closer to surfaces and in smaller foliage spaces than any other local swift species. No information available on diet but it would be surprising if this did not include some items snatched from leaf-tips or suspension threads (see also Glossy Swiftlet).

SOCIAL ORGANIZATION. Nearly always a territorial pair, typically perching together between sorties; or, at most, a pair plus recent offspring (and young disappear from the nesting area only a few weeks after fledging). As far as known, adult pairs remain on their territory year-round (McClure 1979). At no stage do Grey-rumped Treeswift-type gatherings form, although I have seen a large party of Grey-rumps take up residence in the home tree of a pair of Whiskered Treeswifts without displacing them.

MOVEMENTS. None recorded.

SURVIVAL. No information.

SOCIAL INTERACTIONS. No other information.

VOICE. Less noisy than Grey-rumped Treeswift. Has a high-pitched *kweeo*, a peal of shorter notes, *kwee kwee kwi-kwi-kwi-kwi,* and more Grey-rumped Treeswift-like *shi-shi-shi-shew-shi.*

BREEDING

Nest. Sited on the same grade of outer branchlet used as a foraging perch, fully exposed, allowing unobstructed access and an all-round view. As with Grey-rumped Treeswift, a small saucer of salivary cement with feathers included before hardening is built on, or out as a lip to, an often pencil-thin twig; 9–40 m above ground.

Eggs and brood. Egg plain white; no measurements available. Clutch one, the single egg standing proud of the cup and often more than the diameter of the support-twig. Incubation change-overs are usually abrupt although the egg is sometimes left several minutes unattended, implying it may be stuck to the nest. A Selangor egg hatched on or before day 21 and the chick flew soon after day 28, giving an approximately 50-day total development period.

Cycle. Both parents nest-build, incubate and brood, continuing to adding cement and feathers after the egg has been laid. Like Grey-rumped, they tend the nest by straddling it on the support-branch and tenting it completely under breast- and belly-feathers. As with Grey-rumped, nesters cannot be told from birds merely resting on a perch. A timed female took a larger daily share of nest-duties than her mate. A juvenile remained in the parents' territory, receiving occasional feeds, for some three weeks after flying.

Seasonality. Nest-building recorded as early as late February but egg- and chick-dates give evidence of laying only during April–late August; latest fledging in early October (F.G.H. Allen, Madoc 1947, McClure 1979, NRCS).

MOULT. Primaries moult regular-descendantly, with instances of overlapping growth between adjacent feathers out to stage P7, but this is unusual. Order of tail-moult is uncertain but most birds renewing P7 or 8 still carried an old T5 (the streamers). Among 33 adults from throughout the Peninsula and covering all months except May, July, and September–November, 21 showed active wing-moult from late February (P2) to late August (P7 or 8, hence the season is expected to run at least through September), with no starts later than March and incidence 100 percent during April–August. Eight December–January birds showed no moult (BMNH), confirming the seasonality and virtually complete population-level overlap with breeding.

CONSERVATION. Forest-dependent, but it uses disturbed and edge habitat, and is frequent on the submontane slope. No critical issues identified.

Order TROGONIFORMES

Family TROGONIDAE

Trogons: six species

Red-naped Trogon; Nok Khun Phaen Thai-thoi Daeng (Thai); Burung Kesumba Batang (Malay)

Harpactes kasumba (Raffles) 1822, *Transactions of the Linnean Society* 13(2): 282. TL Benkulen, SW Sumatra.

Plate 58

GROUP RELATIONS. Free-standing.

GLOBAL RANGE. Borneo, Sumatra and the Peninsula to latitude about 8°30′N.

IDENTIFICATION/DESCRIPTION. One of the local trio of large trogons. Adult male from male Diard's Trogon *Harpactes diardii* by black rather than maroon-washed cap; ear-coverts and conjoined hind-collar bright red rather than pale pink; peri-orbital skin cobalt-blue rather than purple; necklace bordering black breast white rather than pink; and white on the outer three tail-feathers (T3–5) plain, sharply demarcated from dark parts. Males of smaller species are black only to throat level, without the red hind-collar and pale necklace. A claim that some males show a narrow red rump-band (Chasen 1939) has not been verified. Female from other (smaller) cinnamon-bellied species by contrastingly dark, grey-olive breast, and face as dark as rest of head. Full juveniles resemble the adult female but with wing-coverts barred as broadly buff as black and, typical of trogons, central tail-feathers tapered rather than spade-tipped, without the black apical band. As in other trogons, most of the tarsus is densely feathered black.

Bare-part colours. (Adult) iris dark brown; broad periorbital patch cobalt-blue to, above the eye, clear light blue (male), dull blue (female); tip and culmen black, rest of bill and fleshy margin of mouth cobalt-blue (male), duller blue (female); feet blue-grey.

Size (mm). (Live and skins: 10 males, 10 females; adult): wing 145–149 and 144–152; tail 164–178 and 153–180; bill 20.3–23.8 and 19.4–21.0; tarsus 13.2–14.9 (sexes combined) (BMNH, UMBRP, UMZC).

Weight (g). An adult male, 115.0; adult females, 95.5–105.0 (n=3) (UMBRP).

DISTRIBUTION. No records north of southern Phangnga. Historical summary: *Pha, Kra, Nar, Ked, Kel, Tru, Pra, Pek, Phg, Sel, Neg, Mel, Joh*; extinct *Sin* since the 1920s, possibly later on adjacent Ubin island but no definite dates. There are no other island records.

GEOGRAPHICAL VARIATION. Nominate *kasumba*, also of Sumatra.

STATUS AND POPULATION. Resident, regular and more or less common in the south; (now) local and uncommon to sparse in the north.

HABITATS AND ECOLOGY. The mid stratum and shaded upper interior of evergreen Lowland forest, also peatswamp forest, mature and regenerated back to a layered, closed-canopy stage; at plains level and on slopes to about 600 m, rarely up to the Montane

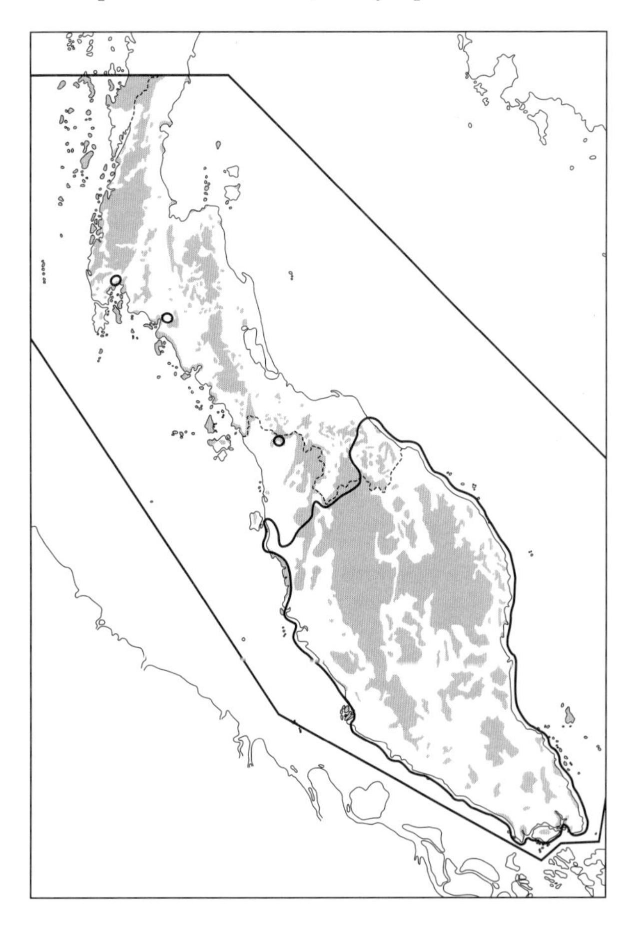

ecotone (a young male above the Gap, Selangor/ Pahang boundary: A.R. Lamont).

FORAGING AND FOOD. Still-hunts from perches in open surroundings, flying short sorties to snatch from foliage and other surfaces. Diet not recorded.

SOCIAL ORGANIZATION. Mostly solitary.

MOVEMENTS. None recorded.

SURVIVAL. No information.

SOCIAL INTERACTIONS. No information.

VOICE. The advertising-call is an even-toned sequence of mainly 3–4, not above six, spaced, mellow but resonant *taup* or *kaup* notes; given by both sexes, the male slightly lower and slower than the female (Boonsong and Round 1991). Probably both sexes (the female definitely) also give a rather soft, short, whirring rattle that is perhaps an alarm-call.

BREEDING

Nest. Only one described: a rounded cavity 1.2 m up a part-rotted 1.6 m tall, 18 cm thick, stump by a forest path; the egg-chamber unlined apart from softened wood fragments.

Eggs and brood. Eggs plain white. Shape and size not recorded. One incubated clutch of two eggs.

Cycle. Daytime checks over one week always flushed the male.

Seasonality. A full clutch monitored during 30 July–4 August (when taken by a predator). A heavily moulting female handled on 12 July showed a brood patch (BR 1978–79, NRCS, UMBRP).

MOULT. Replacement of primaries is regular-descendant, with up to three adjacent inner feathers in overlapping growth, and two out to stage P9. Seventeen of 18 adults covering all months except December, January and May showed active wing-moult, from late March (P1) to late November (P9-10), with general seasonal progression, and completions as of late August. Mid-winter handlings are needed to confirm pattern at population level. Three Johor juveniles were on a later schedule, moulting P3 in October (BMNH, UMBRP). Typical tail-moult is sequential, ending with T1–2, shed not before stage P7. Instances of simultaneous growth of the whole tail in this and other trogon species are likely to have been the result of accidents to these loose-plumaged birds.

CONSERVATION. All trogons favour the full shade of a closed canopy, and are intolerant of disturbance from logging. Restricted occurrence on slopes in the north suggests Red-naped Trogon may already have lost its core habitat in Thailand.

Diard's Trogon; Nok Khun Phaen Hua Dam (Thai); Burung Kesumba Diard (Malay)

Harpactes diardii (Temminck) 1832, *Nouveau Recueil de Planches Coloriées d'Oiseaux* 91: plate 541. TL Pontianak, W Kalimantan.

Plate 58

GROUP RELATIONS. Likely to form a superspecies with *H. ardens* (Philippine Trogon).

GLOBAL RANGE. Borneo, Sumatra and intervening islands, and the Peninsula to latitude about 9°N.

IDENTIFICATION/DESCRIPTION. Near size of Red-naped Trogon, which see. Adult wing-coverts are more finely vermiculated than in Red-naped and, uniquely among local trogons, dark and white parts of the outer tail merge across a zone of black freckling. Female from other brown-headed, pink- or red-bellied trogons by sharply demarcated, darkish brown breast. Similar-sized female Red-headed Trogon, whose range Diard's meets altitudinally, has breast bordered with a white necklace. Juveniles resemble the adult female but are paler pink below, with more coarsely barred wing-coverts (cinnamon as wide as black bars), and show the tail-differences described for Red-naped Trogon.

Bare-part colours. (Adult) iris dark brown to red; periorbital skin pink-violet; tip, cutting-edges and variable area of culmen black, rest of bill and fleshy margin of mouth cobalt-blue (male), duller blue (female); feet flesh- to lavender-tinged grey.

Size (mm). (Live and skins: 19 males, 11 females; adult): wing 140–153 and 140–151; tail 158–175 and 155–167; bill 20.3–23.3 and 19.1–21.9; tarsus 13.6–14.7 (sexes combined) (BMNH, UMBRP).

Weight (g). Adult males, 90.7–110.8 (n=6); adult females, 87.5–106.1 (n=5).

DISTRIBUTION. Not recorded in the far north. Historical summary: *Sur, Nak, Kra, Pht, Tra, Son, Sat, Nar, Pes, Tru, Pek, Phg, Sel, Neg, Mel, Joh*. Extinct *Sin* (Ubin island) for at least 40 years, with no other island records.

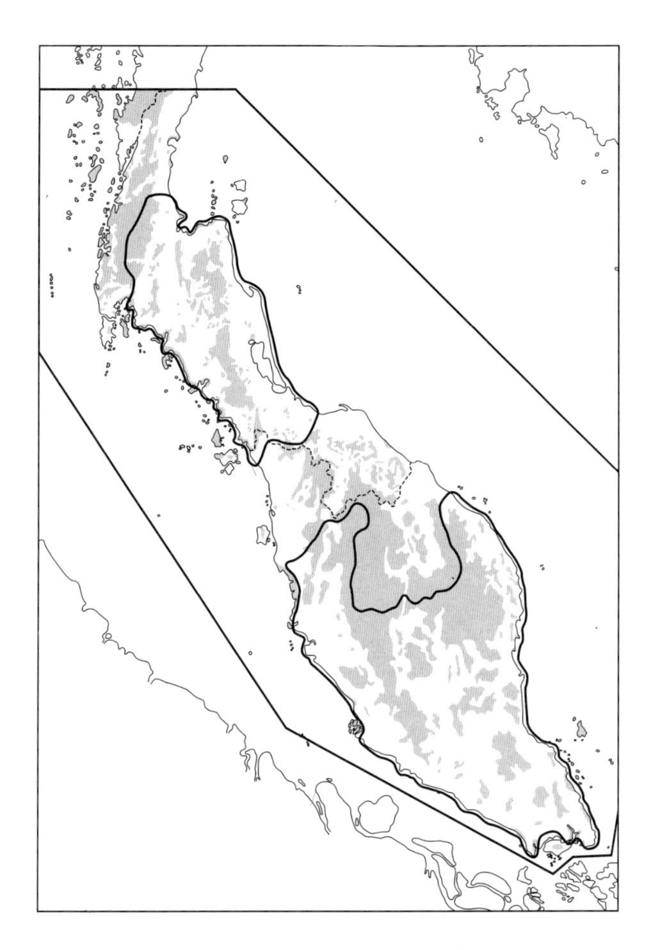

GEOGRAPHICAL VARIATION. Subspecies *sumatranus* Blasius 1896 (TL Sumatra), of the mainland and Sumatra, with deep maroon cap.

STATUS AND POPULATION. Resident, regular and more or less common to (in the north) uncommon. A maximum two pairs made use of separate parts of a 15 ha plot of plains-level understorey in the Pasoh research forest, Negeri Sembilan.

HABITATS AND ECOLOGY. The mid and lower strata of semi-evergreen and evergreen Lowland forest, at plains level and on slopes, recorded to 900 m, near the Montane ecotone, in the south; not above 600 m in Thailand (Boonsong and Round 1991).

FORAGING AND FOOD. Still-hunts from open perches, making sorties to snatch from surrounding plant surfaces. Animal prey not identified, but a record of a bird taking one or more figs (Lambert 1987) appears to be exceptional.

SOCIAL ORGANIZATION. Typically solitary.

MOVEMENTS. None recorded.

SURVIVAL. Only one substantial retrap-interval: a female in the upper Gombak valley, Selangor, ringed as an adult and re-handled on site 63 months later (UMBRP).

SOCIAL INTERACTIONS. No information.

VOICE. The only vocalization reported is a sequence of 10–12 mellow but resonant *khau* notes, the second pitched slightly higher than the first, the rest a falling cadence, even-paced or slightly accelerating then slowing near the end (BMP5); delivered faster than loud calls of other large trogons, but still with all notes distinct (*contra* smaller Scarlet-rumped Trogon *H. duvaucelii*). Given by both sexes, this is evidently the advertising-call.

BREEDING

Nest. Three described: all cavities 1.2–3 m up in rotting stumps of forest trees, in one case close to the stump top; unlined and floored with softened wood fragments. One measured only about 12 cm in any dimension, unexpectedly small for a bird of this size.

Eggs and brood. Eggs glossy, creamy-white. Shape near-spherical. Egg measurements and clutch-size unknown, but a brood of two fledglings reported.

Cycle. Two afternoon checks of a nest at Kuala Lompat, Pahang, flushed the male.

Seasonality. Records of eggs in May and early June, nestlings in March, and recent fledglings in late May and mid June extrapolate to laying from February to at least mid May (BBCB-7, Chasen 1939, ENGGANG-1, NRCS).

MOULT. Replacement of primaries is regular-descendant, with up to three adjacent inner feathers in overlapping growth. Among 26 adults covering all months except December, 17 showed active wing-moult between late March (P2–3) and mid October (P10), with no starts later than June and completions as of August. Others dated October, November and January–March showed none. Tail-moult pattern is as in Red-naped Trogon.

CONSERVATION. Able to use well-regenerated forest, even areas with much bamboo, but like other trogons intolerant of disturbance that breaks up canopy cover. As with Red-naped Trogon, restricted occurrence on slopes in the north suggests most habitat has already been lost from Thailand.

Cinnamon-rumped Trogon; Nok Khun Phaen Taphok See Namtaan (Thai); Burung Kesumba Pelanduk (Malay)

Harpactes orrhophaeus (Cabanis and Heine) 1863, *Museum Heineanum* 4(1): 156. TL Melaka.
Plate 58

GROUP RELATIONS. Free-standing.

GLOBAL RANGE. Borneo, Sumatra and the Peninsula.

IDENTIFICATION/DESCRIPTION. In the shade of the forest understorey, the broadly naked upper eyelid of adult male Cinnamon-rumped and similar-sized Scarlet-rumped Trogons shows up as a bar of brilliant light blue arching swollen and brow-like over the anterior eye; duller blue in females. The black of the male head extends only to throat level while the sooty brown head of the otherwise all-bright-brown adult female shows rich, cinnamon-rufous lores and face-patch. In a good view, fine, black-dominated vermiculation of the wing-coverts, and black-tipped, spade-shaped central tail-feathers help separate her from the all-brown juvenile. Field differences between the latter and young Scarlet-rumped Trogon are subtle: face slightly brighter rufous in Cinnamon-rumped, and cinnamon barring on its wing-coverts about equal to black, versus actually dominating the black in Scarlet-rumped. In the hand, all age/sex-classes of Cinnamon-rumped are identifiable by their stout bill (Wells and Medway 1976).

Bare-part colours. (Adult) iris deep brown, broad bare upper eyelid bright blue (adult male), clear pale blue (adult female); culmen and tip black, rest of bill and fleshy edge of mouth bright cobalt-violet (male), duller blue (female); feet dark fleshy grey.

Size (mm). (Live and skins: 15 males, 15 females; adult): wing 104–111 and 106–114; tail 121–135 and 121–136; bill 16.0–16.6, and depth at anterior margin of nostrils 9.2–10.4 (sexes combined); tarsus 12.7–14.2 (sexes combined) (BMNH, UMBRP).

Weight (g). Adult males, 46.8–60.6 (n=10); adult females, 45.7–60.0 (n=17).

DISTRIBUTION. Historical summary: *Chu, Sur, Pha, Nak, Kra, Ked, Tru, Pek, Phg, Sel, Neg, Joh*, with no island records.

GEOGRAPHICAL VARIATION. Nominate *orrhophaeus*, also on Sumatra.

STATUS AND POPULATION. Resident, regular and more or less common in the south; local and uncommon to sparse in the north. Suspected to be rare in or absent from more seasonal, deciduous to semi-evergreen forest-types. But in southern, plains-level evergreen forest mist-netting suggests this is actually the commonest trogon, difficult to find due only to its

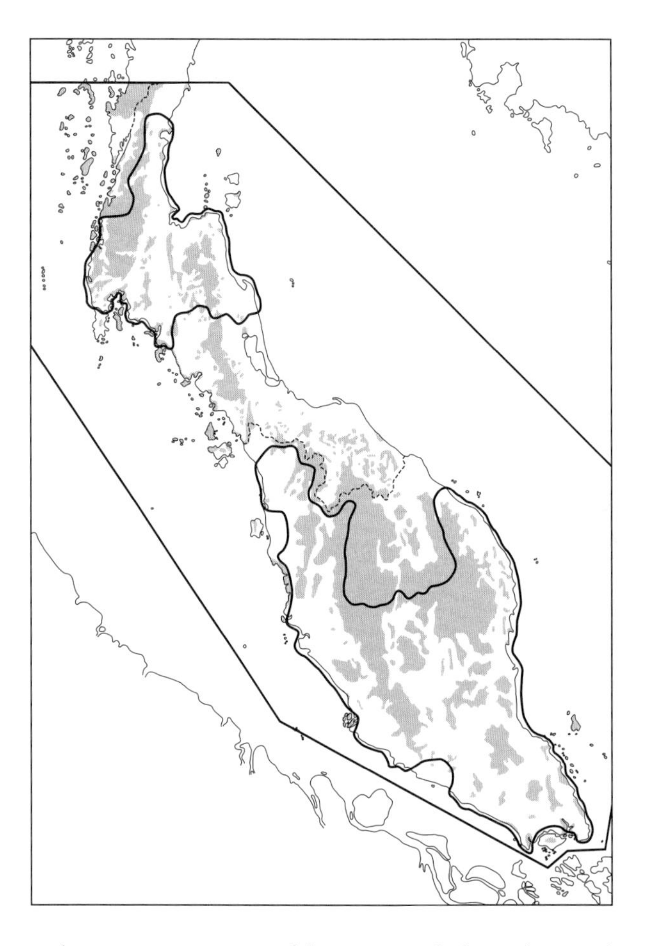

rather consistent use of low, concealed perches and generally silent behaviour. Retrapping of ringed birds showed four pairs made regular use of parts of a 15 ha plot of the Pasoh research forest, Negeri Sembilan.

HABITATS AND ECOLOGY. The under- and, less often, lower mid-stratum of evergreen Lowland forest, mature and regenerated back to a closed-canopy stage, at plains level to only a short distance above the steepland boundary; recorded on slopes to 180 m in central Malaysia, 140 m on the E-central Range in Nakhon Si Thammarat (BR 1968, King 1966).

FORAGING AND FOOD. No information, except that it still-hunts from perches in mostly fairly dense understorey vegetation, within 2–3 m of the forest floor.

SOCIAL ORGANIZATION. Largely solitary.

MOVEMENTS. None reported.

SURVIVAL. Two of 14 ringed in Pasoh forest during 1972–73 were still present on original territories in 1982 (retrap-intervals 109 and 115 months). In (since cleared) Subang forest reserve, Selangor, one was retrapped on site after 156 months.

SOCIAL INTERACTIONS. No information.

VOICE. Not unlike Red-naped Trogon but weaker: a shallowly declining sequence of 3–4 spaced, down-inflected notes, *ta-aup ta-aup ta-aup ta-aup*.

BREEDING

Nest. Three described, all cavities 1–1.5 m up rotten stumps in forest, two by trails, one at the lip of a bank dropping away several metres into a small river. One unlined cavity measured 10 cm deep.

Eggs and brood. Eggs plain white, but no details of shape or size. Full clutch, and one brood, two.

Cycle. Daytime checks at various times show both sexes incubate, and both feed the nestlings.

Seasonality. Eggs in early April and mid June, and nestlings in April (MBR 1986-87, NRCS).

MOULT. Replacement of primaries is regular-descendant, with up to five adjacent inner primaries in overlapping growth. Twenty-four of 25 birds handled during early June–mid October were in active wing-moult, with starts and completions up to and as of about mid August. Seventeen others dated December–early May showed no moult. As in other trogons, simultaneous growth of the full tail is relatively common, but believed not to be the natural pattern.

CONSERVATION. Dependence on plains-level, closed-canopy forest places this trogon in the front rank of species threatened by habitat-loss. Within a few years it is likely to be confined to the few protected areas that have significant forest at this elevation. Taman Negara will be a key site.

Scarlet-rumped Trogon; Nok Khun Phaen Taphok Daeng (Thai); Burung Kesumba Puteri (Malay)

Harpactes duvaucelii (Temminck) 1824, *Nouveau Recueil de Planches Coloriées d'Oiseaux* 49: plate 291. TL Sumatra.

Plate 58

GROUP RELATIONS. Free-standing.

GLOBAL RANGE. Borneo, Sumatra and intervening islands, the Peninsula, and Tenasserim to latitude 14°N.

IDENTIFICATION/DESCRIPTION. All except full juveniles from similarly small-sized Cinnamon-rumped Trogon (which see) by some red or pink on the belly and back to upper tail-coverts (but sharply demarcated dorsally only in adult males). All-brown juvenile from juvenile Cinnamon-rumped by less contrastingly rufous face-patch, and cinnamon-rufous of rather coarsely barred wing-coverts dominating over black; in the hand by weaker, shallower bill. Immature males appear to pass through an intermediate plumage in which wing-covert barring is adult-width but pale bars are cinnamon (female-like) rather than white.

Bare-part colours. (Adult) iris deep brown; narrow eyelid-rim grey-blue, upper lid standing out as a broad, brow-like bar arching over the eye, brilliant blue (male), clear pale blue (female); culmen, tip and outer cutting-edges black, rest of bill and fleshy edge of mouth brilliant cobalt-blue (male), duller blue (female); feet dull pinkish blue to grey-black (the possibility of a sexual difference needs investigating).

Size (mm). (Live and skins: 20 males, 13 females: adult): wing 101–109 and 101–111; tail 113–136 and 113–132; bill 14.4–17.2 and 15.1–16.6, depth at anterior edge nostrils 7.1–7.8 (sexes combined); tarsus 9.0–12.1 (sexes combined) (BMNH, UMBRP).

Weight (g). Adult males, 36.4–43.0 (n=14); adult females, 33.8–43.1 (n=8) (Medway 1972, UMBRP).

DISTRIBUTION. Historical summary: all divisions except *Phu, Ked, Pra, Sin*; with no island records.

GEOGRAPHICAL VARIATION. None recognized.

STATUS AND POPULATION. Resident, regular and more or less common to, in the north, uncommon.

HABITATS AND ECOLOGY. The mid- and, less regularly, under stratum of semi-evergreen and evergreen Lowland forest, including swamp-forest (but no records from peatswamp), mature and regenerated to a more or less closed-canopy stage, at plains level and on slopes. In the south, reaches and marginally crosses the Montane ecotone, with records to 1070 m, but in Thailand not above 400 m (Boonsong and Round 1991).

FORAGING AND FOOD. Still-hunts from open, mid-stratum perches, making rapid sorties to snatch

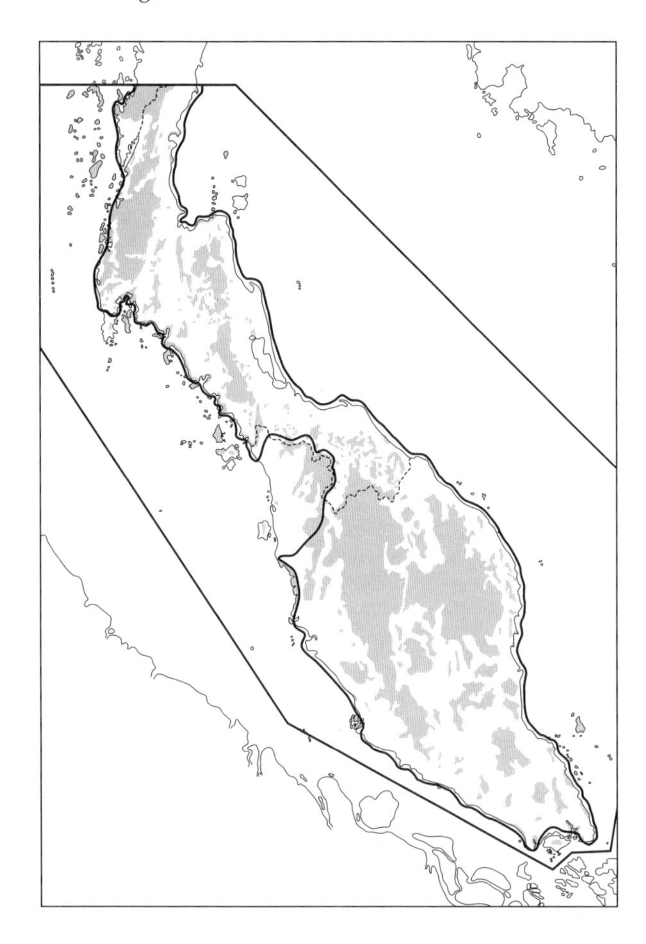

from nearby plant surfaces. Also recorded taking prey in the air; a female flycatching a few metres above a mixed foraging-flock of understratum babblers, whose movements it followed. Robinson (1928) lists phasmids, orthopterans, moths, beetles and 'bugs' amongst prey.

SOCIAL ORGANIZATION. Mainly solitary, but on several occasions pairs have been mist-netted together.

MOVEMENTS. None reported.

SURVIVAL. No information.

SOCIAL INTERACTIONS. No information.

VOICE. Delivered much faster than the advertising-call of any other local trogon species, a short burst of about 12 notes reeling down scale and accelerating to the point where these run together, *yau yau yau-yau-yau-yuyuyu*. A soft, rattling whirr, not distinguished from that of other species, seems to have alarm function. A third call is a squirrel-like scold, *squae*, repeated irregularly, at times with the tail fanned (G.C. Madoc).

BREEDING

Nest. No good description. One tentatively identified was in a hollow of a rotten stump by a forest stream – a typical trogon site.

Eggs and brood. Not reliably described. Full clutch two.

Cycle. No information.

Seasonality. A chick dated 17 March and eggs hatched in May (F.G.H. Allen, BMNH, Chasen 1939).

MOULT. Replacement of the primaries is regular-descendant, with up to three adjacent inner feathers in overlapping growth. Among 63 adults covering all months and the full length of the Peninsula, 31 showed active wing-moult during early February–October, with overall incidence (77 percent) biased to the period May–October; no starts later than June, completions as of early August and no September–October records at less than stage P9. Only one instance of moult during mid October–January: a December male growing P4, but with outer hand already newish.

CONSERVATION. Intolerant of heavy disturbance to canopy cover but ability to use regenerating forest, and wide occurrence on slopes, suggest this species is less threatened by habitat-loss than Cinnamon-rumped or Red-naped Trogons.

Orange-breasted Trogon; Nok Khun Phaen Ok See Som (Thai); Burung Kesumba Harimau (Malay)

Harpactes oreskios (Temminck) 1823, *Nouveau Recueil de Planches Coloriées d'Oiseaux* 31: plate 181. TL Java.

Plate 58

GROUP RELATIONS. Free-standing.

GLOBAL RANGE. SW Yunnan and, except for northern Burma and northern Vietnam, SE Asia to the Greater Sunda islands.

IDENTIFICATION/DESCRIPTION. Size intermediate between the foregoing groups, and red lacking at all stages. Adult male cap to nape grey-olive, upper body chocolate-rufous with finely black-and-white-barred wing-coverts. Adult female entirely grey-olive above, wing-coverts black-and-cinnamon barred, as in females of all *Harpactes* species; both sexes with dark rufous T1, a sharply demarcated slash of white over the outer tail (T4–5), and tail-feathers typically spade-tipped, with a prominent black fringe. Below, chin to upper breast grey-olive, more yellow-washed in males; rest of underparts to belly and flanks yellow (female), apricot-orange paling to yellow back from thighs (male). A young fledgling (sex unknown): entirely light rufous above, pale cinnamon barring on wing-coverts and inner secondaries dominant over narrow bars of black, with other secondaries edged and tipped cinnamon-yellow; chin to breast grey-olive, rest of underparts white with a yellow wash on flanks, and the age-related tail features of other trogon species (see Red-naped).

Bare-part colours. (Adult) iris deep brown (grey in juveniles?), periorbital skin blue; tip and culmen black, rest of bill and fleshy edge of mouth bright cobalt-blue (male), duller blue (female); feet lead-blue.

Size (mm). (Live and skins: 16 males, 10 females; adult): wing 120–127 and 119–130; tail 150–167 and 145–160; bill 14.2–17.8 and 14.7–17.0; tarsus 12.8–13.2 (sexes combined) (BMNH, UMBRP, TISTR).

Weight (g). An adult male, 57.3 (UMBRP).

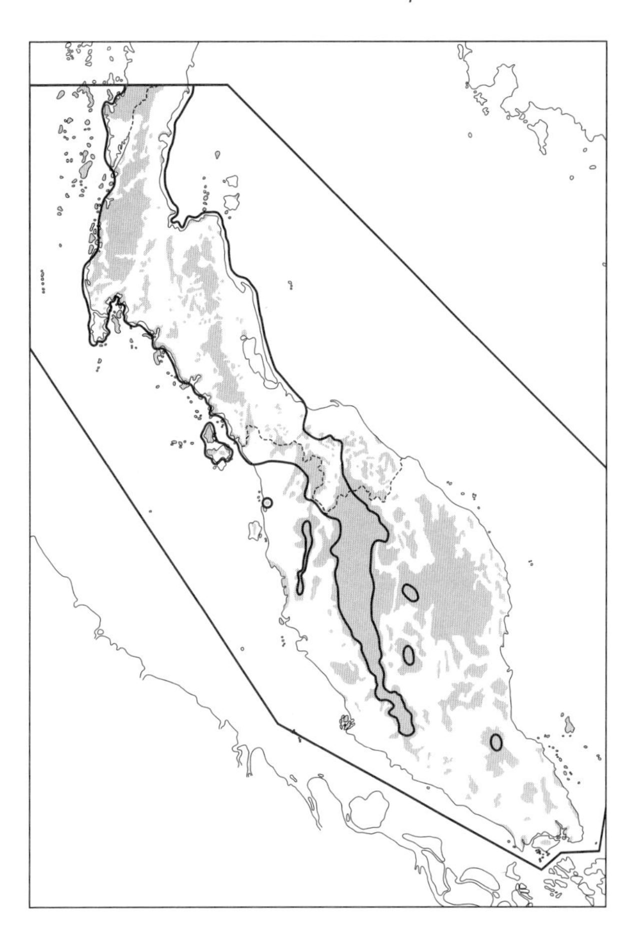

DISTRIBUTION. South to steep slopes along the Pahang/Johor border. Historical summary: all divisions except *Pat, Nar, Tru, Pra, Mel, Sin*, with additional island records from Tarutao and Langkawi.

GEOGRAPHICAL VARIATION. Subspecies *uniformis* Robinson and Kloss 1917 (TL Ban Lamphu La, Trang), also of mainland Sumatra; showing rump and upper tail-coverts concolorous with back.

STATUS AND POPULATION. Resident, regular and more or less common, uncommon only in the far south.

HABITATS AND ECOLOGY. The mid-stratum and lower canopy of semi-evergreen and evergreen Lowland forest, including swamp-forest, mature and disturbed (including heavy incidence of bamboo), at plains level and on slopes; and Lower Montane forest to 1300 m. Plains populations range to not far south of the limit of the Thai-Burmese forest flora, in Perlis and N Kedah. From Yala and mid Kedah south (Bromley 1949), recorded only on hills, rarely below 350 m and near this altitude at its southern terminus in the Endau-Rompin conservation area (Wells 1990).

Active mostly at mid-stratum levels but overnight roost-sites include thin saplings in the understorey.

FORAGING AND FOOD. Still-hunts from open perches, dashing out to snatch from nearby stems and foliage. One record of a bird in a Montane forest mixed-species foraging-flock (ENGGANG-2). Diet undescribed.

SOCIAL ORGANIZATION. Solitary or in pairs; occasional small parties may be family groups (Madoc 1956a).

MOVEMENTS. None reported.

SURVIVAL. No information.

SOCIAL INTERACTIONS. No information.

VOICE. Three (occasionally four) even-pitched notes reminiscent of a Chestnut-backed Scimitar Babbler *Pomatorhinus montanus*, usually with a 1–3-note introduction: *to (to to) tautautau* or *ko (ko ko) kaukaukau*. Boonsong and Round (1991) describe males as shriller and faster than females. The only other vocalization reported is a soft, reedy *shwaek*.

BREEDING

Nest. Two described; a shallow, unlined depression at the top of a 2 m high stump, and a hollow scooped out of the side of a rotted, 15 cm-diameter tree trunk, 1.5 m up, in and at the edge of forest.

Eggs and brood. Eggs are plain, deep cream-coloured, moderately glossy. Shape broad ovate. Size (mm): 26.4 × 20.8, 26.2 × 20.3 (n=2). Full clutch two.

Cycle. No information.

Seasonality. Eggs in late January and early April; a recent fledgling in mid February (BMNH, G.C. Madoc, P.D. Round).

MOULT. Replacement of primaries is regular-descendant. Among 25 adults covering all months except September, ten were in active wing-moult during early March(P3)–August and in late October (P10). Fifteen dated November–February showed none (BMNH, UMBRP).

CONSERVATION. A slope species, not immediately threatened by habitat-loss.

Red-headed Trogon; Nok Khun Phaen Hua Daeng (Thai); Burung Kesumba Gunung (Malay)

Harpactes erythrocephalus (Gould) 1834, *Proceedings of the Zoological Society of London* 2: 25. TL Rangoon.

Plate 58

GROUP RELATIONS. Uncertain; probably closest to Bornean *H. whiteheadi* (Whitehead's Trogon).

GLOBAL RANGE. The Himalayan foothills east from Kumaon and hill-tracts of the far-NE Indian subcontinent; China south from a line Fujian–S Sichuan, including Hainan island; and SE Asia to the Peninsula and Sumatra.

IDENTIFICATION/DESCRIPTION. Size of Red-naped and Diard's Trogons, which it meets on the mid-mountain slope. The adult male is the only trogon with full red head and breast. Adult female from female Diard's by white necklace between brown and red of underparts, white of outer tail (T3–5) plain rather than speckled, stepping rather than slanted across successive feathers, and wing-coverts much more finely vermiculated black and dark cinnamon. Juveniles from adult female by paler, more pink than red underparts, the usual trogon tail-difference, and by paler, more coarsely barred wing-coverts, cinnamon-buff bars dominant over black, but individual feather-pattern complicated by a broad black subapical bar and white tip.

Bare-part colours. (Adult) iris hazel to deep brown; periorbital skin bright pink-violet; culmen and tip black, rest of bill and fleshy margin of mouth bright cobalt-blue (male), duller blue (female); feet lavender- to fleshy blue.

Size (mm). (Skins: 7 males, 3 females; adult): wing 136–139 and 132–142; tail 163–174 and 153–166; bill 17.5–19.7 and 16.8–17.6; tarsus 14.1–17.0 (sexes combined) (BMNH).

Weight (g). Adults, 75.0–86.6 (n=5, the heaviest a female).

DISTRIBUTION. Higher ground of the north end of the E-central Range, the Larut Range, the Main Range between latitudes 5°35′N and 2°41′N (Angsi peak, *Neg*), and on isolated Benom (*Phg*). Historical summary: *Nak, Kel, Pek, Phg, Sel, Neg*.

GEOGRAPHICAL VARIATION. Specimens from the E-central Range (USNM) are closest to Peninsular

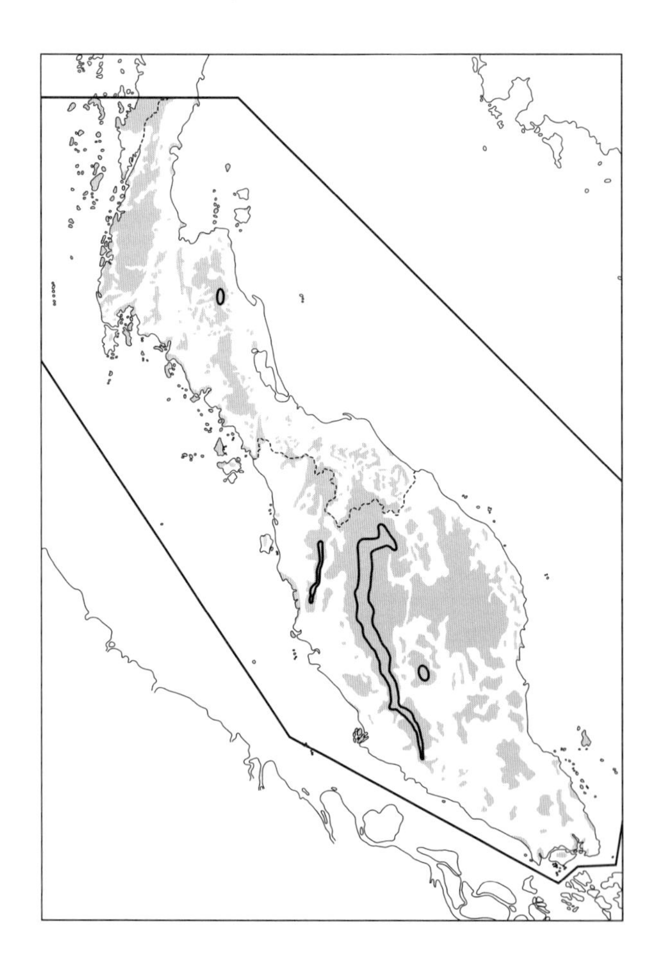

Malaysian endemic *chaseni* Riley 1934 (TL the Gap, Selangor/Pahang divide). From neighbouring continental populations by head and breast of adult male less bright, more vinous-red than the rest of the underparts.

STATUS AND POPULATION. Resident, regular and more or less common.

HABITATS AND ECOLOGY. The mid-stratum interior and sometimes low edge of mature and otherwise closed-canopy evergreen Lowland, Lower Montane and taller-facies Upper Montane forest, not proven to occur below about 700 m (N-central Range specimens all collected at above 800 m). In pristine forest of the Benom slope, found only between 1100–1280 m, i.e., entirely within Lower Montane forest, but on the Main Range has been recorded from submontane levels to 1680 m (McClure 1964, Medway 1972). At the southern limit of range, no true Montane forest occurs on Angsi peak.

FORAGING AND FOOD. Still-hunts typically from relatively open perches, like other mid-stratum trogons, swooping out to snatch from surrounding surfaces.

SOCIAL ORGANIZATION. Typically solitary.

MOVEMENTS. None reported.

SURVIVAL. No information.

SOCIAL INTERACTIONS. No information.

VOICE. A shallowly declining sequence of 4–5 well-spaced, mellow but resonant *tyaup* or *tyauk* notes, plus a light rattle, *tawirrr*.

BREEDING

Nest. Not described.

Eggs and brood. Eggs and clutch not described, but broods of one and two dependant young on record.

Cycle. No information.

Seasonality. On the Main Range, young juveniles in the company of one or a pair of adults on 6 March and 29 May (ENGGANG-1, SINGAV-1).

MOULT. Among 11 Malaysian adults dated January–March, May and October, two show early-stage wing-moult (P1) in late February and May.

CONSERVATION. As for other closed-canopy Montane forest birds, much depends on the course of Thai and Malaysian highland development policies. Within this trogon's range, Luang peak (Nakhon Si Thammarat) and part of Benom (Pahang) have legal sanctuary status; none in place elsewhere.

Order BUCEROTIFORMES

Family BUCEROTIDAE

Hornbills: ten species

Oriental Pied Hornbill; Nok Gek (Thai); Burung Enggang Kelingking (Malay)

Anthracoceros albirostris (Shaw and Nodder) 1807, *Vivarium Naturae, or The Naturalist's Miscellany* 19: 809. TL Chandarnagar, Bengal.

Plate 59

GROUP RELATIONS. Forms a superspecies with allopatric *A. coronatus* and *A. marchei* (Indian and Palawan Pied Hornbills). In the past, widely confused with *coronatus* but smaller, showing greater sexual dimorphism of casque form and with bare mandibular skin of adults bluish rather than pink (Frith and Frith 1983, Kemp 1995).

GLOBAL RANGE. Himalayan foothills and adjacent lowlands east from Dehra Dun, and the far-NE Indian subcontinent; S Yunnan and S Guangxi; and SE Asia to the Greater Sunda islands and Bali.

IDENTIFICATION/DESCRIPTION. Head, upperparts including wings, and chin to square-cut margin across upper breast, green-shot black; rest of underparts and tips of flight-feathers white. Central tail-feathers black, finely tipped white, the remainder grade from black with apical quarter white to, in the south, commonly nearly all white (but most with some black at their concealed base). Among southern birds, this black decreases with age (Frith and Frith 1978) but is not a specifically juvenile character. The black/white interface is usually irregular from feather to feather, and bilaterally asymmetrical in most instances. Sexes differ in overall size (female smaller), bill-colour (blacker in female), and in the form of the casque, developing from a low ridge in the juvenile culmen over a minimum 14 months. This is lower, proportionately smaller in females; higher, larger, and with more forward projection in males. In its final form, a high-standing cylinder with flat rear face inclining back past bill-base, and laterally compressed anterior blade that, in males, projects forward due partly to abrasion of the septum connecting it with the mandible (Frith and Douglas 1978, Frith and Frith 1978).

Flight-action, with bouts of vigorous flapping between rigid, level-winged glides, resembles no other local hornbill species.

Bare-part colours. Iris deep brown (juvenile), dark red-brown (adult female), red (adult male); eyelid dark grey to, in northern birds, part-black; large peri-orbital and mandibular face-patches pinkish-white to white (juvenile), milky blue (adult); bill all ivory-white (young juvenile), black at base and along cutting-edges (adult), in females black also at tip and with red-brown spot near base; posterior face, and sides and tip of anterior blade of full-grown casque black, rest ivory-white; feet greenish black (Frith and Frith 1978, Riley 1938).

Size (mm). (Skins: 3 males, 4 females; adult): wing 272–291 and 255–265; tail 255–273 and 238–259; bill 160–180 and 126–146, casque-length (maximum chord) 119–144 and 81–122; tarsus 51–55 (sexes combined) (BMNH, UMZC).

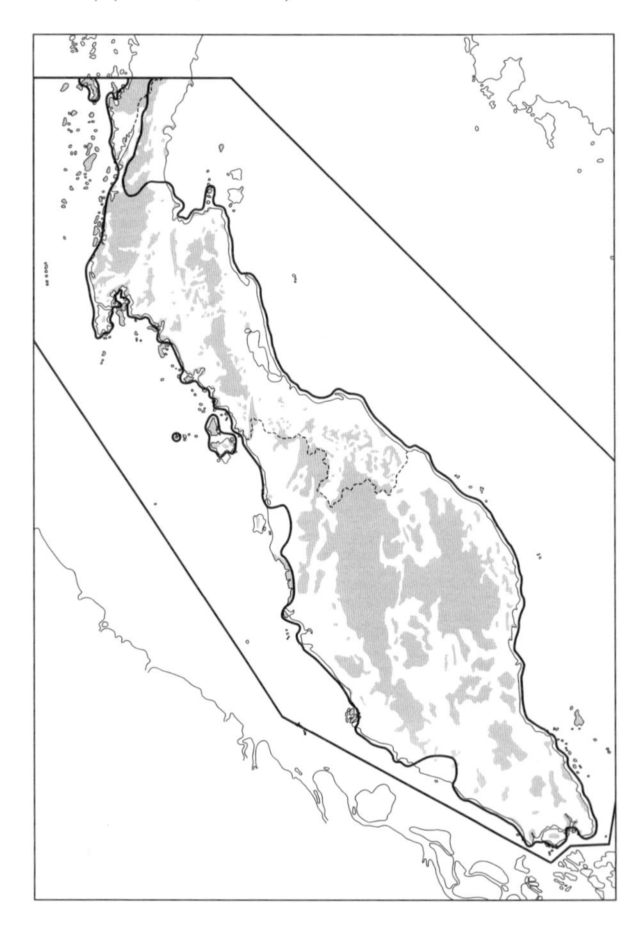

Weight. No data.

DISTRIBUTION. Historical summary: all divisions except *Chu*, *Pra*, *Mel*, with additional island records from Lanbyi (*Pak*), Phanak and Boi Noi (*Pha*), Poda (*Kra*), Libong, Tarutao and Ba Hong (*Sat*), the Langkawi group (Langkawi, Langgun) and Pangkor off the W coast; and the Ang Thong group off the E coast. With loss of forest cover, disappeared from *Sin* possibly in the nineteenth century. Intermittent recent sightings there, including on Berani island, are of presumed wildlife-trade escapes, but birds on the nearby S coast of Johor (Tanjung Sepang area) are likely to be wild, and could still make the crossing.

GEOGRAPHICAL VARIATION. Northern and southern subspecies *albirostris* and *convexus* Temminck 1832 (TL Greater Sunda islands), respectively with outer four tail-feathers mainly black (tips white) and mainly white, appear to have been geographical isolates that have re-met. Frith and Frith (1978) found an average increase of black in the tail of *albirostris* as it approached the range of *convexus*, suggesting possible assortative mating. This has not been checked among wild pairs, but no group segregation has been noticed, and signs of intermediacy from as far away as Java (AMNH, BMNH) show the extent of gene-flow. On present evidence, the Peninsular population as a whole is probably best defined as an *albirostris–convexus* intergrade.

STATUS AND POPULATION. Resident, local and uncommon to more or less common, but in general decline. With other hornbills, pressured by the trade in fledglings, but more tolerant than most of human presence and some habitat fragmentation. It even enters rural settlements, but favours the interface of low-lying terrestrial forest with a coast or significant river, and has disappeared where this forest has been removed.

HABITATS AND ECOLOGY. The canopy and edge of evergreen and semi-evergreen Lowland forest, including peatswamp forest, mature and regenerating, particularly where a watercourse opens out the forest canopy (and survives locally even where only a corridor of woodland has been left along riverbanks). Also occurs in beach-strand woodland and tall secondary-growth, and enters gardens and rubber and palm plantations adjacent to any of the above habitats; strictly at plains level, except on some islands (including Pangkor) where it ranges up the lower slopes of hills to about 150 m.

Bathes during rain-showers by flapping about in wet foliage with wings and tail spread, this behaviour followed by sunning (Frith and Douglas 1978).

FORAGING AND FOOD. Takes small fruit from gap-phase and second-growth vines and trees (e.g., *Vitex pubescens*) but recorded at only a few types of figs, including *Ficus benjamina*, *F. retusa*, and a large, unidentified strangler on the bank of the Tembeling river, Taman Negara. Among the 25 bird-attracting species monitored over several years in forest at Kuala Lompat, Kerau wildlife reserve, visited only *F. pisocarpa* (with 11.6 mm, yellow-orange fruit) (E.F. Allen 1949, Lambert 1989, BR 1972–73). Animal food includes large insects (Frith and Douglas 1978).

SOCIAL ORGANIZATION. Pairs disperse to breed, with no evidence to date of helpers at the nest. Where common, non-breeders flock, with groups of up to 30 recorded in Taman Negara (BR 1972–73), but half this number would be exceptional in most other areas. Ranging behaviour and the age-composition of flocks have not been studied, but they are expected to include many immatures.

MOVEMENTS. None reported.

SURVIVAL. No information.

SOCIAL INTERACTIONS. Casque-form at onset of sexual maturity is not known but given the importance of the casque as a recognition signal in hornbills, breeding is unlikely to occur before full development. Birds of all ages allopreen regularly, especially head, face and neck plumage, and often offer items of food to other flock-members. The stretching of the neck down and forwards in the direction of another individual, with rapid up-flicking of the bill, may serve to advertise casque-form and is thought to be aggressive (Frith and Frith 1978).

VOICE. A rather shrill, ringing, wavering cackle, *kleng-kleng kek-kek-kek-kek-kek-kek*, of 6–8 notes; also a deeper clucking, *kuk-kuk-kuk-kuk-kuk* ... and still softer *kiew-kiew-kiew-kiew* ... (BMP5, Frith and Douglas 1978).

BREEDING

Nest. Three described: holes 5–30 m up trunks of a large *Carapa moluccensis* in coastal swamp-forest, an *Artocarpus rigidus* at the edge of a paddyfield near forest and unidentified tall tree at the edge of a riverside clearing; entrances in all cases plastered up to a narrow slit (15 × 4, 5 × 4 cm), the hard plaster a mixture of droppings (with included seeds), mud and fibrous material (pieces of feather, etc.). Any break while the nest is still occupied is repaired. Brood-chamber unlined, in one instance 30 cm below the entrance-slit. The nest-hole is used in successive seasons.

Eggs and brood. Eggs are dull, glossless white. Shape short elliptical. Size (mm): 51.0–43.6 × 36.7–35.9 (n=5) and (mean of two) 43.6 × 36.4. Full clutch two eggs. No information on incubation or fledging periods, but one record of a female walled in for 87 days.

Cycle. Fruits brought in by the male are regurgitated one by one and fed from the bill-tip.

Seasonality. Eggs in mid January–late March; chicks in March and early and mid May, and an active nest, male delivering food, in early April (BBCB-8, Chasen 1939, Edgar 1933, G.C. Madoc, Madoc 1956a, NRCS, UMZC).

MOULT. In captivity, a young male moulted primaries in the order 3-4-2-1-5-6-7-10-8-9 and 1-2-3-4-5-6-10-8-9-7, out of step by three weeks between wings, starting in early November (at age seven months) and ending in March, with secondaries and tail moulted as of mid and late January (Frith and Douglas 1978). In the wild, active wing-moult of adults recorded in April, July and August, and non-moulters in December–February (BMNH, UMZC). Depending on the timing of breeding, females moult flight- and tail-feathers while walled into the nest (Chasen 1939).

CONSERVATION. Even though common and conspicuous locally, its living-space is vulnerable. Tourism developments bite into the coastal habitat of some erstwhile healthy island populations, and these need monitoring. All hornbill species are under pressure from the trade in fledglings, particularly in Thailand.

Black Hornbill; Nok Ngeuak Dam (Thai); Burung Enggang Gatalbirah (Malay)

Anthracoceros malayanus (Raffles) 1822, *Transactions of the Linnean Society* 13(2): 292. TL Melaka.
Plate 59

GROUP RELATIONS. Free-standing.

GLOBAL RANGE. Borneo and Sumatra and intervening islands, and the Peninsula. Claims of occurrence in SW Thailand and, in the nineteenth century, far-S Indochina (Delacour 1970) have not been substantiated.

IDENTIFICATION/DESCRIPTION. Uniform glossy black except for a long supercilium from the nostril, meeting its partner at the back of nape, either dark grey or white (independent of sex or age), and apical quarter of lateral tail-feathers (T2–5) white. Adult casque high-standing, barrel-shaped, with posterior face inclined behind the base of the bill, and compressed anteriorly into a blade, forward-projecting in adult males; more or less as in Oriental Pied Hornbill but with a series of parallel furrows running the length of its base. Age-groups and sexes are separable by overall size, colour of facial-patches and/or size and colour of bill and casque. The latter develops over more than one year from a narrow ridge within the contour of the upper mandible (Frith and Douglas 1978).

Bare-part colours. Iris dark brown (juvenile), rich red-brown (adult); eyelid orange with black marks; facial skin yellowish (young juvenile), separate peri-orbital and mandibular patches bluish black (adult male), respectively liver-pink and ivory-yellow (adult female); bill and casque white with posterior face and extreme base of the mandibles, including nostril area, black (adult male), all blackish (juveniles and female); feet black (Chasen 1939, Frith and Douglas 1978).

Size (mm). (Skins: 3 males, 4 females; adult): wing 319–325 and 280–288; tail 327–348 and 270–287; bill 171–181 and 124–135, casque-length (maximum chord) 117–125 and 67–76; tarsus 53–54 and 44–49 (BMNH).

Weight. No data.

DISTRIBUTION. Historical summary: *?Ran, Kra, Tra, Sat, Nar, Ked, Kel, Pek, Phg, Sel, Neg, Joh*, with no island records.

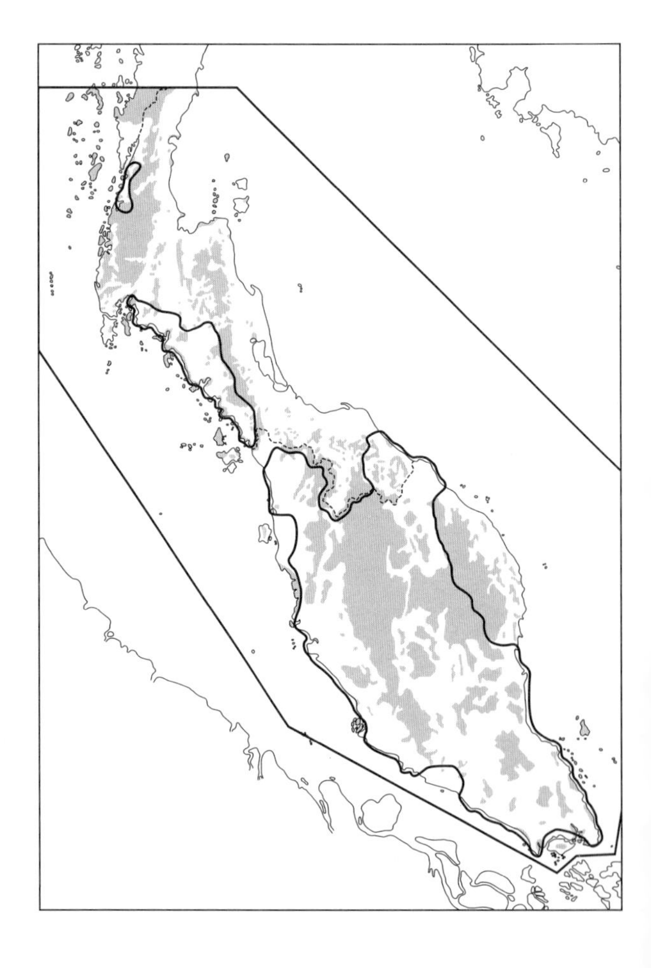

GEOGRAPHICAL VARIATION. None recognized.

STATUS AND POPULATION. Resident and, in the south, more or less regular and common; local and (now) very much rarer in the north, but still present in Hala Bala wildlife santuary, Narathiwat (BCSTB-12).

HABITATS AND ECOLOGY. The edge and canopy of mainly evergreen Lowland forest, mature and regenerating after disturbance (including logging), also peat- and other freshwater swamp-forest; at plains level to not far past the steepland boundary, with records along the foot of the Main Range to 200 m.

During rain-showers, foliage-bathes like Oriental Pied Hornbill (Frith and Douglas 1978).

FORAGING AND FOOD. No reports other than at figs, although unlikely to be a fig specialist. In the Kerau wildlife reserve and Taman Negara, recorded feeding at 17 of 25 bird-attracting *Ficus* species under regular observation, in the fruit-diameter range 7.0–34.8 mm (Lambert 1989).

SOCIAL ORGANIZATION. In Borneo, described as territorial (Leighton 1982), but evidently cohesive groups (age-structure unknown) are also common. Typically of 3–8, where undisturbed in areas of extensive habitat these can sometimes be several times this number. Before clearance of its hinterland, up to 33 recorded in Pasoh research forest, Negeri Sembilan and, in August 1993, 20-plus paid daily visits to a fruiting fig by Kenering lake, Perak (Sutari Supari). A party has been seen close to an active nest, but with no evidence yet of cooperative breeding.

MOVEMENTS. None recorded.

SURVIVAL. No information.

SOCIAL INTERACTIONS. No information.

VOICE. As a group, various grating growls and roars, deep and sonorous; not well described at individual level.

BREEDING

Nest. Only two described: cavities 12 and 27 m up in large trees of mature forest, one a nutmeg *Myristica* sp.; the entrance plastered.

Eggs and brood. No reliable information.

Cycle. Males attending an occupied nest regurgitate food-items every few seconds, passing them individually through the nest-entrance.

Seasonality. A recently hatched chick on 24 February and young of unknown age, but noisy, on 24–27 April (G.C. Madoc, NRCS).

MOULT. Two adult females dated August and November showed none; no other data.

CONSERVATION. More tolerant of secondary and regenerating conditions after logging than other hornbill species, but dependance on plains-level habitat has helped remove it from much former range. On the verge of extinction in Thailand, and near-threatened globally (BTW2).

Rhinoceros Hornbill; Nok Ngeuak Hua Raet (Thai); Burung Enggang Badak (Malay)

Buceros rhinoceros Linnaeus 1758, *Systema Naturae* 10(1): 104. TL Melaka.
Plate 60

GROUP RELATIONS. Free-standing.

GLOBAL RANGE. Java, Borneo, Sumatra and the Peninsula to latitude approximately 7°N.

IDENTIFICATION/DESCRIPTION. Thighs and belly to lower tail-coverts, and tail except for broad black sub-terminal bar, white; rest of head, body and wings glossy black, with no pale tips or wing-bar (although odd white-tipped post-juvenile primaries have been reported in a wild-hatched captive). The sexes are separable by overall size, and eye-, face and casque colour; juveniles also by shape of casque. The latter begins as a round-fronted ridge, with separation of a forward-pointing prow from the mandible helped by abrasion of a thinned-down anterior septum, as in *Anthracoceros* species. Prow straight for at least the first three years of life (BMNH, Frith and Douglas 1978).

Bare-part colours. Iris grey (young juvenile), red (adult male), pearl-white (adult female); eyelids and other periocular skin black (male), dull red (female). Bill and casque-rudiment all yellow (young juvenile), apical half of upper mandible and most of lower ivory-white, shading to yellow then red at base of the upper mandible (colours cosmetic, from preen-oil, hence area of red varies), both mandibles with a basal wedge of black, broader on the lower. Adult casque bright red with front of up-curved horn rich yellow; in males the posterior face black, with black lining the casque-base to continue as a thin stripe separating red from yellow along the sides of the horn; in females, no black on casque, and its posterior face is red. Feet dirty olive.

Size (mm). (Live and skins: 4 males, 2 females; adult): wing 461–477 and 425, 438; tail 350–365 and 350, 350; bill 266–291 and 243, 248, casque-length (maximum chord) 145–158 and 133, 134; tarsus not measured (BMNH, UMBRP).

Weight. No data.

DISTRIBUTION. The southern mainland only. Historical summary: *Son, Sat, Yal, Nar, Ked, Kel, Tru, Pek, Phg, Sel, Neg, Mel, Joh*, with a few nineteenth century reports from Singapore island but no good evidence of residence there, and no other island records. The recent northern limit (recorded May 1988) is Thung Wa district (*Sat*), latitude 7°07′N (J. McLoughlin, Y. Meekeow).

GEOGRAPHICAL VARIATION. Nominate *rhinoceros*, also of Sumatra.

STATUS AND POPULATION. Resident, regular and sparse to more or less common. At the northern edge of its range, few in the northwest (N Kedah and beyond) but up to the early 1970s frequent in parts of Yala and Narathiwat, with good numbers still present in Hala Bala wildlife sanctuary (BCSTB-12, Holmes 1973).

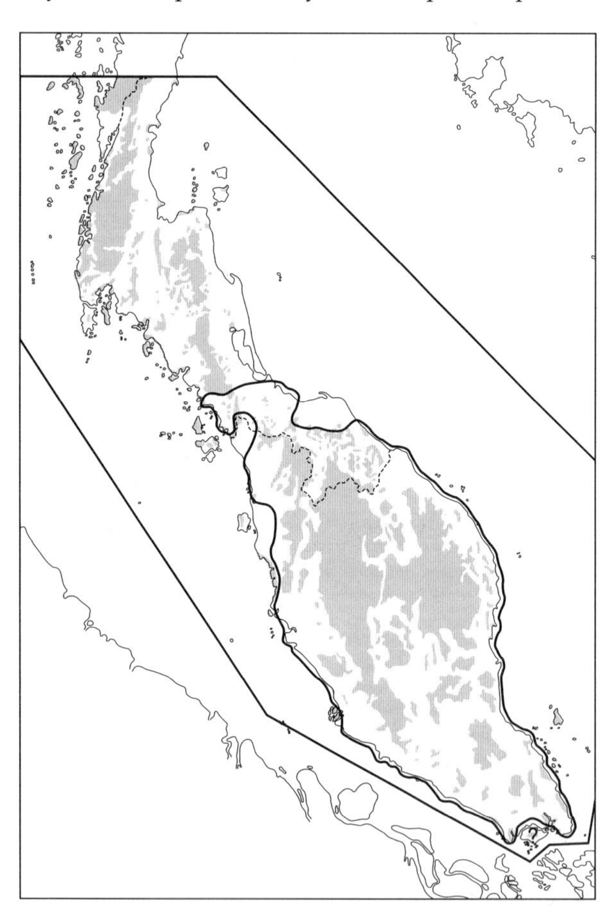

HABITATS AND ECOLOGY. Northern limit of range coincides roughly with the limit of predominantly evergreen (versus semi-evergreen) Lowland forests. Typically, in the canopy of mature Lowland forest, or where plenty of large trees survive after disturbance, also peat- and other freshwater swamp-forests, from plains level to the Montane ecotone. Only a occasional foraging visitor in Montane forest proper, with records to 1400 m (ENGGANG-1).

Foliage-bathes during rain-showers (Frith and Douglas 1978).

FORAGING AND FOOD. Like many hornbills, omnivorous in captivity but the non-fruit, indeed non-fig, part of the wild diet has been little studied. At Kuala Lompat (Kerau wildlife reserve) and in Taman Negara, fed at 13 of 25 bird-attracting *Ficus* species under regular observation, in the fruit-diameter range 7.0–34.8 mm (Lambert 1989), but the piles of hard seeds ejected beneath active nests show figs are only a part of the fruit intake. Among non-fig trees used, Johns (1987) identified *Knema* spp. (Myristicaceae), *Milletia atropurpurea* (Leguminosae), *Castanopsis curtisii* (Fagaceae), *Eugenia* spp. (Myrtaceae) and *Litsea* spp. (Lauraceae). Birds wandering into oil-palm plantation adjacent to logged forest at Tekam (Pahang) took arthropods and small vertebrates (mostly lizards), including from the ground.

SOCIAL ORGANIZATION. Adults with fully formed casques occur mostly in pairs, year-round, and are the territorial social unit. Small groups typically include a pair of adults and one or more (up to four) straight-prowed juveniles, implying possible extended association between parents and offspring of more than one brood (see also Helmeted Hornbill *B. vigil*). Large flocks (25 and 20 at tall strangling figs in Selangor and Taman Negara, and 18 in Narathiwat, in February, April and June) are scarce and of unknown ranging behaviour. They include mostly (perhaps only) straight-prowed birds, suggesting no pairing off or defence of territory begins until casque-growth is complete. There is no evidence yet that Rhinoceros Hornbills roost communally, although young non-breeders may.

MOVEMENTS. None reported.

SURVIVAL. No information.

SOCIAL INTERACTIONS. Little known. Among captives, apparently aggressive bill-twitching is as in Oriental Pied Hornbill. Wild, territorial males chase off intruders (ENGGANG-2), and disputes can develop into noisy fights. One between three birds in the Gombak valley, Selangor (BR 1967), landed them on the forest floor, although what resources (fruit, nest-sites) were actually being defended was not observed. After food-passes at the nest-entrance, breeding mates bill-tap (Johns 1981).

VOICE. While perched, a sharp *kak* and a powerful, sonorous *gronk*, given as the head and bill are flicked vertical. Intention to fly is signalled by switching to a disyllabic *ger-onk* or *ger-honk*, continued as the bird takes off but stopped immediately it re-settles, hence probably with contact function between pair-members on the move. The female receiving food in the nest makes a wheezing noise (Johns 1981).

BREEDING

Nest. Three described: holes in main trunks and a broken crown branch-base of large forest trees (*Palaquium*, *Shorea* spp., including *S. pauciflora*), 12–15 m up; in one instance on the lower side of a leaning trunk, in another orientated away from the prevailing monsoon wind. Entrances were plastered, in one case leaving a slit a few centimetres wide extending 60–80 cm up the full height of the original opening.

Eggs and brood. Not described.

Cycle. Most plastering is from within, by the female. Males service active nests, regurgitating and feeding fruits one by one through the entrance-slit (up to 20 items counted in a session). As with Great Hornbill *B. bicornis*, the female breaks out early and at a Johor nest pair-members took turns to feed re-sealed-in young.

Seasonality. Active nests, contents unchecked, in Pahang, Selangor and Johor in late February, March, May (twice) and early and late June, with inspection of a new site in late May (Johns 1981, G.C. Madoc, NRCS, SINGAV-6, M. Strange).

MOULT. Females are said to moult completely while walled into the nest, but some moult of flight-feathers (sequential, at one or two loci in the primary tract) also occurs when living free. All six free-flying adults (of both sexes) examined showed active wing-moult, in no obvious seasonal progression.

CONSERVATION. Will return to customary nest-holes even after surrounding forest has been disturbed. Monitoring through a logging event and beyond in Tekam forestry concession, Pahang, showed little immediate impact on population density, but six years on only one quarter of original numbers remained (Johns 1987), even though some mature forest survived in the vicinity. Large-bodied hornbills taking high-canopy rather than second-growth food are likely to be affected most by logging. This and other long-term issues (recruitment of young into the population, greater exposure of birds to hunting in degraded forest) need further study.

Great Hornbill; Nok Gok (Thai); Burung Enggang Papan (Malay)

Buceros bicornis Linnaeus 1758, *Systema Naturae* 10(1): 104. TL Sumatra.
Plate 60

GROUP RELATIONS. Free-standing.

GLOBAL RANGE. The W Ghats, Himalayan foothills east from Kumaon and hill-tracts of the far-NE Indian subcontinent; S and W Yunnan; and SE Asia to the Peninsula and Sumatra.

IDENTIFICATION/DESCRIPTION. From Rhinoceros Hornbill by form and colour of casque; white neck (commonly preened yellowish) sharp against black of face and body; white tips to flight-feathers, and a bold white bar across both surfaces of their base (including tips of adjacent coverts), bar often preened yellowish to orange at the leading edge where it receives most attention. Full development of the casque takes not less than three, possibly five, years (Frith and Douglas 1978). Starting as a humped ridge within the contour of the culmen, the rounded posterior end expands well back on the crown, and lateral flanges grow up and forward, initially joined at the tip then abraded to leave a long, open-fronted, eventually more or less level-rimmed trough.

Bare-part colours. Iris blue-grey to whitish (young juvenile), red (adult male), pearl-white (adult female); periorbital skin flesh-pink (young juvenile), all black (adult male), eyelid black and the rest dull red (adult female); adult lower mandible white with yellow tip, upper yellow with red tip (cosmetic colours from preen-oil, hence distribution varies), with a wedge of black across the base of the bill from the nostril, broadest ventrally, and a narrow black line mid-dorsally and mid-ventrally; sides of adult casque yellow, top yellow to reddish and, in male, both ends black, with black along the base, but no black in female casque, which has posterior face red; feet olive-yellow (young juvenile), dirty olive (adult).

Size (mm). (Skins: 5 males, 5 females; adult): wing 465–495 and 440–484; tail 350–383 and 352–400; bill 296–330 and 289–322, casque-length (maximum chord) 143–180 and 137–188; tarsus not measured (BMNH, UMZC).

Weight. No data.

DISTRIBUTION. On the E-coast plain, not recorded south of the Pahang river, but occurs along the Main Range regularly to the head of the Gombak valley (mid Selangor, latitude 3°22'N), with one recent report of a pair on Telapa Buruk peak (*Neg*) (K.T. Yap). No record exists from the W-coast plain south of Perlis/N Kedah but island populations remain in the Langkawi group (Langkawi, Langgun) and on Pangkor (*Pek*), with a high chance that before colonial settlement this and other hornbills also occurred on Penang island. Historical summary: all divisions except *Phu, Pht, Pat, Kel, Pra, Mel, Joh, Sin*, with other W-coast island records from Lanta, Libong and Tarutao.

GEOGRAPHICAL VARIATION. Small nominate *bicornis*, also of Sumatra.

STATUS AND POPULATION. Resident, more or less regular and uncommon to more or less common, even close to the southern terminus, although no large groups have been recorded in the south. Occasional reports from the far south are likely to have been of captives escaped or released in Singapore.

HABITATS AND ECOLOGY. The canopy of near-deciduous to evergreen Lowland forest, mature to lightly disturbed (short gaps between habitat-patches are crossed), at plains level and up slopes into the Lower Montane zone, in the south regularly to about 1400 m (ENGGANG-2). Southernmost records on the eastern plain are from coastal headland forest at Kuantan and, inland, within a few kilometres of the Pahang river at Tekam forestry concession, Jerantut district (BR 1969, 1980–81). Appears not to enter the stretch of swamp-forest between Kuantan and the lower Pahang river, where only Rhinoceros Hornbill has been recorded. They co-occur in eastern dry-land forests, but on the western face of the Main Range in Selangor, for no obvious reason, Great penetrates only a short distance below the Montane ecotone.

Like Rhinoceros Hornbill and *Anthracoceros* species, foliage-bathes during rain (Frith and Douglas 1978).

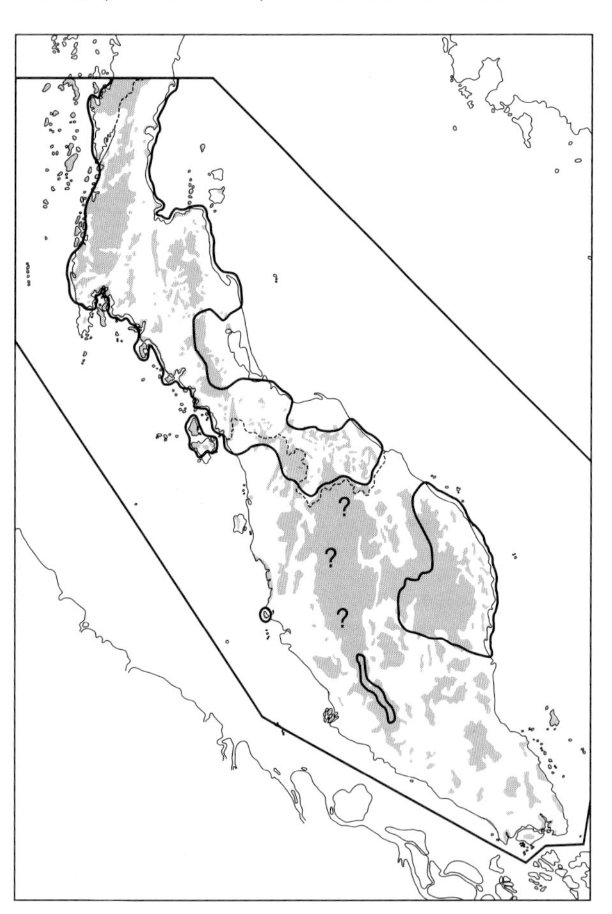

FORAGING AND FOOD. No information.

SOCIAL ORGANIZATION. The adult pair is the presumed territorial social unit, and from Yala and Narathiwat south, largest parties include 3–4 birds only. Larger groups have been recorded in the north, to a maximum 16 at Kaki Bukit, Perlis, in January 1968 – before clearance of then-extensive deciduous and semi-deciduous forests along the Thai border (BMP5). Nothing is known about the age-composition of such flocks, or their ranging behaviour, relationship to neighbouring territorial pairs, etc.

MOVEMENTS. No information.

SURVIVAL. No information.

SOCIAL INTERACTIONS. No specific information, but aggressive displays are said to be similar to those of Rhinoceros and Oriental Pied Hornbills.

VOICE. Pairs indulge in syncopated duetting, with bills flicked up near-vertical; the male gives a deep *kok*, followed with near-overlap by the female. The single-note loud call of perched birds is described as a coarse, guttural *whaaa* or *ruak*. At a distance, the disyllabic flight-call is hard to separate from that of Rhinoceros Hornbill.

BREEDING. No wild nest described but, in Yala, nestlings and young fledglings collected in mid–late May. One successful breeding attempt in captivity gave an incubation period of at most 40 days and fledging period of at least 95 days, for a single chick. The female broke out 26 days before the chick emerged, 112 days after walling herself in (Jurong Bird Park data, UMZC).

MOULT. The female is said to undergo complete moult while sealed into the nest, but this may depend on the timing of the breeding attempt. Seven free-living adults, including two females, showed sequential (single- and double-locus) primary moult during December–February and April, May and July. Three non-moulters during the same months reveal nothing about seasonality, but confirm the process is not continuous (BMNH, UMZC).

CONSERVATION. See Rhinoceros Hornbill. Being scarcer than Rhinoceros in most Malaysian habitats, impacts of logging on its populations in the south should be more severe. Information is needed on its ecology in upland forests.

Helmeted Hornbill; Nok Chon Hin (Thai); **Burung Enggang Tebang Mentua** (Malay)

Buceros vigil J.R. Forster 1781, *Indische Zoologie*: 40. TL Sumatra.
Plate 60

GROUP RELATIONS. Free-standing.

GLOBAL RANGE. Borneo, Sumatra and the Peninsula.

IDENTIFICATION/DESCRIPTION. Bare neck whitish or dark red, and short casque of adult high and nearly flat-fronted. At all ages, face behind eye bright chestnut, the rest of head including shaggy nape-crest, breast and upperparts deep brown, paling on rump and upper tail-coverts; thighs and belly to lower tail-coverts sharply demarcated white. All tail-feathers, including T1, have a broad subterminal black band, as in other *Buceros* species. Laterals (T2–5) are otherwise ash-white, T1 (forming a pair of long streamers) vinous-brown with a white tip. All flight-feathers except inner secondaries are also white-tipped.

Keratin of casque and mandibles is thick, heavy and ivory-like, quite unlike the light sheath over lattice bone of other *Buceros* species. The casque grows over several years, from a low hump on the basal half of the juvenile culmen, and only in full adults is the high front square-cut rather than rounded. By analogy with young Rhinoceros Hornbill behaviour, and from evidence of specimens, this final shape is achieved and maintained by abrasion – which would expose fresh, frontal ivory of the light colour regular in adults. Males acquire red neck-skin before final casque-shape.

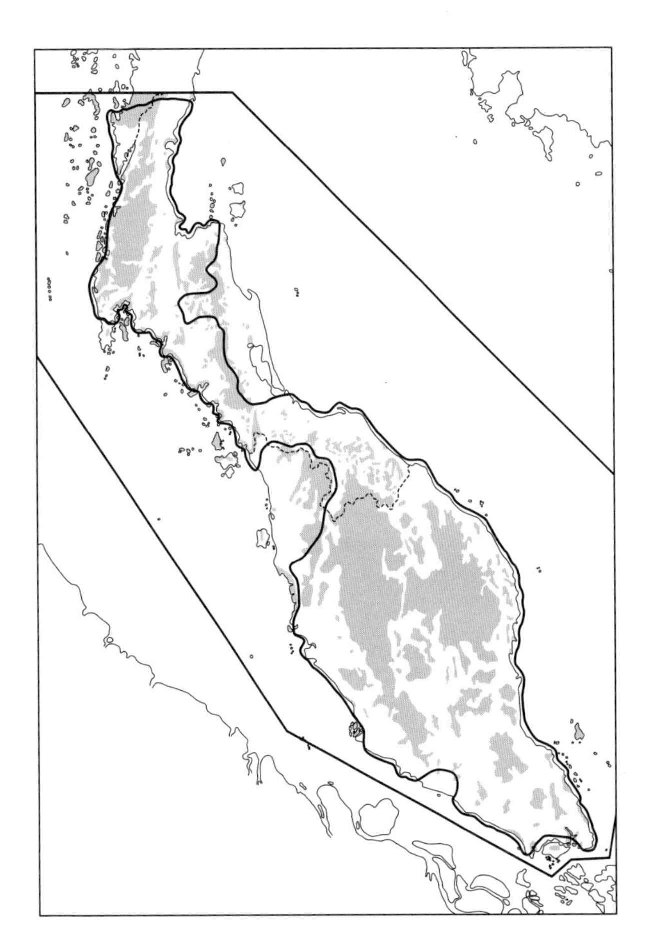

Bare-part colours. (Adults) iris rich red-brown; periorbital skin forward to bill-base, and wrinkled, swollen neck from chin, jaw-line and nape to upper breast and upper mantle levels, dark wine-red (male), milky blue to whitish (juveniles and female); young juvenile bill yellow and casque-rudiment white; adult casque-front and apical half of bill ivory- to orange-yellow, rest of casque and bill-base dark red (all colours cosmetic, from preen-oil, hence variable); feet red-brown.

Size (mm). (Skins: 5 males only; adult): wing 478–500; tail (T1) 685–855; bill 185–200, casque-length (maximum chord) 87–112; tarsus not measured (BMNH).

Weight. No data.

DISTRIBUTION. On the mainland to latitude 10°58'N. Historical summary: all divisions except *Nak, Phu, Pht, Ked, Pra, Mel, Sin*.

GEOGRAPHICAL VARIATION. None recognized.

STATUS AND POPULATION. Resident, more or less regular and, on evidence of calling, relatively common in remote areas, but declining and now sparse in Thailand (probably only in the larger reserves). Based on advertisement-calling, population density is naturally low but if, as suspected (Haimoff 1987), only adult males call, no account has been taken of the presence of elusive, probably slow-maturing pre-adults (see below).

HABITATS AND ECOLOGY. The high canopy of semi-evergreen and evergreen Lowland forest, mostly mature but also logged habitat where much tall timber survives, including large strangling figs and, within its range, the giant legume *Koompassia excelsa*; at all elevations. Also in the Lower Montane zone, recorded to 1400 m (ENGGANG-2), but Montane forest may only be fringe habitat.

FORAGING AND FOOD. Observations in Kalimantan (Leighton 1982) suggest the fruit part of the diet is more strictly figs than in any other hornbill of the area. At Kuala Lompat, Kerau wildlife reserve,

Lambert (1989) recorded attendance at ten of 25 *Ficus* species under study, in the fruit-size range 10.2–34.8 mm, i.e., avoiding the smaller end of the spectrum. Animal food, if any, must be collected at canopy level.

SOCIAL ORGANIZATION. Often alone, but a pair of adults is believed to be the territorial social unit. At Kuala Lompat, Lambert (1987) encountered a maximum three together, including an immature, but more are on record (Dunlop 1961). My one experience of a larger group is from Brunei: an adult male and female, presumed to be a pair, with about seven others (five confirmed), all immature, feeding and resting amicably together in a large-crowned strangling fig. Among the auxiliaries, casque-growth ranged from rudimentary to near-full in a male already with a red neck, implying they were young of several breeding seasons. This allows the possibility that parents tolerate offspring in the territory over several years, at least at certain times of year.

MOVEMENTS. None reported.

SURVIVAL. No direct information but an apparently solitary male has been in Rap Ro wildlife sanctuary, Chumphon, for at least ten years (BCSTB-10).

SOCIAL INTERACTIONS. See above, and under Voice.

VOICE. Syncopated duetting between pair-members described from Kalimantan (Leighton 1982) has not been reported locally. The loud advertising-call, thought to be given only by males, is audible at over 1 km (implying a large territory): even-pitched, pure-tone hoots, *oo* or *hoo*, well-spaced initially but the long sequence slowly accelerates, switching eventually to *tee-<u>hoo</u>* disyllables that soon climax in a wild, laughing crescendo, *tee-hee-hee-haa-haa-haa-haa* ... of about 15 impure notes (with many strong harmonics). Prior to the disyllable-switch the call may abort and re-start; after, it always runs to completion (BMP5, Haimoff 1987). As the monosyllables speed up the bill is pointed vertically; and lowered again and opened as the laugh changes timbre (BR 1970–71).

A sonorous, clanging *ka-hank, ka-hank, ka-hank* . . . has been recorded in a possible alarm context but also as a flight-call (equivalent to the disyllable of other *Buceros*?) when birds were not disturbed. A single staccato note has been heard from members of a party on the move (Dunlop 1961), and in a definite alarm context where feeding birds were flushed from a fruit-tree.

There has been much speculation about the source of loud, apparently non-vocal *kok* or *konk* noises, recorded most often when two or more individuals are known to have been nearby (Dunlop 1961). Museum specimens supply good evidence of heavy abrasion both of the front of the casque and adjacent (thickened) bill, and observations in Taman Negara confirm knocks are made by striking casques together. Two adults (not sexed) perching close clashed frequently over a period of 40 minutes, then kept company in flight and returned together over a long distance when lured by a tape-recording of the flight-call (K.W. Scriven). They are assumed to have been males engaged in a boundary dispute, but knocks are loud and carrying enough to suggest some additional, distant signal function. More observations are needed in the few areas where this great bird is still numerous, but abrasion of the casque is the same in adult females, suggesting they also participate. Possibly, some knocking is against resonating dead wood.

BREEDING. One record: a bird delivering food at a hole in a high branch-stump of a large *K. excelsa* in forest in N Perak, in early August 1993 (C.M. Francis). Egg, brood and development periods are not described.

MOULT. All five males examined (two dated March and September) were moulting primaries, at single loci (BMNH). That central tail-streamers moult asymmetrically, always leaving one intact, has been remarked upon, but this pattern of T1 moult is general in hornbills.

CONSERVATION. Apparent narrowness of the fruit part of the diet suggests Helmeted is among the hornbill species less likely to withstand logging and timber-extraction practices current in Malaysia. With other large hornbills, it is also a traditional quarry, hunted by highly skilled, in some cases now well-armed aboriginal people, e.g., in the upper Perak valley. Given the loss of range suffered through land clearance, long-standing legislation granting these hunters customary access, even in reserves, is overdue for review. Globally near-threatened (BTW2).

Bushy-crested Hornbill; Nok Ngeuak Paak Dam (Thai); Burung Enggang Mengilai (Malay)

Anorrhinus galeritus (Temminck) 1831, *Nouveau Recueil de Planches Coloriées d'Oiseaux* 88: plate 520. TL Sumatra.

Plate 59

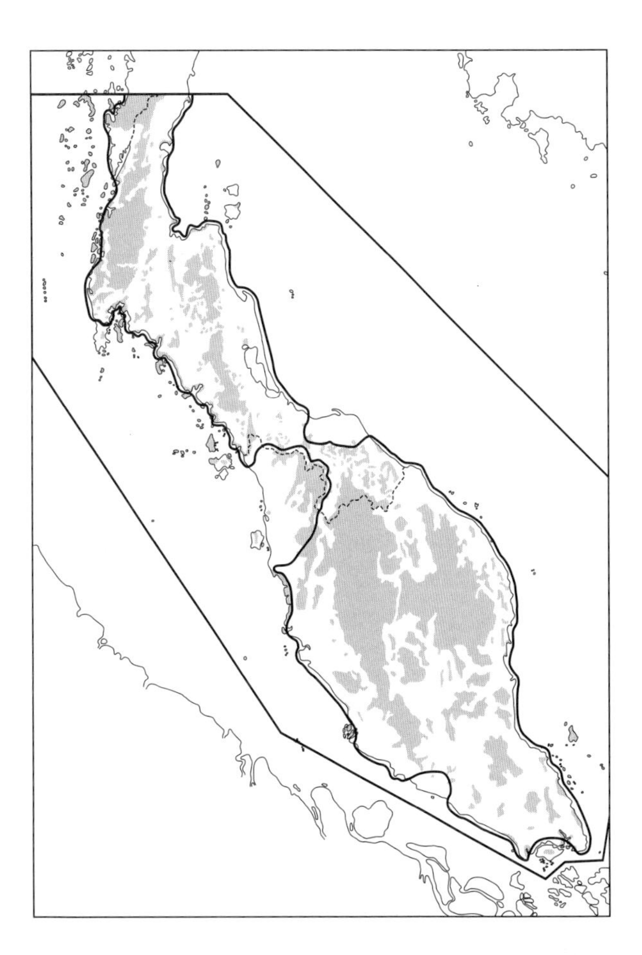

GROUP RELATIONS. Free-standing.

GLOBAL RANGE. Borneo, Sumatra, the Peninsula and Tenasserim to latitude 14°N.

IDENTIFICATION/DESCRIPTION. Head, including broad, drooping nape-crest, body and wings sooty, upperparts with an oily gloss, greyer brown on the belly and lower tail-coverts; basal two thirds of tail dull grey, apex blackish. The casque is a low, narrow ridge with sloping front contour, more or less fully formed by the second year. Sexes are separable on bill-colour; juveniles on both bill and face, and generally browner plumage, paler on the underparts and with some buff edging on wing-coverts.

Bare-part colours. Iris china-blue changing to orange-brown (juveniles), dark crimson (adult); eyelids pink with surrounding periorbital patch bright yellow and mandibular patch cream-yellow (young juvenile), eyelids mottled black-and-white with both skin-patches chalky blue (second-year immature), all skin purplish blue, darkest around eye (adult); bill pale green with yellow tip (young juvenile), ivory-white with base, upper cutting-edge and all except tip of lower mandible, plus casque, variably black (adult female), all black (adult male); feet slaty.

Size (mm). (Skins: 4 males, 2 females; adult): wing 351–372 and 330, 355; tail 270–294 and 263, 276; bill 141–153 and 141 (1 only); tarsus 49–52 and 48 (1 only) (BMNH, UMZC).

Weight. No data.

DISTRIBUTION. Historical summary: all divisions except *Phu, Pat, Ked, Pra, Mel, Sin,* with no island records.

GEOGRAPHICAL VARIATION. None recognized.

STATUS AND POPULATION. Resident, regular and more or less common, less so in Thailand.

HABITATS AND ECOLOGY. The canopy, mid-stratum and, occasionally, understorey of evergreen and semi-evergreen Lowland forest, mature and well-regenerated, also peatswamp forest; at plains level and on hills, occasionally into Montane forest, with records to 1400 m (a party of 15 in Genting Highlands in February: ENGGANG-2). Sometimes enters secondary-growth and overgrown plantations near forest, but these marginal habitats are unlikely to support territories.

FORAGING AND FOOD. Not heavily dependent on figs. Only nine of F.R. Lambert's 25 bird-attracting *Ficus* species under observation in the Kerau wildlife reserve were visited by this hornbill, in the fruit-size range 10.1–27.4 mm. Among non-figs, nutmegs *Myristica* are regular food. A midden below an active nest in Selangor included seeds of palms, Connaraceae, Fagaceae (*Lithocarpus cyclophorus*), Leguminosae, Rutaceae, Sapindaceae (*Sapindus rarak*) and Sterculiaceae (*Sterculia foetida*) (Madge 1969). Most food brought to the nest was fruit, but also included cicadas, a 10 cm phasmid and a lizard. Hunting for animal food has not been studied locally but individuals are believed to exploit disturbance created by the movement of the group to take flushed insects.

SOCIAL ORGANIZATION. Permanently gregarious, and one of only two local hornbill species breeding cooperatively (Madge 1969). Fledglings are recruited directly into the group, which is the basic territorial social unit. Group-size varies in the approximate range 5–15 (BMP5) but is typically in single figures.

MOVEMENTS. None reported.

SURVIVAL. No information.

SOCIAL INTERACTIONS. No information.

VOICE. Various strident, whistling yelps, mono- and disyllabic; individual calls not well described but given in a chorus that swells and fades as members, perched loosely together, join in or drop out: *kleeoo kleeoo kleeeoo, kleea kleea kleea, kloo kloo kloo kloo . . .*, etc. Some territorial hornbills duet but collective vocal advertising to neighbouring groups is rare in SE Asian forest birds, with a nearest parallel among territorial primates.

Other calls include a hen-like cluck and a high-pitched alarm, *aak aak aak*, that halts all other calling as the group slips furtively away. Begging-calls of large young in the nest are a shrill *kwee-wee-wee-wee-weah*, repeated for minutes on end (Madge 1969).

BREEDING

Nest. Only one described: a cavity about 13 m up (i.e., at mid-stratum level) in an approximately 50 cm-thick, living trunk, in lightly logged but well regenerated forest; the entrance plastered back to a slit a few centimetres wide running vertically up the whole length of the original opening (about 30 cm).

Eggs and brood. The female remained in the nest a minimum 75 days (already walled up when first discovered) and her brood of two emerged at least four days apart. No other information.

Cycle. Food delivery bouts involved mainly 1–3 birds, of both sexes, most adult but with some actual or attempted feeding also by birds with juvenile face-colours. Up to 56 items were counted delivered per bout, individually regurgitated and rolled to the bill-tip for transfer through the entrance-slit. Feeders waited in turn and some individuals attended twice.

Seasonality. An active nest in Krabi on 11 January, and one in Selangor in June from which female and first fledgling emerged on 26–27 August (BCSTB-13, Madge 1969). On evidence of alarm-calling S.G. Madge believed the latter nest may have fledged a brood earlier in the same season, but the number of reproductives active per group, hence the number of females likely to breed per year is not known. Evidently the same group inspected the cavity again in the following March.

MOULT. A March male growing primaries at two loci, and asymmetrically between wings (P3,9/6,10), and two non-moulters (male and female) in August – September (BMNH). No other information.

CONSERVATION. Capacity to feed in mid- and lower-stratum vegetation has been cited as a reason for supposing this hornbill is not as heavily pressured by logging as larger species. At Tekam forestry concession, Pahang, the group density detectable per square kilometre in forest 5–6 years after a logging event was about the same as that in untouched forest (Johns 1989). The effect of real remoteness from reservoirs of mature forest has not been tested.

White-crowned Hornbill; Nok Ngeuak Hua Ngawk (Thai); Burung Enggang Jambul Putih (Malay)

Berenicornis comatus (Raffles) 1822, *Transactions of the Linnean Society* 13(2): 339. TL Sumatra.
Plate 61

GROUP RELATIONS. Free-standing. Merged by Kemp (1988) into an enlarged *Aceros* but distinctive biology, appearance and voice persuade that it should continue in a separate genus.

GLOBAL RANGE. Borneo, Sumatra and the Peninsula, and Tenasserim and SW Thailand respectively to latitudes 14° and 15°07′N (P. Poonswad). Old claims from far-S Indochina were rejected by Delacour (1970).

IDENTIFICATION/DESCRIPTION. Sexually dimorphic. Male head including long, spiky, partly forward-pointing crest, neck and underparts to upper belly, tips of flight-feathers except inner secondaries and outermost primary, and entire tail white; thighs and rest of body and wings black, the latter glossy. Female cap to nape and crest, and tail white, but crest-feathers with black bases; the rest of the body, including neck and all underparts, blackish. Juveniles as female except crest shorter, more extensively dark-based; neck and underparts sooty with white fringing down to lower breast; and tail black with only tip white, this interface irregular, mottled and individually variable.

Bare-part colours. Iris pale yellow; facial skin pink changing to light blue (juveniles), dull dark blue (adult); bill bright yellow, changing to horn-green with black patches (juveniles), all black with base of lower mandible dull blue (adult); feet black.

Size (mm). (Skins: 2 males, 3 females; adult): wing 374, 396 and 353–371; tail 417, 460 and 377–440; bill 156, 187 and 138–147; tarsus 60–62 (sexes combined) (BMNH).

Weight. No data.

DISTRIBUTION. Historical summary: all divisions except *Ran, Phu, Pat, Yal, Ked, Kel, Tru, Pra, Pek, Sin.* Likely to have been overlooked elsewhere, but hilly country along the N Johor border (Robinson 1928, Wells 1990b) could be a range terminus. No island records.

GEOGRAPHICAL VARIATION. None recognized.

STATUS AND POPULATION. Resident, more or less regular and common to, in most areas, decidedly uncommon.

HABITATS AND ECOLOGY. The canopy but, more typically, mid- and under-strata and occasionally the floor (Lambert 1987) of semi-evergreen and evergreen Lowland forest, mature and regenerating after disturbance, at plains level and on the submontane slope to about 800 m, with one exceptional record of a party at 1680 m, in Upper Montane forest of Tahan, Pahang (Robinson 1928). At the edge of the mostly hilly Tekam forestry concession (Pahang), seen in oil-palm plantings (Johns 1989). Everywhere, more records are from hills than the level lowlands, but this may be an outcome of greater audibility of calls over slopes. None of the few nests reported was on steep land.

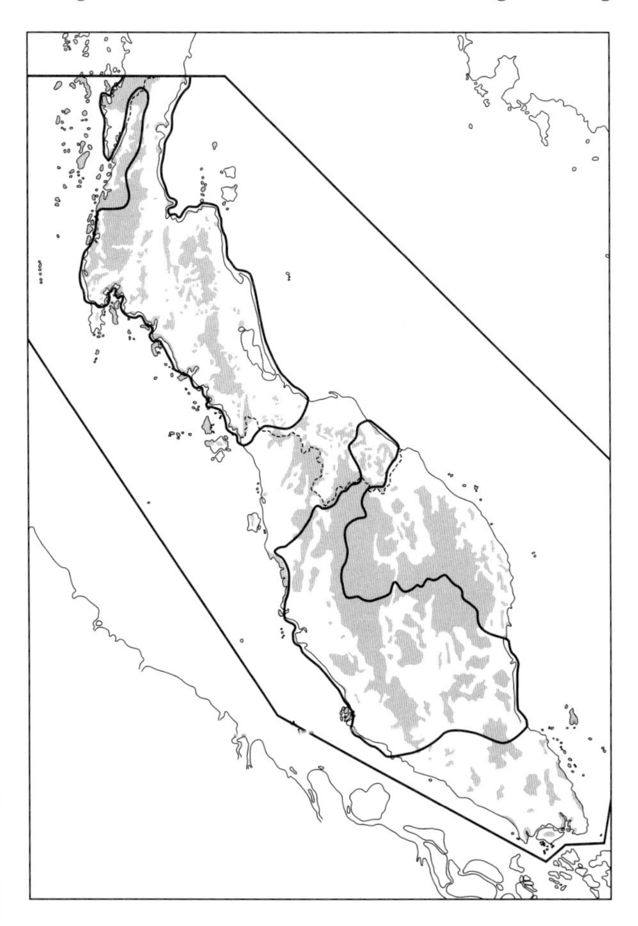

FORAGING AND FOOD. This is the one apparently territorial hornbill never to have been recorded at any of F.R. Lambert's *Ficus* species monitored over nearly three years at Kuala Lompat, Kerau wildlife reserve – even though at least one group (since shown to include breeders) occurred close by. A party of four after figs at the foot of the Main Range in Selangor (ENGGANG-1) must, therefore, be regarded as unusual. Ejected seeds collected from under an active nest have not been identified but lack of attention to figs suggests that the supply of favoured fruit is more continuous than for some other hornbills, or that animal prey more effectively compensates. Birds searching logging debris at Tekam, and visiting nearby oil-palms, are thought to have been hunting, and food brought to a nest in Krabi included lizards, a snake, a rat-like mammal and a small flying squirrel (Johns 1989, P.D. Round).

SOCIAL ORGANIZATION. Alone, in pairs or, frequently, parties of 3–6, age-composition not recorded. The basic territorial social unit is still not confirmed. It may be that territorial pairs tolerate a few pre-breeders (their own offspring?) on a regular basis, or gain some fitness advantage in being part of a foraging-group. Watches at a nest at Kuala Lompat gave no evidence of cooperative breeding, but at one of two recent nests in Krabi the walled-in hen and young were fed by the male plus a helper (C.M. Francis, P.D. Round).

MOVEMENTS. Not reported.

SURVIVAL. No information.

SOCIAL INTERACTIONS. No information.

VOICE. A single deep, soft but resonant *khoo* as birds take flight. The loud advertising-call, given by both sexes, is a sequence of 4–5 couplets of the same sound-quality, *khoo hoo, khoo hoo, khoo hoo . . .* , falling slightly in pitch. Calling birds shallowly bob the tail (Frith and Douglas 1978).

BREEDING

Nest. In level-land forest, a cavity 6–10 m up at mid-stratum level in a relatively slender trunk (once, *Pometia pinnata*); nest-entrance reduced by plastering.

Eggs and brood. Broods of one and two fledglings; no other information.

Cycle. At Kuala Lompat, Pahang, broken-open nest-plaster suggested the female emerged four days before the chick fledged.

Seasonality. The above nest fledged one young on 27 June. Nests in Krabi recorded active in April fledged a single young on 17 June and two in early July (BCSTB-10, 11, NRCS).

MOULT. Three adults, including two females, showed sequential moult of flight-feathers (at 2–3 loci in the primary tract), in February, March and June. A second March male showed none.

CONSERVATION. Able to live in regenerating forest, but a large, shade-adapted carnivore could be hit badly by an actual logging event. Too few contacts with this species have been made in the few studies of logging to be sure of a trend.

Wrinkled Hornbill; Nok Ngeuak Paak Yon (Thai); Burung Enggang Merantau (Malay)

Aceros corrugatus (Temminck) 1832, *Nouveau Recueil de Planches Coloriées d'Oiseaux* 90: plate 531. TL Pontianak, W Kalimantan.

Plate 61

GROUP RELATIONS. Probably free-standing; perhaps close to the Philippine species-pair *leucocephalus* and *waldeni* (Kemp 1988).

GLOBAL RANGE. Borneo, Sumatra and the Peninsula to about 8°N.

IDENTIFICATION/DESCRIPTION. Sexually dimorphic. Male cap to drooping nape-crest, entire body including underparts from crop level, wings and basal one third of tail glossy black; rest of head, neck and tail white, neck often stained yellow and tail orange-buff, cosmetically from preen-oil. Female head and neck black, uniform with rest of body; tail as in male. Juveniles told from adults by bare-part characters.

The fully formed male casque is a narrow, high-standing ridge with vertical front edge and up to three transverse wrinkles, the first developing in year two in a captive – a sudden buckling under apparent mechanical stress (K.W. Scriven). As of year two, males also develop serial corrugations diagonally across the basal half of the lower mandible. Females lack both wrinkles (on a lower, smooth casque) and the corrugations.

Bare-part colours. Iris pale blue-grey (juvenile), grey-brown (adult female), bright red-brown (adult male); eyelid bluish (juvenile), black (adult); peri-orbital skin dull blue (juvenile and female), bright light blue (male); gular pouch dull blue (female), white to yellowish (male); bill yellow with black on undersurface of lower mandible (young juvenile), cream-yellow with same-colour casque and brown base (female), cream-yellow with extreme base and lower rear of casque black, inner two thirds of the lower mandible red-brown, and inner one third of the upper mandible plus rest of the casque bright cherry-red (male); feet dark olive-grey.

Size (mm). (Skin: 2 males, 2 females; adult): wing 404, 425 and 355, 355; tail 265, 288 and 222, 228; bill 176 (1 only) and 144, 151; tarsus 55, 60 and 52, 52 (BMNH, ZDUM).

Weight. No data.

DISTRIBUTION. Not in the north. Historical summary: *Tra, Yal, Pes, Tru, Pek, Phg, Sel, Neg, Mel, Joh,* formerly occasional *Sin* but no report since 1941.

GEOGRAPHICAL VARIATION. Subspecies *rugosus* Begbie 1834 (TL Melaka), also of Sumatra; larger than Bornean nominate *corrugatus*.

STATUS AND POPULATION. Resident overall but nomadic; local and sparse to, occasionally, more or less common. Consistently present, perhaps, only in extensive subcoastal swamp-forest. Now heavily depleted through loss of most of this apparent core habitat but, in the past, indulged in mass movements. One on the coast of Melaka in 1868 involved a temporary roost within town limits (Maingay 1868). Unusual numbers halt to feed for a few weeks or months then disappear for years on end, but nothing is known of the age-classes participating, or of the scope of movements.

Away from core habitat, only a few, small-scale gatherings have been reported in recent decades, including along the Perak river near Grik in 1967 and in Tekam forestry concession, Pahang, in 1980 (BR 1967, A.D. Johns). The very large numbers of *Aceros* hornbills gathered in the upper Perak valley in late 1992 (Sutari Supari 1992), apparently, did not include this species, or it did not participate in their communal roost-movements.

HABITATS AND ECOLOGY. The canopy of tall, closed-canopy, mostly evergreen Lowland forest at plains level and on lower slopes, with an extreme

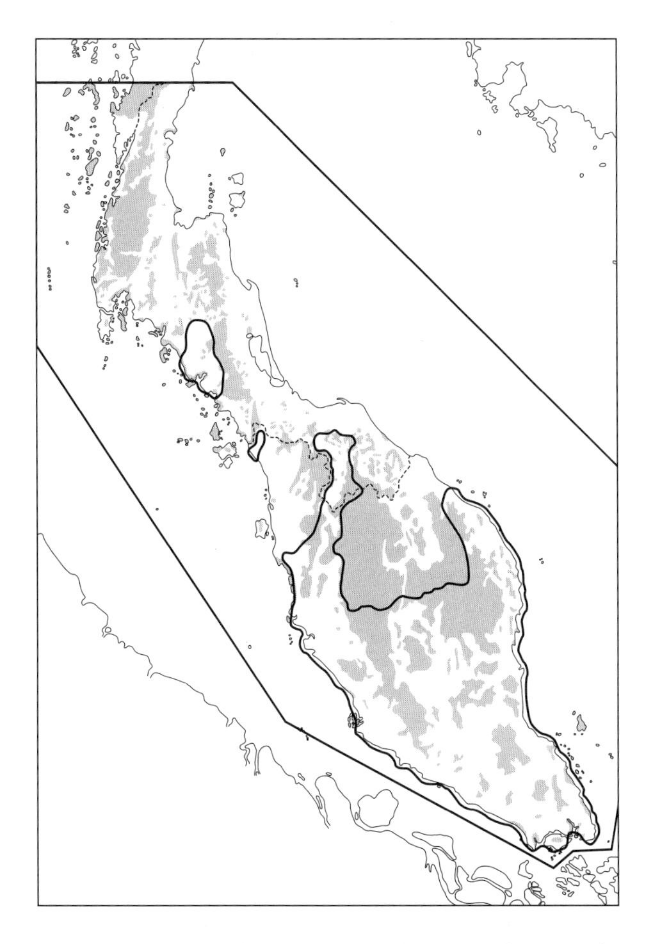

record of two in Yala at 500 m (Holmes 1973). Recently, a pair nested in tall, riverine forest at Kuala Lompat, Kerau wildlife reserve, Pahang (C.M. Francis) but, as stated, core habitat appears to be (or have been) forest of the main lower river valleys and subcoastal peat- and other freshwater swamp-forests.

FORAGING AND FOOD. Ones and twos flushed from fruiting fig trees in Panti swamp-forest and on the Endau river, Johor (ENGGANG-2, SINGAV-6), and F.R. Lambert registered visits to six of his 25 *Ficus* species at Kuala Lompat, in the fruit-size range 11.9–27.7 mm (Lambert 1989). Other parts of the diet are unrecorded, but nomadism is guessed to be linked to the patchy mast-fruiting of non-fig trees in evergreen forest.

SOCIAL ORGANIZATION. Not more than five recorded feeding together, and often solitary during the daytime, even in core habitat. Flocks of 40 and eight over SE Pahang peatswamp forest at dusk (ENGGANG-1) are likely to have been making for a communal roost.

MOVEMENTS. Recognized as nomadic, but no specific information on distances travelled, and there are no island records.

SURVIVAL. No information.

SOCIAL INTERACTIONS. No information.

VOICE. Rather high, sharp, single and double barks, *kak* and *kak-kak* (BMP5), are the only calls recorded, both from a captive male.

BREEDING. No nest described.

MOULT. The few birds examined were non-moulters, showing the process is discontinuous at individual level. No other information.

CONSERVATION. Except at Chalerm Prakiat wildlife sanctuary, Narathiwat (where Wrinkled Hornbill has yet to be found), core habitat as defined here is hardly represented in the nature reserves of the Peninsula. It has been massively cleared and what remains of the swamp-forests of the SE and mid-W coasts of Malaysia is under heavy pressure. Without them, remnant populations of this spectacular bird are unlikely to last (cf. Cinnamon-headed Green Pigeon). Globally vulnerable (BTW2).

Wreathed Hornbill; Nok Ngeuak Gram Chang (Thai); Burung Enggang Bukit (Malay)

Aceros undulatus (Shaw) 1812, *General Zoology or Systematic Natural History* 8(1): 26. TL Java.
Plate 61

GROUP RELATIONS. Free-standing; believed close to *A. subruficollis* (Tenasserim Hornbill) (Kemp 1988).

GLOBAL RANGE. Himalayan foothills east from Bengal and hill-tracts of the far-NE Indian subcontinent; and, except for northern Vietnam, SE Asia to the Greater Sunda islands and Bali.

IDENTIFICATION/DESCRIPTION. Sexually dimorphic. Nostril area and immediate forehead of male dark mahogany-chestnut, this colour contracting to a narrow median stripe then re-widening on hind-crown and drooping nape-crest. Rest of head, ventral neck, extreme tips of primaries 8–10 and complete tail white; sides of crest, back of neck and all remaining plumage black, green-glossed on the wings. Female all black, apart from white tail (see also Tenasserim Hornbill). Casque-growth is slow; by age two years a captive male had developed only the first of its 4–5 flat, transverse 'wreaths' (number eventually balanced by the rate at which they work forward and wear off the front end), and showed only incipient roughness of the sides of the bill, whereas full adults have deep, serial corrugations over the basal one third or more of both mandibles (Frith and Douglas 1978).

Bare-part colours. Iris pale blue (young juvenile), brown (adult female), orange-chestnut to pale red (adult male); eyelid and periorbital skin flesh-pink (juvenile and female), rose-red, eyelid paler (male); gular pouch dull blue (female), bright yellow (male), both sexes with a median transverse black bar, broken mid-ventrally (from nestling stage, showing well before the casque develops: Frith and Douglas 1978); bill all pale yellow (juvenile), ivory-yellow, basal area of corrugations red-brown (adults); in both sexes, casque ivory-white with posterior end brownish and corrugations between wreaths blackish; feet dark, dirty olive.

Size (mm). (Skins: 10 males, 9 females; adult): wing 465–497 and 409–459; tail 280–312 and 250–276; bill 199–218 and 148-181; tarsus 59–65 and 56–57 (BMNH).

Weight. No data.

DISTRIBUTION. Historical summary: all divisions except *Pat, Pra, Sin,* with additional W-coast island records from the Surin group, Lanta, Tarutao and Langkawi.

GEOGRAPHICAL VARIATION. Nominate *undulatus*, of the Sunda region except Borneo.

STATUS AND POPULATION. Resident overall but nomadic, parties searching at random or (more likely) 'trap-lining' round known sources of fruit in very large areas; thus, local and varying from sparse to common, with numbers unstable over time. Greater abundance, hence more frequent contact with Wreathed, makes this behaviour less obvious than in what remains of Wrinkled Hornbill populations, but a heavy fruiting event in the upper Perak valley in 1992 drew the largest aggregation of any hornbill species ever reported in the Peninsula. An evening roost-movement totalling nearly 800 *Aceros*, probably all Wreathed, occurred along just one flight-line over Kenering reservoir on 7 September, dropping to less than 150 over three days, either through shifts away or adoption of other routes between the roost and different feeding areas. None appeared in 1993, but a small resurgence occurred in another area of mass fruiting further up the valley (Bosman and van den Berg 1993).

HABITATS AND ECOLOGY. The canopy of semi-evergreen and evergreen Lowland forest, mature or where well-regenerated and with much tall timber left

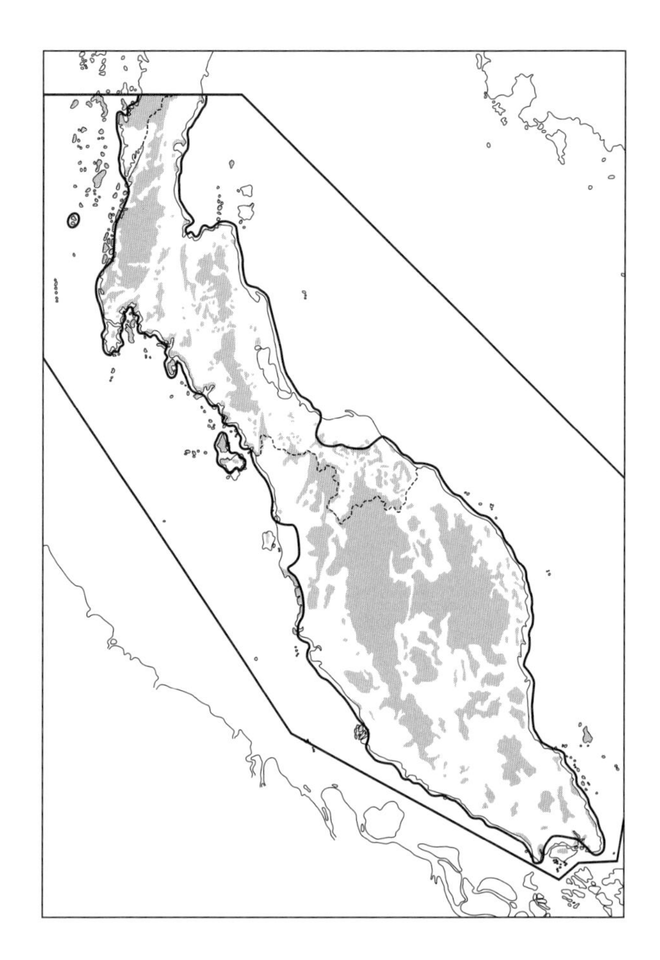

standing, at all elevations; visiting Montane forest to at least 2000 m. *Contra* Wrinkled Hornbill, not recorded in swamp forests of the extreme lowlands.

FORAGING AND FOOD. Observed many times over-flying Kuala Lompat (Kerau wildlife reserve) but in nearly three years of regular monitoring, no visits were registered at any of the 25 *Ficus* species under study there (Lambert 1987). Some of these have been reported used elsewhere, but cannot be a prime attraction. Evidently, fig-rich riverine forest of the Kuala Lompat type does not represent a habitat worth exploring by Wreathed Hornbills. Great mobility and gregariousness are a behaviour that boosts the chance of finding widely scattered, patchily distributed sources of fruit in forest, but the main diet of Wreathed in the Peninsula remains unknown.

SOCIAL ORGANIZATION. It is assumed that individual, already-formed pairs peel away from mobile social groups to nest where good conditions are encountered at an appropriate time, and subsequently move on. At some point, their basic social unit is likely to be the family, but group age-structure has not been studied in the Peninsula. The typical daytime foraging party includes 2–6 birds, but groups may amalgamate when travelling, and flocks heading to roost at Kenering lake in 1992 were in the range 10–30 individuals (SINGAV-6).

MOVEMENTS. Nomadic, but no direct information on journeys, other than the water-crossings inferred from presence, e.g., on the Surin islands, and evident willingness to cross wide habitat-gaps (Allen 1960). Parties on the move often travel at considerable heights, on routes not limited by terrain, and big groups adopt the aerodynamically efficient chevron-skein formation of many large-bodied endurance fliers.

SURVIVAL. No information.

SOCIAL INTERACTIONS. Frith and Douglas (1978) suggest the colourful throat-pouch 'flash' as the bill is flicked vertical during a call is a distant signal attracting other birds; reinforced by the call itself. The exceptionally loud wing-soughing of Wreathed Hornbill in flight must also be obvious to other individuals, at a distance or otherwise out of sight.

VOICE. A roaring, double bark, *wur-wooh*, the second syllable carrying further and, at a distance, all that may be heard. In the upper Perak valley, Bosman and van den Berg (1993) tape-recorded a number of three-note calls from birds positively identified as Wreathed, adding a further complication to separation of this and Tenasserim Hornbill in the field.

The bark is given only while perched, maintains contact between birds out of sight of each other, and may attract others to a group.

BREEDING. No nests reported, confirming Wreathed as one of the least understood hornbill species of the area.

MOULT. Free-living birds replace primaries sequentially, at one or two loci. Eight of 25 adults collected during December–April showed wing-moult in all of these months, with no sign of a pattern of seasonal progression. As with most other hornbills, all they reveal is that moult of individuals is discontinuous.

CONSERVATION. Nomadic behaviour may assist in weathering the impact of logging and forest fragmentation (Johns 1987), but Wreathed Hornbills disappear from (and quit visiting) small remnants of forest at least as fast as do similar-sized territorial species. They are conspicuously common only in the largest continuous areas of Lowland forest, and area may be a prime defining feature of their core habitat.

Tenasserim Hornbill; Nok Ngeuak Gram Chang Paak Riap (Thai); Burung Enggang Belantara (Malay)

Aceros subruficollis (Blyth) 1843, *Journal of the Asiatic Society of Bengal* 12(1): 177. TL Tenasserim.
Plate 61

GROUP RELATIONS. Free-standing and widely sympatric with, rather than a growth-stage of, *A. undulatus* (Kemp 1988). Carries a distinctive feather-louse species, *Chapinia hirta* (the Wreathed counterpart is *C. boonsongi*), has apparently distinguishable calls, and distinctive adult characters that have recently been confirmed by photography at the nest (P. Poonswad).

GLOBAL RANGE. Upper Assam, Burma (including parts of the Mergui archipelago) and western Thailand to the N Peninsula. Claims of occurrence further south, including in NE Sumatra and Banka (E.C. Dickinson, Kemp 1988) need extra investigation.

IDENTIFICATION/DESCRIPTION. Plumage as in Wreathed Hornbill, in all respects, including tone and peculiar pattern of chestnut-mahogany on the head and crest of adult males. Casque also as in Wreathed: low, flat-topped and transversely corrugated, with up to seven wreaths concurrent, covering the basal half of the upper mandible. *Contra* adult Wreathed, sides of bill uncorrugated or they show only a slight roughening at the rear margin of the lower mandible. Otherwise, from Wreathed in the Peninsula by smaller size (adult male roughly 1700 versus 2400–2700 g: BMNH) and lack of a black bar on the gular pouch. Juvenile and casque-growth undescribed.

Bare-part colours. (Adults) iris orange-red (male), orange-brown (female); eyelid and periorbital skin wine-red (male), dull blue (female); gular pouch unmarked bright yellow (male), dull blue (female); bill ivory-yellow with red-brown base and narrow black rear margin to lower mandible; casque ivory-white, posterior end red-brown, with black-brown corrugations between wreaths; feet black with dull grey hind border (male only).

Size (mm). (Skins: 1 male, 1 female; adult): wing 399 and 380; tail 242 and 213; bill 170 and 151; tarsus 44 (male only) (BMNH).

Weight. No more accurate data.

DISTRIBUTION. Historical summary: *Pak, Ran.*

GEOGRAPHICAL VARIATION. None recognized.

STATUS AND POPULATION. A possible nomad but no firm information; only a few specimens have

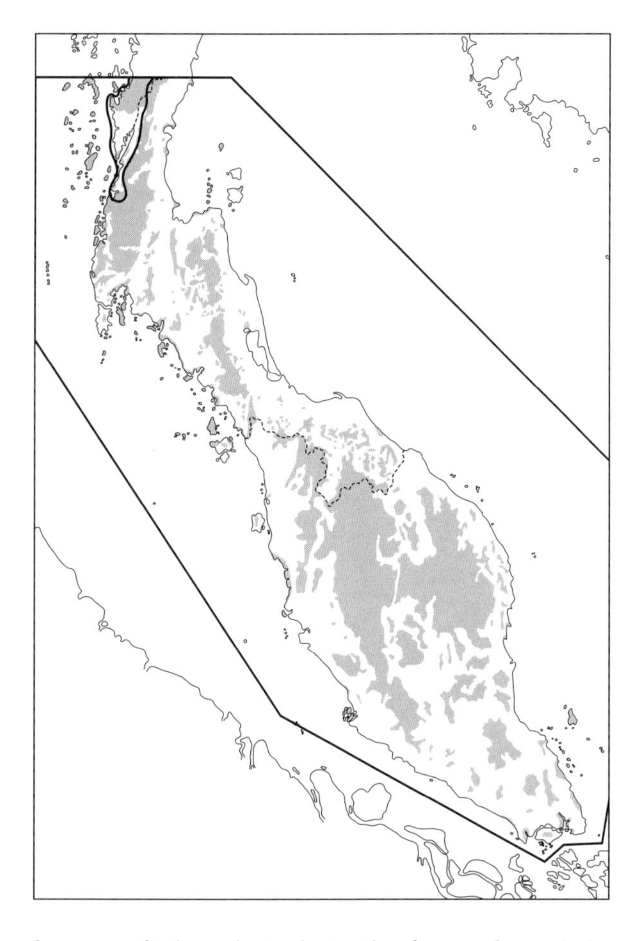

been verified, exclusively in the far north, and the Peninsula may never have been a breeding area. Southward, Robinson (1907, 1910) reported large flocks along the west coast during the NE monsoon season, but linked them with a name '*Hydocissa migratorius*', which belongs in the synonymy of *A. corrugatus*, not of *subruficollis*. FMSM collector E. Seimund believed he, too, shot one out of evening flocks over the Selangor mangroves (Chasen 1939) and, recently, it has been suggested Tenasserim Hornbills were among large numbers of *Aceros* that gathered in the upper Perak valley in August–September 1992 (Ho and Sutari Supari 1994). This remains possible, but none of the above claims can be upheld on evidence available.

HABITATS AND ECOLOGY. The canopy of Lowland forest, in SW Thailand only at river-valley level (Round 1988). No habitat information available from the Peninsula, except that W.L. Abbott's Pakchan localities appear to have been near the coast.

FORAGING AND FOOD. No local information; food brought to a Kanchanaburi nest included fruit and a wide variety of animal prey.

SOCIAL ORGANIZATION. No direct information.

MOVEMENTS. No information.

SURVIVAL. No information.

SOCIAL INTERACTIONS. No information.

VOICE. The only known call is a triple *keh-kek-kehk*, similar in quality to the bark of Wreathed Hornbill but higher-pitched, more quacking, less booming, and apparently always three-noted (Boonsong and Round 1991).

BREEDING. No local record; a Kanchanaburi nest fledged a brood of one.

MOULT. A late December female moulting a T1; no other information.

CONSERVATION. If a genuine low-elevation specialist, possibly now extinct in the Thai part of the Peninsula. The Pakchan situation is unknown but unlikely to be healthy. Globally vulnerable (BTW2).

Order UPUPIFORMES

Family UPUPIDAE

Hoopoes: one species

Common Hoopoe; Nok Garang Hua Khwaan (Thai); Burung Hupu Tunggal (Malay)

Upupa epops Linnaeus 1758, *Systema Naturae* 10(1): 117. TL Sweden.
Plate 59

GROUP RELATIONS. Vocal differences suggest *epops* and Madagascan *marginata* are good species (Fry *et al.* 1988); treatable at superspecies level.

GLOBAL RANGE. Sub-Saharan and N Africa, Eurasia from the Atlantic to Mongolia, Amurland and central Japan; SW Asia, the Indian subcontinent and Sri Lanka; S Tibet; China including Hainan; and SE Asia to the Peninsula. Palaearctic populations migrate, wintering as far as the outer northern tropics. Apparently only small numbers enter SE Asia, straggling to the Peninsula, NE Sumatra, NW Borneo and the northern Philippines.

IDENTIFICATION/DESCRIPTION. A roughly Common Myna *Acridotheres tristis*-sized, sandy coloured, extensively terrestrial bird, with long, thin, slightly decurved bill, and flat, black-tipped crest jutting well back from nape, erectable into a tall, laterally compressed fan. Mainly vinous pink, head to mantle and lesser wing-coverts more rufous, brightest on the crest, which is uniform up to its black tip. Scapulars black and rufous, back to tail black, with a white band across rump and another mid way along the tail. Remaining wing-coverts black, median and greater with white bars; flight-feathers black, primaries with a broad, subterminal white band, secondaries with four white bands. Below, pink-fawn fading to white on belly and lower tail-coverts, flanks and belly boldly streaked black. Apart from slight size-dimorphism, sexes alike; juveniles have a shorter, entirely straight bill. Flight undulating; tail and broad, butterfly-shaped wings show a bold pattern.

Bare-part colours. (Adult) iris hazel-brown to red-brown; bill blackish with pink base; feet dark grey to brownish black.

Size (mm). (Skins: 9 males, 3 females; adult): wing 139–148 and 133–137; tail 96–107 and 91–97; bill 51–66 and 51–52; tarsus 21.9–25.4 and 20.3–22.7 (BMNH, UMZC).

Weight. No data.

DISTRIBUTION. Historical summary: *Pak, Chu, Ran, Sur, Pha, Phu, Kra, Tra, Son, Pat, Sat, Pes, Ked, Pek, Phg, Sel*, with additional island records from Yao Yai, Rang (*Phu*) and Libong off the W coast; and Samui off the E coast.

GEOGRAPHICAL VARIATION. The description is of resident *longirostris* Jerdon 1862 (TL Burma) of the far-NE Indian subcontinent, far-S China and SE Asia. Northern migrant *saturata* Lonnberg 1909 (TL Kyakhta, S Transbaikalia) shows a bold white bar below the black tip of its crest; head and body otherwise more or less as rufous (but fading sandy grey), with similarly patterned wings, back and tail. Measurements of one female: wing 151; tail 103; bill 51; tarsus 20.0 (BMNH).

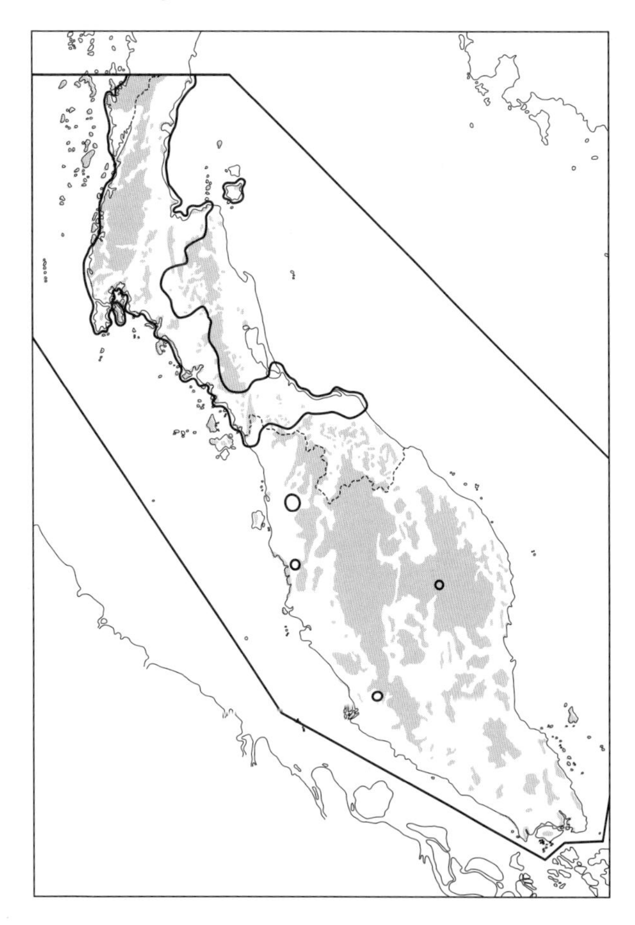

STATUS AND POPULATION. A once locally common resident, including on Phuket and Samui islands (Oates 1890, Robinson 1914b), but with no modern nest records, and has withdrawn from some former range (in the 1930s, bred south to S Kedah). Now local and sparse. Most recent sightings, subspecies undetermined, are winter-dated (late October, December, February: Holmes and Wells 1975, SINGAV-6, Swennen *et al.* 1986) but present and calling in May, hence probably still breeding in Khlong Thom district, Krabi. Palaearctic *saturata* is vagrant (a record from Perak), and rare Hoopoe occurrences south of the former breeding-range are known to have included *longirostris*.

HABITATS AND ECOLOGY. Mainly non-forest habitats, including open, sandy ground below strand woodland and coastal dune scrub, fields, the open margins of rubber plantations and, formerly, rural settlements and suburban gardens; exclusively at plains level but also on level land of the 300 m Phaen Din Samur plateau, Krabi. One record of a migrant or dispersant by a large river through extensive evergreen forest (BR 1967).

FORAGING AND FOOD. Terrestrial; walks and runs in the open, probing into soft ground, and gleaning. Robinson (1927) lists grasshopper and caterpillar prey.

SOCIAL ORGANIZATION. Solitary.

MOVEMENTS. A single record of *U.e. saturata* at Kamunting, Perak, on 5 November (BMNH).

SURVIVAL. No information.

SOCIAL INTERACTIONS. No information.

VOICE. A soft, clear, even-toned, 3–5 note *hu pu pu . . .*, carrying quite far. No other vocalizations reported in this area. Advertising males are said to call incessantly for long periods.

BREEDING

Nest. Cavities, including tree-holes (one 60 cm deep with entrance 7.7 cm wide), hollows in clumps of epiphytes, and under eaves of houses, as low as 1.5 m from the ground. No materials are added.

Eggs and brood. Eggs plain, very pale green-blue. Shape subelliptical. Size (mm): 25.6–25.1 × 17.9 (n=5). Full clutch five. Broods of four and five fledge.

Cycle. No information.

Seasonality. Large nestlings in late February, eggs in late February and May (Madoc 1956a, Oates 1890).

MOULT. Eleven presumed resident *longirostris* dated November and January–March showed no moult, with others on Samui island very worn in May. The November *saturata* was also in very worn, unmoulted plumage (BMNH, Robinson 1914b).

CONSERVATION. Hunting and disturbance are liable to have been a main reason for the decline of resident Hoopoes, and these threats still apply.

Order CORACIIFORMES

Family HALCYONIDAE

Tree kingfishers: eight species

Banded Kingfisher; Nok Ga Ten Lai (Thai); Burung Pekaka Kaing-kaing (Malay)

Lacedo pulchella (Horsfield) 1821, *Transactions of the Linnean Society* 13(1): 175. TL Java.
Plate 63

GROUP RELATIONS. Free-standing.

GLOBAL RANGE. Except in the far north, SE Asia as far as the Greater Sunda islands.

IDENTIFICATION/DESCRIPTION. Smallest of the tree kingfishers in this area, with bright orange-red, slightly uptilted, boat-shaped bill. The sexes are otherwise strongly dimorphic. Long cap-feathers of male banded black-and-white and broadly tipped shining blue (giving a spangled effect when crest is raised), the cap nearly or actually cut off by a broad band of rich chestnut from forecrown across face to hind-neck. Upper body and wing-coverts black with white cross-bars and azure-blue tips, and longish black tail with seven dull violet bars showing beyond upper coverts. Underparts white, with breast to flanks cinnamon-rufous. Female upperparts barred black and rufous-bay, bars narrower (and rufous brighter) on head than on body and wings, and rich rufous bars dominate over black on tail; underparts white, with black barring on flanks and in a narrow zone across breast. Young juveniles are dark- rather than red-billed; otherwise as adults except female ventrally black-barred back to belly and male barred on forehead and malar patch.

Bare-part colours. Iris pale grey to fawn-grey, eyelid-rim red; bill blackish with extreme tip white, to blackish-brown with cutting-edges and lower mandible orange-red and tip yellowish (juvenile stages), all orange-red (adult); feet muddy green.

Size (mm). (Live and skins: 16 males, 20 females; adult): wing 82–91 and 82–90; tail 64–72 and 65–79; bill 36.2–40.5 and 36.6–41.7; tarsus 12.8–15.8 and 13.5–15.3 (BMNH, UMBRP).

Weight (g). Adult males, 40.8–48.5 (n=6); adult females, 46.5–54.3 (n=7) (UMBRP, M. Wong).

DISTRIBUTION. Historical summary: all divisions except *Kel*, with additional island records from Langkawi; extinct *Sin* for at least 40 years.

GEOGRAPHICAL VARIATION. South from about Songkhla, nominate *pulchella*, also of island SE Asia except Borneo. More northerly females tend towards less ventral barring, and males to a slightly more purplish cap, paler rufous underparts and a mid-dorsal narrowing or breaking of the chestnut hind-collar, but these characters vary individually and N-Peninsular '*deignani*' is an intergrade between *pulchella* and continental populations.

STATUS AND POPULATION. Resident, regular and more or less common to common; until recently, numerous on Langkawi island.

HABITATS AND ECOLOGY. From the interior canopy down to ground level in inland semi-evergreen

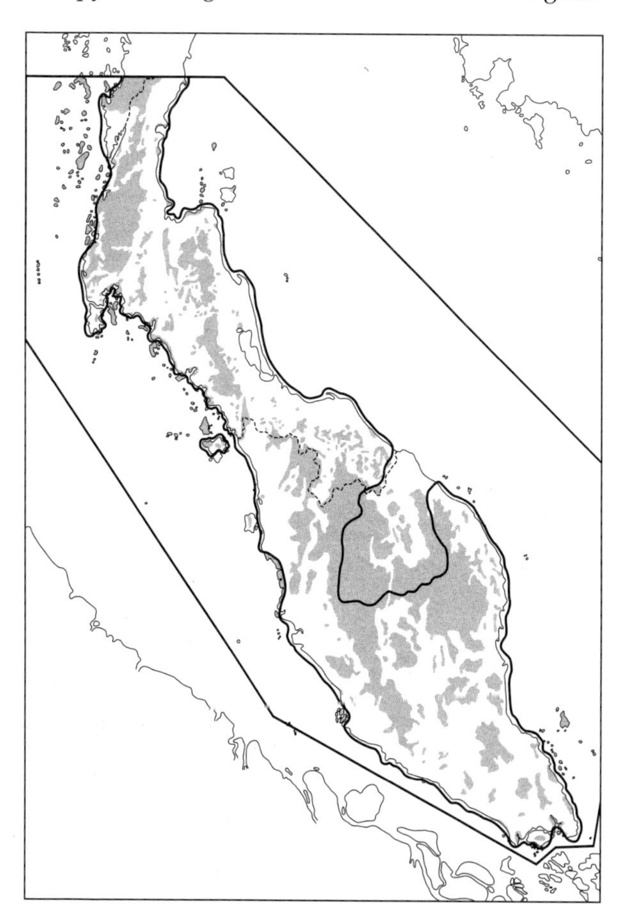

and evergreen Lowland forest, also peatswamp forest, mature and well regenerated after disturbance; at plains level and on slopes, recorded to 820 m but sparse towards the upper limit of range.

FORAGING AND FOOD. Still-hunts from perches over an unknown column-height in forest, but certainly down to within 1–2 m of the forest floor. Also recorded on fallen rotten timber and actually on the ground. Dried earth and insect remains stuck in the lower mandible of a mist-netted male suggest it had been probing. Millipedes, centipedes, woodlice, cockroaches, crustaceans, lizards and small fish have been identified in the diet (Oates 1883, Robinson 1928).

SOCIAL ORGANIZATION. Solitary.

MOVEMENTS. None known.

SURVIVAL. So little susceptible to mist-nets set at ground level that hardly any marked birds have been retrapped; longest interval 14 months, a male in the Pasoh research forest, Negeri Sembilan.

SOCIAL INTERACTIONS. No information.

VOICE. A sharp *wiak, wiak*. The loud advertising-call, given usually from a high perch, is a carrying but slowly dying cadence of up to 15 deliberate, melancholy whistles, *chi-wiu*, starting even-toned but with progressive shift of stress to the first note (BMP5).

BREEDING

Nest. Eggs said to have been taken from holes in forest stream-banks in Perak (E.C.S. Baker) are suspect. At Khao Pra Bang Khram (Krabi), a nest confirmed in an arboreal termitarium, and breeds arboreally elsewhere in its range.

Eggs and brood. Not reliably described.

Cycle. No information.

Seasonality. The Krabi nest active in March–April (CLBS, CLBW, Smythies 1981, U. Treesucon).

MOULT. Primaries are replaced at up to two loci, the outer hand descendantly from P6 or 7. Among 41 adults covering all months and the full length of the Peninsula, 15 showed active wing-moult in mid June (P6) and during August–November (P10 on 22 November). The only records of body- and tail-moult are also from this period. Some non-moulters occurred throughout but with no moult at all during December–May (n=21) (BMNH, UMBRP, M. Wong).

CONSERVATION. Relative commonness at low elevations suggests plains-level forest may be core habitat, and that this kingfisher could be at risk from habitat-loss. In the Peninsula, a species does not have to be rare to be threatened.

Brown-winged Kingfisher; Nok Ga Ten Yai Peek See Namtaan (Thai); Burung Pekaka Dendang (Malay)

Halcyon amauroptera Pearson 1841, *Journal of the Asiatic Society of Bengal* 10(2): 635. TL vicinity of Calcutta.

Plate 62

GROUP RELATIONS. Uncertain. Considered to form a superspecies with *H. capensis* and *H. melanorhyncha* (Stork-billed and Sulawesi Stork-billed Kingfishers) (Fry 1980), but its range lies entirely within that of *capensis* and they are not entirely isolated by habitat.

GLOBAL RANGE. Coasts of the Bay of Bengal, from N Orissa to the Peninsula.

IDENTIFICATION/DESCRIPTION. A very large kingfisher. From Stork-billed by head uniformly tawny-orange, concolorous with the underparts, and mantle, scapulars and wing-coverts, upper tail-coverts and tail dark chocolate-brown, contrasting sharply with bright turquoise-blue back and rump. Fine green fringing of upper tail-coverts is a character shared with juvenile Stork-billed. Sexes similar; juveniles show fine dark fringing on orange parts.

Bare-part colours. Iris hazel-brown, eyelid-rim red; bill red with brownish tip and culmen (juvenile), vermilion-red with extreme tip blackish (adult); feet bright coral-red.

Size (mm). (Live and skins: 7 adults, most not sexed): wing 139–148; tail 79–94; bill 75.4–78.2; tarsus 18.0–19.2 (BMNH, UMBRP, ZDUM).

Weight (g). An adult male, 162 (UMBRP).

DISTRIBUTION. The NW coast only. Historical summary: *Pak, Ran, Pha, Phu, Kra, Tra, Sat,* with additional island records from Lanbyi, the Lanta group (Lanta, Mai Ngam), Libong and satellite Hard Toop, Tarutao national park (Tarutao and Ladang), and the Langkawi group (Langkawi, Dayang Bunting). The southern terminus of mainland range has not been mapped but is north of the Malaysian border.

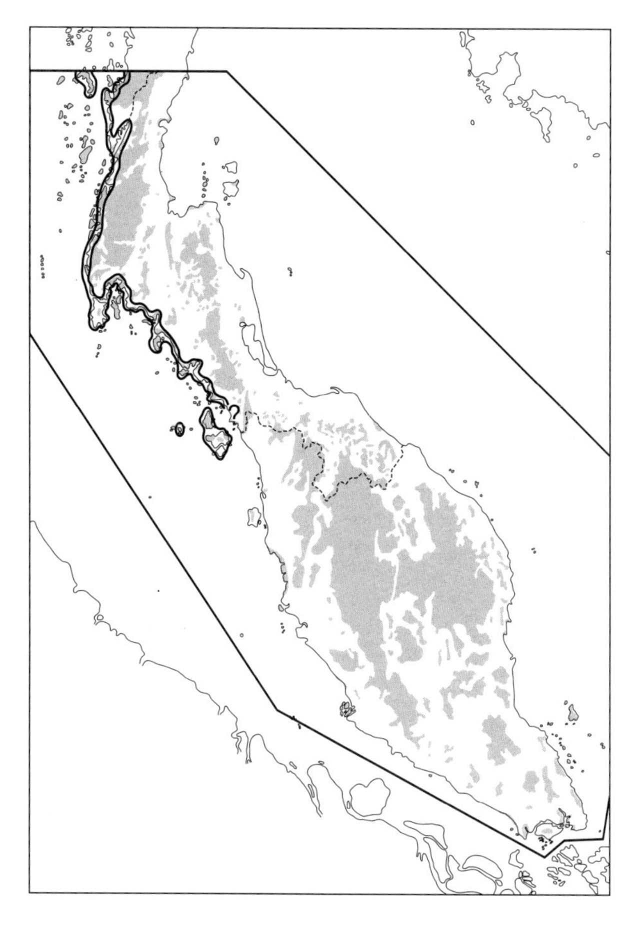

GEOGRAPHICAL VARIATION. None recognized.

STATUS AND POPULATION. Resident, regular and more or less common, but more secretive than Stork-billed Kingfisher.

HABITATS AND ECOLOGY. A mangrove specialist, coastal and on tidal inlets. Emerges onto secluded rocky shores (mangroves and limestone juxtapose on many NW islands) and recorded round the wooded cliff rim of the sinkhole lake on Dayang Bunting island (G.C. Madoc), but never in the open, freshwater habitats used by Stork-billed, even close to mangroves.

FORAGING AND FOOD. Still-hunts from stilt-roots overlooking creeks and is regularly caught in mist-nets set at ground level, suggesting it also hunts below the closed canopy of mangroves, not entirely over water. No record of diet in this area.

SOCIAL ORGANIZATION. Solitary.

MOVEMENTS. None recorded.

SURVIVAL. No information.

SOCIAL INTERACTIONS. No information.

VOICE. A harsh, cackling laugh, not well described; also a short, descending sequence of tremulous whistles, *tree treew-treew*, with slight pause after note one (Boonsong and Round 1991).

BREEDING. Not recorded.

MOULT. Seven adults dated March–April showed none.

CONSERVATION. Globally near-threatened (BTW2) and needs investigating. Given its total attachment to mangroves, may nest arboreally hence depend on retention of big trees or timber old enough to support large holes or termitaria. Over-exploitation and outright clearance of mangroves has become a critical issue in the Peninsula.

Stork-billed Kingfisher; Nok Ga Ten Yai Thammadaa (Thai); Burung Pekaka Buaya (Malay)

Halcyon capensis (Linnaeus) 1766, *Systema Naturae* 12(1): 180. TL Chandarnagar, Bengal.
Plate 62

GROUP RELATIONS. See *H. amauroptera*.

GLOBAL RANGE. The Himalayan foothills and Indian subcontinent east of a line Dehra Dun–Gujarat, Sri Lanka and Bay of Bengal islands; S Yunnan (vagrant); and except for the far NE, SE Asia to the Greater Sunda islands, Bali, and S and W Philippines; also the Lesser Sunda islands as far as Flores.

IDENTIFICATION/DESCRIPTION. Largest local kingfisher, with an enormous red bill. From Brown-winged by head down to malar level dull- or grey-brown to clay-brown (varying individually and perhaps also partly with wear), not concolorous with tawny-orange collar and underparts. Upperparts and tail are variably dark blue to dark greenish blue (greenish especially on the mantle), in not such sharp contrast to bright blue back, rump and central upper tail-coverts. Sexes similar. Juveniles show fine, dark fringing on collar, lower throat and breast, and buff-green fringing to upper tail-coverts.

Bare-part colours. (Adult) iris hazel-brown to dark brown, eyelid-rim coral-red; bill vermilion-red with extreme tip blackish; feet coral-red.

Size (mm). (Skins: 7 males, 3 females; adult): wing 142–151 and 149–153; tail 88–102 and 92–102 (down to 83 in juveniles); bill 78.4–84.0 and 73.3–85.9; tarsus 17.2–20.3 and 18.2–19.0 (BMNH, UMBRP).

Weight. No data.

DISTRIBUTION. Historical summary: all divisions except *Pha*, *Sat*, with additional island records from Langkawi (one sighting by a sea-creek near Kuah on 16 June 1986; perhaps of a wanderer) and Penang off the W coast; Phangan off the E coast; and Tekong, Ubin, St John's, Sentosa, Senang, Pawai, Sudong and Ayer Merbau around Singapore.

GEOGRAPHICAL VARIATION. Subspecies *malaccensis* Sharpe 1870 (TL Melaka), but north from Surat Thani individual variation tends towards the lighter blue upperparts and paler head of continental *burmanica* (Riley 1938).

STATUS AND POPULATION. Resident, regular and uncommon to more or less common, particularly visible on the NW Malaysian rice-plain, perhaps due to well developed wire-perching behaviour in that area, freeing foragers from the need of tree-cover.

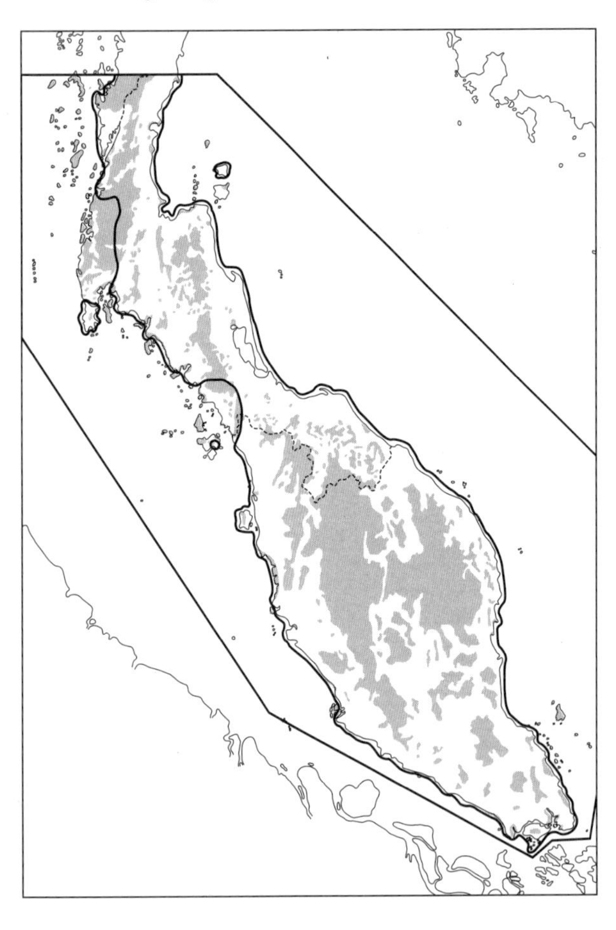

HABITATS AND ECOLOGY. Mostly close to water, including by tidal creeks and inlets, subcoastal lagoons, and occasionally on tree- or palm-backed rocky shores. Regular in mangroves in Malaysia and the NE, apparently not so in the NW within the range of Brown-winged Kingfisher. Inland, in all kinds of open freshwater situations, including along the broader rivers of the plains well into forest country, reservoir margins, paddyland irrigation channels, ponds, large flood-drains, etc., wherever overhanging snags, trees or service-wires provide look-out perches. From the nature of its habitats, occurs strictly at plains level.

FORAGING AND FOOD. Predominantly fish, caught by plunge-diving off a perch typically 2–4m above the water-surface. Chasen (1939) adds crabs, frogs and lizards to the list of prey, and beetle elytra have been found among detritus in a nest (Edgar 1933), suggesting some food is taken from dry land. At the Sanglang river-mouth, Kedah/Perlis border, one or more birds (with other tree kingfisher species) flew out from mangroves to inspect clumps of water-hyacinth floating past on the flood.

SOCIAL ORGANIZATION. Solitary; exceptionally a pair together.

MOVEMENTS. None reported.

SURVIVAL. No information.

SOCIAL INTERACTIONS. On the former Senoko wetland, Singapore, a record of an apparent pair duetting (SINGAV-1).

VOICE. While perched: (1) a rather shrill, descending whistle, *tree-trew (-trew)* or *kwee-kwau (-kou)*; (2) a slow, deliberate rasping, *creak creak cre-ak*; (3) a loud, screaming *whe-awk whe-awk whe-awk*. In flight: (4) a screaming laugh, *kiu-kiu kee-kiu* (or *wiar-wau wir-wau*), usually repeated several times. Perched or in flight: (5) a harsh, dry, cackling laugh, *kek-ek-ek-ek* (Glenister 1951, Boonsong and Round 1991, G.C. Madoc).

BREEDING

Nest. One in the base of a soil termitarium in grass 45 m from a small river, entrance about 10 cm wide, opening into a nest-chamber about 30 cm across; another a large cavity in an arboreal termitarium 6 m up a trunk in secondary forest.

Eggs and brood. Egg glossy, translucent white. Shape short elliptical to near-spherical. Size (mm): 37.9 × 28.5 (n=1). Regular clutch-size unknown, and no other information.

Cycle. No information.

Seasonality. A nestling on 27 March and egg on 18 April (Edgar 1933, G.C. Madoc).

MOULT. Primaries are replaced at one or two loci, sequence not recorded. Eight of 12 adults dated May, July, August and October showed active wing-moult from early May (P1–2) to mid August (P8). Presumed post-juvenile wing-moult of scale-patterned birds occurs more or less year-round, without evidence of progression (P9 or 10 in November–January, March, July and September) (BMNH, BMP5, UMZC).

CONSERVATION. Probably no critical issues.

Ruddy Kingfisher; Nok Ga Ten Daeng (Thai); Burung Pekaka Belacan (Malay)

Halcyon coromanda (Latham) 1790, *Index Ornithologicus* 1: 252. TL Coromandel coast, SE India.
Plate 62

GROUP RELATIONS. Free-standing.

GLOBAL RANGE. Foot of the Himalayas east from Nepal, the NE Indian subcontinent and Andamans; NE China, Korea, S Japan and Taiwan; SE Asia to the Greater Sunda islands and W Philippines; and Sulawesi to the Sula islands. Northern populations migrate, wintering to SE India, and in SE Asia to the Peninsula, Sumatra, Philippines and N Sulawesi; vagrant N Borneo.

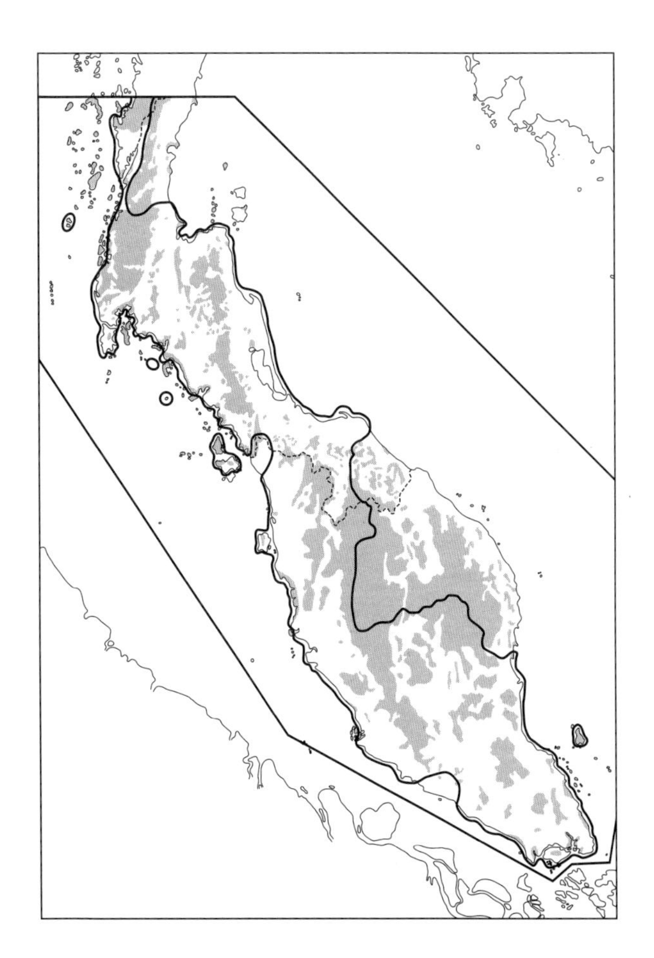

IDENTIFICATION/DESCRIPTION. Size roughly of Collared Kingfisher *H. chloris*. Back and rump silvery white to azure-blue, rest of upperparts including wings and tail orange-rufous, glossed magenta. Below, chin and throat whitish, rest of underparts orange-buff, glossed magenta over breast according to population. Juveniles browner above and dark-fringed over breast and sides of throat, without magenta gloss; back and rump wholly blue rather than silvery (BMP5).

Bare-part colours. Iris deep brown; bill horn-brown with white tip (young juvenile), entirely vermilion-red (adult); feet bright coral-red.

Size (mm). (Live and skins: 4 males, 9 females; adult): wing 105–116 and 106–119 (local juveniles down to 98); tail 59–65 and 58–70; bill 56.9–61.7 and 54.3–63.2; tarsus 15.8–16.8 and 16.5–18.7 (BMNH, BMP5, UMBRP).

Weight (g). Unsexed adults: (1) residents on the Selangor coast, 65.4–91.7 (mean 76.0, n=12); (2) incoming autumn migrants 60.3–79.7 (n=14); (3) mid-winter–mid April migrants in central Malaysia 68.8–86.8 (mean 77.5, n=27), showing no sign of pre-migratory fattening.

DISTRIBUTION. Dates and/or morphology confirm residents south from Krabi, and they are likely to be more widespread. Sightings in the (non-mangrove) Singapore central catchment forest (SINGAV-2) indicate overwintering of migrants to the extreme south, but numbers drop off below latitude 3°N. Historical summary: all divisions except *Chu, Pht, Nar, Pes, Kel, Tru, Mel*, with additional island records from the Surins, Maa (*Kra*), Rok (*Tra*), Tarutao, Langkawi and Penang off the W coast, Tioman (breeders) off the E coast; and Tekong (breeders), Ubin and Ayer Merbau, Singapore.

GEOGRAPHICAL VARIATION. Far southern (Singapore–Johor) residents are subspecies *minor* Temminck and Schlegel 1848 (TL Pontianak, W Kalimantan), darker throughout and smaller than nominate *coromanda* (wing not above 106 mm), with cap, upper body and breast glossed magenta, whereas not all *coromanda* are glossed on the head, and none on the breast. Intergrades have been identified north to Perak (Gyldenstolpe 1917). Northern migrants are all *coromanda*.

STATUS AND POPULATION. Resident, a non-breeding visitor and passage migrant; more or less regular and uncommon to common, particularly on NW islands. Residents are believed to have disappeared from the main island of Singapore possibly as recently as the 1980s: a bird in mangroves at Loyang on 23 September 1989 was ten days outside the confirmed passage season.

HABITATS AND ECOLOGY. North through Malaysia, including on the Langkawi islands, residents occupy exclusively mangrove forest and its immediate landward fringe. In Thailand, to an uncertain southern limit, they also occur inland in freshwater swamp-forest (both mature and re-closed after disturbance), and along forest-lined streams. Wintering migrants occupy both mangroves and inland Lowland forest throughout, extending to dryland habitat in both semi-evergreen and evergreen zones, at plains level and on hills, recorded to 460 m. In the NE, there are autumn-dated records from beach casuarina stands.

In all habitats, both residents and migrants stay entirely within cover during the day and, even where mist-netting shows them to be relatively common, are difficult to locate and observe. Evening emergence to plunge-dive in mangrove creeks, etc., may be bathing behaviour (A.J. Helbig).

In Selangor mangroves and also around the field-station of the University of Malaya in the nearby upper Gombak valley, constant-effort trapping has demonstrated fidelity of migrants to wintering sites, with returns over two and three consecutive seasons.

FORAGING AND FOOD. No specific information.

SOCIAL ORGANIZATION. Territorial and winterers are solitary.

MOVEMENTS. Autumn migrants have been intercepted on small, remote islands, at lights at sea off both coasts, and inland at floodlights on the Main Range, etc., during 25 September–6 December, with fairly recent feather remains on treeless Perak island (N Melaka Straits) in late January. Records of return movement over Fraser's Hill are dated 5–24 April and sightings on the Rok islands during 3–4 May may also have been of passage migrants (BMP5, BMNH, MBR 1982–83, U. Treesucon).

SURVIVAL. Among 14 residents ringed in Selangor mangroves and retrapped a month or more later, a minimum five survived at least one further year, the longest interval 71 months (MAPS).

SOCIAL INTERACTIONS. No information.

VOICE. A descending sequence of 4–5 loud, mournful whistles and a tremulous *quirrr-r-r-r-r* (Boonsong and Round 1991). Calls suspected to be of Ruddy Kingfisher, but not confirmed, include a loud, down-inflected *chor-r-r-u* or *chir-r-r-u*, and a squeaky trilling rather like that of Common Flameback *Dinopium javanense*.

BREEDING. No record of a nest in this area, but in Borneo adopts or makes cavities in arboreal termitaria. Juveniles mist-netted in the Selangor mangroves in May–June; a fledgling on Tioman on 13 July; and one attended by parents on Tekong island, Singapore, on 30 July (MAPS, MBR 1986–87, Robinson 1927).

MOULT. Sequence of primary moult not recorded. Resident adults north from Johor, covering all months except January, September and December, showed active wing-moult in July, August and November. Migrants handled through passage seasons and all intervening months, including retraps through the mid-winter period, showed none, and lack of wear in autumn suggests a moult is completed before arrival. The schedule of first-winterers is unknown, but at least some young migrants arrive in extensively dark-fringed body-plumage (BMNH, BMP5, UMBRP).

CONSERVATION. No residents have been shown to occur off the lowland plain, and inland resident populations are likely to have suffered extensive habitat-loss. On the coast, degradation and clearance of mangroves, reducing their carrying capacity for species needing mature trees for nesting, is a major issue throughout.

White-throated Kingfisher; Nok Ga Ten Ok Khao (Thai); Burung Pekaka Dusun (Malay)

Halcyon smyrnensis (Linnaeus) 1758, *Systema Naturae* 10(1): 116. TL Izmir, W Turkey.
Plate 62

GROUP RELATIONS. Some breeding-range overlap occurs in W Java, but *smyrnensis* and *H. cyanoventris* (Javan Kingfisher) must still be close to superspecies status.

GLOBAL RANGE. S Turkey, Egypt and the E Mediterranean to Iran; the Indian subcontinent, Sri Lanka and Bay of Bengal islands; China south of a line S Sichuan–Fujian including Hainan; and SE Asia to the Peninsula, Sumatra, W Java and, except for western islands, the Philippines. Vagrant Taiwan.

IDENTIFICATION/DESCRIPTION. The familiar, proportionately rather long-tailed, medium-large tree kingfisher of settlements and agriculture, showing a distinctive combination of dark chocolate head to upper mantle and underparts with individually varied extent of white, from throat-spot to large bib-front, often irregular in outline; lesser wing-coverts chestnut, medians black, greaters purple-black with blue tipping; secondaries, scapulars, upper back and tail bright turquoise, lower back to upper tail-coverts brilliant blue. Primaries are black, with a large white basal patch (inner webs of all feathers, lengthening towards P1) conspicuous on both surfaces. Juvenile duller and initially dark-billed; breast-feathering fringed and lesser wing-coverts mottled black.

Bare-part colours. (Adult) iris deep brown, eyelid-rim dull liver-red; bill dark crimson with brownish cutting-edges; feet dark red.

Size (mm). (Live and skins: 16 males, 6 females; adult): wing 113–123 and 114–121; tail 73–82 and 71–82; bill 53.7–64.2 and 54.6–59.6; tarsus 13.0–15.6 and 14.8–16.0 (BMNH, UMBRP, UMZC).

Weight (g). Adults, 66.5–81.0 (n=7) (UMBRP).

DISTRIBUTION. Historical summary: all divisions, with additional island records from Surin Nua (*Ran*), Yao Yai (*Pha*), Phiphi, Libong, Tarutao, the Langkawi group (Langkawi, Langgun), Penang and Pangkor off the W coast; Ang Thong, Phangan and Samui off the E coast; and Tekong, Ubin, Seletar, Berani, Retan Laut, Samulun, Semakau, Senang and Sudong, Singapore.

GEOGRAPHICAL VARIATION. Subspecies *perpulchra* von Madarász 1904 (TL Singapore island), east from the NE Indian subcontinent.

STATUS AND POPULATION. Resident, regular and common to very common. For reasons not yet studied, peak population density is attained in low-

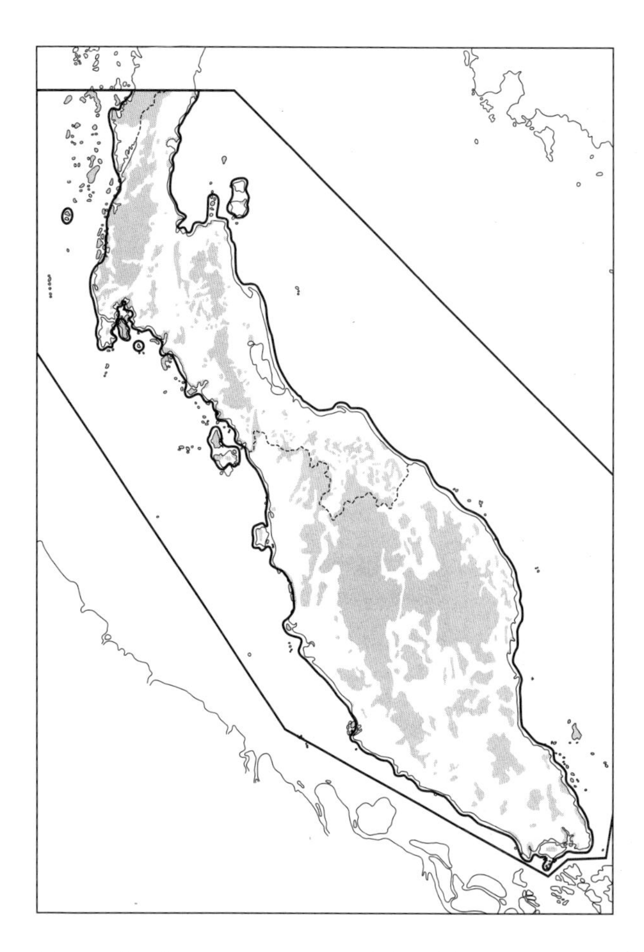

lying oil-palm plantations, and in Malaysia over the last few decades total numbers are likely to have increased.

HABITATS AND ECOLOGY. An almost comprehensive range of open and semi-open habitats at plains level: the degraded, bunded-off landward edge of mangroves, banks of ditches, channels and natural streams (along the edge of large rivers into inland forest), roadsides, paddyland and other open cultivation, rubber and especially oil-palm plantations, parkland, and large (including suburban) gardens. In closed-canopy plantations, interacts with two other tree kingfishers. White-throated and Collared Kingfisher *H. chloris* behave exclusively (Mereek Singh) but, where they meet, White-throated territories invariably include much open space whereas those of Collared do not. The larger Black-capped Kingfisher *H. pileata* excludes both these species from tree-cover.

Ordinarily, not found in closed-canopy mangrove forest or on beaches fronting mangroves, but in N

Kedah occupies both, and hunts there at typical Collared Kingfisher stations on the low-tide mudflat. In mangroves edging the Sanglang river-mouth (Kedah/Perlis border), 15 sightings of tree kingfishers emerging to inspect passing rafts of weed included 13 of White-throated, one of Stork-billed and only one of Collared. This degraded strip of forest, backed by open paddyland, may have lost its capacity to supply Collared Kingfisher nest-sites, and White-throated appears to have taken over some vacated space (MBR 1982–83).

FORAGING AND FOOD. Still-hunts from look-out-perches at heights up to 8–10 m, choosing anything overlooking open ground or water, from a field bund to a bush-top, post, fence, guy or service-wire, or frond or tree branch. Food includes: large orthopterans, cockroaches, mantids, beetles, ants, small scorpions, centipedes (including dangerous *Scolopendra*) and snails (*Achatina* identified); frogs, lizards (full-grown arboreal *Gecko monacha*, *Draco volans* and *Calotes* sp., up to 30 cm long, plus terrestrial skinks *Mabuia* sp.), young birds (White-rumped Shama *Copsychus malabaricus* chicks from a garden nest-box, young Tree Sparrows *Passer montanus* and munias *Lonchura* sp.), and fish up to 10 cm long, caught by plunge-diving. Sallies for swarming termites, and one stomach contained three bees perhaps also taken in flight, and presumed to have been devenomed before swallowing (most prey is branch-swiped). It is often assumed White-throated Kingfishers take anything they can subdue, but individual specialization is suggested by the regularity of fishing in wetlands versus low success observed in some other habitats (only three captures from 22 dives on a drain in a rubber estate), and total lack of interest in an accessible fish-pond by one or more individuals about my Selangor garden taking most kinds of terrestrial food (Batchelor 1958, Bromley 1948, Gibson-Hill 1948a, Glenister 1951, G.C. Madoc, Madoc 1956a, Spittle 1952).

SOCIAL ORGANIZATION. Solitary or in pairs. Forages alone, but in the densest population-patches neighbours can be as little as 100 m apart, and in full view of one another.

MOVEMENTS. Permanently present in favoured habitat. No retrap or recovery has been more than 4 km from site of ringing, but on 3 October 1982 a bird appeared on a drilling platform 200 km off the Terengganu coast (MBR 1982–83). It might have reached there on a supply ship, but distant wandering by a part of the population is implied by occurrence on islands as remote as the Surins and, more generally, by the speed at which this kingfisher colonizes new agriculture.

SURVIVAL. The longest retrap-interval is 66 months, but only small numbers have been marked.

SOCIAL INTERACTIONS. Noisy, raised-wing display by a perched bird (both wings stretched vertically over the back, exposing the white hand-patch) is directed towards an in-coming partner. Given by both pair-members, and a pair in my garden called and wing-displayed intensively during October when a wintering Black-capped Kingfisher took over a wooded corner of their regular space.

VOICE. (1) Song a musical, whinnying trill starting high and reeling down scale over about two seconds, flattening towards the end; succeeded by a long series of trill-bursts, shortening progressively, each down-inflected over nearly an octave, *whihihihihihi . . . hahahahahaha, tirrrr-o, tirrrr-o, tirrrr-o, tirrr-o . . . tirr-o, tirr-o* (bursts sometimes with more than one tail-note, *tirrr-o-o*); (2) a trilling *ji-kurrr*; (3) a piercing *tsik*; (4) in flight, a coarse, screaming laugh, *tjek-tjek-tjek-tjek-tjek-tjek*.

BREEDING

Nest. A horizontal burrow dug into a steep, bare or grassy bank (of sand to stiff clay); entrance diameter 6–8 cm, depth 30–90 cm, nest-chamber up to 23 cm wide × 13 cm high.

Eggs and brood. Egg plain glossy, translucent white. Shape short elliptical. Size (mm): 29.7 × 26.0 (mean, n=11). Full clutch 4–5 eggs. No information on incubation or fledging periods.

Cycle. Both parents attend chicks.

Seasonality. Egg- and chick-dates indicate laying in all months December–late July/early August, with one nest recorded active in October (F.G.H. Allen, BMP5, Edgar 1933, Madoc 1956a, NRCS).

MOULT. Primaries are replaced at up to two loci and with up to three adjacent feathers (out to P6) in overlapping growth. Among 28 adults covering all months except February, April and July–August, ten showed active wing-moult in March, May and September–December (BMNH, UMBRP, UMZC).

CONSERVATION. No critical issues. Ease of monitoring foragers along access-ways through agriculture suggests their possible use as an environmental quality indicator.

Black-capped Kingfisher; Nok Ga Ten Hua Dam (Thai); Burung Pekaka Kopiah Hitam (Malay)

Halcyon pileata (Boddaert) 1783, *Table des Planches Enluminéez d'Histoire Naturelle*: 41. TL Guangzhou, S China.

Plate 62

GROUP RELATIONS. On evidence of ecology, plumage-patterns and feather-protein similarity, in a superspecies with Afrotropical *H. leucocephala* (Grey-headed Kingfisher) (Fry 1980).

GLOBAL RANGE. Breeds in the Indian subcontinent other than the NW, mostly on coasts; Korea, China south and east of a line Liaoning–Hebei–S Sichuan, including Hainan; and western Burma, but not certainly elsewhere in SE Asia. Some populations migrate, reaching Sri Lanka, Bay of Bengal islands and SE Asia to Java and N Sulawesi.

IDENTIFICATION/DESCRIPTION. Jet-black head sharp against white collar and chin to centre breast, and orange-rufous belly, flanks and lower wing-coverts are a diagnostic combination among local tree kingfishers. In flight, shows white patch at base of primaries, as in White-throated Kingfisher, but collar, ventral pattern and rich, royal-blue upperparts are conspicuous at a distance. Sexes alike. For at least part of the winter, juveniles show a scalloped pattern of black fringing on the breast, and fine black streaking on the sides of the throat.

Bare-part colours. (Adult) iris deep brown; bill vermilion-red, darkening at the base of the upper mandible; feet dark red with black edging to scutes.

Size (mm). (Live and skins: 13 males, 6 females; adult): wing 123–133 and 124–137; tail 77–83 and 80–87; bill 62.2–67.5 and 61.6–71.3; tarsus 14.6–16.4 and 14.6–15.1 (BMNH, UMBRP).

Weight (g). Autumn passage to mid winter, 67.9–91.1 (n=16); in March, 78.9–97.2 (n=3) (UMBRP).

DISTRIBUTION. Historical summary: all divisions, with additional island records from the Surins, Ra and the Similan group (*Pha*), Rang (*Phu*), Phiphi, Lanta, Libong, Tarutao national park (Tarutao, Ladang), Langkawi and Dayang Bunting, Perak, Penang, Pangkor, Rembia, Jarak and Pisang off the W coast; Tao (*Chu*), Redang and the Pahang–Johor archipelago (Tulai, Sibu) off the E coast; and Tekong, Ubin, St John's, Hantu, Senang and Ayer Merbau, Singapore.

GEOGRAPHICAL VARIATION. None recognized.

STATUS AND POPULATION. Non-breeding visitor and, on evidence of Melaka Straits lighthouse-strikes, a passage migrant; regular and more or less common, with a very few mid-summer records.

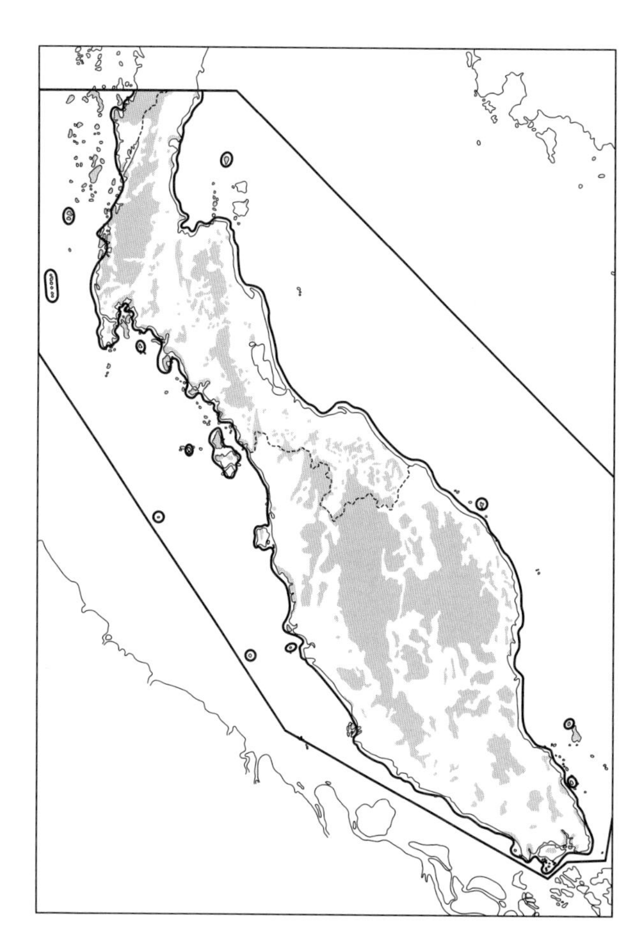

Observations in Selangor indicate numbers wintering inland have declined from the mid 1980s, withdrawing from dry-land habitats of, perhaps, only marginal quality to mainly subcoastal and coastal wetlands.

Loners at Thalae Noi, Kuala Lumpur and on the Linggi river, Negeri Sembilan/Melaka border, in July and August (Anonymous 1981, BR 1964, MBR 1982–83) may have over-summered, but are completely exceptional.

HABITATS AND ECOLOGY. Typical wintering-sites comprise woody cover adjacent to a marine or freshwater wetland, including the creek systems of mangrove forest (holding densest populations), beach strand woodland and the margins of paddyland, marshes (Thalae Noi), ponds, channels and rivers inland. Occasional on rocky shores, including on small islands: a sighting on otherwise completely wooded Jarak island, central Melaka Straits, on 25 January. Large rivers are followed well into inland forest but only as far as they broadly break the tree canopy. Plantation woodland, where streams are typically small and often shaded, is used apparently only in some years and may be sub-optimal, but loners (at least one a juvenile) occupied a part of my garden where it backed on a gully within old rubber in two successive years. Such birds cut into the space of White-throated and, in the south, Collared Kingfishers.

Apart from a few February–early March records at 900–1200 m in the cultivated uplands of Cameron Highlands (Allen 1951b), overwinters strictly at plains level.

Fidelity to a wintering-site demonstrated at the landward edge of mangroves at Rantau Panjang, Selangor, where many marked birds have returned over two or more seasons; as also on Singapore island (MAPS, UMBRP).

FORAGING AND FOOD. Still-hunts from perches typically 1–2 m up, splash-diving or dropping to open ground below trees. At low tide, birds on the seaward edge of mangroves move to the exposed sand- or mudflat, taking up scanning positions on any available look-out, and chasing out any nearby Collared Kingfishers (that hunt in the same manner).

Many crabs are caught on open shores, and compared with White-throated Kingfisher a larger proportion of individuals takes aquatic food. However, winterers at inland dry-land sites often take over the regular hunting perches of other tree kingfishers they supplant.

SOCIAL ORGANIZATION. Solitary in wintering habitat; two or more may associate on migration (BR 1972–73, Ollington and Loh 1993).

MOVEMENTS. Extreme dates of interception of nocturnal migrants at Fraser's Hill in autumn are 26 September and 25 November, with most taken during October. In Singapore, earliest autumn dates are in the range 31 September–18 October (SINGAV-3). Over two seasons, winterers arrived at a well watched inland site in Selangor on 19 and 24 October, and stayed for approximately 145 days, i.e., to late March. Casualty remains on treeless Perak island, Melaka Straits, suggest spring passage runs from not later than the beginning of March, with sightings in Singapore and along the W coast through to May; extreme date (in Singapore) 18 May (BMP5, BR 1972–73, MBR 1986–87).

Records from the Terengganu marine oil-field during 2–5 October (MBR 1982–83) suggest possible direct crossings of the Gulf of Thailand at that season.

SURVIVAL. The five longest retrap-intervals of marked birds, all from subcoastal Selangor, are 37, 44, 63, 64 and 99 months (demonstrating a minimum eight autumn migrations completed).

SOCIAL INTERACTIONS. No information.

VOICE. A penetrating *tsk*, and an occasional cackling laugh, both similar to White-throated Kingfisher.

BREEDING. No population.

MOULT. Eighteen adults covering all months October–March showed no wing-moult, and only two instances of other moult (T1 in early February). Of the few wing-moulters reported otherwise (P1 on 11 and 19 November, P8 on 13 February) at least one was a juvenile, and instances of suspended moult, with 5–9 feathers new at mid winter, appear also to refer to this age-group (BMNH, BMP5, G.W.H. Davison).

CONSERVATION. Probably no critical issues.

Collared Kingfisher; Nok Gin Pieo (Thai); Burung Pekaka Bakau (Malay)

Halcyon chloris (Boddaert) 1783, *Table des Planches Enluminéez d'Histoire Naturelle*: 49. TL Buru island, Moluccas.

Plate 62

GROUP RELATIONS. Free-standing.

GLOBAL RANGE. Coasts and islands of the Red Sea and Gulf of Oman; SW and NE coasts of the Indian subcontinent, and Bay of Bengal islands; mainly coastal SE Asia from W Burma and central Vietnam; Wallacea; southern New Guinea and northern Australia, and the tropical Pacific east to Samoa.

IDENTIFICATION/DESCRIPTION. Top of head to slightly below eye-level and upperparts from mantle, including wings and tail, aquamarine to shining cobalt-blue, brightest on back and rump, greenest on cap and mantle; ear-coverts variably darker than cap; spot in front of eye (below lores) and narrow anterior border of collar black. Otherwise white, including loral bar, spot below eye, broad hind-collar and, except for blackish lower primary-coverts and underside of tail, all underparts. Flanks and centre belly are variably washed buff, but rarely very obviously in the field. Sexes alike, with variability of blue versus green tones, darkness of the ear-coverts, and buffiness of flanks individual, although females average slightly greener, less blue than males on wing-coverts and less brilliant blue on the secondaries. Juveniles duller with broader black collar-margin and fine black scalloping across the breast.

Bare-part colours. (Adult) iris deep brown; upper mandible and bill-tip black, rest of lower mandible flesh-white; feet grey.

Size (mm). (Live and skins: 25 males, 10 females; adult): wing 98–106 and 96–107; tail 57–67 and 59–65; bill 42.4–49.9 and 44.7–49.6; tarsus 14.7–17.1 and 15.0–15.7 (BMNH, MAPS, UMBRP, UMZC).

Weight (g). Coastal resident adults, 47.6–70.9 (mean 58.9, n=66); an April migrant intercepted at Fraser's Hill, 63.0 (MAPS, UMBRP).

DISTRIBUTION. Historical summary: all divisions except *Son, Yal, Nar*, with many additional island records, from the Surins and Similans, Yao Yai, Lanta, Libong, Tarutao national park (Tarutao, Ta Nga), Langkawi, Penang, the Sembilan group, Jarak, the Kelang estuary group, Besar (*Mel*) and Pisang off the W coast; the Ang Thong group, Phangan and Samui, the Perhentian and Redang groups and the Pahang–Johor archipelago (Tulai, Tioman, Rawa, Aur, Sibu) off the E coast; and Tekong, Sahajat, Ubin, Ketam, Seletar, St John's, Sekuda, Sentosa, Retan Laut, Samulun, Sakeng, Hantu, Senang, Pawai, Sudong and Ayer Merbau, around Singapore.

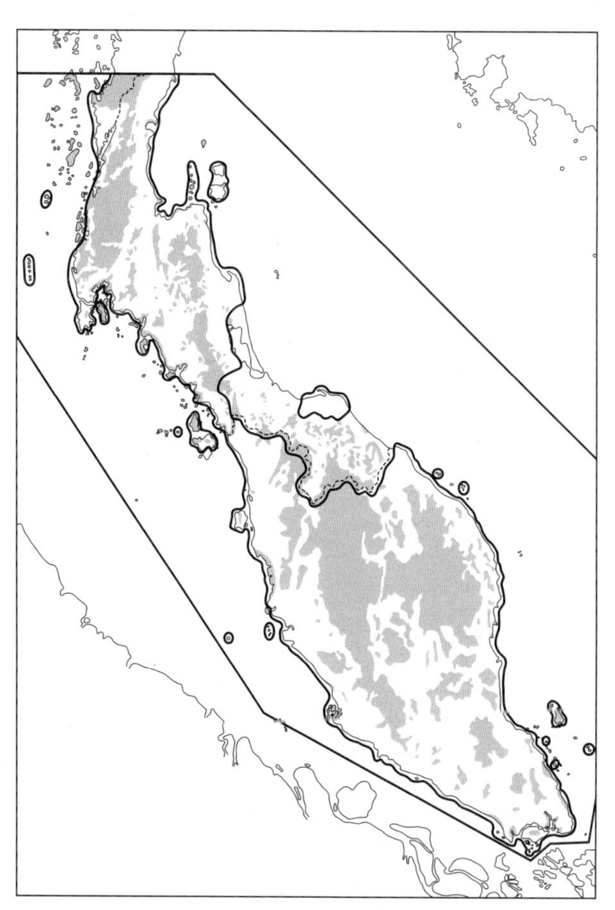

GEOGRAPHICAL VARIATION. Subspecies *humii* Sharpe 1892 (TL Jeram, Selangor), also of NE Sumatra. Migrants have not been distinguished from residents: wing-length and wing-tip shape (P8>7>9>6>10) are the same.

STATUS AND POPULATION. Resident and a possible breeding visitor; regular and common, but movements are little understood. Present year-round on coasts and islands throughout, and has colonized inland habitats apparently from the south: long ago on Singapore island (Bucknill and Chasen 1927), through S and W Johor by 1950, to the Melaka/Negeri Sembilan border in 1953, widely in Negeri Sembilan by the mid 1960s, in Selangor to around Kuala Lumpur by the late 1970s, and in the late 1980s found along the Terengganu river for at least 40 km upstream, as far as Kuala Berang (Batchelor 1954a, BR 1966, 1978–79, Edgar 1954). The few inland records elsewhere, in upper Perak and on the upper Pahang and Kelantan rivers, appear all to have been on likely spring or autumn migration dates (see below).

Ringing in Selangor has shown birds of the mangrove and subcoastal coconut zone to be sedentary residents (BMP5). Migrants would be hard to detect there, and claims of disappearance from plantation habitat in Johor and Melaka during September–early March, plus definitely seasonal passage through the Kuala Lumpur area, have linked migration with the inland population. However, some inland birds stay put. Individuals under observation that moved did so only when their patch was invaded by Black-capped Kingfisher, others nearby remaining on site (Mereek Singh, Yorke 1984). Batchelor's (1954a) guess that inland birds spend the winter on the coast has not been investigated.

HABITATS AND ECOLOGY. The main occupation zone is mangrove forest, mature and well grown after disturbance, adjacent coconut gardens and mixed orchard, coastal strand woodland, and riverine (mostly mangrove) woodland to the limit of tides. Inland habitats include wooded parks and gardens, and especially old, closed-canopy rubber plantation (strongly associated with the colonization front), at plains level. On passage, occasionally in less likely sites, such as clearings in submontane forest (BR 1972–73).

FORAGING AND FOOD. Predominantly by still-hunting from a mound, post, fence, service-wire or, usually, a snag or lower branch of a tree, up to 3–4 m from the ground, with a view over open space that varies from short grass to a creek-bank or exposed beach or tide-flat (see also Black-capped and White-throated Kingfishers). Food on the coast is mainly small crabs and other crustacea (one record of the taking of a tiger prawn from a Little Heron), with only a small proportion of fish, mainly mudskippers (Gibson-Hill 1948a). Inland, large orthopterans, cicadas, beetles, tadpoles, frogs and geckos identified, and Spittle (1952) found remains of a large bee among detritus in a nest. If this had been food it is presumed to have been de-venomed. Most larger items are branch-beaten, and anything caught in the open is carried to a perch for processing.

SOCIAL ORGANIZATION. Solitary or in pairs.

MOVEMENTS. The few direct indications of migration/long-distance dispersal, from night-time interceptions or at improbable day-time sites, including crossing the Main Range at Fraser's Hill and a bird on an oil-rig 200 km off Terengganu, fall in the periods 3 April–13 May and 13–27 September (BR 1974–75, MBR 1982–83).

SURVIVAL. Among 57 birds retrapped on the Selangor coast one-plus months after ringing, at least eight survived a minimum six more years: intervals 75–131 months (MAPS, UMBRP).

SOCIAL INTERACTIONS. Tail-bobbing when perched is a presumed signal behaviour.

VOICE. The commonest advertising-call is a coarse, explosive, commonly five-note laugh falling away and succeeded by loud, discordant disyllables, *jek-jek-jek-jek-jek, ji-jaw, ji-jaw, ji-jaw*. The repertoire needs a fuller description.

BREEDING

Nest. Excavates own burrow (one record of the take-over of a Common Flameback hole) in a still-living or dead tree or palm trunk, or (commonly still active) arboreal termitarium, with one recorded in the polster of a bird's-nest fern; from near ground level to 10 m up. Less often in earth, including a bank and an up-turned tree root-plate. Burrow diameter 6.5–7.5 cm, depth 15–90 cm, according to substrate, widening out into an unlined nest-chamber about 10 cm across. Durable holes are used over more than one season.

Eggs and brood. Egg plain, glossy, translucent white, usually mud-stained. Shape short elliptical. Size (mm): 29.2 × 24.6 (average). Full clutch 2–4, commonly three; one of seven must have included dumped eggs or part of a previously failed clutch. No information on incubation or fledging periods.

Cycle. Up to two broods raised per season.

Seasonality. Excavation noted December–March; egg- and nestling-dates extrapolate to laying during December–July, with exceptional nests recorded active in August and October (Anonymous 1931, Batchelor 1954a, Chasen 1939, Edgar 1933, 1954, G.C. Madoc, MBR 1984–85, NRCS, SINGAV-2, -3, Ryves 1938, Spittle 1949).

MOULT. Primaries are replaced at up to two loci, typically descendant from P1 and P6 or 7. Among 147 handlings covering the Peninsula south of 9°N, and all months except September, active wing-moult occurred during mid May–late January, with latest starts and earliest completions virtually overlapping in August. A large February–April sample showed no primary moult, but some of secondaries and tail (age-group not recorded) up to mid March (BMNH, MAPS, UMBRP, UMZC).

CONSERVATION. No critical issues at the moment, but the Kedah coast situation is a demonstration of what reclamation and degradation of mangrove forest could do to the coastal population generally (see White-throated Kingfisher).

Rufous-collared Kingfisher; Nok Ga Ten Soi Khaw See Namtaan (Thai); Burung Pekaka Rimba (Malay)

Actenoides concretus (Temminck) 1825, *Nouveau Recueil de Planches Coloriées d'Oiseaux* 58: plate 346. TL Sumatra.

Plate 62

GROUP RELATIONS. Fry (1980) includes *concretus* in a superspecies with Philippine *A. hombroni* and *A. lindsayi* (Blue-capped and Spotted Kingfishers).

GLOBAL RANGE. Borneo, Sumatra and intervening islands, the Peninsula and SW Thailand to latitude 11°40'N.

IDENTIFICATION/DESCRIPTION. Cap from centre forehead to hind-crown verditer-green, emerald round its rear margin; supercilium from side of forehead to just behind eye rufous-buff; lores, continuing as a band through the eye and around the rear of the cap, black; broad malar wedge, deep blue. Rest of face, broad hind-collar and underparts orange-rufous, paler on chin, throat and centre belly to lower tail-coverts. Anterior mantle black or blue-black, rest of mantle to wing-coverts, and outer edging of flight-feathers, dark blue in male, olive-green in female, the latter's scapulars and wing-covert feathers each with a round, buff spot; back to centre upper tail-coverts bright azure-blue, lateral upper tail-coverts and tail cobalt-blue. Juveniles as respective adults but duller; female upperparts blacker, and male scapulars and wing-coverts buff-spotted.

Bare-part colours. Iris dark brown; bill all-blackish (young juvenile), culmen to just below level of nostrils blackish, rest of bill, including extreme tip and broad cutting-edges, wax-yellow (adult); feet dirty wax-yellow.

Size (mm). (Live and skins: 25 males, 21 females; adult): wing 102–114 and 104–118; tail 54–66 and 55–65; bill 44.5–53.4 and 43.0–53.4; tarsus 16.9–18.9 and 16.3–18.8 (BMNH, UMBRP).

Weight (g). Adult males, 62.3–83.3 (mean 71.5, n=16); adult females, 59.8–88.1 (mean 75.5, n=16) (UMBRP).

DISTRIBUTION. Historical summary: all divisions except *Chu, Sur, Phu, Pht, Son, Pat, Nar, Ked, Kel, Pra, Mel*; extinct *Sin* for at least 40 years (possibly twice that long), and no other island records.

GEOGRAPHICAL VARIATION. Nominate Sundaic *concretus* in Malaysia; *peristephes* Deignan 1946 (TL Huey Yang, SW Thailand), with paler rufous collar and underparts, whiter belly and, in female, larger buff spots on dorsum, identified north from Trang. Far-northern birds average marginally larger than elsewhere: five adults from Pakchan in the wing-range 111–118 mm.

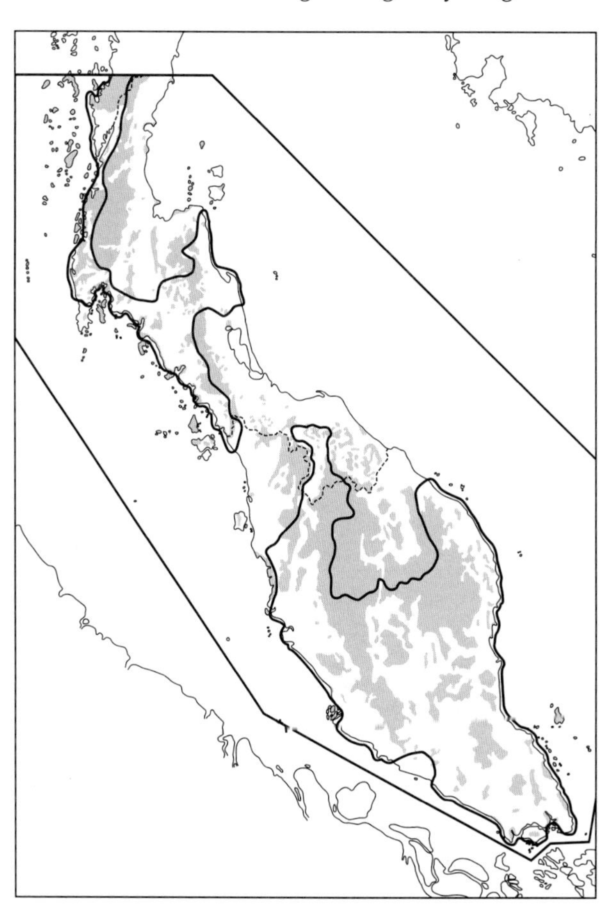

STATUS AND POPULATION. Resident, regular and more or less common, at least in Malaysia, but not very noisy and difficult to find without mist-nets. Regular trapping in the understorey of 15 ha of mature and 17 ha of 20-year regenerating, plains-level Lowland forest in the Pasoh research area, Negeri Sembilan, showed a minimum three pairs regularly entering the former but not more than two the latter.

HABITATS AND ECOLOGY. The understorey to mid-stratum of evergreen and semi-evergreen Lowland forest, mature or regenerated to closed-canopy stage after disturbance, at plains level and on slopes to the Montane ecotone, with small numbers in Lower Montane forest to a recorded upper limit of 1200 m (D. Yong). The only kingfisher resident in Montane forest, emphasizing its non-dependance on fish.

FORAGING AND FOOD. Still-hunts from a shaded perch. Prey includes lizards, small snakes (*Typhlops* and *Doliophis* spp. identified) and isopods (Robinson 1928), i.e., at least some items taken, and perhaps uncovered, on the ground.

SOCIAL ORGANIZATION. Solitary.

MOVEMENTS. None reported.

SURVIVAL. Among 22 adults surviving one-month-plus after ringing at long-term mist-netting sites in Selangor and Negeri Sembilan, longest retrap-intervals are 50, 58 and an extreme 249 months, the oldest bird a male still on its site of ringing at latest handling in June 1993 (C.M. Francis).

SOCIAL INTERACTIONS. No information.

VOICE. A melancholy, slightly up-inflected, wailing whistle, *whoi-i-i* or *kwoi-i-i*, repeated in sustained bouts (with an occasionally inserted, down-turning *whoiu* note), at a rate of about nine calls per ten seconds. A less insistent, wavering sequence, *eer eerlee-er eerlee-er eerlee-er eer*, sound quality not unlike Banded Kingfisher, is also believed to be given by this species; confirmation awaited. The large difference from typical tree kingfisher laugh-calls lends weight to the split from *Halcyon*.

BREEDING

Nest. Only three recorded: burrows bored into sloping ground of the forest floor, entrance 8–10 cm wide; none particularly close to water (nearest streams 16–73 m away).

Eggs and brood. Egg not described, but clutch two.

Cycle. No information.

Seasonality. Active nests, contents unchecked, in May and June; nestlings on 11 May; young juveniles mist-netted June–September (BMNH, BR 1965, H.E. McClure, UMBRP).

MOULT. On limited evidence, replacement of primaries is descendant from two loci, P1 and P7 with, at different stages, up to six adjacent inner- and four outer-row feathers in overlapping growth. Among 117 handlings covering all months, and the length of Peninsula south to Negeri Sembilan, active, bilateral wing-moult occurred during mid April–late October, none through November–March (but some body-moult to late November and two instances of unilateral wing-moult in December) (BMNH, UMBRP).

CONSERVATION. Presence in hill forest suggests no immediate pressure from outright loss of habitat, but is unlikely to survive a logging event that heavily disrupted the canopy (cf. Lowland forest trogons).

Family ALCEDINIDAE

River kingfishers: four species

Oriental Dwarf Kingfisher; Nok Ga Ten Noi Sam Niw (Thai); Burung Pekaka Sepah (Malay)

Ceyx erithacus (Linnaeus) 1758, *Systema Naturae* 10(1): 115. TL Bengal.
Plate 63

GROUP RELATIONS. Forms a superspecies with *C. melanurus* (Philippine Dwarf Kingfisher) (Fry 1980). Lower-order relationships are still in dispute. A one-species arrangement assumes northern black-backed and southern red-backed isolates have re-met and are merging. Ripley and Beehler (1987) analysed a range of characters to test the smoothness of their intergradation through the Peninsula and Sumatra, and found some distributions to be skewed. This evidence of impeded gene-flow suggested hybridization rather than full integration. However, results may not have been free of the influence of a large flow of winter migrants into the area from the north – over 350 intercepted at floodlights on Fraser's Hill and elsewhere since ringing began in the 1960s, exclusively of pure black-backed stock. In summer, such birds have been confirmed south only as far as Ranong where, from timing of wing-moult, they appear to be resident. Red-backs are certainly also resident. Were they hybridizing species, they would have been expected to show a relatively restricted zone of intergradation. In effect, a mix of intermediates fills the whole of the rest of the Peninsula, and beyond, outnumbers pure red-backs more or less everywhere and is certainly self-sustaining.

The zone of interaction is much as between northern and southern Oriental Pied Hornbills, and the preferred interpretation must also be that it is between two formerly isolated populations of a single species.

GLOBAL RANGE. The Himalayan foothills east from Nepal, the NE Indian subcontinent, the W Ghats, Sri Lanka and Bay of Bengal islands; S Yunnan and Hainan; SE Asia from south and west of the Annamite range to the Greater Sunda islands, Bali and the W Philippines; and the Lesser Sunda islands east to Flores. Northern populations migrate, wintering within the southern breeding-range south at least to the Peninsula.

IDENTIFICATION/DESCRIPTION. Pure black-back: cap to nape and back to tail orange-rufous, side of hind-crown and centre of back to upper tail-coverts tipped brilliant magenta; side of face and, in some, side of forehead yellower; a wedge up the centre of the forehead, lores and anterior margin of eye, patch on side of nape (surmounting white neck-flash), mantle, scapulars and wings black, nape-spot and mantle to wing-covert feathers tipped shining ultramarine-blue. Chin to throat white, rest of underparts chrome-yellow, richest across the breast. Pure red-backs lack the forehead and loral spots, and have mantle to scapulars and wing-coverts plain rufous rather than blue and black. All intermediates show at least some rufous on the mantle and wing-coverts, and blue-black variously on the forehead and lores to edge of eye.

Below, juveniles of all grades are white rather than yellow, with a diffuse breast-band of rusty orange. They also show wedge-shaped black tip-marks on the tail-feathers. Like other river kingfishers, flight is direct, on rapidly whirring wings.

Bare-part colours. Iris deep brown; bill blackish tinged dull orange and with extreme tip pale (young juvenile), before post-juvenile moult changing via horn-yellow to the bright orange-red of adult; feet bright orange-red (adult), young juveniles need checking.

Size (mm). Resident red-backs and red-backed intergrades (live: 15 adults, none sexed): wing 54–64; tail

24–30; bill 33.4–39.3; tarsus 8.3–9.2. Summer-dated black-backs (live and skins: 13 adults, most not sexed): wing 57–62; tail 23–32; bill 32.0–34.6; tarsus 8.2–8.6. Migrant black-backs (live: 18 adults, none sexed): wing 54–60; tail 21–26; bill 32.0–35.7; tarsus 7.7–8.6 (UMBRP, ZDUM).

Weight (g). Among adults, most not sexed, *rufidorsum* and red-backed intergrades average heaviest, 15.2–21.5 (mean 18.0, n=51); summer-dated (resident) extensively black-backed intergrades are intermediate, 13.2–18.0 (mean 16.4, n=11); overwintering northern *erithacus* lightest, 13.0–16.4 (mean 14.9, n=20). Few in-coming autumn migrants fall outside this winter range (maximum 18.5 g), and no obvious fattening occurs before spring departure.

DISTRIBUTION. Historical summary: all divisions except *Pes*, pure red-backs recorded south from Surat Thani, also on Tekong island but, apparently, now extinct on the neighbouring main island of Singapore; pure black-backs (independent of status) to the extreme south in winter, with island records strictly at passage or wintering dates from Libong, Tarutao, Langkawi, Penang, Rembia (*Pek*), Jarak and Pisang off the W coast; and Perhentian Besar and Redang off the E coast.

GEOGRAPHICAL VARIATION. Migrants are exclusively black-backed nominate *erithacus*; residents are *erithacus* in the far north, red-backed *rufidorsum* Strickland 1846 (TL Melaka) elsewhere, with intermediates greatly outnumbering parental types probably everywhere.

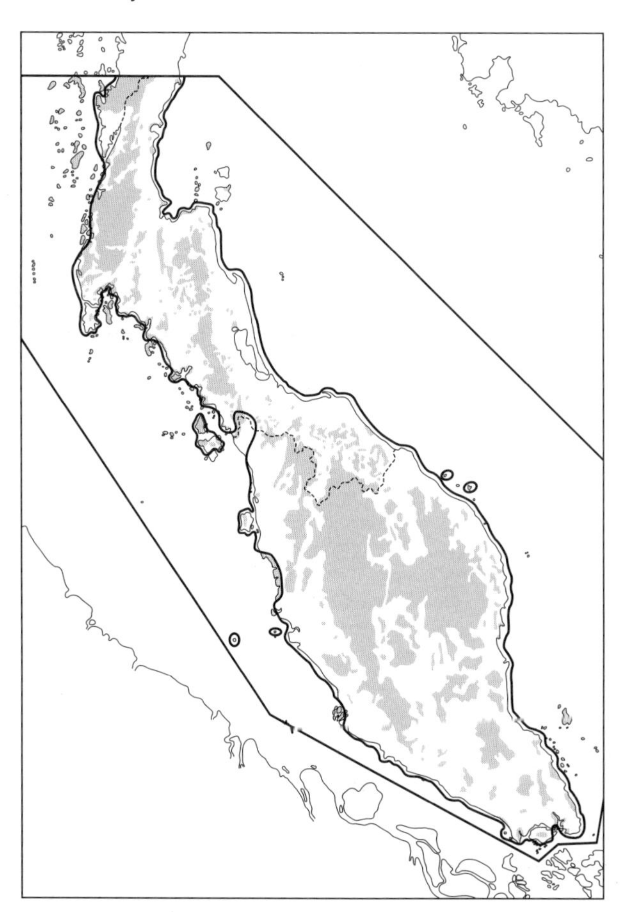

STATUS AND POPULATION. Resident, a non-breeding visitor and, from evidence of strikes on Melaka Straits lighthouses (One-Fathom Bank, Angsa, Undan, etc.), passage migrant; regular and more or less common. This is one of very few species in which individuals of different migratory status have been demonstrated to meet as a single population. At the Pasoh research forest, Negeri Sembilan, overwintering black-backs on 15 ha of primary understorey outnumbered resident red-backs/intergrades five to two, but in a year when red-backs/intergrades were missing, eight black-backs overwintered. Nearby, a similar area of regenerating forest with more swampy habitat again held nearly the same total winter density, but dominated throughout by red-backs/intergrades. It is suspected these show a slightly greater preference for wet sites but this has not been demonstrated objectively. At neither site did the number of red-backs rise during summer absence of migrants, but the combined winter densities were close to that of an all-resident population in comparable forest near Kuching, Sarawak (Fogden 1976).

HABITATS AND ECOLOGY. Mangroves, and the under-stratum of inland evergreen and semi-evergreen Lowland forest, mature and regenerating, also riverside peatswamp forest, tall secondary-growth, and sometimes overgrown rubber gardens; at all elevations, and into Lower Montane forest, recorded to 1300 m. Everywhere, favours damp ground and valley bottoms, close to streams and other shaded surface water, but by no means all activity-space is wetland.

Retrapping of ringed birds suggests both residents and migrants, including first-winterers, establish individual (but overlapping) home-ranges in forest. At Pasoh, returning winterers demonstrated between-season fidelity to site, one adult occupying partly the same patch during three successive winters (Wells 1990).

FORAGING AND FOOD. Robinson (1928) recorded insects, including mayflies and winged ants, picked off stream surfaces. Food brought to nestlings and fledglings included small fish and worms (BR 1978–79, SINGAV-6).

SOCIAL ORGANIZATION. Solitary.

MOVEMENTS. Night-flying autumn migrant *erithacus* have been intercepted at lights from the crest of the Main Range down to sea-level, and at coastal and off-shore lighthouses, during 4 August–3 January (BR 1976–77). Peak southward passage is in September–October, but at Pasoh research forest, latitude 2°59′N, no overwinterers arrived before late October, with most there only as of November. Earlier movements are guessed to be onward, into Indonesia. In spring, some leave winter spaces by the end of February, with none found after 20 March. Night-time northbound migrants have been intercepted at lights during 12 March–2 May, but with few records after the first third of April (BMP5, SINGAV-3, A.B. van den Berg).

The only evidence of movement by red-backed birds comes from a single occurrence on a ship in the Melaka Straits (CLBS).

SURVIVAL. Among in-coming migrants intercepted at lights, a mean 65 percent are first-winterers (BMP5), implying northern black-backs have a relatively low rate of survival. Few marked birds of any population have been tracked for more than one year; longest retrap-interval 20 months for residents, 25 months for migrants (UMBRP).

SOCIAL INTERACTIONS. No information.

VOICE. In flight, a piping, *Alcedo*-like note, but higher-pitched.

BREEDING

Nest. Burrows in the steep sides of a track, stream and drainage-ditch, and the flank of a low (still active) soil termitarium; in and at the edge of forest. Entrance 3.8–4.5 cm wide, tunnel 15–52 cm deep, opening to a nest-chamber 10–13 cm across. Rotten leaves found lining one chamber are likely to have been carried in before the kingfishers took possession (implying burrows are re-used).

Eggs and brood. Eggs are plain, translucent white and highly glossed. Shape near-spherical. Size (mm): 22.1–20.0 × 17.9–16.7 (n=5). Clutch three, and a report of a brood of three. No information on incubation or fledging periods.

Cycle. No information.

Seasonality. From Perak to Negeri Sembilan, eggs during early March–May, nestlings in May, dependant fledglings in late June and early August, and dark- or yellow-billed juveniles mist-netted in June and August (F.G.H. Allen, Chasen 1939, R.V. Lansdown, G.C Madoc, Ryves 1938, SINGAV-3, UMBRP).

MOULT. Primaries are replaced at up to three loci, moult moving ascendant and descendant from P3 or 4 and descendant from P7 or 8. Among 106 handlings of resident adults covering the Peninsula south to Negeri Sembilan, and all months, wing-moult occurred during mid June–late September, with only one later instance (P6), and some tail-moult up to late December.

Adult migrants follow a more protracted schedule. Many on southward passage have suspended with about half their primaries renewed and, while still on passage in November, a few re-activate. In wintering habitat, no moult has been found in October, but is near-general by late November, and all flight-feathers are replaced before the end of February (instances of body- and tail-moult into March). First-winterers moult into adult body-plumage and tail over the same period but do not appear to change flight-feathers (BMP5, RTFD, M. Wong, UMBRP, UMZC).

CONSERVATION. Boonsong and Round (1991) have speculated residents in Thailand are restricted to low elevations. In Malaysia, they extend far up the submontane slope, hence may be less at risk from outright habitat-loss. The impact on foraging of stream-fouling during logging operations has not been studied.

Common Kingfisher; Nok Ga Ten Noi Thammadaa (Thai); Burung Pekaka Cit-cit (Malay)

Alcedo atthis (Linnaeus) 1758, *Systema Naturae* 10(1): 109. TL Egypt.
Plate 63

GROUP RELATIONS. Forms a superspecies with Afrotropical *A. semitorquata* (Half-collared Kingfisher) (Fry 1980).

GLOBAL RANGE. Breeds in N Africa and, excluding central Asia, temperate-zone Eurasia from the Atlantic to Sakhalin and Japan; in SW Asia, the Indian subcontinent and Sri Lanka; China including Taiwan and Hainan; SE Asia to northern Sumatra; and Wallacea and coastal New Guinea to the Bismarck and Solomon archipelagos. Northern continental populations migrate, wintering in and beyond the southern breeding-range, in S and SE Asia to the Bay of Bengal and Greater Sunda islands, Bali and the Philippines; and to an uncertain eastern limit in Wallacea.

IDENTIFICATION/DESCRIPTION. Cap to upper mantle dark aquamarine, cross-barred bright azure-blue and with black feather-tips; scapulars and wing-coverts are dark aquamarine, washed blue, and all except primary and secondary coverts spangled brilliant blue. Lower mantle and back to upper tail-coverts brilliant blue; flight-feathers blackish with bright aquamarine edging to outer webs; tail aquamarine to royal-blue. A broad, bright aquamarine malar-stripe cuts off rufous of lores and band from rear margin of eye through ear-coverts to bold white lateral neck-flash (some Blue-eared Kingfishers have cheeks rufous but only juveniles show it out to neck-flash). Chin to throat white, rest of underparts warm buff to rich rufous. The sexes differ mainly on bill-colour. Juveniles are duller, with a grey cast to rufous parts and zone of sooty grey fringing across the breast.

Bare-part colours. (Adult) iris deep brown; bill black with extreme base of lower mandible and mouth-line coral-red (male), basal half to most of lower mandible coral-red (female); feet coral-red.

Size (mm). (Live and skins: 13 males, 15 females; adult): wing 67–74 and 69–80; tail 24–33 and 25–32; bill 38.8–42.4 and 36.2–41.5; tarsus 7.9–9.0 and 8.3–9.4 (BMNH, UMBRP, ZDUM).

Weight (g). Adults, status unknown, 24.0–27.6 (n=8).

DISTRIBUTION. Historical summary: all divisions except *Kel*, with additional island records at passage or wintering dates from Loughborough, the Surins, Yao Yai, Rang (*Phu*), Lanta, Libong, the Tarutao national park group (Tarutao, Ladang, Ta Nga), Langkawi, Dayang Bunting and Paya (*Ked*), Penang, Jarak and Pisang off the W coast; Redang, Tulai and Tioman off the E coast; and Tekong, Ubin, Seletar, Sentosa, Sakeng, Senang and Sudong, Singapore.

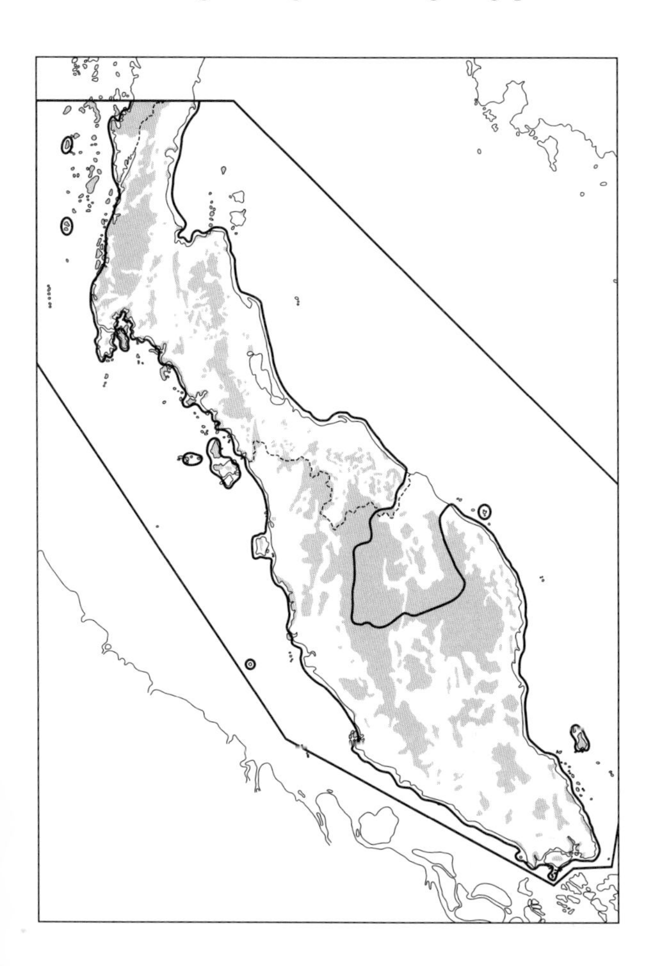

GEOGRAPHICAL VARIATION. All populations are subspecies *bengalensis* Gmelin 1788 (TL Bengal), of the N Indian and E and SE Asian range.

STATUS AND POPULATION. Non-breeding visitor and passage migrant, regular and more or less common; and on the Malaysian W-coast plain from Perak to the Negeri Sembilan/Melaka border a sparse breeder, presumed to be resident.

HABITATS AND ECOLOGY. Tidal creeks and aquaculture ponds in the mangrove zone, open marshland (including the natural Thalae Noi/Songkhla wetland), and streams, channels, rivers, ponds and lagoons at all distances inland on the deforested plain; into forest only along margins of rivers that broadly open the canopy. Habitats of migrants and residents are not known to differ, but the few accepted nest-records are all from well inland.

FORAGING AND FOOD. Most food is aquatic, but crabs and small mudskippers are sometimes taken from exposed tide-flats (Gibson-Hill 1948a). Along the NW Malaysian coast, Helbig (1987a) found 90 percent of capture-attempts were plunge-dives off scanning-perches (on exposed twigs, pole-tops, etc., mostly within 1–2 m of the surface), 2.6 percent dives from a hover position, and 0.9 percent direct from level flight. The rest were aborted. Fifty-three percent of completed forays were successful, capturing mainly fish and prawns (about 60 and 30 percent of diet items); body-lengths roughly in the range 15–45 mm. Fish, in particular, were branch-swiped before being swallowed, and processing time varied with prey-size (to an extreme 8.5 minutes). Conversion to fresh weight suggested individuals consumed up to 60 percent of body-weight equivalent daily, and needed a mean 38 captures to secure this.

SOCIAL ORGANIZATION. A. J. Helbig found coastal winterers are more or less territorial but that in areas of high population density a given home-range overlapped up to four others, with minimum conflict.

MOVEMENTS. The few records away from wintering habitat (including interceptions at lights on Fraser's Hill, on a Terengganu off-shore oil-rig and small islands of the Melaka Straits) fall during 23 August–30 November and mid–late April (BMP5, MBR 1982–83). Earliest dates on the ground in Selangor, including over several seasons at a constant-effort mist-netting plot in reedbeds near Kuala Lumpur, are in the range 23–26 August; and in Singapore (outside the known breeding-range), from 14 August to 1 September (BIRDLINE-2, SINGAV-4). Latest spring dates in the far south (Singapore, SE Johor) are in early May (extreme 9 May) (Howes *et al.* 1986, SINGAV-6).

SURVIVAL. No information.

SOCIAL INTERACTIONS. No specific information.

VOICE. The only vocalization recorded in the area is the flight-call, 2–3 high-pitched, rippling squeaks.

BREEDING

Nest. Burrows in steep earth banks, one in an active soil termitarium; close to open water (including of a fish-pond), but one by a road through a rubber estate was 180 m from water. Tunnel-width 3.5 cm, and length to nest-chamber 15–30 cm; the chamber unlined except for degraded oral pellets.

Eggs and brood. Eggs plain, glossy, translucent white. Shape elliptical. Size (mm): 22.3 × 17.4, 21.8 × 16.9 (n=2). Two clutches of two, one fresh the other part-incubated. No other information.

Cycle. No information.

Seasonality. In Perak and Selangor, eggs in January and on 20 February (Batchelor 1958, Edgar 1933, Robinson 1927). An entry in the diary of V.W. Ryves (1938) suggests that he confused Common with Blue-eared Kingfisher *A. meninting*, and that his records of nests in May and June (cf. BMP5) should be transferred to the latter species.

MOULT. Primaries are replaced at two loci, apparently descendant from P1 and P8, the latter coincident with P3, 4 or 5, but sometimes preceded by independent moult of P10. One example of post-juvenile moult (P6 in mid September) may have been regular-descendant.

Among 38 adults (status unknown) from throughout the Peninsula, and covering the period September–April, 12 showed active wing-moult from September to late March. Suspensions occurred throughout, including in April.

CONSERVATION. No critical issues.

Blue-eared Kingfisher; Nok Ga Ten Noi Lang See Namngern (Thai); Burung Pekaka Bintik-bintik (Malay)

Alcedo meninting Horsfield 1821, *Transactions of the Linnean Society* 13(1): 172. TL Java.
Plate 63

GROUP RELATIONS. Fry (1980) includes it in a superspecies with African *A. quadribrachys* (Shining-blue Kingfisher) and E Wallacean/Australasian *A. azurea* and *A. websteri* (Azure and Bismarck Kingfishers).

GLOBAL RANGE. Himalayan foothills east from Nepal and the NE Indian subcontinent, W Ghats, Sri Lanka and the Andamans; S Yunnan; SE Asia south and west of the Annamite range to the Greater Sunda islands, Bali and W Philippines; Lombok, Sulawesi and the Sula group.

IDENTIFICATION/DESCRIPTION. From similar-sized Common Kingfisher by exclusively rich blue rather than green tones, and by flight-call. Ground-colour of head and scapulars to wing-coverts is blue-black rather than aquamarine, with brilliant barring and spangling; remaining upperparts shining blue, brightest on the back; primary coverts and flight-feathers black and tail blue-black. Most adults show a dull, grey-brown-tinted breast-band across rufous underparts, but distinct from juvenile-type fringing.

Rufous lores and white neck-flash are standard, as in Common Kingfisher, but the rest of the face-pattern varies. Adult males and a proportion of females (the oldest?) are solidly blue down to malar level. Most females, including birds with clearly adult bare-part colours, show an incomplete malar-stripe past which rufous spreads up cheeks and ear-coverts to near eye-level, but not to neck-flash, or a complete malar-stripe above which variable amounts of rufous are isolated in one or more patches (reduced, it is guessed, at successive moults). Juveniles lack a malar-stripe and have side of face entirely rufous, including out to the neck-flash. They are generally duller than adults, especially on the underparts, and more or less dark-mottled across the breast.

Bare-part colours. Iris deep brown; bill horn-black with mouth-line pale and extreme tip white (juvenile), blackish with mouth-line, extreme base of lower and matching cutting-edge of upper mandible coral-red (male), mouth-line and most or all of lower mandible, often also with apical quarter of upper mandible, or (quite commonly) entire bill, coral-red (female). No fully blue-faced bird has an all-red bill and many with rufous on the face have it bicoloured – hence the all-red condition is believed to be intermediate (and guessed to be exclusive to females), darkening first along the culmen (BMNH). Some careful mark-and-release work should clarify this issue.

Size (mm). (Live and skins: 13 males, 11 females; adults): wing 61–65 and 61–66; tail 23–27 and 23–29; bill 41.2–43.9 and 37.8–42.3; tarsus 7.8–9.0 (sexes combined) (BMNH, UMBRP, M. Wong).

Weight (g). Adults, 17.9–23.3 (n=15, most not sexed but females span this range).

DISTRIBUTION. Historical summary: all divisions except *Nar, Pes, Kel, Pra,* with additional W-coast island records from Tarutao, Langkawi and Penang.

GEOGRAPHICAL VARIATION. Nominate *meninting*, also of the Greater Sunda islands.

STATUS AND POPULATION. Resident, regular and more or less common.

HABITATS AND ECOLOGY. Mangroves and the under-stratum of evergreen and semi-evergreen Lowland forest, mature and regenerating, also peatswamp forest and tall secondary-growth, near small to moderate streams that no more than partly break the canopy. Moves out to the forest edge and shaded edge of impoundments, occasionally also along streams through tree plantations abutting forest, but only exceptionally visits rivers open enough to attract Common Kingfisher. There are no good records from above the steepland boundary.

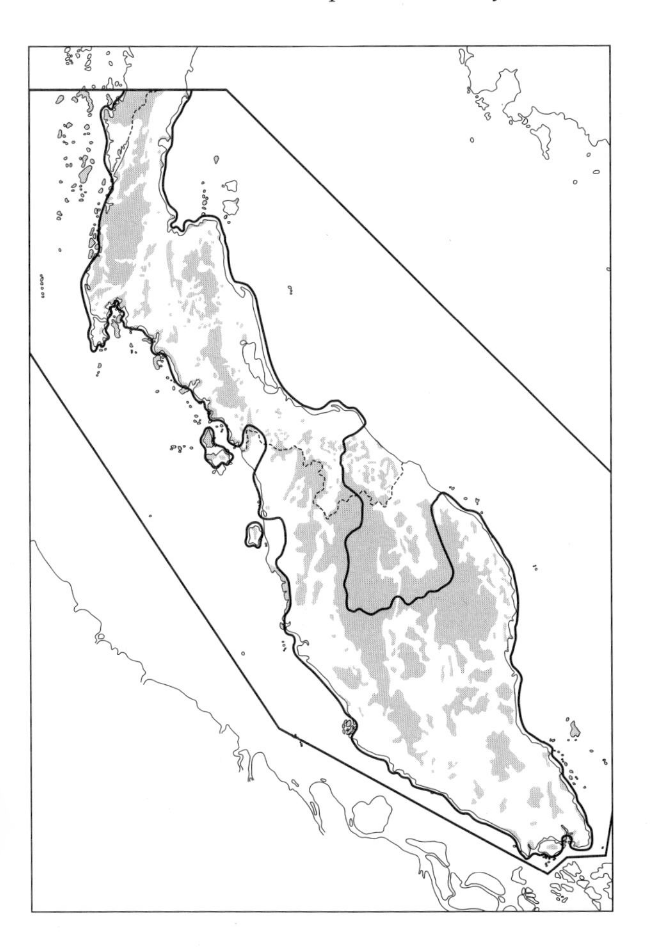

FORAGING AND FOOD. No reliable information.

SOCIAL ORGANIZATION. Solitary.

MOVEMENTS. None reported.

SURVIVAL. No information.

SOCIAL INTERACTIONS. No information.

VOICE. The flight-call is a thin, shrill squeak, like Common Kingfisher but including only a single note (Boonsong and Round 1991).

BREEDING

Nest. Burrows dug in the earth side of a soil-pit, a road-cutting and deep drainage channel; one 60 cm below the lip of a 3 m drop, in and at the edge of forest, and on a rubber estate. Tunnel-width 5 cm, length to nest-chamber 30–60 cm. One active burrow was close to several others abandoned incomplete, or perhaps used previously.

Eggs and brood. Eggs plain, very glossy white. Shape near-spherical. Two clutches of five.

Cycle. No information.

Seasonality. Eggs in Perak, Negeri Sembilan and Melaka during 9–28 May, and on 28 June. A February record from Perak is based on material in the Baker collection (BMNH); treated as unconfirmed. In Negeri Sembilan and Krabi, young juveniles on 22 August and 30 January (E.C.S. Baker, Chasen 1939, C. Robson, Ryves 1938, ZRCNUS).

MOULT. Primaries are replaced at up to three loci, apparently descendant from P1 and 5, and P10 independant but in several instances coincident with P5. Among 52 handlings covering all months except September, December and February, many non-moulters occurred throughout. The eight instances of active wing-moult were during April–August and in early October, including a ringed individual at stage P1,5,10 (start?) in mid April and completing (S4) in early August. On this schedule, another starting in late July would not have finished by October (BMNH, UMBRP, M. Wong).

CONSERVATION. Its stronghold is plains-level forest, and even though able to use regenerating and secondary-growth, response to the devastation of forest streams during logging has not been studied.

Blue-banded Kingfisher; Nok Ga Ten Noi Thaeb Ok Dam (Thai); Burung Pekaka Bukit (Malay)

Alcedo euryzona Temminck 1830, *Nouveau Recueil de Planches Coloriées d'Oiseaux* 86: text. TL Java. Plate 63

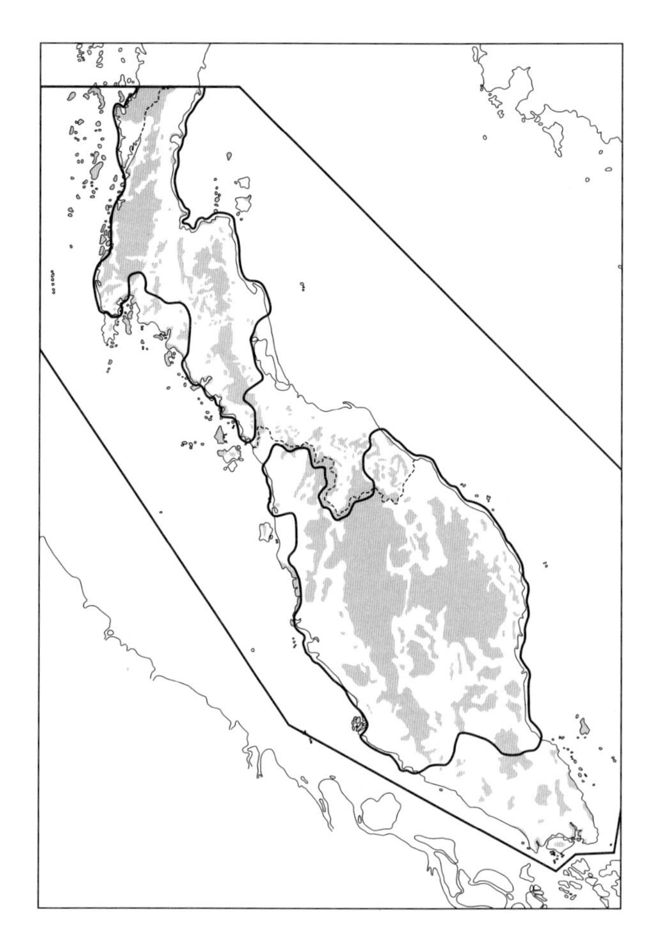

GROUP RELATIONS. Free-standing.

GLOBAL RANGE. The Greater Sunda islands, the Peninsula, and SW Thailand and Tenasserim to latitudes 14°58′ and about 16°N.

IDENTIFICATION/DESCRIPTION. Has the same direct flight, fast and low along streams, as other *Alcedo* species, but is noticeably larger (twice the mass of partly syntopic Blue-eared Kingfisher). Silvery azure of lower mantle to rump is conspicuous in flight. Upper tail-coverts are bluer than rump; rest of upperparts including head, wings and tail black, generally bluer on the malar area, with fine cross-barring on cap buff to bright blue (individually variable), and bright blue tips to median and greater wing-coverts. Both sexes show a rufous spot on the lores and orange-rufous tip to long white neck-flash. They differ in underpart colour: male white with a broad zone of bold, blackish- to brilliant blue fringing across the breast, and flanks to belly and lower tail-coverts washed rufous-buff, the flanks black-streaked; female chin and throat also white, otherwise rich rufous, without a breast-band. Juvenile not described.

Bare-part colours. (Adult) iris deep brown; mouth-line dusky red, rest of bill blackish (male), with lower mandible pale reddish (female); feet fleshy to red. Juvenile inadequately described but said to be black-footed (Robinson 1928).

Size (mm). (Live and skins: 11 males, 13 females; adult): wing 82–88 and 80–92; tail 35–40 and 37–40; bill 45.0–50.8 and 48.8–50.7; tarsus 11.9–13.7 and 12.5–12.9 (BMNH, UMBRP, ZDUM).

Weight (g). Adult males, 40.6–45.2 (n=5); adult females, 38.7–48.5 (n=9).

DISTRIBUTION. Possibly not south of the Endau drainage, Pahang/Johor border. Historical summary: all divisions except *Phu, Kra, Son, Pat, Yal, Pes, Tru, Pra, Mel, Joh, Sin*; with no island records.

GEOGRAPHICAL VARIATION. Subspecies *peninsulae* Laubmann 1941 (TL Melaka), also of Sumatra, Banka and Borneo; the female lacking a breast-band.

STATUS AND POPULATION. Resident and more or less regular but uncommon; pairs are widely spaced along rivers and probably territorial. Secretive behaviour makes censusing difficult, but at constant-effort mist-netting sites on the upper Gombak river, Selangor, never more than one pair, and possible off-spring, were taken in any one year (UMBRP).

HABITATS AND ECOLOGY. Medium-sized, permanently flowing streams, both under and breaking the canopy, from back-mangroves inland through tall, plains-level evergreen and semi-evergreen Lowland forest, and up slopes along the larger torrents, recorded to 820 m (Robinson 1909). The widely held view that this kingfisher is most abundant on hill-streams probably cannot be sustained, although it happens to be the only *Alcedo* in that habitat.

FORAGING AND FOOD. From bill-morphology, assumed to be mainly piscivorous, but no direct information from this area.

SOCIAL ORGANIZATION. Typically solitary, with no recent support for W.R. Davison's claim (Oates 1883) that it often associates in pairs.

MOVEMENTS. None reported.

SURVIVAL. The few retraps have been within-season or, at most, between consecutive years.

SOCIAL INTERACTIONS. No information.

VOICE. Flight-call like that of Common Kingfisher but harsher (Robinson 1928); better descriptions are needed.

BREEDING. The only records are still the two clutches of (four and five) eggs said to have been taken in early February from the banks of streams at 450–600 m in the Larut Range, Perak (E.C.S. Baker); treatable as only tentatively identified.

MOULT. Only one of 21 adults covering February–July, September and December showed any moult, a female growing T1,3–5 on 19 May (BMNH, UMBRP). Pattern and timing of wing-moult unknown.

CONSERVATION. Core habitat has not been defined. Provisionally, occurrence on hill-slopes suggests less threat from forest-loss than to Blue-eared Kingfisher, but where a few of the latter's smaller streams may escape the impact of a logging event, no larger streams escape. Response to disturbance needs study.

Family MEROPIDAE

Bee-eaters: four species

Red-bearded Bee-eater; Nok Jab Khaa Khrao Daeng (Thai); Burung Berek-berek Janggut Merah (Malay)

Nyctyornis amictus (Temminck) 1824, *Nouveau Recueil de Planches Coloriées d'Oiseaux* 52: plate 310. TL Benkulen, SW Sumatra.

Plate 64

GROUP RELATIONS. Free-standing.

GLOBAL RANGE. Borneo, Banka, Sumatra, the Peninsula and to about 17°N in Tenasserim and 14°58′N in SW Thailand.

IDENTIFICATION/DESCRIPTION. Bigger, proportionately broader-winged (P10 well developed), with heavier, more strongly decurved bill than local *Merops* bee-eaters, and lacks their black eye-mask. Adult forehead to forecrown shining lilac-pink, shading to mauve then green (male), vermilion-red with narrow upper band of mauve before green (female); lores to chin, throat and centre breast bright red, elongated tips of chin- to breast-feathers forming the often puffed-out 'beard'. Point of chin and narrow rim round bill sky-blue; eyelid-rim feathering the same in males, turquoise in females. Otherwise, grass-green, paler on the lower breast and belly, which are obscurely streaked dark green; lower wing-coverts cinnamon and underside of flight-feathers black; underside of the tail brassy yellow with broad black tip, and the outer web of its outermost feather all black. Apart from slight blue round the bill, young juveniles are mostly plain green, unstreaked ventrally, belly to lower tail-coverts buff-white and underside of tail dull grey-yellow, merging into rather than sharply demarcated from black tip. Adult colours are acquired during a single moult of 1.5-plus months.

Bare-part colours. Iris brownish (young juvenile), bright orange-yellow (adult); bill black, base of lower mandible lead-grey; feet pale grey-green.

Size (mm). (Skins: 14 males, 8 females; adult): wing 127–133 and 124–129; tail 112–125 and 112–118; bill 53.2–60.5 and 50.6–56.2 (juveniles below 50.0); tarsus 14.2–16.1 and 14.0–16.1 (BMNH, UMZC).

Weight. No data.

DISTRIBUTION. Historical summary: all divisions except *Phu, Pat, Pra, Sin*; also on Penang island.

GEOGRAPHICAL VARIATION. None recognized.

STATUS AND POPULATION. Resident, regular and more or less common; estimated population density in mature, plains-level Lowland evergreen forest two birds per 20 ha.

HABITATS AND ECOLOGY. The open, upper mid-stratum and interior canopy of semi-evergreen and evergreen Lowland forest, mature and well-regenerated after disturbance, at all elevations; in Lower Montane forest to about 1300 m. Exceptionally, also in old, unkempt rubber plantations and gardens, with several records of loners that settled for periods of weeks to several months in well-wooded suburbs (BR 1974–75, Glenister 1951, MBR 1986–87).

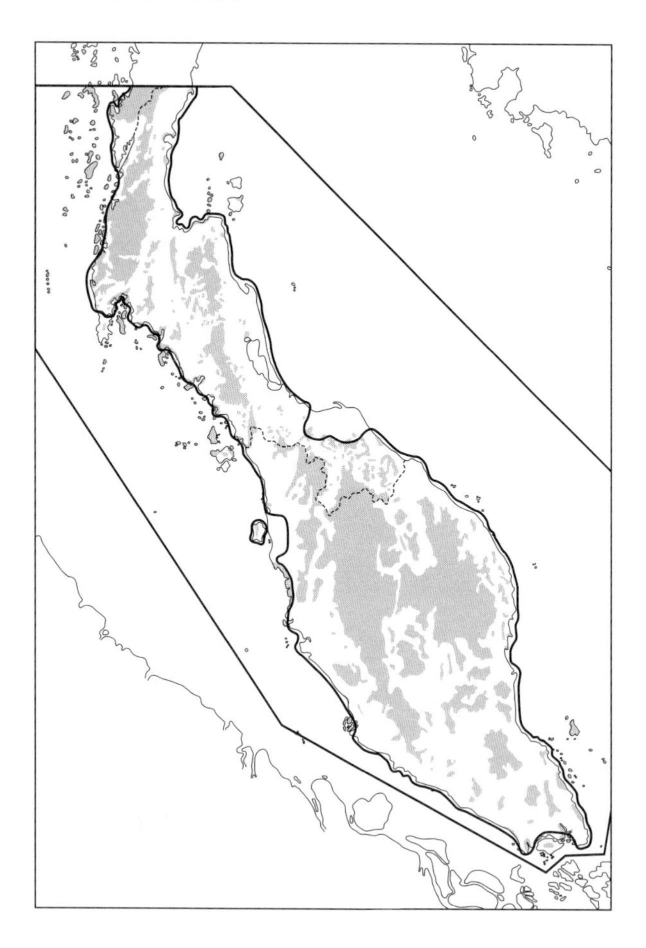

FORAGING AND FOOD. Said to clamber about after food, and items such as roaches in stomach contents seem likely to have been taken from surfaces. However, a typical bee-eater dash through the open canopy or free airspace between crowns after flying prey spotted from a lookout-perch in canopy foliage is the only behaviour well described. Along quiet roads through forest, sometimes hunts from service-wires as does related Blue-bearded Bee-eater *N. athertoni* north of the Peninsula. Has been known to feed low in gardens, with exceptional use of verandah rails as a lookout, and a record of a foraging bird stunned by flying into a ground-floor window (BR 1978–79, Glenister 1951). Photographs and oral pellet analyses (BR 1978–79, C. Kurian) support field identification of cicadas and large xylocopid (carpenter) bees as common food. Robinson (1928) lists bees, wasps, termites, butterflies, and large roaches. At least bees are thoroughly branch-swiped before being swallowed, but there are no reports of the de-venoming of hymenoptrans by rubbing recorded in *Merops* species.

SOCIAL ORGANIZATION. Mostly solitary; occasionally a loosely associating pair.

MOVEMENTS. None reported. Dispersants settled into unusual non-forest sites have included both adults and juveniles.

SURVIVAL. No information.

SOCIAL INTERACTIONS. No information.

VOICE. Deep, gruff, rasping chuckles, tending to fall in both pitch and volume: *kar kar kah kah*, with longer variants *kar ka-ka-ka-ka-ka* and *kah-kah-kah ku-ku-ku*, etc., given with beard puffed and crown-feathers raised. While calling, has been noticed making a few sideways steps then hopping round to face the reverse direction (Glenister 1951). Often answered by a neighbour (mate?), and a perched bird called once as raptors glided past. Courting birds give harsh croaks, *kork kark kwala-kark*, etc. Other close-range calls are a repeated *quark* and trisyllabic *ka-ka-tau* (G.C. Madoc).

BREEDING

Nest. In forest, burrows (one 1.2 m deep) excavated in the low bank of small paths and streams, and one into a soil termitarium.

Eggs and brood. Eggs plain, translucent white. A clutch of two eggs possibly incomplete, but identifications of three and five are not regarded as confirmed. No other information.

Cycle. Both pair-members excavate and both feed nestlings. In Pasoh research forest, a pair carried food from perch to perch between the canopy and ground, then waited near the burrow for a chick to put its head out and beg.

Seasonality. Burrow-excavation in early January and February, and egg- and chick-dates extrapolate to laying during February–August (clutches confirmed in both these months). Nestlings in late March, and two flying young attended by an adult on 11 June (Allen 1961, BR 1976–77, Kelsall 1891, Madoc 1956a, NRCS, Robinson 1928, P.D. Round).

MOULT. The few moulters handled suggest replacement of primaries is regular-descendant, with up to three mid-tract feathers in overlapping growth. Among 33 adults from the length of the Peninsula, and covering all months except June, July and September, ten showed active wing-moult during early April (P1–2)–November (P9), with completions from August. Post-juvenile acquisition of head- and beard-colours noted in July, September and November, with tail-moult (T1 and T5 in different individuals) in early September (BMNH, UMZC).

CONSERVATION. Relatively common in most of the hill-forest part of its range, hence perhaps not at great risk from habitat-loss.

Blue-throated Bee-eater; Nok Jab Khaa Khaw See Faa (Thai); **Burung Berek-berek Pirus** (Malay)

Merops viridis Linnaeus 1758, *Systema Naturae* 10(1): 117. TL Java.
Plate 64

GROUP RELATIONS. Free-standing.

GLOBAL RANGE. China south of a line Fujian–S Henan–Yunnan, including Hainan; continental SE Asia south and east of a line mid Laos–SW Thailand to the Greater Sunda islands and the Philippines. Probably most N-hemisphere populations migrate, wintering within the western breeding range (only?), between at least central Vietnam and Sumatra.

IDENTIFICATION/DESCRIPTION. Bright but variably intense blue of the adult chin to upper throat merges into emerald-green of the breast, with no interposed gorget. Clear azure-blue back to upper tail-coverts, conspicuous in flight against darker mantle, wings and tail, is also a feature of Bay-headed Bee-eater *M. leschenaulti*, but the latter is smaller and has different calls. Sexes similar; males average brighter and slightly larger, but variation in the length of unworn tail-streamers is largely individual (more in males: Stader 1996). Juveniles lack streamers, are duller, with chin buff-white, throat green rather than blue and, as in same-stage Bay-headed Bee-eater, cap to mantle the same green as the wings (versus dark chestnut in adults). Some breeding-season adults continue to show a scatter of green cap-to-mantle feathers, and many winterers aged adult by their worn tail-streamers (and guessed to be northern migrants) appear all-green. In both groups, such feathers are only green-tipped, not retained from juvenile plumage.

High overhead, difficult to separate from Blue-tailed Bee-eater *M. superciliosus*. In direct flight, Blue-throated flaps in longer bouts, with shorter interposed glides, and contact-calls are slightly richer and deeper, but differences are subtle.

Bare-part colours. (Adult) iris red; bill black; feet slaty grey.

Size (mm). (Live and skins: 11 males, 4 females; adult): wing 110–115 and 109–110; tail including unabraded streamers 132–167 and 121 (1 only); bill 39.4–43.2 and 36.7–40.9; tarsus 11.3–12.1 (sexes combined) (BMNH, UMZC).

Weight (g). Breeding-season adults, sexes not separated but probably including some laying females, 28.4–45.0 (mean 34.8, n=159).

DISTRIBUTION. Absent from the far northwest, which lies outside the global range-limit. Historical summary: all divisions except *Pak, Ran, Pha,* with additional island records from Libong and, at breeding dates, Langkawi, Penang and Pangkor off the W coast; Phangan and Samui off the E coast; and Ubin, Ketam, Seletar, St John's and Retan Laut, Singapore.

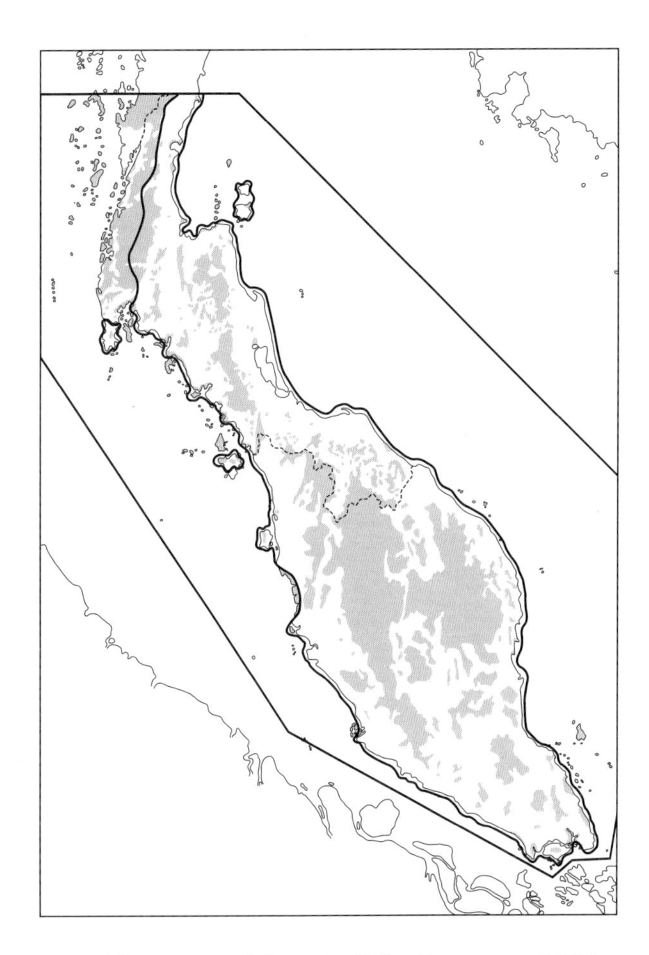

GEOGRAPHICAL VARIATION. All populations are nominate *viridis*, of the global range except the Philippines. There is evidence that brightness of breeding adults varies locally, between colonies (L.D. Stader).

STATUS AND POPULATION. A proportion of breeders may be resident, but the recovery in southern Sumatra of a bird ringed at a Selangor nesting-colony confirms an assumption from field observations (BMP5) that at least some migrate out of the Peninsula. Otherwise, a non-breeding visitor and probable passage migrant; regular and more or less common.

Towards the end of the breeding-season, small groups of adults and juveniles gather to forage from trees, service-wires, etc., in plantations, open woodland and wooded parks and gardens. First arrival in these habitats varies by several weeks but, in Selangor, is never before late June, and all birds have gone by early September. It is now recognized that parties of Blue-throats also appear this early in forest (eight, including several apparent juveniles, in the upper canopy at Pasoh, Negeri Sembilan, on 23 June; others in the Tembeling drainage, Taman Negara, in early July: BR 1970–71, 1978–79). Up to two weeks ahead of earliest obvious through-passage, these too could be of local origin. Whether they then leave on the schedule of garden birds, or stay to join later-arriving forest winterers has not been discovered.

HABITATS AND ECOLOGY. Breeders occupy a variety of open habitats, including subcoastal and, locally, beach dunes (nesting to within a few metres of the high-tide line), river sand-banks, abandoned dredge-mine land, grazing-grounds, large lawns and other open grassland. Post-breeders disperse to lightly wooded habitats and, as stated, perhaps true forest. Overwinterers occupy tall mangroves and inland Lowland forest, including peatswamp forest, plus mature tree plantations and tall secondary-growth, at plains level and on the submontane slope, recorded to 670 m (BR 1969, Medway 1972). All forage in the top canopy, down to mid-stratum level where tracks, streams or logging have opened out free space within the stand. On Singapore island, but nowhere else, small numbers of uncertain status occur at mid winter in atypically open habitats (SINGAV-1, -4).

Hunting in woodland limits heat-stress, combated in full sunlight by lowering the legs during flight to increase skin-surface exposure (Bryant 1983). Drinks and bathes by splashing onto an open water-surface.

FORAGING AND FOOD. The tracking of colour-tagged breeders in Johor showed that they travelled out to forage over a radius of 3–5 km from the colony (Stader 1996). Most food is taken in swift aerial sorties from lookout-perches high on exposed branches, service-wires, aerials, etc., above all kinds of open and wooded habitats, but with some hawking of swarming termites, ants, etc., during longer forays, often at a considerable height. Non-breeders are likely to eat such prey on the wing, but dangerous hymenopterans are branch-swiped and de-venomed by rubbing on a perch before being swallowed (Fry 1984). By weight, identifiable prey in oral pellets from mainland Penang included 56 percent dragonflies, 35 percent hymenopterans (mainly honey bees) and eight percent beetles, with some flies, and small bones thought to have been from lizards (Avery and Penny 1978). Others pellets from a Penang island breeding-colony contained mostly hymenopteran parts (meliponine sweat bee to carpenter bee size), with lesser numbers of dragonflies, bugs and beetles (some scarabs and chafers up to 42 mm long) (Fry 1984). Pellets of this species are a maximum 22 mm long.

SOCIAL ORGANIZATION. Nesting assemblages vary from lone pairs to extensive colonies of more than 1000 birds, but most are in the range 5–20 pairs. Blue-throats also forage, and migrate, in small parties, usually of not above 15 birds although groups on the move sometimes merge into larger flocks (BBCB-8). Non-breeders roost socially including, in late February, about 1000 presumed winterers counted into an isolated tree on the Pekan town sportsfield, Pahang (MBR 1986–87).

Colour-tagging at well-studied colonies in Selangor and Johor has shown that not all adults occurring during the breeding-season attempt to nest on site, or even visit regularly. These are likely to have included birds that failed in the previous season, and some failed individuals do not reappear at all. This contributes to a variable but relatively low rate of return overall, and after bad years only a few individuals are able to re-pair with the partner of a previous season.

Cooperative breeding does not seem to be well developed in this species, and pairs at only about one nest in 20, in some years, are assisted by a helper attending the brood (Stader 1996). However, DNA fingerprinting has shown that near-relatives, especially of paired males, tend to be neighbours; also that a minority of chicks is either the offspring of extra-pair (cuckold) matings, generally by the male with an outside female, or is entirely the offspring of relatives (neighbouring pairs?), and must have been dumped as eggs (Stader 1994).

MOVEMENTS. Earliest parties crossing north over Singapore are dated 23 and 25 January, with a first spring landfall reported at Cape Rachado, north end of the Melaka Straits narrows, on 11 February. Passage reaches peak intensity during March–early April then declines through to May, with a latest accepted record on 7 May. These dates cover both arrival of adults at W-coast nesting-colonies (which colour-tagging shows continues into May: Stader 1989a) and the equally protracted departure of migrants north out of Malaysia (passage in progress over central Thailand by late February, but some attendance at southern woodland and forest wintering-sites up to late April/early May: BBCB-8, BR 1965, MBR 1982–83).

Southward passage over both upland forests and the coastal plains runs from the second week of July to late October (extreme dates 7 July, 27 October). This inland movement intensifies through September–October (BBCB-7, BCSTB-11) apparently as northern migrants arrive to overwinter locally, whereas no exiting for Indonesia across SW and S coasts has been recorded later than early September; most during August. Such early departure is believed to be of local breeders, among which the last garden-forager date is 12 September and the latest within-season retrap of a summer bird 1 September (BMP5). The one overseas recovery is of an adult ringed at Sungai Buloh breeding-colony on 9 April, killed in December/early January while wintering in Lampung province, latitude 5°30′S, southern Sumatra (P.T. Green). Other retraps of foragers up to 24 km away from the colony in July and August (McClure 1974) appear likely to have been of birds dispersing before migration.

Small parties of mid August migrants timed between points along a measured N–S stretch of beach near Cape Rachado averaged 40.3 kph in still air. On the same day, flight-bearings of 16 parties watched out to sea off the Cape averaged 180°. Assuming no serious wind-drift, they should have crossed to Sumatra in 134 minutes. On this basis, and allowing about nine hours of daytime flying, Selangor breeders should complete their migration to southern Sumatra in only about 2.5 days, including overnight roost-stops.

SURVIVAL. Between good and bad periods at Sungai Buloh nesting-colony, rates of return of marked adults in the following season have varied from 67 down to only 15 percent. No individual retrap-intervals have been longer than 14 months, but colour-tagging has shown that some missing birds merely stay away rather than die (Stader 1989a, 1996).

SOCIAL INTERACTIONS. Courting birds flicker the tail and puff out throat-feathers. Before copulation the female squats horizontally on the perch, with bill inclined up. Beside her, the male stretches and sleeks himself vertically, and may bow a few times before mounting. Both sexes initiate matings, females mostly early in the season, males more commonly later, when the chance of copulations resulting in fertilization increases. Those initiated by the male mostly involve him carrying an insect, eaten by the female, and occasionally she is fed several in succession (Stader 1989b, 1996).

VOICE. Foragers and migrants communicate constantly. The commonest contact-calls are a liquid *ter-rip-terrip-terrip* or faster *terrip-rrip-rrip*, and a deeper *trrurrip*, all with a richer, 'fruitier' quality than similar calls of Blue-tailed Bee-eater.

BREEDING

Nest. Chooses light, diggable soils with a high sand content, allowing rapid drainage to a considerable depth. Most burrows are excavated into level ground, less often a low, usually shallow slope. Only a few colonies have been found on a sheer face: five pairs under the lip of a deep sandpit, five in a riverside sand-cliff, and about 15 pairs in the upper third of a sheer, 4–5 m gravel-pit face, all sites with water at the cliff-foot. Burrows are 7 cm wide × 1–3 m deep, in flat ground angled uniformly down, or fairly sharply then more shallowly, and some then rise slightly to end 45–60 cm underground. The nest-chamber is up to 45 cm long, low but widening out to 20 cm or more, unlined except for accumulating pellet-remains and droppings.

Eggs and brood. Eggs are plain, slightly glossy, translucent white. Shape short elliptical. Size (mm): 23.3 × 20.5 and 21.5 × 19.5 (means, n–11 and 3); one unusually large egg 25.4 × 21.0. Full clutch 3–6, mean 3.7 (n=59), incubated apparently from close to the start of laying, so that hatching is staggered, over 3–9 days in a sample of five Selangor broods. The nestling period is about 30 days, and the largest recorded brood of flying young is four, but commonly only 1–2 chicks survive to fledging. Full-grown, they undergo a 15–16 percent loss of mass (from around adult weight) prior to fledging.

Asynchronous hatching in larger broods must help smooth out the peak of demand on adult food-getting. If food declines, it also promotes brood-reduction through sibling aggression, where small, featherless chicks (below age 15 days) are wounded by the sharp, hooked bill-tip of larger siblings. Younger chicks are more likely to die if significantly wounded, wounding is more frequent if the next-older chick is itself in poor condition, and older chicks are more aggressive when hungry; hence the connection between siblicide and food-provisioning is direct. Significantly, if dumped eggs are accepted only after the incumbent female has herself started laying, chicks standing the lowest chance of fledging will be those with the highest chance of having an extra-pair parent. At Selangor and Johor colonies, productivity was greatest from clutches laid at mid season, in May.

Cycle. Burrows are excavated only by established pairs, and more than one burrow may be dug before laying begins. Pair-members share work, one on watch while the other digs, and both incubate and tend nestlings and flying young. Broods are provisioned at a mean rate of twice per hour (varying with brood-size), by male and female alternating, or operating shifts. One or both (and sometimes relatives) also roost in the nest-burrow, but Molesworth (1952) describes a pair directing its exceptional brood of four underground then leaving to roost elsewhere.

Seasonality. An unusually heavy downpour at a level-land site can cause the abandonment and re-starting of an entire colony's nesting effort, adding to variation of timing year to year. From Narathiwat south to Singapore, first exploratory visits to colony-sites occur any time during late February–early April (not before early April on seasonal Langkawi island), with population build-up through March–April, and some new arrival also in May. First burrows are started in late March, and eggs laid during mid April–mid July, with earliest nestlings in April, young on the wing as of late May and, in Selangor, a few burrows still active as late as early August (BMP5, Bryant and Hails 1983, Bryant and Tatner 1990, Edgar 1933, P.T. Green, Molesworth 1950, 1952, Spittle 1949, L.D. Stader, Stader 1989a, 1996).

MOULT. Replacement of adult primaries appears to be regular-descendant, with 2–4 adjacent middle-tract feathers in overlapping growth. At Selangor breeding colonies, a very few adults (breeding status unknown) moult one or two inner primaries in June (earliest record P1–2 on 1 June), but many must depart unmoulted (five July–August birds showed none). In October–November, most presumed winterers (including green-capped adults) are at mid-stage wing-moult (out to between P3 and P5), and have reached P9 or 10 by February. These may then also be growing new tail-streamers (T1), although some forest birds remain streamerless as late as early April (BMP5). Different populations are likely to have different schedules, and age-related differences also need research. Three mid-July juveniles were moulting P8–9 or 9, and may have renewed the wing-tip precociously (before migration?).

CONSERVATION. Breeding-sites in the Peninsula are degraded both by natural processes and interference. This bee-eater adjusts by being opportunistic in site-choice, and able to nest in groups of greatly varying size, occasionally down to lone pairs. Break-up of a large colony through loss of its customary site may disrupt only in the short term, but fewer and fewer big sites remain secure in themselves, or in terms of good local foraging habitat (see Blue-tailed Bee-eater).

Blue-tailed Bee-eater; Nok Jab Khaa Hua Khieo (Thai); Burung Berek-berek Sawah (Malay)

Merops superciliosus Linnaeus 1766, *Systema Naturae* 12(1): 183. TL Madagascar.
Plate 64

GROUP RELATIONS. Fry (1984) has lumped south and east Asian–Australasian Blue-tailed with green-tailed Madagascan Bee-eater *M. superciliosus* of Madagascar to E Africa. In the NW Indian subcontinent, Blue-tails meet the range of Blue-cheeked Bee-eater *M. persicus*, but with no demonstrated breeding overlap, and these similar birds are treatable as a superspecies.

GLOBAL RANGE. Breeds through southern and eastern Africa, the Comoros and Madagascar; the Indian subcontinent from N Pakistan, and Sri Lanka; China south and west of a line S Sichuan–Guangdong, including Hainan; continental SE Asia to the Peninsula and the Philippines; Sulawesi; and New Guinea to New Britain. Many populations migrate, those in the northern part of the Asian range south to winter within and beyond southern continental breeding limits, through the Bay of Bengal islands and Greater and Lesser Sundas possibly as far as Timor.

IDENTIFICATION/DESCRIPTION. Cap non-contrasting. Slightly larger overall than Blue-throated and obviously larger than Bay-headed Bee-eater *M. leschenaulti*, both of whose juveniles also have mostly green cap and mantle. Rump and upper tail-coverts are darker blue, concolorous with flight-feathers, scapulars and tail; not in striking contrast to the rest of the dorsum. In flight, sails more than smaller species, showing off copper-tawny under-wing with grey-black trailing-edge.

The general tone of green parts is copper-shot olive, with yellow of chin and upper throat cut off by a copper-brown gorget much broader than in Bay-headed Bee-eater. At close range, adults show a fine light blue fringe above the bill and along black mask to above eye, and broader band of the same along lower border of the mask; more or less absent in the generally duller, streamerless juvenile.

Bare-part colours. (Adult) iris red; bill black; feet slaty grey.

Size (mm). (Live and skins: 6 males, 6 females; adult): wing 128–136 and 127–135 (juveniles down to 121); tail including unabraded streamers 128–153 and 129–142; bill 41.7–48.2 and 40.5–47.5; tarsus 11.8–13.0 (sexes combined) (BMNH, UMBRP).

Weight (g). Adults, most not sexed, 32–45 (mean 38.5, n=32) (Fry 1984, UMBRP).

DISTRIBUTION. Historical summary: all divisions, with additional island records from Libong, Tarutao, Langkawi, Penang, Jarak (migrants, provisionally of

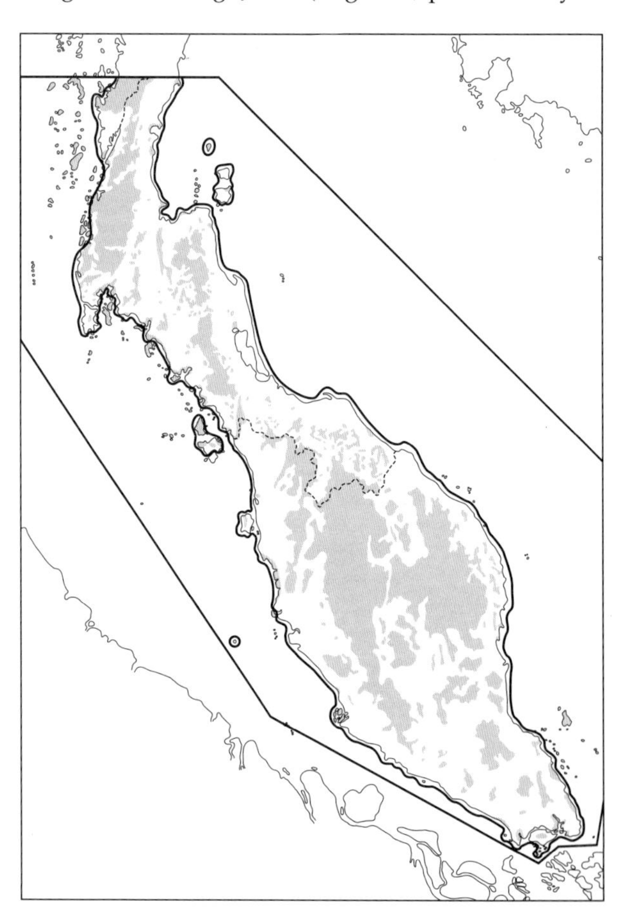

this species), the Kelang estuary group (Tengah), Besar (*Mel*) and Pisang off the W coast; Tao, Phangan and Samui off the E coast; and Tekong, Ubin, Lazarus, St John's, Senang and Sudong, Singapore.

GEOGRAPHICAL VARIATION. Variation through Asia–Australasia is slight, and Fry (1984) recognizes only subspecies *philippinus* Linnaeus 1766 (TL Philippines) throughout.

STATUS AND POPULATION. Passage migrant, non-breeding visitor and sparse breeder; regular and common. The one confirmed nesting-colony is at Padang Kamunting, west side of Penang island, far to the south of main continental breeding-limits. Among much larger numbers of the two other *Merops* species, this has held a small and fluctuating population of generally below 50 pairs of Blue-tails for many decades (Cairns 1957). When last checked, in early April 1990, not above 25 birds brought in food to active burrows, and with the building of a school on an important block of former nesting-habitat, disturbance there has recently increased.

Off-season dispersal away from Padang Kamunting has not been studied but could account for odd summer (June–early August) records in nearby Kedah, Pattani and Songkhla (BMNH, R. Gregory-Smith, Holmes and Wells 1975). A small group in N Kedah paddyland on 8 August still had full-length tail-streamers, suggesting they had not dug or used burrows that year. May records from Samui and Phangan islands (Surat Thani) (Robinson 1914b) are now known to be within the span of northward migration (ENGGANG-2), but include a juvenile of the year from Samui that must have originated in the Peninsula. This leaves open the possibility of one or more additional breeding-sites, even though Boonsong and Round (1991) map Blue-tailed Bee-eater as strictly on passage in southern Thailand.

Most overwintering begins south of the Malaysian border but small numbers occur at mid winter on Langkawi island and, on the E-coast plain, north at least as far as Thalae Songkhla.

HABITATS AND ECOLOGY. Padang Kamunting breeding-station is a mosaic of bare sand, sparse grass-tufts, scattered scrub and a few poor rubber trees on the flat ground of a former beach, extending discontinuously more than 1 km between subcoastal coconuts and paddyland. Winterers occupy the same range of non-forest habitats, from beach scrub to suburban gardens, indeed many of the same foraging perches, as summering Blue-throated Bee-eaters, but with greater use of paddyland, dredge-mine swamps and other such completely open wetlands, where they heavily depend on man-made scanning perches: service- and pole guy-wires, etc. Winter roosting is strongly social, locally with other bee-eaters (Batchelor 1958), in isolated clumps of tall trees inland and frequently in mangroves. Undisturbed sites become traditional, as on Tengah island, Kelang estuary, where records extend over 20 years. Some draw on a large catchment. The favoured part of Tengah is 10 km from nearest mainland foraging-grounds, but 5000–10 000 birds have been recorded there in late November, well after the end of autumn passage (MBR 1984–85). Four-figure gatherings have also been recorded in Singapore mangroves, at Seletar and Serangoon, but not in the same years and these neighbouring roosts are likely to have succeeded one another (BR 1965, SINGAV-1). Such roosts may attract passage migrants but, within sight of Tengah island, coasting parties have also been seen to halt in flooded scrub directly on their flight-paths.

A mid-season retrap demonstrates year-to-year fidelity to a wintering-site, on a dredge-mine wetland near Kuala Lumpur (UMBRP).

FORAGING AND FOOD. Largely as Blue-throated Bee-eater. In early April, breeders bringing food into the Penang island colony all carried dragonflies, probably from nearby flooded paddyland. By weight, prey identified in a sample of pellets from dry, harvested paddyland on the nearby mainland comprised 69 percent dragonfly and 23 percent hymenopteran parts (honey bees, *Vespa* wasps and sphecid potter-wasps), with traces of beetles, termites, damselflies, bugs, orthopterans and dipterans (Avery and Penny 1978). Pellets from under a lookout perch at an open, stream-side site in Kuala Lumpur included, by item, 89 percent hymenopterans (mainly honey bees, including some large *Apis dorsata*, with various wasps, ants, ichneumons, etc.), and only four percent dragonflies, with occasional dipterans, orthopterans, bugs, beetles and butterflies. Uniquely, one contained the vertebrae of a small, surface-feeding mosquito fish *Gambusia affinis* (Fry 1984). Some from the Seletar winter roost, Singapore, contained mostly hymenopterans (honey bees, wasps, and two-plus species of ants), with traces of scarab and dung beetles (BMP5). Fry describes the taking of large, dangerous wasps in flight from below and their transport back to a processing perch at the tip of the up-tilted bill, avoiding a collision should the prey escape. Regularly attends swarms of termites and ants, feeding without returning to perches, and passage migrants stop to forage in late evening, some carrying prey (including crepuscular dragonflies) as they head directly off to roost.

SOCIAL ORGANIZATION. Gregarious throughout.

MOVEMENTS. Migrating bee-eaters normally roost overnight, but one struck the Kuala Selangor lighthouse during autumn passage, presumably at night, and occasionally I have heard flocks pass high over the Kuala Lumpur area well after dark.

Most migration data are from the W-coast plain of Malaysia and islands of Singapore. At mid latitudes (S Perak to Melaka), earliest autumn arrival varies year to year by about four weeks, between 11 August and the first week of September, but with no records in Singapore before 10 September (BIRDLINE 13, BR 1967), suggesting early W-coast passage diverts away, presumably to Indonesia via the Melaka Straits. Overall, passage runs to the last week of October, peaking in mid October at 150–200 birds per hour (BR 1964), countable anywhere across the coastal plain north of Cape Rachado (Negeri Sembilan). From the Cape, over 1000 per hour have been counted out to sea towards Sumatra. At all times, numbers reaching Singapore are much smaller.

In spring, winterers begin moving off regular sites by early March but initial northward passage is leisurely, parties stopping to forage morning and evening at many of these same sites almost daily. Passage reaches peak level in late March and early April, with none passing Singapore after mid April, but parties arriving off the sea at Cape Rachado and light movement recorded over Selangor well into May; latest date 25 May, at Kuala Selangor (A. Jeyarajasingam).

Spring movement along the Malaysian NE coast, reported as far as the Thai border during the first two weeks of April, is in nothing like the numbers over the W-coast plain, and there are few records at either season of this species crossing the Main Range inland (*contra* Blue-throated Bee-eater).

SURVIVAL. No additional information.

SOCIAL INTERACTIONS. No information.

VOICE. Contact-calls among winter foragers include a loud *rillip, rillip, rillip*, a shorter *trrrit trrrit trrrit*, rapid *tri-tri-trip* and intermittent, emphatic *chip*, repeated once or twice. Among groups of perched birds, a sharper *pit* is common. Vocalizations of breeders have not been separately described.

BREEDING

Nest. At Padang Kamunting in April 1990, all burrows confirmed to belong to this species were in flat ground, in patches of sprawling herbs, grass-tufts and dried cattle dung; not on bare sand. Cairns (1957) records burrow-lengths there of 2.1–3.7 m, but this seems unlikely to be typical.

Eggs and brood. No information.

Cycle. No information.

Seasonality. Burrow-excavation is said to begin in late February or early March, with eggs during March–late May (Cairns 1957) and, from behaviour of adults, circumstantial evidence of chicks at my visit on 4 April.

MOULT. Replacement of primaries is likely to be regular-descendant, but little seasonal sense has been made of the few wing-moult records obtained so far. An adult female dated mid June, from its worn plumage probably a local post-breeder, had suspended after renewing P1–2 (cf. Blue-throated Bee-eater). Four October birds had suspended between P6 and P8, and a fifth was growing P9; three in January were growing P10; and in February and March had all completed. Juveniles in active wing-moult recorded in October, December and late April, anomalously, all at between stage P4 and P6 (BMNH, UMBRP). P4 in a streamered, only slightly worn Pattani female on 31 April seems equally unlikely, unless failed breeders start early.

CONSERVATION. Decisive action, with the full involvement of the local community, is needed to protect the Padang Kamunting breeding-site from further encroachment and interference. The value of one of the Peninsula's largest, mixed-species bee-eater colonies as a nature-tourism attraction on Penang appears not to have been appreciated. Elsewhere, intensification of chemical pesticide-usage in paddylands is likely to reduce the quality of an important wintering habitat (measurable in terms of changes in dragonfly abundance).

Bay-headed Bee-eater; Nok Jab Khaa Hua See Som (Thai); Burung Berek-berek Senja (Malay)

Merops leschenaulti Vieillot 1817, *Nouveau Dictionnaire d'Histoire Naturelle* 14: 17. TL Sri Lanka.
Plate 64

GROUP RELATIONS. Free-standing.

GLOBAL RANGE. Foothills of the Himalayas and adjacent lowlands east from Dehra Dun and the NE Indian subcontinent south to Orissa, the W Ghats, Sri Lanka, and Andamans; S and W Yunnan; and SE Asia to Sumatra, Java and Bali.

IDENTIFICATION/DESCRIPTION. A small bee-eater; adults with distinctive copper-bay cap to mantle, and cream-yellow chin and throat bordered below by a chevron-shaped gorget, dark chestnut with posterior fringe of black, separated from green breast by a further narrow band of yellow. Rest of body, wings and tail grass-green to, on inner secondaries and belly to lower tail-coverts, blue-green, with back to upper tail-coverts light azure-blue, conspicuous in flight (cf. Blue-throated Bee-eater). Sexes alike, and in all age-groups tail shallowly forked, without streamers. Juvenile duller, with paler throat, gorget rudimentary and, except for nape, cap to mantle green, concolorous with wings.

Bare-part colours. Iris red-brown (juvenile), red (adult); bill black; feet dark grey.

Size (mm). (Skins: 5 males, 9 females; adult): wing 106–108 and 103–108; tail 74–81 and 78–81; bill 34.7–40.1 and 35.7–40.5; tarsus 9.8–12.0 (sexes combined) (BMNH).

Weight (g). Breeding-season adults, none sexed, 23.0–33.1 (mean 27.2, n=65) (Fry 1984).

DISTRIBUTION. Breeds to mid Perak and Terengganu; absent from the south of the Peninsula. Historical summary: all divisions except *Chu, Pht, Son, Neg, Mel, Joh, Sin,* with probable to proven breeding populations on additional W-coast islands: Yao Yai (*Pha*), Libong, Tarutao, Langkawi and Penang.

GEOGRAPHICAL VARIATION. Nominate *leschenaulti*, of the continental range and Sri Lanka, with a fully black eye-mask.

STATUS AND POPULATION. Resident, with no evidence of more than non-breeding dispersal; regular and uncommon to, locally, common. Southernmost reports of breeding are from ex-mining land at Chemor, latitude 4°43′N on the W-coast plain (BMP5) and, on the E coast, the south end of Setiu lagoon, N Terengganu.

HABITATS AND ECOLOGY. Nests amid open scrub on coastal dunes and other sandy ground inland, including in relatively small swidden- and other clearings in woodland; in steep banks of rivers and streams, road-cuts, etc., and on abandoned tin-tailings and dredge-mine land. Has lost some Malaysian breeding habitat with the widespread conversion of redundant buffalo grazing-grounds to plantation agriculture. Post-breeders behave like Blue-throated Bee-eaters, dispersing away from colony-sites to gather in parties in and at the edge of mature tree plantations, wooded parks, gardens and golf-courses, tall secondary-growth and the canopy of original forest, especially where logging or other disturbance has opened out the stand; at plains level and on hills to 750 m.

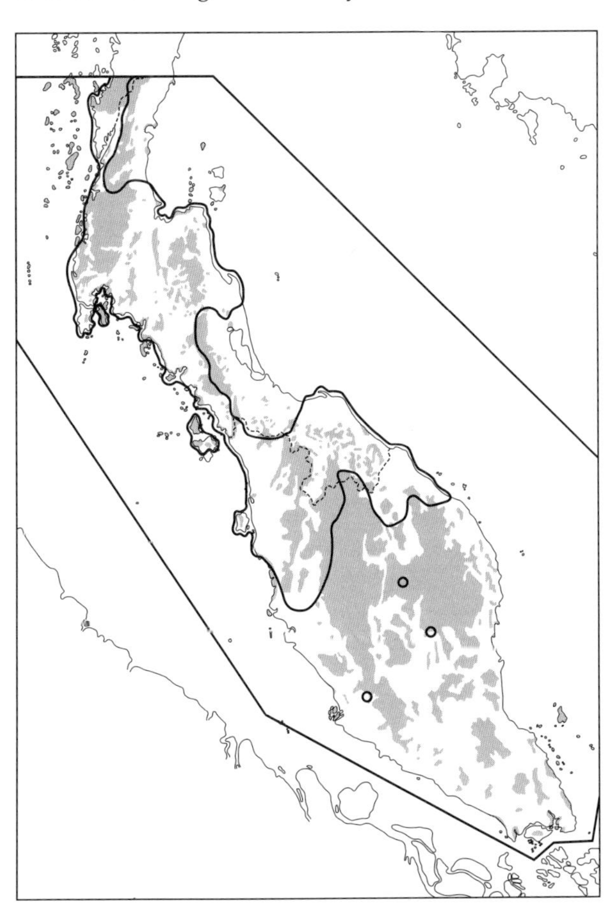

FORAGING AND FOOD. Flies generally shorter sallies and, in open habitat, commonly from rather lower scanning perches than the other *Merops* species, including on the same service-wires but also low fences, small bush-tops, low boughs, cane-grass fronds, etc., only 1–2 m from the ground. Tactics change in forest, where parties of non-breeders operate at crown height, as do Blue-throated Bee-eaters in this habitat. Two pellets from a grassy reservoir-bank on Penang island contained mainly remains of hymenopterans: prominently the small social wasp *Polybioides raphigastra*, also honey-bees *Apis indica* and the large *A. dorsata*, and some very small forms (Pagden 1958). A bird in open casuarina strand on Penarik spit, Setiu, Terengganu, caught dragonflies.

SOCIAL ORGANIZATION. Breeding-groups range from single to several hundred pairs but typical colonies are in the range 5–15, with burrows often well spread out. Where common, sometimes large numbers roost gregariously in a customary, isolated tree-crown. In forest, non-breeders forage in parties that occasionally associate with wintering Blue-throated Bee-eaters (BR 1978–79).

MOVEMENTS. No true migration detected, but range expands erratically south by a few to over 100 km during the non-breeding season. Dispersal away from breeding-sites has occurred by July (no exact dates available), with records of parties in the Kinta and Perak river-valleys south to Parit and Batu Gajah, latitude 4°27′N, Perak state, and strays reported twice (in July and November) around Kuala Lumpur (BMP5, Edgar 1947). East of the Main Range, collected in forest somewhere near the foot of Tahan, modern Taman Negara (Hartert 1902) and during October–November 1979 fairly common, consorting with Blue-throated Bee-eaters, in the selectively logged Tekam forestry concession, latitude 4°00′N, but none there in the following winter (BR 1978–79). Near Chemor, back in tin tailing breeding-habitat on 1 December but elsewhere in Perak some are still in forest at the beginning of January.

SURVIVAL. At the Padang Kamunting breeding-colony in the late 1960s, 80 percent of ringed adults returned between years.

SOCIAL INTERACTIONS. No information.

VOICE. A soft, airy *chewy-chewy-chewy . . .* and, in flight, slightly deeper, burring *prruip, prruip, prruip* or *churit, churit, churit* (Cairns 1957, Boonsong and Round 1991).

BREEDING

Nest. Burrows are excavated in flat ground, or slight irregularities in flat ground, in the same sandy soils favoured by the other *Merops* species; also in high, steep road-cuttings, earth-cliffs along streams, etc., usually near the top, and typically well spaced. Burrow diameter is about 4 cm and extreme lengths of around 3 m have been reported, but influenced by substrate hardness.

Eggs and brood. Eggs not described and there are no reliable records of clutch-size, but broods of 1–4 nestlings reported, as in Blue-throated Bee-eater.

Cycle. For most of the breeding period, one or both pair-members roosts in the burrow.

Seasonality. Burrow-excavation begins earlier than in other *Merops* bee-eaters; noted during early January–mid February in the NW, north from Penang, including on Penang and Langkawi islands, with burrows active (stage unknown) in January in Perak. Digging in early April in N Terengganu suggests a later schedule, perhaps linked to the later end to NE monsoon rains on that coast, but more information is needed. Overall, egg- and nestling-dates extrapolate to laying during February–April, with latest nestlings in mid May (BMP5, BR 1962, 1965, 1968, Cairns 1957, Müller 1882, Riley 1938).

MOULT. Hardly known. At Padang Kamunting, earliest records of active wing-moult among adults are dated 14 May (P1–2, P2–3) (BMP5), and a Phuket female suspended after renewing P1–3 in early March may have been an early failed breeder. Pattani and Narathiwat juveniles dated mid June and late July were moulting P5–6 and P8 (regular-descendant).

CONSERVATION. Like Blue-throated Bee-eater, an opportunist breeder in groups of widely varying size. The largest colony recorded in the Peninsula, at the Padang Kamunting site, Penang island, is at risk from encroachment and disturbance.

Family CORACIIDAE

Rollers: two species

Indian Roller; Nok Takhaab Thung (Thai); Tiong Gajah (Malay)

Coracias benghalensis (Linnaeus) 1758, *Systema Naturae* 10(1): 106. TL Bengal.
Plate 64

GROUP RELATIONS. Forms a superspecies with Sulawesian *C. temminckii* and, possibly, African *C. naevia* (Purple-winged and Rufous-crowned Rollers).

GLOBAL RANGE. E Arabia, S Iraq and Iran; the Indian subcontinent, Sri Lanka and islands south to the Maldives; SE Tibet, S Sichuan and Yunnan; and mainland SE Asia to the Peninsula.

IDENTIFICATION/DESCRIPTION. There have been naive misidentifications of dark-billed, juvenile Dollarbird as this species but, at all ages, upperparts including mantle, back, scapulars and inner secondaries are light grey-green and underparts to upper belly vinous-grey; never blackish. They share a purple- to bright blue-streaked throat, but dark blue and aquamarine wing-coverts, light blue thighs to lower tail-coverts and, in adults, light blue cap are the only other bright parts Indian Roller shows when perched. Purple- to light blue rump and upper tail-coverts; purple-blue based, light blue tail; zones of aquamarine, vivid light blue and deep blue across the wing-coverts and flight-feathers, and blue underwing flash on take-off, with a pale 'window' showing on both surfaces of the primaries as in Dollarbird. Sexes alike; juveniles are duller, head concolorous with body and lacking bright colours.

Bare-part colours. (Adult) iris mid brown, eyelid-rim and skin immediately behind eye yellow-orange; bill black; feet horn-yellow.

Size (mm). (Skins: 1 female; adult): wing 179; tail 113; bill 37.1; tarsus 25.7 (BMNH).

Weight. No data.

DISTRIBUTION. Principally along the eastern coastal plain, south to about 5°30'N; perhaps only an occasional dispersant in the west, as far as 7°52'N, at Aow Tong (*Tra*). Historical summary; *Chu, Pha, Phu, Kra, Pht, Tra, Son, Pat, Yal, Nar, Kel, Tru*, with no other island records.

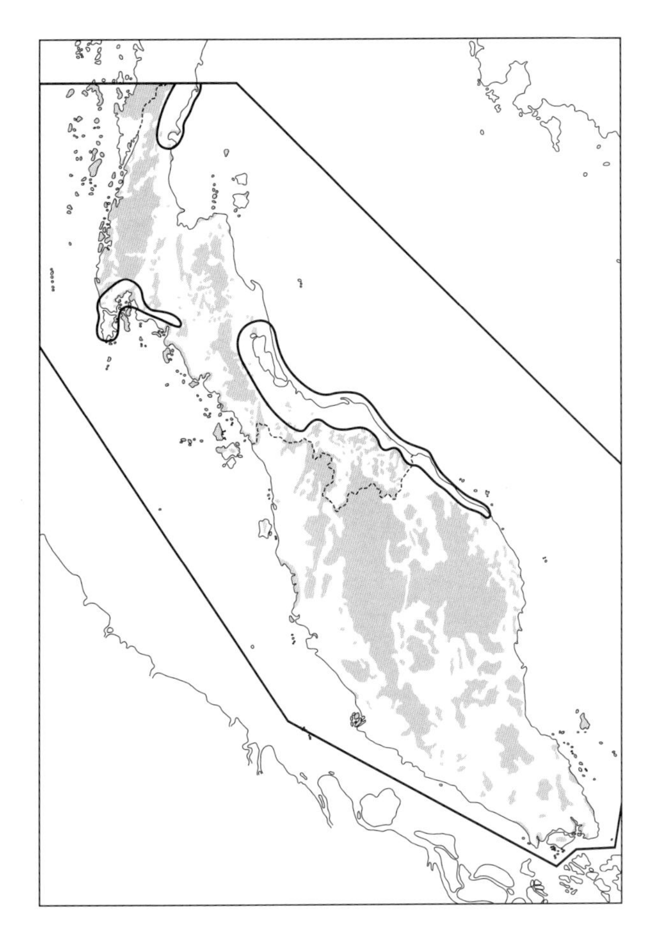

GEOGRAPHICAL VARIATION. Subspecies *affinis* McClelland 1840 (TL Assam), of the global range east from Sikkim.

STATUS AND POPULATION. Resident, more or less regular and uncommon to locally common; dispersing (Holmes 1973) but with no sign of true migrants. On the E coast, breeding-range limits have been stable for many decades.

HABITATS AND ECOLOGY. Light strand (including casuarina) woodland, patchy dune scrub, coconut plantations, open marshland, margins of paddyland and other field-edge cover, and quiet roadsides; wherever dead tops, service-poles, overhead wires or even piles of road-metal (G.C. Madoc) supply hunting perches with a view over open ground.

FORAGING AND FOOD. Still-hunts from exposed, mostly medium-height perches, power-flying or planing down to snatch prey from the ground or low vegetation. Said also to aerial-forage, especially around grass-fires, but this cannot be common behaviour. Diet poorly known in this area, but breeding birds collect large arthropods. At least some items are thoroughly branch-swiped before being eaten or fed to young.

SOCIAL ORGANIZATION. Territorial, but pair-members separate to forage alone. Only occasionally do two birds perch near each other, but tolerant of Dollarbirds close by, with these two roller species recorded nesting in adjacent palm trunks.

MOVEMENTS. Territory-holders are believed to be sedentary, but in the north apparent dispersants occur erratically up to 25 km away from nearest regular breeding localities.

SURVIVAL. No information.

SOCIAL INTERACTIONS. No information.

VOICE. A rasping scream at intruders approaching a nest-site, but no vocalizations are well described.

BREEDING

Nest. Ten on record have all been in the hollow tops of tall (9–12 m), dead and crownless coconut palms, entered vertically; none described in more detail. On the palm-covered Penarik spit, Terengganu, four breeding pairs each occupied their own patch of trunks killed by lightning or pathogens, well separated from one another but in at least one case shared with a pair of nesting Dollarbirds.

Eggs and brood. Eggs and clutch undescribed, but a fledged brood of two.

Cycle. No information.

Seasonality. In Kelantan and Terengganu, nests active but contents unchecked during April; nestlings in mid April and early May; earliest fledglings in late April (Berwick 1952, Lewin 1957, NRCS).

MOULT. A female dated 27 November showed none; no other information.

CONSERVATION. No critical issues, but the Setiu lagoon area (including Penarik Spit), a key site in N Terengganu, is being over-run by tourist developments.

Dollarbird; Nok Takhaab Dong (Thai); Tiong Batu (Malay)

Eurystomus orientalis (Linnaeus) 1766, *Systema Naturae* 12(1): 159. TL Java.
Plate 64

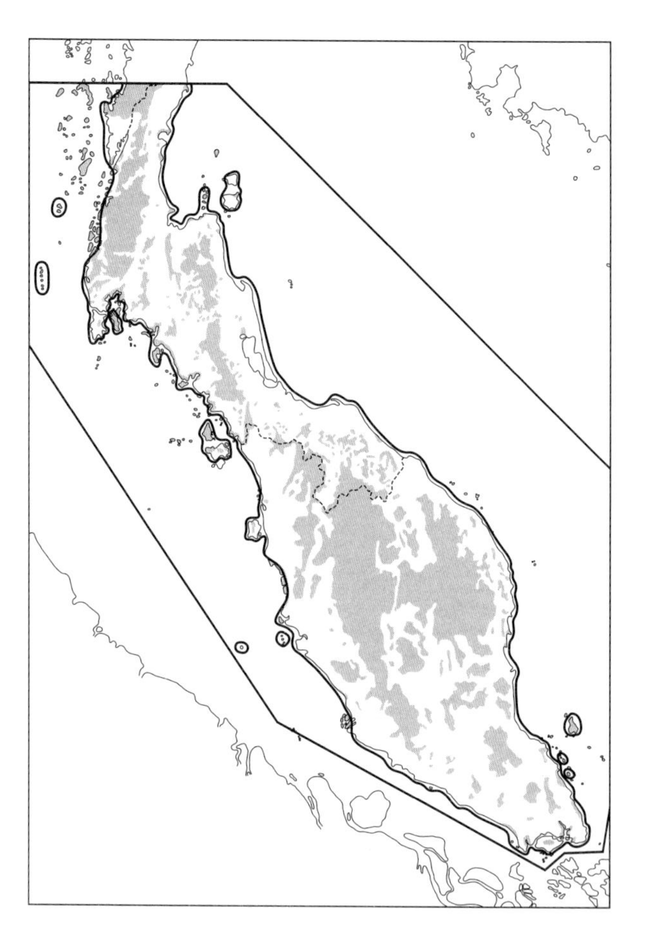

GROUP RELATIONS. Forms a probable superspecies with larger, E Wallacean *E. azureus* (Purple Roller); breeding-ranges have not been proved to overlap.

GLOBAL RANGE. The Himalayan foothills east from Ambala and the far-NE Indian subcontinent, SW India, Sri Lanka and the Andamans; SE Tibet; Pacific Russia south from Amurland, southern Japan, Korea, and China south and east of a line Heilongjiang–Ningxia–Sichuan; SE Asia; Wallacea; New Guinea and the Solomons; and northern and eastern Australia. Higher-latitude populations migrate, as far as the Greater Sunda islands from the north; Micronesia, Sulawesi and E Java Sea islands from the south.

IDENTIFICATION/DESCRIPTION. Broad-shouldered and broad-headed, generally blackish, with orange-red bill and feet conspicuous at a distance. Head to upper mantle and upper breast dull sooty brown with an oily sheen, lightening to dull verditer on the upper body and scapulars, brighter on the wing-coverts. Large throat-patch ultramarine-blue with brilliant cobalt-blue shaft-streaks; rest of lower body and lower wing-coverts bright verditer. Flight-feathers, alula, primary coverts and tail black, with extent of blue a population-variable. Sexes alike; juveniles as adult but duller, with little or no throat-streaking, and bare-part differences. In typical flight-modes, wings appear rather long relative to tail, flexed at the wrist, and with a more or less circular, milky-blue window ('silver dollar') near the base of the hand, conspicuous on both surfaces.

Bare-part colours. Iris deep brown, eyelid-rim orange-red; bill blackish (juvenile, including arriving first-winter migrants), bright orange-red, upper mandible with terminal nail black (adult); feet dull, dark red (juvenile), bright orange-red (adult).

Size (mm). (Live and skins: 26 males, 15 females; adult): wing 179–205 and 178–195; tail 96–105 and 89–104; bill 29.2–35.7 and 28.0–34.3; tarsus 17.6–20.7 and 19.2–21.7 (BMNH, UMZC, ZDUM).

Weight (g). A resident adult, 117.9; two autumn migrants, subspecies not recorded, 123.8, 129.6 (UMBRP).

DISTRIBUTION. Historical summary: all divisions, among which dates and behaviour confirm residents everywhere except *Ran, Pha, Son, Pat, Sat, Nar, Pes, Pra*; with other island records from Langkawi off the W coast; Phangan, Samui and the Pahang–Johor archipelago (Tioman, Babi Tengah) off the E coast; and Tekong and Ubin, Singapore. Also, but apparently only at passage or wintering dates, on the Surins, Similans, Yao Yai, Lanta, Muk, Libong, Tarutao, Penang, Pangkor, Rembia, Jarak and Pisang off the W coast; the Ang Thong group and Sibu (*Joh*) off the E coast; and Sentosa, Singapore.

GEOGRAPHICAL VARIATION. Residents are nominate *orientalis*, breeding north and west to the NE Indian subcontinent, and this also occurs as a migrant: relatively short winged (not above 195 mm), outer webs of alula, primary coverts and secondaries only finely margined blue, if at all; blue on the primaries not past level of 'dollar', and upper surface of tail verditer only at its extreme base (under the coverts). Other migrants are northeastern *abundus* Ripley 1942 (TL Nanking, lower Changjiang valley): mostly longer winged (11 adults 186–205 mm, no male below 189), with outer webs of alula, primary coverts, flight-feathers and all except central tail-feathers almost entirely ultramarine-blue, and tail-base verditer to well beyond covert-level.

STATUS AND POPULATION. Resident, a non-breeding visitor and, from records on remote Melaka

Straits islands and lighthouses (One-Fathom Bank) during both migration seasons, a passage migrant to and from Indonesia; regular and common. Collections from the Melaka Straits show *abundus* is roughly twice as common as *orientalis* in this migration stream (Gibson-Hill 1950e).

HABITATS AND ECOLOGY. A wide spectrum of wooded and semi-wooded habitats offering exposed loafing and lookout perches: including mangroves, casuarina and other strand woodland, inland forests, including paperbark and other swamp-forests, particularly edges of clearings and where logging has opened out the stand to leave relic timber emergent above the general vegetation level; also mature plantations (especially coconut), orchards and wooded gardens. In otherwise open agriculture or rural settlements makes common use of overhead service-wires, tall aerials, etc. Except while migrating, more or less strictly at plains level; a party of five in forest at 1200 m on Fraser's Hill (Madoc and Allen 1952) and one hunting in a clearing on the 880 m summit of Raya, Langkawi island, in late March were evidently on the move. The extent of habitat-overlap between winterers and residents is unknown.

FORAGING AND FOOD. Said to take prey from the ground, *Coracias*-fashion, but this must be exceptional. The common hunting mode is aerial capture of free-flying insects, either in sorties from a high lookout perch or during longer patrols at tree-top to far above canopy height. Particularly active late in the day and spends long periods, until last light, attending ant and termite swarms. Large cicadas, mantids, ants and orthopterans have been identified among other prey.

SOCIAL ORGANIZATION. Residents associate mostly in pairs, often perching together and jointly defending breeding-territory against conspecifics. Migrants travel alone or in small parties, and may forage together. Winter termite swarms commonly attract several, feeding without interference, and 30-plus presumed migrants have been counted together over a Singapore reservoir in early March (SINGAV-3).

MOVEMENTS. Migrates diurnally and also at night, over a broad front that takes in both coasts and their island-systems, with crossings of the Main Range inland to above 1200 m. Earliest autumn arrival dates are 13 October, small parties heading south over inland Negeri Sembilan, 16 October at the Fraser's Hill floodlights, and 17 October over open country in the Selangor lowlands (BMP5, Cant 1957–58). Night migration continues to at least late November (latest capture at Fraser's on 22 November). Remains of casualties on Perak island, N Melaka Straits, in the first week of March are the earliest sign of spring return, with day-moving parties recorded elsewhere to 16 April.

SURVIVAL. No information.

SOCIAL INTERACTIONS. Courtship-feeding is common, and pair-members sitting side-by-side rapidly and shallowly bob (flick) heads at each other. Combined confrontation of an intruder by a territorial pair involved aerial-chasing and mates perching close together with their throat-hackles fluffed out, much head-bobbing and loud calling.

VOICE. All calls are rather low-pitched, hoarse and rasping: commonly a *skatch-skatch*, with faster, four-note *kej-kej-kej-kej*, and single *tchek* and *tcherk* notes from pair-members communicating while perched near one another. In flight, a hoarse, repeated *jek jek jek jek jek* . . . Over several minutes after courtship-feeding, and while mates were still perched close together, a male gave irregular, up to half-second bursts of a coarse, apparently non-vocal stridulating sound seen to coincide with rapid bill-clattering.

BREEDING

Nest. Holes of wood-boring birds such as parakeets and larger woodpeckers (including of White-bellied Woodpecker *Dryocopus javensis*, taken over after sustained harassment of the owners), 9–13 m up dead trees at the edge of logged inland forest; and in tall mangrove trees and a dead nibong palm *Onchosperma*. Also adopts the hollow top of a tall, dead and crownless coconut palm, occasionally close to similar, active nests of Indian Roller and Long-tailed Parakeet.

Eggs and brood. Eggs glossy, plain white. Shape ovate. Full clutch two; no other information available.

Cycle. A pair spent two months harassing and finally ousting breeding White-bellied Woodpeckers, and a further two months before bringing off young of their own. Both parents attend nestlings and fledglings.

Seasonality. An active nest, stage unchecked, in February; courtship-feeding, copulation and hole-prospecting during March–late May; eggs May; nestlings during April–late June; fledglings mid-May–late June; with one record of attendance at a tree-hole on 1 October (Chasen 1939, Madoc 1956a, G.C. Madoc, G. Noramly, NRCS, SINGAV-2, -3, -4).

MOULT. Unexpected in coraciiforms, adults show what appears to be regular-descendant replacement of primaries, with up to three adjacent middle-tract feathers in overlapping growth, and two at the wing-tip. Among 27 adult *orientalis* covering the length of the Peninsula, and all months except June and September, i.e., including presumed residents, seven were in active wing-moult during late February–early October, approaching completion (at P9–10 or 10) as of mid July. Migrants of both subspecies (all age-groups) trapped on autumn passage, and *abundus* in all months up to late February, show relatively unworn plumage and no moult, suggestive of completion before autumn arrival (BMNH, UMBRP).

CONSERVATION. No critical issues.

Order PICIFORMES

Family INDICATORIDAE

Honeyguides: one species

Malaysian Honeyguide; Nok Phraan Pheung (Thai); Burung Gembala Lebah (Malay)

Indicator archipelagicus Temminck 1832, *Nouveau Recueil de Planches Coloriées d'Oiseaux* 91: plate 542. TL Pontianak, W Kalimantan.

Plate 68

GROUP RELATIONS. Uncertain; apparently with closer African than other Asian affinities. From vocalizations, perhaps nearest to the *I. variegatus–maculatus* (Scaly-throated and Spotted Honeyguide) superspecies.

GLOBAL RANGE. W and SW Thailand from latitude about 16°N (so far, no record from Tenasserim) to the Peninsula, Sumatra and Borneo.

IDENTIFICATION/DESCRIPTION. Shape and size of a medium *Pycnonotus* bulbul but with thicker, more finch-like bill than any local bulbul species. Adults dull, darkish brown above, sharp against white chin and upper throat at jaw level. Apart from some whitish edging on wing-coverts and rump, upper body-feathering, flight- and tail-feathers edged rather bright olive-green. Inner leading-edge of lesser wing-coverts chrome-yellow in the adult male, probably exposable during displays but mostly covered when at rest. Lower throat to breast and anterior flanks clear, pale grey; remaining underparts including lower wing-coverts creamy white, with upper belly and rear flanks boldly streaked black. Tail rounded, the outermost feather-pair reaching only half way to tip, the next two pairs with inner web mainly white. Apart from the yellow and some size-dimorphism, sexes alike. Juveniles apparently as female but not reliably described.

Bare-part colours. Iris dark brown (juvenile and possibly adult female; needing confirmation), blood-red (adult male); upper mandible and bill-tip black, rest of lower mandible pinkish brown; feet dark grey.

Size (mm). (Live: 6 males, 6 females; adult): wing 96–103 and 79–90; tail 65–73 and 50–63; bill 14.2 (1 only) and 13.5–14.6; tarsus 13.8–15.2 (sexes combined) (BMNH, UMBRP).

Weight (g). Adults, sex of most not recorded, 35.2-42.1 (n=7) (M. Wong, UMBRP).

DISTRIBUTION. Under-recorded. Historical summary: *Sur, Nak, Kra, Pht, Tra, Kel, Pek, Phg, Sel, Neg, Mel*, with no island records.

GEOGRAPHICAL VARIATION. None recognized.

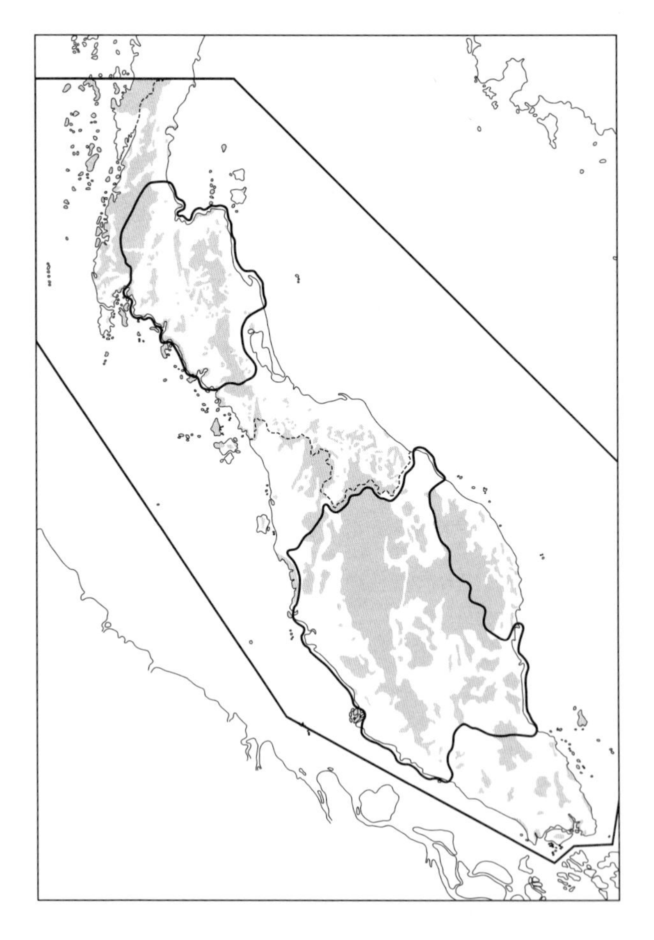

STATUS AND POPULATION. Resident, local and sparse to uncommon; hard to find when not calling. In 2 km^2 of the Pasoh research forest, Negeri Sembilan, only one calling-station was located at any one time, but the relationship between callers, females and probable non-vocal subordinates (including, apparently, other adult males) is not known. These are liable to contribute to a higher than obvious overall population density.

HABITATS AND ECOLOGY. Mature evergreen and semi-evergreen, dry-land Lowland forest, mainly at plains level, with a few records from submontane slopes, into the lower edge of Montane forest at about 900 m on the Pahang slope of Tahan (Taman Negara) and 1050 m on the Main Range (R. Gregory-Smith, Robinson 1928). On two occasions, birds have been mist-netted in smaller-stature regenerating forest, but close to mature stands. Callers occupy mostly the canopy and mid-stratum, but several captures at ground level show foragers sometimes move lower down the forest column.

Male advertisement-calling has been reported only in mature forest. At Pasoh, a station of several years' standing was abandoned soon after a wind-storm cleared a big opening next to the favoured tree. Another was established about 800 m away soon after.

FORAGING AND FOOD. No data from the Peninsula. In Borneo, where recorded from a wider range of habitats, a stomach is said to have contained bees, bee larvae and comb wax (Smythies 1981).

SOCIAL ORGANIZATION. Calling-stations are tenanted more or less continuously, sometimes over periods of several years (one at Khao Pra-Bang Khram, Krabi, for at least eight years) (BCSTB-12, Wong 1984), and appear to be inherited. It has been guessed, though not confirmed, that only one male has occupancy at a time but, evidently, others wait in the vicinity for an opening. In Sungai Dusun wildlife reserve, N Selangor, checks on a site from which a calling male had been removed in early February showed it re-occupied by late March, the new incumbent consistently present (and noisy) over five days of observations (BMP5).

MOVEMENTS. None reported.

SURVIVAL. No information.

SOCIAL INTERACTIONS. At two regularly checked calling-stations in Krabi and Negeri Sembilan, incumbent males showed evidence of being stimulated to vocalize by the arrival of people, and by even a crude imitation of the first note of the call; also of stopping when observers moved on (P.D. Round, Wong 1984). One of these birds is also reported to have moved around actively while calling, but a Sumatran bird I watched at only a few metres' range, on a vine unusally close to the ground, remained absolutely still throughout and continued calling as I moved away. A male collected in early February had enlarged testes, implying its calling-site may have been a mating station.

There is no evidence Malaysian Honeyguides 'guide', although proximity to bee-nest food has not been checked, and nothing is known about behaviour towards non-human bee-predators.

VOICE. The male advertising-call is a sharp, grating monosyllable with slight downward inflection followed immediately by a sustained, slowly rising, bleating rattle, *graui, krrrr-a-a-a-a-a-aii.* Audible at up to 100 m away, it is repeated at intervals in long bouts from perches in the interior high canopy of a large forest tree.

BREEDING. No record. Brood-hosts have not been identified.

MOULT. The only records are of adults growing P4–5 in mid May and P2 in mid June, with replacement of at least the inner primary tract regular-descendant. Others dated December, February, March, July and September showed no moult (BMNH, BMP5).

CONSERVATION. Calling reported on slopes to at least 300 m, but most records are from forest at plains level. If this is core habitat, Malaysian Honeyguide is among those forest species at risk from habitat-loss. Globally near-threatened (BTW2).

Family PICIDAE

Piculets and woodpeckers: 27 species

Speckled Piculet; Nok Hua Khwaan Jiw Thong Lai (Thai); Burung Belatuk Kerdil Berbintik (Malay)

Picumnus innominatus Burton 1836, *Proceedings of the Zoological Society of London* 3: 154. TL Sikkim.

Plate 65

GROUP RELATIONS. Free-standing.

GLOBAL RANGE. The W Ghats, Himalayas and NE Indian subcontinent; SE Tibet; China south of a line Sichuan–Shaanxi–lower Changjiang valley; and (mainly) uplands of SE Asia to Sumatra and Borneo.

IDENTIFICATION/DESCRIPTION. Smaller than nuthatch species of the same forest and like nuthatches, and also other piculets, soft-tailed, relying mostly on strong feet at a climbing prop. Head-pattern superficially *Picoides*-like: cap olive-grey, malar-stripe and band from lores through eye to ear-coverts black, white between, and with a narrow white supercilium from above eye to side of nape, but the piculet upper body and wing-coverts are rather bright, unpatterned olive. Underparts whitish, all feathers with a bold, central spot of black, largest on the breast and forming bars on the flanks. Inner webs of central tail-feathers white and a white subterminal band slants across the three outer pairs; tail otherwise black. Sexes differ on forehead colour: black with feather-tips orange in the male, concolorous with rest of cap in the female. Juveniles resemble the adult female but are duller overall.

Bare-part colours. (Adult) iris brown, periorbital skin black; upper mandible and extreme bill-tip black, rest of lower mandible grey; feet blue-grey.

Size (mm). (Live and skins: 3 males, 2 females; adult): wing 55–56 and 55, 57; tail 29–32 and 29, 31; bill 11.5–11.7 and 11.0, 11.5; tarsus 12.3–12.6 and 11.8, 12.9 (BMNH, UMBRP).

Weight (g). An adult male, 10.0 (UMBRP).

DISTRIBUTION. Malaysian mountains, including the Larut Range, the Main Range (but recorded so far only between Cameron Highlands and Fraser's Hill) and on Tahan, Taman Negara. Historical summary: *Kel, Pek, Phg, Sel*.

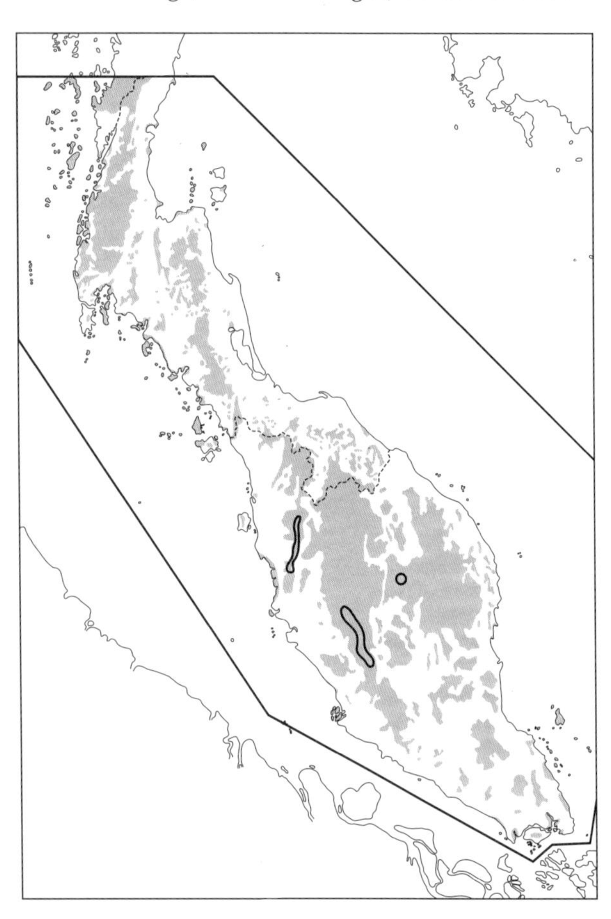

GEOGRAPHICAL VARIATION. Subspecies *malayorum* Hartert 1912 (TL Hijau peak, Larut Range), of the global range east to southern Yunnan.

STATUS AND POPULATION. Resident, regular and uncommon to more or less common.

HABITATS AND ECOLOGY. The mid-stratum and understorey of Lower Montane and the lower fringe of Upper Montane forest, recorded between about 1000–1400 m.

FORAGING AND FOOD. Loners or at most a parent and dependant juvenile commonly attend mixed-species foraging-flocks, mainly of small passerines. Actively searches and taps on thin branches, vines and scrambling bamboos, sometimes perching crosswise while opening pits in bark, ant-containing stems, etc., at which feeding occurs for up to several minutes before the bird flies on to rejoin the moving flock (Dunlop 1960, Short 1973). No prey identified; at only a few metres range, items passed by an adult female to a juvenile were too small to be checked.

SOCIAL ORGANIZATION. Mostly solitary. That mixed foraging-flocks never include more than a single adult suggests several (non-exclusive) possibilities, including active avoidance behaviour, a divergence of foraging behaviour between the sexes, and attendance only while the flock moves within the piculet's own territory. None of these has been investigated.

MOVEMENTS. None reported.

SURVIVAL. No information.

SOCIAL INTERACTIONS. A full-grown juvenile fed bill-to-bill by a female waited silently behind the forager, showing no soliciting behaviour.

VOICE. An occasional thin, sharp *tsik* is the only vocalization reported (Short 1973), and there is no local record of drumming.

BREEDING. No conclusive record. At Fraser's Hill over two consecutive days in mid March, L.L. Short watched a male excavate a hole in a frond-rib hanging about 10 m up off a dead palm, but it is not known if this was actually used. A dependent juvenile attended by a parent on 7 May.

MOULT. Eight adults dated February, March, late June, August and November showed none (BMNH, UMBRP). No other information.

CONSERVATION. No current threat, but pressure for development on the Main Range could lead to problems of habitat-fragmentation in the foreseeable future.

Rufous Piculet; Nok Hua Khwaan Jiw Ok Daeng (Thai); Burung Belatuk Kerdil Api (Malay)

Sasia abnormis (Temminck) 1825, *Nouveau Recueil de Planches Coloriées d'Oiseaux* 62: plate 371. TL Java.

Plate 65

GROUP RELATIONS. See White-browed Piculet *S. ochracea*.

GLOBAL RANGE. Java, Borneo, Belitung and Sumatra, and the Peninsula north to latitude 10°52′N (BMNH, Baker 1919–1920).

IDENTIFICATION/DESCRIPTION. Even smaller than Speckled Piculet. Adults are rather bright yellow-olive above, including outer webs of flight-feathers; underparts including face to slightly above level of eye rich orange-chestnut, with a golden wash across lower breast; lower wing-coverts creamy white; longest upper tail-coverts and tail black. The sexes are separated on colour of forehead and forecrown, back to level of eye: golden yellow in males, chestnut in females. Apart from blackish tail, juveniles are uniform dark olive-green dorsally, head and underparts dark olive-washed grey.

Bare-part colours. Iris brown (juvenile), red (adult); loral skin to lanceolate eye-patch pale grey (juvenile), liver-purple (adult); bill uniform black (juvenile), upper mandible black, lower pale yellow (adult); feet dirty yellow (juvenile), orange (adult).

Size (mm). (Live and skins: 14 males, 20 females; adult): wing 53–56 and 52–56; tail 20–25 and 19–24; bill 12.9–14.0 and 12.4–14.2; tarsus 12.6–13.9 and 13.0–14.3 (BMNH, UMBRP).

Weight (g). Adult males, 8.5–11.1 (n=8); adult females 7.6–9.8 (n=19) (UMBRP).

DISTRIBUTION. Possibly not in the far NW. Historical summary: all divisions except *Pak*, *Ran*, *Phu*, *Pra*, *Mel*, *Sin*, with no island records.

GEOGRAPHICAL VARIATION. Nominate *abnormis*, of the global range except Nias island, W Sumatra.

STATUS AND POPULATION. Resident, regular and common.

HABITATS AND ECOLOGY. Dense understorey vegetation of evergreen and semi-evergreen Lowland forest, and peatswamp forest, mature and regenerating after disturbance; at plains level and on slopes to the Montane ecotone, less commonly into Lower Montane forest to about 1300 m (Bromley 1952). Potentially, overlaps the range of Speckled Piculet, although most Montane records of Rufous are from isolated peaks on which Speckled appears to be absent, e.g., Rabong (Kelantan), Tapis (Pahang).

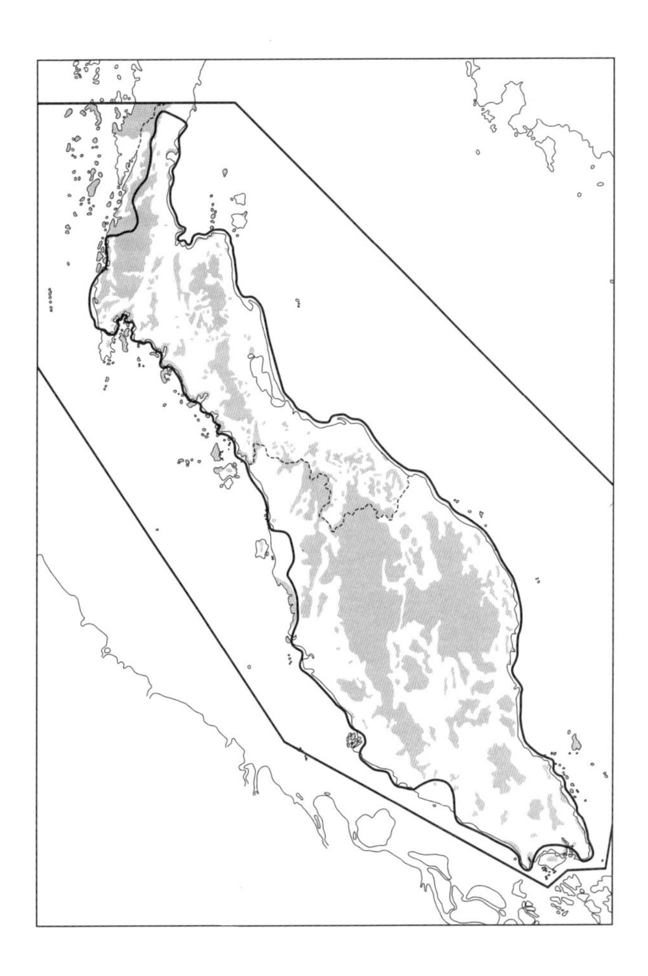

FORAGING AND FOOD. Gleans from, and taps on, thin stems, creepers, bamboos, tall gingers, etc., perching crosswise and sometimes acrobatically, lingering longest while tapping at the internodal sheath of bamboos but generally moving faster between feeding-sites than the more stolid Speckled Piculet (Short 1973). In mature forest, a heavy preponderance of females over males taken in mist-nets set at ground level (ratio 6 : 1 in a large sample) is unlikely to reflect the real sex ratio, but could be due to some behavioural difference, such as males foraging higher in the vegetation column. Foraging-niche divergence between the sexes of woodpeckers is known mostly from the N temperate zone, and this possibility deserves to be investigated (see also the woodpecker genus *Hemicircus*). Curiously, juveniles are netted even less often than males.

Prey is said to include ants, spiders and beetles (Robinson 1928).

SOCIAL ORGANIZATION. Commonly solitary, but family parties travel as cohesive groups (Short 1973). Mist-netting on a sample plot of the Pasoh research forest, Negeri Sembilan, showed a large amount of space overlap between adults. Less than 30 percent of birds marked made regular use of the 15 ha covered and the two most frequently retrapped individuals (both female) moved widely, probably to beyond the plot boundaries.

MOVEMENTS. After intervals of several years, two females in continuous forest at Pasoh were retrapped some 800 m from site of ringing (UMBRP).

SURVIVAL. Longest retrap-intervals are 68 and 86 months (UMBRP, M. Wong).

SOCIAL INTERACTIONS. No information.

VOICE. A soft *pik* and a shrill but emphatic rattle, *kep-kep-kipkipkipkipkip*. A slower version, *kep, kep, kep, kep . . .*, is given in alarm/anxiety situations. An approximately one-second drum starts fast then slows to more spaced beat-pairs, with or without a signing-off note, *dadadadada . . . da-da da-da da-da (da)*. When given on a bamboo culm it is remarkably loud for the size of the drummer.

BREEDING

Nest. Only two on record, holes less than 2.5 cm wide, both less than 1 m from the ground, in a stump and a thin sapling. Use of bamboo culms (BMP5) has not been confirmed. Appropriate-sized, mistakable, holes in bamboos are made by the tree mouse *Chiropodomys gliroides*.

Eggs and brood. A brood of two; no other information.

Cycle. No information.

Seasonality. Active nests in late May and (with well grown chicks) mid June; single recent fledglings escorted by an adult on 21 June and 14 July; and female with oviduct still hypertrophied also dated 14 July (Allen 1958, BCSTB-13, Madoc 1956a, P.D. Round, UMBRP).

MOULT. Replacement of primaries is regular-descendant, with up to three adjacent inner-tract feathers in overlapping growth. Among 86 handlings of adults mainly in Selangor and Negeri Sembilan, and covering all months, active wing-moult occurred between 8 June (P1–2) and 10 December (P9–10), with late starts and early completions overlapping in late September–early October and incidence 50 percent or more during August–October. Within-season retrapping showed individuals complete wing-moult in 3.5–4 months.

CONSERVATION. Common use of regrowth and mountain-slope forest implies this piculet is not at significant risk.

White-browed Piculet; Nok Hua Khwaan Jiw Khiw Khao (Thai); Burung Belatuk Kerdil Kening Putih (Malay)

Sasia ochracea Hodgson 1836, *Journal of the Asiatic Society of Bengal* 5: 778. TL Nepal.
Plate 65

GROUP RELATIONS. Most populations show a liver-red periorbital patch, as in Rufous Piculet, but the one entering the Peninsula, and in possible contact with Rufous Piculet, has a black patch. These birds narrowly overlap by latitude, and use similar habitats, but have not yet been found in the same areas, hence are validly treatable as a superspecies.

GLOBAL RANGE. The Himalayas east from Garhwal and the far-NE Indian subcontinent; SE Tibet; Yunnan to Guizhou and Guangxi; and SE Asia to the N Peninsula.

IDENTIFICATION/DESCRIPTION. Adults as respective sexes of Rufous Piculet except for a narrow white stripe from rear edge of eye over the top of the ear-coverts, and yellow-olive of dorsum confined to crown and wings. Neck and remaining upperparts (apart from black long upper tail-coverts and tail) are golden cinnamon, brightest on the rump. The local juvenile has not been described.

Bare-part colours. (Adult) iris red, loral skin to lanceolate eye-patch slaty black; upper mandible black, lower mandible blue-grey (a male), yellow (a female, but this claimed difference could be age-related, and needs research); feet orange (BMNH).

Size (mm). (Skins: 1 male, 1 female; adult): wing 52 (male only); tail 21 and 21; bill 13.4 and 12.8; tarsus 12.9 and 12.6 (BMNH).

Weight. No data.

DISTRIBUTION. Historical summary: *Pak, Chu, Ran, Pha*; the southern limit of regular occurrence unknown, but only one record from Phangnga.

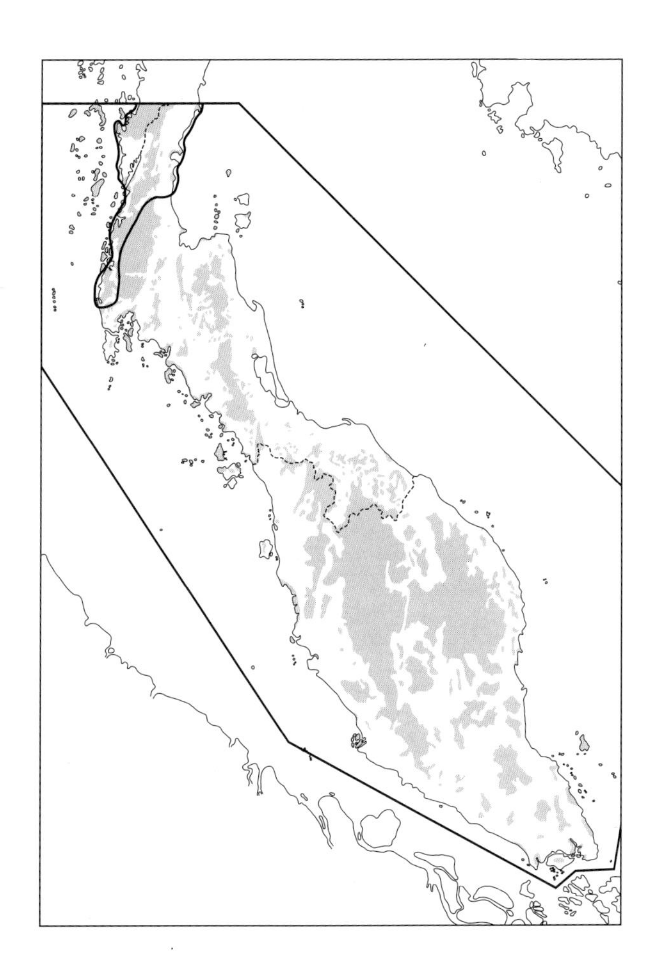

GEOGRAPHICAL VARIATION. Near-endemic *reichenowi* Hesse 1911 (TL Thayet river, latitude 13°50′N, Tenasserim).

STATUS AND POPULATION. Resident; no information on other aspects.

HABITATS AND ECOLOGY. Scarcely known. At Khlong Naka, Ranong, a sighting on a large bamboo culm in valley-bottom forest at about 50 m above sea-level (P.D. Round), a typical situation for Rufous Piculet elsewhere in the Peninsula.

FORAGING AND FOOD. No specific information.

SOCIAL ORGANIZATION. No information.

MOVEMENTS. None reported.

SURVIVAL. No information.

SOCIAL INTERACTIONS. No information.

VOICE. No information.

BREEDING. No records.

MOULT. Two dated February and March showed none. No other information.

CONSERVATION. Situation unknown, but elsewhere able to use regrowth and disturbed forest.

Brown-capped Woodpecker; (no Thai name); Burung Belatuk Belacan (Malay)

Picoides moluccensis (Gmelin) 1788, *Systema Naturae* 13(1): 439. TL Melaka.
Plate 65

GROUP RELATIONS. Short (1982) includes S Asian *nanus* in a species *moluccensis*, but in doing so creates a long range-gap in northwestern SE Asia, through which suitable habitats seem plentiful. More research is needed.

GLOBAL RANGE. The Indian subcontinent and Sri Lanka; the Malay Peninsula, Greater Sunda islands and Bali; and Lesser Sunda islands east to Alor.

IDENTIFICATION/DESCRIPTION. Size of Eurasian Tree Sparrow *Passer montanus* and slightly smaller than similar-looking Grey-capped Woodpecker *P. canicapillus*, but the difference is of little value in isolation. Both show a strong, dark stripe back from eye to side of neck, bolder than malar-stripe which in Brown-capped is, in turn, bolder than ventral streaking, clearly demarcating white lower face from throat. Brown-capped is generally sooty rather than black, appearing less crisply pied than Grey-capped. The white barring of its upper body broadens to dominate over dark parts on upper tail-coverts, and continues laterally over scapulars and wing-coverts, leaving only the leading-edge of the wing all-dark, hence the 'ladder-back' pattern in this species has no clear edge. Crown smoky brown, commonly appearing all dark (SINGAV-2). Tail sooty, white-barred laterally, white spotted at the centre, hence overlapping the variability of pattern seen in Grey-capped Woodpecker. The minute red mark above the ear-coverts of the male is exposed only during display movements; not otherwise detectable, even at close range. There are no other sexual differences and, apart from being slightly duller overall and lacking red, juveniles resemble adults.

Bare-part colours. (Adult) iris light red-brown; bill slate-grey, darker on upper mandible; feet greenish grey.

Size (mm). (Live and skins: 8 males, 8 females; adult): wing 71–77 and 72–78; tail 33–36 and 28–36; bill 15.0–16.3 and 15.4–16.0; tarsus 13.5–14.8 and 14.1–15.1 (UMBRP, BMNH).

Weight (g). Unsexed adults, 14.9 and 15.2 (UMBRP).

DISTRIBUTION. The far south and the W coast to latitude approximately 5°N. Historical summary: *Pra, Pek, Sel, Neg, Joh, Sin,* with additional island records from Penang and the Kelang estuary group (Ketam) off the W coast; and Tekong, Ubin, Sakeng, Senang, Sudong and Ayer Merbau, Singapore.

GEOGRAPHICAL VARIATION. Subspecies *moluccensis*, of the Sunda region.

STATUS AND POPULATION. Resident, regular and more or less common to common, within a limited local range and a restricted array of habitats.

HABITATS AND ECOLOGY. On the mainland, found only in mangrove forest, at or close to the landward edge of which it meets, and appears to be excluded by, Grey-capped Woodpecker. Both are in expected habitats on Penang island but in Singapore and satellites, where careful searching over recent years indicates Grey-capped no longer occurs, Brown-capped has invaded plantations and the light woodland of parks, gardens and planted roadsides inland. Large trees are preferred, and it operates at mid and canopy levels, but in mangrove forest will follow the vegetation 'skin' down to comparatively low levels in areas of disturbance or stunted growth. Everywhere, rot-softened dead branches and other narrow stems appear essential for roost- and nest-hole excavation, and in non-mangrove habitats of Singapore a negative correlation has been noted between occurrence of Brown-caps and numbers of Coppersmith Barbets, with similar nest-site preferences (SINGAV-1).

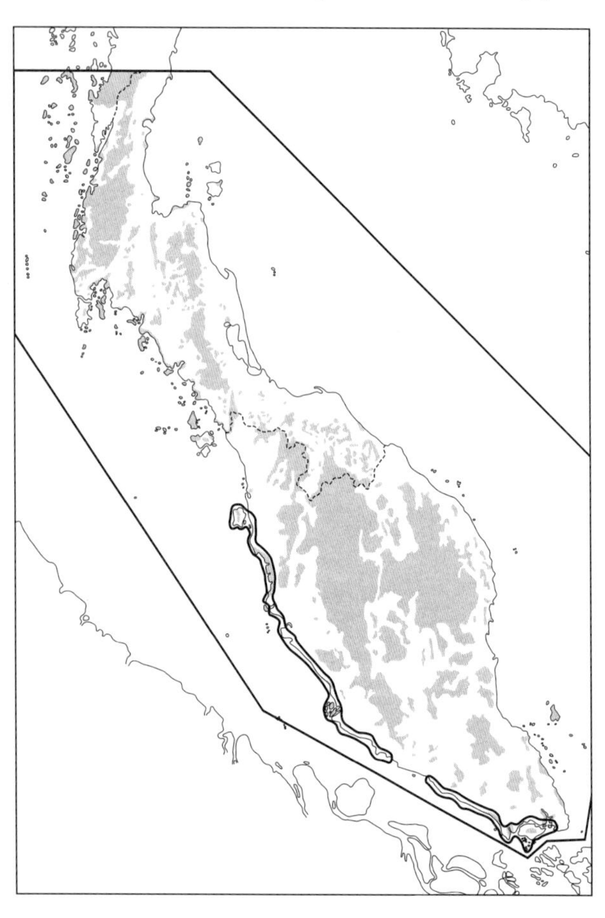

FORAGING AND FOOD. Hunts mainly over branches and twigs, generally avoiding large beams and main trunks, and is also said to search leaves (Spittle 1952). Forages by surface-gleaning and by tapping, probing and flaking outer layers of bark, mainly but not exclusively of living wood (Short 1973). Prey appears mostly to be small arthropods, but fig-like fruits as well as insect larvae have been identified among food taken to nestlings (SINGAV-1, -3).

SOCIAL ORGANIZATION. Adults forage alone, and there is no information on the behaviour of the family parties typical of most breeding woodpeckers.

MOVEMENTS. None reported.

SURVIVAL. No information.

SOCIAL INTERACTIONS. As with Grey-capped Woodpecker, drumming is weak but in open situations, and depending on substrate, the sound carries 50 m or more.

VOICE. A shrill, rapid trill *pihihihihi . . .*, as in Grey-capped Woodpecker but weaker, is the only vocalization reported. The drum is high-pitched, brief (less than one second), even and very rapid (17–20 beats), repeated at rates of 6–8 bursts per minute during bouts lasting up to five minutes (Short 1973).

BREEDING

Nest. A tunnel 15–30 cm deep, and with entrance about 4 cm wide, excavated in dead, part-rotted wood, usually of a narrow branch or stem, mostly close to an emergent tip orientated anywhere between vertical and horizontal, and entered always on the overhung side. Recorded less than 2 m up in scrubby mangroves but most nests are 3–18 m above ground or water. There are also records from artificial sites over water, including bamboo mooring-poles, old jetty timbers and the uprights of permanent, off-beach fish-traps.

No record exists of the tree species preferred in mangrove forest but, inland, nests have been reported in yellow flame *Peltophorum pterocarpum* and coral tree *Erythrina* spp., common in parks and gardens.

Eggs and brood. Eggs are glossy, plain, rather translucent white. Shape ovate to short elliptical. Size (mm): 19.2–17.7 × 13.6–13.3 (n=3). Full clutch two eggs, and broods are regularly of two. Incubation and fledging periods not measured.

Cycle. Both pair-members excavate the nest and both incubate and tend nestlings and fledglings. A pair monitored at an inland site in Singapore fledged two young from a hole in a yellow flame on 23 March, were seen copulating on 11 May and fed a second brood at the same site on 11 June.

Seasonality. Thirty-three records of active nests or dependent fledglings, from Singapore north to Perak, occupy all months March–August, on dates that imply egg-laying during February–August and final broods off in September (BMP5, Edgar 1933, MBR 1986–87, Ollington and Loh 1993, SINGAV-1, 2, -3, -4).

MOULT. Moult of primaries apparently regular-descendant. Among 15 adults covering July–October and December–February, six showed active wing-moult during early July (P4)–early December (P9), with starts up to August and completions as of October. None of the six dated January–February showed any moult.

CONSERVATION. Much mangrove habitat has been lost but capacity to use thin stems, and the health of inland populations, suggests no immediate threat.

Grey-capped Woodpecker; Noh Hua Khwaan Daang Khre (Thai); Burung Belatuk Kasturi (Malay)

Picoides canicapillus (Blyth) 1845, *Journal of the Asiatic Society of Bengal* 14: 197. TL Ramree island, W Burma.

Plate 65

GROUP RELATIONS. In a superspecies with more or less parapatric NE Asian *P. kizuki* (Japanese Woodpecker) (Short 1982). The sound-quality of their vocalizations is rather different, *kizuki* with a distinctive buzz.

GLOBAL RANGE. The Himalayan foothills east from Pakistan, and hill-tracts of the far-NE Indian subcontinent; Ussuriland, Korea, China south and east of a line NE provinces–Gansu–Sichuan, including Taiwan and Hainan; and SE Asia to Sumatra and Borneo.

IDENTIFICATION/DESCRIPTION. Slightly larger, more robust than Brown-capped Woodpecker. In isolation, better identified by crisper, more definitely black-and-white dorsal patterning and other plumage details. Forehead to nape medium grey, bordered black (most noticeable in rear view), and the bold black band from behind the eye down side of neck to upper breast level cuts off a white supercilium that expands posteriorly to constrict black of upper neck into a fairly narrow median-dorsal stripe. Malar-stripe weak, hardly distinguishable from dark streaking of throat, hence pale cheek poorly demarcated at the jaw-line. Black-and-white dorsal ladder-barring of mantle, back, long scapulars and inner secondaries clearer than in Brown-capped Woodpecker, edged by all-black short scapulars and lesser wing-coverts (mostly white-barred in Brown-cap). Underparts white, variably pale grey- to faintly yellow-washed, and dark-streaked back from breast and sides of throat. Flight-feathers black, outer webs finely and inner webs boldly notched white; tail variably all white-barred to barred laterally with centre plain black. Apart from a small red fleck at the top rear margin of the ear-coverts of the male, exposed only during display (as in Brown-capped), the sexes are similar. Juveniles as adults, but duller and without the red.

Bare-part colours. (Adult) iris dull pinkish to red-brown; bill slate-grey, blacker on upper mandible; feet grey-green.

Size (mm). (Skins: 18 males, 13 females; adult): wing 76–86 and 77–89; tail 32–40 and 32–40; bill 13.9–17.8 and 15.2–17.4; tarsus 13.8–14.7 and 13.5–16.0 (BMNH).

Weight. No data.

DISTRIBUTION. Historical summary: in all divisions except *Phu, Kel, Pra, ?Mel* (a *Picoides* at the landward edge of Melaka mangroves not positively identified), with island records from Yao Yai, Libong and Penang off the W coast; and Samui off the E coast. Apparently extinct *Sin*, with no specimen-records since the late nineteenth century.

GEOGRAPHICAL VARIATION. Subspecies *auritus* Eyton 1845 (TL Melaka), also of the Riau archipelago. Claimed variation in strength of ventral wash and boldness of streaking within the Peninsula (Riley 1938, Robinson 1927) is more individual than geographical.

STATUS AND POPULATION. Resident, regular and uncommon to more or less common.

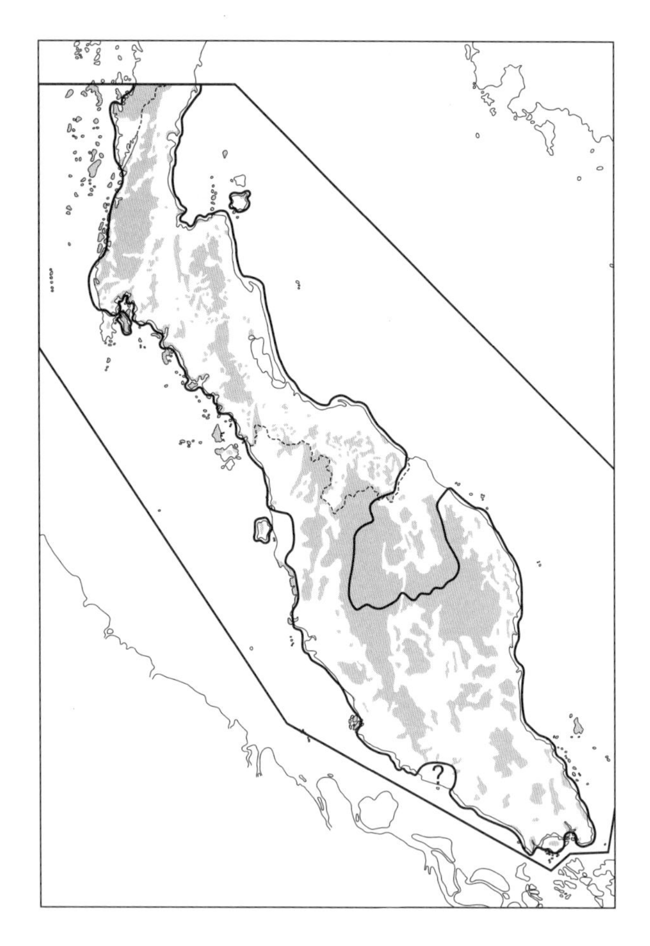

HABITATS AND ECOLOGY. The high canopy, including emergent crowns, of mature semi-evergreen and evergreen Lowland forest, down to mid-profile levels in edge and disturbed situations; also mature tree plantations, wooded gardens, parkland timber, rough secondary-growth and coastal strand (including casuarina) woodland. Perhaps also enters the landward fringe of mangrove forest, but more observations are needed. Occurs mainly at plains level, but in inland forest and edge habitats some are on hill-slopes, with a few records up to the Montane ecotone (ENGGANG-2). Abundance in closed-canopy forest has not been measured, but much more visible and audible in its other habitats. As Brown-capped, relies on dead, rot-softened spurs for excavating roost- and nest-holes.

FORAGING AND FOOD. Even in open habitats, invariably stays high, at mid to upper crown levels. Like Brown-capped, moves relatively fast, surface-gleaning and tapping and flaking bark-fragments of mainly narrow branches and twigs. Also searches through leaf-bases, often perching crosswise and moving acrobatically (Short 1973). Prey apparently mostly small arthropods, but no specific identifications.

SOCIAL ORGANIZATION. Forages mostly alone, but presumed family parties of 3–4 birds have been seen together up to December.

MOVEMENTS. None reported.

SURVIVAL. No information.

SOCIAL INTERACTIONS. As with Brown-capped, the weak, high-pitched drum carries hardly over 50 m and has been recorded only in contact situations: by a bird interacting with another foraging in an adjacent tree; also at a new nest-site, where given persistently by a pair-member until its mate arrived.

VOICE. Of similar sound-quality to Brown-capped but more variants on record: a thin, repeated disyllable, *pik-it* and a single, sharp *pik* contact-note, the latter also often introducing a high, even-pitched trill, *pik-pihihihihihi . . .* The pursuer in a chase-flight broke the latter into spiderhunter-like, spaced triplets, *pihihi, pihihi, pihihi . . .* A bird foraging in a party introduced the trill with more complex, rippling, nuthatch-like notes, *pik-chirru-chirru-pihihihihi . . .*

The approximately half-second, even-toned drum is thin, high-pitched and very fast, given irregularly and intermittently while foraging. At regular (dead-wood) drumming-sites near the nest, repeated at rates of around 11 bursts per minute in bouts lasting up to five minutes.

BREEDING

Nest. The only records are from semi-open sites; none from forest, and none described in detail; in narrow, dead stems and mostly near-vertical spurs, commonly close to a broken or rotted-off tip, 6–15 m above ground (but likely to be much higher in original forest).

Eggs and brood. One successful nest monitored in my Selangor garden fledged only a single young, but parties of up to four birds imply some broods are of two. No other information.

Cycle. Both pair-members excavate and a pair working on a dead *Acacia auriculiformis* completed a hole in just two days, at least one bird roosting in it as of the second night. Both members also incubate and tend young. An early morning incubation change-over was completed in just a few seconds; the arriving bird called briefly outside the entrance, the sitter flying out and away immediately and silently (minimizing detection although, later, young in this nest were lost to a predator).

Seasonality. Active nests reported in all months February–September, on dates that suggest all laying, and last broods away, within this season (although no records are from north of central Malaysia).

MOULT. Replacement of primaries is regular-descendant. Among 42 adults from the full length of the Peninsula, and covering all months, 18 showed active wing-moult during late April (P1)–late October (P6–7), with starts up to June, completions apparently as of August, and incidence over 70 percent during May–July (BMNH).

CONSERVATION. Relative abundance and proven breeding in non-forest habitats implies no serious threat, but in Malaysia loss of habitat through replacement of old rubber with apparently uninhabitable oil-palm, removal of mature crop-trees and elimination of shelter-belts is on-going as plantation agriculture intensifies.

Rufous Woodpecker; Nok Hua Khwaan See Taan (Thai); Burung Belatuk Biji Nangka (Malay)

Celeus brachyurus (Vieillot) 1818, *Nouveau Dictionnaire d'Histoire Naturelle* 26: 103. TL Java.
Plate 66

GROUP RELATIONS. Free-standing; the sole representative in Asia of an otherwise Neotropical genus (Short 1982).

GLOBAL RANGE. The Himalayan foothills east from Garhwal, the eastern and southern Indian subcontinent, and Sri Lanka; SE Tibet; China south of a line Fujian–Guizhou–Yunnan, including Hainan island; and SE Asia to the Greater Sunda islands.

IDENTIFICATION/DESCRIPTION. A medium-small, compact woodpecker. Dull rufous above including wings, slightly darker and browner on head and tail; upperparts, mostly but not always including head and upper neck, barred black-brown, both bars and spacing widening on the wing-coverts, flight-feathers and tail. Below, chin and throat black, feathers narrowly fringed buff to rufous in a subdued scaly pattern; rest of underparts dull rufous-brown, a variable width of the breast plain, otherwise narrowly barred to scalloped black-brown (several bars per feather) back to lower tail-coverts. Adult male from other sex/age-classes by a small area of dark red feathering immediately below the eye.

Bare-part colours. (Adult) iris hazel-brown to dark brown, eyelid-rim greyish black; bill black, slaty at base of lower mandible; feet dirty grey-green to brown-olive.

Size (mm). (Live and skins: 17 males, 14 females; adult): wing 110–122 and 109–118; tail 52–60 and 51–62; bill 24.8–28.4 and 23.0–28.7; tarsus 19.1–22.6 and 19.7–23.2 (BMNH, UMBRP, UMZC, ZDUM).

Weight (g). Adults, sexes not separated, 62.0–72.4 (n=10) (UMBRP).

DISTRIBUTION. Historical summary: all divisions except *Son*, with additional island records from Penang off the W coast; and Ubin, St John's and Sentosa, Singapore.

GEOGRAPHICAL VARIATION. Endemic *squamigularis* Sundevall 1866 (TL Melaka), averaging larger (longer-winged) in the far north, where it intergrades with bigger, paler, less intensely barred *williamsoni* of S Tenasserim–SW Thailand (Robinson and Kloss 1921–24).

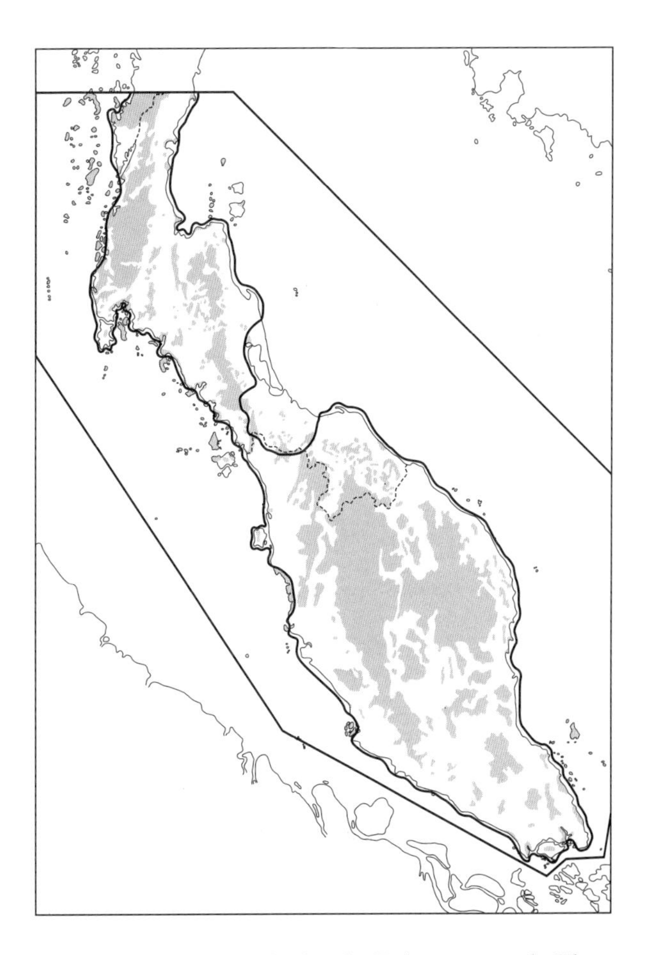

STATUS AND POPULATION. Resident, regular and more or less common.

HABITATS AND ECOLOGY. The canopy, including emergent crowns, of semi-evergreen and evergreen Lowland forest, mature and disturbed, from the landward edge of mangroves to the Montane ecotone and, locally, into the lowest zone of Lower Montane forest, recorded to 1050 m (MBR 1976–77). Follows the 'skin' of forest down at the edge of clearings; also in secondary-growth, strand (including casuarina) woodland, the subcoastal coconut belt, rubber and teak plantations (especially where overgrown), mature orchards and nearby wooded gardens and parkland.

The aromatic resin gummed to plumage of nearly all Rufous Woodpeckers, most often on the cap, back and tail-tip, has been guessed to be of plant origin but could equally well be from nest-defending termites (see also Banded and Crimson-winged Yellownapes, and Heart-spotted Woodpecker).

FORAGING AND FOOD. Invariably at crown level, surface-gleaning and tapping bark of living branches in the shaded interior. Not recorded excavating for food and hunts mostly while on the move, but stops to probe cracks in bark, holes in coconuts, etc., and waits on food-sources such as ant columns (Short 1973, Taylor 1961). Said to take mainly ants but a few local details available. Occasionally joins mixed-species flocks of foraging passerines (SINGAV-1).

SOCIAL ORGANIZATION. Forages mostly alone or in pairs, but family parties of 3–4 birds behave cohesively.

MOVEMENTS. None reported.

SURVIVAL. The longest retrap-interval is 36 months, at site of ringing (UMBRP).

SOCIAL INTERACTIONS. Head-swinging display-movements by two closely approaching males; also by a pair conducting a new fledgling (Short 1973, Taylor 1961). Males drum often, loudly enough to be advertising.

VOICE. The long advertising-call is a squealing rattle of 4–16 (commonly around eight) notes delivered at a rate of nine per second, evenly paced except for a short, fast tail, *kyi kyi kyi kyi kyi kyi kyi kyi-i-i-i*; the sequence drops very slightly in pitch throughout but with tail distinctly down-turned. Short (1973) describes brief, 3–5-note *keek* and *kweek* series, the latter given in conflict situations. At least one of a party of three foragers (pair and offspring?) called persistently with loud, rasping *dreik* and more stressed *dre-ik* notes.

The drum is an approximately two- (occasionally up to five-) second burst, rapid but suddenly and characteristically slowing down towards the end, *dadadadadadada-da–da–da—dat*.

BREEDING

Nest. Commonly stated to burrow into arboreal ant-nests (*Crematogaster* spp.). Holes in such nests are common, but only two of the breeding attempts reported were in ant-nests. Others were holes bored directly into trunks, e.g., of casuarinas and palms (including a dead Malayan date *Phoenix paludosa*), typically about 4 m up. One had an entrance 7.7 cm wide, nest-chamber 15 cm down.

Eggs and brood. Eggs are plain, glossless white. Shape short elliptical. Size (mm): 24.6 × 18.2, 24.4 × 17.9 (n=2). Full clutch two and, commonly, two young fledge.

Cycle. No information.

Seasonality. Poorly known. Egg-, chick- and new fledgling-dates extrapolate to laying during January–late April, but the overall season is unlikely to be this short (copulation seen in late August) (Edgar 1933, ENGGANG-1, Howes *et al.* 1986, R.R. Kersley, G.C. Madoc, NRCS).

MOULT. Replacement of primaries evidently regular-descendant. Among 71 adults from the full length of the Peninsula, and covering all months, 21 were in active wing-moult during late March (P1)–mid December (P9–10), with starts up to late August, completions as of September (possibly earlier), and incidence over 70 percent in July and August. None of 21 dated January–mid March showed any wing-moult (BMNH, UMBRP).

CONSERVATION. Extensive, permanent presence in non-forest habitats implies no critical threat.

White-bellied Woodpecker; Nok Hua Khwaan Yai See Dam (Thai); Burung Belatuk Perut Putih (Malay)

Dryocopus javensis (Horsfield) 1821, *Transactions of the Linnean Society* 13(1): 175. TL Java.
Plate 67

GROUP RELATIONS. Free-standing.

GLOBAL RANGE. Hill-tracts of the W, SW and, possibly, E Indian subcontinent, and the Andamans; S Sichuan and Yunnan; and SE Asia to the Greater Sunda islands (now extinct in Bali?), and the Philippines; with a northern isolate in the Korean Peninsula and formerly the Nansei islands (Tsushima).

IDENTIFICATION/DESCRIPTION. Great size and diagnostic pied plumage. Through most of the Peninsula, white confined to belly, rear flanks, lower tail-coverts and thighs (the latter spotted and barred black), fine flecking on ear-coverts, chin and throat, and variable fringing on lower breast. In the north, variable amounts also on back and rump, and base and extreme tips of primaries. The sexes differ on head-pattern: male malar-patch and complete cap with hind-crown crest scarlet; female malar and cap black, only the hind-crown crest scarlet. Juveniles resemble the female but with face streaked rather than flecked white.

Bare-part colours. (Adult) iris pale yellow, eyelid-rim dark blue-grey; upper mandible black, lower slaty grey; feet slaty grey.

Size (mm). (Live and skins: 10 males, 11 females; adult): wing 219–237 and 218–233; tail 154–168 and 151–166; bill 55.8–61.8 and 51.6–60.0; tarsus 35.6–39.9 and 33.5–39.8 (BMNH, M. Wong).

Weight (g). An adult male, 250.0; an adult female, 256.4 (UMBRP, M. Wong).

DISTRIBUTION. Few recent records north of Malaysia. Historical summary: all divisions except *Chu, Ran, Pha, Nak, Son, Pat, Pes*, with additional W-coast island records from Lanta (1995), Penang (none since 1989) and Pangkor.

GEOGRAPHICAL VARIATION. Nominate *javensis*, of the Sunda region, but variable white barring on the back and rump, and white extreme tips of primaries 5–8 show populations north from Trang intergrade with continental *feddeni* (BMNH, Chasen 1939).

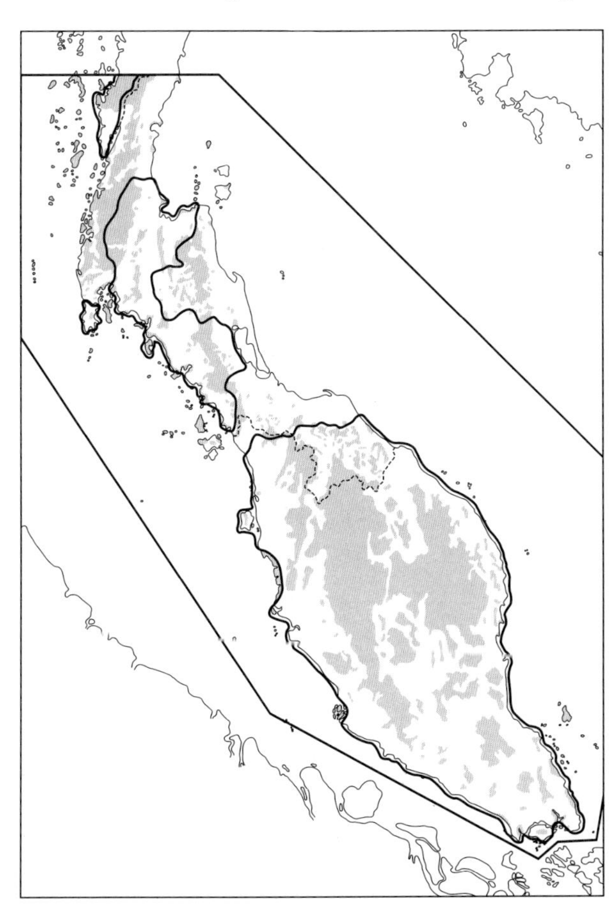

STATUS AND POPULATION. Resident, more or less regular and uncommon to more or less common on the southern mainland; now very local, believed close to extinction, in the Thai provinces. The modern Singapore population has never been more than a few individuals (BR 1976–77), most recently reported from the central catchment woodlands in mid 1994 (OBCB-20).

HABITATS AND ECOLOGY. Tall, semi-evergreen and evergreen Lowland forest, and peatswamp forest, mature to well regenerated with a good supply of large trees remaining (some feeding and even nesting occurs in isolated, edge trees); formerly also mangrove forest but most of the important back-zone of this habitat has been deforested, and hardly any of the rest retains trees large enough, or with enough dead wood, for nesting, foraging or even roosting purposes (birds roost alone in holes in dead snags). The only recent record is from the Krabi mangroves (Parr 1988), most or all of which are now under harvesting licence. Locally, enters old rubber plantation near forest.

Most of the range is at plains level, not above the steepland boundary, although recorded on steep terrain to 300 m in the Endau-Rompin conservation area, Pahang.

FORAGING AND FOOD. Taps bark of living trees mainly at interior-canopy level, but particularly attracted to dead, including rot-softened, wood at all levels, from high emergent snags to tall stumps and large dead-falls. Laterally hacks then flakes off large pieces of dead bark (Short 1973), actively breaks into dead wood and also excavates large and conspicuous pits (leaving a tell-tale carpet of large chips beneath the feeding-site). Foragers degrade rotten wood relatively fast and White-bellied Woodpeckers are obviously commoner in forests with a large supply of dead trees. Animal prey not identified locally; from Selangor, a single record of fruit-eating.

SOCIAL ORGANIZATION. Forages alone or in pairs. Both sexes drum (Short 1973) and elicit distant responses, the power of the drum fitting the apparently large size of territories.

MOVEMENTS. None reported.

SURVIVAL. No information.

SOCIAL INTERACTIONS. Males partly raise the crest in response to calls and drumming (Short 1973), and a pair interacting while perched close to one another jerked bodies from side to side (SINGAV-1). Drums powerfully on resonating dead wood, mostly at mid-morning and in late afternoon, in bouts of a few to 15 minutes, depending on responses.

VOICE. A loud, explosive yelp, *kiauk*, with shorter, softer versions, *kuk, kyuk*, and doubled *kiau-kiauk*, repeated in irregular order. In flight, notes run into a loud, far-carrying rattle, *kiau-kiau-kiau-kiau-kiau . . .* One or both members of a pair perched close together gave a low *ch-wi, ch-wi, ch-wi, ch-wi . . .* Drum-bursts of up to about two seconds accelerate towards the end (the longest from a rate of about 12 up to 19 beats per second) (BMP5, Short 1973).

BREEDING

Nest. Five described, all in dead trunks, one of a plantation rubber tree, others of forest trees standing relic in secondary-growth or recently cleared ground close to forest; in the main trunk, 9–15 m up, two directly below the base of large branches. One entrance-hole measured 10 × 12 cm wide, with tunnel 28 cm down to the nest-chamber.

Eggs and brood. Not described.

Cycle. Both sexes excavate, with a male seen 'indicating' a nest to his mate perched 2 m away by a bout of rapid tapping beside the entrance-hole. Both also incubate (males reported taking over in late evening), and both tend young.

Seasonality. Excavation in December and January, incubation during late December–February, young in the nest late January–March (Hutchinson 1950, NRCS, Short 1973).

MOULT. Order of primary moult regular-descendant. Among 29 adults covering the length of the Peninsula south to Johor, and all months except April and June, nine showed active wing-moult from mid May (P4, P1–2) to mid October (P7–8), with completions as of September. November adults were in fresh plumage and none of 19 dated November–March showed any further moult. An instance of early-stage post-juvenile wing-moult: P1–2 in mid March (BMNH, M. Wong).

CONSERVATION. A declining species, suffering from loss of core, plains-level forest. Able to feed in disturbed habitats where these retain a large supply of dead trunks, but once the canopy is opened acceptable relic stands also attract aggressive competitors for tree-holes, notably Dollarbird *Eurystomus orientalis*. G. Noramly followed three woodpecker nesting-attempts in relic forest on the campus of the Malaysian National University, Selangor, during which holes were excavated and young hatched, but parents were consistently harassed by pairs of Dollarbirds whenever they flew near the nest. Only one attempt is suspected to have succeeded. At least one other fell to a predator, and noisy attentions of the Dollarbirds probably helped advertise the position of the nest. In all cases, Dollarbirds ultimately took possession of nest-holes.

Banded Yellownape; Nok Hua Khwaan Daeng Lai (Thai); **Burung Belatuk Merah** (Malay)

Picus mineaceus Pennant 1769, *Indian Zoology*: plate 4. TL Java.
Plate 66

GROUP RELATIONS. Free-standing.

GLOBAL RANGE. The Greater Sunda islands, the Peninsula, and Tenasserim and SW Thailand respectively to about 12°30′N and 13°N (BBCB-9).

IDENTIFICATION/DESCRIPTION. At rest on an exposed snag, the posture is typically hunched, with crest lowered, sloping off the nape (see also Common Flameback). Long posterior feathers of crest lemon-yellow; hind-neck and upper mantle dark olive barred buff-white, feather-tips brightening to yellow-green on the lower mantle and bright lime-yellow on back and rump; scapulars, upper wing-coverts and outer webs of secondaries and inner primaries dark red; flight-feathers otherwise black-brown, inner webs barred and outer webs of primaries notched buff-white on both surfaces. Upper tail-coverts and tail black-brown. Below, lower face and chin to upper breast cinnamon-rufous, rest of underparts stone-white densely barred black-brown; lower wing-coverts mottled the same. The sexes differ in extent of red on the head: forehead to nape-crest, down face to below eye-level and back to rear ear-coverts in males, back only from forecrown and not enclosing eye in females; also in the patterning on rufous parts: none in males; forehead to side of face (around eye), chin, throat and, in some cases, upper breast finely freckled in females (feather-tips dark brown then whitish).

In juveniles, red of head is duller and restricted to hind-crown and nape-crest, leaving rest of cap and face dull rufous-brown; upper breast spotted and barred, the barring of remaining underparts less crisp, more widely spaced and on a rufous-buff rather than stone-white ground; and rump correspondingly brown-and-white-barred rather than yellow.

Bare-part colours. Iris brown (juvenile), red (adult), narrow eyering dark grey-green; upper mandible black, lower bluish white; feet dull grey-olive to greenish.

Size (mm). (Live and skins: 15 males, 15 females; adult): wing 126–135 and 124–137; tail 72–87 and 66–83; bill 26.7–33.5 and 26.2–32.6; tarsus 23.5–25.0 and 23.7–24.8 (BMNH, UMBRP, UMZC).

Weight (g). Adults, sexes not separated, 85.0–105.0 (n=7); brown-eyed juveniles down to 74.7 (UMBRP).

DISTRIBUTION. Historical summary: all divisions except *Pha*, *Yal*, with additional island records from Pangkor (*Pek*). The still-unidentified woodpecker on Tioman island is a yellownape (BR 1980–81), Banded being one of three possibilities.

GEOGRAPHICAL VARIATION. Subspecies *malaccensis* Latham 1790 (TL Melaka), also of mainland Sumatra, Banka, Belitung and northern Borneo.

STATUS AND POPULATION. Resident, regular and common in the south, now uncommon in the Thai provinces (Boonsong and Round 1991).

HABITATS AND ECOLOGY. Older mangroves, evergreen and semi-evergreen Lowland forest, mature and disturbed, and, less commonly, Lower Montane forest to about 1200 m; also strand (including casuarina) woodland, scrub with scattered trees and other secondary-growth, tree plantations, parkland and wooded gardens. Everywhere, requires dead wood for drumming and nest- and roost-hole excavation, and commonly forages on dead wood. Often calls, occasionally drums, or sits stolidly for extended periods on an exposed dead snag. Like Rufous and Heart-spotted Woodpeckers, and Crimson-winged Yellownape, sometimes tarred with an aromatic gum, especially on anterior cap, underparts and wing- and tail-tips.

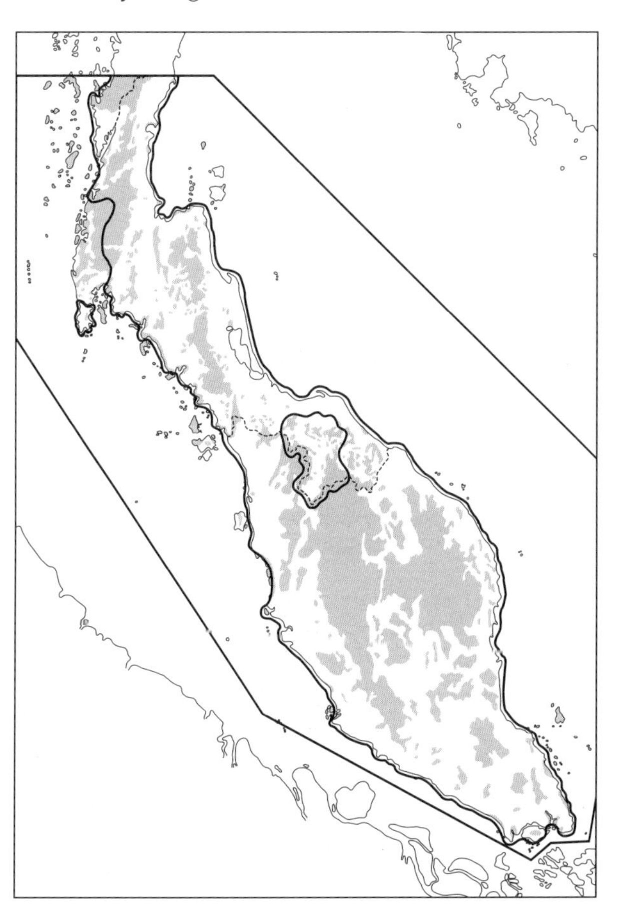

A pair in Terengganu coastal strand woodland lost a nest- or roost-hole to Lineated Barbets *Megalaima lineata* (Lewin 1957).

FORAGING AND FOOD. In inland forest, hunts from the lower canopy down to the under-stratum but in other habitats mainly at mid- to crown levels. Taps, gleans and probes bark surfaces, rotten wood and epiphyte root-masses, often among fairly dense foliage (Short 1973). Lingers at good sites hence progress is typically rather slow, but in the Singapore central catchment woodland one observed in a mix-species foraging-flock, mostly of passerines (SINGAV-1).

SOCIAL ORGANIZATION. Territorial pairs, but commonly forages alone.

MOVEMENTS. None reported.

SURVIVAL. The longest of very few retrap-intervals, 71 months (UMBRP).

SOCIAL INTERACTIONS. Territory-edge interactions between males include crest-raising, side-to-side body-swinging, and vocalizing. Drums sparingly, on dead wood. The individual burst is a fast, high, even-paced, monotone rattle of about one second, repeated in bouts at intervals down to about 30 seconds.

VOICE. The loud advertising-call, given with up-tilted bill, is a single screaming *kwier*, often answered by a neighbouring bird (mate?); occasionally repeated at a typically deliberate pace, usually not more than five times but one of a pair working on a nest-hole gave a run of 20. A robust, rasping *cherwerk-cherwerk-cherwerk* . . ., accompanying body-swing display, is common during pair-interactions in the early breeding period and also when young fledge.

BREEDING

Nest. Invariably in dead, often rot-softened wood of a bare trunk, tall stump or snag of a dead branch (on the overhung face where sloping), in the open and also within an otherwise living crown, 8–20 m up. Silk-cotton *Ceiba pentandra* and batai *Albizzia falcataria* are among trees commonly used in non-forest situations. One entrance-hole measured 5 cm wide, nest-chamber 30 cm down.

Eggs and brood. Eggs are plain, glossy, slightly translucent white. Shape elliptical to near-ovate. Size (mm): 27.7–26.9 × 20.5–19.5 (n=5). Full clutch 2–3 eggs but the few records of fledging have been of only single young, implying brood-reduction.

Cycle. Both partners excavate, and at the start of the breeding-season nest-holes may be worked intermittently 1–2 months before they are finally occupied. Both also incubate and tend young. Incubation-switches (regular at dusk) are swift and silent, or with not more than a single call from the arriving partner. A parent tending a large nestling shook its head violently, apparently to regurgitate a food-bolus which was then fed deep into the offspring's gullet.

Seasonality. Hole-excavation leading to breeding-attempts recorded during early November–early May; active nests, contents unchecked, as of early January; and nestlings during February–late August (fledging from early March to early September). At one well-watched hole, nestlings in February and May are believed to have been successive broods of a single pair (BBCB-7, Edgar 1933, Lewin 1957, G.C. Madoc, NRCS, Short 1973).

MOULT. Replacement of primaries apparently regular-descendant, with not more than two adjacent feathers in overlapping growth. Among 61 adults from the length of the Peninsula and covering the year, 20 showed wing-moult in all months except December, February, April and June. Starts (P1) are dated May–September, with only inner-tract moult during that period, versus only mid- and outer-tract moult during November–March. Fluctuating monthly incidence: 40–100 percent during July–November, below 25 percent during December–April, is further evidence of seasonality overall, but loosely enough synchronized probably for some activity year-round (see also Laced Woodpecker). Extreme start and finish dates imply individual wing-moult may require more than seven months (BMNH, UMBRP, UMZC, ZDUM).

CONSERVATION. From its wide range of resident habitats, evidently not at serious risk.

Lesser Yellownape; Nok Hua Khwaan Lek Ngawn Leuang (Thai); Burung Belatuk Tengkuk Kuning Kecil (Malay)

Picus chlorolophus Vieillot 1818, *Nouveau Dictionnaire d'Histoire Naturelle* 26: 78. TL Bengal.
Plate 66

GROUP RELATIONS. Forms a superspecies with *P. puniceus* (Crimson-winged Yellownape), which it replaces altitudinally (Short 1982).

GLOBAL RANGE. The Himalayas and hill-tracts of the Indian subcontinent and Sri Lanka; uplands of Fujian, Yunnan and Hainan; and of SE Asia to the Peninsula and Sumatra.

IDENTIFICATION/DESCRIPTION. Nape-crest orange-yellow and sides of face olive, with a long, white moustache-line from bill-base back under eye to lower border of ear-coverts. Upperparts olive, brightest on the body and washed yellowish on rump and upper tail-coverts; wing-coverts bronzy green, primaries and outer secondaries rufous-brown with outer webs edged olive-green, unbarred (*contra* Greater Yellownape), and inner webs notched white. Below, brown-olive with spots and short bars from the side of the lower breast to flanks and tibia white. Head-pattern differs between the sexes: in males, malar-stripe and variable amount of the cap red, some completely from forehead but, commonly, only the rim (and even this often broken posteriorly), with any red showing on the otherwise olive-black crown reduced to fine tips. In females, only a supercilium from eye to nape is red, with malar-patch greenish. Young juveniles lack all red and are more extensively and heavily marked white below.

Bare-part colours. Iris brown (juvenile), red (adult); bill-tip and upper mandible except cutting-edge blackish, base of lower mandible yellowish, rest of bill slate-blue; feet dirty grey-green (Robinson 1928).

Size (mm). (Skins: 4 males, 2 females; adult): wing 121–124 and 125, 126; tail 86–91 and 85, 91; bill 26.4–27.1 and 26.4, 26.9; tarsus 21.6–22.5 and 21.5, 22.4 (BMNH).

Weight. No data.

DISTRIBUTION. On the Larut Range, the Main Range, recorded from Genting Highlands north to Cameron Highlands, and eastern outlier Benom (BR 1967). Historical summary: *Pek, Phg, Sel.*

GEOGRAPHICAL VARIATION. Endemic *rodgeri* Hartert and Butler 1898 (TL Hijau peak, Larut Range).

STATUS AND POPULATION. Resident, regular and uncommon to more or less common.

HABITATS AND ECOLOGY. Lower and Upper Montane forest, mature and disturbed, recorded from about 1200 to 1820 m.

FORAGING AND FOOD. Searches mostly upper trunks and main branches at canopy level. Short (1973) lists surface gleaning, tapping and flaking, probing and excavation of pits. Except when working at an opening, it tends to move on quickly. Loners join mixed-species flocks of foraging passerines (Bromley 1952), in which L.L. Short saw only females,

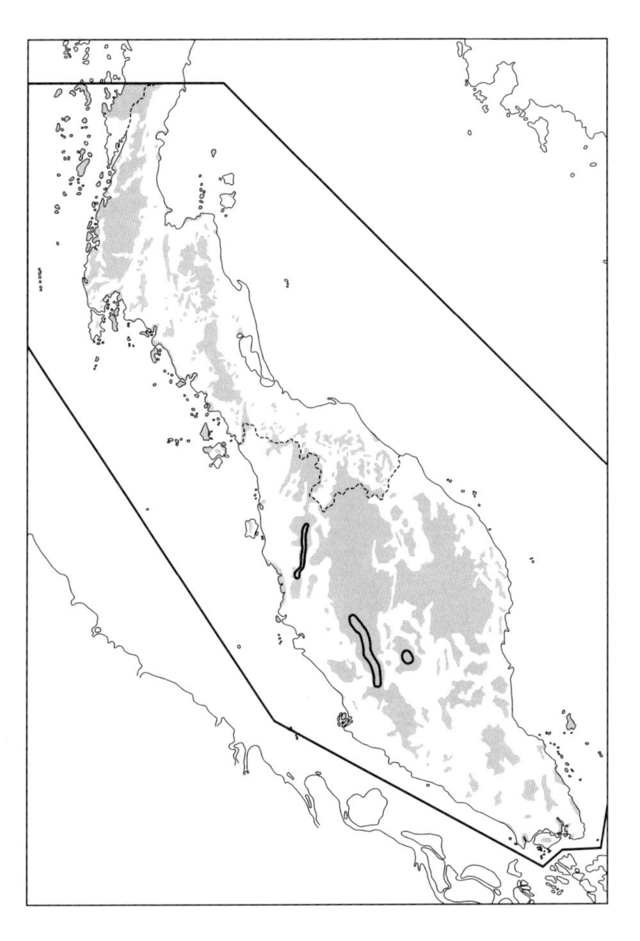

suggesting a possible behavioural divergence between the sexes.

SOCIAL ORGANIZATION. Independant adults tend to space themselves while foraging, and generally do not keep company, but family parties persist until at least the stage of post-juvenile moult.

MOVEMENTS. No information.

SURVIVAL. No information.

SOCIAL INTERACTIONS. Crest-raising, as individuals approach one another (Short 1973).

VOICE. The loud call is a rather high-pitched, drawn-out wail, *kweee-ooe*, repeated at intervals of a few seconds; each call twice as long (about 0.5 seconds), shriller and more obviously disyllabic than the similar vocalization of Banded Yellownape, potentially in the same habitat, but less disyllabic than the equivalent call of more closely related Crimson-winged Yellownape. A soft, kitten-like note, *meay*, has been heard from feeding birds (G.C. Madoc).

BREEDING

Nest. The only record, 4 m up the trunk of a dead tree in disturbed Lower Montane forest; no details available.

Eggs and brood. Not described.

Cycle. Both sexes incubate.

Seasonality. The active nest is dated February. An identification of fledglings at Fraser's Hill in June is now in some doubt (Allin and Edgar 1948, BMP5).

MOULT. P2 on 30 May and T1 on 11 October are the only records. Other adults dated February, March and May showed no moult (BMNH).

CONSERVATION. No current threat, but much depends on the nature of the development that might in future be allowed in the highlands, especially on the Main Range.

Crimson-winged Yellownape; Nok Hua Khwaan Peek Daeng (Thai); Burung Belatuk Mas (Malay)

Picus puniceus Horsfield 1821, *Transactions of the Linnean Society* 13(1): 176. TL Java.
Plate 66

GROUP RELATIONS. See Lesser Yellownape.

GLOBAL RANGE. The Greater Sunda islands, the Peninsula, and Tenasserim and SW Thailand, respectively, to 11°20'N and 13°N.

IDENTIFICATION/DESCRIPTION. Cap crimson, sharply demarcated against olive-green cheek at slightly above eye-level, and nape-crest yellow. Rest of head and body, together with tertials, tips of inner secondaries and lower wing-coverts, olive-green, brightest on the upperparts (to yellowish on back and rump), palest on chin and throat; flanks and, variably, belly and lower breast spotted and barred whitish (compare Lesser Yellownape). Upper wing-coverts and outer webs of flight-feathers crimson-red, except for P9–10 which, like tail, are all blackish. The sexes differ in face-pattern: male with a contrasting red malar-stripe, absent in female whose lower face is uniform olive. Young juveniles resemble the female but have cap dark olive rather than red.

Bare-part colours. Iris grey (young juvenile), dark red (adult), with broad bare eyelids lavender-green (adult); upper mandible except cutting-edge black, rest of the bill yellow, or with lower mandible tip brownish; feet pale olive-green.

Size (mm). (Live and skins: 19 males, 9 females; adult): wing 123–132 and 128–137; tail 77–92 and 81–86; bill 29.2–34.0 and 29.4–34.5; tarsus 22.9–26.8 and 21.1–25.2 (BMNH, UMBRP).

Weight (g). Adult males, 77.6 and 82.8 (UMBRP).

DISTRIBUTION. Historical summary: in all divisions except *Pha, Phu, Pht, Pat, Pra,* but extinct *Sin* for at least 30 years, and with no other island records.

GEOGRAPHICAL VARIATION. Subspecies *observandus* Hartert 1891 (TL Deli, NE Sumatra), of the global range except Java; mainland birds averaging slightly larger than those of Sumatra and Borneo.

STATUS AND POPULATION. Resident, regular and more or less common.

HABITATS AND ECOLOGY. The edge and interior of semi-evergreen and evergreen Lowland forest, mature and disturbed, also peatswamp forest and old paperbark *Melaleuca* stands, at plains level and on slopes to the Montane ecotone; occasionally into Lower Montane forest to about 1100 m (ENGGANG-3). Erratic in coastal strand woodland, secondary-growth with tall trees, tree- and palm plantations, and wooded gardens. Unlike Banded Yellownape, shows no good evidence of a stable population away from original forest.

In Pasoh research forest, a male excavated a roost-hole some 20 m up a dead snag projecting vertically from the crown of a tree, above the level of surrounding regenerating forest.

Like Rufous and Heart-spotted Woodpeckers, and Banded Yellownape, plumage sometimes fouled with an aromatic gum, particularly on cap, underparts and tail- and wing-tips. Nasute head-capsules of worker termites stuck along the fringe of a gummed tail of a museum skin (BMNH) prove nothing but lend weight to a suggestion of the gum being an insect product.

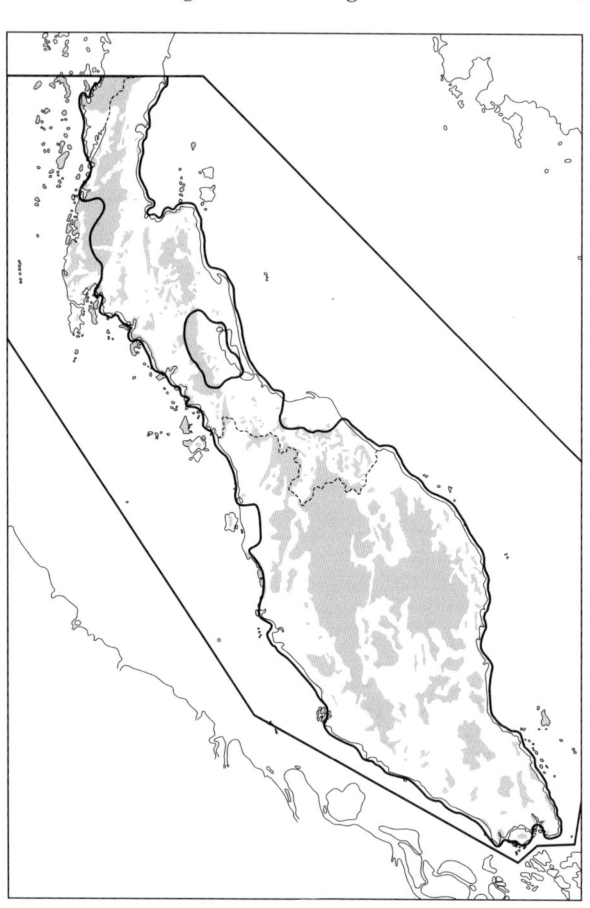

FORAGING AND FOOD. Hunts in situations equivalent to Lesser Yellownape, on the upper trunk and main crown branches of relatively tall trees. Taps, probes, excavates, gleans and flakes bark surfaces; lingers at good sites but generally moves on fairly quickly (Short 1973).

SOCIAL ORGANIZATION. Apparently territorial pairs, but commonly alone when foraging.

MOVEMENTS. None reported.

SURVIVAL. No information.

SOCIAL INTERACTIONS. An encounter between pair-members involved crest-raising, sideways body-swinging and drumming by the male (Short 1973). Drums mostly alone, on dead, resonating snags. Bursts are fast; one of 0.9 seconds included 14 beats, more or less regularly paced but of uneven strength (Short 1973).

VOICE. The common loud advertising-call is a wailing disyllable, *kwee-lu*, less often extended to a 3–5-note *kwee-ler-lu, kwee-ler-ler-lu*, etc., given with crest raised and bill up-tilted. Bouts of apparent territorial advertising from tree-top height last from a few to 20 minutes. Other calls include a low *week-eek* as pair-members meet.

BREEDING. No details beyond a pair bringing food to young in a Selangor nest on 26 March (G. Noramly). A fledgling recorded in BMP5 has been re-identifed as Banded Yellownape.

MOULT. Replacement of primaries is regular-descendant. Among 53 adults from the full length of the Peninsula and covering all months, 29 showed wing-moult during early May(P2) – early January (P8–9), with starts (P1) up to mid September, no records to late August past stage P5 (versus most beyond stage P6 from October), earliest completions as of October, and a monthly incidence of 70–100 percent during June–November. Sixteen dated February–April were all non-moulters, implying arrest, or sufficient population synchrony to allow a genuine break in activity (compare Banded Yellownape and Laced Woodpecker *Picus vittatus*). Post-juvenile wing-moult (P3) on 19 October would not have been completed by January.

CONSERVATION. Abundance in submontane slope-forest suggests no immediate threat to this species.

Greater Yellownape; Nok Hua Khwaan Yai Ngawn Leuang (Thai); Burung Belatuk Tengkuk Kuning Besar (Malay)

Picus flavinucha Gould 1834, *Proceedings of the Zoological Society of London* 1: 120. TL Darjeeling, NE India.

Plate 66

GROUP RELATIONS. Forms a superspecies with *P. mentalis* (Chequer-throated Woodpecker), which it replaces altitudinally (Short 1982).

GLOBAL RANGE. The Himalayas east from Garhwal and hill-tracts of the NE Indian subcontinent; SE Tibet; uplands of Fujian to Guangxi, Sichuan and Yunnan, and Hainan island; and of SE Asia to the Peninsula and Sumatra.

IDENTIFICATION/DESCRIPTION. Cap down to just above eye-level dark olive, washed chestnut-brown, and nape-crest bright yellow; rest of upperparts including wing-coverts and outer webs of inner secondaries olive-green, brightest on the body. Primaries, outer secondaries and inner webs of inner secondaries boldly barred chestnut and black (*contra* Lesser Yellownape); and tail blackish. Side of face olive, a broad malar-stripe and chin to upper throat (separated by a streak of bronze-brown), pale yellow in males, poorly contrasting dull rufous in females; lower throat of both sexes chequered black and white (black with white feather-edging, clearer in the female). Rest of underparts plain grey-olive (without the white side-markings of Lesser Yellownape), lower wing-coverts lime-yellow barred dark olive. There is no good description of the local juvenile.

Bare-part colours. (Adult) iris red-brown; bill slate-black, lower mandible slightly paler, tinged blue-green; feet greenish slate.

Size (mm). (Skins: 6 males, 5 females; adult): wing 142–153 and 143–152; tail 98–113 and 103–114; bill 35.6–38.0 and 33.3–37.1; tarsus 25.0–28.1 and 24.1–26.7 (BMNH, UMZC).

Weight. No data.

DISTRIBUTION. The Larut Range, the Main Range recorded from Genting Highlands north to Cameron Highlands and (provisional sight-records only) on outlying Benom (*Phg*). Historical summary: *Pek, Phg, Sel.*

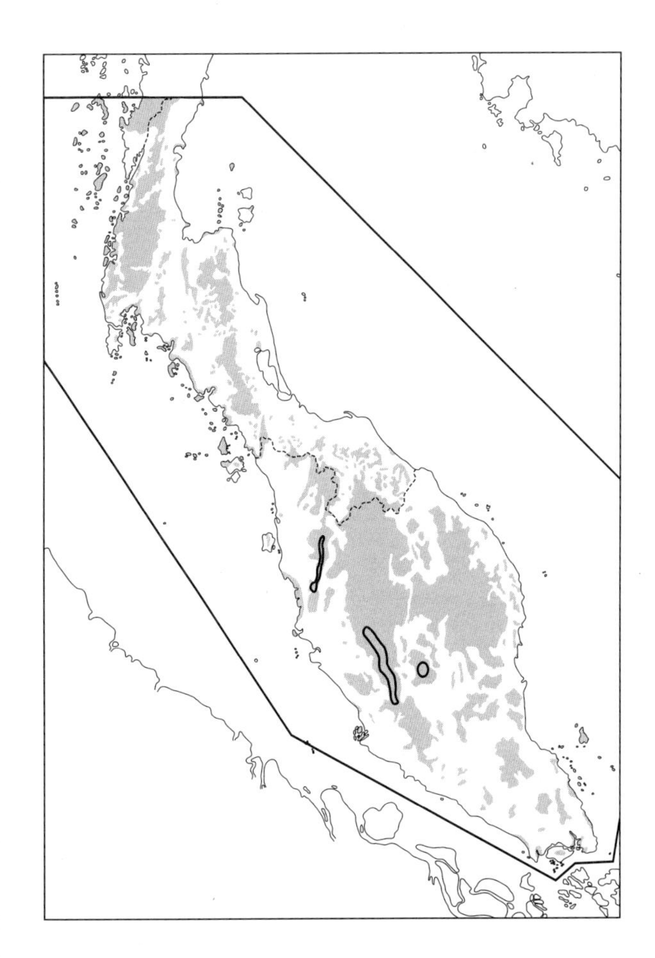

GEOGRAPHICAL VARIATION. Small, endemic *wrayi* Sharpe 1888 (TL Inas peak, Larut Range).

STATUS AND POPULATION. Resident, regular and (on the Main Range) common.

HABITATS AND ECOLOGY. Lower to Upper Montane forest, mature or lightly disturbed, from about 920 to at least 1890 m (McClure 1964). Roost- or nest-holes confirmed to belong to this species have all been in trunks of dead trees or large palms (*Caryota*), but records are too few to confirm a dependance on dead wood.

FORAGING AND FOOD. Gleans and probes over the whole vegetation column, from near ground-level to the top canopy, and on substrates ranging from main trunks to branches, vines, leaf-bunches and trapped litter (Short 1973). Foragers commonly stay well concealed amongst foliage and tend to progress rather slowly, although one reported accompanying a mixed-species flock of foraging passerines (SINGAV-2).

SOCIAL ORGANIZATION. Pair-members often forage together, and cohesive family parties are conspicuous by their noise.

MOVEMENTS. None reported.

SURVIVAL. No information.

SOCIAL INTERACTIONS. Crest-raising as birds meet.

VOICE. A robust, explosive disyllable, *kyau-yak* or *kyau-yok*, and a piercing *pieu* or *kieu*.

BREEDING

Nest. Only one confirmed: approximately 5 m up the trunk of a 25 cm diameter, partly rotten, dead tree at the edge of a forest clearing; entrance 5.8 cm wide, tunnel dropping 20.5 cm to an oval-shaped nest-chamber up to 11.5 cm across. Other occupied holes used, perhaps, only as roosts, have all been in rotten trunks, not less than 4 m above ground.

Eggs and brood. A brood of two, one sibling substantially larger (older? better fed?) than the other, but both left the nest. Surprisingly for so common a bird, no other information.

Cycle. Both partners incubate and both tend young.

Seasonality. The above pair laid in February, began feeding-visits in the first week of March, and fledged young in the last week. Other possible active nests on 21 March and 2 April (Cramer 1941, ENGGANG-1, G.C. Madoc).

MOULT. P10 in early September and T1 in late November are the only instances. Nine adults dated December–March showed no moult (BMNH, UMZC).

CONSERVATION. No current threat, but comments under Lesser Yellownape apply to most Montane birds in the Peninsula.

Chequer-throated Yellownape; Nok Hua Khwaan Khaw Lai (Thai); **Burung Belatuk Ranting** (Malay)

Picus mentalis Temminck 1826, *Nouveau Recueil de Planches Coloriées d'Oiseaux* 65: plate 384. TL Java.

Plate 66

GROUP RELATIONS. See Greater Yellownape.

GLOBAL RANGE. The Greater Sunda islands, Banka, the Peninsula, and Tenasserim to latitude about 12°20'N.

IDENTIFICATION/DESCRIPTION. Nape-crest yellow. Rest of cap, upper body and outer median wing-coverts rather bright olive-green, sharp against crimson-red of remaining wing-coverts and outer webs of secondaries. Rest of flight-feathers black-brown, primaries and inner webs of secondaries boldly notched to barred chestnut (as in Greater Yellownape, which has green rather than red wing-coverts); tail black. Side of face from above eye-level grey-green, with broad malar-stripe white-speckled green in males, plain chestnut in females. Below, throat (and chin in the male) white, boldly and densely streaked ('chequered') black; point of female chin chestnut. Both sexes show a broad, bright chestnut band across the upper breast, curving up the side of the neck to end on the nape, at the base of the crest. Remaining underparts plain olive-green; lower wing-coverts mottled chestnut and dark brown. Juveniles resemble adults but are duller, with an area of chestnut at or very close to the tip of the outer web of the primaries, and no white speckling on the male malar-stripe. A claimed rufous tinge to the underparts requires confirmation.

Bare-part colours. (Adult) iris red-brown, broad eyelids olive-green; upper mandible black, lower pale lead-blue; feet olive-green.

Size (mm). (Live and skins: 11 males, 12 females; adult): wing 132–143 and 130–144; tail 86–101 and 89–100; bill 32.6–38.0 and 34.2–38.2; tarsus 24.2–26.5 and 23.7–27.0 (BMNH, UMBRP, UMZC).

Weight (g). Adults, sexes not separated, 82.2–121.0 (n=10) (UMBRP).

DISTRIBUTION. Historical summary: all divisions except *Chu, Ran, Phu, Pat, Ked*, but extinct *Sin* for at least 30 years, and with no other island records.

GEOGRAPHICAL VARIATION. Subspecies *humii* Hargitt 1889 (TL Kelang, Selangor), of the global range except Java.

STATUS AND POPULATION. Resident, regular and more or less common in the evergreen south; local and uncommon north of Malaysia, from approximately the Thai-Burmese forest floristic boundary.

HABITATS AND ECOLOGY. The most completely forest-dependent Lowland *Picus*. Inhabits dry-land evergreen and, to a lesser extent, semi-evergreen Lowland forest, forest-edge and occasionally secondary-growth with tall trees, at plains level and on slopes to the Montane ecotone. Above the ecotone, excluded by Greater Yellownape; on mountains outside the latter's range in the Peninsula it continues into Lower Montane forest, with records to 1220 m (BMP5).

FORAGING AND FOOD. Hunts throughout the forest vegetation column, but mainly in the mid-stratum and lower canopy, on living and dead bark surfaces of trunks, major branches, stems and creepers, and at epiphyte masses. Main modes of foraging are gleaning and probing, with only occasional tapping or excavating, consistent with generally fast onward movements (Short 1973). Regularly joins both Lowland and Montane forest mixed-species foraging-flocks, or flocks may actually form around a woodpecker. L.L. Short describes instances of the 'marking' of a Chequer-throat by up to three Ferruginous Babblers *Trichastoma bicolor*, which moved in close as soon as it began active foraging.

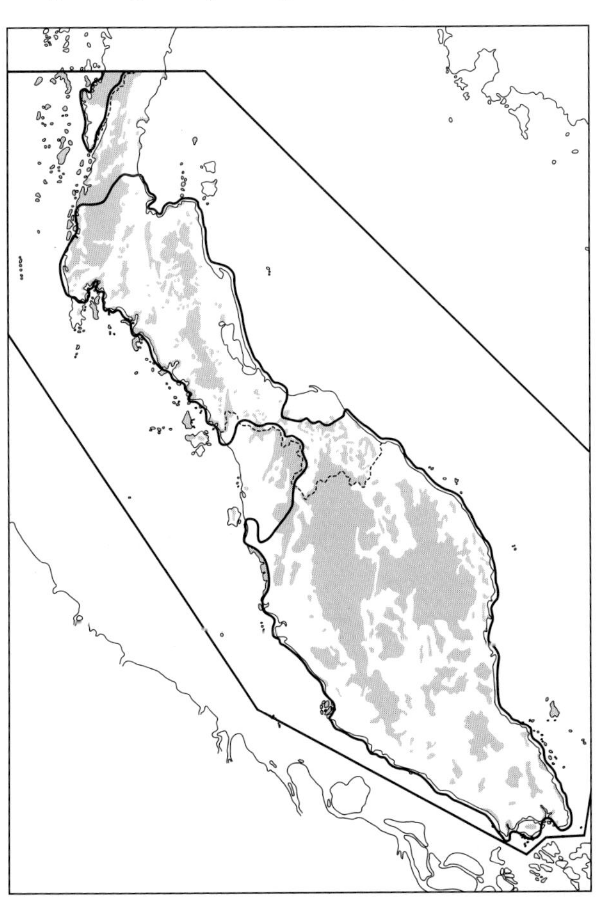

SOCIAL ORGANIZATION. Forms cohesive family parties while offspring are dependent, but independent adults forage mostly alone. Never more than one individual attends a mixed-species flock.

MOVEMENTS. None reported.

SURVIVAL. No information.

SOCIAL INTERACTIONS. Crest-raising as pair-members approach one another.

VOICE. Surprisingly little known. Short (1973) describes a single *kyi-ee*, with a distinct tail, and a briefer *kyik*, etc., from foragers. More observations are needed.

BREEDING

Nest. Only three reported, all 5–6 m up dead, rot-softened trunks, including two of trees standing out of the canopy of secondary-growth, the third in a coconut palm on the edge of forest. No other details available.

Eggs and brood. Eggs are plain matt white. Shape short elliptical. One probably full clutch of three. No other information.

Cycle. No information.

Seasonality. Eggs in March and April; a juvenile accompanying parents on 9 August (Chasen 1939).

MOULT. Replacement of primaries is regular-descendant, with not more than two adjacent feathers in overlapping growth, but across the whole tract to P9–10. Among 47 adults covering the Peninsula south from Pakchan, and all months, 25 showed wing-moult during mid May (P1)–mid December (P8), with starts (P1) up to September, earliest completions probably in November, and incidence 80-plus percent during May–November. Seventeen dated January–April were all moult-free, but individual progress implies a minority of moulters could have been active well outside observed limits, suggesting the seasonal break at population level may involve arrests or suspensions. An instance of post-juvenile wing-moult: P1 on 12 March (BMNH, UMBRP).

CONSERVATION. By its narrower ecological tolerance, perhaps more at risk from habitat-loss than other lowland *Picus* species, but still well distributed on the submontane slope, hence judged not to be under immediately threat.

Laced Woodpecker; Nok Hua Khwaan Khieo Paa Phai (Thai); Burung Belatuk Bakau (Malay)

Picus vittatus Vieillot 1818, *Nouveau Dictionnaire d'Histoire Naturelle* 26: 91. TL W Java. Plate 68

GROUP RELATIONS. Eastern *vittatus* and western *viridanus* (Streaked-breasted Woodpecker) have been treated as conspecific but diverge ecologically to occupy separate sets of habitats where they meet in far-W and SW Thailand (Boonsong and Round 1991), suggesting they are better considered members of a superspecies.

GLOBAL RANGE. S Yunnan; continental SE Asia west to E Burma, SW Thailand and Tenasserim, then in the southern Peninsula, E lowlands of Sumatra, Java and Bali.

IDENTIFICATION/DESCRIPTION. Apart from a fringe of black from bill-base to ear-coverts, entire cap back to nape vermilion-red in the male, all-black with some white bases showing through along the sides in the female. Rest of upperparts including wing-coverts bright olive-green, suffused lime-yellow on the back and rump. Flight-feathers sooty black with outer webs barred white and, inwards along the tract, secondaries progressively edged green through which these bars show only obscurely, but their inner webs remain boldly notched white. Tail black. Side of face from bill-base to ear-coverts clear grey, finely vermiculated black-and-white from lores back around eye, streaked white, and white-margined over the ear-coverts and malar-stripe; the latter black with white speckling. Below, chin to upper breast and side of neck plain light olive-green with a coppery tinge, the rest of the underparts patterned: lime-cream with a dark olive stripe down either side of each feather, back from thighs and belly stripes meeting apically to produce a scalloped effect, with some dark penetrating back along the shaft. In some individuals, this scalloped pattern extends onto the lower breast. Lower wing-coverts are white with black flecking. Juveniles as adult except ventral patterning more obscure, and cap of male mottled black, to all-black posteriorly.

Bare-part colours. (Adult) iris dark red to red-brown; upper mandible black, lower yellow-horn darkening to greenish or black at tip; feet glaucous-green.

Size (mm). (Live and skins: 11 males, 9 females; adult): wing 126–139 and 125–136; tail 88–106 and 84–104; bill 31.9–36.8 and 32.0–35.0; tarsus 26.1–28.3 and 24.8–28.3 (BMNH, UMBRP).

Weight (g). Adult nominate *vittatus*: males, 95.0–126.0, (n=49); females, 94.2–121.0 (n=35). *P.v. connectens* is slightly heavier: males, 127.9 and 128.0; a female, 126.6 (UMBRP).

DISTRIBUTION. Southern and western mainland coastal plains north to Sitiawan district (latitude 4°13'N) and the E coast north to Rompin district, Johor/Pahang border. Historical summary: *Pek, Sel, Neg, Mel, Joh, Sin*, with an outlying population in the Langkawi group (Langkawi, Dayang Bunting) (*Ked*) and other island records from Ubin and Sentosa, Singapore.

GEOGRAPHICAL VARIATION. Nominate *vittatus* of the Sunda region on Singapore and the mainland; local endemic *connectens* Robinson and Kloss 1919 (TL Langkawi islands) in the Langkawi group, not separated by Short (1982) although slightly larger: wing minimum 135 mm versus not above 133 in nominate *vittatus*, and said to be clearer green on the wing-coverts, but this subtle colour-difference could be a wear factor.

STATUS AND POPULATION. Resident, regular and common near coasts, less so inland.

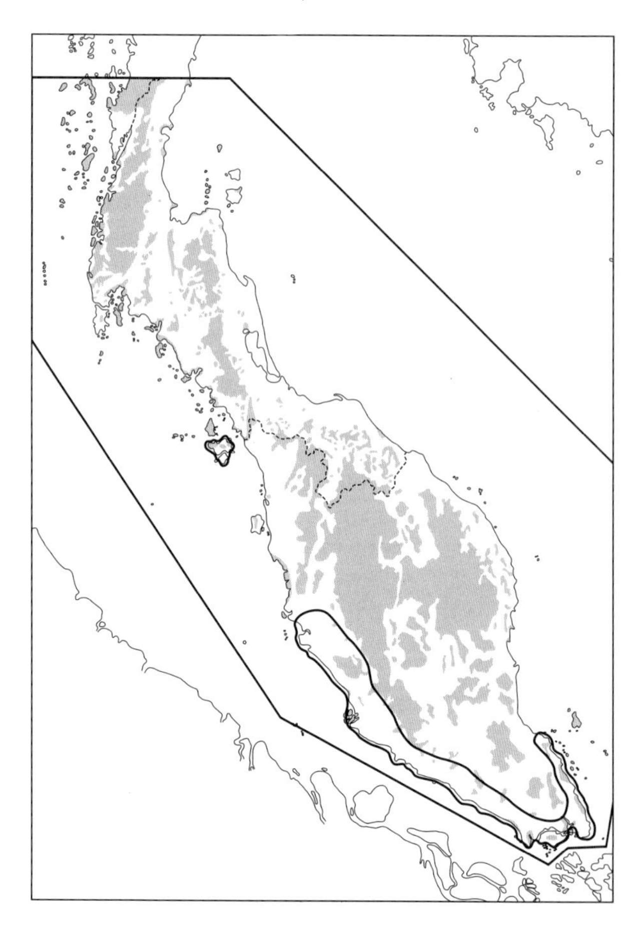

HABITATS AND ECOLOGY. On the mainland, mangroves and coastal strand woodland are core habitat. Out of these, landward invasion of the conjoined coconut–orchard belt, secondary (including swampy) scrub, oil-palm and rubber plantations (especially where over-mature, neglected and supplying plenty of dead stumps), and nearby wooded gardens and parkland began by about the early 1930s (Edgar 1933). Inland numbers have increased particularly since the 1970s, with quite rapid, stepwise settlement of habitat-patches up to 30 km from the sea but, so far, strictly at plains level (BR 1978–79, 1982–83). In the Langkawi group, where it is the only *Picus* woodpecker present, extends to inland dry-land forest, as far as the lower slopes of the hills.

FORAGING AND FOOD. Hunts throughout the vegetation column, on both living and dead stems, trunks and branches of all sizes, plus the bases of palm-fronds, and searches dead, pendant fronds; occasionally also in live foliage. The main modes are tapping and probing, less often excavating (Short 1973) and, on dead snags, even works its way behind sheets of exfoliating bark. Also feeds on the ground (where it hops), probing rotten deadfalls and directly into litter and soil, including mangrove mud. Dependant fledglings sometimes come to the ground to be fed (Short 1973).

To the mainly animal diet is added occasional fruit: a female in Singapore seen to dig the flesh out of a rambutan *Nephelium lappaceum* (SINGAV-3).

SOCIAL ORGANIZATION. Forages alone and in pairs; also in cohesive family parties.

MOVEMENTS. None reported.

SURVIVAL. Two ringed as adults and retrapped on site 116 and 120 months later (BMP5) are still the oldest on record.

SOCIAL INTERACTIONS. Sideways body-swinging as birds approach one another. The half- to one-second drum, on dead wood, is a fast, rather low-pitched, even-paced monotone delivered at 23 beats per second (Short 1973), in long bouts, at intervals of as little as five seconds up to three minutes.

VOICE. Loud, explosive notes, *chaak*, *chauk* or *kyauk*, and a disyllabic *chaakauk*, are given singly or in short series, by loners and in company. A sharp *kaek*, repeated 2–3 times, is a response to intruders. At close quarters, pair-members interact with a low, squeaking *tiku-tiku*, repeated (Lewin 1954). More observations are needed.

BREEDING

Nest. Excavates mainly dead trunks, but some livewood sites are on record; in core habitats, commonly mangrove trees and palms, but with records also in casuarinas, 0.5–9 m above ground. Inland, in a dead mango *Mangifera* and a hog-plum *Spondias*, but obviously much under-recorded.

Eggs and brood. Eggs are plain, faintly glossy, slightly translucent white. Shape elliptical, of varied breadth. Size (mm): 26.7 × 19.2 and 27.7 × 21.3 (means of two clutches). It is not known whether a record of a clutch of four eggs is unusual; there are no reports of this many young fledging.

Cycle. Both partners incubate and both tend nestlings and fledglings.

Seasonality. Egg-, nestling- and young fledgling-dates extrapolate to laying during February–June, with earliest fledglings off the nest in March and a latest brood of small chicks on 20 July, although Madoc mentions an apparently active nest in October (Edgar 1933, Lewin 1954, G.C. Madoc, Madoc 1956a, McClure and Husain Osman 1968, Short 1973, SINGAV-2, -4, -6).

MOULT. Replacement of primaries is regular-descendant. Among 185 adults from the full local range, including 171 handlings of 136 individuals over a decade at Rantau Panjang, Selangor coast, and covering all months except October, active wing-moult occurred during late May–February, with starts up to late November and evidence from retrap data of an individual moult-span of 4–5 months. Lack of moult in the March–April sample suggests a break at population-level but, unless interrupted, latest moulters are liable to continue into this period.

CONSERVATION. Declining on Singapore island, it is believed due to loss of mangroves and other coastal vegetation. At least where mangroves and coconut plantations meet, not threatened on the mainland, but stability of inland colonists cut off from core habitats is still uncertain. Coastal land-clearance for tourism and other developments on Langkawi, and recent forest-burning on Dayang Bunting island, have reduced the security of *connectens*, and further checks are needed.

Streaked-breasted Woodpecker; Nok Hua Khwaan Khieo Khaw Khieo (Thai); Burung Belatuk Jati (Malay)

Picus viridanus Blyth 1843, *Journal of the Asiatic Society of Bengal* 12: 1000. TL Arakan, W Burma.
Plate 68

GROUP RELATIONS. See Laced Woodpecker.

GLOBAL RANGE. Burma and adjacent W and SW border areas of Thailand, to the northern Peninsula.

IDENTIFICATION/DESCRIPTION. Marginally larger than Laced Woodpecker; otherwise the same except for underparts: green-buff from chin to upper breast, cream-white thereafter, patterned throughout, not just from lower breast or belly. Dark olive stripes along the length of each web are bolder than in most Laced Woodpeckers, meet at the feather-tip everywhere and are flanked by a dark shaft-streak and subsidiary dark fringing along web margins. The whole effect is of streaks rather than scalloping, denser than in Laced Woodpecker. Sexes differ as in Laced, and juveniles are duller than adults, males with black showing through on the cap. They are also more obscurely marked below, indeed, some are sufficiently heavily green-washed on the breast to be mistaken in the field for Laced.

Bare-part colours. (Adult) iris red-brown, eyelid slate-grey; upper mandible black, lower yellow to greenish yellow, blackening at the tip; feet sage-green.

Size (mm). (Skins: 20 males, 15 females; adult): wing 131–141 (124, 126 possibly not adult) and 129–141; tail 90–104 and 90–106; bill 32.7–40.0 and 33.9–37.6; tarsus 25.1–30.1 and 26.5–28.6 (BMNH).

Weight. No data.

DISTRIBUTION. South to the Songkhla/Kedah border. Historical summary: *Pak, Chu, Ran, Sur, Pha, Nak, Phu, Kra, Pht, Tra, Son, Pat, Yal, Pes, Ked*, and with additional W-coast island records from Ra and Phra Thong, the Phangnga bay group (Boi Yai, Yao Noi, Yao Yai), Maphrao and Rang (*Phu*), Lanta, Muk and Libong.

GEOGRAPHICAL VARIATION. Short (1982) admits no subspecies.

STATUS AND POPULATION. Resident, regular and uncommon to more or less common.

HABITATS AND ECOLOGY. Mangroves and strand (including casuarina) woodland, and inland dry-land semi-evergreen (possibly not evergreen) Lowland forest, mature and disturbed (commonest in patches of regrowth), at plains level and on low slopes. Also, tree (including teak and rubber) plantations, especially where overgrown, emerging to forage in individual trees isolated on open ground.

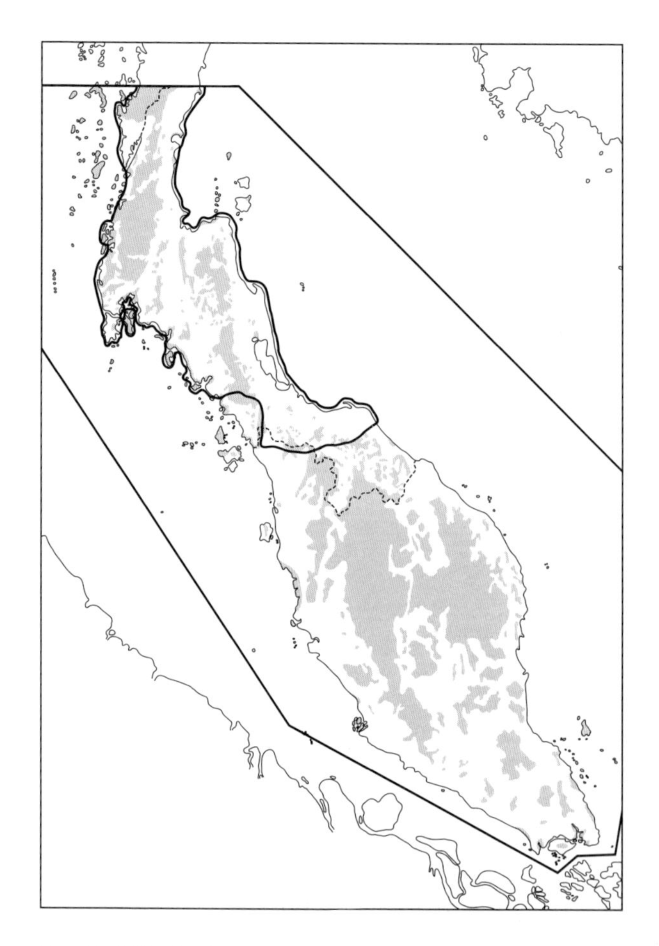

FORAGING AND FOOD. Forages on the ground and over the whole column-height of forest vegetation, from sapling stems of the understorey to epiphyte-laden branches in the top canopy. No data on animal prey, but one report of the taking of small drupes from a forest crown.

SOCIAL ORGANIZATION. Solitary or in pairs.

MOVEMENTS. None reported.

SURVIVAL. No information.

SOCIAL INTERACTIONS. Drums, but not well described; no other information.

VOICE. The commonest loud call is an explosive, down-inflected *kwiep* or *kiek* (similar to continental Thai Laced Woodpecker); less often an equally sharp, slightly down-inflected *chiorr* or *chiaar*, repeated at longish intervals (and given by a male foraging alone in an isolated tree.

BREEDING. Known only from an occupied nest at the landward edge of Libong island mangroves in mid April (J.A. Wolstencroft).

MOULT. Replacement of primaries appears to be regular-descendant. Among 41 adults covering the Peninsula south to Pattani, and all months except October–November, 11 showed active wing-moult during mid May (P3)–early December (P8–9). Twenty-six dated January–April were all non-moulters, indicating a longer seasonal break than in Laced Woodpecker populations (BMNH).

CONSERVATION. Loss of plains-level inland forest and degradation of mangroves have made deep inroads into the range of this species, and nothing is known about its stability once isolated from these core habitats. More research is needed, particularly into nesting requirements.

Grey-faced Woodpecker; Nok Hua Khwaan Khieo Hua Dam (Thai); Burung Belatuk Gunung (Malay)

Picus canus Gmelin 1788, *Systema Naturae* 13(1): 434. TL Norway.
Plate 68

GROUP RELATIONS. Free-standing.

GLOBAL RANGE. Across temperate-zone Eurasia from W Europe to Sakhalin, Hokkaido and Korea, south in Asia to the N Caspian, Altai and N Mongolia, thence China south and east of a line NE provinces–Sichuan, including Taiwan and Hainan; SE Tibet; the lower Himalayas and hill-tracts of the NE Indian subcontinent; and SE Asia to the Peninsula and Sumatra.

IDENTIFICATION/DESCRIPTION. Lores and entire cap to nape black, the adult male with a triangle of orange-red from the mid-point of the fore- to the mid-crown. Rest of upperparts dark olive, tinged glossy bronze on the wing-coverts and with lime-yellow flecks strong on the rump, sparse on the back and upper tail-coverts (plus a few on the mantle of a male); flight-feathers and tail brown-black, the former narrowly barred white on their outer webs. Side of face plain dark grey, with no white streaks or edging, and long malar-stripe plain black. Chin and throat light grey-green merging into the dark olive of remaining underparts. The one male examined showed a narrow, broken necklace of small, lime-yellow flecks across the breast; absent from females. Lower wing-coverts barred black-and-white. Juveniles have not been described from the Peninsula (BMNH, ZRCNUS).

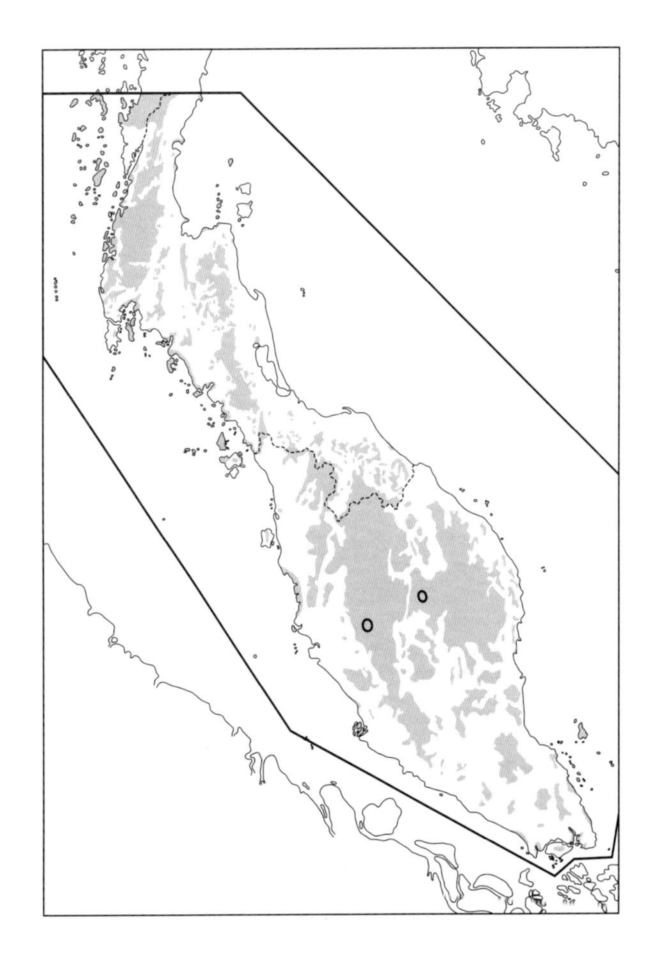

Bare-part colours. (Adult) iris red-brown; bill black; feet green-lead (Robinson 1928).

Size (mm). (Skins: 1 male, 3 females; adult): wing 136 and 138–143; tail 100–108 (females only); bill 44.2 and 40.5–44.5; tarsus 28.6 and 26.7–29.3 (BMNH, ZRCNUS).

Weight. No data.

DISTRIBUTION. The Main Range, recorded so far only at Cameron Highlands, and on Tahan, Taman Negara. Historical summary: *Kel, Phg*.

GEOGRAPHICAL VARIATION. Taman Negara birds are endemic *robinsoni* Ogilvie-Grant 1908 (TL Tahan mountain). The Main Range population has never been handled.

STATUS AND POPULATION. Resident, local and sparse. Known on Tahan from five specimens, including of two pairs, collected in July 1905, October 1920 and April 1922 (Ogilvie-Grant 1908, Gibson-Hill 1949b), and on Cameron Highlands from two sightings of lone males, both responding to mimicked calls, in April 1968 and February 1990 (S.G. Madge, F. Schepers).

HABITATS AND ECOLOGY. One record on Tahan from Lower Montane forest at about 920 m, all the others (including of pairs), there and on the Main Range, in Upper Montane forest between about 1500 and 1800 m. The Tahan pairs were collected in a tall screw-pine *Pandanus* and stand of conifers, probably *Dacrydium* sp., with other records from broad-leaved forest; in one instance, regrowth.

FORAGING AND FOOD. No information.

SOCIAL ORGANIZATION. No additional information.

MOVEMENTS. No information.

SURVIVAL. No information.

SOCIAL INTERACTIONS. No information.

VOICE. A male long-call is the only vocalization reported: a sequence of 6–8 clear whistles, *pew* or *kyie*, accelerating and dropping slightly in pitch towards the end (compare Bay Woodpecker). Imitation of this call produced a strong reaction, in one instance luring a bird over more than 200 m, implying it has territorial advertisement function.

BREEDING. Not recorded.

MOULT. A male growing P3 (P1–2 new, rest of tract very worn) on 25 October is the only record. Females dated April and early July appear not to have started (BMNH, ZRCNUS).

CONSERVATION. Status and distribution on the Main Range need investigating but presence around the Cameron Highlands settlement area implies some ability to withstand habitat disturbance.

Olive-backed Woodpecker; Nok Hua Khwaan Sam Niw Lang See Plai (Thai); Burung Belatuk Pinang Rimba (Malay)

Dinopium rafflesii (Vigors) 1831, Lady Sophia Raffles's *Memoir of the Life and Public Services of Sir Thomas Stamford Raffles, F.R.S. &c. Catalogue of Zoological Specimens*: 669. TL Sumatra.

Plate 67

GROUP RELATIONS. Free-standing.

GLOBAL RANGE. Borneo, Banka, Sumatra and the Peninsula, and SW Thailand and Tenasserim respectively to about 13°N and 16°N.

IDENTIFICATION/DESCRIPTION. Medium sized, about that of flamebacks, and from them in the field mainly by underparts behind pale cinnamon chin and throat solidly dark olive-brown (with buff-white spotting on the flanks mostly hidden in perched birds). Cap to nape produced into a tall, anvil-shaped crest, bright red in males, black in females. Lores from nostril, narrow forehead-band, and malar stripe cinnamon-rufous. Rest of face and side of neck black, broken by a white stripe from eye to nape (under the crest) and another from under the eye expanding down the side of the neck to the wing-base. Remaining upperparts, including outer webs of secondaries, bright olive; mantle- to rump-feathering edged shining brassy yellow, with touches of red on the rump an individually variable feature of some males. Primaries dull black, with grey-brown tips conspicuous when folded against the black of upper tail-coverts and tail.

Juveniles resemble the female, apart from greener underparts and smoky grey rather than cinnamon on the head. Young males have red tips to rear crest-feathers.

Bare-part colours. (Adult) iris dark brown; bill slaty blue, paler on the lower mandible; feet dark greenish grey.

Size (mm). (Live and skins: 13 males, 10 females; adult): wing 140–153 and 144–156; tail 102–111 and 102–117; bill 33.6–40.1 and 33.5–37.3; tarsus 24.5–28.8 and 25.5–26.9 (BMNH, UMBRP).

Weight (g). An adult male, 104.9 (UMBRP).

DISTRIBUTION. Probably under-recorded in the north. Historical summary: all divisions except *Ran, Pha, Phu, Pht, Son, Pat, Sat, Yal, Pes, Ked, Kel, Tru, Pra*; extinct *Sin*, including Ubin island, for at least 30 years.

GEOGRAPHICAL VARIATION. Nominate *rafflesii*, of the species range except Borneo (Short 1982). Shows a shallow cline of decreasing size north to south: none of either sex with wing over 150 mm recorded south of Trang, but some Pakchan birds as small as the smallest from Johor.

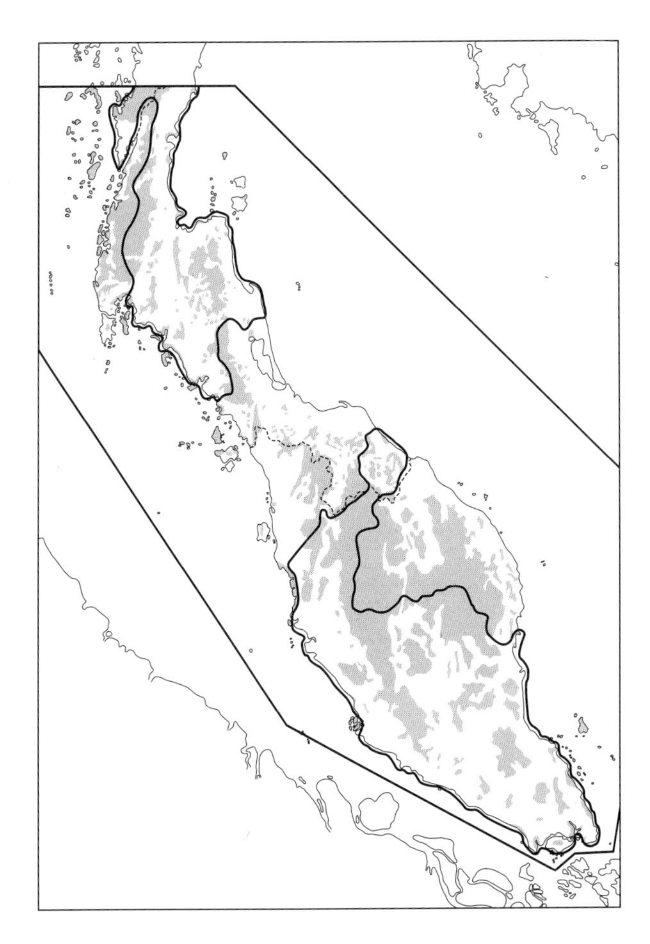

STATUS AND POPULATION. Resident, in the south regular and uncommon to more or less common, in the north local and sparse.

HABITATS AND ECOLOGY. Semi-evergreen and evergreen Lowland forest, mature and well regenerated after disturbance, locally also peatswamp forest (Chalerm Prakiat wildlife sanctuary), at plains level, less commonly on hill-slopes to the Montane ecotone, with a few records from Lower Montane forest to about 1200 m. Only exceptionally out of forest cover; at Pasoh research forest, Negeri Sembilan, a visit by a male to a dead stump 150 m beyond the forest edge (Short 1973) could have been to a foraging-site within this individual's formerly tree-covered territory.

FORAGING AND FOOD. Hunts mainly in the lower- and mid-stratum of the vegetation column, mostly by tapping and surface-gleaning on fallen timber, saplings and the lower boles of larger trees (Short 1973).

SOCIAL ORGANIZATION. A solitary forager.

MOVEMENTS. None reported.

SURVIVAL. No information.

SOCIAL INTERACTIONS. At close quarters between pair-members, crest-raising and, by males, bowing, head-swinging and, in one instance, courtship-feeding of a female with ants (Short 1973).

VOICE. Long, probable advertising-calls are a fast, staccato laugh of about 2–4 seconds that spectrographic analysis shows to be made of up of notes delivered at a rate of around ten per second, intervals expanding towards the end of longer examples, slowing them down audibly: *chachachachachacha . . . chacha cha cha*. Also has loud, single-note, *chak* calls, and a male reacting to a nearby female (mate?) gave a low *ch-wee, chwee, chwee* (BMP5, Short 1973).

BREEDING

Nest. Two, 4.5 and 9 m up small trunks (one 25 cm thick) of the forest interior, one standing in water. No other details.

Eggs and brood. Not described.

Cycle. Both pair-members excavate.

Seasonality. Hole-excavation in early and mid March, and apparent incubation in early April (ENGGANG-2, Short 1973).

MOULT. Replacement of primaries is regular-descendant. Among 28 adults from the length of the Peninsula, covering all months except January, 13 showed active wing-moult during late April–November, with no likelihood of starts before April and no late-stage examples before September. Nine dated December–March were all non-moulters. An instance of tail-moult (T1) in July (BMNH, UMBRP, M. Wong).

CONSERVATION. Capacity of this woodpecker to withstand typical levels of destruction during logging operations without access to reservoirs of undisturbed habitat has not been investigated.

Common Flameback; Nok Hua Khwaan Sam Niw Lang Thong (Thai); Burung Belatuk Pinang Muda (Malay)

Dinopium javanense (Ljungh) 1797, *Konglige Vetenskaps Academiens Handlingar* 18: 137 and plate 6. TL Jakarta, W Java.

Plate 67

GROUP RELATIONS. In a superspecies with *D. shorii* (Himalayan Flameback). Ranges overlap widely but habitat-preferences diverge where *javanense* meets *shorii* in the far-NE Indian subcontinent and Burma (Short 1982).

GLOBAL RANGE. SW India and the far-NE Indian subcontinent; S Yunnan; and SE Asia to the Greater Sunda islands, Bali and W Philippines (the Palawan group to Busuanga).

IDENTIFICATION/DESCRIPTION. Entire cap including anvil-shaped nape-crest black with short white streaks (rather than spots on shorter crest of Greater Flameback *Chrysocolaptes lucidus*) in females; shining blood-red with narrow black border from above eye round rear base of crest in adult males. In both sexes, black continues mid-dorsally down the neck, is joined at lower-nape level by a stripe from the eye, and spreads on to the upper mantle and inner leading-edge of the wing. A third black (malar-) stripe runs the length of the jaw and expands down side of neck to breast, with a fine branch behind jaw up towards the eye-band and ventral branch that joins its opposite number across the lower throat to run forward as a narrow, median gular stripe. Chin and rest of throat, supercilium isolated above eye-stripe, and broad band across face between stripes white, in a bold pattern. Some show white invading the malar-stripe to split off a subsidiary band along the lower edge of the jaw, but this is not detectable in the field (*contra* Greater Flameback). Rest of mantle and wing-coverts shining brassy yellow, to more olive-yellow on outer webs of secondaries; back and rump bright red; upper tail-coverts and tail black. Flight-feathers also black, with bold white dots along inner webs, and longer primaries tipped grey-white. Remaining underparts, from throat-band, white with all feathers fully margined black, giving a scalloped pattern boldest at sides of breast where the black is stepped in at feather-corners. Frequently, neck and breast are stained cinnamon to tawny.

See Greater Flameback for further points of separation between these species.

Bare-part colours. Iris dark brown; bill lead-grey, paler blue-grey at base of lower mandible; feet green-tinged lead-grey.

Size (mm). (Skins: 15 males, 13 females; adult): wing 131–146 and 130–142 (juveniles down to 122); tail 81–94 and 76–96; bill 29.8–35.8 and 28.3–33.6; tarsus 23.1–26.2 and 21.4–24.4 (BMNH, UMZC).

Weight (g). Adult males, 63.9–90.4 (mean 76.4, n=26); adult females, 63.5–79.1 (mean 69.3, n=29).

DISTRIBUTION. Historical summary: all divisions except *Chu*, *Son*, with additional island records from Libong, Penang and Pangkor off the W coast; and Ubin, St John's and Ayer Merbau, Singapore.

GEOGRAPHICAL VARIATION. Subspecies *javanense*, also of Sumatra and W-central Java, in the far north intergrading with larger *intermedium* Blyth 1845 (TL Ramree island, NW Burma). As of latitude about 10°N, most have wing 140 mm or over. A few of this size occur south to Trang province, but the upper limit recorded in Malaysia is 136 mm.

STATUS AND POPULATION. Resident, regular and common.

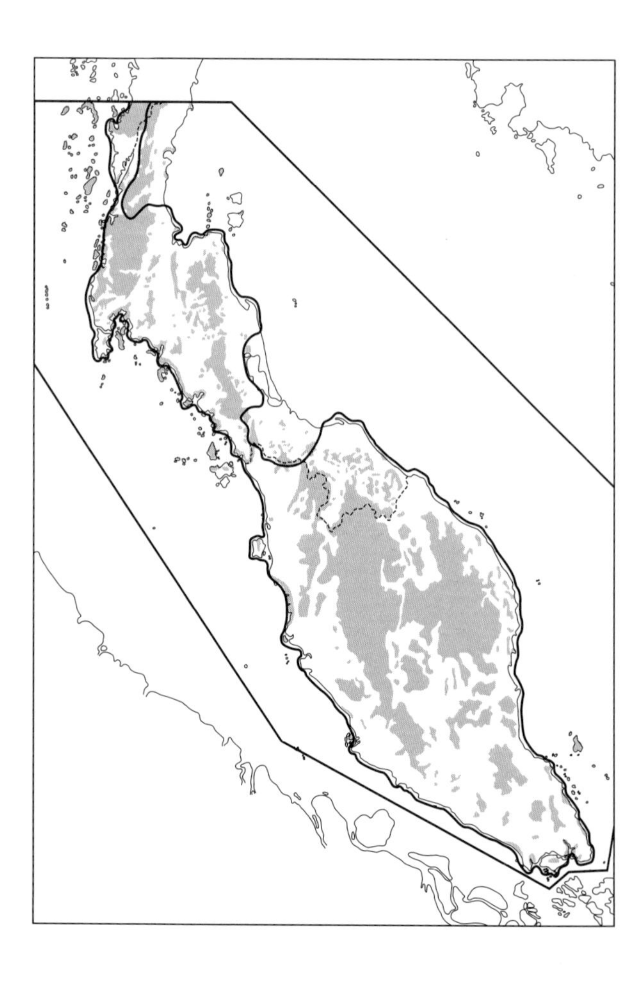

HABITATS AND ECOLOGY. Mangrove forest, strand (including casuarina) woodland, subcoastal paperbark stands and many wooded habitats of the interior low country, including coconut, oil-palm, rubber and (locally) teak plantations, orchards, parkland and well wooded gardens, exclusively at plains level. There are a few records from logged-over semi-evergreen forest, but other than mangrove forest avoids natural, closed-canopy cover.

Several peculiar pieces of behaviour have not been explained, including one or a pair of birds perched a metre or so apart on some totally exposed snag, silent and completely motionless for long periods, without interacting and not obviously engaged in any comfort activity, such as sunning. Another is the thorough, and regular, rubbing of chin to belly on a favoured patch of bark (linked perhaps with the staining of ventral plumage). This has been recorded on a smooth-barked species of *Albizzia* (Leguminosae) and white chempaka *Michelia alba* (Magnoliaceae), the latter peeled back to the green wood. Some unidentified *Michelia* exudate is also preened onto back-plumage (Harrison 1958).

FORAGING AND FOOD. In mangrove forest, uses a wider range of tree species than Greater Flameback (Noske 1991). Hunts mostly by probing and gleaning, and usually maintains fairly fast progress, over the full height of trunks and main crown branches, up palms to the frond-base, and on fronds themselves (Short 1982). Pushes deeply into holed coconuts (Spittle 1952) but there is no evidence holes are actually cut by woodpeckers themselves. Also attracted to emerging alate termites, snapping them up during clumsy aerial sallies through the swarm, with frequent returns to a perch.

SOCIAL ORGANIZATION. Family parties, pairs and loners.

MOVEMENTS. None reported.

SURVIVAL. Of 35 birds in subcoastal coconut plantation and adjacent mangrove edge at Rantau Panjang, Selangor, ringed and re-handled at least one month later, a minimum six survived not less than four more years and a minimum three over eight years; longest retrap-intervals 102, 124 and 126 months (UMBRP).

SOCIAL INTERACTIONS. Crest-raising and occasional body-swinging during encounters, including between pair-members. The drum is short, fast, relatively low and soft, unlikely to carry far and perhaps not a territorial advertisement e.g., given by a male while its mate and an offspring were close by.

VOICE. Noisy. Piercing, even-paced, more or less level-toned, 2–4-second trills or rattles of brief notes delivered at rates of 4–22 per second: *ki-ki-ki-ki-ki-ki-ki* . . . to *kiddddddddddddt* (Short 1973). Flight-calls are a series of generally short, 3–9-note sequences at intermediate speed: *didididit*, etc. A low, rasping *zerk-zerk-zerk-zerk* . . . noted during pair-interactions.

BREEDING

Nest. Typically 4–12 m up, rarely as low as 2 m, and more often in dead than living trunks, including both trees and palms. Coconut (the commonest site), rubber, paperbark, mango *Mangifera foetida*, batai *Albizzia* spp., and cashew are on record and, in mangrove forest, *Sonneratia* and *Xylocarpus* species. Most nest-tunnels are at least 30 cm deep.

Eggs and brood. Eggs are plain, variably translucent white. Shape subelliptical to short elliptical. Size (mm): 23.1 × 19.2 and 26.4 × 18.2 (means of two clutches). Full clutch three but, commonly, fewer chicks fledge.

Cycle. Excavation of a nest-hole may extend over at least two months before laying and incubation begin (Short 1973). Both parents tend nestlings, and an adult has been seen leaving a nest carrying what appeared to be a faecal sac. One of a pair of young in my garden that flew on about 20 May was still closely following the parents, begging and being fed on 10 June.

Seasonality. Copulations, and egg- and chick-dates extrapolate to laying during February–July, with records of active nests, contents unchecked, also in September and October (Edgar 1933, Madoc 1956a, NRCS, SINGAV-2, -3, Spittle 1949).

MOULT. Replacement of primaries is regular-descendant, from retrap data, spanning about five months. Among 106 adults, covering all months and the length of the Peninsula (and including 66 handlings of 40 individuals over twelve years at Rantau Panjang, coastal Selangor), active wing-moult occurred during June–early March, with evidence of starts from May to August and earliest completions in October, but very low incidence as of December suggests late moulters may suspend (BMNH, BMP5, UMBRP, UMZC).

CONSERVATION. No critical issues.

Greater Flameback; Nok Hua Khwaan See Niw Lang Thong (Thai); Burung Belatuk Pinang Tua (Malay)

Chrysocolaptes lucidus (Scopoli) 1786, *Deliciae Florae et Faunae Insubricae* 2: 89. TL Mindanao, Philippines.

Plate 67

GROUP RELATIONS. Free-standing.

GLOBAL RANGE. Himalayan foothills east from Garhwal, the NE Indian subcontinent, and the E and W Ghats and Sri Lanka; S and SW Yunnan; and SE Asia to the Greater Sunda islands, Bali and the Philippines.

IDENTIFICATION/DESCRIPTION. Dark brown immediately above the bill, rest of cap and crest black with white spots in females, glossy blood-red margined black back from bill-base in males. A second black band from the lores through the eye expands across the face and down the side of the neck, with a dorsal connection to the rear crest-base cutting off a broad white supercilium (as in Common Flameback), and fine ventral branch that subdivides (a) to run forward along the jaw, splitting again into a pair of narrow black malar-stripes that encloses a lens of white, (b) to join its opposite number and run forward as a narrow median gular stripe. Rest of face, chin, throat and hind-neck from crest-base white, with some black mottling where white of neck meets the body. Mantle, wing-coverts, tertials and outer webs of secondaries olive-yellow edged brassy to rich yellow with, in some males (of all ages), quite extensive red. Back and rump glossy blood-red, upper tail-coverts, tail and flight-feathers black, inner webs of the latter with bold white spots, and tips ash-grey. Below, from throat-level, white (or stained tawny), feathers edged black in a scalloped pattern on breast, giving way to black shafts and bars back to lower tail-coverts. Juveniles have back and rump feathers mainly black, white and olive, only tipped red, and the young male head shows red only on the crest.

From Common Flameback in the field by crest-profile (a more cropped shaped), white-spotted rather than streaked cap of female, bill-proportions (about equal to, versus hardly more than half, head-length), white hind-neck, and adult eye-colour (Noske 1991). Malar pattern and fourth toe are usually confirmable only at close range.

Bare-part colours. Iris brown to red-brown (juvenile), pale yellow (adult); bill bluish horn; feet greenish slate.

Size (mm). (Skins: 20 males, 13 females; adult): wing 144–166 and 149–168; tail 77–89 and 75–89; bill 41.2–53.8 and 44.6–53.6; tarsus 29.2–33.7 and 27.7–32.8 (BMNH).

Weight (g). An adult male, 131.2; a female, 128.9 (UMBRP).

DISTRIBUTION. Widespread on both coastal plains south to Perlis and Narathiwat, beyond which strictly the W and S coasts. Mid-nineteenth century specimens collected by A.R. Wallace on Penang island and recent sightings in the Merbok estuary, S Kedah, reduce the supposed NW Malaysian range-gap, and there is no reason why stretches of suitable coastal habitat should not once have been available all the rest of the way to the border. Historical summary: all divisions except *Pht, Son, Pat, Kel, Tru, Phg, Neg*; extinct *Sin* for at least 50 years and on Penang island perhaps for longer (BMNH), but with other island records from Surin Tai and Kam Yai (*Ran*), Yao Yai, Nakha Yai (*Phu*), Libong, Tarutao and Langkawi off the W coast; and Samui off the E coast.

GEOGRAPHICAL VARIATION. As in *Dinopium* species, Greater Flameback shows a rough cline of decreasing size (wing-length) north to south: most

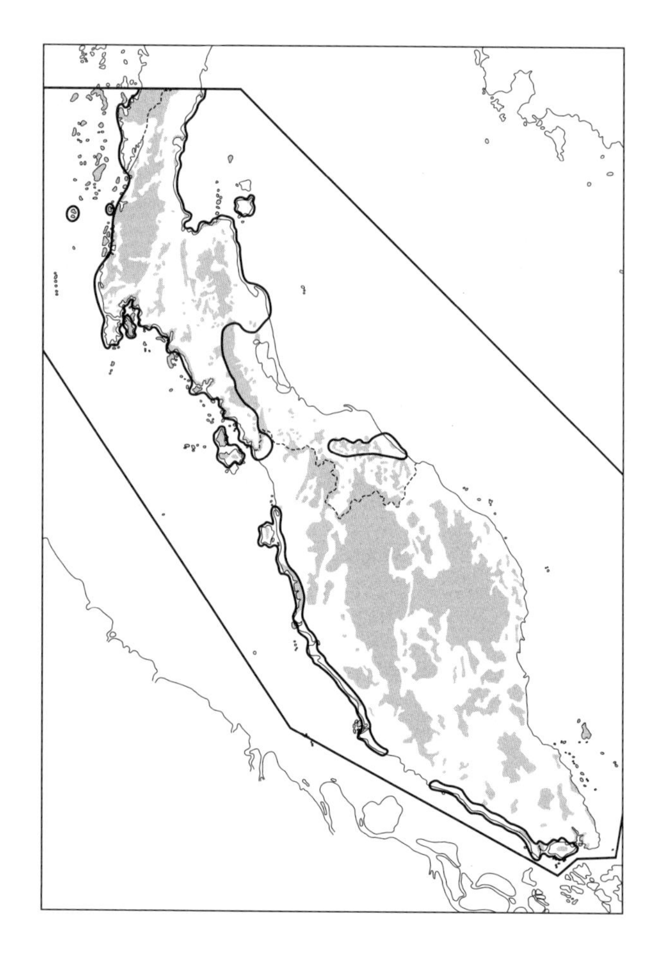

far-northern individuals 160 mm or over, none this big in Malaysia, and down to an extreme 144 mm in the far south, but with largest Singapore specimens (158) still larger than smallest birds from Pakchan (154). Additional data from neighbouring Indonesia show smallness continues through Sumatra and satellite islands but that the cline reverses in the far south, such that W Javan and N Peninsular populations seem not to be separable. Short (1982) and Mees (1986) steered alternative courses around this classical subspecies problem, respectively, by ignoring the W Java situation and by including all W Sunda-region populations in N Peninsular *indomalayicus* Hesse 1911 (TL Phuket). Lumping solves the Java question at the expense of inner tropical birds which, despite some variation, genuinely are small. To deny them their name *chersonesus* Kloss 1918 (TL S Johor) is out of line with treatment of other woodpeckers of the area.

Phuket island is positioned well within the zone of the N–S cline, but most Phuket specimens seen have been large. The option then is to accept *chersonesus*, shelve the Java question in the expectation that more research will reveal new characters, and to follow Short in treating *indomalayicus* as a synonym of northern *guttacristatus* Tickell 1833 (TL forests of Borabhum and Dhalbhum, Bihar). Within the Peninsula, *chersonesus* has commonly been accepted as the bird of southern mangroves. How far north it should actually be recognized seems quite arbitrary, but southernmost records of wing-length 160 mm or more are from Tarutao island (Satul) and, on the mainland, mid Trang (BMNH, Robinson 1917).

STATUS AND POPULATION. Resident, more or less regular but uncommon, outnumbered by Common Flameback except in some of its wooded inland habitats.

HABITATS AND ECOLOGY. Well-grown mangroves throughout (Parr 1988, Swennen *et al.* 1986), with some evidence of a preference for foraging in older *Avicennia alba* trees towards the accreting front of the forest (Noske 1991), but also visits (and nests in) back-mangrove and larger dry-land trees at its immediate edge. Along the Malaysian W coast, Greater Flamebacks occur about as far north as this habitat-combination is still available. On Langkawi island and as of about the Thai border they spread inland, into coconut, teak, and old (rather open) rubber plantings, secondary scrub and bamboo growth (including within areas of shifting cultivation) where there are taller relic trees, and the edge of deciduous and semi-deciduous forest; all exclusively at plains level.

FORAGING AND FOOD. Hunts by vigorous tapping, probing, de-barking and gleaning exposed surfaces, and excavating substantial pits in both live and dead wood of trunks and main branches (down to about 5 cm diameter), mostly at mid to upper column levels (6 m and above). In mangroves near the Selangor river-mouth, a pair used exclusively *Avicennia alba* trees, actively selected within a zone mainly of *Bruguiera parviflora*. Both in mangroves and inland, also attracted to dead stumps, not necessarily tall ones (Noske 1991, Short 1973).

SOCIAL ORGANIZATION. Often in fairly closely associating pairs. Parties of three probably included a juvenile.

MOVEMENTS. None recorded.

SURVIVAL. No information.

SOCIAL INTERACTIONS. Crest-raising and head-swinging during pair and family-group encounters (Short 1973). The advertising drum is a powerful, fast burst of up to 2.2 seconds, falling off in loudness but, at the same time, accelerating (20 up to 30 beats per second, as shown by spectrographic analysis) (Short 1973).

VOICE. Generally similar to Common Flameback: loud rattle-calls of up to 3.5 seconds, but delivered at variable speed, producing a wavering effect not recorded in Common Flameback. Also a single, high-pitched *keek* and other abrupt mono- and disyllablic notes, single or repeated, given when perched and also in flight (Short 1973).

BREEDING

Nest. Only one confirmed, 9 m up a dead tree at the landward edge of mangroves, with two other holes in the same trunk, one fresh-looking.

Eggs and brood. Not described.

Cycle. Both pair-members tend chicks and fledglings.

Seasonality. On the Malaysian W coast, young in the nest on 19 January, and dependent juveniles accompanying parents during late February–April and July) (ENGGANG-2, Short 1973).

MOULT. Replacement of primaries is regular-descendant. Among 29 adults covering the length of the Peninsula and all months except September and October, eight showed active wing-moult between mid February (P1–2) and early August (P6), with evidence of starts until some time after mid July; but a good sample of November–January birds (n=16) were all non-moulters (BMNH).

CONSERVATION. The decreasing area and stature of mangrove forest is a serious issue throughout the Peninsula.

Bamboo Woodpecker; Nok Hua Khwaan Paa Phai (Thai); Burung Belatuk Buluh (Malay)

Gecinulus viridis Blyth 1862, *Journal of the Asiatic Society of Bengal* 31: 341. TL Toungoo, S Burma.
Plate 68

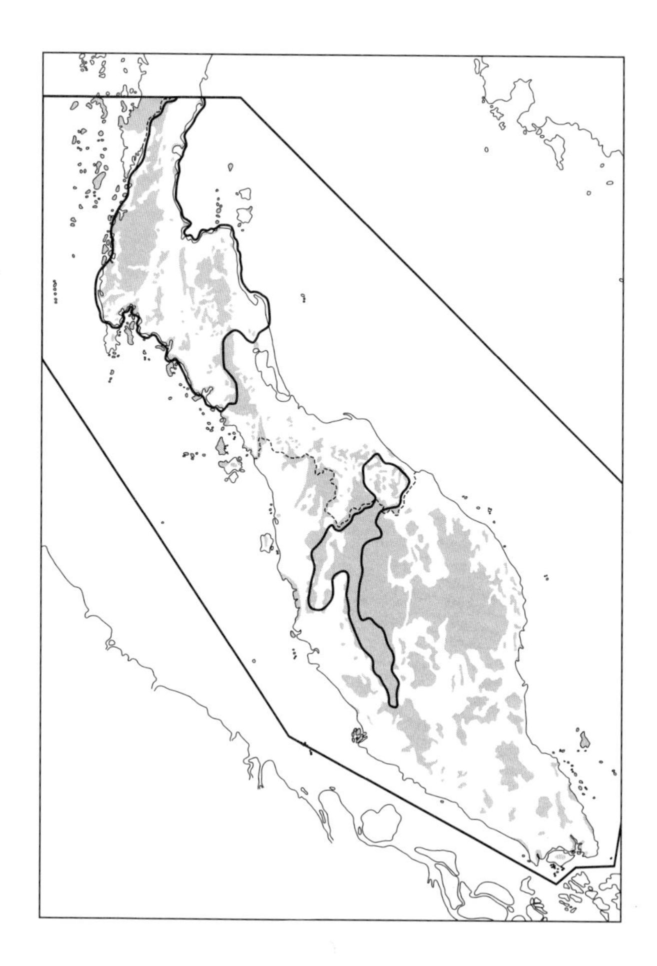

GROUP RELATIONS. Short (1982) lumps *viridis* with parapatric, outer tropical *G. grantia* (Pale-headed Woodpecker). Some of the latter's eastern populations are extensively green, but all have barred tails, versus plain in *viridis*. No intergradation has been reported where ranges most closely approach, in NW Laos, and they are better treated as a superspecies.

GLOBAL RANGE. E-central Burma, NW Thailand and marginally into NW Laos, south through Tenasserim and W Thailand to the Peninsula.

IDENTIFICATION/DESCRIPTION. Plain olive-green, including unbarred outer webs of secondaries; head lighter and brighter than body, tinted golden-olive down to malar level, with forecrown to nape of male bright red. Both sexes show a conspicuously pale bill, and some dull red feather-edging on the rump. Juveniles duller, gold-olive on head confined to feather-edging, male red on nape only, and some females showing virtually no red on rump. Below, grey of chin and throat shades to blackish, with olive wash on belly and flanks. Three-toed, toes all angled forward when climbing bamboo (Short 1973).

Bare-part colours. Iris hazel- to deep brown; bill bluish white, palest at tip; feet greenish grey (Robinson and Kloss 1921–24).

Size (mm). (Live and skins: 12 males, 7 females; adult): wing 126–132 and 127–135; tail 80–88 and 85–90; bill 26.4–30.1 and 24.6–28.0; tarsus 25.7–28.0 and 25.7–27.0 (UMBRP).

Weight (g). Adult males, 68.9–74.6 (n=5); adult females 65.0, 73.5 (UMBRP).

DISTRIBUTION. Apparently absent from the far south. Historical summary: *Chu, Ran, Sur, Pha, Nak, Kra, Tra, Nar, Pek, Phg, Sel*, with no island records.

GEOGRAPHICAL VARIATION. Nominate *viridis* at the northern limit of the Peninsula, endemic *robinsoni* Kloss 1918 (TL Genting Bidai, Selangor/Pahang boundary), a shade darker and with smaller white spots on the inner webs of the primaries, elsewhere.

STATUS AND POPULATION. Resident and more or less regular but generally uncommon. The type of *robinsoni*, from a low pass on the Main Range at 3°18′N, is the southernmost record of the species.

HABITATS AND ECOLOGY. Not found away from forest with much bamboo, hence mostly in habitat regenerating after heavy disturbance. In the south, large-stemmed bamboos are gap-phase invaders mainly on slopes, and most Malaysian records are from the Main Range, to a general altitude-limit of about 1200 m but locally as high as 1400 m (Genting Highlands, where disturbance has continued up into Montane forest: ENGGANG-2). More widespread in the north, into plains-level bamboo country well clear of mountains (BBCB-6, Robinson and Kloss 1921–24).

FORAGING AND FOOD. Hunts evidently mainly on bamboos, from ground level over at least the first 5 m of both living and dead culms, by surface-gleaning, tapping and, sometimes, excavating (Short 1973). Reported sap-drinking from a wound in a bamboo (BBCB-6).

SOCIAL ORGANIZATION. Often in fairly closely associating pairs.

MOVEMENTS. None reported.

SURVIVAL. No information.

SOCIAL INTERACTIONS. The drum, on bamboo, is a low but quite loud, monotone burst of about one second, fast with a slight terminal slow-down. Given by loners and also while pair-members are together. No other information.

VOICE. Loud, clear, presumed advertising-calls are of up to 18 (commonly about eight) individually up-inflected notes, hastily repeated, *kweikweikweikwei* . . . or *koikoikoikoi* . . .; also a staccato laugh with sharp terminal up-sweep, *jihahaha-jihahaha-jiweik*. Single-noted *pit*, *kwa*, etc. (Short 1973), are probably close-range contact-calls.

BREEDING

Nest. Only one reported: a hole in the top third of an internode 5 m up a dead culm in a clump of the large bamboo *Gigantochloa scortechinii*. When first found, the wall was being tapped from the inside, loud enough to attract attention 20 m away.

Eggs and brood. Not described.

Cycle. No information.

Seasonality. A Selangor nest found on 28 April; the female in residence (incubating?) on 19 May (MBR 1982–83).

MOULT. Replacement of primaries is regular-descendant. Among 19 adults covering the whole local range, and all months except August and October, seven showed active wing-moult from June (three at P2) to November (P9–10), with evidence of completions possibly as early as late September. None of twelve dated December–May was moulting, confirming the seasonality (BMNH, UMBRP).

CONSERVATION. No critical issues. Optimum habitat is the product of forest disturbance.

Maroon Woodpecker; Nok Hua Khwaan Daeng (Thai); Burung Belatuk Punggur (Malay)

Blythipicus rubiginosus (Swainson) 1837, *The Natural History of the Birds of Western Africa* 2: 150. TL Melaka.

Plate 66

GROUP RELATIONS. Free-standing.

GLOBAL RANGE. Borneo, Sumatra, the Peninsula, and Tenasserim and SW Thailand, respectively, to 11°20′N and 13°N (Kaeng Krachan).

IDENTIFICATION/DESCRIPTION. The only medium-sized, at a distance all-blackish-looking woodpecker with conspicuously pale yellow, proportionately long bill. Face back to crown and upper throat dull clay-brown with bright cinnamon shafts, shading to sooty black elsewhere, with dark wine-crimson upperparts, including wing-coverts, outer webs of secondaries and outer edging of inner primaries. Tail blackish and rest of flight-feathers sooty brown, both with stone-buff bars narrow, hardly noticeable in the field. Lower wing-coverts are also barred stone-buff. Sexes separated by sides of stubby nape-crest bright red in males. In the hand, males also show a faint red wash over the malar area and breast. Juveniles are duller throughout, only faintly red on rear head and upperparts, with inconspicuous stone-grey barring on rear body and wing-coverts.

Bare-part colours. Iris grey-brown to brown (juvenile), blood-red (adult); bill waxy yellow, tinged greenish as the base; feet dark olive-brown.

Size (mm). (Live and skins: 29 males, 31 females; adult): wing 119–127 (both sexes); tail 63–69 (76) and 60–69 (75); bill 32.6–38.3 and 31.8–35.7; tarsus 21.6–26.1 and 21.8–25.3 (BMNH, UMBRP, ZDUM).

Weight (g). Adult males, 73.0–88.0 (n=10); adult females 76.2–92.0 (n=13) (UMBRP).

DISTRIBUTION. Historical summary: all divisions except *Phu, Pat, Yal, Mel, Sin*; possibly extinct *Sin*, but proof of historical occurrence is lacking (Gibson-Hill 1950a). There are no other island records.

GEOGRAPHICAL VARIATION. None recognized (Short 1982).

STATUS AND POPULATION. Resident, regular and common. Constant-effort mist-netting on a 15 ha plot in mature plains-level forest at Pasoh, Negeri Sembilan, showed up to five adults entered it regularly.

HABITATS AND ECOLOGY. The understorey and lower mid-stratum of mature to well regenerated semi-evergreen and evergreen Lowland forest, also peatswamp forest, at all elevations; less commonly past the Montane ecotone to an upper limit of about

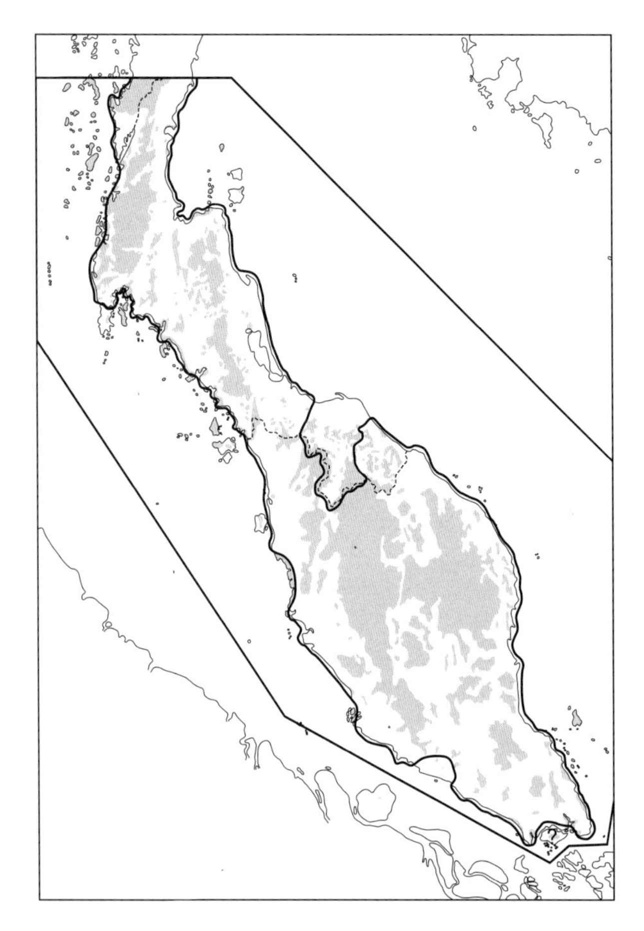

1500 m, at the boundary of Upper Montane forest (ENGGANG-2). Ranges into contiguous secondary-growth and overgrown tree plantation (rubber, teak), but not found more than a few hundred metres outside well-structured natural forest.

FORAGING AND FOOD. Searches rotten timber on the forest floor, and the first few metres column-height of both live and dead trunks, by hacking, excavating, and ripping aside epiphytes and lodged debris (Short 1973).

SOCIAL ORGANIZATION. Forages mostly alone.

MOVEMENTS. None reported.

SURVIVAL. No significant records.

SOCIAL INTERACTIONS. Anxious birds flick wings while calling (Short 1973). Not known to drum.

VOICE. A sharp *kik* or an up-inflected *kik-ik*, with contact or low-level alarm function; constantly repeated while foraging. Longer calls include (1) a sequence of 7–11 high, squealing notes, *pyee pyee pyee pyee . . .*, given at a rate of about four notes per second, steadily falling in pitch; (2) a slightly longer, slightly faster sequence not dropping in pitch but whose individual notes are inflected, *pyiu-pyiu-pyiu-pyiu-pyiu . . .*; (3) fast, screaming rattles of about 12 notes per second, wavering in pitch (Short 1973).

BREEDING. No details of nest or eggs available, but both pair-members tend nestlings and flying young. At Pasoh research forest, Negeri Sembilan, one or more noisy nestlings on 25 February and a juvenile following parents on 14 February.

MOULT. Replacement of primaries is regular-descendant and from evidence of retrapping ringed birds extends over a minimum seven months, but the high overall percentage of non-moulters confirms it is normally discontinuous. Among 90 handlings of adults from throughout the Peninsula, active moult occurred year-round, with starts (P1 or 1–2) recorded in January–March, July, September and October, and completions in February, April, June, August and September, implying no seasonality (BMNH, BMP5, UMBRP, ZDUM).

CONSERVATION. An understorey species potentially sensitive to logging impacts. Responses need study.

Bay Woodpecker; Nok Hua Khwaan Daeng Lang Lai (Thai); Burung Belatuk Bulan (Malay)

Blythipicus pyrrhotis (Hodgson) 1837, *Journal of the Asiatic Society of Bengal* 6: 108. TL Nepal.
Plate 66

GROUP RELATIONS. Free-standing.

GLOBAL RANGE. The Himalayas east from central Nepal and hill-tracts of the far-NE Indian subcontinent; China south from Fujian, Hunan and Sichuan, including Hainan; and uplands of continental SE Asia as far as the Peninsula.

IDENTIFICATION/DESCRIPTION. Shape and proportions, including of pale bill, resemble Maroon Woodpecker, but Bay is larger, with dorsal patterning conspicuous. In a fleeting view at the lower margin of its range, confusion with female Orange-backed Woodpecker *Reinwardtipicus* is a possibility, but the latter's white upper body, black tail and distinctive pin-headed shape are unlikely to be missed. Forehead, face and chin to throat pale clay-brown, shading above and below to vinous-washed, sooty brown. Wings, upper tail-coverts and tail are all barred rufous-chestnut and black: rufous dominant on tail, black dominant on wing-coverts and flight-feathers, except that their rufous bars broaden distally, to about half the width of black on tertials and inner secondaries. As in Maroon Woodpecker, adult males are identified by bright red on the side of the stubby nape-crest. In juveniles, the entire upperparts are broadly barred, and cap and upper neck boldly streaked rufous-chestnut and black (cap-feathers rufous with black sides).

Bare-part colours. (Adult) iris hazel-brown; bill pale waxy yellow; feet dark sooty brown.

Size (mm). (Live and skins: 4 males, 2 females; adult): wing 140–144 and 137, 140; tail 76–81 and 77, 80; bill 40.1–45.2 and 41.3, 44.4; tarsus 22.6–27.1 and 25.6, 25.8 (BMNH, UMBRP).

Weight (g). Adults, sexes not separated, 110–122 (n=5) (McClure 1964, UMBRP).

DISTRIBUTION. Recorded only on the Main Range, so far, between Cameron Highlands and Genting Highlands, and on eastern outlier Benom (BMP5). Historical summary: *Pek, Phg, Sel.*

GEOGRAPHICAL VARIATION. Endemic *cameroni* Robinson 1928 (TL Mengkuang Lebar peak, Genting Highlands).

STATUS AND POPULATION. Resident, regular and more or less common.

HABITATS AND ECOLOGY. The understorey, mid-stratum and edge of Lower and Upper Montane forest between about 1000–1800 m.

FORAGING AND FOOD. Taps, probes and gleans saplings, vines, live and dead trunks, and fallen timber; and excavates large pits especially in rotten wood. Like Maroon Woodpecker, also probes into and tears out epiphytes and trapped debris (G.C. Madoc, Short 1973). One record of a bird accompanying a mixed-species foraging-flock.

SOCIAL ORGANIZATION. Forages alone or in loosely associating pairs.

MOVEMENTS. None reported.

SURVIVAL. No information.

SOCIAL INTERACTIONS. Wing-flicks while calling, like Maroon Woodpecker (Short 1973). Not known to drum.

VOICE. The loud advertising-call is a 1.5 to 3-second sequence of 7–14 well separated notes on a gently declining scale, *kweep kweep kweep kweep . . . wep-wep-wep*, i.e., as Maroon Woodpecker but accelerating (interval closing and frequency flattening) towards the end, and generally lower-pitched, not squealed. Another characteristic call is a rhythmic ('clockwork')

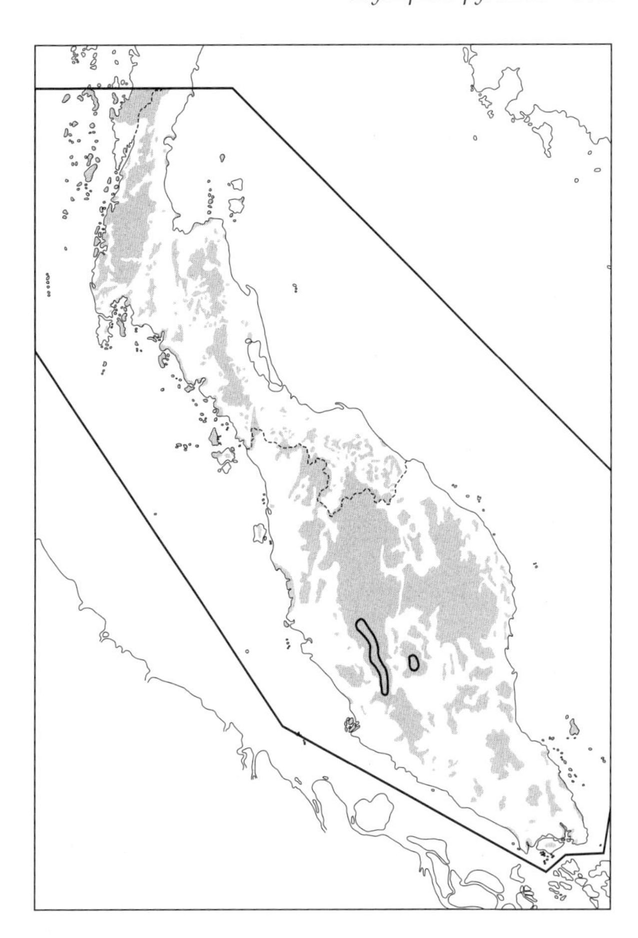

rattle of varying length, *kirera-rarera-rarera . . .* Also gives single-note calls, *keeu, kit*, etc. In the same habitat, a deceptively woodpecker-like vocalization of the same form and general length as the Bay Woodpecker advertising-call, but richer-toned: *ploi ploi ploi ploi . . . plu-plu-plu*, is believed given by Black Laughingthrush *Garrulax lugubris*.

BREEDING

Nest. Only three reported, 6–9 m up in and at the edge of forest, in one instance in a fairly large dead tree in a forest gap.

Eggs and brood. Not described.

Cycle. An incubation changeover noted at mid-day: the male called and as his mate left immediately took her place.

Seasonality. Nestlings in February and incubation in late February-early March; female on, stage uncertain, early April (ENGGANG-1, Madoc 1956a, NRCS).

MOULT. Five adults dated October, February and March showed none. No other information (BMNH, UMBRP).

CONSERVATION. Unlikely to be disturbed on Benom but forests of the relevant stretch of the Main Range are threatened by road-building and land-clearance.

Orange-backed Woodpecker; Nok Hua Khwaan Lang See Som (Thai); Burung Belatuk Ranum (Malay)

Reinwardtipicus validus (Temminck) 1825, *Nouveau Recueil de Planches Coloriées d'Oiseaux* 64: plate 378. TL Java.

Plate 67

GROUP RELATIONS. Free-standing.

GLOBAL RANGE. The Peninsula to the Greater Sunda and intervening islands.

IDENTIFICATION/DESCRIPTION. Another woodpecker with proportionately long, partly pale bill, but larger than *Blythipicus* species, characteristically thin-necked, and with small head and low-peaked ('cropped') crown-crest dull red in the adult male, dark grey-brown in the female. Hind-neck and mid-dorsal band down body white, changing to bright yellow on back and rump in females, rich orange or, occasionally, red-washed in males (but this area concealed until the bird flies). Rest of upperparts, including wings, blackish brown, and upper tail-coverts and tail black. Tertials have a basal bar and shaft-spot of rufous; all other flight-feathers except outermost primary show three broad, bright rufous-chestnut bands (see Bay Woodpecker). Below, female dull grey-brown; male, from centre throat to belly, dark, dull red. In both sexes, the ventral neck-colour contracts over throat and chin into a narrow gular stripe, bordered white in females, yellow (spilling over onto the side of the face) in males. Young juveniles resemble the adult female. Noticeably rattle-winged flight.

Bare-part colours. (Adult) iris orange-brown to brown (female), orange-red to red (male); upper mandible dark horn, lower mandible pale grey-white or yellow-tinged, extreme bill-tip whitish; feet pink-tinged brown.

Size (mm). (Live and skins: 16 males, 13 females; adult): wing (150) 154–163 and 151–159; tail 78–89 and 79–86; bill 41.9–52.9 and 42.0–48.1; tarsus 29.1–31.5 and 28.3–29.7 (BMNH, UMBRP, UMZC).

Weight (g). An adult male, 151.9 (UMBRP).

DISTRIBUTION. North to latitude 8°30'N. Historical summary: *Nak, Kra, Pht, Tra, Son, Sat, Yal, Nar, Ked, Kel, Tru, Pra, Pek, Phg, Sel, Neg, Mel, Joh.* Extinct *Sin* for at least 30 years (SINGAV-2), and with no modern records from Penang; there are no other island records.

GEOGRAPHICAL VARIATION. Subspecies *xanthopygius* Finsch 1905 (TL E Kalimantan), of the global range except Java. Chasen (1939) describes an exceptional Johor male with back and rump as nearly red as in the nominate *validus*, but flecking or a wash of red on the rump is a widespread individual variable.

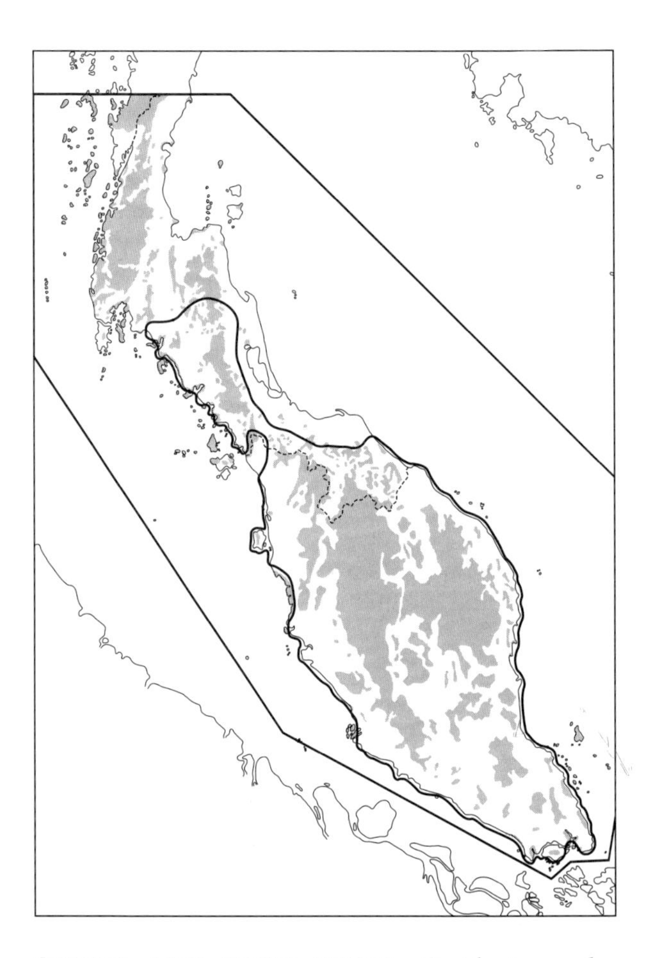

STATUS AND POPULATION. Resident, regular and uncommon to more or less common.

HABITATS AND ECOLOGY. The edge and interior of evergreen, but not certainly semi-evergreen, Lowland forest, mature and disturbed; occasionally also peatswamp forest, mostly at plains level but uncommonly on slopes up to the Montane ecotone, and sparse in Lower Montane forest, with records to 1220 m. Locally, invades old and overgrown rubber plantings, especially where dead stumps and over-mature trees remain.

FORAGING AND FOOD. Hunts throughout the vegetation column, from ground level (including on fallen timber) to the main canopy, on trunks, large branches and lianes, and favours dead and rotting wood. Main search-modes are tapping, bark-flaking and excavating, and rot-softened wood is broken up extensively.

SOCIAL ORGANIZATION. Forages alone, but often also in pairs, with mates sometimes feeding side by side. Parties of 4–7 reported from Johor (Hutchinson 1950) probably included families, but exceed the possible size of a single brood and need investigating.

MOVEMENTS. None reported.

SURVIVAL. No information.

SOCIAL INTERACTIONS. Crest-raising and a sudden jerking out from the perch, with head and neck arched up, and wings spread (and flicked), have been seen during aggressive encounters, including when supplanting Dollarbirds (likely nest-hole competitors) (G.C. Madoc, Short 1973). In Air Keroh forest, Melaka, a fast, half-second drum came from approximately where an Orange-backed Woodpecker had concealed itself, but a Banded Yellownape was active close by and the source of the sound was not confirmed. There is no other evidence of a drum by this species.

VOICE. Shows closest vocal affinity with *Blythipicus* (Short 1973). Loud calls include a squealing burst delivered at 5–6 notes per second, with emphatic up-inflected ending, *jekek-ek-ek-ek-ek-ek-ek-ek . . .-jatik*, and a faster rattle of similar short notes but without the terminal flourish. A burst of separated disyllables, *kliu kliu kliu kliu . . .* has been heard from a female. Shorter calls include single, sharp *jik* or *jek* notes and an up-inflected *jekik*; all like the components of longer sequences.

BREEDING

Nest. Only two reported, about 5 m up dead trunks in forest.

Eggs and brood. Eggs are plain white and fairly glossy. Shape elliptical. Size (mm): 25.9 × 20.5, 27.2 × 20.5 (n=2). Two clutches of two eggs were not confirmed as complete, but fledged broods have been of only one and two young.

Cycle. No direct information.

Seasonality. Eggs in January and June; dependent fledglings following parents in February and March (Chasen 1939, Short 1973).

MOULT. Replacement of primaries is regular-descendant and moult of the individual discontinuous, but activity in 18 (70 percent) of a well-spread sample of 26 adults suggests a long individual duration. Collected from Trang to Johor, in all months except October, they show population-level moult is virtually continuous. With starts as far apart as February and September, no seasonal trend is detectable in this amount of data (cf. Maroon Woodpecker). Tail-moult finishes with T1, dropped not earlier than P8 (BMNH, UMBRP, UMZC).

CONSERVATION. Estimates of population density are needed to identify core habitat.

Buff-rumped Woodpecker; Nok Hua Khwaan Lai Taphok Leuang (Thai); Burung Belatuk Awan (Malay)

Meiglyptes tristis (Horsfield) 1821, *Transactions of the Linnean Society* 13(1): 177. TL Java.
Plate 65

GROUP RELATIONS. Uncertain; continental *M. jugularis* (Black-and-buff Woodpecker) shows morphological and foraging-behaviour parallels. They might form a superspecies, but doubt exists about range- and habitat-limits in SW Thailand.

GLOBAL RANGE. The Greater Sunda and intervening islands, the Peninsula, and SW Thailand and Tenasserim respectively to 14°09′N (near Sai Yoke, Kanchanaburi) and 14°N (Tavoy).

IDENTIFICATION/DESCRIPTION. See Grey-and-buff Woodpecker. Small size, short, tapering, non-red crest, buffy lores and eyering, and contrastingly dark eye and bill are the most immediate field-characters. The ground-colour of the entire head and underparts is creamy buff, apart from the above parts and chin, densely pencilled black, finely on the head, progressively coarser on the underparts, back to flanks, thighs and lower tail-coverts. Most far-northern birds are solidly black on lower breast and belly, and a few such individuals occur south to Selangor. Back and rump are plain *café-au-lait* to white, but mostly concealed in the perched bird. Remaining upperparts, including upper tail-coverts, black, narrowly tipped and barred whitish, and 2–3 white notches show beyond the coverts on both webs of otherwise black tail-feathers. Sexes separable by the male's short red malar-stripe. Juvenile males are said to have red flecks on the forehead but this seems to be unusual. The regular juvenile character in both sexes is a scaly rather than barred cap, in which pale feathers have a black base and fine, all-round blackish edging.

Bare-part colours. Iris deep brown; bill black, with extreme tip whitish in juvenile; feet pinkish grey (juvenile), dark slate-grey (adult).

Size (mm). (Skins: 25 males, 25 females; adult): wing 92–102 and 91–101; tail 41–49 and 42–48; bill 19.8–23.0 and 19.9–22.6; tarsus 18.3–20.6 and 18.4–20.2 (BMNH, UMZC).

Weight. no data.

DISTRIBUTION. Historical summary: all divisions, but extinct *Sin*, including on Ubin island, for at least 30 years; possibly also gone from Penang island, from where there are no modern records.

GEOGRAPHICAL VARIATION. Subspecies *grammithorax* Malherbe 1862 (TL Malay Peninsula), of the global range except Java (Short 1982).

STATUS AND POPULATION. Resident, regular and more or less common.

HABITATS AND ECOLOGY. The canopy and edge of dry-land semi-evergreen and evergreen Lowland forest, mature and disturbed, at plains level and on slopes; and recorded in Lower Montane forest to 1300 m.

FORAGING AND FOOD. Hunts mainly on small, outer branches and among foliage, following the 'skin' of forest at all levels, including down to small trees at its edge and in areas of regrowth; more or less exclusively by probing and gleaning. Small colonies of ants nesting between leaves are a particular target, commonly taken while following in the wake of a mixed-species foraging-flock (that perhaps stirs defending insects into showing themselves). Also recorded swallowing small figs (BR 1972–73).

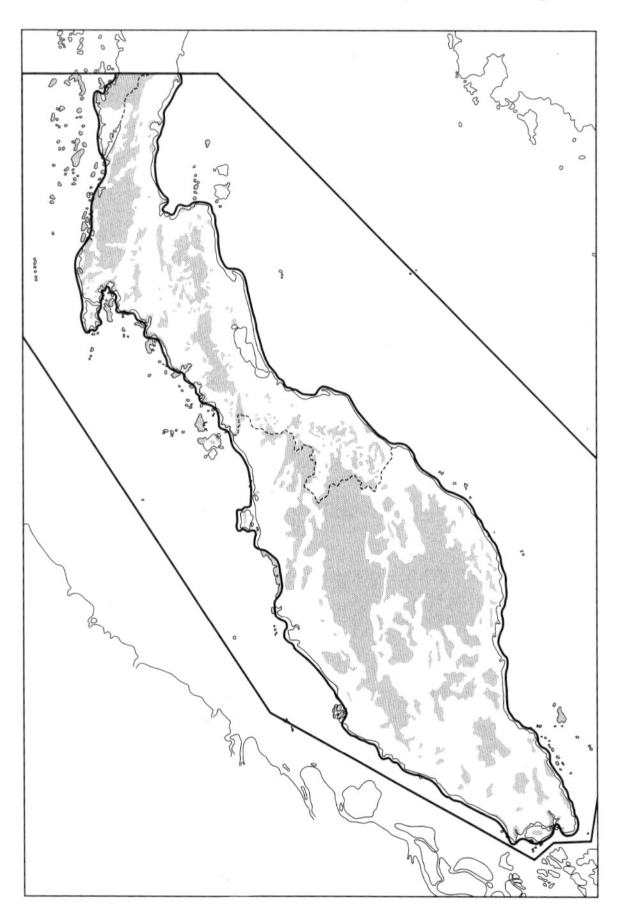

SOCIAL ORGANIZATION. Forages mainly alone, sometimes in pairs. Records of parties of up six (BMNH) are presumed to include dependant young, but six would be more than a single family. Both loners and pairs have been seen in mixed-species foraging-flocks (Short 1973), but more than a single bird is unusual.

MOVEMENTS. None reported.

SURVIVAL. No information.

SOCIAL INTERACTIONS. Head-swinging display between pair-members. Drum bursts, on dead wood, are 1–3 seconds long, with beats distinct but rather weak, and are probably only a short-range communication. Often given with the mate close by, and pair-members counter-drum (Short 1973).

VOICE. A shrill trill of two-plus seconds, fast and with slight rise in pitch mid way. Brief, single- and double-note calls recorded from pair-members interacting at a nest-site, and a *chit* sound heard in flight (Boonsong and Round 1991, Short 1973).

BREEDING

Nest. Only a few reported, 2.5–8 m up broken-off trunks and tall stumps, live and dead, standing at or out of the forest-edge, in clearings and in one instance facing a rubber plantation.

Eggs and brood. One clutch of two eggs; no other details available.

Cycle. Both pair-members excavate the nest-hole.

Seasonality. Hole-excavation in March and April, copulation on 19 March, eggs on 21 March and an active nest, stage undetermined, on 10 March (BMP5, Chasen 1939, Short 1973).

MOULT. Replacement of primaries is regular-descendant. Among 91 adults from the length of the Peninsula and covering all months, 40 showed active wing-moult during February (P1, P2)–mid November (P8), but at a low incidence until April, with starts until July virtually overlapping earliest completions in July/August. A small December and January sample (n=8) was all of non-moulters, and a population finish by the end of the year seems likely (BMNH). Instances of early-stage post-juvenile wing-moult are dated mid-March, April and June.

CONSERVATION. Relative abundance implies plains-level Lowland forest and edge are core habitat, in which case potentially at risk from habitat-loss.

Buff-necked Woodpecker; Nok Hua Khwaan Lai Khaw Theb Khao (Thai); Burung Belatuk Tuki-tuki (Malay)

Meiglyptes tukki Lesson 1839, *Revue Zoologique par la Société Cuvierienne*: 167. TL Sumatra.
Plate 65

GROUP RELATIONS. Free-standing.

GLOBAL RANGE. Borneo, Sumatra and intervening islands, the Peninsula, and SW Thailand to 12°50′N.

IDENTIFICATION/DESCRIPTION. Adult head down to malar level, upper body, wings and tail rufescent olive-brown, with interposed black-brown on the hind-neck. Narrow, well-spaced bars across both webs of inner secondaries, outer-web notches on other flight-feathers, and bars on the outer part of both webs of tail-feathers cream-buff. From behind the jaw a large band of creamy yellow expands down the side of the neck to the wing-base. Below, chin to neck finely and densely pencilled rufous-cream and black; lower neck and upper breast solidly black; lower breast black with fine, well-spaced bars of buff; centre of belly and thighs plain rufescent olive; and flanks to lower tail-coverts barred dark olive-brown and cream-buff, in about equal strength. Sexes separable by male's broad red malar-stripe. Young juveniles like adult female but with brown parts possibly less rufescent. Red flecking claimed on the forehead of some young males is not a regular juvenile character.

Bare-part colours. Iris grey-brown to dark brown (juvenile), red-brown to dark red (adult); bill horn-brown with pinkish tinge (young juvenile), upper mandible black, lower pale blue-grey (adult); feet pinkish brown (juvenile), olive-brown to olive-grey (adult).

Size (mm). (Live and skins: 45 males, 40 females; adult): wing 97–109 and 97–107; tail 56–65 and 55–69; bill 23.1–27.3 and 23.2–26.3; tarsus 20.1–22.1 and 19.5–22.7 (BMNH, UMBRP).

Weight (g). Adult males, 51.3–62.1 (69.5) (n=16); adult females 43.5–64.2 (n=13) (UMBRP).

DISTRIBUTION. Historical summary: all divisions except *Pha, Phu, Pes, Kel*. Extinct *Sin*, including Ubin island, for at least 30 years; perhaps also gone from Penang island, where modern records are lacking.

GEOGRAPHICAL VARIATION. Nominate *tukki*, of the global range except the W Sumatran islands.

STATUS AND POPULATION. Resident, regular and common; commonest woodpecker species of the understorey of evergreen forest, at peak population density in mature forest. In Pasoh research forest, Negeri Sembilan, eight adults made regular use of a 15 ha plot of mature growth whereas only four used a near-equivalent area of 20-year regenerated forest nearby (UMBRP).

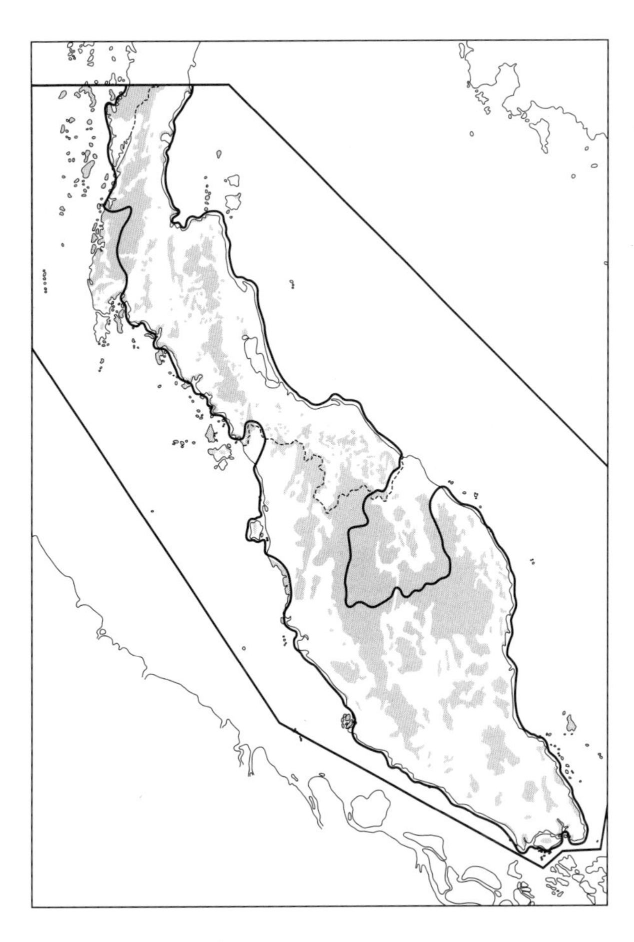

HABITATS AND ECOLOGY. Mainly the denser under-stratum of evergreen and semi-evergreen Lowland forest, mature and regenerated back to closed-canopy structure, also peatswamp forest; at plains level and on slopes to the Montane ecotone. Much less common in Lower Montane forest where recorded to about 1250 m (ENGGANG-1). Exceptionally, wanderers reach sometimes-isolated patches of overgrown plantation and tall secondary-growth, but are not known to survive there long-term.

FORAGING AND FOOD. Hunts over stumps and trunks (from live to rotten), branches, vines, thin stems and foliage at all levels in the non-emergent vegetation column, but with heavy emphasis on dense under-stratum and lower mid-stratum, down to ground level (including at fallen rotten wood).

Main foraging-modes are gleaning and probing, with hacking only into rot-softened wood. Except when working at rotten stumps, tends to move on rather quickly, and one or more commonly join, or follow, mixed-species foraging-flocks, a behaviour also recorded in Montane forest (Short 1973, SINGAV-2).

SOCIAL ORGANIZATION. Social, commonly foraging side by side with other individuals. What are assumed to be pair-members maintain close contact year-round, and parties are frequent, sometimes larger than can be accounted for by a single brood. Seven birds caught together in a mist-net comprised a pair of adults and five immatures, at a date (2 March) suggesting broods of more than one breeding-season could have been involved.

MOVEMENTS. None reported.

SURVIVAL. The longest reported retrap-interval among ringed birds is 63 months (MBR 1986–87).

SOCIAL INTERACTIONS. Head-swinging displays at an encounter between two males. One record of drumming on a large, dead *Schizostachyum* sp. bamboo culm but, as in Buff-rumped Woodpecker, the otherwise rather weak drum must function mainly at close range. Pair-members counter-drum (Short 1973).

VOICE. A fast, approximately two-second trill, similar to Buff-rumped Woodpecker but not as high-pitched; answered at a distance. During short-range interactions, gives a rattling *wik-wik-wik-wik-wik* . . . at about ten notes per second, and brief *dwit* and *pee* notes, alone or in short series. The drum is a variable burst of 1–3 seconds, fast (up to 22 beats per second), but long bursts tend to slow down towards the end (Short 1973).

BREEDING

Nest. Three described: 1.5–4.2 m up rotting trunks from which the bark was exfoliating, entrance-hole 4.2 cm wide. One had been excavated just below a large, sheltering bracket-fungus.

Eggs and brood. A clutch of two. No other information.

Cycle. Both parents incubate, and both tend nestlings.

Seasonality. Excavation in late February, eggs on 7 and 30 June, nestlings in mid April, May and June (F.G.H. Allen, G.C. Madoc, Ogilvie 1954, Short 1973, ZRCNUS).

MOULT. Replacement of primaries is regular-descendant, and retrapping shows individual wing-moult spread over some 5–6 months. Among 178 handlings, year-round and throughout the Peninsula, active wing-moult occurred in all months except March and April (n=18), with starts spread between May and September and completions during October–February (last individuals probably into March, with several records of T1 moult in March and April). One male finishing (P9–10) on 13 February had restarted (P1) by the following 4 August (C.M. Francis, UMBRP, UMZC, M. Wong).

CONSERVATION. Heavy use of the fully shaded understorey of forest implies this species could be sensitive to logging impacts in its core habitat.

Grey-and-buff Woodpecker; Nok Hua Khwaan Khre Ok Thao (Thai); Burung Belatuk Daun (Malay)

Hemicircus concretus (Temminck) 1821, *Nouveau Recueil de Planches Coloriées d'Oiseaux* 15: plate 90. TL Java.

Plate 65

GROUP RELATIONS. Uncertain. Their habitat-preferences are not well defined but shows significant range-overlap with Heart-spotted Woodpecker *H. canente*. Short (1982) treats them as free-standing.

GLOBAL RANGE. The Greater Sunda and intervening islands, the Peninsula, and SW Thailand to latitude 13°N (BBCB-9).

IDENTIFICATION/DESCRIPTION. Small, stubby, with 'tailless' appearance and outsize, upstanding, anvil-shaped crest. Head and underparts clear mid grey, with a fine, whitish moustache-line produced down the side of the neck. Mantle, scapulars, wing-coverts and upper tail-coverts white to rufous-cream, each feather with three large, round to heart-shaped black dots, almost filling web-space and producing a scaled effect by restricting most white to an apical fringe; back grey with cream fringing, rump uniform cream-white. Tertials as scapulars, but white reduced to outer-web notches on inner secondaries, and remaining flight-feathers all-black. Lower wing-coverts cream-white with black-spotted leading-edge. Outer tail-feathers have cream bars, tail otherwise plain black. Sexes separable by the male's bright red cap, from bill-base over the eye not quite to the peak of the crest; uniform grey in female.

Juveniles have upperparts, including wing-coverts, broadly edged cream, tertials almost all buff-cream with only small black markings. Some also show fine dark fringing on the rump. Below, grey with dull buff-cream fringing, and rear flanks black, broadly edged cream. The juvenile crest is full-sized, its whole front buff-orange with variable black fringing (both sexes). Some show red on the crest peak, possibly as a moult-stage, but this is uncertain.

Shortness of the tail is most obvious in flight, which is slow for a woodpecker, and direct rather than undulating, at least between neighbouring tree-crowns.

Bare-part colours. (Adult) iris pink- to red-brown or red; upper mandible slaty, lower paler grey, bill-tip blackish; feet olive-slate (Chasen 1939, Riley 1938).

Size (mm). (Live and skins: 20 males, 9 females; adult): wing 84–90 and 83–90; tail 26–30 and 28–32; bill 20.7–23.0 and 18.3–19.8; tarsus 14.9–17.6 and 14.5–16.4 (BMNH, UMBRP).

Weight (g). An adult male, 31.5 (UMBRP).

DISTRIBUTION. Historical summary: all divisions except *Phu, Pat, Kel, Tru, Pra*; extinct *Sin*, including on Ubin island, for at least 30 years.

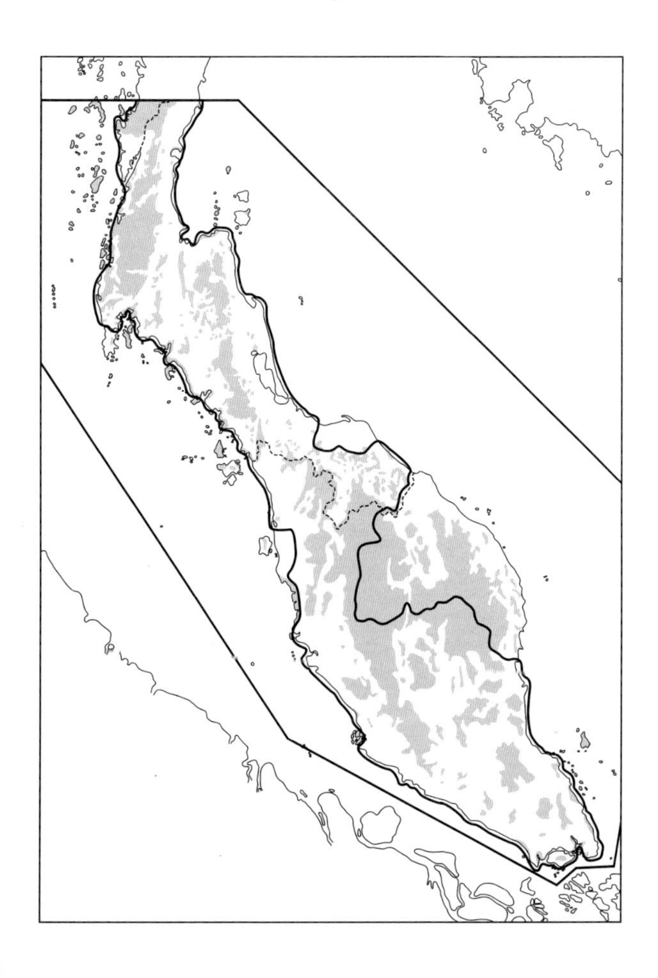

GEOGRAPHICAL VARIATION. Subspecies *sordidus* Eyton 1845 (TL Melaka), of the mainland, hence near-endemic.

STATUS AND POPULATION. Resident, regular and uncommon to, in the south, still more or less common.

HABITATS AND ECOLOGY. The canopy of evergreen and semi-evergreen Lowland forest, and peatswamp forest, mature and regenerating with some tall trees retained, at plains level and up slopes to the Montane ecotone; locally and erratically also into Lower Montane forest, with records to about 1100 m (BMP5).

FORAGING AND FOOD. Hunts over upper trunks and crown branches out to terminal twigs and foliage, following the 'skin' of the forest, thus from high canopy levels down to relatively small trees in patches of regrowth and at the forest edge. Foraging-modes include gleaning from surfaces, tapping, probing and flaking, with acrobatic behaviour and passerine-like perching when searching fine twigs and leaf-bunches (Short 1973). One watched from a tree-platform for nearly two hours worked a patch of dead branches, hammering small pits, probing and bark-gleaning. Has been seen taking insects off the skin of figs but, unlike Buff-rumped Woodpecker, not to take the fruit itself (BR 1972–73). The male's mean 14 percent longer bill (ranges non-overlapping) suggests some divergence of foraging between the sexes. Short (1973) describes males as varied in their choice of feeding-sites, moving between trunks, branches and foliage, whereas some females he watched concentrated entirely on small branches. Whether such a difference might connect with bill-form is not yet known.

Normally rather fast movements allow the joining of mixed-species foraging-flocks.

SOCIAL ORGANIZATION. Forages alone, often also in pairs, and recorded in parties of up to ten, much larger than can be accounted for by a single family (BMP5). Several records of clusters of holes, up to eight together, in one instance with two occupied (Chasen 1939, G.C. Madoc, NRCS, Short 1973), suggest the possibility of other group activities.

MOVEMENTS. None recorded.

SURVIVAL. No information.

SOCIAL INTERACTIONS. Raises crest during encounters. The weak drum seems to be a short-range signal, given by both sexes, in two instances at a nest-hole with another individual (mate?) present (MBR 1984–85, Short 1973).

VOICE. High-pitched but quite loud and resonant calls of one second or longer range from a rattled *kik-ki-ki-ki-ki-ki . . .* or *ti-ti-tee-tee-tee . . . tee-tee-ti*, or slightly expanded *toitoitoitoitoi . . .* at about 11 notes per second, to trills twice that speed. The latter waver in pitch; one given by a perched male was punctuated by a single lower note: *fififififif-tyu-fifififififififififi-tyu-fifi-fififififi . . .*, the bird jerking its head forward with each *tyu* as though catching its breath. Various short monosyllables, *pit, tsip*, etc., are given in flight, including during chases, and a disyllablic *ki-u* by a bird giving crest-raising display (Short 1973).

BREEDING

Nest. 9–14 m up, in dead wood; a group of holes in the underside of a leaning branch; others near the tops of tall snags, all in or at the edge of forest, including regrowth. Entrance-holes are typically oval.

Eggs and brood. Not described.

Cycle. At one of a line of eight holes, a male excavated over two days, in company of a drumming female that was seen to inspect the hole on the second day.

Seasonality. Excavation in the company of other individuals, or occupation of a hole during daytime, in late December, February, April and July (Chasen 1939, MBR 1986–87, NRCS, Short 1973).

MOULT. Replacement of primaries is regular-descendant. Among 32 adults from Phuket south to Johor, and covering all months except May, twelve showed active wing-moult in all months except March, September, December and January, with no discernible seasonal progression (BMNH, UMBRP).

CONSERVATION. Like many canopy species, probably able to withstand selective logging that leaves a fair relic stand. Damage to remaining trees could temporarily increase the supply of dead wood and potential hole-sites.

Heart-spotted Woodpecker; Nok Hua Khwaan Khre Juut Hua Jai (Thai); Burung Belatuk Daun Rintik (Malay)

Hemicircus canente (Lesson) 1830, *Centurie Zoologique, ou Choix d'Animeaux Rares, Nouveaux ou Imparfaitment Connus*: 215. TL Pegu, S Burma.

GROUP RELATIONS. See Grey-and-buff Woodpecker.

GLOBAL RANGE. The W Ghats, Satpura hills and NE Indian subcontinent; and, except for northern Burma and northern Vietnam, SE Asia as far as the Peninsula.

IDENTIFICATION/DESCRIPTION. Line drawing, on page 579. Shape and comportment as Grey-and-buff Woodpecker. Adult male has cap and crest all black to below eye level, forehead to fore-crown with no more than fine white apical spotting. Limits of black the same in adult female, but cap from bill-base to half way up crest cream-white. Scapulars, lesser and median wing-coverts, inner secondaries and rump cream-white, long scapulars, median coverts and inner secondaries each with a large, heart-shaped, subapical black spot. Rest of upper body, tail, and remaining wing-coverts and flight-feathers black, black of hind-neck and mantle divided by a narrow collar of white. The depth of the larger heart-marks on the secondaries is an individual variable. Below, chin to throat greyish white, whiter at the sides; rest of underparts olive-grey, blackening on lower tail-coverts; lower wing-coverts plain cream. Juveniles of both sexes resemble adult female except that pale parts are washed cinnamon-buff, and scapular and body feathers are finely fringed white. Below, chin and throat darker medially, leaving a long white marginal strip of white from bill to neck (the best guide to ageing). Rest of under-body less olive, more charcoal grey.

Males are absolutely larger than females, and bill dimorphism (mean 14 percent longer in males) is as great as in Grey-and-buff Woodpecker.

Bare-part colours. (Adult) iris brown or red-brown; bill black; feet slaty black (Robinson and Kloss 1921–24).

Size (mm). (Skins: 8 males, 8 females; adult, from Pakchan and neighbouring S Tenasserim): wing 96–99 and 90–95; tail 32–36 and 31–34; bill 23.1–25.3 and 19.9–22.2; tarsus 16.4–19.1 and 15.3–17.6 (BMNH).

Weight. No data.

DISTRIBUTION. The far north only. Historical summary: *Pak, Ran, ?Pha.* J. Darling's 1879 record from SE Phangnga (Hume 1880) was backed by no specimens, has not been repeated and, on balance, is likely to have been an error. His description of a nest there is a reasonable fit for one of a small *Picoides* species. Occurrence claimed in the hills of Nakhon Si Thammarat province (Short 1982) seems to be due to confusion of Khao Luang mountain with a peak of the same name on the Tenasserim/SW Thailand divide, north of the Peninsula as defined here (Meyer de Schauensee 1946)

GEOGRAPHICAL VARIATION. None recognized.

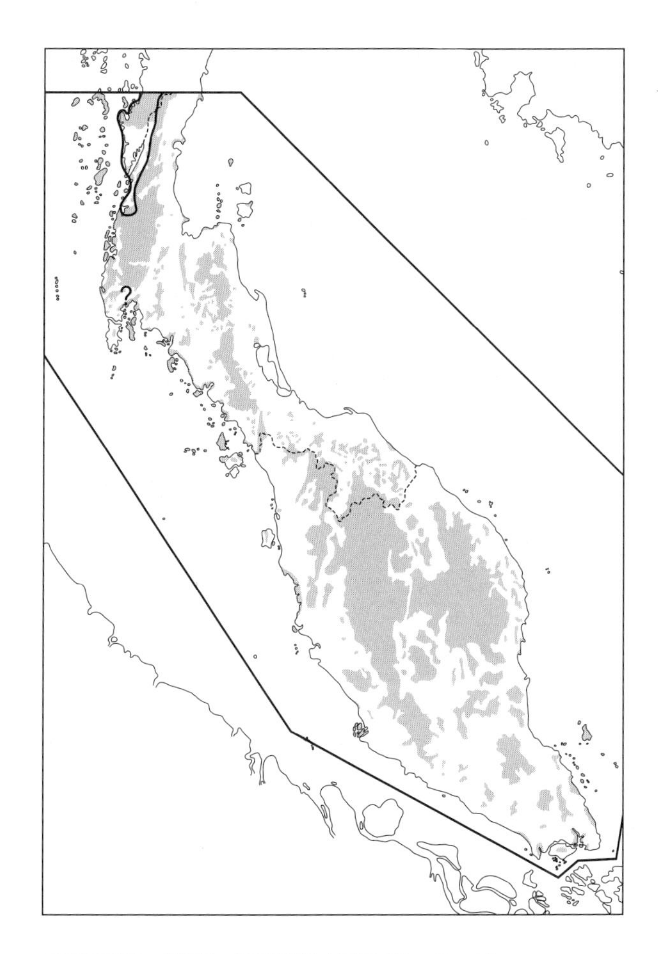

STATUS AND POPULATION. Resident, apparently local, and uncommon to sparse.

HABITATS AND ECOLOGY. Dry-land semi-evergreen and evergreen Lowland forest, apparently mainly at the edge and in clearings, but perhaps overlooked at canopy height; also in heavily disturbed forest with invading bamboo (Oates 1890). At plains level and on slopes to at least 1000 m altitude, but hardly any information is specifically from the Peninsula.

Bristly feathering on the back of both sexes is often smeared with aromatic resin (Bock and Short 1971, Hume and Davison 1878) – see also Rufous Woodpecker and Banded and Crimson-winged Yellownapes.

FORAGING AND FOOD. No local information, but in continental Thailand high, dead snags are favoured foraging sites (P.D. Round). Bill dimorphism implies some divergence of foraging between the sexes, but this has not been investigated (see Grey and-buff Woodpecker).

SOCIAL ORGANIZATION. Pairs and family parties (Hume and Davison 1878).

MOVEMENTS. No information.

SURVIVAL. No information.

SOCIAL INTERACTIONS. No information.

VOICE. No information.

BREEDING. J. Darling's nest-details from Phangnga, recorded as this species but suspicious on geographical grounds:

Nest. Two metres up a dead stump in sparse bamboo and tree jungle, entrance-hole 3.8 cm wide, tunnel running in 10 cm then down 16.7 cm to a nest-chamber 13 cm across.

Eggs and brood. Eggs white, stained creamy. Shape subelliptical. Size (mm): 23.3 × 17.2, 23.1 × 17.2 (n=2). One clutch of two, not necessarily complete.

Cycle. No information.

Seasonality. Eggs on 2 July (Oates 1890).

MOULT. Among 16 adults dated November–January, March–May, all April-dated birds (seven) were in active wing moult, at P4 or 5 (one P1, 4). One was at P4 on 20 March; all others showed none, the May individual evidently a late starter still with old plumage (BMNH).

CONSERVATION. More information needed.

Heart-spotted Woodpecker

Great Slaty Woodpecker; Nok Hua Khwaan Yai See Thao (Thai); Burung Belatuk Kuda (Malay)

Mulleripicus pulverulentus (Temminck) 1826, *Nouveau Recueil de Planches Coloriées d'Oiseaux* 66: plate 389. TL Java.

Plate 67

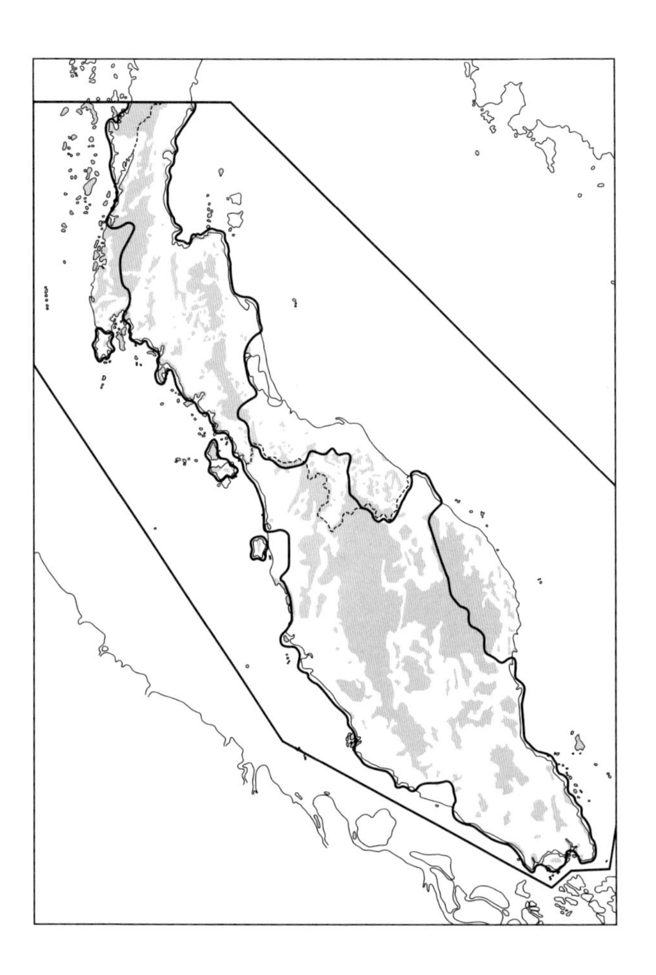

GROUP RELATIONS. Free-standing.

GLOBAL RANGE. Himalayan foothills east from Himachal Pradesh and hill-tracts of the far-NE Indian subcontinent; S Yunnan; and, except for northern Vietnam, SE Asia to the Greater Sunda islands and W Philippines (Balabac and Palawan).

IDENTIFICATION/DESCRIPTION. Largest Old World woodpecker, with long, powerful bill, disproportionately thin-looking head and neck (close-feathered except for a slight nape-crest), and heavy, slightly undulating flight on noisy wings. Adult chin and throat sharply demarcated buff-yellow, feather-tips rosy pink in males. Rest of plumage slaty grey, head, neck and upper breast paler due partly to whitish feather-tips lending a frosted to (on the breast) speckled appearance; uniformly darker elsewhere except that, with some variation, the apical 1 cm of the outer web of primaries is edged white. The sexes are separable by throat-colour, also by the male's rose-pink malar-patch (a long oval isolated at mid jaw level) and, in the hand, variable pink spangling from bill-base to brow. Juveniles lack the pale frosting and speckling, and their chin and throat are white.

Bare-part colours. (Adult) iris deep brown with a bluish cast; bill pale horn to lead-blue, blacker at the tip and on the culmen, but with pronounced dorso-lateral ridge horn-white.

Size (mm). (Skins: 16 males, 14 females; adult): wing 220–237 and 221–247; tail 153–166 and 143–162; bill 59.4–72.3 and 61.8–67.6; tarsus 37.7–43.3 and 35.4–40.3 (BMNH).

Weight. No data.

DISTRIBUTION. Historical summary: all divisions except *Pha, Son, Pat, Nar, Tru, Pra, Mel,* with additional W-coast island records from Lanta, Tarutao, Langkawi, Penang and Pangkor, from which a party has been recorded crossing sea to nearby Pangkor Laut (BR 1978–79, G. Noramly, Robinson 1917).

GEOGRAPHICAL VARIATION. Nominate *pulverulentus,* also of Sumatra and Java, grading towards paler, continental *harterti* through the Thai provinces (mainly from the latitude of Trang but a few pale individuals found south to Langkawi island: BMNH). Deignan's '*celadinus*' is this intergrading population.

STATUS AND POPULATION. Resident, more or less regular and sparse to more or less common. In general decline, and probably most island populations are at risk. There are no modern records from Phuket or Penang, and on Singapore island the only reports over more than a decade have been of one or more calling in the Nee Soon area of the central catchment woodlands, in August 1990 and February 1992 (SINGAV-4, -6).

HABITATS AND ECOLOGY. Inland, mostly the high canopy of evergreen and semi-evergreen Lowland forest, also peatswamp forest, mature and well-regenerated with plenty of big trees retained; at plains level to not far above the steepland boundary, with records to about 200 m. Reported a few times in young regrowth (ENGGANG-2), but ordinarily dependent on big, tall trees. Their complete removal in forestry operations, plus landward clearance and loss of contact with dry-land forest, are the probable main reasons why this woodpecker has retreated from most of its former mangrove range (recent reports only in Krabi: Parr 1988).

Pairs and groups make long flights at top-canopy level around apparently large home ranges that sometimes incorporate space outside the forest margin, where favoured trees stand relic in clearances or across short water-gaps.

FORAGING AND FOOD. Recorded in small trees to within 3 m of the ground, but this is exceptional. The bulk of foraging occurs high on trunks and main-crown branches of big trees, live and dead. The principal mode is gleaning, but Great Slaty Woodpeckers also probe, tap, flake bark and excavate (Short 1973).

SOCIAL ORGANIZATION. Individuals roost alone (Short 1973), but by day are more social than many other woodpeckers of the area. Pairs keep regular company and forage close by, and parties of 3–5 birds (assumed to include juveniles, but sometimes more than a likely family unit) are regular.

MOVEMENTS. No reports, unless recent occurrences in Singapore have been of dispersants from the mainland or Riau archipelago.

SURVIVAL. No information.

SOCIAL INTERACTIONS. Between presumed pair-members, head- and body-swinging; also active chasing while clambering and hopping among branches, with wings and tail spread, and throat-patch conspicuous (Short 1973). In India and Burma described as drumming loudly (HBI, Smythies 1953), but no drum identified in this area.

VOICE. The loudest, presumed territorial or long-range contact-call is a powerful whinny of 3–5 notes, *yoik-hoi-hoi-hoi-hoi*, even or falling away in pitch, and given while perched. Other vocalizations include a mew and a rich, resonant *tloik* or *juik*, single or in a short series, given both while perched and in flight. Longer versions respond to, and elicit, whinnying calls by a nearby partner (Short 1973).

BREEDING

Nest. A minimum 9 m up in tall mangrove trees (*Sonneratia, Lumnitzera* spp.) and, inland, likely nest-holes (attended by pairs) 9–45 m up trunks and on major boughs of tall trees, live and dead, including the giant legume *Koompassia excelsa,* within forest or standing relic above regrowth.

Eggs and brood. Eggs plain white. One clutch of two not necessarily complete, but no broods reported larger than this. No other information.

Cycle. Both adults excavate, but do not necessarily use a fresh hole at each breeding attempt. A.T. Edgar observed a pair abandon one in favour of another nearby that had already reared Dollarbirds and Brown Boobooks in a previous season, but which they themselves may well have made originally. Excavating adds to a store of potentially usable holes, where some are temporarily usurped by other bird species, and also mammals (L.L. Short added a large flying squirrel *Petaurista* sp. to the list).

Seasonality. Hole-excavation in March, April and late July; eggs on 16 August, fledglings during early July–late August (Chasen 1939, Holmes 1973, NRCS, Short 1973).

MOULT. Replacement of primaries is regular-descendant. Among 30 adults covering the length of the Peninsula and all months except September, 16 showed active wing-moult during July–February, with high incidence throughout this period. No starts were earlier or later, probably, than June and September, and no completions observed earlier than January (the most advanced individual still growing central tail-feathers T1 on 15 January). The March–June sample (n=11) was all of non-moulters. T1 is dropped not earlier than P9 (n=5).

CONSERVATION. On the plus side, able to use logged-over forest where removal of large timber has not been excessive, but core plains-level habitat is heavily fragmented and continues to shrink at a fast rate.

Family CAPITONIDAE

Barbets: 12 species

Fire-tufted Barbet; (no Thai name); Burung Takur Jambang Api (Malay)

Psilopogon pyrolophus S. Müller 1835, *Tijdschrift voor Natuurlijke Geschiedenis en Physiologie* 2: 339 and plate 8. TL Sumatra.

Plate 69

GROUP RELATIONS. Free-standing. Indochinese *M. legrandieri* (Red-vented Barbet) shows similarities of head-pattern, but is clearly a *Megalaima* species.

GLOBAL RANGE. Mountains of Sumatra and Peninsular Malaysia.

IDENTIFICATION/DESCRIPTION. The large barbet of Montane forest, with proportionately longer, more graduated tail than *Megalaima* species. Deep, flat-sided, pale-green bill with vertical black bar, and yellow-and-black breast-band below green throat, are diagnostic. Forehead, lores back to eye, and long rictal bristles black, the nasal tuft tipped red. Band across forecrown, at eye-level, lavender-grey with lateral spur of emerald-green extending behind eye; rest of cap to upper neck dark, dull maroon (slightly blacker in the female). A large face-patch (cheek to ear-coverts) pale lavender-grey. Rest of body, wings and tail plain grass-green; lower wing-coverts yellow. Juveniles as adult except head (especially cap) duller, paler, with face-patch browner grey.

Wing-beats distinctively noisy, and the rasping, insect-like call resembles no other bird of the area.

Bare-part colours. (Adult) iris chestnut-red, peri-orbital skin dark olive; bill pale apple-green with vertical black bar just beyond its mid point; feet sage-green.

Size (mm). (Skins: 9 males, 5 females; adult): wing 120–126 and 117–125; tail 100–112 and 97–109; bill 31.2–37.7 and 31.7–36.2; tarsus 29.7–32.3 and 30.0–31.8 (BMNH, UMBRP).

Weight (g). Adults, sexes not separated, 115–149 (n=20) (McClure 1964, UMBRP).

DISTRIBUTION. The Larut Range, the Main Range recorded from Ulu Langat (S Selangor/Pahang divide) north to latitude 5°35′N, and on outlying Benom (Medway 1972). Historical summary: *Pek, Phg, Sel.*

GEOGRAPHICAL VARIATION. None recognized.

STATUS AND POPULATION. Resident, regular and common; since it regularly feeds in regenerating growth along roadsides, etc., the most often-seen mountain barbet.

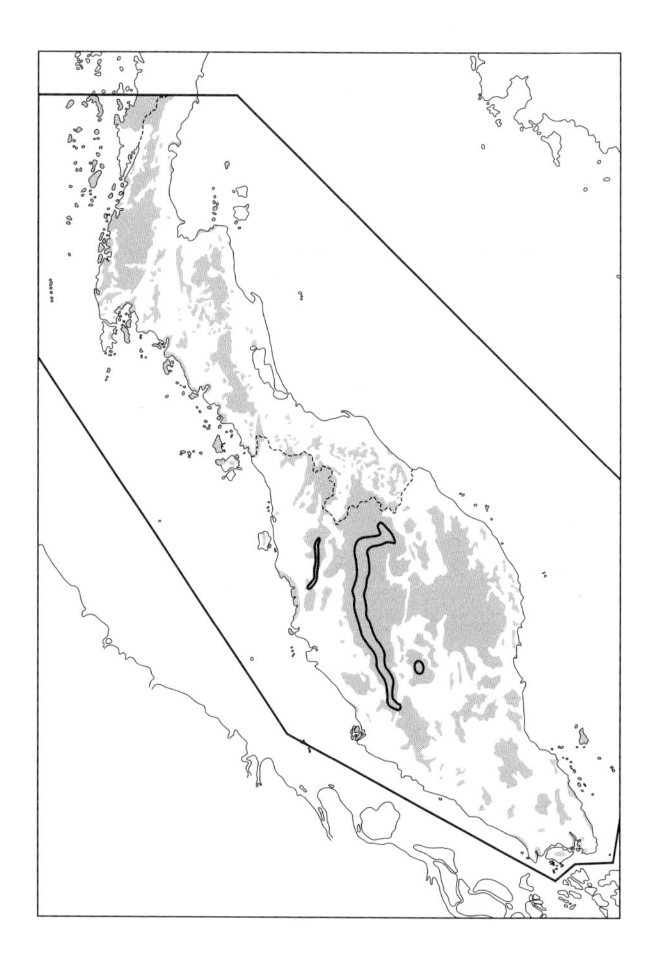

HABITATS AND ECOLOGY. Mid and canopy levels, and the edge of Montane forest, recorded from 2012 m, high in the Upper Montane zone (McClure 1964), down to and, in disturbed vegetation or at favoured fruiting figs, occasionally just below the Montane ecotone. Claims of occurrence as low as 670 m (Robinson 1909) have not been confirmed and, in continuous mature forest of the Benom slope, not found below 1070 m, i.e., not even to the ecotone (BMP5).

FORAGING AND FOOD. Figs are important over a wide size-range, from tiny fruit of *Ficus vasculosa* (the only species taken that has actually been identified) up to a diameter of 25 mm or more. Larger, tough-skinned types are mashed in the bill before being swallowed. Among non-figs in the diet, Robinson (1928) mentions fruit of an epiphytic melastome, probably *Medinella*. Also captures large arthropods, and loners sometimes join mixed-species foraging-flocks of passerines.

SOCIAL ORGANIZATION. Adults forage mostly alone or, at fruit sources, sometimes in loosely associating pairs or groups of 3–5 (BR 1974–75), but these do not behave cohesively. Where they meet in fruiting trees, etc., commonly displaces smaller, co-occurring Black-browed Barbet *Megalima oorti*.

MOVEMENTS. None reported.

SURVIVAL. No information.

SOCIAL INTERACTIONS. No information.

VOICE. The loud, presumed advertising-call, answered by neighbours, is a sequence of rasping, burring notes, the first 3–4 well spaced, but accelerating, running together and rising to an abruptly terminated crescendo, the last 1–2 notes falling away slightly: *zurr zurr zurr zurr-zur-zur... zr-zr-zr-zr-z-zzzzzzz-z-z*. Likened to cicada song although the resemblance is only in general quality of sound. At the start of the call, body held horizontal but it rises to near-vertical as tempo increases. Other calls are an incisive *tsink*, and, from a young juvenile, a rasping *teenk* (Glenister 1951, G.C. Madoc).

BREEDING

Nest. Little documented for so common a bird. Holes in large (including dead) trunks and in the lower side of an inclined branch, in and at the edge of mountain forest. No other details recorded.

Eggs and brood. Not described.

Cycle. No information.

Seasonality. Active nests, stage unchecked, in February; nestlings during February–early April; and a recent fledgling near Fraser's Hill on 7 May (Allen 1953, G.C. Madoc, Madoc 1956a).

MOULT. Among 16 adults handled in January–April, June and October–November, three showed mid-stage primary moult, in March and (twice) October (BMNH, UMBRP). Months covered may exclude the main season.

CONSERVATION. Ability to use forest regenerating after disturbance suggests no serious threat, but the overall ecology of this barbet is little known.

Lineated Barbet; Nok Phoradok Thamadaa (Thai); Burung Takur Kukup (Malay)

Megalaima lineata (Vieillot) 1816, *Nouveau Dictionnaire d'Histoire Naturelle* 4: 500. TL Java.
Plate 68

GROUP RELATIONS. Uncertain. Very similar to S Asian *M. zeylanica* (Brown-headed Barbet), and their vocalizations differ only subtly, but ranges overlap in the Himalayan foothills and NE Indian subcontinent. Habitat-limits need more research.

GLOBAL RANGE. Himalayan foothills east from Nepal and the NE Indian subcontinent; S and SW Yunnan; continental SE Asia to the Peninsula, and Java and Bali.

IDENTIFICATION/DESCRIPTION. The only medium-large, green-bodied barbet of non-forest habitats, and the only species with a yellow bill, conspicuous, bright yellow skin around a darkish eye, and cream-streaked brown head and breast. All sex/age-classes are much the same (Riley 1938).

Bare-part colours. (Adult) iris red-brown to dark brown, periorbital skin bright yellow; bill orange-horn; feet pale yellow.

Size (mm). (Skins: 5 males, 2 females; adult): wing 122–129 and 121 (1 only); tail 75–79 and 71, 72; bill 29.6–34.5 and 34.2 (1 only); tarsus 26.2–33.9 and 29.7, 31.9 (BMNH, UMZC).

Weight. No data.

DISTRIBUTION. The northern two thirds of the Peninsula. Historical summary: all divisions except *Sur, Nak, Sel, Neg, Mel, Joh, Sin*, with no additional island records.

GEOGRAPHICAL VARIATION. Subspecies *hodgsoni* Bonaparte 1850 (TL Nepal). Deignan (1963) identified smaller nominate *lineata* in the south, but latitudinal differentiation in an actively advancing non-forest bird is inherently unlikely. More measurements are needed.

STATUS AND POPULATION. Resident, regular, common, and spreading south along both coastal

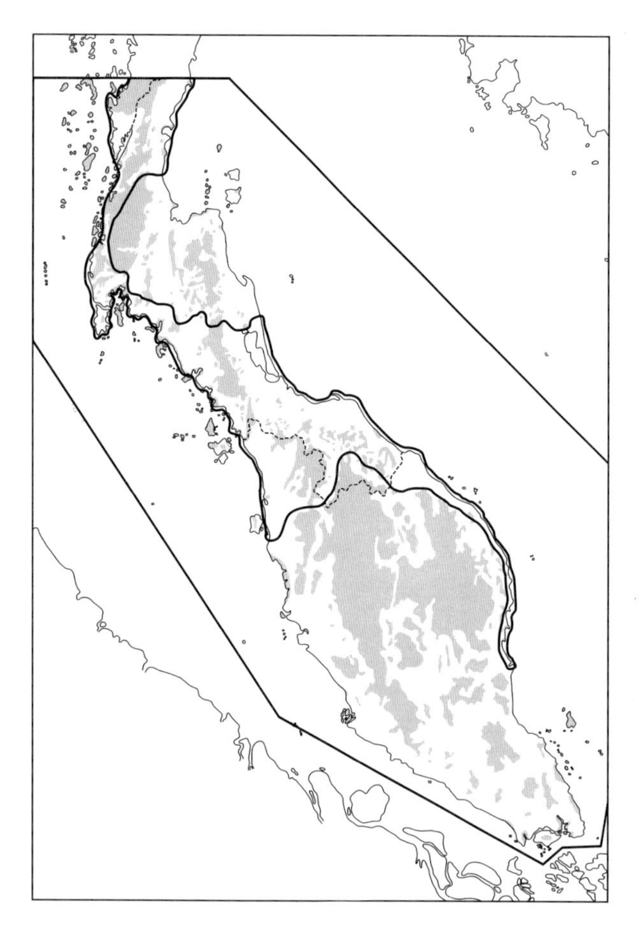

plains. On the E coast, present at Dungun (latitude 4°46′N) by 1900, Kemaman in the 1940s, a few kilometres north of Kuantan (Pahang) in 1964 and at Pekan Lama, south shore of the Pahang estuary, in May 1995 (Berwick 1952, BR 1964, Bromley 1949, A. Jeyarajasingam). In the west, long present in Kedah, now also mainland Penang (Seberang Prai) (K. Kumar). Inland, it is on the Pengkalan Hulu plateau, N Perak, perhaps reached from Yala as Malaysian approaches are still mostly ringed by forest.

HABITATS AND ECOLOGY. The landward edge of mangrove forest, beach (including casuarina) strand, paperbark woodland, coconut and rubber gardens (but avoids extensive plantations), orchards, wooded parks and gardens (well into towns), and isolated trees scattered across agriculture and other open land; at plains level, and on the settled Pengkalan Hulu plateau at about 300 m.

FORAGING AND FOOD. A breeding pair took half-ripe jambu *Eugenia* (Myrtaceae) fruit for themselves but fed their nestlings fruit of a species of *Litsea* (Lauraceae); also large invertebrates including spiders, orthopterans and mantids. Some animal food is captured on the ground (Berwick 1952, 1952b).

SOCIAL ORGANIZATION. When not breeding, typically solitary.

MOVEMENTS. None reported.

SURVIVAL. No information.

SOCIAL INTERACTIONS. No information.

VOICE. The advertising-call is a dull, wooden, *ho-prrub*, monotonously repeated in bouts of up to 40 calls at a rough rate of one every second, usually from a perch well concealed in foliage. Said to have another, four-note call (Berwick 1952) but details are wanting.

BREEDING

Nest. Holes 5–12 m up, mostly in living trunks and main branches, with records from a laurel *Litsea* sp., *Morinda citrifolia*, paperbark, casuarina, rubber, and just below the broken-off peak of a coconut palm. One entrance measured 7.7 cm wide, the tunnel 20 cm deep. Excavates its own holes but also takes over (at least occasionally usurps) those of other species, including Banded Yellownape *Picus mineaceus*.

Eggs and brood. Eggs slightly glossy, plain white. Shape long ovate. Size (mm): 29.2–27.2 x 20.8–20.5 (n=4). Full clutch said to be four but no record of a brood of that size fledging.

Cycle. Both parents tend nestlings, one waiting on the departure of the other if they happen to arrive with food simultaneously. Faecal sacs are carried away from the hole.

Seasonality. Active nests, stage unchecked, in March; eggs on 24 April; nestlings in April. A much longer season (September–May) has been claimed for Kedah (Berwick 1952, 1952b, Bromley 1949, ENGGANG-2, Lewin 1957, G.C. Madoc, Madoc 1956a, NRCS).

MOULT. Replacement of at least inner primaries is regular-descendant. Active wing-moult recorded in early June (P2) and mid August (P8), and a second August adult had recently completed. Others dated February, March and May showed none (BMNH, UMZC).

CONSERVATION. No critical issues.

Gold-whiskered Barbet; Nok Phoradok Khrao Leuang (Thai); Burung Takur Misai Emas (Malay)

Megalaima chrysopogon (Temminck) 1824, *Nouveau Recueil de Planches Coloriées d'Oiseaux* 48: plate 285. TL Sumatra.

Plate 69

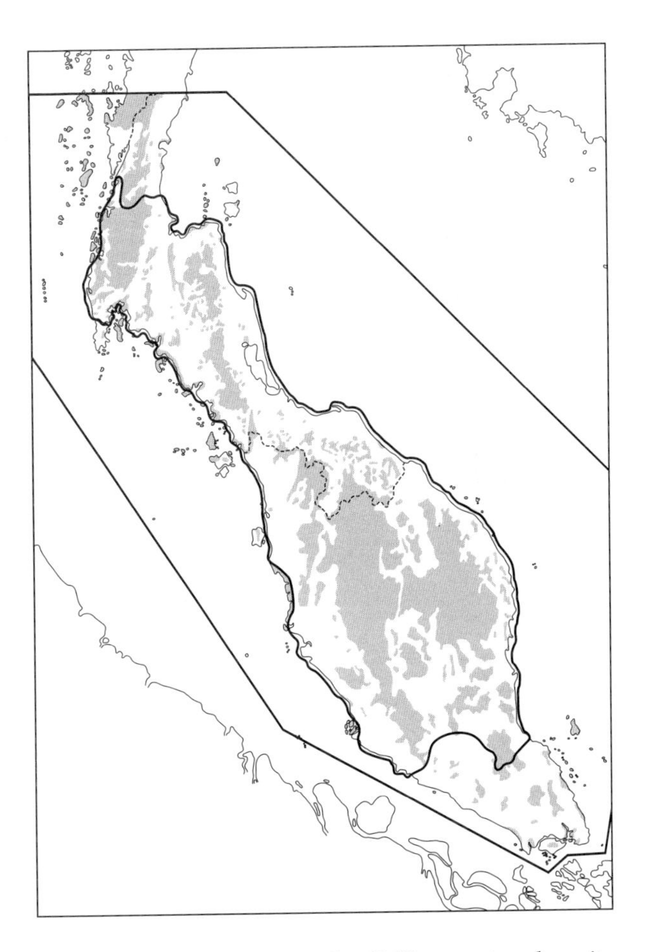

GROUP RELATIONS. Probably free-standing.

GLOBAL RANGE. Borneo, Sumatra, the Peninsula and SW Thailand to latitude about 11°30′N.

IDENTIFICATION/DESCRIPTION. Largest local barbet, from Red-crowned by larger, more conspicuous gold-yellow malar-patch, lavender rather than bright blue chin and throat, and buff-brown fore-crown rather than completely red cap. Red on the head is confined to lores, around base of upper mandible, and feather-centres of the otherwise blue hind-crown to nape. Sexes similar. Juveniles duller throughout, with lores orange rather than red, fore-crown yellow-tinged, and throat more violet (BMNH, Robinson 1928); there is no evidence of an all-green juvenile head-plumage in this species.

Bare-part colours. (Adult) iris red-brown, peri-orbital skin black; bill black, shading to lead-grey at base of lower mandible; feet olive-green.

Size (mm). (Live and skins: 12 males, 10 females; adult): wing 122–133 and 126–134; tail 74–80 and 72–78; bill 42.8–46.4 and 44.6–50.0; tarsus 31.2–33.8 and 31.3–34.8 (BMNH, UMBRP, UMZC).

Weight (g). An unsexed adult, 156 (UMBRP).

DISTRIBUTION. No reports from the far north or far south. Historical summary: all divisions except *Pak, Chu, Phu, Mel, Sin*, and no other island records.

GEOGRAPHICAL VARIATION. Endemic *laeta* Robinson and Kloss 1918 (TL Tangga peak, Negeri Sembilan), with richer yellow malar-patch than nominate Sumatran birds, although the Malaysian W-coast plain is said to hold intermediates (Chasen 1934).

STATUS AND POPULATION. Resident, regular and uncommon to common.

HABITATS AND ECOLOGY. Mainly the high canopy of semi-evergreen and evergreen Lowland forest, mature and where a good residue of tall trees, including fruit-sources, remains after logging; occasionally also out short distances from forest to fruiting trees in tall secondary-growth. Selects hilly and undulating terrain, up slopes to the lower fringe of Montane forest, with records to 1070 m (one exceptional Main Range encounter at 1500 m: BMP5). At plains level, typically sparse (or absent) in the extreme lowlands, with only a handful of records ever from subcoastal peatswamp forest (ENGGANG-2). Thus, hardly known in Johor south of hilly country along its northern border with Pahang (I.D. Teesdale).

FORAGING AND FOOD. Like most other forest barbets, Gold-whiskered takes many figs. In the upper Gombak valley, Selangor, seen at high-crowned, canopy-fruiting *Ficus glabella* and *F. sumatrana* (McClure 1966), and visited 22 of 25 bird-attracting *Ficus* species under regular observation in Kerau wildlife reserve and Taman Negara (Lambert 1989). Over a fruit-diameter range 5.4–34.8 mm, attention increased with fruit-size, peaking as of about 28 mm (*F. dubia, stupenda* and *subcordata*), but one small-fruited species, *F. obscura*, mean fig-diameter only 7.1 mm, remained unexpectedly attractive even though fruiting in the understorey rather than this bird's usual canopy habitat.

Adults also take alate termites, and unidentified insects and a lizard were fed to a fledgling (J.R. Howes, Lambert 1987).

SOCIAL ORGANIZATION. Typically solitary, but attraction to large-crowned, mass-fruiting trees may result in several birds (up to five counted) gathering to feed together. These show no obvious cohesive behaviour, and comings and goings are individual, but at times birds call, and a chorus around a fruit-source may attract late-comers. Fogden (1970) thought this might be a form of altruism, but in a localized food-surplus situation individual tree-top foragers might also gain directly from company through collective vigilance, allowing more efficient feeding. Callers are notoriously hard to pinpoint in a leafy canopy, but the situations in which this and other barbet species vocalize while feeding need analysing in more detail – with scope for experimentation.

MOVEMENTS. None reported.

SURVIVAL. No information.

SOCIAL INTERACTIONS. No definite information.

VOICE. A mellow but powerful, resonant hoot, *ke<u>tob</u>*, monotonously repeated at about 25 calls per ten seconds, from high perches well concealed in foliage. Also, a sequence of strident, rattling trills, in bursts that space out, slow and shorten progressively, down to not more than 3–5 notes. Trills are given other than while feeding, but are of unknown function.

The advertising disyllable is given more or less year-round, but erratically, and often in concert with other *Megalaima* species of the same habitat. At times, many barbets of several species, including Gold-whiskered, call persistently over a wide area, and at others are virtually or completely silent, as stated, for reasons not yet well understood.

BREEDING

Nest. Excavates its own holes, 6–17 m up in rot-softened wood of dead trees in and at the edge of forest (one in a tree drowned at the edge of a new reservoir). Extra holes are dug in the same or neighbouring trees, apparently as roosts. They accumulate from previous years, and two instances of a nesting association with Black-thighed Falconets have been reported, the falconets using old barbet holes while the probable former owners themselves bred only a few metres away. Structural details are lacking.

Eggs and brood. Eggs, clutch two, claimed for this species were slightly glossy, plain white, short elliptical in shape, but measurements quoted are smaller than expected and more certain identifications are needed.

Cycle. Both adults excavate, and some pairs appear to raise more than one brood per season in the same hole.

Seasonality. Records of hole-excavation in February and August; nestlings in early May and late June (successive broods perhaps of a single pair), and November (E.C.S. Baker, BCSTB-13, Chasen 1939, G.C. Madoc, Molesworth 1955, NRCS).

MOULT. Among 23 adults covering most of the Peninsula, and all months except July, eight showed active wing-moult during early April–mid November (BMNH, UMZC). Apparent mid-stage records from June onwards imply only weak synchrony, but more information is needed on the pattern of flight-feather replacement in individuals.

CONSERVATION. Concentration on slope-land forest implies no immediate threat from habitat-loss, but removal of large-fruited strangling figs from the canopy via the logging of their host-trees is an issue over the whole altitudinal range of this species (Lambert 1991).

Red-crowned Barbet; Nok Phoradok Lak See (Thai); <u>Bu</u>rung <u>Ta</u>kur Mah<u>ko</u>ta <u>Me</u>rah (Malay)

Megalaima rafflesii (Lesson) 1839, *Revue Zoologique par la Société Cuvierienne*: 137. TL Sumatra.
Plate 69

GROUP RELATIONS. Free-standing.

GLOBAL RANGE. Borneo, Sumatra and intervening islands, and the Peninsula, with a record at latitude 11°20′N in S Tenasserim (Riley 1938).

IDENTIFICATION/DESCRIPTION. Closest in size to Gold-whiskered Barbet, and also has a yellow malar-patch, but this is smaller and the surrounding head-pattern differs distinctively: entire cap from bill to nape, a small spot below eye and large spot on side of throat bright blood-red; chin, throat and long supercilium shining cobalt-blue, sharp against black feather-bases; lores to ear-coverts black. The sexes are similar. Juveniles are much duller, with red spots, particularly the throat-spot, small and obscure, malar-patch smaller, and blue parts turquoise rather than cobalt. There is no evidence of a green-headed plumage-stage.

Bare-part colours. Iris chestnut-brown (adult); bill black, lower base whitish (juvenile), slaty (adult); feet pale olive-grey.

Size (mm). (Live and skins: 19 males, 10 females; adult): wing 115–126 and 117–124; tail 64.2–70.2 and 65.1–70.9; bill 37.4–42.1 and 37.6–43.3; tarsus 29.1–31.1 and 27.1–30.0 (BMNH, UMZC).

Weight (g). An unsexed adult, 99 (UMBRP).

DISTRIBUTION. No records from the far north. Historical summary: all divisions except *Pak, Chu, Ran, Pha, Nak, Phu, Pht, Son, Pat, Sat, Yal, Kel, Pra*, and formerly on Ubin island, Singapore.

GEOGRAPHICAL VARIATION. None currently recognized; subspecies rejected on the basis that variations in body-size and tone of blue parts are aged-linked or individual rather than geographical (Mees 1986, Voous 1961).

STATUS AND POPULATION. Resident, regular and common, wherever good tracts of suitable plains-level habitat survive. Forest clearance has near-eliminated it from Thailand.

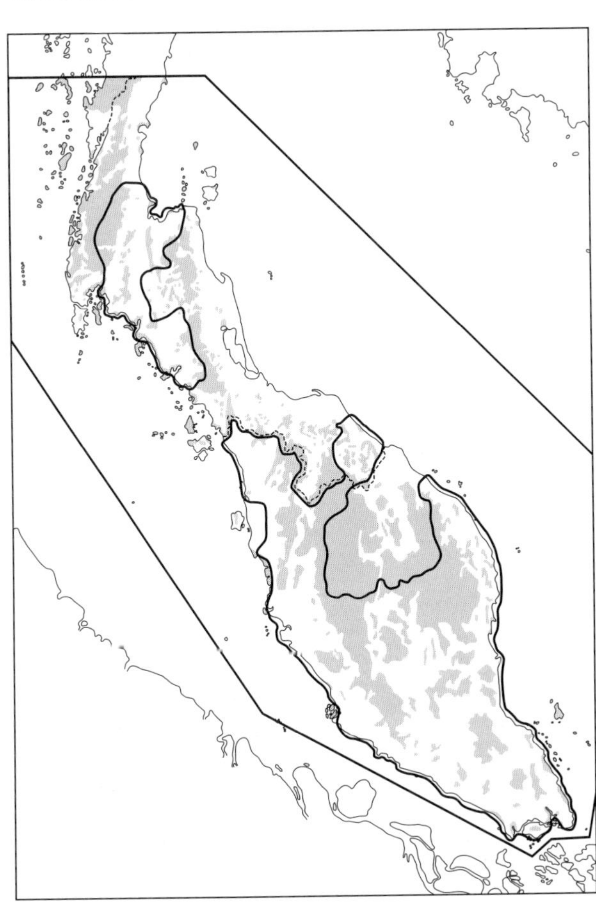

HABITATS AND ECOLOGY. As with Gold-whiskered Barbet, the canopy of semi-evergreen and evergreen Lowland forest, including peatswamp forest and tall paperbark woodland, mature and well regenerated after disturbance. Shares habitat with Gold-whiskered Barbet around the base of hills. In undulating terrain, locally, they can be equally common, but typically occupy complementary habitat-zones, Red-crowned commonest in level, low-lying plains and hardly present past the steepland boundary. The ecological significance of the terrain-break for these mainly high-canopy species has not been investigated, but *Megalaima* barbets of given size-classes are commonly partitioned by altitude.

FORAGING AND FOOD. A bird seen taking fruit of a canopy-height vine in Pasoh research forest, Negeri Sembilan, and this species was among visitors to a mass-fruiting banyan, *Ficus microcarpa*, by the Tembeling river, Taman Negara (BR 1972–73). In the same area, none visited a fruiting *Ficus virens* fed at by all other local *Megalaima* species, including Gold-whiskered, and Lambert (1987) never encountered a Red-crowned Barbet at any of his many forest *Ficus* species under observation at Kuala Lompat, Kerau wildlife reserve. Takes some animal food, including borer grubs excavated from rotten wood (BMP5), and has been recorded a few times in, or following, mixed-species foraging-flocks, mainly of insectivorous passerines (SINGAV-2). The fact of survival on Singapore island where three, possibly four, smaller (regular fig-eating) barbets have disappeared within a century (Lim 1992) suggests unusual attributes.

SOCIAL ORGANIZATION. Typically solitary.

MOVEMENTS. None reported.

SURVIVAL. No information.

SOCIAL INTERACTIONS. No information.

VOICE. An even-toned sequence of 10–15 rich, mellow hoots delivered at a steady rate of three per second, except for a noticeably longer pause after the second, or first and second note(s): *hoop hoop, hoop-hoop-hoop-hoop . . .*, given typically from a high perch deep in foliage. This species has not been confirmed to possess rattle- or trill-calls.

BREEDING

Nest. Burrows into rot-softened wood, including of entirely dead trees. One nest-hole 4.5 m up. No other details available.

Eggs and brood. Eggs and clutch undescribed, but broods of one and two fledglings reported from Singapore and Krabi.

Cycle. Both pair-members excavate, in alternating shifts, and dig more holes than they actually use for breeding (see also Gold-whiskered Barbet).

Seasonality. Excavation (but not necessarily of nest-holes) during late January–April and in July, nestlings in April and dependant fledglings in mid and late May (BBCB-7, BCSTB-11, BR 1978–79, MBR 1986–87, NRCS, SINGAV-2).

MOULT. Order of primary replacement uncertain, but it starts at P1. Among 36 adults covering most latitudinal range, and all months except May and June, 13 showed active wing-moult during early April (P1)–mid September (P8 to P10), with latest starts and early completions overlapping in July and incidence 60-plus percent in all months July–September. Birds dated October–March (n=18) showed no moult (BMNH, UMZC).

CONSERVATION. Special to forest of the level lowlands, it is in the front rank of species threatened by outright habitat-loss. Already gone from virtually all former Thai range (Boonsong and Round 1991), and populations are highly fragmented everywhere. Near-threatened globally (BTW2).

Red-throated Barbet; Nok Phoradok Khang Daeng (Thai); Burung Takur Raya (Malay)

Megalaima mystacophanos (Temminck) 1824, *Nouveau Recueil de Planches Coloriées d'Oiseaux* 53: plate 315. TL Sumatra.

Plate 69

GROUP RELATIONS. Free-standing.

GLOBAL RANGE. Borneo, Sumatra, the Peninsula, and Tenasserim and SW Thailand respectively to 14°N and 14°58′N (Bung Kroeng Kavia, Kanchanaburi: BBCB-4).

IDENTIFICATION/DESCRIPTION. A medium-sized barbet with proportionately larger bill than others in its mass-class. The only local *Megalaima* that is strongly sexually dimorphic. In both adults, hind-crown, spot on the lores and a larger one at the side of the throat, red, but all duller in the female. Males have chin and upper throat bright red; lower throat (between the spots) bright cobalt-blue; forehead to forecrown shining, brassy yellow; spot at base of lower mandible lemon-yellow and emerald-green; and narrow supercilium from lores over eye to rear of ear-coverts black. Females have all these parts shades of blue-green, in only mild contrast to grass-green body. Except for slight red on the lores, young juveniles are entirely green-headed. Young males develop yellow on the forehead before any other red.

Bare-part colours. Iris red-brown (adult); upper mandible and bill-tip black, rest of lower mandible paling to lead-blue (juvenile and adult female), bill all-black (adult male); feet greenish grey to slaty.

Size (mm). (Skins: 17 males, 12 females; adult): wing 94–101 and 94–102; tail 51–59 and 51–57; bill 32.3–39.0 and 32.6–38.9; tarsus 24.7–28.4 and 25.3–27.7 (BMNH, UMZC).

Weight (g). Adult males, 71.0, 74.9 (UMBRP).

DISTRIBUTION. Historical summary: all divisions except *Mel*, *Joh*, but is present along the Pahang/Johor border and the southern gap is unlikely to be real. Also recorded from Rang island (*Phu*).

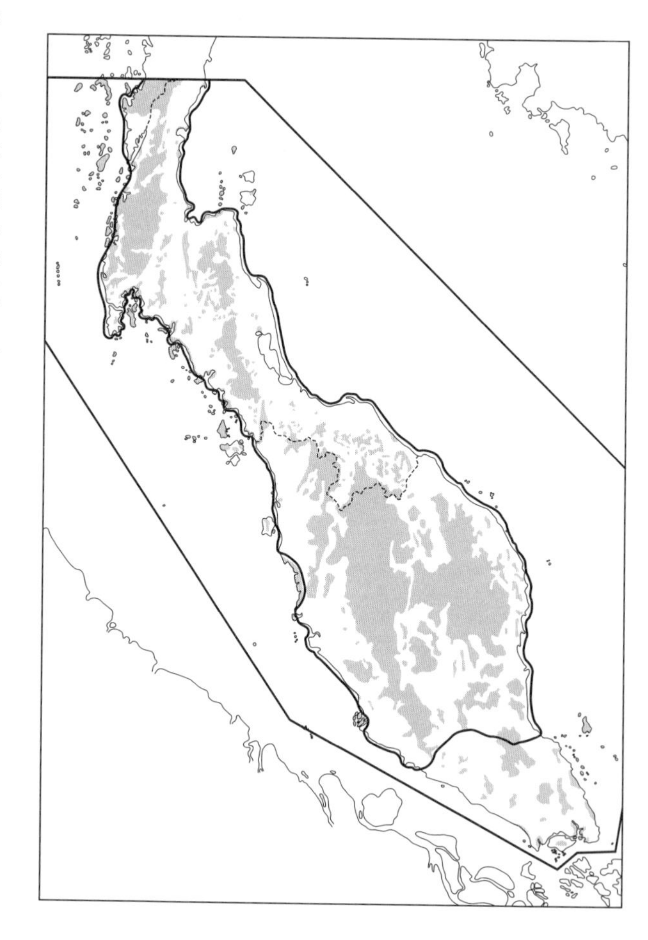

GEOGRAPHICAL VARIATION. Nominate *mystacophanos*, of the global range except W Sumatran islands.

STATUS AND POPULATION. Resident, regular and common except, apparently, in the far south. The only recent record in Singapore is of an apparent loner calling during two weeks of March 1989 (SINGAV-3), indicating a possible small (new?) presence in the central catchment woodland; but in the Republic chance of an escape or release from captivity can never be ruled out.

HABITATS AND ECOLOGY. Mainly the canopy, occasionally (including when nesting) down to mid- and lower-stratum levels, in semi-evergreen and evergreen Lowland forest, mature and regenerated back to closed-canopy structure after disturbance; also in peatswamp forest. Occurs at all elevations including, in Malaysia, marginally into Lower Montane forest, with records on the Main Range to 1040 m, but none from Thailand above 750 m (ENGGANG-2, Boonsong and Round 1991).

FORAGING AND FOOD. A fig-cropper, like most forest barbets. Recorded at a large-crowned *Ficus sumatrana* in the upper Gombak valley, Selangor (McClure 1966), and from 18 of 25 bird-attracting *Ficus* species under observation in the Kerau wildlife reserve and Taman Negara (Pahang), in the minimum fruit-diameter range 5.4–27.4 mm (Lambert 1989). Among these, peak attention was given to *F. parietalis* (an understorey species) and *F. trichocarpa*, mean minimum fruit-diameters 14.8 and 15.5 mm. Also among the barbet species visiting a forest-edge banyan *F. microcarpa* (BR 1972–73). Bark-taps, possibly after arthropods, and recorded taking winged termites (Hume and Davison 1878, Lambert 1987, Short 1973a).

In the Kerau wildlife reserve, a female fed a dependant fledgling figs on all six visits observed (NRCS).

SOCIAL ORGANIZATION. Solitary or in pairs; not known to gather at fruit-sources in greater numbers than this.

MOVEMENTS. None reported.

SURVIVAL. No information.

SOCIAL INTERACTIONS. Courtship-feeding of a small snail to a female by a male, after the item had been branch-beaten (BMP5).

VOICE. A slow, prolonged bout of rather dull, single and double clucks, *chok*, *chok-chok*, in alternating or irregular sequence. Less commonly, the call is just of single notes, delivered at a rate of about one per second. Also, a succession of loud, rather high-pitched rattle-trills that slow and shorten progressively, down to only two notes per burst.

BREEDING

Nest. A hole 6 m up a dead tree standing through the canopy of low, regenerating forest; and in the forest interior, two instances of holes excavated in still-active, arboreal ant-nests or termitaria, one only 3 m up a dead stump in an area prone to flooding.

Eggs and brood. Eggs plain, rather glossy white. Shape short elliptical. Size (mm): 27.7 × 21.2, 27.7 × 20.5 (n=2). A report of a clutch of four requires confirmation.

Cycle. Two consecutive evening checks on a nest found the female incubating.

Seasonality. Eggs or incubation-behaviour in January and March, courtship-feeding in late June, hole-excavation (but not necessarily for nesting) in early July, and dependant fledglings on 28 May and 11 August (BMP5, BR 1972–73, Chasen 1939, NRCS, UMZC).

MOULT. Moult of primaries starts from P1. Among 48 adults covering the Peninsula south to Selangor, and all months except August, 15 showed active wing-moult during late April (P2–3)–September (P4 and P8), with overall incidence 70 percent-plus in June–July, starts to at least June and completions as of July (BMNH, UMBRP, UMZC). Zero incidence during October–March (n=17) implies retarded individuals may arrest or suspend before completion, but more information is needed on sequence of replacement of flight-feathers.

CONSERVATION. See Gold-whiskered Barbet.

Golden-throated Barbet; Nok Phoradok Khang Leuang (Thai); Burung Takur Gunung (Malay)

Megalaima franklinii (Blyth) 1842, *Journal of the Asiatic Society of Bengal* 11: 167. TL Darjeeling, NE India.

Plate 69

GROUP RELATIONS. Free-standing. In Borneo, its habitat-slot is filled by *M. pulcherrima* (Golden-naped Barbet) but this seems not to be a guide to relationships.

GLOBAL RANGE. The Himalayas east from Nepal and hill-tracts of the far-NE Indian subcontinent; SE Tibet; Yunnan and SW Guangxi; and higher mountains of SE Asia as far as the Peninsula.

IDENTIFICATION/DESCRIPTION. Similar in size and shape to Black-browed Barbet *M. oorti*, which it replaces altitudinally. Both have bright yellow chin and throat, red forehead, a yellow patch on the crown centre, and red centre to the nape, flanked by black and with a fine posterior fringe of bright blue forming a hind-collar; but Golden-throated lacks a red spot on the side of the throat, has a silver-grey rather than blue face and, in Malaysia (where the two species meet), the black of the brow is broken between eye and hind-crown. It is also the only local barbet with blue in the wing (margins of lesser wing-coverts and flight-feathers). A small orange spot at the base of the lower mandible is noticeable only at close range. The sexes are much the same, but females are duller on the throat and less broadly margined blue on the wings. Juveniles have much duller wing and head colours, with reds especially paler, and no mandibular spot.

Bare-part colours. (Adult) iris dark red-brown; bill black paling to blue-grey at the base; feet grey-green.

Size (mm). (Skins: 9 males, 2 females; adult *minor*): wing 92–98 and 97, 98; tail 57–64 and 61, 64; bill 22.0–25.5 and 26.0 (1 only); tarsus 24.6–26.0 and 24.9, 26.6 (BMNH, UMZC).

Weight (g). Unsexed adult *minor* from Cameron Highlands, 63.5 (n=54) (McClure 1964).

DISTRIBUTION. South end of the E-central Range, the Larut Range, the Main Range where recorded between Ulu Langat and Cameron Highlands, and on eastern outliers Benom and Tahan, plus the latter's northern satellite Rabong. Historical summary: *Tra, Pht, Kel, Pek, Phg, Sel.*

GEOGRAPHICAL VARIATION. Subspecies *minor* Kloss and Chasen 1926 (TL Hijau peak, Larut Range) in Malaysia. Restricted-range *trangensis* Riley 1934 (TL Nom Plu peak, Trang) is very slightly larger (wing 98–101 mm) with longer, heavier bill (26–28 mm) and black brow complete back to hind-crown level (as in northern continental populations).

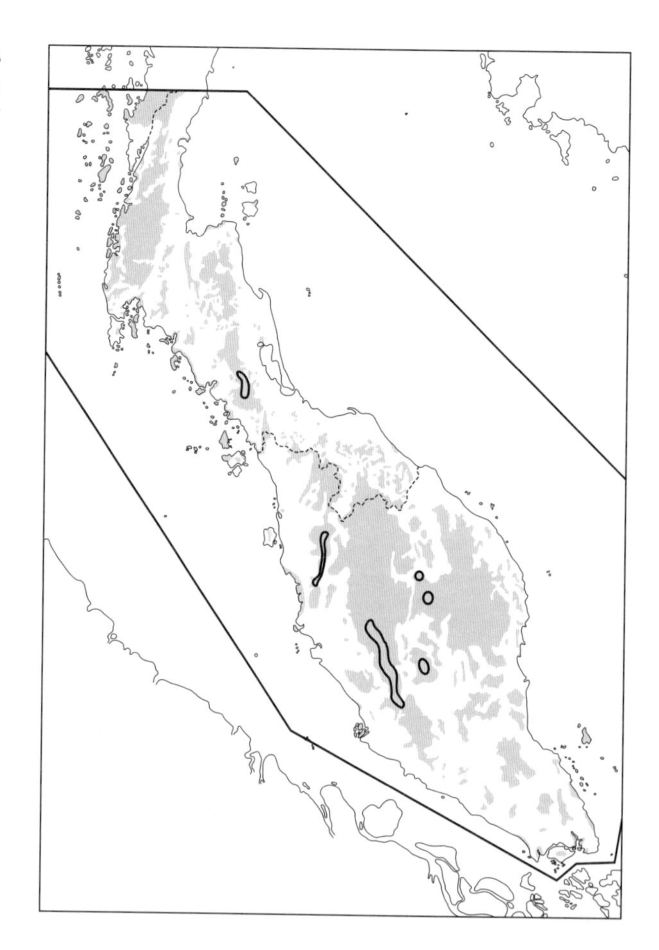

STATUS AND POPULATION. Resident, regular and, in Malaysia, common within a strictly delimited habitat zone. Sometimes-tiny pockets of population occur in the top 50 m or less of summit terrain. *M.f. trangensis* is known from only five specimens collected by W.L. Abbott nearly a century ago (Riley 1938), and has not been looked for since.

HABITATS AND ECOLOGY. In Malaysia, upper member of a trio of morphologically similar species that replace one another by altitude. Confined there to Upper Montane forest typically not below about 1400 m but limit dictated locally by the effect on vegetation of summit-height, aspect, slope, etc. (thus, down to 1350 m on Benom and on a few Main and Larut Range ridges, 1300 m). On the Trang slope, which lacks a middle-zone species, *trangensis* is recorded as low as 760 m (Riley 1938), where no longer even in Montane let alone Upper Montane forest. Its slightly larger bill may help adapt it to occupation of more habitats than in Malaysia. This barbet ranges from canopy level well down into the interior of Upper Montane forest; behaviour in other forest-types is unrecorded.

FORAGING AND FOOD. Golden-throated Barbets rarely wander below their typical calling-zone which, in Malaysia, is above that of most mass-fruiting fig species. Montane forest appears to offer a more dependable range of non-fig fruit options than Lowland forest, but more observations are needed.

SOCIAL ORGANIZATION. Mainly solitary.

MOVEMENTS. None recorded.

SURVIVAL. No information.

SOCIAL INTERACTIONS. No information.

VOICE. A brisk, yelping *ke-triuk*, given in a steady sequence at a rate of 12 calls per ten seconds. Birds advertising with this call rotate the body and head through a wide arc, concealing the exact location of the sound-source (G.C. Madoc). A rattle-trill call exists but needs proper description. An adult with a fledgling gave brief alarm-rattles, and a bird just released after ringing a whinnying *tehihi, tehihi*.

BREEDING

Nest. Only one described, a hole 4.5 m up a dead tree, entrance 4.5 cm wide, tunnel to nest-chamber 26 cm deep.

Eggs and brood. Eggs not described and regular clutch-size unknown. The above nest contained a single chick.

Seasonality. A new nestling on 16 March, recent fledglings on 23 March and 4 May (Allin and Edgar 1948).

MOULT. Information is needed on flight-feather replacement patterns. One of two August adults was growing P9; 11 others dated December–January and March–April showed no moult (BMNH, UMZC).

CONSERVATION. No critical issues as yet.

Black-browed Barbet; (no Thai name); Burung Takur Bukit (Malay)

Megalaima oorti (S. Müller) 1835, *Tijdschrift voor Natuurlijke Geschiedenis en Physiologie* 2: 341 and plate 8. TL Sumatra.

Plate 69

GROUP RELATIONS. Uncertain. *M. asiatica* (Blue-throated Barbet) and *M. incognita* (Moustached Barbet) occupy equivalent habitat-space in mostly interdigitating SE and E Asian ranges, avoiding each other by altitude in patches of overlap (none between Black-browed and Blue-throated), and have similar advertising vocalizations. They may form a superspecies, to which might perhaps be added Bornean *M. monticola* (Mountain Barbet). At the same time, occupants of other equivalent barbet habitats in the region are not close relatives (see *M. franklinii*).

GLOBAL RANGE. Uplands of Taiwan, Guangxi and Hainan; and in SE Asia, S Laos, S Vietnam, the Peninsula and Sumatra.

IDENTIFICATION/DESCRIPTION. See Golden-throated Barbet. From it by side of face up to level of eye, side of nape and zone around throat clear, bright blue; and by bold black supercilium over eye unbroken to rear margin of ear-coverts. Also by lack of blue in the wing but, surprisingly, this is not a strong field-character. If they should ever be shown to meet in the northern Peninsula, from Blue-throated Barbet *M. asiatica* by yellow parts (the main plumage-character separating Black-browed from presumed immediate relatives). Sexes alike; juveniles as adult but duller, red parts in particular fainter and smaller.

Bare-part colours. Iris red-brown, broad eyelid sage-green; bill dark horn with yellow marks (juvenile) (Robinson 1928), slaty black paling to lead-grey at the base (adult); feet grey-green.

Size (mm). (Skins: 11 males only; adult): wing 92–96; tail 59–67; bill 21.7–23.8; tarsus 22.8–25.4 (BMNH).

Weight. No data.

DISTRIBUTION. The Larut Range including southern outlier Bubu, the Main Range recorded from Telapa Buruk peak, Negeri Sembilan, north to latitude 5°35'N (the E-W Highway), on eastern outliers Benom and Tahan, Tahan satellites Tulang Rabong and Rabong, and Lawit peak off the north tip of the E-Coast Range. Historical summary: *Kel, Tru, Pek, Phg, Sel, Neg.*

GEOGRAPHICAL VARIATION. Nominate *oorti*, also of Sumatra.

STATUS AND POPULATION. Resident, regular, and common wherever found.

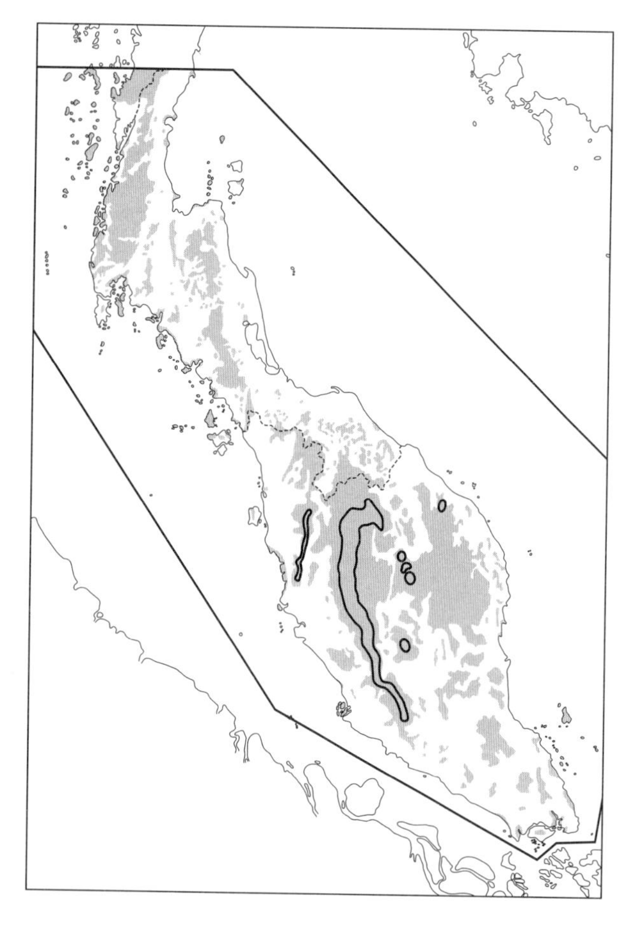

HABITATS AND ECOLOGY. The canopy of steep-land Lowland and Lower Montane forest, mature and well regenerated, typically between about 750 and 1300 m but locally variable (thus only above 900 m, hardly down to the forest ecotone, on the Larut Range slope). Middle member of an altitudinal trio. On vocal evidence, species-replacement is mostly abrupt, but in untouched forests of the Benom and Rabong slopes short gaps occurred between Black-browed and Golden-throated Barbet ranges. Black-browed seems not to use the latter's space anywhere but in disturbed forest of Main Range valleys has occasionally been seen deep within the calling-zone of its lowland counterpart, Yellow-crowned Barbet *M. henricii*, at large, mass-fruiting fig trees attended by both these species down to 250 m (ENGGANG-1).

In Montane forest, often displaced by larger Fire-tufted Barbet (Newmark 1955), including from feeding-sites. At Fraser's Hill, none visited a small-figged *Ficus vasculosa* fruiting at understorey level and fed at by various montane frugivores, including up to five Fire-tufted Barbets (BR 1974–75).

FORAGING AND FOOD. Takes canopy-level fruit everywhere including, at critical altitudes, figs attracting most submontane barbet species. In Montane forest, one also observed exploring a shallow pit in a dead snag.

SOCIAL ORGANIZATION. Except where a few converge on a fruit-source, mostly solitary.

MOVEMENTS. None recorded.

SURVIVAL. No information.

SOCIAL INTERACTIONS. No information.

VOICE. A brisk tokatruk, not unlike the call of Golden-throated Barbet, but with reciprocal stress, the third syllable purred or vibrated slightly when heard at close range; given in long, steady bouts at a rate of about one call per second (BMP5). A rattle-call is less strident than that of most congeners, with separate notes more easily distinguishable, shortening down to bursts of just a few (commonly three) notes.

BREEDING

Nest. Holes in dead trees, in two instances at the edge of Lower Montane forest, 9 and 10.5 m above ground.

Eggs and brood. Not described.

Cycle. No information.

Seasonality. Active nests, stage unchecked, in mid March and early October (Allin and Edgar 1948, NRCS).

MOULT. Twelve adults from the Larut and Main Ranges, and Tahan, collected in all months January–late May, showed no wing- or tail-moult, implying the process is seasonal.

CONSERVATION. See Fire-tufted Barbet.

Blue-throated Barbet; Nok Phoradok Khaw See Faa (Thai); Burung Takur Muka Biru (Malay)

Megalaima asiatica (Latham) 1790, *Index Ornithologicus* 1: 201. TL Calcutta.
Plate 69

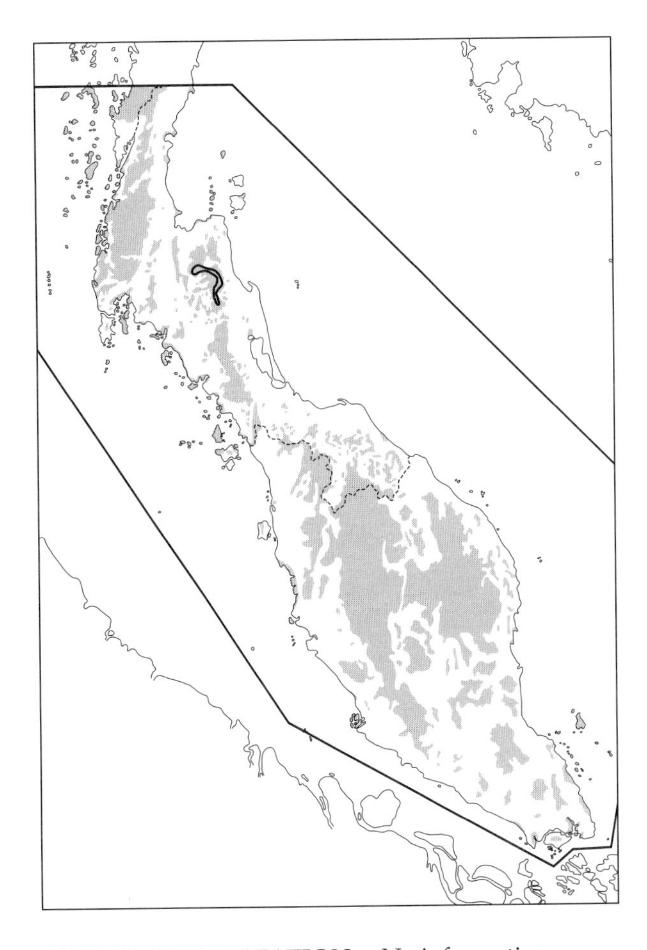

GROUP RELATIONS. See Black-browed Barbet.

GLOBAL RANGE. The Himalayas and the far-NE Indian subcontinent; Guangxi and Yunnan; and northern and western SE Asia to the Peninsula.

IDENTIFICATION/DESCRIPTION. Lores, forehead, centre hind-crown and spot at side of throat red; rest of crown to sides of nape clear blue with faint black shaft-lines; a bold black stripe from level of eye back over ear-coverts; rest of face, chin and throat clear blue – the most obvious character in the field. From Black-browed by lack of yellow parts. Sexes are alike; juveniles duller and paler, with red reduced, and the chin is white (BMNH, Robinson 1928).

Bare-part colours. (Adult) iris red-brown; bill-tip and, except for its lower base, upper mandible black, rest of bill pale yellowish; feet grey-green.

Size (mm). (Skins: 5 males, 2 females; adult): wing 97–102 and not measured; tail 59–63 and 61, 63; bill 26.6–28.3 and 28.9, 29.8; tarsus 25.3–27.7 and 27.5, 27.7 (BMNH).

Weight. No data.

DISTRIBUTION. North end of the E-central Range, from the Surat Thani/Nakhon Si Thammarat divide south to the limit of Montane forest at latitude about 8°15'N. Historical summary: *Sur, Nak.*

GEOGRAPHICAL VARIATION. Endemic *chersonesus* Kloss and Chasen 1927 (TL Khao Luang) isolated by four degrees of latitude from nearest continental populations. Red nape-patch relatively small, broadly separated from black supercilium by blue, and blue of crown clear, not contrasting with face as it does in northern birds.

STATUS AND POPULATION. Resident, regular and apparently common (King 1966).

HABITATS AND ECOLOGY. Montane forest, recorded from 885 m, close to the Lowland ecotone, where it must hear or meet the occasional Yellow-crowned Barbet, to at least 1520 m (highest local summit 1800 m). No Upper Montane specialist occurs within its range and Blue-throated Barbet continues up into at least part of that zone (its bill-size is as in the Trang population of Golden-throated Barbet, which also occupies multiple habitats).

FORAGING AND FOOD. No information.

SOCIAL ORGANIZATION. No information.

MOVEMENTS. None recorded.

SURVIVAL. No information.

SOCIAL INTERACTIONS. No information.

VOICE. No information for this subspecies.

BREEDING. Not recorded. A juvenile collected in late September (BMNH).

MOULT. Among seven adults dated March, June and September, two showed wing-moult in late June (P1) and late September (P4) (BMNH), on a typical forest barbet schedule.

CONSERVATION. No critical issue beyond small natural range. The highest peak occupied (Khao Luang) is a conservation area.

Yellow-crowned Barbet; Nok Phoradok Hua Leuang (Thai); Burung Takur Mahkota Kuning (Malay)

Megalaima henricii (Temminck) 1831, *Nouveau Recueil de Planches Coloriées d'Oiseaux* 88: plate 524. TL Sumatra.

Plate 69

GROUP RELATIONS. Probably free-standing; allopatric relatives live in different forest zones and have very different vocalizations.

GLOBAL RANGE. Borneo, Sumatra except the far south, and the Peninsula to latitude about 8°20'N.

IDENTIFICATION/DESCRIPTION. Medium-sized, in the range of Golden-throated, Black-browed and Blue-throated Barbets. Forehead to forecrown and side of rest of crown back to nape, bright yellow; centre cap, chin and throat clear, pale blue; hind-collar red and spot at the side of the throat orange-red; lores and short stripe back from eye velvety black. Sexes similar; young juveniles are all-green-headed, developing light blue chin and throat, and yellow forehead, before other bright cap-colours or red markings appear.

Bare-part colours. (Adult) iris dark brown, eyelids black; bill slaty black; feet grey-green (Chasen 1939).

Size (mm). (Skins: 10 males, 6 females; adult): wing 95–102 and 94–100; tail 51–58 and 50–56; bill 25.4–29.1 and 26.3–27.9; tarsus 23.8–25.7 and 23.2–25.6 (BMNH).

Weight (g). An unsexed adult, 55 (Lambert 1989).

DISTRIBUTION. Not recorded north of Krabi and southern Nakhon Si Thammarat. Historical summary: all divisions except *Pak, Chu, Ran, Sur, Pha, Phu, Pat, Pra*. If it ever genuinely occurred there wild, extinct *Sin* for a least a century. There are no other island records.

GEOGRAPHICAL VARIATION. Nominate *henricii*, of the global range except Borneo.

STATUS AND POPULATION. Resident, regular and common in the south; uncommon north of about latitude 6°N.

HABITATS AND ECOLOGY. The canopy of evergreen, evidently also semi-evergreen, Lowland forest (possibly not in more deciduous variants), mature and well regenerated with a good residue of old trees, and also in peatswamp forest; at plains level and on slopes, locally up to the Montane ecotone. Recorded at 970 m in disturbed forest on the Larut Range (Bromley 1952) but commonly not this high, e.g., not above 760 m on the untouched slope of Benom (Medway 1972), meeting vocal Black-browed Barbet apparently without overlap in both areas (but see that species).

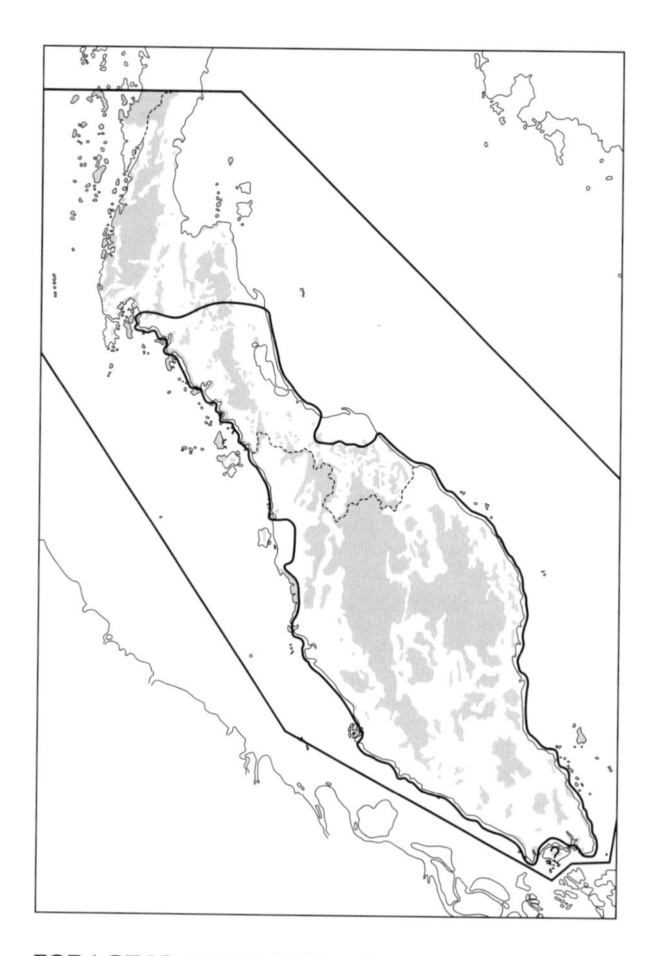

FORAGING AND FOOD. Attracted to mass-fruiting *Ficus*. Fed at 18 of 25 species regularly taken by birds at Kuala Lompat, Kerau wildlife reserve, in the fig-diameter range 5.4–27.4 mm, but avoided understratum species (including those drawing other barbet species) and concentrated activity in the high canopy. Most visits were to *F. crassiramea* and *F. cucurbitina*, mean minimum fruit-sizes 17.5 and 20.3 mm (Lambert 1989). Elsewhere, recorded at banyans *F. microcarpa* on the edge of forest in Taman Negara (BR 1972–73) and, in the upper Gombak valley, Selangor, visited large-crowned, canopy-height *F. sumatrana* and *F. glabella* (McClure 1966). A radio-tagged bird followed over three days spent 70 percent of daytime at or around a fruit-source, but on intervening nights roosted 700 m away in the crown of a tall forest emergent (Lambert 1989a).

Birds gleaning and bark-tapping along the main-crown branches of a tall dipterocarp *Shorea acuminata* in Pasoh research forest may have been after animal prey.

SOCIAL ORGANIZATION. Except in company of young juveniles or when a few converge on a fruiting crown, solitary.

MOVEMENTS. No additional information.

SURVIVAL. No information.

SOCIAL INTERACTIONS. No information.

VOICE. A short rattle followed typically by four (occasionally two or six) deliberately paced, even-toned clucks, *trrrk, tuk tuk tuk tuk*; the whole call about one second long, and repeated end-to-end such that it is difficult to position the rattle between calls, but a bout of calling is always signed off with clucks.

BREEDING

Nest. No definite record. A pair excavated what may have become a nest-hole in a large branch of a forest tree, 9 m up at mid-stratum level (BMP5).

Eggs and brood. Not described.

Cycle. No information.

Seasonality. Hole-excavation in mid March; a recent fledgling attended by an adult in late June; green-headed juveniles in mid and late May, and early July (BMNH, BMP5, BR 1978–79).

MOULT. A record of double-locus moult of primaries (P5–6, 9–10) appears not to be typical. Among 18 adults covering January–April and August–September, five showed active wing-moult from early August (P5) to mid September (P9, P10), with presumed starts (P1) up to late August. January–April birds (n=9) were all non-moulters. An instance of post-juvenile wing-moult: (P1) on 11 August (BMNH).

CONSERVATION. See Gold-whiskered Barbet.

Blue-eared Barbet; Nok Phoradok Naa Paak Dam (Thai); Burung Takur Akar (Malay)

Megalaima australis (Horsfield) 1821, *Transactions of the Linnean Society* 13(1): 181. TL Java.

Plate 69

GROUP RELATIONS. May form a superspecies with *M. eximia* (Bornean Barbet) but relative habitat- and altitude-limits needs more study.

GLOBAL RANGE. Himalayan foothills and adjacent terai lowlands east from E Nepal, and the far-NE Indian subcontinent; W and SW Yunnan; and SE Asia to the Greater Sunda islands and Bali.

IDENTIFICATION/DESCRIPTION. The smallest all-green-bodied barbet, by far, and size is obvious in the field even in isolation. Forehead to forecrown black or a black-blue mix, and short malar-stripe black; large spot behind malar-stripe and stripe from rear edge of eye over the ear-coverts bright red; and a red to pink-plush spot under the eye. Lores and rest of cap verditer-blue; chin and throat light verditer-blue, black bases of lower throat-feathers showing through to form a variable-sized median patch; tail washed blue on both surfaces. Rictal and nasal bristles are proportionately very long in this species, reaching beyond the bill-tip. The sexes are similar. Juveniles are all-green – and start to sing before they moult.

Bare-part colours. (Adult) iris dark red-brown; bill slate-black paling to slate-blue at base of lower mandible; feet sage-green.

Size (mm). (Skins: 17 males, 8 females; adult): wing 74–79(82) and 73–79; tail 37–45 and 36–43; bill 17.2–20.1 and 17.5–20.2; tarsus 17.7–20.9 and 17.3–19.5 (BMNH, UMZC).

Weight (g). An unsexed adult, 27 (Lambert 1989).

DISTRIBUTION. Historical summary: all divisions except *Pra*, but extinct *Sin* for at least 30 years. There are no other island records.

GEOGRAPHICAL VARIATION. Subspecies *stuarti* Robinson and Kloss 1919 (TL Khlong Tung Sai, Phuket), also of Tenasserim and SW Thailand, with ear-coverts verditer-blue, throat-patch weak and spot below eye pink-plush, occurs to about latitude 6°N. Replaced in the south by *duvaucelii* Lesson 1830 (TL Sumatra), which has ear-coverts more or less black, throat-patch bolder, and spot below eye red. Intergrades have been identified in NW Malaysia (including Perlis), and a small amount of eye-spot colour-variation occurs more widely.

STATUS AND POPULATION. Resident, regular and common. At least in dry-land evergreen forest, intensity of calling and numbers congregating at fruit-trees indicate Blue-eared Barbet maintains a higher population density than larger *Megalaima* species.

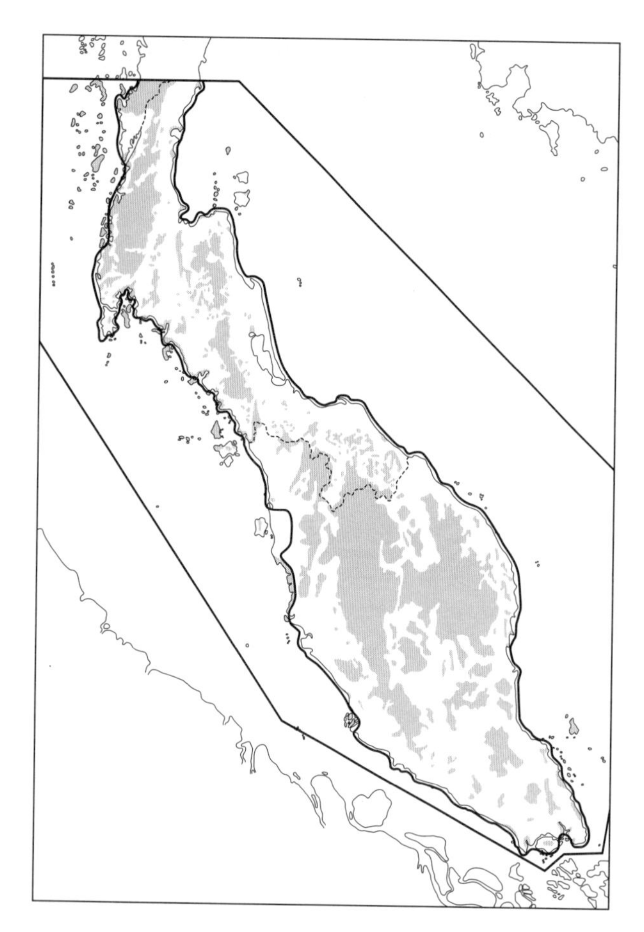

HABITATS AND ECOLOGY. The canopy of semi-evergreen and evergreen Lowland forest, mature and where a good supply of old trees remains after disturbance, also in peatswamp forest; at plains level and on slopes to the Montane ecotone (in disturbed forest to slightly above it, at 975 m on the Larut range: Bromley 1952). Exceptionally, wanders out into old tree plantation (Batchelor 1958, ENGGANG-2), but uses modified habitats apparently much less often than in some other parts of its range, e.g., Borneo.

FORAGING AND FOOD. At Kuala Lompat, Kerau wildlife reserve, attended 21 out of 25 bird-attracting *Ficus* species under observation, in the fig-diameter range 5.4–27.7 mm, visit-frequency increasing towards the lower end of this range and most activity focused on diameters 11.6 mm (*F. pellucido-punctata*) or less (Lambert 1989). Two under-stratum species attracting other barbets, including *Ficus obscura* in the prime fruit-size range, were not visited and, like Yellow-crowned Barbet, Blue-eared focuses its foraging on the upper canopy. In the Gombak valley, Selangor, recorded at large-crowned, canopy-fruiting *Ficus sumatrana* and *F. glabella* (McClure 1966), species not on the Kuala Lompat list.

SOCIAL ORGANIZATION. Typically solitary but, where barbets converge on a fruiting crown, Blue-eared is commonly represented by many more individuals than any larger congener.

MOVEMENTS. None recorded.

SURVIVAL. No information.

SOCIAL INTERACTIONS. The one barbet commonly defending patches of fruit in a crown, chasing off both conspecifics and other, larger frugivores (Lambert 1987).

VOICE. A brisk, rather high-pitched clucking, *tarrek tarrek tarrek* . . ., delivered in long, monotonous bouts at a rate of about 16 calls per ten seconds, and as a faster version in which the first syllable is reduced. Also, a single, loud *pleow* and a rattle-trill, the latter repeated approximately once per second (BMP5, Boonsong and Round 1991) and higher-pitched than in larger congeners of the same forests.

BREEDING

Nest. A hole about 12 m up a main trunk and another in a broken-off dead branch that had fallen into the crown of a small, bank-top tree; both in forest-edge situations. One entrance 3 cm wide, vertical depth of tunnel to nest-chamber 20.5 cm.

Eggs and brood. Not described.

Cycle. No information.

Seasonality. Hole-excavation in early April; young, green-headed juveniles during late April–mid August (BMNH, BR 1974–75, G.C. Madoc).

MOULT. Replacement of primaries is regular-descendant, with up to three adjacent inner-tract feathers in overlapping growth. Among 48 adults from the full length of the Peninsula and covering all months except November, 14 showed active wing-moult during mid June (P3–5)–early September (P4, P4–5, P7), stages that imply earlier and later extreme dates, but with starts up to July and incidence during July–September 100 percent. The other 34 dated late October–May showed no moult (BMNH, UMZC).

CONSERVATION. Abundance in slope-land forests suggests no crisis from habitat-loss, but removal of canopy-fruiting strangling figs as host-trees are logged threatens the food-resources of most Lowland forest barbet species.

Coppersmith Barbet; Nok Tee Thong (Thai); Burung Takur Tukang Besi (Malay)

Megalaima haemacephala (P.L.S. Müller) 1776, *Natursystem, Supplements*: 88. TL Lamao, Luzon, Philippines.

Plate 68

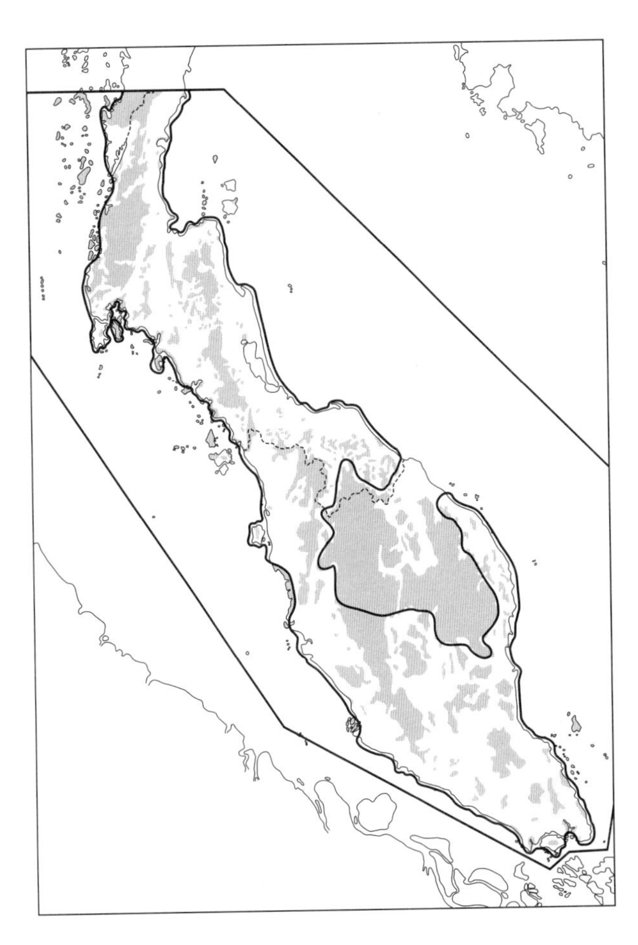

GROUP RELATIONS. Probably free-standing.

GLOBAL RANGE. The Indian subcontinent except the far NW, and Sri Lanka; SW Yunnan; and, except for the extreme NE, SE Asia to Sumatra, Java, Bali and the Philippines.

IDENTIFICATION/DESCRIPTION. Marginally larger than Blue-eared Barbet. Only adults have striking head-colours, but all age-classes show orange-red feet and rather bright olive-green upperparts. Anterior cap of adults red, bordered posteriorly with black that encircles face to join a broad black malar-stripe; lores black; short supercilium arching over eye and a broad band below eye cream-yellow. Similar yellow of chin and throat is succeeded by a broad red band across upper breast, fringed below with yellow; rest of underparts creamy white, streaked dark olive. Sexes similar. Juveniles are duller throughout, lack all red, show only a trace of cream over the eye, and are dark olive rather than black on the head.

Bare-part colours. (Adult) iris brown, eyelid dark red; bill slate-black, paling at the base; feet orange-red.

Size (mm). (Live and skins: 15 males, 11 females; adult): wing 77–84 and 76–83; tail 30–34 and 32–34; bill 18.2–20.4 and 17.2–20.5; tarsus 17.6–21.4 and 18.8–20.1 (BMNH, UMBRP, UMZC).

Weight. Unsexed adults, 34.5–39.4 (n=6) (UMBRP).

DISTRIBUTION. Historical summary: all divisions except *Kel*, with additional island records from Yao Yai, Lanta, Penang and Pangkor off the W coast; and Sentosa and St John's, Singapore.

GEOGRAPHICAL VARIATION. Subspecies *indica* Latham 1790 (TL Calcutta), of the global range except the Sunda islands and Philippines.

STATUS AND POPULATION. Resident, regular and common; in response to forest clearance, has colonized the southern third of the Peninsula within the last 70–80 years. On the W-coast plain, present in the middle Perak valley in the 1870s (Kelham 1881–83); had reached latitude 4°N (Sitiawan district, S Perak) by 1933, was in Kuala Lumpur by 1939, S Negeri Sembilan by 1948, Melaka town by 1951, and Singapore by early 1957 (Allen 1951c, Chasen 1934, 1939, Garr 1957, Gibson-Hill 1949b). Now common to the extreme south, with first records from the S archipelago of Singapore in 1980 (BR 1980–81). Progress down the E-coast plain is undocumented, but advanced from a southern limit on the Nerus river, N Terengganu, some time after 1910 (BMP5).

HABITATS AND ECOLOGY. The landward fringe of mangrove forest (Parr 1988, SINGAV-3), and overflies logged deciduous (but no other) forest to reach favoured fruit-trees some distance in from the edge. Otherwise, strictly in man-altered habitats, favouring dead timber of abandoned rubber plantations, etc., trees scattered through open agriculture, roadside avenues, wooded gardens and parkland, to well within town limits. Operates typically at crown-top level, often resting and sometimes calling, fully exposed, on the pinnacle of a dead snag.

FORAGING AND FOOD. At least as dependant on figs as any of its forest congeners, gathering particularly at fruit-flushes of *Ficus benjamina*, the commonest small-figged banyan of non-forest (including town) situations. Animal food includes alate termites, taken in sallies from a perch (Bromley 1948), and both figs and large arthropods have been identified among items fed to nestlings (SINGAV-1, -3).

SOCIAL ORGANIZATION. Several may converge on a mass-fruiting crown, without obvious aggression. As far as is known, Coppersmiths night-roost alone, in tree-holes, but they sometimes loaf socially: several records during late September–early December of up to 18 adults together in open crowns (including casuarina), not obviously associated with a fruit-source (MBR 1986–87, SINGAV-3).

MOVEMENTS. No information.

SURVIVAL. No information.

SOCIAL INTERACTIONS. One record of a laying or incubating bird being fed fruit by its partner.

VOICE. Long, monotonous, even-paced bouts of a dull, percussive *wouk* or *tounk*, at a rate of about 24 notes per ten seconds. Advertising adults swing the head while calling, disguising the position of the sound-source (Wingate 1953), although some calling is from totally exposed perches on dead snags where such behaviour would be irrelevant. Apparent males also call around the nest-hole, before and into the laying period. Juveniles begin to sing before they acquire full adult head-colouring (see also Blue-eared Barbet).

BREEDING

Nest. Excavates holes 4–15 m up in rot-softened wood of dead snags or entirely dead trees, commonly in relatively thin stems or branches but sometimes in the main trunk, and always on the overhung side where leaning; one in a broken-off branch trapped in a fork. Over several consecutive seasons, nest-holes in a particular yellow flame tree *Peltophorum pterocarpum* in Singapore were disguised by hanging flaps of bark (SINGAV-4). Other nest-trees include: rubber, durian, jacaranda, *Sonneratia* sp., *Adenanthera pavonina*, *Acacia auriculiformis*, *Albizzia* spp., *Eucalyptus deglupta*, and *Fagraea fragrans*. The variety implies species may be less important than site, wood-texture, etc.

Eggs and brood. Eggs not described and the regular full clutch is unknown, but broods of 1–4 fledge.

Cycle. Individual holes are used for up to two broods per season, presumably by the same pair.

Seasonality. From many records: hole-excavation during late December–mid June, incubation as of January, nestlings (including second broods) in all months February–July; fledglings as of mid March, (BR 1974–75, Edgar 1933, ENGGANG-2, NRCS, SINGAV-1, Wingate 1953).

MOULT. Replacement of primaries appears to be regular-descendant. Among 35 adults from Phangnga south to Perlis, covering all months except June, October and December, eight showed active wing-moult during early April (P1)–late September (P9), with incidence 100 percent over this period. The balance dated November–early April showed none. Two instances of post-juvenile wing-moult: stage P5 in late June and late October (BMNH, UMBRP, UMZC).

CONSERVATION. No critical issues.

Brown Barbet; Nok Jawk Paa Hua Toh (Thai); Burung Takur Dahan (Malay)

Calorhamphus fuliginosus (Temminck) 1830, *Nouveau Recueil de Planches Coloriées d'Oiseaux* 83: text. TL Pontianak, W Kalimantan.

Plate 68

GROUP RELATIONS. Free-standing; no near relatives identified (Prum 1988).

GLOBAL RANGE. Borneo, Sumatra and the Peninsula.

IDENTIFICATION/DESCRIPTION. Medium-small by Asian barbet standards. Orange-peach foot-colour approaches Coppersmith Barbet but otherwise completely unlike any other species. Cap and entire upperparts dull, dark brown, with stiff, shiny black shafts on forehead, and obscure, pale clay edging on mantle and back; sides of face to jaw level rufous-brown. Below, chin and throat washed rust-red, intensity varying individually, independent of sex and geography; flanks dark brown; rest of underparts silky white to cream- or brown-tinged white. Lacks the elongated rictal bristles of other local barbets, and the colour of the proportionately large, robust bill differs between the sexes. Juveniles told from adults only by cream-buff tips to long scapulars and inner secondaries, and wing-coverts fringed rufous. Said to be yellower below, but on no evidence seen by me.

Bare-part colours. (Adult) iris hazel-brown (female), pale red or red-brown (male); periorbital skin cinnamon-brown, close to rest of face-colour; bill reddish brown (female), all-black (male); feet orange-pink. Young male bill as female, blackening from tip and along culmen-ridge.

Size (mm). (Live and skins: 14 males, 11 females; adult): wing 81–86 and 78–87; tail 47–52 and 46–52; bill 23.0–26.2 and 22.4–25.0; tarsus 21.4–23.8 and 20.9–22.9 (BMNH, UMBRP).

Weight (g). Adults, 45.0–47.1 (n=3) (UMBRP, Wong 1985).

DISTRIBUTION. Historical summary: all divisions except *Ran, Pat, Pra,* but extinct *Sin* for at least 40 years. An extra island record from Lanta (*Kra*).

GEOGRAPHICAL VARIATION. Subspecies *hayii* Gray 1831 (TL Melaka), also of Sumatra. Characters of a supposed northern subspecies, *detersus* Deignan 1960 (TL Ban Sichol, Surat Thani) – paler, brighter cream-white underparts with throat less rufous – are individually variable throughout the Peninsula, hence do not separate it from *hayii*.

STATUS AND POPULATION. Resident, regular and more or less common to (in Malaysia) common.

HABITATS AND ECOLOGY. The mid-stratum to canopy, and crowns at the edge of, semi-evergreen and evergreen Lowland forest, mature and re-closing after disturbance, also peatswamp forest; at plains level and up slopes. In undisturbed, continuous forest of the Benom outlier, recorded to 760 m (Medway 1972), but where disturbance has occurred reaches or crosses the Montane ecotone, recorded to 1000 m on Genting Highlands. Wanders out of forest into nearby secondary-growth and rubber (Batchelor 1958).

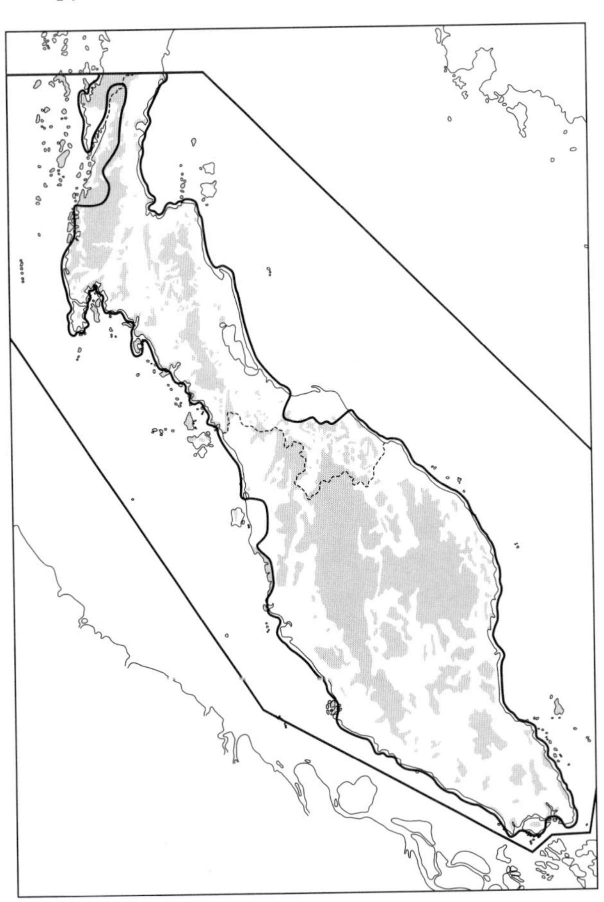

FORAGING AND FOOD. Searches foliage and the surface and crevices of bark on branches and trunks apparently for animal food; a large green orthopteran identified among food items (including fruit) taken to nestlings (NRCS). Many observations of fruit-eating by adults otherwise suggest the habits of adults do not differ much from those of other local barbets. At Kuala Lompat, Kerau wildlife reserve, took figs from 22 of 25 bird-attracting *Ficus* species, in the fruit-diameter range 5.4–27.7 mm (Lambert 1989), and in Taman Negara and the Gombak valley, Selangor (McClure 1966), seen at additional species *F. glabella* and *F. microcarpa*. Also eats flowers; a bird climbing down and systematically stripping the pendant inflorescence of a large, white-blossomed epiphytic orchid.

SOCIAL ORGANIZATION. Moves about in cohesive parties of up to ten individuals, but at fruit-sources they associate only loosely and not all may feed in a given crown at any one time (Lambert 1987). Group behaviour may have more to do with the hunting of animal prey. A dispersed nester, but a watch at a nest with chicks suggested at least one helper attended, additional to the pair (cf. CLBS, MBR 1984–85).

MOVEMENTS. None reported.

SURVIVAL. No information.

SOCIAL INTERACTIONS. No information.

VOICE. Thin, asthmatically wheezing whistles and squeaks: *pseeoo*, a repeated *see see see . . .*, and more abrupt *tsuk, tsuk, tsuk . . .* Members of a group communicate incessantly.

BREEDING

Nest. A hole in the overhung side of a dead branch-stub, about 0.5 m out from the main trunk, and three others excavated in arboreal termitaria, 2.5–20 m up in the interior of forest, including peatswamp forest. Gum and termite head-capsules stuck on plumage, taken as evidence of feeding on termites (Robinson 1928), may actually result merely from excavating in active nests. Observations are needed.

Eggs and brood. Eggs and clutch not reliably described, but two broods were of three nestlings each.

Cycle. Over five days of watching, a pair servicing large nestlings visited approximately every 20 minutes, typically with a gap from 1100 to 1500 hours, and entered periodically to remove faecal masses.

Seasonality. Nestlings in March, May and early September (Chasen 1939, NRCS).

MOULT. Replacement of primaries is mostly single-locus and regular-descendant, but one instance of P10 dropped synchronously with P6/7. Among 45 adults covering the length of the Peninsula and all months, 29 showed active wing-moult scattered, un-barbet-like, through most of the year, with starts (P1 or 1–2) as far apart as February and October, and monthly incidence 50 percent or more in February, March and June–October (BMNH, UMBRP).

CONSERVATION. In Malaysia, abundance on the submontane slope and use of forest regenerating after logging suggest no critical threat, but extent of dependance on strangling figs needs further study.

REFERENCES AND OTHER SOURCES

Aagaard, C.J., 1932. A New Bird for Siam. *Journal of the Siam Society, Natural History Supplement* 8: 341–342.

ABBBS. Data from the Australian Bird and Bat Banding Schemes, Canberra.

Abbott, I., 1978. Lancelin island, Western Australia. *Corella* 2: 40–42.

Abdulali, H. and Grubh, R.B., 1970. A new race of the Black-crested Baza *Aviceda leuphotes* (Dumont), from the Andaman Islands. *Journal of the Bombay Natural History Society* 67: 137–138.

Abdul Rahman Ismail, 1981. *Senarai nama-nama burung Semenanjung Malaysia dan Asia Tenggara.* Department of Wildlife and National Parks, Kuala Lumpur.

Allen, E.F., 1948. Nidification and other field notes on some Malayan birds. *Malayan Nature Journal* 3: 82–86.

——————, 1949. Changes in the status of some birds in Lower Perak. *Malayan Nature Journal* 4: 77–79.

——————, 1951. The Nicobar Pigeon (*Caloenas n. nicobarica*). *Malayan Nature Journal* 5: 154–155.

——————, 1951a. Two new birds in the Straits of Malacca. *Malayan Nature Journal* 5: 155–157.

——————, 1951b. Short notes on migratory birds. *Malayan Nature Journal* 5: 174–179.

——————, 1951c. Southern Distribution of the Coppersmith Barbet. *Malayan Nature Journal* 5: 206–207.

Allen, E.F. and Berwick, E.J.H., 1950. Nesting localities of terns off the south Perak coast. *Malayan Nature Journal* 5: 33–34.

Allen, F.G.H., 1949. A mating between Changeable Hawk-Eagles in different Colour Phases. *Malayan Nature Journal* 4: 42.

——————, 1951. The Breeding of the Rose-Ringed Paroquet in Singapore. *Malayan Nature Journal* 5: 205.

——————, 1952. Some notes on birds at Fraser's Hill. *Malayan Nature Journal* 7: 84–90.

——————, 1952a. A very late nesting of the Crested Tree-swift. *Malayan Nature Journal* 7: 135–136.

——————, 1953. Further notes on birds nesting at Fraser's Hill. *Malayan Nature Journal* 8: 16–22.

——————, 1955. Singapore Bird Notes. *Malayan Nature Journal* 10: 82.

——————, 1956. The nesting of the Bay headed Bee-eater. *Malayan Nature Journal* 10: 164.

——————, 1957. Some notes on the birds of Cameron Highlands. *Malayan Nature Journal* 11: 39–41.

——————, 1958. Birds nesting on the Genting Sempah. *Malayan Nature Journal* 13: 1 6.

——————, 1960. Wreathed Hornbills. *Malayan Nature Journal* 14: 214–-215.

——————, 1960a. A nest of the Spine-tailed Swift *Chaetura g. gigantea. Ibis* 102: 126–127.

——————, 1961. Further notes on breeding birds of Fraser's Hill. *Malayan Nature Journal* 15: 45–47.

——————, 1961a. The Common Shoveller *Spatula clypeata. Malayan Nature Journal* 15: 62.

——————, 1961b. A nest of the Spinetail Swift: *Chaetura g. gigantea. Malayan Nature Journal* 15: 63–64.

Allin, E.K., 1941. Notes on some Malayan Bitterns and the Yellow Crowned Bulbul. *Malayan Nature Journal* 1: 110–112.

Allin, E.K. and Edgar, A.T., 1948. Notes on the nesting of some birds of the Malayan mountains. *Malayan Nature Journal* 3: 51–57.

Amadon, D., 1974. Taxonomic notes on the Serpent-eagles of the genus *Spilornis. Bulletin of the British Ornithologists' Club* 94: 159–163.

——————, 1978. Remarks on the taxonomy of some Australian raptors. *Emu* 78: 115–118.

——————, 1982. The genera of Booted Eagles: *Aquila* and Relatives. *Journal of the Yamashina Institute for Ornithology* 14: 108–121.

AMNH. Data from the bird collection of the American Museum of Natural History, New York.

Anderson, J., 1887. List of Birds, chiefly from the Mergui Archipelago, collected for the Trustees of the Indian Museum, Calcutta. *Journal of the Linnean Society* 21: 136–153.

Andrew, P., 1992. *The Birds of Indonesia, a checklist (Peter's Sequence).* Indonesian Ornithological Society, Jakarta.

Andrews, T., 1993. The first record of Chinese Egret on Java. *Kukila* 6: 133.

Annandale, N. and Robinson, H.C., 1903. Supplement and Map. *Fasciculi Malayenses*: i-xlii.

Anonymous, 1931. Nesting habits of the White-collared Kingfisher (Halcyon chloris humii, Sharpe). *Bulletin of the Raffles Museum* 5: 121.

——————, 1954. News from Local Branches: Malacca Museum – Natural History Section. *Malayan Nature Journal* 9: 39–40.

——————, 1955. News from Local Branches: Malacca. *Malayan Nature Journal* 9: 141–144.

——————, 1955a. News from Local Branches: Malacca. *Malayan Nature Journal* 10: 38–41.

——————, 1958. News from Local Branches. Selangor Branch: an outing to the mangrove swamps off Port Swettenham. *Malayan Nature Society* 12: 194.

——————, 1981. *Ecological Studies for Conservation of Shore Birds in Songkhla Lake*, volume 1. Office of the National Environment Board of Thailand, publication 1981-007, Bangkok.

ANSP. Data from the bird collection of the Academy of Natural Sciences, Philadelphia.

Archibald, G., 1992. A Bird's Eye View of Cambodia. *Bugle* 18(2): 1–3.

Argeloo, M., 1993. Black-headed Gulls wintering in Sulawesi (and notes on their occurrence elsewhere in the Indo-Australia region). *Kukila* 6: 110–114.

Ash, J.S., 1984. Bird observations on Bali. *Bulletin of the British Ornithologists' Club* 104: 24–35.

——————, 1993. Raptor migration on Bali, Indonesia. *Forktail* 9: 3–11.

Ashby, H.K., 1951. Snipe in Kelantan. *Malayan Nature Journal* 5: 161–162.

Avery, M.L. and Penny, N.D., 1978. Analysis of pellets from Blue-tailed and Blue-throated Bee-eaters in Province Wellesley. *Malayan Nature Journal* 32: 223–226.

AWB. Data from the files of Asian Wetland Bureau.

Baker, E.C.S., 1916. The game birds of India, Burma and Ceylon. *Journal of the Bombay Natural History Society* 24: 200–223.

———, 1919–20. Notes on a collection of bird-skins formed by Mr. E.G. Herbert, C.M.Z.S., M.B.O.U. *Journal of the Natural History Society of Siam* 3: 177–216, 409–443; 4: 25–43.

———, 1922–30. *The Fauna of British India including Ceylon and Burma. Birds* (second edition), volumes 1–7. Taylor and Francis, London.

———, 1930. *The Game-Birds of India, Burma and Ceylon*, volume III, *Pheasants and Bustard-Quail.* Bombay Natural History Society and Bale and Danielsson, London.

———, 1934–35. *The nidification of birds of the Indian Empire.* Volumes 3–4. Taylor and Francis, London.

———. *Manuscript Notes*, volumes 35, 36, 37, 45, 46. Unpublished, Library of the Natural History Museum, Tring.

Baker, H.R., 1907. Some birds of Singapore. *Journal of the Bombay Natural History Society* 17: 755–763.

Bakewell, D.N., 1989. Sekinchan Harrier Roost. *Enggang* 2(1): 18.

Baltzer, M.C., 1990. A report on the wetland avifauna of South Sulawesi. *Kukila* 5: 27–55.

Barrett, S., 1987. Notes on the birds of Sibu island, Malaysia. *Singapore Avifauna* 1(4): 14–15.

Barton, D., 1982. Notes on skuas and jaegers in the western Tasman Sea. *Emu* 82: 56–59.

Bartels, M., 1908. *Xenorhynchus asiaticus* (Lath.) auf Java nachgewiessen. *Ornithologische Monatsberichte* 16: 165.

Batchelor, D.M., 1954. Mount Ophir. *Malayan Nature Journal* 8: 167–168.

———, 1954a. Some birds of Asahan, Malacca. *Malayan Nature Journal* 9: 50–52.

———, 1955. The Red Breasted Snipe. *Malayan Nature Journal* 10: 32–33.

———, 1958. A checklist of the birds seen at Asahan, Malacca. *Malayan Nature Journal* 12: 164–182; 13: 14–29.

———, 1960. Migrating raptores. *Malayan Nature Journal* 14: 178–180.

BBCB. Recent Reports (compiler P.D. Round). *Bangkok Bird Club Bulletin* 3 (1986); 4 (1987); 5 (1988); 6 (1989); 7 (1990); 8 (1991); 9 (1992).

BCSTB. Recent Reports (compiler P.D. Round). *Bird Conservation Society of Thailand Bulletin* 10 (1993); 11 (1994); 12 (1995); 13 (1996).

Beadle, D. and Whittaker, A., 1985. Sabah Survey Report. Pages 79–117 in D. Parish and D.R. Wells (editors), *INTERWADER Annual Report 1984.* INTERWADER, Kuala Lumpur.

Becking, J.H., 1971., The breeding of *Collocalia gigas. Ibis* 113: 330–334.

———, 1981. Notes on the breeding of Indian cuckoos. *Journal of the Bombay Natural History Society* 78: 201–231.

Bell, T.R., 1902. Note on the habits of *Rallina superciliaris*, Sharpe, and *Gorsachius melanolophus*, Blyth. *Journal of the Bombay Natural History Society* 14: 393–395.

Berthold, P., 1967. Zur Creme-Färbung von *Ducula bicolor* (Scopoli). *Journal für Ornithologie* 108: 491–493.

Berwick, E.J.H., 1947. Notes on some lowland birds now occurring in Cameron Highlands. *Malayan Nature Journal* 2: 38–40.

———, 1952. Notes on some birds in Kelantan and Trengganu. *Malayan Nature Journal* 7: 10–14.

———, 1952a. The Nicobar Pigeon. *Malayan Nature Journal* 7: 39.

———, 1952b. Bird Notes from Kelantan. *Bulletin of the Raffles Museum* 24: 183–198.

Bijlsma, R.G. and de Roder, F., 1986. Notes on Nordmann's Greenshank *Tringa guttifer* in Thailand. *Forktail* 2: 92–94.

BIRDLINE. The Birdline Singapore monthly newsletter (compiler R.F. Ollington). Privately circulated. 1992 (numbers 1–5), 1993 (numbers 6–15), 1994 (number 21).

Bishop, K.D., 1992. New and interesting records of birds in Wallacea. *Kukila* 6: 8–34.

Blakers, M., Davies, S.J.J.F. and Reilly, P.N. (editors), 1984. *The Atlas of Australian Birds.* Royal Australasian Ornithologists Union and Melbourne University Press, Melbourne.

Blasco, F. and Belan, M.F., 1995. *A Vegetation Map of Tropical Continental Asia.* Institut de la Carte Internationale de la Végétation, Toulouse.

BLC. Data from the private collection of Dr Boonsong Lekagul, Bangkok.

BMNH. Data from the collection of the Natural History Museum (sub-department of Ornithology), Tring, United Kingdom.

BMP5. Medway, Lord and Wells, D.R., 1976. *The Birds of the Malay Peninsula.* Volume V: *Conclusion, and survey of every species.* H.F. and G. Witherby, London.

Bock, W.J. and Short, L.L., 1971. 'Resin secretion' in *Hemicircus* (Picidae). *Ibis* 113: 234–236.

Bonhote, J.L., 1901. On the Birds collected during the 'Skeat Expedition' to the Malay Peninsula, 1899–1900. *Proceedings of the Zoological Society of London*: 57–81.

Boonsong Lekagul, 1968. *Bird Guide of Thailand.* Association for the Conservation of Wildlife and Kurusapa Ladprao Press, Bangkok.

Boonsong Lekagul and Cronin, E.W., 1974. *Bird Guide of Thailand* (second edition). Association for the Conservation of Wildlife and Kurusapa Ladprao Press, Bangkok.

Boonsong Lekagul and Round, P.D., 1991. *A Guide to the Birds of Thailand.* Saha Karn Bhaet Co., Bangkok.

Bosman, C.A.W. and van den Berg, A.B., 1993. *Birds and mammals of the MNS Belum Expedition, Perak, Malaysia in October-November 1993.* Unpublished report to the Malayan Nature Society, Kuala Lumpur.

Boswall, J., 1978. Overlooked and new birds from Phuket Province, Thailand. *Natural History Bulletin of the Siam Society* 27: 198.

Boswall, J. and Frith, C.B., 1978. First record of the Japanese Sparrowhawk, *Accipiter gularis*, on Phuket. *Natural History Bulletin of the Siam Society* 27: 192–193.

Boswall, J. and Kanwanich, S., 1978. The birds of Phi Phi Le island, Krabi, Thailand. *Natural History Bulletin of the Siam Society* 27: 83–92.

Bourne, W.R.P., 1960. The petrels of the Indian Ocean. *Sea-Swallow* 13: 26–29.

——————, 1966. Observations of sea birds. *Sea-Swallow* 18: 9–39.

——————, 1967. Observations of seabirds and review of literature. *Sea-Swallow* 19: 51–76.

——————, 1983. Reports of seabirds received in 1973–1977. *Sea-Swallow* 33: 39–53.

Bourne, W.R.P. and Dixon, T.J., 1973. Observations of seabirds. *Sea-Swallow* 22: 29–60.

——————, 1975. Observations of seabirds. *Sea-Swallow* 24: 65–88.

Bowler, J., Howes, J. and Long A., 1985. Wader observations on the north coast of Java. Pages 143–149 in D. Parish and D.R. Wells (editors) *INTERWADER Annual Report 1984*. INTERWADER, Kuala Lumpur.

BR. Bird Report (editors Lord Medway, I.C.T. Nisbet, D.R. Wells). *Malayan Nature Journal* 17: 123–144 (1962); 18: 133–167 (1963); 19: 160–194 (1964); 20: 59–80 (1965); 21: 34–50 (1966); 21: 185–200 (1967); 23: 47–77 (1968); 25: 43–61 (1969); 27: 30–49 (1970–71); 28: 186–213 (1972–73); 36: 61–85 (1974–75); 36: 197–218 (1976–77); 38: 113–150 (1978–79); 39: 279–298 (1980–81). [See Malayan Bird Report].

Brandt, J.H., 1966. Notes on the Collocalia of Micronesia and peninsular Thailand. *Oologists' Record* 40: 61–68.

Brazil, M.A., 1991. *The Birds of Japan*. Christopher Helm and A. and C. Black, London.

Bretagnolle, V., Carruthers, M., Cubitt, M., Bioret, F. and Cuillandre, J.-P., 1991. Six captures of a dark-rumped, fork-tailed storm-petrel in the northeast Atlantic. *Ibis* 133: 351–356.

Briffett, C., 1990. Update on countdown at Sibu island, Malaysia. *Singapore Avifauna* 4(2): 28–31.

Brockelman, W.Y. and Nadee, N., 1977. Preliminary survey and biogeographic analysis of the birds of the Surin Islands, Thailand. *Natural History Bulletin of the Siam Society* 26: 213–226.

Bromley, E.H., 1941. Notes on Malayan birds. *Malayan Nature Journal* 1: 140–146.

——————, 1948. The swarming of termites. *Malayan Nature Journal* 3: 93–95.

——————, 1948a. Voice of the Giant Spinetail Swift, and breeding of the Banded Bay Cuckoo. *Malayan Nature Journal* 3: 153.

——————, 1948b. Further notes on the nesting of mountain birds. *Malayan Nature Journal* 3: 212–213.

——————, 1949. Notes on the Birds of Some Parts of Kedah. *Bulletin of the Raffles Museum* 19: 120–132.

——————, 1952. A Note on Birds seen at Maxwell's Hill, Perak, April 1950 and February 1951. *Bulletin of the Raffles Museum* 24: 199–218.

——————, 1953. A Pelican at Malacca. *Malayan Nature Journal* 8: 64.

——————, 1954. News from Local Branches: Malacca. *Malayan Nature Journal* 9: 77–78.

Brooke, R.K., 1969. *Hemiprocne coronata* is a good species. *Bulletin of the British Ornithologists' Club* 89: 168–169.

——————, 1971. Geographical variation in the Little Swift *Apus affinis* (Aves, Apodidae). *Durban Museum Novitates* 9(7): 93–103.

——————, 1972. Generic limits in old world Apodidae and Hirundinidae. *Bulletin of the British Ornithologists' Club* 92: 53–57.

Bruce, M.D., 1978. Records of birds from Timor: some additions and corrections. *Bulletin of the British Ornithologists' Club* 98: 127–128.

Bryant, D.M., 1983. Heat stress in tropical birds; behavioural thermoregulation during flight. *Ibis* 125: 313–323.

Bryant, D.M. and Hails, C.J., 1983. Energetics and growth patterns of three tropical bird species. *Auk* 100: 425–439.

Bryant, D.M. and Tatner, P., 1990. Hatching asynchrony, sibling competition and siblicide in nestling birds: studies of Swiftlets and Bee-eaters. *Animal Behaviour* 39: 657–671.

BTW2. Collar, N.J., Crosby, M.J. and Stattersfield, A.J., 1994. *Birds To Watch 2. The World List of Threatened Birds*. Birdlife Conservation Series No. 4. Birdlife International, Cambridge.

Buckley, F.G., 1968. Behaviour of the Blue-crowned Hanging Parrot *Loriculus galgulus* with comparative notes on the Vernal Hanging Parrot *L. vernalis*. *Ibis* 110: 145–164.

Bucknill, J.A.S. and Chasen, F.N., 1927. *Birds of Singapore and South-east Asia* (second edition 1990). Tynron Press, Thornhill.

Butler, A.L., 1899. The nidification of some Malayan birds. *Journal of the Bombay Natural History Society* 12: 421–423, 772–773.

——————, 1899a. Occurrence of the Black-winged Kite (*Elanus caerulescens*) Desf. and the Short-toed Eagle (*Circaetus gallicus*) Gmel., in the Malay Peninsula. *Journal of the Bombay Natural History Society* 12: 423–424.

——————, 1899b. Birds collected and observed in the Larut Hills, Perak, in March and April 1898. *Journal of the Straits Branch of the Royal Asiatic Society* 32: 9–30.

——————, 1900. The birds of the Larut Hills. *Journal of the Straits Branch of the Royal Asiatic Society* 34: 99.

BWP. Cramp, S. and Simmons, K.E.L. (editors), 1977–85. *Handbook of the Birds of Europe, the Middle East and North Africa*, volumes 1–4. Oxford University Press, Oxford.

Cairns, J., 1940. Birds of Penang and Province Wellesley. *Malayan Nature Journal* 1: 29–34, 73–77, 118–127.

——————, 1952. Two rare birds in Penang. *Malayan Nature Journal* 7: 72–73.

————, 1952a. Rare Visitors and Passage Migrants in Penang. *Malayan Nature Journal* 7: 133–134.

————, 1953. Studies of Malayan Birds. *Malayan Nature Journal* 7: 173–179.

————, 1953a. A miscellany of notes. *Malayan Nature Journal* 8: 27–31.

————, 1953b. Rare Visitors and Passage Migrants in Penang. *Malayan Nature Journal* 8: 66–69.

————, 1954. The Yellow Bittern. *Malayan Nature Journal* 9: 11–15.

————, 1954a. Notes on two families of Yellow Bittern. *Malayan Nature Journal* 9: 28–31.

————, 1955. Footnote on the Yellow Bittern (*Ixobrychus sinensis*). *Malayan Nature Journal* 9: 132.

————, 1955a. A miscellany of bird notes from Penang. *Malayan Nature Journal* 10: 17–30.

————, 1956. The Night Heron. *Malayan Nature Journal* 10: 145–148.

————, 1957. Penang Bee-eaters. *Malayan Nature Journal* 11: 114–120.

————, 1963. New Breeding Records of Malayan Birds. *Journal of the Bombay Natural History Society* 60: 140–159.

Cant, R.G.H., 1957–58. A note on some swamp birds on a tin mine in Selangor. *Malayan Nature Journal* 12: 11–14, 153–157.

Chalmers, M.L., 1986. *Annotated checklist of the birds of Hong Kong*. Hong Kong Bird Watching Society, Hong Kong.

Chasen, F.N., 1923. An Introduction to the Birds of Singapore Island. *Singapore Naturalist* 1(2): 87–112.

————, 1923a. A rare petrel. *Journal of the Malayan Branch of the Royal Asiatic Society* 1: 255–256.

————, 1924. Remarks on the Ornithology of the Islands near Singapore. *Singapore Naturalist* 1(3): 22–36.

————, 1925. Further remarks on the Birds of Singapore Island. *Singapore Naturalist* 1(5): 71–73.

————, 1932. Notes on some Migratory Birds from Pulau Pisang, West Coast of Johore. *Bulletin of the Raffles Museum* 7: 3–7.

————, 1933. Notes on the Birds of Christmas Island, Indian Ocean. *Bulletin of the Raffles Museum* 8: 55–87.

————, 1934. Noteworthy Records of Birds from Perak. *Bulletin of the Raffles Museum* 9: 89–91.

————, 1935. A Handlist of Malaysian Birds. *Bulletin of the Raffles Museum* 11: i-xx, 1–389.

————, 1939. *The Birds of the Malay Peninsula*, volume IV: *The birds of the low-country jungle and scrub*. H.F. and G. Witherby, London.

————, Unpublished field diary held with the Zoological Reference Collections, National University of Singapore.

Chasen, F.N. and Hoogerwerf, A., 1941. The birds of the Netherlands Indian Mt. Leuser Expedition 1937 to North Sumatra. With a general survey, an itinerary and field-notes by A. Hoogerwerf. *Treubia* 18 (supplement): 1–125.

Chasen, F.N. and Kloss, C.B., 1927. Notes on Oriental birds. *Journal of the Federated Malay States Museums* 13: 275–280.

————, 1928. On a Collection of Birds from the Anamba Islands, South China Sea. *Journal of the Malayan Branch of the Royal Asiatic Society* 6: 43–63.

————, 1928a. Some Notes on Malaysian Waders. *Journal of the Malayan Branch of the Royal Asiatic Society* 6: 68–69.

————, 1928b. Birds from Mt. Benom, Pahang; the Kledang Hills, Perak; and the Islands of Penang, Tioman and Aor. *Journal of the Malayan Branch of the Royal Asiatic Society* 6: 70–75.

————, 1931. Notes on Malaysian Birds. *Bulletin of the Raffles Museum* 5: 80–82.

Chavalit Vidthayamon, 1985. First record of the Masked Booby (Aves, Sulidae; *Sula dactylatra*) for Thailand. *Natural History Bulletin of the Siam Society* 33: 53.

Cheke, A.S., 1966. Notes on seabirds seen on a journey across the Indian Ocean. *Ibis* 108: 628–630.

Cheng Tso-hsin, 1987. *A Synopsis of the Avifauna of China*. Science Press, Beijing, and Paul Parey, Hamburg.

Christidis, L. and Boles, W.E., 1994. *The Taxonomy and Species of Birds of Australia and its Territories*. Royal Australasian Ornithologists Union Monograph 2. RAOU, Melbourne

CHULA. Data from the Zoology Museum collection, Chulalongkorn University, Bangkok.

Clancey, P.A., 1995. The name of a proposed eastern race of the Greenshank. *Bulletin of the British Ornithologists' Club* 115: 190.

Clark, W.S., 1992. The taxonomy of Steppe and Tawny Eagles, with criteria for separation of museum specimens and live eagles. *Bulletin of the British Ornithologists' Club* 112: 150–157.

Clark, W.S. and Banks, R.C., 1992. The taxonomic status of the White-tailed Kite. *Wilson Bulletin* 104: 571–579.

CLBP. Dickinson, E.C., Kennedy, R.S. and Parkes, K.C., 1991. *The Birds of the Philippines. An annotated check-list*. British Ornithologists Union, Tring.

CLBS. van Marle, J.G. and Voous, K.H., 1988. *The Birds of Sumatra. An annotated check-list*. British Ornithologists Union, Tring.

CLBW. White, C.M.N. and Bruce, M.D., 1986. *The Birds of Wallacea. An annotated check-list*. British Ornithologists Union, London.

Colebrook-Robjent, J.F.R., 1978. An oviduct egg of the Indian Cuckoo *Cuculus micropterus*. *Bulletin of the British Ornithologists' Club* 98: 40.

Collias, N.E. and Saichuae, P., 1967. Ecology of the Red Jungle Fowl in Thailand and Malaya with reference to the origin of domestication. *Natural History Bulletin of the Siam Society* 22: 189–209.

Colston, P.R., 1980. The first and second records of the Short-tailed Shearwater *Puffinus tenuirostris* for the Malay Peninsula and other *Puffinus* records. *Bulletin of the British Ornithologists' Club* 100: 205–206.

Colston, P.R. and Burton, P.J.K., 1988. A field guide to the Waders of Britain and Europe. Hodder and Stoughton, London.

Compost, A. and Milton, G.R., 1986. An early arrival of the Malayan Night-Heron *Gorsachius melanolophus* in Java? *Kukila* 2: 88–90.

Condon, H.T., 1975. *Checklist of the Birds of Australia. Part I Non-passerines.* Royal Australasian Ornithologists Union, Melbourne.

Connors, P.G., McCaffery, B.J. and Maron, J.L., 1993. Speciation in golden-plovers, *Pluvialis dominica* and *P. fulva*: evidence from the breeding grounds. *Auk* 110: 9–20.

Cook, J.P., 1911. Uncommon birds of Burma. *Journal of the Bombay Natural History Society* 21: 265–267.

Cooper, W.A., 1948. Birds recorded from a Trengganu garden. *Malayan Nature Journal* 3: 97–98.

Cramer, E.D.H., 1941. Notes on the nesting of a woodpecker. *Malayan Nature Journal* 1: 138–139.

Cranbrook, Earl of, and Wells, D.R., 1981. Observations of fledgling cuckoos and their fosterers in Gunung Mulu National Park. *Sarawak Museum Journal* 29:147–149.

d'Abreu, E.A., 1910. Note on Blyth's Baza (*Baza jerdoni*). *Journal of the Bombay Natural History Society* 20: 518.

Danielsen, F. and Skov, H., 1986. *Observations of waterbirds along the coast of South-east Sumatra, July-August 1985.* Unpublished report, Copenhagen.

Davison, G.W.H., 1978. Studies of the crested Argus, II Gunong Rabong 1976. *World Pheasant Association Journal* 3: 46–53.

———, 1979. Studies of the Crested Argus, III Gunong Rabong 1977. *World Pheasant Association Journal* 4: 76–80.

———, 1980. The evolution of the Crested Argus. *World Pheasant Association Journal* 5: 91–97.

———, 1980a. The type locality of *Rheinardia ocellata* Rothschild. *Bulletin of the British Ornithologists' Club* 100: 141–143.

———, 1981. Diet and dispersion of the Great Argus *Argusianus argus*. *Ibis* 123: 485–494.

———, 1981a. Habitat requirements and the food supply of the Crested Fireback. *World Pheasant Association Journal* 6: 40–52.

———, 1981b. Sexual selection and the mating system of *Argusianus argus* (Aves: Phasianidae). *Biological Journal of the Linnean Society* 15: 91–104.

———, 1982. Sexual displays of the Great Argus Pheasant *Argusianus argus*. *Zeitschrift für Tierpsychologie* 58: 185–202.

———, 1982a. Systematics within the genus *Arborophila* Hodgson. *Federation Museums Journal* 27: 125–134.

———, 1983. The eyes have it: ocelli in a rainforest pheasant. *Animal Behaviour* 31: 1037–1042.

———, 1983a. Behaviour of Malay peacock pheasant *Polyplectron malacense* (Aves: Phasianidae). *Journal of the Zoological Society of London* 201: 57–65.

———, 1985. Avian spurs. *Journal of the Zoological Society of London* 206: 353–366.

———, 1986. Sexual selection in tropical forest birds. *Sains Malaysiana* 15: 185–197.

———, 1986a. Breeding behaviour of Crested Wood Partridges in captivity. *Avicultural Magazine* 92: 18–22.

———, 1987. The Birds of Ulu Endau, Johore, Malaysia, with Special Reference to Birds of Heath and Fan Palm Forests. *Malayan Nature Journal* 41: 425–433.

———, 1991. Who was Gunung Tahan's first conqueror? Disputes based on collected specimens and 'calls' of the Crested Argus. *Enggang* 3(2): 25–27.

———, 1992. Display of the Mountain Peacock-Pheasant. *World Pheasant Association Journal* 15/16: 45–56.

———, 1992a. Brood division and sibling relationships in captive Crested Wood Partidges (*Rollulus rouloul*). *Gibier Faune Sauvage* 9: 719–728.

Davison, W., 1889. Journal of a trip to Pahang, &c. with H.E. The Governor, August, 17th to 27th, 1889. *Journal of the Straits Branch of the Royal Asiatic Society* 20: 83–90.

de Korte, J., 1991. Status and conservation of Indonesia's seabird colonies. Pages 225–247 in J.P. Croxall (editor), *Seabird Status and Conservation: A Supplement.* ICBP Technical Publication 11, Cambridge.

de Silva, R.I., 1991. Status and conservation of breeding seabirds of Sri Lanka. Pages 205–211 in J.P. Croxall (editor), *Seabird Status and Conservation: A supplement.* ICBP Technical Publication 11, Cambridge.

Deignan, H.G., 1945. The Birds of Northern Thailand. *United States National Museum Bulletin* 186: i-iv, 1–616.

———, 1948. The races of the Black-crested Baza. *Auk* 65: 284–285.

———, 1950. The races of the Collared Scops Owl, Otus bakkamoena Pennant. *Auk* 67: 184–201.

———, 1952. The Correct name for the Malayo-Sumatran Race of the Chestnut-breasted Malkoha (Cuculidae). *Bulletin of the Raffles Museum* 24: 219.

———, 1956. Eastern Races of the White-rumped Swift, *Apus pacificus* (Latham), with a footnote by C.A. Gibson-Hill. *Bulletin of the Raffles Museum* 27: 147–149.

———, 1963. Checklist of the Birds of Thailand. *United States National Museum Bulletin* 226: i-x, 1–263.

Delacour, J., 1947. *Birds of Malaysia.* Macmillan, New York.

———, 1970. The contribution of Gilbert Tirant to Indochinese ornithology. *Natural History Bulletin of the Siam Society* 23: 325–329.

———, 1977. *The Pheasants of the World* (second edition). Spur Publications and The World Pheasant Association, Hindhead.

Delacour, J. and Jabouille, P., 1931. *Les oiseaux de l'Indochine Francaise.* Volumes 1–4. Exposition Coloniale Internationale 1931, Paris.

Delacour, J. and Mayr, E., 1945. The family Anatidae. *Wilson Bulletin* 57: 3–55.

———, 1945a. Notes on the taxonomy of the birds of the Philippines. Tree Swifts (Family Hemiprocnidae). *Zoologica* 30: 105–117.

Dementiev, G.P. and Gladkov, N.A. (editors), 1951–54.

The birds of the Soviet Union, Volumes 1–6. [English translation, Israel Program for Scientific Translations, Jerusalem].

Devillers, P., 1977. The skuas of the North American Pacific coast. *Auk* 94: 417–429.

Diamond, J.M., 1975. Assembly of Species Communities. Pages 342–444 in M. Cody and J.M. Diamond (editors), *Ecology and Evolution of Communities*. Harvard University Press, Cambridge, Massachusetts.

Dickinson, E.C., 1966. Notes upon a collection of birds made by Frank Gill Esq. off the west coast of Peninsular Thailand. *Natural History Bulletin of the Siam Society* 21: 243–249.

————, 1975. The identity of *Ninox scutulata* Raffles. *Bulletin of the British Ornithologists' Club* 95: 104–105.

————, 1989. A review of the larger Philippine swiftlets of the genus *Collocalia*. *Forktail* 4: 19–53.

Dodsworth, P.T.L., 1913. Eggs of the Malay Eagle Owl, *Huhua orientalis* (Horsf). *Journal of the Bombay Natural History Society* 22: 394.

Duckett, J.E., 1984. Barn Owls (*Tyto alba*) and the 'second generation' ratbaits utilised in oil palm plantations in Peninsular Malaysia. *The Planter* 60: 3–11.

————, 1987. Birds of Prey as feeders on Oil Palm (*Elaeis guineensis*) – A Note on New Malaysian Record. *The Planter* 63: 21–23.

————, 1991. *The evaluation of Management Techniques in the Biological Control of Rats in Oil Palm Plantations*. M.Phil. thesis, Silsoe College, Cranfield Institute of Technology.

Duckett, N., 1978. Notes on the Collared Scops Owl – *Otus bakkamoena*. *Malayan Naturalist* September 1978: 18–20.

Dunlop, S.W.C., 1960. Birdwaves. *Malayan Nature Journal* 14: 222–223.

————, 1961. Hornbills. *Malayan Nature Journal* 15: 67–68.

DuPont, J.E., 1971. *Philippine Birds*. Delaware Museum of Natural History, Delaware.

Eck, S., 1976. Die vögel der Banggai-Inseln, insbesondere Pelengs. *Zoologische Abhandlungen Staatliches Museum für Tierkunde in Dresden* 34: 53–100.

Edgar, A.T., 1933. Notes on the Nidification of some Perak Birds. *Bulletin of the Raffles Museum* 8: 121–162.

————, 1947. Notes on Malayan Birds. *Malayan Nature Journal* 2: 1–19.

————, 1954. A note on the White Collared Kingfisher (*Halcyon chloris humii* Sharpe). *Malayan Nature Journal* 9: 90–93.

Ellis, D.H., Kepler, A.K. and Kepler, C.B., 1990. Evidence for a fall raptor migration pathway across the South China Sea. *Journal of Raptor Research* 24: 12–18.

ENGGANG. Newsletter of the Malaysian Nature Society Bird Group. 1(1988), 2(1989), 3(1990).

Erftemeijer, P.L.A., van Balen, S. and Djuharse, E., 1988. *The Importance of Segara Anakan for Conservation, with Special Reference to its Avifauna*. Asian Wetland Bureau/INTERWADER-PHPA Report No. 6, Bogor.

Etchécopar, R.D. and Hüe, F., 1966. Présence de *Larus brunnicephalus* Jerdon à Penang (Malaisie). *Oiseau* 36: 65–67.

Evans, H.W., 1950. A 'Tock-tock' Record? *Malayan Nature Journal* 5: 37.

Eve, R. and Guigue, A.M., 1982. Birds on Ko Libong, Southern Thailand. *Natural History Bulletin of the Siam Society* 30: 91–99.

Ewins, P.J., Bazely, D.R. and Recher, H.F., 1990. Communal roosting of the Eastern Reef Egret. *Corella* 14: 29.

FAO, 1982. *Maungmagan, Moscos Islands and Mergui Archipelago. Report on a preliminary survey, April 1982*. UNDP/FAO Nature Conservation and National Parks Project. FAO, Rangoon.

————, 1983. *Report on a Reconnaissance of part of the Pakchan Reserved Forest and Lampi Island, Tenasserim*. Working People's Settlement Board. FAO, Rangoon.

FMSM. Federated Malay States Museums. The colonial Malayan museums system.

Foenander, E.C., 1956. Bee-eaters diving into water for floating insects. *Malayan Nature Journal* 10: 126.

Fogden, M.P.L., 1970. *Some aspects of the ecology of bird populations in Sarawak*. D.Phil thesis, Oxford University.

————, 1972. The seasonality and population dynamics of equatorial forest birds in Sarawak. *Ibis* 114: 307–343.

————, 1976. A Census of a Bird Community in Tropical Rain Forest in Sarawak. *Sarawak Museum Journal* 24: 251–267.

Frith, C.B., 1978. Short-tailed Shearwaters *Puffinus tenuirostris* in the Andaman Sea area, Indian Ocean. *Emu* 78: 95–97.

————, 1981. Utilization of a Single Brief Termite Eruption by Predators. *Natural History Bulletin of the Siam Society* 29: 173–174.

Frith, C.B. and Douglas, V.E., 1978. Notes on ten Asian hornbill species (Aves: Bucerotidae); with particular reference to growth and behaviour. *Natural History Bulletin of the Siam Society* 27: 35–82.

Frith, C.B. and Frith, D.W., 1978. Bill growth and development in the Northern Pied Hornbill. *Avicultural Magazine* 84: 20–31.

————, 1983. A systematic review of the hornbill genus *Anthracoceros* (Aves, Bucerotidae). *Zoological Journal of the Linnean Society* 78: 29–71.

Fry, C.H., 1980. The evolutionary biology of kingfishers (Alcedinidae). *The Living Bird* 18: 113–160.

————, 1984. *The Bee-eaters*. T. and A.D. Poyser, Calton.

Fry, C.H., Keith, S. and Urban, E.K., 1988. *The Birds of Africa*. Volume 3. Academic Press, London.

Gairdner, K.G., 1914. Notes on the fauna and flora of Ratburi and Petchaburi districts. *Journal of the Natural History Society of Siam* 1: 27–40.

Galdikas, B.M.F., Shapiro, G.L. and Katz, F., 1985. Danau Burung; bird lake in southern Indonesian Borneo. *Ardea* 73: 189–190.

Garr, J.J., 1957. Coppersmith Barbet (*Megalaima haemacephala indica*). *Malayan Nature Journal* 11: 132–133.

Gast, S. and King, B., 1985. Notes on Philippine birds, 7. Recent records of the Chinese Egret *Egretta leuphotes* from Luzon, Mindoro and Palawan,

Philippines. *Bulletin of the British Ornithologists' Club* 105: 139–141.

Gee, R.E., 1962, 'Pelicans'. *Malayan Nature Journal* 16: 151–152.

Gibson-Hill, C.A., 1947. Notes on the Birds of Christmas Island. *Bulletin of the Raffles Museum* 18: 87–165.

————, 1948. The storm-petrels occurring in the northern Indian Ocean, and adjacent seas. *Journal of the Bombay Natural History Society* 47: 443–448.

————, 1948a. A note on the food habits of three kingfishers occurring on Singapore Island. *Journal of the Bombay Natural History Society* 48: 146–152.

————, 1948b. The Brown Booby. *Malayan Nature Journal* 3: 67–69.

————, 1948c. The Malayan Swiftlets. *Malayan Nature Journal* 3: 190–200.

————, 1949. Ornithological Notes from the Raffles Museum, 1–4. *Bulletin of the Raffles Museum* 19: 98–119.

————, 1949a. Bird and Mammal Type Specimens formerly in the Raffles Museum Collections. *Bulletin of the Raffles Museum* 19: 133–198.

————, 1949b. An annotated checklist of the birds of Malaya. *Bulletin of the Raffles Museum* 20: 1–299.

————, 1949c. Notes on the nesting of the Bridled Tern on the Malayan coast. *Malayan Nature Journal* 4: 19–23.

————, 1950. Ornithological Notes from the Raffles Museum, 5–8. *Bulletin of the Raffles Museum* 21: 106–131.

————, 1950a. A Checklist of the Birds of Singapore Island. *Bulletin of the Raffles Museum* 21: 132–183.

————, 1950b. Notes on the Birds of the Cocos-Keeling Islands. *Bulletin of the Raffles Museum* 22: 212–270.

————, 1950c. Notes on the Sea Birds breeding in Malayan Waters. *Bulletin of the Raffles Museum* 23: 5–64.

————, 1950d. Ornithological Notes from the Raffles Museum, 9–14. *Bulletin of the Raffles Museum* 23: 65–126.

————, 1950e. Birds recorded from Pulau Jarak, Malacca Strait. *Bulletin of the Raffles Museum* 23: 263–299.

————, 1950f. Pulau Perak. *Malayan Nature Journal* 5: 1–4.

————, 1950g. A note on the Crested Tree-Swift. *Malayan Nature Journal* 5: 5–8.

————, 1952. Ornithological Notes from the Raffles Museum, 15–22. *Bulletin of the Raffles Museum* 24: 220–343.

————, 1952a. A Revised List of the Birds known from the Rhio-Lingga Archipelago. *Bulletin of the Raffles Museum* 24: 344–380.

———— (editor), 1953. The Cambridge University Expedition to the North-Eastern Malayan States, and to Upper Perak, 1899–1900. *Journal of the Malayan Branch of the Royal Asiatic Society* 26: 1–174.

————, 1956. Birds recorded from the Aroa Islands, Malacca Strait. *Bulletin of the Raffles Museum* 27: 155–179.

————, 1956a. Ornithological Notes from the Raffles Museum, 23–25. *Bulletin of the Raffles Museum* 27: 180–191.

Giles, F.H., 1936. A description of the swifts (Collocalia francica and Collocalia innominata), the birds which build edible nests. *Journal of the Siam Society, Natural History Supplement* 10: 137–160.

Gilliard, T.E. and McCroy, M., 1970. Notes on Birds from the Tamrau Mountains, New Guinea. *American Museum Novitates* 2420: 1–28.

Glenister, A.G., 1951. *The Birds of the Malay Peninsula, Singapore and Penang*. Oxford University Press, London.

Goodwin, D.E., 1967. *Pigeons and doves of the world.* British Museum (Natural History), London.

Grant, A., 1990. North Keeling: a Seabird Paradise. *Birds International* 2: 36–45.

Green, A.J., 1992. *The status and conservation of the White-winged Wood Duck Cairina scutulata.* IWRB special publication 17, Slimbridge.

Gregory-Smith, R., 1995. *Birds of Sintok; An Annotated Checklist*. Universiti Utara Malaysia, Sintok.

————, 1995a. *Birds of Perlis and Kedah, including Langkawi.* Institute of Biodiversity and Environmental Conservation, Universiti Malaysia Sarawak, Kuching.

Grubh, R.B., 1978. Field identification of some Indian vultures (*Gyps bengalensis, G. indicus, G. fulvus,* and *Torgos calvus*). *Journal of the Bombay Natural History Society* 75: 444–449.

Gurney, J.H., 1879. On the occurrence of Ninox borneensis in Java, and a large Form of Scops lempiji in Sumatra. *Ibis* series 3(4): 470–471.

Gyldenstolpe, N., 1916. Zoological Results of the Swedish Zoological Expeditions to Siam 1911–1912 & 1914–1915. *Kungliga Svenska Vetenskapsakademiens Handlingar* 56: 1–160.

————, 1917. On birds and mammals from the Malay Peninsula. *Arkiv för Zoologi* 10: 1–31.

Hackett, S.J., 1989. Effects of varied electrophoretic conditions on detection of evolutionary patterns in the Laridae. *Condor* 91; 73–90.

Haile, N.S., 1964. Notes on birds on Spratly island, Amboyna Cay and Swallow Reef, South China Sea. *Sabah Society Journal* 11: 135–137.

Hails, C.J. and Amirrudin, A., 1981. Food samples and selectivity of White-bellied Swiftlets *Collocalia esculenta. Ibis* 123: 328–333.

Hails, C. and Jarvis, F., 1987. *Birds of Singapore.* Times Editions, Singapore.

Hails, C.J. and Turner, A.K., 1984. The breeding biology of the Asian Palm Swift *Cypsiurus balasiensis. Ibis* 126. 74–81.

————, 1985. The rôle of fat and protein during breeding in the White-bellied Swiftlet (*Collocalia esculenta*). *Journal of Zoology, London (A)* 206: 469–484.

Haimoff, E.H., 1987. A spectrographic analysis of the loud calls of Helmeted Hornbills *Rhinoplax vigil. Ibis* 129: 319–326.

Hale, W.G., 1971. A revision of the taxonomy of the

Redshank *Tringa totanus*. *Zoological Journal of the Linnean Society* 50: 199–268.

———, 1973. The distribution of the Redshank, *Tringa totanus*, in the winter range. *Zoological Journal of the Linnean Society* 53: 177–236.

Hall, B.P., 1956. First record of the Chinese Lesser Crested Tern, *Thalasseus zimmermanni*, from Thailand. *Bulletin of the British Ornithologists' Club* 76: 87.

Hamilton, A.W., 1923. Some bird names in Kedah. *Journal of the Malayan Branch of the Royal Asiatic Society* 1: 378–381.

Hancock, J. and Kushlan, J., 1984. *The Herons Handbook*. Croom Helm, London.

Hancock, J.A., Kushlan, J.A. and Kahl, M.P., 1992. *Storks, Ibises and Spoonbills of the World*. Academic Press, London.

HANZAB. Marchant, S. and Higgins, P.J. (co-ordinators), 1990–93. *Handbook of Australian, New Zealand and Antarctic Birds*. Volumes 1–2. Oxford University Press, Melbourne.

Harrison, C.B., 1958. Strange behaviour of a Woodpecker. *Malayan Nature Journal* 12: 124.

Harrison, C.J.O., 1969. Some comparative notes on the Peaceful and Zebra Doves (*Geopelia striata* ssp) with reference to their taxonomic status. *Emu* 69: 66–71.

Harrison, P., 1985. *Seabirds, an Identification Guide*. Croom Helm, London and Sydney.

Hartert, E., 1889. Zur Ornithologie der indisch-malayischen Gegenden. *Journal für Ornithologie* 37: 345–440.

———, 1902. On birds from Pahang, eastern Malay Peninsula. *Novitates Zoologicae* 9: 537–580.

———, 1920. *Die vögel der Paläarktischen Fauna*. Volume 2. Friedländer, Berlin.

Hartert, E. and Butler, A.L., 1898. A few notes on birds from Perak, Malay Peninsula. *Novitates Zoologicae* 5: 506–508.

Hawkins, A.F.A. and Howes, J.R., 1986. *Preliminary assessment of coastal wetlands and shorebirds in South-west Peninsular Malaysia*. INTERWADER, Kuala Lumpur.

Hayman, P., Marchant, J. and Prater, T., 1986. *Shorebirds. An identification guide to the waders of the world*. Croom Helm, London.

HBI. Salim Ali and Ripley, S.D., 1978–83. *Handbook of the Birds of India and Pakistan* (second edition). Volumes 1–4. Oxford University Press, Bombay.

Helbig, A.J., 1987. Records of Javan Pond-Heron *Ardeola speciosa* and Dusky Warbler *Phylloscopus fuscatus* in Peninsular Malaysia in March 1986. *Forktail* 3: 57–59.

———, 1987a. Ökologie des Eisvogels (*Alcedo atthis*) in einem südasiatischen überwinterungsgebeit. *Journal für Ornithologie* 128: 441–456.

Herbert, E.G., 1923–26. Nests and eggs of birds in Central Siam. *Journal of the Natural History Society of Siam* 6: 81–123, 215–222, 293–311, 323–356.

Hickey, J.J. and Anderson, D.W., 1969. The Peregrine Falcon: life history and population literature. Pages 3–42 in J.J. Hickey (editor), *Peregrine Falcon populations. Their biology and decline*. University of Wisconsin Press, Madison.

Hislop, J.A., 1956. Notes from the National Park. *Malayan Nature Journal* 10: 122–125.

Ho Hua Chew and Sutari Supari, 1994. Plain-pouched in Perak? A spectacular movement of hornbills. *Singapore Avifauna* 8: 37–40.

Holmes, D.A., 1973. Bird notes from southernmost Thailand, 1972. *Natural History Bulletin of the Siam Society* 25: 39–66.

———, 1976. A record of White-winged Wood Duck *Cairina scutulata* in Sumatra. *Bulletin of the the British Ornithologists' Club* 96: 88–89.

———, 1977. Faunistic notes and further additions to the Sumatran avifauna. *Bulletin of the British Ornithologists' Club* 97: 68–71.

———, 1990. Notes on the occurrence of the White-winged Wood Duck *Cairina scutulata* on the west coast of North Sumatra. *Kukila* 5: 69–72.

———, 1991. Note on the status of the White-shouldered Ibis in Kalimantan. *Kukila* 5: 145–147.

Holmes, D.A. and Wells, D.R., 1975. Further observations on the birds of South Thailand. *Natural History Bulletin of the Siam Society* 26: 61–78.

Holttum, R.E., 1950. Reflections on the seasonal behaviour of two common birds in Singapore. *Malayan Nature Journal* 5: 96–97.

Holyoak, D.T., 1973. Significance of colour dimorphism in Polynesian populations of *Egretta sacra*. *Ibis* 115: 419–420.

Hoogerwerf, A., 1953. Some notes about the nature reserve Pulau Panaitan (Prinseneiland) in Strait Sunda. *Treubia* 21: 481–505.

———, 1965. Notes on Indonesian birds with special reference to the avifauna of Java and the surrounding small islands (Parts 1–3). *Treubia* 26: 1–56, 133–157, 211–291.

———, 1966. On the occurrence of *Nycticorax caledonicus* in Java. *Ardea* 54: 81–87.

———, 1967. On the validity of *Charadrius alexandrinus javanicus* Chasen and the occurrence of *Charadrius alexandrinus ruficapillus* Temm. and of *Charadrius peronii* Schl. on Java and in New Guinea. *Philippine Journal of Science* 95: 209–214.

———, 1969–71. On the ornithology of the rhino sanctuary Udjung Kulon in West Java (Indonesia). *Natural History Bulletin of the Siam Society* 23: 9–65; 24: 79–135.

Hope Sworder, G., 1928. A Predatory Kingfisher. *Malayan Naturalist* 2(1): 48.

Hopwood, J.C., 1919. Notes on some nests recently found in south Tenasserim. *Journal of the Bombay Natural History Society* 26: 853–859.

———, 1921. The nidification of the Masked Finfoot, (*Heliopais personata*). *Journal of the Bombay Natural History Society* 27: 634–637.

Hornaday, W.T., 1878. Account of a naturalist's visit to the Territory of Selangor. *Journal of the Straits Branch of the Royal Asiatic Society* 3: 124–131.

———, 1885. *Two years in the jungle; the experiences of a hunter and naturalist in India, Ceylon, the Malay Peninsula and Borneo*. Charles Scribner's Sons, New York.

Howes, J.R., 1988. Nordmann's Greenshank *Tringa*

guttifer: status and threats. *Asian Wetland News* 1: 12.
——————, 1988a. A Note on the Foraging Behaviour of the Masked Finfoot (*Heliopais personata). Enggang* 1(3): 13.
Howes, J.R. and Bakewell, D.N., 1989. *Shorebird Studies Manual.* Asian Wetland Bureau Publication 55, Kuala Lumpur.
Howes, J.R., Hawkins, A.F.A. and Parish, D., 1986. *Preliminary survey of wetland and shorebirds along the East Coast of Peninsular Malaysia.* INTER-WADER, Kuala Lumpur.
Howes, J.R. and Lambert, F.R., 1987. Some notes on the status, field identification and foraging characteristics of Nordmann's Greenshank *Tringa guttifer. Wader Study Group Bulletin* 49: 14–17.
Hubbard, J.P., 1976. Status of the night herons (*Nycticorax*) of the Philippines and vicinity. *Nemouria* 19: 1–10.
Hume, A.O., 1879. A first Tentative List of the Birds of the western half of the Malay Peninsula. *Stray Feathers* 8: 37–72, 151–163.
——————, 1880. The Birds of the Western Half of the Malay Peninsula, third notice. *Stray Feathers* 9: 107–132.
Hume, A.O. and Davison, W.R., 1878. A Revised List of the Birds of Tenasserim. *Stray Feathers* 6: i-viii, 1–524.
Hurrell, L.H., 1961. Migration and Movements of Birds of Prey over Singapore. *Bulletin of the National Museum, Singapore* 30: 97–100.
Hutchinson, G., 1950. Woodpeckers in Johore. *Malayan Nature Journal* 5: 36–37.
ICF. Data from the files of the International Crane Foundation.
Indrawan, M., 1991. A winter flock of Pheasant-tailed Jacanas at Ciamis, West Java. *Kukila* 5: 138–140.
Inglis, C.M., 1918. An addition to the game birds of Burma. The Long-billed Partridge (*Rhizothera longirostris*, Temm.) in Tenasserim. *Journal of the Bombay Natural History Society* 26: 291–292.
Inskipp, C. and Inskipp, T., 1985. *A Guide to the Birds of Nepal.* Croom Helm, London.
Inskipp, T., Lindsey, N. and Duckworth, W., 1996. *An Annotated Checklist of the Birds of the Oriental Region.* Oriental Bird Club, Sandy.
Itoh, S., 1991. Geographical variation of the plumage polymorphism in the Eastern Reef Heron (*Egretta sacra*). *Condor* 93: 383–389.
Jespersen, P., 1933. Observations on the oceanic birds of the Pacific and adjacent waters. *Videnskabelige Mededelsar fra Dansk Naturhistorisk Forening i København* 94: 187–204.
Johns, A.D., 1981. Observations on the nesting of the Rhinoceros Hornbill, *Buceros rhinoceros. Malayan Nature Journal* 35: 173–177.
——————, 1986. Effects of selective logging on the ecological organization of a peninsular Malaysian rainforest avifauna. *Forktail* 1: 65–79.
——————, 1987. The use of Primary and Selectively logged Rainforst by Malaysian Hornbills (Bucerotidae) and Implications for their Conservation. *Biological Conservation* 40: 179–190.
——————, 1987a. *Long-term effects of selective logging operations on Malaysian wildlife: a case study in the Tekam Forest Reserve, Pahang, Peninsular Malaysia.* Unpublished report to the Forest Research Institute of Malaysia.
——————, 1989. Recovery of a Peninsular Malaysian rainforest avifauna following selective timber logging: the first twelve years. *Forktail* 4: 89–105.
Johns, A.D. and Thorpe, R.I., 1981. On the occurrence of long-distance movement in the Yellow-wattled Lapwing *Vanellus (= Lobipluvia) malabaricus* (Boddaert). *Journal of the Bombay Natural History Society* 78: 597–598.
Johnsgard, P.A., 1978. *Ducks, Geese and Swans of the World.* University of Nebraska Press, Lincoln and London.
——————, 1993. *Cormorants, Darters and Pelicans of the World.* Smithsonian Institution Press, Washington D.C.
Johnstone, R.E., 1978. North Fisherman Island, Western Australia. *Corella* 2: 43–45.
Johnstone, R.E., van Balen, S. and Dekker, R.W.R.J., 1993. New bird records from the island of Lombok. *Kukila* 6: 124–127.
Jørgensen, A., 1949. Siams Vadefugle. *Dansk Ornithologisk Forenings Tidsskrift* 43: 60–68, 150–162, 216–237, 261–279.
Junge, G.C.A., 1941. Biological results of the Snellius Expedition. X Aves. *Temminckia* 6: 100–108.
——————, 1948. Notes on some Sumatran birds. *Zoologische Mededelingen, Rijksmuseum van Natuurlijke Historie te Leiden* 29: 311–326.
Kahl, M.P., 1971. Social behaviour and taxonomic relationships of the storks. *The Living Bird* 10: 151–170.
Kalai, A.R., 1984. *The ranging, hunting behaviour, nesting behaviour and activity patterns of the Black-shouldered Kite, Elanus caeruleus.* Unpublished dissertation, Zoology Department, University of Malaya.
Kang Nee, Hails, C.J. and Sigurdsson, J.B., 1991. Nest construction and egg-laying in edible-nest Swiftlets *Aerodramus* spp. and implications for nest harvesting. *Ibis* 133: 170–177.
Kasprzyk, M.J., Forster, R.A. and Harrington, B.A., 1987. First Northern Hemisphere record and first juvenile plumage description of the Cox's Sandpiper (*Calidris paramelanotos*). *American Birds* 41: 1359–1364.
Kelham, H.R., 1881–83. Ornithological notes made in the Straits Settlements and in the Western States of the Malay Peninsula. *Journal of the Straits Branch of the Royal Asiatic Society* 9: 109–140; 11: 1–29, 171–205.
Kelsall, H.J., 1891. Note on the nest and eggs of *Nyctiornis amicta. Journal of the Straits Branch of the Royal Asiatic Society* 24: 169–170.
——————, 1894. Account of a trip up the Pahang, Tembeling and Tahan rivers, and an attempt to reach Gunong Tahan. *Journal of the Straits Branch of the Royal Asiatic Society* 25: 33–65.
——————, 1894a. List of birds collected or observed during a trip across Johore. *Journal of the Straits Branch of the Royal Asiatic Society* 26: 17–19.
Kemp, A.C., 1988. The systematics and zoogeography of Oriental and Australasian hornbills (Aves :

Bucerotidae). *Bonner Zoologische Beiträge* 39: 315–345.

———, 1995. *The Hornbills*. Oxford University Press, Oxford.

Kemp, A.C. and Crowe, T.M., 1994. Morphometrics of falconets and hunting behaviour of the Black-thighed Falconet *Microhierax fringillarius*. *Ibis* 136: 44–49.

Kempe, J.E., 1947. Note on the Migration of Swinhoe's Snipe and the Fantail Snipe in Malaysia. *Journal of the Bombay Natural History Society* 46: 730–731.

Kennedy, R.S., Mayer, S. and Fisher, T.H., 1984. Notes on Philippine birds, 3. First sight records of the Javan Pond Heron *Ardeola speciosa* from the Philippines. *Bulletin of the British Ornithologists' Club* 104: 102–103.

Kennerley, P.R. and Bakewell, D.N., 1987. Nordmann's Greenshank in Hong Kong: a review of the identification and status. *Hong Kong Bird Report 1986*: 83–100.

Kennerley, P.R., Hoogendoorn, W. and Chalmers, M.L., 1995. Identification and systematics of large white-headed gulls in Hong Kong. *Hong Kong Bird Report 1994*: 127–156.

Kidd, E.R.G., 1961. Grey-rumped Tattler in Johore. *Malayan Nature Journal* 16: 175–176.

———, 1978. Some notes on the birds of Brunei. *Brunei Museum Journal* 4: 115–164.

King, B., 1966. *List of bird skins and specimens collected in Thailand from 1 March 1964 to 30 June 1966 under MAPS programme*. Unpublished report to Centre for Thai National Reference Collections, Bangkok.

———, 1987. The Waterfall Swift *Hydrochous gigas*. *Bulletin of the British Ornithologists' Club* 107: 36–37.

King, B., Dickinson, E.C. and Woodcock, M.W., 1975. *A Field Guide to the Birds of South-East Asia*. Collins, London.

King, W.B., 1967. *Seabirds of the tropical Pacific Ocean*. United States National Museum, Washington D.C.

Kiørboe, T., 1991. Seabirds observed in the Andaman Shelf Sea off Phuket, Thailand, 1990–91. *Natural History Bulletin of the Siam Society* 39: 85–90.

Kloss, C.B., 1906. Some birds of Tiuman Island. *Journal of the Straits Branch of the Royal Asiatic Society* 45: 280–281.

———, 1911. On mammals and birds from Trengganu. *Journal of the Federated Malay States Museums* 4: 135–143.

———, 1911a. On mammals and birds from the lowlands of Pahang. *Journal of the Federated Malay States Museums* 4: 144–166.

———, 1911b. On mammals and other vertebrates from the Trengganu archipelago. *Journal of the Federated Malay States Museums* 4: 175–212.

———, 1911c. On mammals and birds from the hills of Negri Sembilan. *Journal of the Federated Malay States Museums* 4: 219–229.

———, 1911d. Notes on birds new to, or rare in, the Malay Peninsula (second series). *Journal of the Federated Malay States Museums* 4: 229–232.

———, 1926. The Laughing Gull (*Larus ridibundus*) in the Straits of Singapore. *Journal of the Malayan Branch of the Royal Asiatic Society* 4: 157.

Knystautas, A., 1987. *The Natural History of the USSR*. Century, London.

Lack, D., 1956. The species of *Apus*. *Ibis* 98: 34–62.

Lambert, F.R., 1987. *Forest fig phenology and avian frugivores in Malaysia*. Ph.D. thesis, University of Aberdeen.

———, 1987a. Bat-hawk or Peregrine Falcon at Templer Park? *Oriental Bird Club Bulletin* 6: 34–35.

———, 1988. Pigeons as seed predators and dispersers of figs in a Malaysian lowland forest. *Ibis* 131: 521–527.

———, 1989. Fig-eating by birds in a Malaysian lowland rain forest. *Journal of Tropical Ecology* 5: 401–412.

———, 1989a. Daily ranging behaviour of three tropical forest frugivores. *Forktail* 4: 107–116.

———, 1991. The Conservation of Fig-eating Birds in Malaysia. *Biological Conservation* 58: 31–40.

Lambert, F.R. and Marshall, A.G., 1991. Keystone characteristics of bird-dispersed *Ficus* in a Malaysian lowland rain forest. *Journal of Ecology* 79: 793–809.

Lane, B. and Davis, J., 1987. *Shorebirds in Australia*. Nelson, Melbourne.

Langham, N.P.E., 1976. The status of the avifauna of Pulau Perak. *Federal Museums Journal* 21: 69–84.

———, N., 1980.Breeding biology of the Edible-nest Swiftlet *Aerodramus fuciphagus*. *Ibis* 122: 447–461.

Langham, N.P.E., Wells, D.R. and Charles, J.K., 1973. Vertebrates on Pulau Perak in March 1973. *Malayan Nature Journal* 26: 95–98.

———, 1974. Further notes on the vertebrates of Pulau Perak, July 1973. *Malayan Nature Journal* 28: 13–17.

Lansdown, R.V., 1987. Recent extensions in breeding range of the Yellow Bittern *Ixobrychus sinensis*. *Forktail* 3: 61–63.

———, 1988. Some Calls, Displays and Associated Morphology of the Cinnamon Bittern (*Ixobrychus cinnamomeus*) and their possible functions. *Colonial Waterbirds* 11: 308–310.

———, 1989. Displays of the Sumatran Heron *Ardea sumatrana*. *Colonial Waterbirds* 12: 113–114.

———, 1990. Chinese Egret. *Oriental Bird Club Bulletin* 11: 27–30.

Leighton, M., 1982. *Fruit resources and patterns of feeding, spacing and grouping among sympatric Bornean hornbills (Bucerotidae)*. Ph.D. thesis, University of California, Davis.

Lekagul, B. (See Boonsong Lekagul).

Lenton, G.M., 1980. *The ecology of Barn Owls (Tyto alba) in the Malay Peninsula with reference to their use in rodent control*. Ph.D. thesis, University of Malaya.

———, 1984. Moult of Malayan Barn Owls *Tyto alba*. *Ibis* 126: 188–197.

———, 1984a. The feeding and breeding ecology of Barn Owls *Tyto alba* in Peninsular Malaysia. *Ibis* 126: 551–575.

———, 1985. History, distribution and origin of

Barn Owls *Tyto alba* in the Malay Peninsula. *Bulletin of the British Ornithologists' Club* 105: 54–58.

Lewin, H.G.D., 1954. A nest of the Bamboo Green Woodpecker. *Malayan Nature Journal* 9: 16–18.

————, 1957. The status of some resident birds on the East Coast. *Malayan Nature Journal* 11: 35–38.

————, 1960. Petrels in Malayan waters. *Malayan Nature Journal* 14: 128.

Leyne, E.G., 1941. Peafowl in Selangor. *Malayan Nature Journal* 1: 113–114.

Lim Chan Koon, 1994. *Variasi protein dan sistematik Burung Layang-layang Perut Putih (White-bellied Swiftlets) dari tiga koloni di Semenanjung Malaysia.* Unpublished dissertation, Zoology Department, University of Malaya.

Lim Kim Seng, 1987. An unusual cuckoo encounter. *Singapore Avifauna* 1(7): 18–19.

————, 1987a. Preliminary Notes on the Birds of Seletar Island. *Singapore Avifauna* 1(10): 26–27.

————, 1989. Storming the Singapore Straits. *Singapore Avifauna* 3(10): 30–31.

————, 1992. *Vanishing Birds of Singapore.* Singapore Nature Society, Singapore.

Livezey, B.C., 1991. A phylogenetic analysis and classification of recent dabbling ducks (tribe Anatini) based on comparative morphology. *Auk* 108: 471–507.

Loke Wan Tho, 1954. Photographing the Yellow Bittern in Penang. *Malayan Nature Journal* 9: 81–83.

Ludgater, S.J., 1952. The Black-crested Baza. *Malayan Nature Journal* 7: 43.

Maccoll, N.S., 1962. Collared Scops Owls. *Malayan Nature Journal* 16: 230–232.

MacDonald, K.C., 1908. Notes on birds in the Amherst district, Lower Burma. *Journal of the Bombay Natural History Society* 18: 912–913.

Mackenzie M.J.S. and Kear, J., 1976. The White-winged Wood Duck. *Wildfowl* 27: 5–17.

Madge, S.G., 1969. Notes on the breeding of the Bushy-crested Hornbill *Anorrhinus galeritus. Malayan Nature Journal* 23: 1–6.

Madoc, G.C., 1936. On the nidification of some Malayan Birds. *Bulletin of the Raffles Museum* 12: 124–133.

————, 1947. An introduction to Malayan birds (revised edition). *Malayan Nature Journal* 2: i-iv, 1–123.

————, 1950. Field Notes on some Siamese Birds. *Bulletin of the Raffles Museum* 23: 129–190.

————, 1950–51. Notes on some birds occurring in Thailand and Malaya. *Malayan Nature Journal* 5: 47–57, 123–133, 184–191.

————, 1954. The Birds of Pulau Perak. *Malayan Nature Journal* 9: 19–24.

————, 1955. Pulau Perak. *Malayan Nature Journal* 9: 130–131.

————, 1956. The Birds observed during two short visits to the Aroa Islands. *Bulletin of the Raffles Museum* 27: 150–154.

————, 1956a. *An Introduction to Malayan Birds* (revised edition). Malayan Nature Society, Kuala Lumpur.

————, 1956b. Observations on two Malayan cuckoos. *Malayan Nature Journal* 10: 97–103.

————, 1956c. A further note on the Lesser Cuckoo. *Malayan Nature Journal* 10: 134–138.

————, 1957. An ornithological note on Pulau Jarak. *Malayan Nature Journal* 11: 101–103.

————, 1960. A visit to Gunong Tahan. *Malayan Nature Journal* 14: 95–107.

Madoc, G.C. and Allen, F.G.H., 1952. Ornithological Notes made at Fraser's Hill, March, 1951. *Bulletin of the Raffles Museum* 24: 164–182.

————, 1956. Postscript to Pulau Perak. *Malayan Nature Journal* 10: 131–133.

Maingay, A.C., 1868. Notes on rare and little known Malayan mammals and birds. *Proceedings of the Asiatic Society of Bengal*: 194–198.

Malling Olsen, K., 1989. Field identification of the smaller skuas. *British Birds* 82: 143–176.

Mann, C.F., 1987. A checklist of the birds of Brunei Darussalam. *Brunei Museum Journal* 6: 170–212.

————, 1987a. Notable bird observations from Brunei, Borneo. *Forktail* 3: 51–56.

————, 1989. More notable bird observations from Brunei. *Forktail* 5: 17–22.

MAPS. Data from the files of the Migratory Animal Pathological Survey.

Marshall, J.T., 1966. Relationships of certain owls around the Pacific. *Natural History Bulletin of the Siam Society* 21: 235–242.

————, 1978. Systematics of smaller Asian night birds based on voice. *American Ornithologists Union Ornithological Monograph* 25: i-v, 1–58.

Mason, V., 1989. *Birds of Bali.* Periplus Editions, Singapore.

Mayr, E., 1945. *Birds of the Southwest Pacific.* Macmillan, New York.

————, 1949. Geographical variation in *Accipiter trivirgatus. American Museum Novitates* 1415: 1–12.

Mayr, E. and Amadon, D., 1941. Birds collected during the Whitney South Sea expedition XLVI. Geographical variation in *Demigretta sacra* (Gmelin). *American Museum Novitates* 1144: 1–11.

Mayr, E. and Short, L.L., 1970. *Species taxa of North American Birds. A contribution to comparative systematics.* Nuttall Ornithological Club, Cambridge, Massachusetts.

MBR. Malayan Bird Report (editor D.R. Wells). *Malayan Nature Journal* 43: 116–147 (1982–83); 43:148–171 (1984–85); 43: 172–210 (1986–87).

McAllan, I.A.W. and Bruce, M.D., 1988. *The birds of New South Wales – a working list.* Biocon Research Group, Turramurra, Australia.

McClure, H.E., 1961. Garden birds in Kuala Lumpur, Malaya. *Malayan Nature Journal* 15: 111–133.

————, 1963. English Vernacular Names of the Birds of the Malaysian Subregion. *Malayan Nature Journal* 17: 75–121.

————, 1963a. Some bird 'rarities'. *Malayan Nature Journal* 17: 173–178.

————, 1963b. Northern visitors to Malaya. *Malayan Nature Journal* 17: 232–234.

————, 1964. Avian bionomics in Malaya: 1. The avifauna above 5000 feet altitude on Mount Brinchang, Pahang. *Bird-Banding* 35: 141–183.

————, 1966. Flowering, fruiting and animals in

the canopy of a tropical rain forest. *Malayan Forester* 29: 182–203.

————, 1967. The composition of mixed species flocks in lowland and sub-montane forests in Malaya. *Wilson Bulletin* 79: 131–154.

————, 1974. *Migration and Survival of the Birds of Asia*. United States Army Medical Component, SEATO Medical Project, Bangkok.

————, 1979. Nesting of the White-whiskered Tree Swift in Malaya. *Condor* 81: 308–311.

McClure, H.E. and Hussein bin Othman, 1965. Avian bionomics of Malaya 2. The effect of forest destruction upon a local population. *Bird-Banding* 36: 242–269.

McClure, H.E. and Husain bin Haji Osman, 1968. Nesting of birds in a coconut-mangrove habitat in Selangor. *Malayan Nature Journal* 22: 18–28.

McDonald, E.M., 1940. Breeding season of the Whistling Teal (*Belibis*). *Malayan Nature Journal* 1: 65.

McGowan, P., 1991. Ecology and behaviour of the Malaysian peacock pheasant – a threatened tropical rain forest species. *World Pheasant Association News* 34: 11–14.

Medway, Lord, 1962. The swiftlets (*Collocalia*) of Java and their relationships. *Journal of the Bombay Natural History Society* 59: 146–153.

————, 1966. Observations on the Fauna of Pulau Tioman and Pulau Tulai. 4. The Birds. *Bulletin of the National Museum of Singapore* 34: 39–52.

————, 1966a. Field characters as a guide to the specific relations of swiftlets. *Proceedings of the Linnean Society of London* 177: 151–172.

————, 1972. The Gunong Benom Expedition 1967. 6. The distribution and altitudinal zonation of birds and mammals on Gunong Benom. *Bulletin of the British Museum (Natural History), Zoology* 23: 105–154.

Medway, Lord and Lim, R.P., 1970. Post-juvenile dispersal of Night Herons in Malaya. *Bird-Banding* 41: 265–274.

Medway, Lord and Pye, J.D., 1977. Echolocation and the systematics of swiftlets. Pages 225–238 in B. Stonehouse and C. Perrins (editors), *Evolutionary ecology*. Macmillan, London.

Medway, Lord and Wells, D.R., 1969. Dark orientation by the Giant Swiftlet *Collocalia gigas*. *Ibis* 111: 609–611.

————, 1971. Density and diversity of birds at Kuala Lompat, Pahang. *Malayan Nature Journal* 24: 238–247.

Medway, Lord and Yong Ghong Chong, 1970. Barn Owl pellets from Kulai, Johore. *Malayan Nature Journal* 23: 171–172.

Mees, G.F., 1971. Systematic and faunistic remarks on birds from Borneo and Java, with new records. *Zoologische Mededelingen, Rijksmuseum van Natuurlijke Historie te Leiden* 45: 225–244.

————, 1973. The status of two species of migrant swifts in Java and Sumatra (Aves, Apodidae). *Zoologische Mededelingen, Rijksmuseum van Natuurlijke Historie te Leiden* 46: 197–207.

————, 1975. A list of the birds known from Roti and adjacent islets (Lesser Sunda Islands). *Zoologische Mededelingen, Rijksmuseum van Natuurlijke Historie te Leiden* 49: 115–140.

————, 1975a. Identiteit en status van *Sterna bernsteini* Schlegel. *Ardea* 63: 78–86.

————, 1977. The subspecies of *Chlidonias hybridus* (Pallas), their breeding distribution and migrations. *Zoologische Verhandelingen, Rijksmuseum van Natuurlijke Historie te Leiden* 157: 1–64.

————, 1977a. Geographical variation of *Caprimulgus macrurus* Horsfield (Aves, Caprimulgidae). *Zoologische Verhandelingen, Rijksmuseum van Natuurlijke Historie te Leiden* 155: 1–47.

————, 1981. The Sparrow-Hawks (*Accipiter*) of the Andaman Islands. *Journal of the Bombay Natural History Society* 77: 371–412.

————, 1982. Birds from the lowlands of southern New Guinea (Merauke and Koembe). *Zoologische Verhandelingen, Rijksmuseum van Natuurlijke Historie te Leiden* 191: 1–188.

————, 1985. Comments on species of the genus *Hirundapus* (Aves: Apodidae). *Verhandelingen der Koninklijke Nederlandse Akademie van Wetenschappen (C)* 88: 63–73.

————, 1985a. *Caprimulgus macrurus* Horsfield and related forms, a re-evaluation (Aves, Caprimulgidae). *Verhandelingen der Koninklijke Nederlandse Akademie van Wetenschappen (C)* 88: 419–428.

————, 1986. A list of the birds recorded from Bangka Island, Indonesia. *Zoologische Verhandelingen, Rijksmuseum van Natuurlijke Historie te Leiden* 232: 1–176.

Meeswat, K. and Prentice, R.C., 1984. Observations on the ecology of the birds of the Kukut Sanctuary. Pages 50–72 in A.G. Marshall (editor), *The Kukut Project. The biological resource potential of Kukut area of Lake Songkla, Southern Thailand. First Annual Report, 1983/84*. Prince of Songkhla University, Thailand.

Meinertzhagen, A.C., 1924. A review if the genus *Burhinus*. *Ibis* series 11(6): 329–356.

Melville, D.S. and Round, P.D., 1982. Further Records of the Asian Dowitcher *Limnodromus semipalmatus* from Thailand, with Notes on its Distribution and Identification. *Natural History Bulletin of the Siam Society* 30: 199–204.

Meyer de Schauensee, R., 1934. Zoological Results of the Third De Schauensee Siamese Expedition, Part II. – Birds from Siam and the Southern Shan States. *Proceedings of the Academy of Natural Sciences of Philadelphia* 86: 165–280.

————, 1946. On Siamese Birds. *Proceedings of the Academy of Natural Sciences of Philadelphia* 98: 1–82.

Meyer de Schauensee, R. and Ripley, S.D., 1940. Zoological results of the George Vanderbilt Sumatran Expedition, 1936–1939. Part I – Birds from Atjeh. *Proceedings of the Academy of Natural Sciences of Philadelphia* 91: 311–368.

Milledge, D.R., 1977. One year's observations of

seabirds in continental shelf waters off Sydney, N.S.W. *Corella* 1: 1–12.
Milton, G.R., 1985. Notes on the distribution of the Masked Finfoot *Heliopais personata* in Indonesia. *Kukila* 2: 41–43.
Milton, G.R. and Marhadi, A., 1989. *An investigation into market-netting of birds in West Java, Indonesia.* Unpublished report to PHPA/WWF/IUCN, Bogor.
MNC. Data from the collection of Muzium Negara (the Malaysian National Museum).
Mohamed Basri Wahid and Abdul Halim Haji Hassan, 1985. The effects of *Elaeidobius kamerunicus* Faust on rat control programmes of oil palm estates in Malaysia. *Palm Oil Research Institute of Malaysia Occasional Paper* 14: i–iv, 1–50.
Mohamed Nazim Yaacob, Tunku. Unpublished data from the Zoo Negara (National Zoo) bird collection, Kuala Lumpur.
Molesworth, B.D., 1950. The nesting of the Chestnut-headed Bee-eater. *Malayan Nature Journal* 5: 76–78.
——————, 1952. Further notes on the nesting of the Chestnut-headed Bee-eater. *Malayan Nature Journal* 7: 148.
——————, 1955. A possible nesting association. *Malayan Nature Journal* 9: 116–118.
Morse, R.A. and Liago, F.M., 1968. The Philippine Spine-tailed Swift *Chaetura dubia* McGregor as a honey bee predator. *Philippine Entomologist* 1: 138–143.
Mueller, O. and Hails, C.J., 1985. Surveying and ringing in Singapore. Pages 119–126 in D. Parish and D.R. Wells (editors), *INTERWADER Annual Report 1984*. INTERWADER, Kuala Lumpur.
Müller, A., 1882. Die Ornis der Insel Salanga. *Journal für Ornithologie* 30: 353–448.
Mundkur, T., Yus Rusila Noor, Rudyanto and Lane, B., 1992. *A status overview of shorebirds in Malaysia and Indonesia*. Asian Wetland Bureau, Kuala Lumpur.
Nadchatram, M., 1964. Black Eagles rather than Changeable Hawk-Eagles. *Malayan Nature Journal* 18: 172–173.
Nadee, N., 1982. Lesser Crested Tern, *Sterna bengalensis*, a new Bird for Thailand. *Natural History Bulletin of the Siam Society* 30: 205–206.
Nakhasathien, S., 1984. *Report on research planning in detail for forest recovery in forest watershed of Khlong Saeng, Chiew Larn Dam Project, Surat Thani Province* [in Thai]. Wildlife Conservation Division, Royal Thai Forest Department, Bangkok.
——————, 1987. The discovery of Storm's Stork *Ciconia stormi* in Thailand. *Forktail* 3: 43–49.
Nash, S. and Nash, A.D., 1987. An observation of Pied Imperial Pigeons *Ducula bicolor* on Air (Ayer) Islet, the first record for Lombok. *Kukila* 3: 48–49.
Nelson, J.B., 1975. The breeding biology of frigatebirds – a comparative review. *Living Bird Annual* 14: 113–156.
——————, 1978. *The Sulidae: Gannets and Boobies*. University of Aberdeen and Oxford University Press, Oxford.
Newmark, G.N., 1955. Birds seen at Maxwell's Hill, April, 1955. *Malayan Nature Journal* 10: 9–12.
Newton, I., 1972. *Finches*. Collins, London.
Nieboer, E., 1973. *Geographical and ecological differentiation in the genus Circus*. Vrije Universiteit te Amsterdam.
Nisbet, I.C.T., 1968. The utilization of mangroves by Malayan Birds. *Ibis* 110: 348–352.
NNML. Data from the collection of the Nationaal Natuurhistorisch Museum, Leiden, supplied by G.F. Mees and R.W.R.J. Dekker.
Noramly Muslim and Noramly, G., 1985. Layang-layang, island paradise for seabirds. *Nature Malaysiana* 10: 14–23.
Noske, R.A., 1991. Field identification and ecology of the Greater Golden-back *Chrysocolaptes lucidus* in Malaysia. *Forktail* 6: 72–74.
——————, 1995. The ecology of mangrove forest birds in Peninsular Malaysia. *Ibis* 137: 250–263.
NRCS. Data from the Zoology Department Nest Record-Card Scheme, University of Malaya .
Oates, E.W., 1878. Notes on the nidification of some Burmese birds. *Stray Feathers* 7: 40–52.
——————, 1883. *A Handbook to the Birds of British Burmah*. Volumes 1–2. Porter and Dulau, London.
—————— (editor), (1890). *The Nests and Eggs of Indian Birds by A.O. Hume, C.B.* (second edition). Volumes 2–3. R.H. Porter, London.
OBCB. Recent Reports/From the Field (editors A. Gretton, C. Robson). *Oriental Bird Club Bulletin* 3 (1986): 33–36; 7 (1988): 34–40; 8 (1988): 32–36; 9 (1989): 38–44; 11 (1990): 40–48; 12 (1990): 40–44; 13 (1991): 47–52: 14 (1991): 48–52; 15 (1992): 43–47: 16 (1992): 50–52: 17 (1993): 49–53; 20 (1994): 55–61; 22 (1995): 56–62; 23 (1996): 49–53.
Ogilvie, C.S., 1949. Nesting habits and early life of the Crested Green Wood Quail *Rollulus roulroul*: Malay-Siul. *Malayan Nature Journal* 4: 80–84.
——————, 1952. Nature notes from King George V National Park 1950. *Malayan Nature Journal* 7: 15–18.
——————, 1954. Notes on some birds nesting in King George V National Park. *Malayan Nature Journal* 9: 53–56.
Ogilvie-Grant, W.R., 1906. Report on the Birds. *Fasciculi Malayenses*, Zoology Part III: 65–123.
——————, 1908. The Gunong Tahan Expedition. Report on the Birds. *Journal of the Federated Malay States Museums* 3: 15–57.
Oliver, T.M., 1958. Birds at Cameron Highlands. *Malayan Nature Journal* 12: 186–187.
Ollington, R.F. and Loh, E., 1992. *1991 Singapore Bird Report*. Privately circulated.
——————, 1993. *1992 Singapore Bird Report*. Privately circulated.
Olson, P.D., Marshall, R.C. and Gaal, A., 1989. Relationships within the genus *Falco*: a comparison of the electrophoretic pattern of feather proteins. *Emu* 89: 193–203.
Olson, S.L., 1973. A classification of the Rallidae. *Wilson Bulletin* 85: 381–416.

Pagden, H.T., 1952. A Bird Migration. *Malayan Nature Journal* 7: 41–43.
——————, 1955. Falconets and Grasshoppers. *Malayan Nature Journal* 10: 81–82.
——————, 1958. Bay-headed Bee-eater. *Malayan Nature Journal* 13: 90–91.
Pan, K.A., 1987. Notes on the breeding behaviour of Southern Pied Hornbill (*Anthracoceros convexus*) in Peninsular Malaysia. *Journal of Wildlife and Parks* 6 and 7: 53–57.
————, 1987a. The study of species composition and behaviour of sympatric hornbills in Besout, Perak. *Journal of Wildlife and Parks* 6 and 7: 89–93.
Parish, D., 1985. Ground surveys in the Thai Peninsula. Pages 43–68 in D. Parish and D.R. Wells (editors), *INTERWADER Annual Report 1984*. INTERWADER, Kuala lumpur.
——————, 1985a. Ground surveys in Peninsular Malaysia 1984. Pages 69–78 in D. Parish and D.R. Wells (editors), *INTERWADER Annual Report 1984*. INTERWADER, Kuala Lumpur.
Parish, D. and Ardseungnern, S., 1989. Swinhoe's Storm Petrel *Oceanodroma monorhis*; a species new for Thailand. *Bulletin of the British Ornithologists' Club* 109: 9–11.
Parish, D. and Wells, D.R. (editors), 1984. *INTERWADER '83 Report*. INTERWADER, Kuala Lumpur.
Parkes, K.C., 1958. Specific relationships in the genus *Elanus*. *Condor* 60: 139–140.
Parker, S.A., 1981. Prolegomenon to further studies in the *Chrysococcyx 'malayanus'* group (Aves, Cuculidae). *Zoologische Verhandelingen, Rijksmuseum van Natuurlijke Historie te Leiden* 187: 1–56.
Parr, J.W.K., 1988. *An evaluation of mangroves and mudflats at Krabi, South Thailand*. Asian Wetland Bureau, Kuala Lumpur.
Parry, M. Ll., 1954. A Blue-faced Booby? *Malayan Nature Journal* 9: 25.
Payne, R.B. and Risley, C.J., 1976. Systematics and evolutionary relationships among the herons (Ardeidae). *Miscellaneous Publications of the Zoological Museum, University of Michigan* 150: 1–115.
Perennou, C., Rose, R. and Poole, C., 1990. *Asian Waterfowl Census 1990*. IWRB and Asian Wetland Bureau, Slimbridge.
PERHILITAN. Data from the files of the Malaysian Federal Department of Wildlife and National Parks.
Petersen, S., 1991. A record of White-shouldered Ibis in E Kalimantan. *Kukila* 5: 144–145.
Phillips, T.J., 1960. Dabchicks (*Podiceps ruficollis capensis*). *Malayan Nature Journal* 14: 228.
——————, 1961. Wigeon, Jacanas and Dabchicks. *Malayan Nature Journal* 15: 72–73.
Phillips, W.W.A., 1978. *Annotated checklist of the Birds of Ceylon (Sri Lanka)* (revised edition). Wildlife and Nature Protection Society of Ceylon and Ceylon Bird Club, Colombo.
Pierce, G.J., Spray, C.J. and Stuart, E., 1993. The effect of fishing on the distribution and behaviour of waterbirds in the Kukut area of Lake Songkla, Southern Thailand. *Biological Conservation* 66: 23–34.
Pook, J., 1992. Banding Round-up Complete List. *The Stilt* 20: 51–76.
Pratt, D.H., Bruner, P.L. and Berret, D.G., 1987. *A Field Guide to the Birds of Hawaii and the Tropical Pacific*. Princetown University Press, Princeton.
Prentice, C., 1989. Breeding Long-tailed Nightjar in Kuala Selangor Nature Park. *Enggang* 2(4): 13.
Prigogine, A., 1973. Le Statut de *Phodilus prigoginei*. *Gerfaut* 63: 177–186.
Primrose, A.M., 1911. Blyth's Baza (*Baza jerdoni*). *Journal of the Bombay Natural History Society* 20: 1152.
Prum, R.O., 1988. Phylogenetic interrelationships of the barbets (Aves: Capitonidae) and toucans (Aves: Ramphastidae) based on morphology with comparisons to DNA-DNA hybridization. *Zoological Journal of the Linnean Society* 92: 313–343.
Rahmani, A.R., 1989. Status of the Black-necked Stork *Ephippiorhynchus asiaticus* in the Indian subcontinent. *Forktail* 5: 99–110.
Ratnam, L., 1976. Night Heron. *Nature Malaysiana* 1(2): 23–27.
——————, 1977. Storks and Kuala Gula. *Nature Malaysiana* 2(4): 38–45.
Reichel, J.D., Glass, P.O. and Stinson, D.W., 1994. Status of the Common Buzzard *Buteo buteo* in the northern Mariana Islands, Pacific Ocean. *Emu* 94: 53–55.
Ridley, H.N. (with Kelsall, H.J.), 1894. List of birds observed or collected during trip in Pahang. *Journal of the Straits Branch of the Royal Asiatic Society* 25: 60–65.
Riley, J.H., 1938. Birds from Siam and the Malay Peninsula in the United States National Museum collected by Drs Hugh M. Smith and William L. Abbott. *United States National Museum Bulletin* 172: 1–581.
Rintoul, D., 1949. White-bellied Swiftlets. *Malayan Nature Journal* 4: 93.
Ripley, S.D., 1977. *Rails of the World. A Monograph of the Family Rallidae*. Feheley Publishers, Toronto.
——————, 1982. *A Synopsis of the the Birds of India and Pakistan* (second edition). Bombay Natural History Society, Bombay.
Ripley, S.D. and Beehler, B.M., 1987. The species status of the Malaysian three-toed kingfishers (*Ceyx*) – a re-assessment. *Bulletin of the British Ornithologists' Club* 107: 145–151.
Roberts, T.J., 1991. *The Birds of Pakistan*. Volume 1. *Regional studies and non-passerines*. Oxford University Press, Karachi.
Roberts, T.J. and King, B., 1986. Vocalizations of the owls of the genus Otus in Pakistan. *Ornis Scandinavica* 17: 299–305.
Robinson, D. and Seywald, G., 1987. The birth of Blyth's Hawk Eagle. *Malaysian Naturalist* 41(2): 16–18.
Robinson, H.C., 1905. List of a small collection of mammals, birds and batrachians from Gunong

Angsi, Negri Sembilan. *Journal of the Federated Malay States Museums* 1: 25–30.

———, 1906. A visit to the Aroa Islands, with a list of the birds found there. *Journal of the Federated Malay States Museums* 2: 8–16.

———, 1907. A hand-list of the birds of the Malay Peninsula, south of the Isthmus of Kra. *Journal of the Federated Malay States Museums* 2: 66–83.

———, 1909. The birds at present known from the mountains of the Malay Peninsula. *Journal of the Federated Malay States Museums* 2: 164–222.

———, 1909a. Notes on birds new to, or rare in, the Malay Peninsula. *Journal of the Federated Malay States Museums* 4: 129–133.

———, 1910. *A Hand-list of the Birds of the Malay Peninsula, south of the Isthmus of Kra.* Government Printer, Kuala Lumpur.

———, 1911. A list of a small collection of mammals and birds from the mountains of Ulu Langat, Selangor. *Journal of the Federated Malay States Museums* 4: 235–241.

———, 1911a. On a Horned Owl, new to the Malay Peninsula. *Journal of the Federated Malay States Museums* 4: 246–247.

———, 1911b. A scientific expedition to Temengoh, Upper Perak: zoology of Temengoh. *Journal of the Straits Branch of the Royal Asiatic Society* 57: 12–14.

———, 1913. Occurrence of the Crab-Plover (*Dromas ardeola*) in the Malay Peninsula. *Journal of the Bombay Natural History Society* 22: 199–200.

———, 1913a. Notes on birds new to, or rare in, the Malay Peninsula (third series). *Journal of the Federated Malay States Museums* 5: 15–22.

———, 1914. List of a small collection of birds and mammals from Gunong Kerbau, Perak. *Journal of the Federated Malay States Museums* 5: 23–27.

———, 1914a. On a collection of birds from the Siamese province of Bandon, N.E. Malay Peninsula. *Journal of the Federated Malay States Museums* 5: 83–110.

———, 1914b. The zoology of Koh Samui and Koh Pennan. *Journal of the Federated Malay States Museums* 5: 128–152.

———, 1917. On a collection of birds from Pulau Langkawi and other islands on the north-west coast of the Malay Peninsula. *Journal of the Federated Malay States Museums* 7: 129–191.

———, 1919. Notes on the vertebrate fauna of the Pahang-Johore archipelago. I. A list of Birds from Pulau Tinggi. *Journal of the Federated Malay States Museums* 7: 325–329.

———, 1927. *The Birds of the Malay Peninsula* Volume I: *The commoner birds.* H.F. and G. Witherby, London.

———, 1928. *The Birds of the Malay Peninsula.* Volume II: *The birds of the hill stations.* H.F. and G. Witherby, London.

———, 1928a. Occurrence of the White-breasted Fruit-dove in Kuala Lumpur. *Malayan Naturalist* 2(1): 46.

Robinson, H.C. and Chasen, F.N., 1936. *The Birds of the Malay Peninsula.* Volume III: *Sporting birds; birds of the seashore and estuaries.* H.F. and G. Witherby, London.

Robinson, H.C. and Kloss, C.B., 1910–11. On Birds from the Northern Portion of the Malay Peninsula, including the Islands of Langkawi and Terutau; with Notes on other rare Malayan Species from the Southern Districts. *Ibis* 52: 659–675; 53: 10–80.

———, 1914. On a further collection of mammals and birds from the hills of Negri Sembilan. *Journal of the Federated Malay States Museums* 5: 51–57.

———, 1915. List of a small collection of mammals and birds from the Krau river, western Pahang. *Journal of the Federated Malay States Museums* 5: 169–175.

———, 1916. The natural history of Kedah Peak. *Journal of the Federated Malay States Museums* 6: 219–244.

———, 1918. On a collection of birds from the Province of Phuket, Peninsular Siam. *Journal of the Natural History Society of Siam* 3: 87–119.

———, 1921–24. The Birds of South-West and Peninsular Thailand. *Journal of the Natural History Society of Siam* 5: 1–397.

———, 1921. Nine new Oriental birds. *Journal of the Federated Malay States Museums* 10: 203–206.

———, 1922. Birds from the One Fathom Bank lighthouse, Straits of Malacca. *Journal of the Federated Malay States Museums* 10: 253–255.

———, 1922a. A list of birds collected on Pulau Rumpia, Sembilan islands. *Journal of the Federated Malay States Museums* 10: 255–259.

———, 1922b. List of birds collected on Pulau Jarak, Straits of Malacca. *Journal of the Federated Malay States Museums* 10: 259–260.

———, 1922c. Three new Oriental birds. *Journal of the Federated Malay States Museums* 10: 261–262.

———, 1923. Mammals and birds from the hills of Nakon Sri Tamarat, Peninsular Siam. *Journal of the Federated Malay States Museums* 11: 58–63.

———, 1924. On a large collection of birds chiefly from West Sumatra made by Mr E. Jacobson. *Journal of the Federated Malay States Museums* 11: 189–347.

Robson, C.R., Eames, J.C., Nguyen Cu and Truong Van La, 1993. Further recent records from Viet Nam. *Forktail* 8: 25–52.

Rohwer, S., 1990. Foraging differences between white and dark morphs of the Pacific Reef Heron *Egretta sacra*. *Ibis* 132: 21–26.

ROM. Data from the collection of the Royal Ontario Museum, Toronto.

Round, P.D., 1983. Five bird species new for Thailand. *Bulletin of the British Ornithologists' Club* 103: 77–79.

———, 1988. *Resident forest birds in Thailand.* ICBP Monograph 2, Cambridge.

———, 1989. Bird of the Month, Black Kite. *Bangkok Bird Club Bulletin* 6(2): 9–10.

Round, P.D., Amget, B., Jintanugol, J. and Treesucon,

U., 1988. A summary of the larger waterbirds in Thailand. *Tigerpaper* 15: 1–9.

Round, P.D., Dobias, R.J., Komolphalin, K. and Duangkhae, S., 1982. Notes and new distributional information on birds in western Peninsular Thailand. *Natural History Bulletin of the Siam Society* 30: 15–24.

Rozendaal, F., 1990. Vocalizations and taxonomic status of *Caprimulgus celebensis*. *Dutch Birding* 12: 79–81.

RTFD. Data from the Wildlife Conservation Division, Royal Thai Forest Department, Bangkok.

Ruttanadakul, N. and Ardseungnern, S., 1987. *Evaluation of shorebird hunting in Pattani Province, South Thailand.* Interim Report. INTERWADER/Prince of Songkhla University, Kuala Lumpur.

Ryves, V.W., 1938. *Notes on Birds; Federated Malay States.* Volume 1 (1915–1938). Unpublished diary held with the Zoological Reference Collections, National University of Singapore.

Salomonsen, F., 1983. Revision of the Melanesian Swiftlets (Apodes, Aves) and their conspecific forms in the Indo-Australian and Polynesian Regions. *Kongelige Danske Videnskabernes Selskab Biologiske Skrifter* 23(5): 1–112.

Salvadori, T., 1889. Viaggo di Leonardo Fea nella Birmania e nella regione vicine XIX. *Annali del Museo Civico di Storia Naturale di Genova* 27: 369–438.

Saunders, C.J., 1923. Bird Notes. *Singapore Naturalist* 1(2): 112–114.

SBNR. Data from ringing operations at Sungai Buloh Nature Reserve, Singapore.

Scott, D.A. (editor), 1989. *A Directory of Asian Wetlands.* IUCN, Gland and Cambridge.

Sebastian, A.C., 1987. *Beberapa aspek ekologi pengeraman di dalam Lang Laut (Haliaeetus leucogaster) Gmelin di Telok Bahang, Pulau Pinang.* Unpublished dissertation, School of Biological Sciences, Science University Malaysia.

Sebastian, A.C., Hughes, R.N. and Hurrell, P.H., 1993.*Integrating ash pond management with shorebird conservation, tourism and education at Stesen Janaletrik Sultan Salahuddin Abdul Aziz, Kapar, Selangor Darul Ehsan.* Asian Wetland Bureau, Kuala Lumpur.

Serventy, D.L., Serventy, V. and Warham, J., 1971. *The handbook of Australian Sea-birds.* Reed, Sydney.

Sharpe, R.B., 1886. Notes on some birds from Perak. *Proceedings of the Zoological Society of London*: 350–353.

————, 1887. On a second collection of birds made by Mr L. Wray in the main range of mountains of Perak. *Proceedings of the Zoological Society of London*: 431–443.

————, 1888. List of a collection of birds made by Mr L. Wray in the main range of mountains of the Malay Peninsula, Perak. *Proceedings of the Zoological Society of London*: 268–281.

Sheldon, F.H., 1983. The birds of the Mantanani islands. *Sabah Society Journal* 7: 165–175.

————, 1987. Phylogeny of herons estimated from DNA-DNA hybridisation data. *Auk* 104: 97–108.

Sheldon, F.H. and Manuel, M.A., 1985. The sympatry of night herons in Borneo. *Bulletin of the British Ornithologists' Club* 105: 76–78.

Short, L.L., 1973. Habits of some Asian woodpeckers (Aves, Picidae). *Bulletin of the American Museum of Natural History* 152: 253–364.

————, 1973a. 'Woodpecking' by a Red-throated Barbet. *Auk* 90: 909–910.

————, 1978. Sympatry in woodpeckers of lowland Malayan forest. *Biotropica* 10: 122–133.

————, 1982. *Woodpeckers of the World.* Delaware Museum of Natural History, Greenville.

Sibley, C.G. and Ahlquist, J.E., 1990. *Phylogeny and Classification of Birds. A study in molecular evolution.* Yale University Press, New Haven.

Sibley, F.C. and Clapp, R.B., 1967. Distribution and dispersal of central Pacific Lesser Frigatebirds *Fregata ariel*. *Ibis* 109: 328–337.

Siegel-Causey, D., 1988. Phylogeny of the Phalacrocoracidae. *Condor* 90: 885–905.

Silvius, M.J., Chan Hung Tuck and Shamsudin Ibrahim, 1987. *Evaluation of wetlands of the West Coast of Peninsular Malaysia and their importance for natural resource conservation.* World Wildlife Fund Malaysia, Kuala Lumpur.

Silvius, M.J. and Verheugt, W.J.M., 1989. The status of storks, ibises and spoonbills in Indonesia. *Kukila* 4: 119–132.

Silvius, M.J., Verheugt, W.J.M. and Johan Iskandar, 1985. Coastal surveys in South-east Sumatra. Pages 133–142 in D. Parish and D.R. Wells (editors), *INTERWADER Annual Report 1984*, Kuala Lumpur.

————, 1986. *Coastal wetlands inventory of Southeast Sumatra.* ICBP, Cambridge and University of Utrecht.

SINGAV. Recent, nesting and trip reports. *Singapore Avifauna: Bulletin of the Singapore Nature Society Bird Group* (editor Lim Kim Seng) 1 (1987); 2 (1988); 3 (1989); 4 (1990); 6 (1992); 8 (1994); 9 (1995).

Siti Hawa Yatim, 1990. Short notes on band recovery of waders from Kuala Selangor, Selangor; Thailand and Hong Kong. *Journal of Wildlife and Parks* 9: 43–44.

Slater, C.A. and Slater, L.J., 1988. Frigatebirds roosting on Pulau Rengis, Malaysia. *Singapore Avifauna* 2(4): 23–25.

Slater, P., 1971. *A field guide to Australian Birds. Non-passerines.* Oliver and Boyd, Edinburgh.

Smal, C.M., 1989. Research on the use of Barn Owls *Tyto alba* for Biological Control of Rats in Oil Palm Plantations: 1986–1989. Pages 342–346 in the Proceedings of the 1989 PORIM International Oil Palm Development Conference, Kuala Lumpur.

Smythies, B.E., 1953. *The Birds of Burma* (revised edition). Oliver and Boyd, Edinburgh.

————, 1957. An Annotated Checklist of the Birds of Borneo. *Sarawak Museum Journal* 7: i-xv, 523–818.

————, 1960. *The Birds of Borneo.* Oliver and Boyd, Edinburgh.

———, 1981. *The Birds of Borneo* (third edition, editor the Earl of Cranbrook). Sabah Society and Malayan Nature Society, Kuala Lumpur.

Snow, D.W. (editor), 1978. *An Atlas of Speciation in African Non-Passerine Birds*. British Museum (Natural History), London.

Somadikarta, S., 1986. *Collocalia linchi* Horsfield & Moore – a revision. *Bulletin of the British Ornithologists' Club* 106: 32–40.

Sonobe, K. and Washington, J.W. (editors), 1982. *A Field Guide to the Birds of Japan*. Wild Bird Society of Japan, Tokyo.

Spittle, R.J., 1949. Nesting habits of some Singapore birds. *Bulletin of the Raffles Museum* 21: 184–204.

———, 1952. Feeding habits of some Singapore birds. *Malayan Nature Journal* 7: 23–32.

Stader, L., 1989. Blue-throated Bee-eaters in Sungai Buloh. An ongoing study. *Enggang* 2(4): 10–11.

———, 1989a. News from the Bee-eater Colony (May 1989). *Enggang* 2(5): 10.

———, 1989b. News from the Bee-eater Colony (June 1989). Mating behaviour. *Enggang* 2(6): 13.

———, 1989c. News from the Bee-eater Colony. The Breeding Birds. *Enggang* 2(8): 13–14.

———, 1994. *Breeding behaviour of a tropical bird: a study of the Blue-throated Bee-eater (Merops viridis) using a relational database and DNA fingerprinting*. Ph.D thesis, University of Stirling.

———, 1996. Breeding behaviour of the Blue-throated Bee-eater (*Merops viridis*): 1. General behaviour and ecology. *Wallaceana* 77: 1–7.

Stanford, J.K., 1936. On the breeding of the Pied Harrier (*Circus melanoleucos* Pennant) in Northern Burma. *Journal of the Bombay Natural History Society* 39: 179.

Starks, J., 1985. Interwader surveys in Thailand. Pages 27–42 in D. Parish and D.R. Wells (editors), *INTERWADER Annual Report 1984*. INTERWADER, Kuala Lumpur.

Stokes, T., 1988. *A review of the birds of Christmas Island, Indian Ocean*. Australian National Parks and Wildlife Service, Canberra.

Stoliczka, F., 1870. A contribution to Malayan ornithology. *Journal of the Asiatic Society of Bengal* 39(4): 277–334.

Storer, P.J., 1976. *A study of the waterfowl at Thale Noi Waterfowl Reserve Area*. Unpublished report to the Conservation Division of the Royal Thai Forestry Department, Bangkok.

———, 1978. A biological survey of a lowland evergreen scrub forest and meadowland in southern Thailand. *Natural History Bulletin of the Siam Society* 27: 93–114.

Stresemann, E., 1912–13. Ornithologische Miszellan aus dem Indo-Australischen Gebeit. *Novitates Zoologicae* 19: 311–351; 20: 289–324.

Stresemann, E., 1931. Notes on the Systematics and Distribution of some Swiftlets (Collocalia) of Malaysia and adjacent subregions. *Bulletin of the Raffles Museum* 6: 83–101.

Stresemann, E. and Amadon, D., 1979. Falconiformes. Pages 271–425 in E. Mayr and G.W. Cotterell (editors), *Check-list of Birds of the World*. Volume 1 (second edition). Museum of Comparative Zoology, Cambridge, Massachusetts.

Stresemann, E. and Stresemann, V., 1961. Die handschwingen Mauser der Kuckucke (Cuculidae). *Journal für Ornithologie* 102: 317–352.

Stresemann, V. and Stresemann, E., 1966. Die Mauser der Vögel. *Journal für Ornithologie* (supplement) 107: 1–448.

Subharaj, R., 1988. Discovered at last! A Night Heron Heronry in Singapore. *Singapore Avifauna* 2(2): 32–34.

Summers-Smith, D., 1981. Some New Bird Records from Phuket Province, Thailand. *Natural History Bulletin of the Siam Society* 29: 175–178.

Sutari Supari, 1987. The breeding of the Red Junglefowl (*Gallus gallus*) in Pulau Ubin. *Singapore Avifauna* 1(11): 20–23.

———, 1992. Hornbills and Fish-Eagles. *Singapore Avifauna* 6(2): 25–27.

Sutter, E., 1955. Über die Mauser einiger Laufhühnchen und die Rassen von *Turnix maculosa* und *sylvatica* im indo-australischen Gebeit. *Verhandlungen der Naturforschenden Gesellschaft in Basel* 66: 85–139.

Swennen, C., Howes, J.R., Ruttanadakul, N., Stikvoort, E. and Ardseungnurn, S., 1986. *Evaluation of the littoral ecosystem at three sites in South Thailand in 1985*. INTERWADER/Prince of Songkhla University Report 1, Kuala Lumpur.

Swennen, C. and Marteijn, E.C.L., 1985. Wader feeding ecology studies in the Malay Peninsula. Pages 13–26 in D. Parish and D.R. Wells (editors), *INTERWADER Annual Report 1984*. Kuala Lumpur.

———, 1985a. First record of the White-tailed Tropicbird *Phaethon lepturus* for Thailand. *Natural History Bulletin of the Siam Society* 33: 139–140.

———, 1987. Notes on the feeding behaviour of the Milky Stork *Mycteria cinerea*. *Forktail* 3: 63–66.

———, 1988. Foraging behaviour of Spoon-billed Sandpipers *Eurhynorhynchus pygmeus* on a mudflat in Peninsular Thailand. *Natural History Bulletin of the Siam Society* 36: 85–88.

Swennen, C., Ruttanadakul, N., Ardseungnern, S. and Howes, J.R., 1987. Foraging behaviour of the Crab Plover *Dromas ardeola* at Ko Libong, Southern Thailand. *Natural History Bulletin of the Siam Society* 35: 27–33.

Taylor, E.M., 1961. Observations on a woodpecker. *Malayan Nature Journal* 15: 62–63.

Thang Hooi Chiew, 1995. *Sustainable forest management and conservation practices*. Report to the Malaysian Timber Council.

TISTR. Data from the Thai National Collection, Thailand Institute for Scientific and Technological Research, Bangkok.

Tuck, G. and Heinzel, H., 1978. *A field guide to the seabirds of Britain and the world*. Collins, London.

UMBRP. Data from the University of Malaya Bird-Ringing Project.

UMZC. Data from the collection of the University Museum of Zoology, Cambridge.

USNM. Data from the collection of the United States National Museum of Natural History, Washington D.C.

van Balen, S., 1984. Sight records of the Black Baza *Aviceda leuphotes* on Java. *Ardea* 72: 234.

————, 1991. Jaegers in Indonesian waters. *Kukila* 5: 117–124.

————, 1991a. Faunistic notes from Bali with some new records. *Kukila* 5: 125–132.

van Balen, S. and Compost, A.R., 1989. Overlooked evidence of the Short-toed Eagle *Circaetus gallicus* on Java. *Kukila* 4: 44–46.

van Balgooy, M.M.J., Kurtak, B.H., Littke, W.R., Widjojo, P. and Weinheimer, E.A., 1977. A biological reconnaissance of Tasek Pulau Langgun, a sink-hole lake in the Langkawi district. *Sains Malaysiana* 6: 1–27.

van den Berg, A.B., Smeenk, C., Bosman, C.A.W., Haase, B.J.M., van der Niet, A.M. and Cadée, G.C., 1991. Barau's Petrel *Pterodroma baraui*, Jouanin's Petrel *Bulweria fallax* and other seabirds in the northern Indian Ocean in June-July 1984 and 1985. *Ardea* 79: 1–14.

van der Linde, M., 1996. A new breeding species for the Philippines: the Pied Harrier *Circus melanoleucos*. *Forktail* 11: 172–173.

van Oort, E.D., 1911. On two rare petrels *Oceanodroma monorhis* and *Aestrelata aterrima*. *Notes from the Leyden Museum* 33: 111–112.

van Rhijn, J.G., 1991. *The Ruff*. T. and A.D. Poyser, London.

van Tets, G.F., 1976. Australasia and the origin of shags and cormorants, Phalacrocoracidae. *Proceedings of the XVI International Ornithological Congress* (1974): 121–124.

Vaurie, C., 1959. Systematic Notes on Palearctic Birds. No. 38 Alcedinidae, Meropidae, Upupidae and Apodidae. *American Museum Novitates* 1971: 1–25.

————, 1964. Systematic Notes on Palearctic Birds. No. 53. Charadriidae: The Genera *Charadrius* and *Pluvialis*. *American Museum Novitates* 2177: 1–22.

————, 1965. *The Birds of the Palearctic Fauna. A systematic reference: Non-passeriformes*. H.F. and G. Witherby, London.

Veit, R.R. and Jonsson, L., 1987. Field identification of smaller sandpipers within the genus *Calidris*. *American Birds* 41: 213–236.

Verheugt, W.J.M., Skov, H. and Danielsen, F., 1993. Notes on the birds of the tidal lowlands and floodplains of South Sumatra Province, Indonesia. *Kukila* 6: 53–84.

Verhoeye, J. and King, B., 1990. Notes on three raptor species new to Flores. *Kukila* 5: 65–68.

Violani, C., 1980. On the Wedge-tailed Green Pigeon *Treron sphenura etorques* of Sumatra. *Bulletin of the British Ornithologists' Club* 100: 223–226.

Voous, K.H., 1960. *Atlas of European Birds*. Nelson, London.

————, 1961. Birds collected by Carl Lumholtz in Eastern and Central Borneo. *Mededelser fra det Zoologiske Museum, Osla* 10: 127–180.

Voous, K.H. and Payne, H.A.W., 1965. The grebes of Madagascar. *Ardea* 53: 9–31.

Vowles, R.S. and Vowles, G.A., 1985. Notes on the birds of Borneo. *Bulletin of the British Ornithologists' Club* 105: 72–73.

Ward, P., 1968. Origin of the avifauna of urban and suburban Singapore. *Ibis* 110: 239–255.

Ward, P. and Wood, B., 1967. Parrot damage to oil-palm fruit in Johore. *The Planter* 43: 1–3.

Waterstradt, J., 1902. Kelantan and my trip to Gunong Tahan. *Journal of the Straits Branch of the Royal Asiatic Society* 37: 1–27.

Watson, G.E., Zusi, R.L. and Storer, R.E., 1963. *Preliminary field guide to the birds of the Indian Ocean*. United States National Museum, Washington D.C.

Wattel, J., 1973. *Geographical differentiation in the genus Accipiter*. Nuttall Ornithological Club Publication 13, Cambridge, Massachusetts.

Waugh, D.R. and Hails, C.J., 1983. Foraging ecology of a tropical aerial feeding bird guild. *Ibis* 125: 200–217.

Webber, M.L., 1954. Bird Notes from Johore. *Malayan Nature Journal* 9: 100.

Weigant, W. and van Helvoort, B., 1987. First sighting of *Tachybaptus ruficollis* on Bali. *Kukila* 3: 50–51.

Wells, D.R., 1972. The genus *Cuculus*: two amendments to the 'Handbook of the Birds of India and Pakistan'. *Journal of the Bombay Natural History Society* 69: 179–185.

————, 1975. The Moss-nest Swiftlet *Collocalia vanikorensis* Quoy and Gaimard in Sumatra. *Ardea* 63: 148–151.

————, 1985. The forest avifauna of Western Malesia and its conservation. Pages 213–232 in A.W. Diamond and T.E. Lovejoy (editors), *Conservation of Tropical Forest Birds*. ICBP Technical Publication 4, Cambridge.

————, 1986. Further parallels between the Asian Bay Owl *Phodilus badius* and *Tyto* species. *Bulletin of the British Ornithologists' Club* 106: 12–15.

————, 1988. Birds. Pages 167–195 in Earl of Cranbrook (editor), *Key Environments: Malaysia*. Pergamon Press, Oxford.

————, 1990. Migratory birds and tropical forest in the Sunda region. Pages 357–369 in A. Keast (editor), *Biogeography and ecology of forest bird communities*, SPB Academic Publishing, The Hague.

————, 1990a. Taman Negara and ornithology. *Journal of Wildlife and Parks (special issue to commemorate the Golden Jubilee of Taman Negara, 1939–1989)* 10: 326–332.

————, 1990b. Bird diversity in the Sungai Kinchin Area, Pahang, Malaysia. *Malayan Nature Journal* 43: 326–332.

————, 1991. Status and conservation of seabirds breeding in Malaysian waters. Pages 213–223 in J.P. Croxall (editor), *Seabird Status and Conservation; a supplement*. ICBP Technical Publication 11, Cambridge.

Wells, D.R. and Becking, J.H., 1975. Vocalizations and status of Little and Himalayan Cuckoos *Cuculus poliocephalus* and *C. saturatus*, in Southeast Asia. *Ibis* 117: 366–371.

Wells, D.R. and Medway, Lord, 1976. Taxonomic and faunistic notes on birds of the Malay Peninsula. *Bulletin of the British Ornithologists' Club* 96: 20–34.

Wells, K.L., 1958. A Note of Birds at Grik, Upper Perak. *Malayan Nature Journal* 12: 121–124.

WFVZ. Data from the collection of the Western Foundation of Vertebrate Zoology, Camarillo, California.

White, C.M.N., 1974. Three water birds of Wallacea. *Bulletin of the British Ornithologists' Club* 94: 9–11.

————, 1975. Further notes on birds of Wallacea. *Bulletin of the British Ornithologists' Club* 95: 106–109.

Whitmore, T.C., 1984. *Tropical Rain Forests of the Far East* (second edition). Oxford University Press, Oxford.

Whitten, A.J., 1989. Pelicans at Cengkareng. *Kukila* 4: 64.

Wilds, C. and Newlon, M., 1983. The identification of Dowitchers. *Birding* 15: 151–166.

Wilkinson, R., Dutson, G., Sheldon, B., Darjono and Yus Rusila Noor, 1991. The avifauna of the Barito Ulu region, central Kalimantan. *Kukila* 5: 99–116.

Williamson, W.J.F., 1916. A list of birds not previously recorded from Siam, with notes. *Journal of the Natural History Society of Siam*, 2: 59–65.

————, 1916a. The Giant Ibis. *Journal of the Natural History Society of Siam* 2: 71–72.

————, 1918. New and noteworthy bird-records from Siam. *Journal of the Natural History Society of Siam* 3: 15–42.

Wingate, J., 1953. The nesting of a pair of Coppersmith Barbets. *Malayan Nature Journal* 8: 32–34.

Wolfe, E.D.B., 1951. The Nicobar Pigeon – 2. *Malayan Nature Journal* 5: 204.

————, 1951a. A Bird Mimic. *Malayan Nature Journal* 5: 207.

Wong, M., 1984. Behavioural indications of an African origin for the Malaysian Honeyguide *Indicator archipelagicus*. *Bulletin of the British Ornithologists' Club* 104: 57–61.

————, 1985. Understorey birds as indicators of regeneration in a patch of selectively logged West Malaysian rainforest. Pages 249–263 in A.W. Diamond and T.E. Lovejoy (editors), *Conservation of Tropical Forest Birds*. ICBP Technical Publication 4, Cambridge.

Wood, B.J., 1968. *Pests of Oil Palms in Malaysia and their Control*. Incorporated Society of Planters, Kuala Lumpur.

Wray, L., 1890. Journal of a collecting expedition to the mountains of Batang Padang, Perak. *Journal of the Straits Branch of the Royal Asiatic Society* 21: 123–165.

WWFM. Data from the Worldwide Fund for Nature Malaysia resource library.

Wyatt-Smith, J., 1951. The Nicobar Pigeon – I. *Malayan Nature Journal* 5: 203–204.

————, 1951a. Distribution of the Pied Imperial Pigeon. *Malayan Nature Journal* 5: 208.

————, 1997. Manual of Malayan Silviculture for Inland Forest. Volume 1, parts I–III (second edition). *Malayan Forest Records* 23.

Yorke, C.D., 1984. Avian community structure in two modified Malaysian habitats. *Biological Conservation* 29: 345–362.

Young, C.G., 1940. Notes on the Christmas Island Frigate Bird on the east coast, and the Japanese Martin in Kelantan. *Malayan Nature Journal* 1: 62.

————, 1941. Notes on some migratory birds in Malaya. *Malayan Nature Journal* 1: 149–156.

ZDUM. Data from the Zoology Department museum collection, University of Malaya, Kuala Lumpur.

ZRCNUS. Data from the Zoological Reference Collections, National University of Singapore.

INDEXES

The four indexes cover only the species accounts and are strictly nomenclatural. They are self-contained and apart from plate numbering in common (given in brackets throughout) have not been designed to interact. Thai and Malay names direct the reader only to species-account headers. To find the full range of other mentions, consult Scientific and English name indexes together. In both of these, bold page references are to the start of the relevant main account, others to subsidiary mentions.

SCIENTIFIC NAMES

Names of families, genera, species and subspecies.

Extralimital taxa, including members of superspecies, are entered only under their genus heading.

SPECIES NAMES IN ENGLISH

SPECIES NAMES IN ROMANIZED THAI

The widely-used prefix 'Nok' (bird) is omitted as understood. Note that no Thai-language names have been formed for species not on the Thailand national list.

SPECIES NAMES IN MALAY

The widely used prefix 'Burung' (bird) is omitted as understood.

ISBN 0-12-742961-1